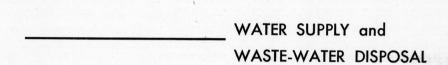

WATER SUPPLY and
WASTE-WATER DISPOSAL

WATER SUPPLY
and
WASTE-WATER
DISPOSAL

Gordon Maskew Fair

Abbott and James Lawrence Professor of
Engineering and Gordon McKay Professor of
Sanitary Engineering, Harvard University

John Charles Geyer

Professor of Sanitary Engineering
The Johns Hopkins University

With a chapter on Water Chemistry by
John Carrell Morris
Associate Professor of Sanitary Chemistry
Harvard University

JOHN WILEY & SONS, INC., NEW YORK
CHAPMAN & HALL, LIMITED, LONDON

91064
2-57

Library of Congress Catalog Card Number: 54–9504

Printed in the United States of America

This treatise on water supply and waste-water disposal [1] is intended for the student of civil and sanitary engineering, no matter whether he is in college or established in the practice of his profession. With this reader in mind, we have addressed ourselves to the presentation of principles rather than practice, of methodology rather than method, and of rationality rather than rule of thumb. Our ability to keep to this purpose is, in a sense, a measure of the devotion and success of engineers, chemists, and biologists in their search for new and fundamental concepts. It will become evident that the "degree of empiricism" in the engineering of water supplies and waste-water systems remains high in spite of great labors, that many concepts are oversimplified, and that others must be subjected to further test and refinement. The profession has by no means arrived at the point where sanitary design has become an orderly process of calculation based upon the fundamental physical, chemical, and biological behavior of water and waste water. But this observation should not be discouraging. Rather should it impel the student of water supply and wastewater disposal to take part in needed investigation and experimentation. If he does, he will gain much personal satisfaction and meet more fully his obligation to the profession.

To give emphasis to principles, we have chosen a structural rather than a functional treatment of the subject matter. This has made for an integrated discussion of water supply and waste-water disposal in contrast to the compartmentalization of these subjects that currently characterizes other books in this field. Water and waste water, like "the Colonel's Lady and Judy O'Grady, are sisters under their skins." The quantities of water consumed and waste water discharged are

[1] We have used the term "waste-water disposal" in the title of this book rather than the term "sewerage" in order to mark the fact that this book is concerned with the collection and disposal not only of sanitary sewage and combined sewage but also of storm water and water-carried industrial wastes, both by themselves and in combination with sanitary sewage.

substantially the same, because most of the water supplied to a community or industry becomes waste water. Rainfall and runoff lie at the base of water supply as well as waste-water disposal. The hydraulic problems of water works are no different from those of sewage works. Changes in the physics, chemistry, and biology of water and waste water reflect but the varying concentrations of their impurities. The natural purification of streams and other bodies of water, too, is altered only in proportion to the intensity of their pollution. The principles of water purification and of waste-water treatment are the same, although equal accomplishment may not be registered for both and certain operations are better adapted to one than to the other. Because these identities exist, we have tried to shake off the *ad hoc* thinking that has characterized much of the past writing on water supply and waste-water disposal. For the same reason, we have attempted to avoid duplication of statement by giving free rein to the exchange of ideas between the two subjects.

To include as much material as possible and make room for illustrative examples, we have resorted to a number of expedients. Descriptions of materials, methods, equipment, and structures have been kept short. The excellence of manufacturers' catalogues has, indeed, made the illustration and discussion of their products superfluous. New methods of construction and specialized structural design are constantly evolved. Their presentation seems to us a responsibility of current journals. Tables of raw data, such as statistics of water consumption and sewage discharge for individual municipalities, of rainfall and runoff for individual regions, of water quality and sewage strength for individual communities, and of the results of operating individual water-purification and waste-water treatment plants, are dispensed with. Generalized figures, formulations, and graphical representations take their place. Many of the illustrations in the book are but "thumbnail sketches." Application of this technique conserves space. At the same time its pedagogic objective is to show only the most essential elements of a given structure, piece of equipment, or apparatus. Finally, the style of the book is not discursive. Its pages must be studied, not read.

In spite of the husbanding of space, we have been forced to omit some interesting topics and to abridge others. Important are unusual ways of water and waste-water treatment that have been applied on a limited scale in the past or that, still in the developmental stage, give promise of being applied successfully in the future.

Roughly, the first half of this treatise (Chapters 1–16) deals with the collection and distribution of water and with the collection and removal of waste water. The second half (Chapters 17–30) takes up the treatment of water and waste water and the natural purification of water. In our experience, each half is readily covered in the hours commonly allotted to water supply and waste-water disposal in a semester of instruction.

We have made the elements of water sanitation our opening chapter, because the water engineer must, at all times, be aware of these elements in the planning, design, construction, and operation of water and waste-water works. If he is not, he will endanger the health of the community or industry that his works are to serve. The second and third chapters are concerned with water supply and waste-water disposal systems as a whole. They are intended to form a frame of reference for the subjects that are singled out for detailed discussion in the body of the treatise.

Chapter 4, Statistical Analysis of Quantitative Information, has been prepared because many of the data upon which water supply and waste-water disposal are based can be put to service only by subjecting the collected information to statistical analysis. The statistical approach to the analysis of quantitative information is used in succeeding chapters, more particularly Chapter 5, Quantities of Water and Waste Water, and Chapters 7–9 on applied hydrology. These chapters are preceded by a general discussion of the elements of hydrology, Chapter 6. Like the first chapter of this book, this chapter has as one of its purposes the introduction of the reader to elements of the culture as well as the art and science of water supply and waste-water disposal.

Chapters 10–13 discuss specific problems of water supply: the collection of water, its transmission to the community, and its distribution through the community. Chapter 14, Water Supply and Drainage of Buildings, forges the link between the water-distribution system and the waste-water-collection system. The succeeding two chapters, Chapters 15 and 16, treat of the flow of water in sewers and their appurtenances and of the collection of sewage and storm drainage.

The second half of the book opens with three chapters on the physical, chemical, and biological properties of water and waste water, Chapters 17–19. They are followed by chapters on the examination of water and waste water and on standards of water quality, Chapters 20 and 21. These five chapters, together with Chapter 1, lay the foundation for an understanding of water quality and for a perception of the purposes and possible accomplishments of water purification and waste-water treatment. Included in Chapter 21 is a summary of the unit operations of water and waste-water treatment that are discussed in the six succeeding chapters, Chapters 22–27.

The last three chapters of the book (Chapters 28–30) deal with the natural or self-purification of water, industrial water supply and waste-water disposal, and rural water supply and waste-water disposal. Since the water supply of swimming pools calls for much the same pattern of management as does rural water supply, bathing waters are discussed in Chapter 30.

The Appendix includes tables that simplify computations or summarize basic information of a physical or chemical nature. A diagram facilitates the solution of the Hazen-Williams formula for the flow of water in pipes. Appended, too, are classified lists of reference works, serial publications, monographs, and papers that supplement the references to original sources found in the footnotes of individual chapters.

The teacher or reader who prefers to concern himself with water supply and waste-water disposal separately rather than conjointly will discover that, without doing too much violence to the primary purpose of this treatise, he can make the different chapters or sections of this book fall reasonably well into the presently conventional sequence of topics. However, he will not be able to avoid some repetition. For the study of water supply, a satisfactory sequence is formed by Chapters 1 (Sections 1–7, 12), 2, 4, 5 (Sections 1–9), 6, 7 (Sections 1, 2, 8, 10), 8, 9, 10, 11, 12, 13, 14 (Sections 1–5), 17, 18, 19 (Sections 1, 2), 20 (Sections 1–16), 21 (Sections 1–4, 9–11), 22 (Sections 1–16), 23, 24, 25 (Sections 12, 14), 27, 28 (Sections 1–4), 29 (Sections 1–6), and 30 (Sections 1–5, 8, 9). Similarly, a satisfactory sequence for the study of waste-water disposal is established by Chapters 1 (Sections 1–3, 8–12), 3, 4, 5 (Sections 1–6, 10, 11), 6, 7 (Sections 1, 3–10), 14 (Sections 1, 6–11), 15, 16, 17, 18, 19, 20, 21 (Sections 1, 5–11), 22, 23 (Sections 1–4, 8), 24 (Sections 1–3), 25, 26, 27 (Sections 1–13, 16–20), 28, 29 (Sections 1, 7–13), and 30 (Sections 1–3, 6, 7).

In writing this book, we have made free use of materials included in our own publications, more particularly those sections in *Sewage Treatment* [2] by Karl Imhoff and Gordon M. Fair and in *The Microscopy of Drinking Water* [3] by George C. Whipple, Gordon M. Fair, and M. C. Whipple, for which one of us was responsible. Only occasional reference is made to the sources of these materials in the pages of this book. We, therefore, acknowledge our indebtedness to Professor M. C. Whipple and to Dr. Imhoff. Their thinking is bound to be reflected also in the present volume.

As members of university departments of sanitary engineering at

[2] John Wiley & Sons, New York, 1940.
[3] John Wiley & Sons, New York, 1927.

Harvard and Hopkins, we cannot fail to be under heavy obligation to our colleagues in these departments. They have, indeed, shared the burden of producing this book. We are grateful to them for their interest, encouragement, and assistance. We acknowledge with special thanks the preparation of Chapter 18, Elements of Water Chemistry, by Dr. J. C. Morris and the critical reading of Chapter 19, Biology of Water and Waste Water, by Dr. S. L. Chang, both of Harvard University. We are grateful, too, to Mrs. William Hutchinson, Secretary of Dunster House, Harvard College, for the typing of the manuscript— a task beyond the call of duty.

GORDON M. FAIR
JOHN C. GEYER

Dunster House, Cambridge, Mass.
Whitehead Hall, Baltimore, Md.
August, 1954

CONTENTS

xi

1-1. General Considerations. Water sanitation is made the subject of the opening chapter of this book because the requirements of sanitation distinguish water supply and waste-water disposal from all other hydraulic undertakings of an engineering nature. An awareness of sanitary injunctions inheres in the underlying hydrological investigations, in the hydraulic and structural designs by which the necessary engineering works are created, and in the management of the completed systems. If the requirements of sanitation are not fulfilled all along this line, the engineering works that supply water and dispose of waste waters must fail of their purpose. On the other hand, if health is built into such works, the engineer responsible for them can take just pride in Pindar's words: [1] αριστον μεν ύδωρ (*ariston men hudor*)— "best of all things is water."

Throughout the world, the planning, design, construction, and supervision of water supplies and waste-water disposal systems has long been the responsibility of civil engineers. The underlying engineering activities call for the exercise of skills commonly possessed in largest measure by this, the oldest, group of civilian engineering practitioners. That drinking water could convey enteric diseases, such as cholera and typhoid fever, and that sewage often harbored the causative agents of these diseases was discovered toward the middle of the nineteenth century and scientifically substantiated towards the end of that century. Chemical and biological (including in particular bacteriological) research eventually provided the tools for controlling the water-borne diseases and otherwise insuring the safety as well as the palatability and economic usefulness of water. At the same time, these researches identified the nature of sewage and other water-carried wastes from household and industry and provided the means for the protection of

[1] From an ode written in 460 B.C.

1

water against contamination [2] and pollution [3] by sewage and related waste matters.

The civil engineer who developed competence in those aspects of chemistry and biology that are important in water supply and waste-water disposal became known as a sanitary engineer. Skilled in the hydraulic control of water, it was but natural for him to take part, in the course of time, in the suppression of diseases other than the enteric water-borne diseases in which water or water-dwelling organisms were also implicated. Examples of such activities are the sanitation of swimming pools and other bathing places, and the control of malaria and other insect-borne diseases in which the insect vectors can be attacked in their aquatic habitat by hydraulic and related engineering operations. Familiarity with the engineering aspects of disease control led sanitary engineers to accept responsibility, too, for the solution of problems not so directly related to water but concerned in general with the preservation and promotion of the public health. Since air, water, food, heat, and light constitute the five essentials for human existence, and since their sanitary supply involves engineering activities in many ways, sanitary engineering [4] has ultimately concerned itself with all of them in some degree. This book, however, deals with but one of these five: water and water-carried wastes.

1-2. Community Sanitary Works and Facilities. Water is introduced into municipalities for many purposes: (1) for drinking and culinary uses; (2) for bathing and washing; (3) for heating and air-conditioning systems; (4) for the watering of lawns and gardens; (5) for street sprinkling; (6) for recreational use in swimming and wading pools; (7) for display in fountains and cascades; (8) for the creation of hydraulic and steam power; (9) for numerous and varied industrial processes; (10) for the protection of life and property against fire; and (11) for the removal by water carriage of offensive and potentially dangerous wastes from household (sewage) and industry (industrial wastes). To provide for these varying uses, which total about

---

[2] Contamination of water is the introduction or release into it of potentially pathogenic organisms or of toxic substances that render the water hazardous and, therefore, unfit for human consumption or domestic use.

[3] Pollution of a body of water is the introduction into it of substances of such character and in such quantity that its natural quality is so altered as to impair its usefulness or render it offensive to the senses of sight, taste, or smell. Contamination may accompany pollution.

[4] The term *public-health engineering* can be used interchangeably with the term *sanitary engineering;* it is sometimes employed in a more restrictive sense to identify the activities of engineers who are attached to departments of public health.

100 gallons per capita per day (gpcd) in average North American residential communities and 150 gpcd in large industrial cities, the supply of water must be satisfactory in quality and adequate in quantity, readily available to the user, relatively cheap, and easily disposed of after it has served its purposes. The engineering works that make possible this manifold use of water are: (*a*) the water works, or water supply system, and (*b*) the waste-water works, or waste-water disposal system.[5]

The water works collect water from its natural source, purify it if necessary, and deliver it to the consumer. The waste-water works collect the sewage or spent water of the community—about 70 per cent of the water supplied, together with varying amounts of entering ground and surface water. Surface runoff resulting from rainstorms and melting snow and ice is either collected by the system of drains that also carries away the waste waters of household and industry (combined sewerage), or the runoff is collected in an independent or separate system of storm drains (separate sewerage). The collected sewage or waste water is discharged, when required after suitable treatment, usually into a natural drainage channel, or receiving body of water, of the region; more rarely onto land. Often the same body of water must serve both as a source of water and as a recipient of sewage and storm drainage. It is this dual use of water in nature and within communities and industrial premises that establishes the most impelling reasons for water sanitation.

The interdependence of water supply and waste-water disposal is the more pronounced the greater the urbanization of a region and the farther advanced its sanitary economy. The connecting link between water supply and waste-water disposal is the plumbing system, or system of water supply and drainage within dwellings, commercial establishments, and industries. Refuse collection is essentially independent of the two, except as garbage is ground and discharged into sewers and except as refuse incinerators are operated in connection with sewage-treatment works. Figure 1-1 illustrates, from the point of view of the householder, the progress from the individualistic practices of rural populations to the communal services that are provided for the urban dweller. The associated problems of sanitation are briefly indicated.

[5] The terms *sewage works* and *sewerage system* are, strictly speaking, more limited in concept than the terms *waste-water works* and *waste-water disposal system*. As a general rule, however, they are employed to describe the collection and disposal of all types of water-carried wastes and also of storm-water runoff.

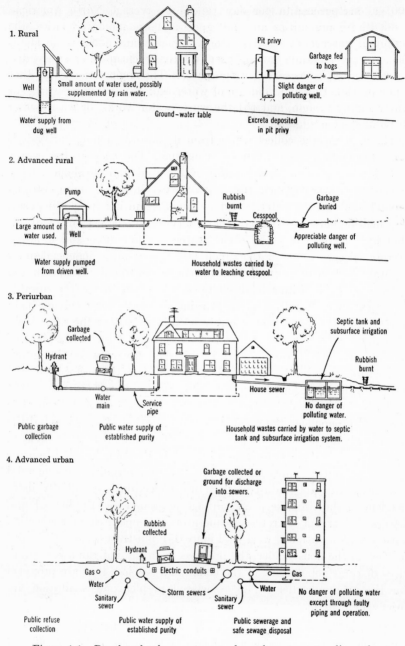

Figure 1-1. Rural and urban water-supply and waste-water disposal.

1-3. Background in History. "Sanitation," as stated by Reynolds,[6] "has its history, its archeology, its literature, and its science. Most religions concern themselves with it, sociology includes it within its sphere, and its study is imperative to social ethics. Some knowledge of psychology is necessary to understand its development and retardation, an esthetic sense is required for its full appreciation, (and) economics determine, to a large degree, its growth and extent. . . . Whoever, indeed, would study this subject with a knowledge worthy of its magnitude must consider it from all angles and with a . . . wealth of learning."

The history of water sanitation has its roots in antiquity. There the design, construction, and management of public water supplies and waste-water disposal systems were allied to the growth of capital cities and religious or trade centers. Developed as installations of considerable magnitude and complexity, their remnants stand as monuments to sound, yet daring, feats of early engineering. Notable among the great structures of antiquity are the aqueducts and sewers of Rome [7] and her colonial dependencies.

As against the mere supplying of adequate quantities of water of unknown sanitary quality, the hygienic control of water supply and waste-water disposal is of quite recent origin. It, too, is associated with the growth of cities which resulted, in this instance, from the industrial revolution of the nineteenth century. The scientific discoveries and engineering inventions of the late eighteenth and early nineteenth century paved the way for the creation of centralized industries. To these people flocked for employment. The standard of living of vast numbers of men was thereby improved; but absence of adequate community organization created slums through which the apocalyptic horsemen of pestilence and death often rode their steeds unchecked. The community facilities of the mushrooming industrial cities were quickly overtaxed. In particular the need for the abundant distribution of safe water and for the effective disposal of human excrement and other wastes could not be met through the means and knowledge immediately at hand. Too often, water was

---

[6] Reginald Reynolds, *Cleanliness and Godliness,* George Allen and Unwin, London, 1943.

[7] Sextus Julius Frontinus, water commissioner of Rome, A.D. 97, reports the existence of nine aqueducts supplying water to Rome and varying in length from 10 to over 50 miles and in cross-section from 7 to over 50 sq ft. Clemens Herschel (*Frontinus and the Water Supply of the City of Rome,* Longmans, Green & Co., New York, 1913) has estimated their aggregate capacity at 84 mgd. The great sewer, known as the *cloaca maxima,* which was constructed to drain the Roman Forum, is still in service.

drawn from polluted rivers or from shallow wells in crowded sections of the community and "distributed in courts by standpipes on intermittent days. The fatigue of fetching it was so great that they (the inhabitants of the courts) only used it for purposes which they deemed of absolute necessity, such as cooking; they rarely bestowed much of it on their clothes or persons." [8]

Although cities had for centuries been provided with sewers, these drains were intended for the purpose of carrying away the runoff from storms. The discharge of fecal and other wastes into sewers was forbidden well into the nineteenth century, although there had been clandestine use of sewers for this purpose before that time.[9] Before sanitary sewerage became an accepted method of municipal cleansing, "many dwellings of the poor were arranged round narrow courts having no other opening to the main street than a narrow covered passage. In these courts there were several occupants, each of whom accumulated a heap. In some cases, each of these heaps was piled up separately in the court, with a general receptacle in the middle for drainage. In others a pit was dug in the middle of the court for the general use of all the occupants. In some the whole courts up to the very doors of the houses were covered with filth." [10] In the great cities of the world, large numbers of people inhabited basements and cellars. "In very many cases the vaults and privies were situated on the same or a higher level, and their contents frequently oozed through walls into the occupied apartments beside them." [11] The privies themselves were often "too small in size and too few in number, and without ventilation or seat covers." [11]

Search for a remedy for foul conditions such as these ultimately led to the suggestion that human excrement be discharged into existing storm drains. The system of combined sewers was thereby created, and the early drainage works of most metropolitan communities were

[8] *First Report of the Metropolitan Sanitary Commission,* London, 1848.

[9] That storms helped to cleanse cities, at least superficially, can be judged from descriptions such as that of a city shower of October, 1710, cased in the satire of Jonathan Swift: "Now from all parts the swelling kennels flow, and bear their trophies with them as they go: Filth of all hues and odour, seem to tell what street they sail'd from, by their sight and smell."

[10] *Report from the Poor Law Commissioners on an Inquiry into the Sanitary Conditions of the Labouring Population of Great Britain,* 1842, *Local Reports,* p. 2. (In this quotation, the past tense replaces the present tense of the original.)

[11] *Report of the Council of Hygiene and Public Health of the Citizens' Association of New York upon the Sanitary Condition of the City,* 1865. (In this quotation, the past tense replaces the present tense of the original.)

elaborated in accordance with this scheme. The storm drains had justifiably been constructed so as to terminate in the nearest water courses. When sewage was emptied into the drains, they carried into the water courses quantities of wastes that, more often than not, over-taxed the receiving capacity of those waters. The nuisances that had apparently been so happily removed from dwellings by water carriage of waste matters were concentrated within waters that flowed through or past the communities. First the smaller and then the larger bodies of water, especially during hot weather, began to "seethe and ferment under a burning sun, in one vast open *cloaca*." [12] As a result, "large (surrounding) territories were at once, and frequently, enveloped in an atmosphere of stench so strong as to arouse the sleeping, terrify the weak, and nauseate and exasperate everybody." [13]

To cope with this new situation, many of the smaller streams were converted into sewers; but the larger bodies of water remained open to view and sensory disapprobation, until the discharge of waste matters into them was diminished by interception of the dry-weather flow and treatment of the collected waste waters.

The men who guided communities out of this morass did so by awakening the social and sanitary consciousness of the people and of their representatives in government. They included doctors, lawyers, engineers, writers,[14] and statesmen. Towering above all was Sir Edwin Chadwick, by training a lawyer, by calling a crusader for health. His was the chief voice in the *Report from the Poor Law Commissioners on an Inquiry into the Sanitary Conditions of the Labouring Popula-tion of Great Britain,* 1842. Communities are indebted to him for his general contributions to the advancement of the public health; the engineering profession for his specific interest in sanitary works, in-cluding his advocacy of employing tile sewers and the separate system of sewerage. The latter he epitomized in the statement "The rain to the river and the sewage to the soil." Closely associated with Chad-wick was Sir John Simon, first Medical Officer of Health of London (1848) and author of *English Sanitary Institutions* (1860).

In the United States, the counterparts of Edwin Chadwick and Dr. John Simon were played by Lemuel Shattuck of Boston and Dr.

[12] W. Budd, *Typhoid Fever,* 1873, relative to the condition of the Thames dur-ing the hot months of 1858 and 1859.

[13] E. C. Clark, *Report on the Main Drainage Works of the City of Boston,* 1885, quoting excerpts from one of the Annual Reports of the Board of Health.

[14] Charles Dickens, in commenting upon the slums of London at a public meet-ing in 1850, said that he "knew of many places in London unsurpassed in the accumulated horrors of their neglect by the *dirtiest* old spots in the *dirtiest* old towns under the *worst* old governments in Europe."

Stephen Smith of New York. Shattuck was the principal author of the *Report of the Sanitary Commission of Massachusetts* (1850) which led to the creation of the Massachusetts State Board of Health (1869). This board eventually established an engineering division (1886) and assigned to it the task of protecting the purity of inland waters. Stephen Smith was responsible for the *Report of the Council of Hygiene and Public Safety of the Citizens' Association of New York upon the Sanitary Condition of the City* (1865). The revelations of this document forced the passage of the Metropolitan Health Law (1866).

The researches of two outstanding medical authorities fall into this period, which has aptly been called the Great Sanitary Awakening: those of John Snow, who, in 1849, demonstrated to a world that had not yet witnessed the discoveries of Louis Pasteur the role of fecal pollution of drinking water in the epidemicity of cholera; and those of William Budd, who from 1857 onward investigated typhoid fever, its nature, mode of spreading, and prevention.

Early leaders among engineers were James Simpson, who in 1829 built the filters of the Chelsea Water Company for the purpose of improving the quality of Thames River water; Sir Robert Rawlinson, who, as Superintendent Inspector of the General Board of Health (1848), conducted the engineering studies necessary for the construction of sanitary works in industrial Britain; Sir John Bazalgette, who started the main drainage of London in 1850; and John Roe, who accepted Chadwick's suggestion that vitrified tile pipe be used in sewer lines. Similar functions were performed in the United States by Julius W. Adams, who in 1857 constructed the first comprehensive system of sewerage in Brooklyn, N. Y.; James P. Kirkwood, who in 1871 built the first sizeable water filters at Poughkeepsie, N. Y.; and Hiram F. Mills, who in 1886, as the engineer-member of the Massachusetts State Board of Health, gave direction to its newly formed engineering division and caused the work of that division to be supported and advanced by the sanitary researches of the Lawrence Experiment Station of the Board.

More recent developments in water supply and waste-water disposal are discussed later in this book in connection with individual subject matters.

Sanitation of Water Supplies

1-4. General Considerations. To meet the general requirements of sanitation, water supplies must possess two attributes: wholesomeness and palatability. These are intertwined. If water is not attractive to the senses of sight, taste, and smell—if it disgusts the consumer

—people will shun its use and either drink amounts that are insufficient to meet physiological needs or seek water from sources that, although they deliver a liquid that is more pleasant to the senses, may in fact be contaminated or otherwise hygienically unsafe or dangerous.

1-5. Wholesomeness of Water. To be wholesome, water must be (a) uncontaminated and hence unable to infect its user with a water-borne disease; (b) free from poisonous substances; and (c) free from excessive amounts of mineral and organic matter.

a. Safety from Infection. The water-borne diseases fall into five categories according to the nature of the organisms that cause infectious disease: bacteria, protozoa, worms, viruses, and fungi. Water itself would not become the means of spreading disease, however, were it not for its pollution by the excreta (1) of persons acutely ill with an intestinal or related infection or (2) of apparently healthy carriers of the responsible organisms.

The enteric, water-borne, bacterial infections include typhoid fever, paratyphoid fever (salmonellosis), bacillary dysentery (shigellosis), and cholera. Most of the conscious efforts in water supply and waste-water disposal have been, and continue to be, directed to the removal or destruction of these pathogenic organisms. Water-borne outbreaks of undulant fever (brucellosis) and tularemia have been reported but are of unusual occurrence. Hemorrhagic jaundice, or Weil's disease, is acquired, in addition to other ways, by swimming in polluted water. Rats have a part as carriers of the spirochete responsible for this disease which, as a water-borne infection, is normally confined to particular situations such as the canals of Holland.

Typhoid fever, at the beginning of the present century a scourge which even in some of the larger communities of North America exacted an annual death toll of more than 115 per 100,000 population,[15] has been placed under control by proper methods of water supply, filtration, and disinfection in particular, and by other sanitary safeguards, such as safe methods of waste-water disposal, milk and food supply, and the control of flies. The fact that civilized communities have been relatively free from attack for a generation, however, has left them more vulnerable to infection than before, because their inhabitants have not had an opportunity to acquire immunity to this disease. A community-wide invasion of the water supply might, therefore, be expected to strike down a far larger proportion of the

---

[15] Pittsburgh, Pa., from 1902 to 1907 before filtration of the public water supply was introduced. Because the case fatality of this disease may be estimated to have been 1 in 10, the typhoid morbidity may be estimated to have been 1,150 per 100,000 population.

population than succumbed to the disease in the epidemics of the past when typhoid fever was more prevalent than today. This warning applies to other water-borne infections as well. It is one that should spur the responsible agencies to continual vigilance.

Water-borne paratyphoid fever (salmonellosis) and bacillary dysentery (shigellosis) are probably of more frequent occurrence than our statistics indicate. The groups of diseases vary widely in severity and individual response. Mild outbreaks are probably never reported. The fact that man shares some of the paratyphoid organisms with domestic animals, such as hogs, poultry, and dogs, is not adequately recognized.

Cholera, which was pandemic during the nineteenth century, is confined at present principally to the Asiatic continent. The rapid communication with other parts of the world by air transport has renewed interest in the potential hazard of new epidemics.

Although it is estimated that between 5 and 10% of the American people are carriers of amebic cysts, the reported incidence of water-borne amebic dysentery (amebiasis) has been small.[16] The probable reason for this is (1) the number of cysts excreted by carriers, which is relatively much lower than the number of typhoid organisms excreted by carriers of that disease, and (2) the effective removal of the cysts from water by natural purification and by filtration. The large size of amebic cysts (15 microns) relative to that of bacteria (1 to 2 microns) accounts in part for their more active removal. It is to the contamination of water distribution systems by back-flow from house drainage systems and by cross-connections with unsafe water supplies that we must probably look for most outbreaks of water-borne amebic dysentery. By such means a heavy charge or "slug" of excrement can be carried to nearby consumers and infect them. Normal methods of water disinfection do not destroy amebic cysts, and higher than normal dosages of chlorine must be resorted to in order to assure safety from amebic dysentery when the presence in water of the causative agent is suspected. There are other, possibly water-borne, protozoal infections, too. However, they are of such rare occurrence as to be of little general significance.

The eggs of some intestinal worms and the larvae of others undoubtedly find their way from human and animal carriers (either directly or from the soil) into water courses and so possibly into water

---

[16] There are but three water-borne epidemics of amebic dysentery on record, all of them in Chicago, Ill. The first of these was confined to the patrons of two hotels; the second, to firemen and spectators at a stockyard fire; and the third to workers in an industrial establishment.

supplies. The numbers in which these organisms are discharged from the alimentary tract are relatively so small, however, and the organisms themselves are relatively so large that no widespread infections from this source have been reported. Sporadic infection may well take place under grossly insanitary conditions. Infection by the larval form (cercariae) of the blood flukes (schistosomes) is another matter. Here the snail host of this worm liberates large numbers of cercariae into water. Infection does not occur in the water itself but when the larvae are forced into the skin by the drying of water droplets. Fortunately, schistosomiasis does not occur in many regions of the world because of the absence of a suitable snail host. Although none of the snails through which man is infected are indigenous to the United States, the snail hosts and larvae of certain schistosomes that cause "swimmer's itch," a skin disease (cercarial dermatitis), are found in some parts of the country. They are transported from one body of water to another by water fowl. In certain regions of the world, the minute crustacean *Cyclops* contains the larvae of the guinea worm, a species of filaria that infects man.

About water-borne virus infections we know all too little at the present time. However, we do have knowledge of at least one virus—that of infectious hepatitis or epidemic jaundice—being spread by drinking water. We also know that other viruses—among them that of infantile paralysis or poliomyelitis—occur in the stools of patients suffering from specific virus diseases. Present indications are that the normal portal of entry of poliomyelitis virus into the human body may be through the intestinal tract as well as the nose and throat. Hence, it might conceivably be a water-borne disease of swimming pools and bathing beaches as well as of drinking-water supplies. Epidemiological evidence, however, is still overwhelmingly against this hypothesis.

About certain other gastrointestinal upsets, apparently water-borne, possibly of virus origin, and associated with heavy pollution of the water supplies of the communities in which they have occurred, we still have much to learn.

The only fungus that may be suspected of being allied to water in its spread is that associated with histoplasmosis. So little is known about the epidemiology of this disease at the present time, however, that judgment as to the possibility of water-borne infection must be reserved.

b. Freedom from Poisonous Substances. Three types of toxic contaminants may conceivably be encountered in public water supplies under normal conditions: (1) natural contaminants in water that has come into contact with poisonous mineral formations; (2) natural contaminants in water associated with specific aquatic growths; (3) acquired contaminants that enter water from water-works structures, principally metallic pipes, or from water-treatment practices; and (4) acquired contaminants traceable to industrial and similar wastes that have been discharged into water courses.

Natural mineral contaminants include the elements fluorine, selenium, arsenic, and boron. With the exception of fluorine, these natural contaminants are seldom encountered in sufficient concentration in drinking water to cause damage. The mottling of teeth, observed widely in the middle and south west of North America is definitely associated with the presence in water of excessive amounts of fluorides. Small concentrations of fluorides, on the other hand, appear to reduce the prevalence of dental caries. Fluorides, therefore, must be regarded as both beneficent and dangerous minerals. Excessive amounts of nitrates in water are held to be responsible for an illness (methemoglobinemia or nitrate-cyanosis) of formula-fed infants. Reduction of the nitrates to nitrites in the intestinal tract and absorption into the blood stream, where the nitrites combine with the hemoglobin, deprives the organs and tissues of needed oxygen; cyanosis (a blue color of the skin) is the symptom of the poisoning.

The sudden death of cattle following the ingestion of water supporting luxuriant growths of blue-green algae and the isolation of a toxic principle from these growths have been reported. Ordinarily, such water would be too repulsive to man to endanger him. The possibility of poisoning from these natural contaminants, however, cannot be completely discounted. A case in point is the poisoning caused by the consumption of mussels that contain large numbers of the dinoflagellate *Gonyaulax catenella* [17] at certain seasons of the year.

Contaminants acquired within the distribution system by corrosion of metallic pipes are often the reason for consumer complaints. Soft waters are highly corrosive, particularly those that contain appreciable quantities of carbon dioxide. Among the metals still employed in water-works systems, lead is the only one of proved toxicity. It is a cumulative poison, the resulting disease being called plumbism. Copper, zinc, and iron are objectionable chiefly because they impart a metallic taste to water if they are present in significant amounts. They may also discolor either the water itself (zinc and iron), fixtures (copper and iron), fabrics (iron), or other objects with which they

---

[17] A small protozoon that occurs in sea water, often in sufficient numbers to give the water a red appearance. This organism invades mussel beds upon occasion and is ingested by them without harm to themselves.

come into contact. Excessive amounts of copper have been reported to produce nausea.

The chemical treatment of water for coagulation, disinfection, destruction of algae and water weeds, or corrosion control is in essence a source of potential contamination. The chemicals employed are ordinarily harmless in themselves or so low in concentration as to be non-toxic. Nevertheless, it should be one of the tenets of the engineering profession to refrain from the addition of new substances to water until the possibility of their being toxic in themselves or producing toxic effects by unsuspected action within the water system has been adequately explored.

All conceivable kinds and varieties of toxic contaminants may be contributed to water by industrial or commercial operations. Their control is a matter of proper treatment and disposal of the wastes that contain them. The possibility of their presence in water supplies is sometimes unsuspected. To guard against them, establishments employing or producing toxic compounds, such as cyanides and hexavalent chromium, should be surveyed thoroughly for hazards of water pollution caused by normal as well as by unusual operations or occurrences.

c. *Freedom from Excessive Amounts of Mineral and Organic Matter.* Whereas the harmfulness of infecting organisms and toxic contaminants is self-evident, there are certain qualities of water supplies that touch upon the fringe of wholesomeness but that cannot be directly incriminated. Excessive mineralization is one; excessive presence of organic matter—living and dead—is another.

Highly mineralized waters frequently possess laxative properties. These are particularly associated with the presence in water of magnesium and sulfate ions. Highly mineralized or hard waters consume much soap before a lather is created and lay down scales when the water is heated or evaporated. Although most hard waters are less corrosive than soft ones, because most of them deposit protective coatings on metallic pipe surfaces, the presence of acids and acid radicals—chlorides and sulfates—may render them very corrosive. The significance of caustic alkalinity, present in some natural waters in the West, but associated ordinarily with the liming of water for softening or corrosion control, has not yet been fully established. Excessive hardness may have some bearing on irritations of the skin of sensitive individuals (winter chapping and dishpan hands).

Related to mineralization but of opposite significance is (1) the absence from the waters of the glaciated regions of the United States of iodine, a lack of adequate amounts of this element being associated with endemic goiter; and (2) insufficient alkalinity that renders water corrosive. While deficient alkalinity is readily made up by the addition of lime or soda ash, the remedy for iodine deficiency does not seem to lie in the medication of the water by addition of iodides, but in the regulation of the iodine content of table salt and the distribution of corrective tablets to school children. The use of iodized salt and iodide tablets is more economical than the periodic iodizing of water supplies. It also makes the water at all times available to individuals who have an iodine idiosyncrasy or who are suffering from a thyroid disease that is adversely affected by iodine intake. The addition to water of physiologically needed quantities of fluorides for the control of dental caries, on the other hand, appears to be justified for as long as a more economical method of providing needed amounts of fluorides cannot be devised.

There is no direct evidence of the harmfulness of excessive amounts of organic matter in water. Bad odors, tastes, and appearance, however, issue warnings to our primitive protective instincts. It seems only reasonable to heed them in the absence of proof to the contrary.

1-6. Palatability of Water. Water may be unsafe without being unsavory and the reverse: unsavory without being unsafe. The interrelation of the two has already been pointed out. To be palatable, water should be free, or significantly so, from color, turbidity, taste, and odor, of moderate temperature in summer and winter, and aerated. At least four human perceptions are involved in judging these qualities. They involve the senses of sight (color and turbidity), taste, smell (odor), and touch (temperature). If the pleasant sound of running water is recognized as one of its qualities, the sensory appeal of water becomes complete.

   a. Color and Turbidity. Color is commonly of vegetable origin, like the "meadow-tea" that Thoreau saw in the brooks of New England. Water may become discolored, however, also by industrial wastes, by natural sources of iron and manganese, and by the products of corrosion. To appeal to the visitor as well as the native, the color of water should be low. So far as individual communities are concerned, however, the accustomed color of the supply may be quite high without eliciting comment. Much the same situation holds for turbidity. A muddy water, in which turbidity is due to suspended clay particles, is more obnoxious to those who do not live in regions in which, according to Mark Twain, "a tumblerful of river water contains an acre of land," than it is to the indigenous population. Turbidity may be due not only to the erosion of clay banks but also to the discharge of industrial wastes, the liberation of products of corrosion, and the growth of algae and other plankton organisms.

Coagulation, sedimentation, and filtration make it possible to turn out a water that contains almost no coloring or dispersed matter. Today's public demands a sparklingly clear water.

b. *Taste and Odor.* The words taste and odor are generally used loosely and, to a certain extent, interchangeably. Actually there are but four tastes—sour, salt, sweet, and bitter—which are strictly confined in their preception to the taste buds of the tongue. Odors appear to be without limit in number, and they are known to change in quality as the concentration of the odorous compounds, or the intensity of their smell, is varied. However, careful screening of odors has identified certain fundamental odors from which all odors can be compounded. The smallest number in a suggested classification is four: sweet or fragrant, sour or acid, burnt or empyreumatic, and goaty or caprylic.[18] Odors are sensed through the olfactory area which is situated high in the human nose. Minute cilia, or hairlike receptors, extend from the cells that cover the olfactory nerve fibers. Perception of odors is commonly assumed to require the absorption of the molecules of odorous substances by the watery and oily covering of the olfactory area; but other mechanisms of olfaction have also been suggested.

Tastes and odors are associated with the presence in water of the following: (1) decaying organic matter; (2) living algae and other microscopic organisms that contain essential oils and other odorous compounds; (3) iron and manganese and metallic products of corrosion; (4) industrial wastes, particularly phenolic substances; and (5) in connection with the disinfection of water, chlorine and its substitution compounds. The metallic, or chalybeate, taste of water from hot springs was described by Dickens as the "taste of hot flat irons."

Generally speaking, water should not possess a taste or odor that is sufficiently marked to impress itself upon the user without his first searching for its presence. It is unfortunate that there should frequently be allied to chlorination—so important to the attainment or assurance of water safety—the production or accentuation of odors and tastes.

Fortunately superchlorination (including its direction into the break-point reaction), ammonia-chlorine treatment, addition of chlorine dioxide, use of activated carbon, and dechlorination offer means for preventing or destroying tastes and odors that are connected with this economical and effective method of water disinfection. The pre-

[18] E. C. Crocker, *Flavor,* McGraw-Hill Book Co., New York, 1945.

vention of odors and tastes associated with algae and related organisms by the judicious application of copper sulfate to water that might otherwise support objectionable growths of these organisms is also important.

c. *Temperature.* Warm water tastes or, more concisely, feels flat. Surface waters fluctuate in temperature with the seasons, whereas ground water holds close to the annual average within slight departures. In the summer, the temperature of deep lakes and reservoirs decreases sharply from top to bottom. By shifting the depth of draft, therefore, it may be possible to draw relatively cool water even during hot weather. So far as provisions permit, this should be done, not only to obtain water cooler than that near the surface, but often also to draw water that contains fewer algae and is generally more attractive, or more amenable to treatment.

1-7. Sanitary Control of Water Quality. The sanitary control of water quality enters into every phase of technical water-works activity. It starts with the preparation and supervision of the catchment area or source of supply; it follows the conduits through the purification works into the distribution system; and it terminates at the fixture or equipment from which or into which water is drawn. Each part of the works presents problems of control that are peculiar to it. For all parts, however, eternal vigilance is the price of security.

a. *Source of Supply.* A naturally clean water can be drawn only from a clean source or watershed. Water-works managers, therefore, should be thoroughly familiar with the catchment area of their supply or, in the case of large streams and lakes as well as ground-water works, with the vicinity of the source. These areas should be visited at all seasons of the year and in all conditions of weather—during summer and winter, and during drought and flood—in order that the varying hazards to water quality may be fully uncovered and remedied. Much can be done to safeguard and improve natural water quality by sanitation of the catchment area, drainage of swamps, prevention of soil erosion, reforestation and afforestation, encouragement of proper farming practices (contour plowing), preparation of reservoir sites in advance of filling, control of the growth of water weeds and plankton (algae), and shifting the depth of draft. Regulation and supervision of recreational activities—camping, picnicking, swimming, boating, and fishing—as well as ice harvesting, are parts of the problem. Protection of the source of supply during construction and repairs is another important responsibility.

b. *Purification Works.* Modern water-purification works can be elaborated in great variety to meet the needs of the community. Regardless of the quality of the raw water, an effluent of any desired composition can be produced by suitable treatment methods. Economic considerations, however, exert a controlling influence, once sanitary requirements have been met.

All water delivered to a community should normally be disinfected, no matter how clean and presumably safe the water may be in its natural state or following other processes of treatment. This does not mean, however, delivering, in place of water, a dilute disinfectant to the consumer on the last tap.

c. *Conduit and Distribution System.* The masonry or metallic structures that carry water to the community and distribute it to the consumers are subject to attack by water. In turn they may change the quality of the water that they convey. It is within the responsibility and power of designers to adjust the materials employed to the quality of the water carried, and within the responsibility and power of operators to adjust the qualities of the water conveyed to the materials employed. Corrosion of metals and disintegration of cement and concrete can be held within reasonable limits. No conduit should go into service, upon installation or repair, without having been disinfected.

Perhaps of greatest importance in the sanitary maintenance of distribution works is (1) the control and elimination of cross-connections of the public supply with polluted or otherwise unsafe private supplies, and (2) the prevention, in plumbing systems, of backflow or siphonage of polluted water from fixtures and other portions of the drainage system into the water piping of buildings. Water purveyors should have the right to regulate and inspect all water piping on private property or to cooperate in such regulation and inspection with other duly constituted authorities. Chlorine or ammonia-chlorine residuals will keep down bacterial growths within distribution systems and so imply a clean bill of health, but their ability to neutralize "slugs of pollution" liberated within the system is open to question. However, these residuals do serve as traveling sentinels of safety. Their disappearance should arouse suspicion.

Sanitation of Waste-Water Disposal

1-8. General Considerations. It has been pointed out before that water supply and waste-water disposal are closely interrelated activities in community service. Whereas the safety and palatability of its water supply primarily involves the exercise of selfish concern for the community served, the motivation for the sanitary disposal of its waste waters must often be a sense of neighborly responsibility toward persons and communities that are dependent, in one way or another, upon the water courses into which sewage and industrial wastes are discharged. It is because of this difference in interest that the sanitation of receiving bodies of water has progressed slowly and that judicial as well as advisory functions have had to be assumed by governmental health agencies in order to preserve the desirable purity of such waters.

To meet the general requirements of sanitation, waste-water disposal systems must perform two functions: (1) reliable and inoffensive collection of waste matters from household and industry, and (2) safe disposal of the water-carried wastes into water or, less commonly, onto land. If the second function is disregarded, as it was in early drainage works, the collection system will merely transfer the potential hazards and nuisance associated with the wastes from the immediate premises of dwellings and industrial establishments to the terminus of the system; in particular to the receiving waters that constitute the ultimate drainage channels of a region. Runoff from rainstorms and from melting ice and snow, collected in rigidly separated storm-drainage systems presents few, if any, sanitary hazards, however.

1-9. Objectionable Properties of Sewage and Industrial Waste Waters. As is true for drinking water, much of our interest in systems of waste-water disposal, too, stems from the primitive warnings of our sense of smell that decay means danger; and so it does very frequently where food is concerned. However, the odors arising from decaying sewage matters and industrial wastes, once called sewer gases and implying danger, are not the immediate carriers of infection. Although high concentrations of hydrogen sulfide, which is one of the most odoriferous products of the anaerobic decomposition of waste matters, are toxic to man, sewer odors are ordinarily innocuous, though frequently obnoxious. Because of the possible presence in underground structures of toxic and inflammable gases, including illuminating gas escaping from gas mains, and because of the possible inadequacy of oxygen in such structures, workmen descending into manholes, sewers, and appurtenant structures must always be alert to these dangers. Precautions against poisoning, asphyxiation, and explosion should become part of the operational routine of such workers.

Until it was recognized, upon the advent of bacteriology, that the living agents of disease were associated with the flowing sewage rather than its gases of decomposition, sanitary thought was primarily directed towards means for controlling the penetration of sewer air into habitations. Engineers, however, should knowingly differentiate between the obnoxious attributes of sewage and industrial wastes, such as unsightliness and bad smell, which have no bearing or but an indirect bearing on health, and the true hygienic hazards that are involved in collecting and disposing of sewage and other waste waters.

There is probably no infectious or parasitic disease to which man may succumb the agents of which do not find their way, at some time, into sewage. Whether the responsible organisms issue from the intestinal tract, the respiratory system, or the surfaces of the human body, the habits of civilized man are such that his excretions, secretions, and ablutions are committed to the sewerage system. In order to impart disease, however, sewage or sewage-polluted substances must come into contact with susceptible persons in such manner as to infect them. Fortunately, the number of diseases that lend themselves to widespread transmission through sewage is relatively small and consists principally of the classical water-borne diseases: typhoid, paratyphoid, bacillary dysentery, and cholera (see Section 1-5).

Again as is true for drinking water, the modes of transmission and routes of infection are ordinarily well defined; but they may be quite devious. If we include infections conveyed by excreta as well as by sewage, and sewage sludge, we may cite numerous ways in which disease is spread from these sources. We may also slightly expand the list of possible infections beyond those of the classical water-borne diseases. Modes of transmission other than through drinking water are: (1) through watercress, or shellfish harvested from or stored in sewage-polluted water (typhoid, paratyphoid, and bacillary dysentery); (2) through vegetables and fruits contaminated by excreta, sewage, or sewage sludge (typhoid, paratyphoid, the dysenteries, parasitic worms, and infectious hepatitis); (3) through exposure to soil contaminated by human excreta (hookworm); (4) through all manner of food contaminated by flies and other vermin that feed upon human excreta (typhoid, paratyphoid, the dysenteries, and infectious hepatitis); (5) through milk contaminated by utensils that have been washed in polluted water (typhoid, paratyphoid, and bacillary dysentery); (6) through fish from polluted waters and eaten raw or too soon after salting (flukes and tapeworms); and (7) through bathing or other exposure to polluted water (Weil's disease and schistosomiasis). An unusual chain of infection is that through the milk of cows that have acquired tuberculosis from the sewage of tuberculosis sanatoria discharged into streams running through pastures.

The role of bathing waters in spreading infections other than those associated with drinking water is discussed in Section 30-8.

Although the unsightliness of sewage and industrial wastes is of no direct hygienic concern, it constitutes an objectionable attribute and must be given consideration in the design and operation of waste-water disposal systems. Unsightliness is particularly obnoxious when it interferes with the recreational enjoyment of bodies of water into which waste matters are discharged or when it injures the prospect of a city that could otherwise take pride in the beauty of the sheets of water in which it could be mirrored.

1-10. Sanitary Control of Waste Water. The sanitary control of waste water enters into every phase of technical waste-water disposal. It starts, where water supply ends, at the fixtures or appurtenances that receive water for discharge into the waste-water system; it follows the collecting system through the treatment works; and it terminates only after the streams or other bodies of receiving water have been returned to the condition of relative purity desired for them.

Waste-water works have as their primary objective not only the safe collection of waste matters from household and industry but also the safe disposal of these waste matters. When the waste waters are discharged into receiving waters this involves the prevention of damage of many kinds: (1) contamination or pollution of water supplies for man, beast, and industry; (2) contamination or pollution of bathing places, shellfish layings, and ice supplies; (3) creation of conditions offensive to sight or smell; (4) infection and destruction of food fish and other valuable aquatic life; and (5) other impairment of the usefulness of natural waters for recreation, commerce, or industry. When the waste waters are discharged onto land either directly (sewage) or indirectly (sewage sludge), the contamination of crops used by man and beast becomes an added consideration.

a. Collection Works. Within the system of drains that constitute the water-carriage system, waste matters should be transported steadily and rapidly to the point of disposal. The system should be self-cleansing and as hydraulically tight as is economically justifiable.

Within buildings, sewage should never be permitted to seep from the metal drains and stacks that convey it from plumbing fixtures to the tile building sewer and tile or masonry public sewer. The drainage portion of plumbing systems (including venting systems), furthermore, should not permit foul air to escape into occupied spaces; neither should there be an opportunity for roaches and other vermin to find shelter or convenient routes of travel within the drainage system. Similar safeguards should be provided in industrial premises.

Tile and masonry sewers are seldom so tight that they will not lose some of their contents by seepage into the surrounding soils, or that

they will not take in ground water. Both these occurrences are undesirable. But their elimination or control is economically justifiable
only when leakage endangers water supply, for example, or when
entrance of ground water becomes excessive. Water-pipe, rather than
sewer-pipe, materials and methods of laying should then be employed
in order to insure maximum tightness of the collecting conduits.
Where sewers are underdrained and the drains empty into water
courses, the outlets should receive sanitary supervision.

In combined systems, the hazards created by the discharge of sewage and industrial wastes along with flood runoff through storm-water
overflows must be clearly recognized. Although the amount of waste
matter released is seldom in excess of 1% of that contained in the
annual flow of sewage and industrial wastes when intercepters are
designed to carry the maximum dry-weather flow (close to twice the
average dry-weather flow), the ensuing pollution and contamination
of receiving waters and bathing beaches may be quite heavy at times.
It is for this reason that public health authorities prefer separate
systems to combined systems.

Catchbasins may breed mosquitoes, including species that carry
virus infections such as dengue.

b. Treatment Works. Like modern water-purification plants, modern waste-water treatment works can be built to meet almost any
specified performance requirements. Actual choice of works is determined by economic considerations within the framework of sanitary
needs. Much depends upon the nature of the hygienic, esthetic, and
economic interests that are to be safeguarded. A treatment plant becomes part of the regional economy and as such should be integrated
into the general plan of the drainage area. Particular consideration
should be given to the intelligent conservation and exploitation of the
regional water resources.

Where conditions permit, we may forgo treatment. In other circumstances, it may be worth while to treat the waste waters so completely that they approach drinking water in quality although they
may not, purposely, be used as such. Chadwick's advice that sewage
be carried to the soil implies the utilization of the fertilizing constituents of the sewage.[19]

[19] Recommending the employment of the sewage of Paris for the irrigation of
farms along the Seine, Victor Hugo (in *Les Misérables*) asks the following question and gives the following answer: "Do you know what those piles of ordure
are, collected at the corners of streets, those carts of mud carried off at night
from streets, the frightful barrels of the night-man, and the fetid streams of subterranean mud which the pavement conceals from you? All this is a flowering
field, it is green grass, it is mint, thyme, and sage; it is game, it is cattle, it is

The agricultural utilization of sewage, or of the by-products of sewage treatment, however, presents potential sanitary hazards that must be guarded against. Ordinarily, the principal agricultural value of sewage is its use for the irrigation of crops in semiarid regions in which water cannot be supplied more cheaply from other sources. Nevertheless, the full use of the waste matters of communities remains a challenge, and the sanitary solution of the problem awaits a better answer than it has received so far.

c. *Receiving Waters.* Unless waste water is disposed of by irrigation, it must be emptied, either raw or after suitable treatment, into the available regional drainage channels. Such discharge is called disposal by dilution. But more than a mere physical dilution or dispersion of waste matters and living organisms in additional volumes of water takes place. The natural or self-purifying power of the water is marshaled for action. This includes the biological decomposition of waste organic substances, the die-away of pathogenic organisms, and the operation of certain physical, especially subsiding, and chemical forces. In the course of time, these will effect the ultimate return of polluted waters to the normal standards of clean surface waters in nature.

The discharge of raw or treated waste water into receiving waters is circumscribed in an engineering sense by the capacity of these waters for self-purification—whether they be streams and canals, lakes and ponds, or tidal estuaries and coastal waters. In a balanced economy, the treatment and discharge of waste waters should be regulated to make as much use of this self-cleansing power of water as is consistent with the proper safeguarding of receiving waters against damage.

There corresponds to the self-purification of surface waters a self-purification also of ground waters. The forces involved are similar in nature, but they differ in intensity. Filtration through the pores of fine-textured geological formations often becomes a potent force for natural purification.

Self-purification does indeed offer an answer to the question raised by Samuel Taylor Coleridge after a visit to the city of Cologne towards the end of the eighteenth century: "The river Rhine, it is well known, doth wash your city of Cologne; but tell me, nymphs, what power divine shall henceforth wash the river Rhine?"

the satisfied lowing of heavy kine; at night it is perfumed hay, it is gilded wheat, it is bread on your table, it is warm blood in your veins, it is health, it is joy, it is life."

Accomplishments of Water Sanitation

1-11. General Considerations. The accomplishments of water sanitation are not reflected alone by statistics of sickness and death traceable to water-borne infections. They are allied, in important measure, also to the enhancement of human comfort and well-being. The amenities created by an abundant and palatable supply of water, by the water-carriage system of sewerage, and by clean streams, ponds, lakes, and shore waters are many. How acceptable a supply of good water can be to a community that has lacked it is well illustrated by the celebration in 1848 on Boston Common of the introduction into that city of a new supply of water from Lake Cochituate. For this celebration, James Russell Lowell was prompted to write a poem that includes the words: "My name is Water: I have sped through strange, dark ways, untried before, by pure desire of friendship led, Cochituate's ambassador; he sends four royal gifts by me, long life, health, peace, and purity."

Of house drainage, Stobart [20] has well said: "There is no truer sign of civilization and culture than good sanitation. It goes with refined senses and orderly habits. A good drain implies as much as a beautiful statue. And let it be remembered that the world did not reach the Minoan [21] standard of cleanliness again until the great sanitary movement of the late nineteenth century."

Unfortunately, there are no ready means for measuring human comfort and well-being, whereas sickness and death are determinable facts. Less reliance can be placed, however, on records of illness than on records of death, because the reporting of illness is seldom complete and the diagnosis, except in time of epidemics, is often uncertain or incomplete. For purposes of comparison, rates of morbidity and mortality are employed. It is common practice to express these rates respectively as the number of cases of a specific disease and the number of deaths resulting from this disease within a region or community per 100,000 population per annum. The ratio of deaths to cases is called the case fatality. Of interest in water sanitation are not only the annual rates of morbidity and mortality but also the number of outbreaks of water-borne disease and the causes of these outbreaks.

[20] J. C. Stobart, *The Glory That Was Greece* (revised by F. N. Pryce), Appleton-Century Co., New York, p. 29, 1935.

[21] Named after King Minos of Crete. Archeologists have found that the palace of Knossos on this island contained bathrooms, a latrine flushed by rain water, and tile drains.

1-12. Accomplishments Exemplified. The accomplishments of water sanitation in terms of reduced sickness and death as well as the number and intensity of outbreaks can be exemplified most closely for water supply. Here cause and effect can be more nearly established. The accomplishments of waste-water sanitation cannot be evaluated as directly. However, we can adduce some evidence in

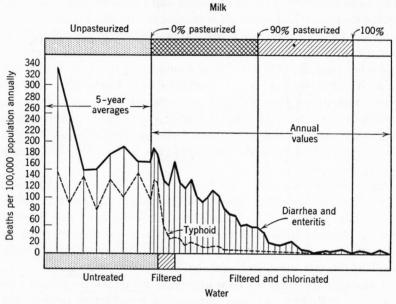

Figure 1-2. Effect of water purification and milk pasteurization on the death rates from typhoid fever in all age groups and from diarrhea and enteritis in children under 2 years of age in a city drawing water from a polluted river.

terms of the record of enteric diseases in rural areas in which safe methods of excreta disposal are provided.

a. Water Supply. The effects of water sanitation on the death rates from typhoid fever in two typical North American communities are shown in Figures 1-2 and 1-3. Figure 1-2 records the experience of a city [22] supplied with drinking water from a polluted stream. In the course of its history, this city first introduced slow sand filtration of the water and later chlorination of the filtered supply. The effects of these operations are clearly illustrated. In order to show that other factors, too, contribute to the reduction in enteric disease, the history of diarrhea and enteritis in children under two years of age, which is probably more closely related to milk supply than to water

[22] The city of Pittsburgh, Pa., which takes its supply from the Allegheny River.

supply, is also recorded statistically in Figure 1-2. Other sanitary improvements, undoubtedly, had a part in lowering the rates of both diseases in this community. Figure 1-3 gives the record of a city [23] supplied with drinking water from a relatively clear lake. This city resorted to chlorination before adding coagulation, sedimentation, and

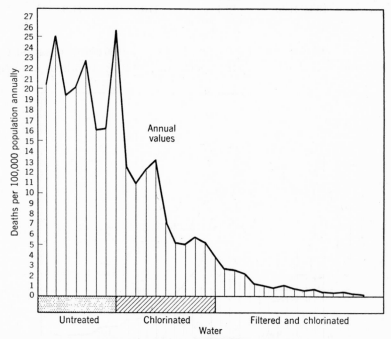

Figure 1-3. Effect of water purification on the death rate from typhoid fever in a city drawing water from a clear lake.

rapid sand filtration. Again the effects are clearly manifest. Both communities were able, in the course of time, to reduce their death rates from typhoid fever well below 1 per 100,000 per annum. At such levels, there is no longer reason to suspect that the disease is acquired from the drinking water of the community.

The reported average annual number of outbreaks of water-borne typhoid fever in the United States for the periods 1920 to 1929, 1930 to 1936, and 1938 to 1945 and their relative intensity are shown in Table 1-1.[24]

[23] The city of Detroit, Mich., which is supplied from Lake St. Clair.

[24] Data from (1) Abel Wolman and A. E. Gorman, "Water-Borne Outbreaks in the United States and Canada, and Their Significance," *J. Am. Water Works Assoc., 31,* 225 (1939); and (2) from Rolf Eliassen and R. H. Cummings, "Analysis of Water-Borne Outbreaks, 1938–45," *J. Am. Water Works Assoc., 40,* 509 (1948).

TABLE 1-1.   Water-Borne Typhoid Fever in the United States

Period	Outbreaks per annum	Typhoid cases per annum	Typhoid cases per outbreak
1920–1929 *	23.0	942	41.0
1930–1936	24.1	452	19.2
1938–1945	12.4	170	11.0

* 47 states only.

b. Excreta Disposal. The effect of sanitary excreta disposal on the incidence of typhoid and paratyphoid in a state [25] in which a deter-

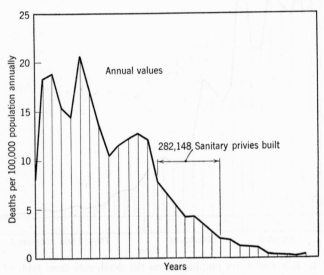

Figure 1-4.   Reduction in the death rate from typhoid fever by sanitation of excreta disposal.

mined effort was made to construct an adequate number of sanitary privies is shown in Figure 1-4. Improvements in other sanitary conditions probably occurred at the same time.

Leach and Maxcy [26] have listed rates of typhoid fever per 100,000 population in communities of different sizes or types (Table 1-2).

TABLE 1-2.   Typhoid Fever and Size or Type of Community

Size or type	Rural	500–1,000	1,000–2,500	2,500–5,000	5,000–10,000	10,000–25,000	>25,000
Morbidity	52	443	307	180	165	118	63

[25] West Virginia.

[26] C. N. Leach and K. F. Maxcy, "The Relative Incidence of Typhoid Fever in Cities, Towns, and Country Districts of a Southern State," *Pub. Health Rept., 41,* 705 (1926).

These values may be interpreted as showing relatively good sanitary protection (1) in rural areas because of lack of contact, and (2) in larger communities because of good community sanitation, including both water supply and waste-water disposal.

We may well end this introductory chapter with the admonition of Disraeli, provoked during a discussion in Parliament of the Public Health Act, described as the most complete code of sanitary law in existence: "The public health is the foundation on which repose the happiness of the people and the power of a country. The care of the public health is the first duty of a statesman." It is likewise the first duty of the water engineer.

2-1. General Features of Water-Supply Systems. Water-supply systems generally comprise (1) collection works; (2) purification works, where needed; and (3) transportation and distribution works. Their relative functions and positions in a surface-water supply are outlined in Figure 2-1. The collection works either tap a source of water that is continuously adequate in quantity to satisfy present and reasonable future demands, or they convert an intermittently inadequate source into a continuously adequate supply by storing surplus water for use during periods of insufficiency. If the water is not satisfactory in quality at the point of collection, purification works render the collected water suitable for the purposes it is to serve. Polluted and hence potentially infected water is disinfected; esthetically unattractive or unpalatable water is treated to make it attractive and palatable; water containing iron or manganese is subjected to deferrization or demanganization; corrosive water is modified chemically to render it non-corrosive; and excessively hard water is softened. The transportation and distribution works convey the collected and purified water to the community and there dispense it to consumers in ample volume and at adequate pressure. The amount of water delivered is measured so that an equable charge can be made for its use.

2-2. Required Capacity. Water-supply systems are designed to meet the needs of the community for a reasonable number of years into the future. For purposes of comparison the quantity of water consumed by a community is expressed as the average annual rate of use in gallons per capita per day (gpcd). Seasonal, monthly, daily, and hourly variations from this average are often expressed as percentages of the average. In North America, the spread in consumption is large: from 35 to 500 gpcd approximately, varying in particular with the industrial water requirements of different communities. Rates of 90 to 130 gpcd are most common, and a generalized average of 100 gpcd is a useful guide to normal requirements in the absence of unusually large industrial consumers.

28

In determining the capacity of the individual components of the system, consideration is given to the service that is expected of them. Distribution systems, for example, must be able to furnish water to combat and control serious conflagrations while still meeting the maximum coincident draft expected for domestic and industrial purposes. Fire demands are a function of the size and value of the properties to be protected which are reflected by the size of the community as a whole. For an average American city of 100,000 people, for example, the *stand-by* capacity of the distribution system leading to the high-value district just about equals the average rate of draft that would prevail if fires did not have to be considered. For smaller or larger communities, the stand-by capacity falls or rises about in proportion to the square root of the population.

2-3. Sources of Supply. The source of water determines the nature of the collection, purification, and distribution works. Sources of water and their development may be classified as follows:

1. Rain water.[1]
   a. From roofs, stored in cisterns for small individual supplies.
   b. From larger, prepared catchment areas, or "catches," stored in reservoirs, for large communal supplies.
2. Surface water.
   a. From streams, natural ponds, and lakes of adequate capacity, by continuous draft.
   b. From streams with adequate flood flow, by intermittent, seasonal, or selective draft of clean flood waters, and their storage in reservoirs adjacent to the stream, or otherwise readily accessible from it.
   c. From streams with inadequate dry-weather flow but adequate annual discharge, by continuous draft made possible through the storage of the necessary proportion of flows in excess of daily use in an impounding reservoir created by a dam thrown across the stream valley.
3. Ground water.
   a. From natural springs.
   b. From wells.
   c. From infiltration galleries, basins, or cribs.
   d. From wells or galleries and possibly springs, the flow into which is increased by water from another source (1) spread on the surface of the gathering ground, (2) carried into charging basins or ditches, or (3) lead into diffusion galleries or wells.
   e. From wells or galleries, the flow into which is maintained by recharging the ground with the water previously removed from the same area for cooling and related purposes.

All these supplies normally tap fresh-water sources. On board ship and in certain, normally very arid, regions in which fresh water is not

[1] Strictly speaking, rain water is collected as surface runoff.

immediately available, salt, or brackish, water may be supplied for all but drinking and culinary uses. Ships usually carry needed fresh water, particularly drinking water, in "water tanks," but they may produce fresh water in part by evaporation of sea water. Where fresh water is not directly available for community supply, it is either hauled in by road, rail, or water, or it is supplied as a whole or in part by evaporation of salt or brackish water. Some brackish or saline waters are economically amenable to desalting by ion-exchange processes as well as chemical precipitation methods.

Municipal supplies may be drawn from a single source or from a number of different ones. The water from multiple sources is ordinarily mixed before distribution to the community provided that the component waters or their mixtures are safe and satisfactory in quality. Dual public water supplies of unequal quality are unusual in North America. They are frowned upon by health authorities because of the ever-present hazard of their being interconnected, wittingly or unwittingly.

2-4. Collection of Rain Water. Rain is rarely the immediate source of municipal water supplies,[2] and the use of rain water is generally confined (1) to farms and rural settlements usually in semiarid regions devoid of satisfactory ground-water or surface-water supplies, and (2) to some hard-water communities in which, because of its softness, roof drainage is employed principally for household laundry work and general washing purposes, while the public supply satisfies all other requirements. In most hard-water communities, the installation and operation of municipal water-softening plants can ordinarily be justified economically. Their introduction is desirable and does away with the need for supplementary rain-water supplies and the associated objection of their possible cross-connection[3] with the public supply.

For individual homesteads, rain water running off the roof is led through gutters and downspouts to a rain barrel or cistern situated on the ground or below it (see Figure 1-1). Barrel or cistern storage converts the intermittent rainfall into a continuous supply. For municipal service, roof water may be combined with water collected from sheds or catches on the surface of ground that is naturally impervious or rendered so by grouting, cementing, paving, or similar means.

---

[2] A notable example is the water supply of the communities on the Islands of Bermuda on which streams are lacking and ground water is brackish.

[3] A *cross-connection* is a junction between water supply systems through which water from a doubtful or unsafe source may enter an otherwise safe supply.

The gross yield of rain-water supplies is proportional to the receiving area and the amount of precipitation. Some rain, however, is blown off the roof by wind, evaporated, or lost in wetting the collecting area and conduits and in filling depressions or improperly pitched gutters. Also, the first flush of water contains most of the dust and other undesirable washings from the catchment surfaces and may have to be wasted. The combined loss is particularly great during the dry season of the year. A cutoff, switch, or deflector in the downspout permits selecting the quality of water to be stored. Sand filters are successfully employed to cleanse the cistern water and prevent its deterioration (1) by the growth of undesirable organisms and (2) by the bacterial decomposition of organic materials, both of which may give rise to tastes, odors, and other changes in the attractiveness and palatability of the water.

Storage to be provided in cisterns depends upon seasonal rainfall characteristics and commonly approximates one-third to one-half the annual needs in accordance with the length of dry spells. If the water is to be filtered before storage, stand-by capacity in advance of filtration must be provided if rainfalls of high intensity are not to escape. Because of the relatively small catchment area available, roof drainage cannot be expected to yield an abundant supply of water for man and beast, and a close analysis of storm rainfalls and seasonal variations in precipitation must be made if catchment areas, stand-by tanks, filters, and cisterns are to be proportioned and developed properly.

Example 2-1. Make a rough estimate of the gallons of water that can be caught by 3,000 sq ft of horizontally projected roof area (the average area of American farm buildings) in a region in which the average annual rainfall is 15 in.

Gross yield = $3,000 \times 15/12 \times 7.5 = 28,100$ gal annually = 77 gpd.

Net yield approximates $\frac{2}{3}$ gross yield = 18,800 gal annually = 51 gpd.

About half the net yield, or 9,400 gal = 1,250 cu ft, must be stored to secure the use of this water.

2-5. Collection of Surface Water. In North America, by far the largest volume of water for municipal use is taken from surface sources. The quantities of water that can be gathered from these sources vary directly with the size of the catchment area, or water shed, and with the difference between the amount of water precipitated upon and lost by evapotranspiration [4] from this area. The significance of these relations to water supply is illustrated in Figure

[4] The term *evapotranspiration* is generally assumed to include all water lost to the atmosphere, whether by evaporation, transpiration, guttation, or other processes.

2-1. Where the surface-water and ground-water sheds do not coincide, there may be a loss of ground water to an adjacent catchment area, or there may be a slight gain.

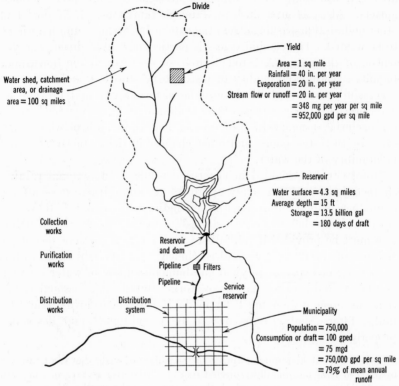

Figure 2-1. Rainfall, runoff, storage, and draft relations in the development of surface-water supplies.

a. Continuous Draft. Communities situated on or near streams, ponds, or lakes may take their supplies from these sources by continuous draft if stream flow and pond, or lake, capacity are sufficient at all seasons of the year to permit withdrawal of the requisite volumes of water.[5] The collecting works for such supplies include ordi-

[5] Examples of continuous draft from streams are the water supplies of Montreal, P. Q., St. Lawrence River; Philadelphia, Pa., Delaware and Schuylkill rivers; Pittsburgh, Pa., Allegheny River; Cincinnati, O., and Louisville, Ky., Ohio River; Kansas City, Mo., Missouri River; Minneapolis and St. Paul, Minn., Mississippi River; St. Louis, Mo., Missouri and Mississippi rivers; and New Orleans, La., Mississippi River.

Examples of continuous draft from lakes are furnished by Burlington, Vt., Lake Champlain; Syracuse, N. Y., Lake Skaneateles; Toronto, Ont., Lake On-

narily (1) an intake structure in the form of a crib, gatehouse, or intake tower; (2) an intake conduit; and (3) in many places, a pumping station. On small streams that serve communities of moderate size, an intake or diversion dam may have to be constructed to create sufficient depth of water to submerge the intake pipe and protect it against ice. When intakes are situated in the immediate vicinity of the community, the water drawn must generally be lifted from the source to the distribution system and prior to that to purification works which are generally needed (see Figure 2-2).

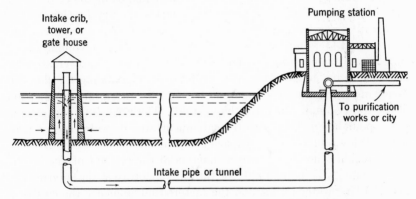

Figure 2-2. Continuous draft of water from large lakes and streams.

Waters drawn from large streams are commonly polluted by the wastes from upstream communities and must almost always be purified before use. Cities situated on large lakes must protect themselves against their own discharges of sewage and industrial-process waters as well as those of neighboring municipalities. Intakes are, therefore, placed as far away from shore as economically feasible, and purification plants ordinarily become necessary parts of the water-supply system. Treatment of the sewage of the community is generally indicated.

b. Selective Draft. It may be desirable to leave low-water flows in streams undisturbed in order to meet existing water needs of the valley or because the pollution carried by the stream is too highly concentrated to permit satisfactory purification. Only flood waters in excess of basic needs, or cleaner in composition, may then be led into reservoirs constructed in meadow lands adjacent to the stream or

tario; Buffalo, N. Y., and Cleveland, O., Lake Erie; Detroit, Mich., Lake St. Clair; Chicago, Ill., and Milwaukee, Wis., Lake Michigan; and Duluth, Minn., Lake Superior.

otherwise available nearby.[6] The amount of water so stored must equal the demand for water during the season of unavailable stream flow. If draft is confined to a quarter year, for example, the reservoir must hold at least three-fourths of the annual supply. In spite of its selection, the stored water may have to be purified.

c. *Impoundage.* In search for clean water and water that can be brought to the community by gravity, engineers have developed supplies from upland streams. Ordinarily these streams are tapped near their source in high and sparsely settled regions. To be of use, their annual discharge must equal or exceed the demands of the community they are to serve, and, since their flows during the dry portions of the year will generally fall short of concurrent municipal requirements, their flood waters must generally be stored in sufficient volume to assure a continuous supply. The necessary reservoirs are created by throwing dams across the stream valley and impounding the flows in excess of current use (see Figure 2-3). In this way a large proportion of the total annual runoff can be utilized. The area draining towards the impoundage is known as the catchment area or water shed. Economical development of its capacity depends upon the value of water in the region concerned and is a function of the amount of and variation in runoff, the accessibility of the catchment area, the interference with existing water rights, and the factors that influence the cost of a dam and reservoir. Storage must include allowances for evaporation from the new-water surface created by the impoundage and may have to sustain established minimum flows in the stream below the dam (compensating water). The supplementation of surface storage by increased ground storage in the flooded area and the gradual dissipation of surface storage by siltation are also allowed for when these effects are significant.

Intake structures are either incorporated in the impounding dams or kept separate from them. Other important parts of impounding reservoirs are (1) spillways which must safely discharge floods in excess of reservoir capacity and (2) diversion conduits which must carry the runoff of the stream that is to be impounded safely past the construction site until the reservoir is completed and its spillway can go into

[6] London, England, meets part of its water needs from the Thames River by storing relatively clean flood waters in large basins surrounded by dikes in the Thames Valley. The Boston, Mass., Metropolitan Water Supply diverts the freshets of the Ware River through a tunnel (1) to the Wachusett Reservoir which impounds the waters of the previously existing Wachusett supply, and (2) to the subsequently completed Quabbin Reservoir which impounds the neighboring Swift River.

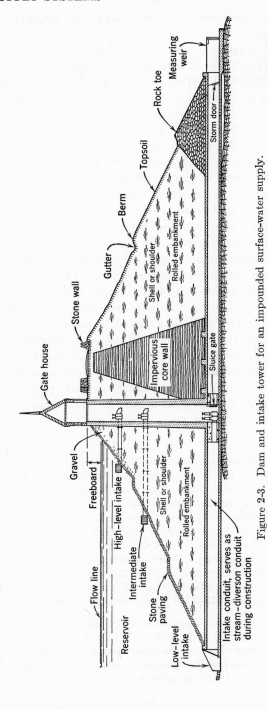

Figure 2-3. Dam and intake tower for an impounded surface-water supply.

action. The design of these ancillary structures requires the analysis of flood records.

Impounded supplies [7] may be sufficiently safe, attractive, and palatable to permit use of their waters without treatment other than protective disinfection. High color, caused by the decomposition of organic matter in swamps and on the flooded valley bottom, odors and tastes associated with this decomposition or engendered by the growth of algae, especially during the years of initial filling, turbidity (finely divided clay or silt) carried into streams or reservoirs by surface wash, wave action, or bank erosion, and the development of recreational uses of water sheds and reservoirs may, however, call for more complete treatment of the stored flows.

Much of the water flowing in streams or reaching ponds, lakes, and reservoirs in times of drought, or when precipitation is frozen, is made up of seepage from the ground. It is nevertheless classified as surface runoff rather than ground water. Discharge of seepage from the ground and recharge of ground water from surface sources are governed by the relative levels of water on the surface and in the ground (see Figure 2-4). Release of water from storage in the ground or from snow persisting until midsummer in high mountains may contribute markedly to the dry-weather flow of a stream and thus be the determining factor in the yield of a given area. Although surface waters are derived from rainfall, the relations between rainfall, runoff, and infiltration are so involved that engineers rightly prefer to base their calculations of yield upon stream gagings. These should extend over a considerable number of years if they are to present adequate information.

Example 2-2. Certain rough estimates of the yield of surface-water sheds and storage requirements are shown in Figure 2-1. Rainfall is used as the point of departure, merely for illustration of the rainfall-runoff relationship, and the following conversion factors and approximations are employed:

a. 1 in. per sq mile = 17.378 mg. Hence 20 in. per sq mile annually = $20 \times 17.378 = 348$ mg annually or 348/365 = 0.953 mgd.

b. This stream flow of about 1 mgd (1.547 cfs) per sq mile is a good average for the well-watered sections of North America. Not all of this runoff can be developed economically by storage. For 75% use (750,000 gpd per sq mile), about half a year's supply must be stored. For a catchment area of 100 sq miles, therefore, the storage = $0.75 \times 100 \times 180 = 13.5$ billion gal. In semiarid regions,

---

[7] Examples of untreated, impounded, upland supplies are the Croton River, Catskill, and Delaware River supplies of New York, N. Y., and the Wachusett and Quabbin supplies of the Metropolitan District of Boston, Mass.

Examples of treated impounded supplies are those of Baltimore, Md.; Providence, R. I.; Hartford, Conn.; Springfield, Mass.; and Springfield, Ill.

storages of three times the mean annual stream flow are not uncommon; i.e., water is held over from wet years to supply the demands during dry years.

c. For an average consumption of 100 gpcd, the drainage area of 100 sq miles and impoundage of 13.5 billion gal will serve a municipality with $100 \times 750,000/100 = 750,000$ people.

d. For water supply by continuous draft, low-water flows rather than average annual yields govern. In well-watered sections of North America, these approximate 0.1 cfs or 64,600 gpd per sq mile. A catchment area of 100 sq miles, therefore, can supply without storage only $100 \times 64,600/100 = 64,600$ people against 750,000 people when proper storage is provided.

2-6. Collection of Ground Water. Smaller in their daily delivery, but many times more numerous than surface-water supplies, are the municipal and private ground-water supplies of North America. Ground waters are drawn (1) from the pores of alluvial (water-borne), glacial, or aeolian (windblown) deposits of granular materials such as sand, gravel, and sandstone; (2) from the solution passages, caverns, cleavage planes, fissures, or fractures of rocks including limestone, slate, shale, and igneous rocks; and (3) from combinations of these unconsolidated and consolidated geological formations (see Figure 2-4). Ground-water supplies have an intake or catchment area much like that of surface-water supplies, except that the catch, or recharge, is by infiltration of water into the openings of the ground rather than by runoff over its surface. The intake area may be nearby or situated at a considerable distance from the point of water collection, especially when flow is confined within a water-bearing stratum, or *aquifer*,[8] that underlies an impervious stratum, or *aquiclude*.[9]

The maximum yield of ground-water sources is directly proportional to the size of the intake area and to the difference between the amount of precipitation and the loss by evapotranspiration and storm runoff. Flow extends laterally across the full width of the aquifer. Vertically, flow reaches as far below the earth's surface as do the open pores and passages of the ground and as close to the earth's surface as the ground is filled or saturated with water that is able to move. If the upper surface of the ground water is free to rise and fall with seasonal changes in recharge, flow is unconfined or free, and the water surface, or *ground-water table*, slopes downward more or less like the ground surface. Under these conditions, the ground water moves at right angles to the water-table contours. If the water-bearing stratum dips beneath an impervious layer, flow becomes con-

[8] The word *aquifer* comes from the Latin *aqua*, water, and *ferre*, to bear.

[9] The word *aquiclude* comes from the Latin *aqua*, water, and *cludere*, to shut or close.

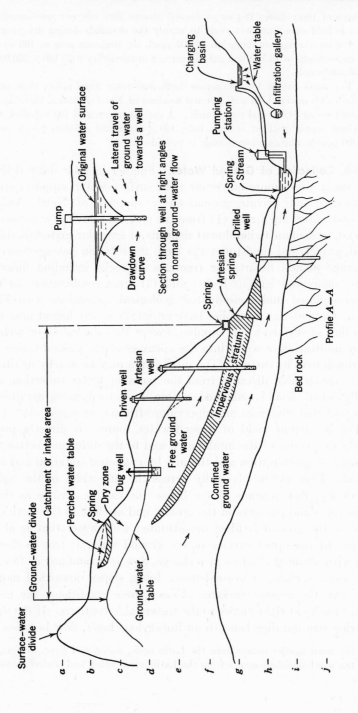

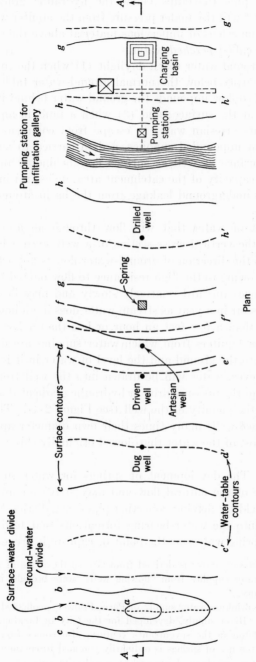

Figure 2-4. Groundwater and its development as springs, wells, and infiltration galleries.

fined as in a pipe that dips below the hydraulic grade line, and
artesian water [10] will rise under pressure from the aquifer when tapped.
Water caught on a lens of impervious material above the true ground-
water table is called *perched* water.

Springs of ground water reach daylight (1) when the surface of the
earth drops sharply below the normal ground-water table; (2) when
an obstruction to flow impounds the ground water behind it and forces
it to overflow at the surface; and (3) when a fault in an impervious
stratum permits artesian water to escape from confinement. In the
development of impounded supplies, a dam carried to bed rock will
impound subsurface as well as surface flow behind it and so utilize
the full water capacity of the catchment area, unless raising the water
surface causes underground leakage from the basin around the reservoir.

The amount of water that will flow through an area of ground
equivalent to the vertical cross-section of a well, even a large one, at
right angles to the direction of ground-water flow is not great, because
ground water, owing to the high resistance to flow offered by the pores
of the soil, moves forward relatively slowly and may be expected to
travel about as far in a year as stream water does in an hour. Natural
rates of more than a few feet an hour or less than a few feet a year
are unusual for aquifers from which water supplies are drawn. If a
well is sunk into the ground and the level of water in it is lowered by
pumping, however, water will be drawn into the well from all directions, because of the pressure drop or hydraulic gradient that is thereby
established in the vicinity of the well (see Figure 2-4). This makes it
possible to space wells many times their own diameter apart and yet
to intercept most of the water that flowed originally through the intervening space.

a. Springs. The development of springs for water supply [11] aims
at the capture of the natural flow and may strive for an increase in
the natural yield by driving collecting pipes or galleries, more or less
horizontally, into the water-bearing formations that feed the spring.
Pollution of spring waters at the point of capture is prevented (1) by

[10] The term *artesian water* is derived from *Artois,* the name of a province of
France, where water supplies from "flowing wells" were brought in as early as
the twelfth century.

[11] Some of the drinking-water supply of Paris, France, is collected from springs.
Part of the New River supply, developed for the City of London, England, by
Sir Hugh Middleton in the seventeenth century, also comes from springs. In
North America, the use of springs is ordinarily confined to communities of small
size, a number of springs being harnessed by a collecting conduit.

the exclusion of shallow seepage waters from the spring through the encirclement of the spring by a water-tight chamber that penetrates well into the aquifer and (2) by diversion of surface runoff in the immediate vicinity of the spring. Some springs are known to yield less than 1 gpm; a few more than 50 mgd.

b. Wells. These structures are dug, driven, bored, or drilled into the ground, depending upon the geological formations through which they must pass and the depth to which they must reach. Dug wells and driven wells are usually confined to soft ground, sand, and gravel and to shallow depths, normally less than 100 ft. Bored and drilled wells are generally used in hard ground and rock and may be sunk to depths measuring hundreds and even thousands of feet.[12] In the well-watered regions of the world, successful wells of moderate depth and diameter in hard rock may be expected to yield from 1 to 50 gpm,[13] whereas similar wells in coarse sand and gravel and in coarse sandstone will deliver from 50 to 500 gpm. Wells in deep aquifers will yield 100 gpm or more in favorable circumstances.

Except in hard rock, particularly limestone, without sand or gravel cover, wells are generally not polluted by lateral seepage into them but by entrance of pollution at or near the surface of the ground. Water-tight casings or seals extending into the aquifer and at least 10 ft below the surface of the ground, together with diversion of surface runoff from the well area and protection against its being inundated by the flooding of nearby streams, will insure the safety of the water drawn from otherwise good ground.

c. Infiltration Galleries. Ground water traveling towards a stream or lake from neighboring uplands can be intercepted by digging a trench or driving a tunnel more or less at right angles to the direction of flow and carrying the water entering the resulting infiltration gallery [14] to a pumping station. Water may be drawn from both sides of the collecting conduit, or the river side may be blanked off to exclude the often less satisfactory seepage water received from the river itself. Infiltration basins and trenches are similar in conception and are in essence large, shallow, open wells. Filter cribs built into stream

[12] Memphis, Tenn., is the largest municipality in the United States supplied by ground water. There are about 30 wells 8 and 12 in. in diameter and 450 to 1,400 ft deep. The ground-water table reaches within 15 to 50 ft of the surface when no water is being pumped.

[13] The yield of ground water is commonly expressed in gallons per minute because the pumps needed to lift the water from the ground are conventionally rated in gallons per minute; 1 gpm = 1,440 gpd.

[14] The water supply of Des Moines, Ia., is drawn from an infiltration gallery as is that of Brussels, Belgium.

bottoms catch the underflow of the stream. The driftways and stopes of mines may collect much water. Galleries may be driven into mountainsides specifically for this purpose, or abandoned mines may be salvaged for this use. Infiltration galleries may produce as much as a million gallons of water daily per thousand feet of gallery. Their use is indicated particularly in aquifers of shallow depth, or where deep saline water must be excluded.

d. *Recharging Devices.* As outlined in Section 2-3, the yield of groundwater works may at times be increased or maintained by water spreading or diffusion. The necessary structures are built in the vicinity of the collecting works and within the ground-water shed. Charging ditches or basins [15] are filled with river or lake water by gravity or pumping. In water spreading by the flooding method, water is ordinarily diverted from a stream and flows into the ground-water area. In either instance, the added waters leach into the ground to increase the natural flow. The incentive to these arrangements is either to augment a dwindling or inadequate supply or to utilize natural filtration as a means of water purification. The gathering of a more uniformly cool water is also a consideration. In extreme cases, a badly polluted surface water may be partially purified before being led into the charging structure.[16] Diffusion galleries and wells may return to the ground waters that have been abstracted from it for use such as cooling purposes.

Collection works for ground water usually include pumps. The water flows to these pumps from the well field either by gravity, often through deep-lying conduits, or under negative pressure through suction mains. Wells can also be equipped with individual pumps, especially when the water table lies at a considerable depth below the surface of the ground.

Ordinarily, ground water is clean, palatable, and cool. In its passage through the ground, however, the water may acquire constituents that render it unpalatable, unattractive, corrosive, or hard (soap-consuming). These properties may have to be remedied by suitable treatment.

In studying the yield of ground-water areas, the engineer must acquire adequate knowledge of the geology as well as the hydrology of the region. Much can be learnt from past experience with similar supplies in nearby areas, but ultimate judgment must generally rest upon the behavior of test wells driven for exploratory purposes.

[15] The collecting works at Des Moines, Ia., include charging basins.

[16] Frankfort, Germany, at one time filtered the polluted Main River water before leading it into a charging gallery.

Example 2-3. Make a rough estimate of the yield of an aquifer 20 ft deep through which water moves at a rate of 3 ft a day (a) if all the ground water laterally within 500 ft of the well comes fully within its influence, and (b) if a gallery 1,000 ft long collects water from both sides.

(a) $20 \times 1,000 \times 3 \times 7.5/1,440 = 310$ gpm.

(b) $20 \times 1,000 \times 2 \times 3 \times 7.5/1,000,000 = 0.90$ mgd.

2-7. Purification of Water.

Some of the waters collected from surface [17] or ground sources are satisfactory in quality for all common municipal uses. Such waters need to be protected only by disinfection. Others contain objectionable substances in varying quantities, and these substances must be removed, reduced to tolerable limits, destroyed, or otherwise changed in character before they are sent to the consumer. Impurities are acquired in the normal passage of water through the atmosphere, over the earth's surface, or through the pores of the ground. They are associated in their pollutional aspects with man's activities and, in particular, with his own use of water in household and industry and his discharge of spent water into natural water courses. Water can acquire impurities also within the water-supply system. Some of the heavy metals, such as lead, copper, zinc, and iron, are traceable to corrosion of metallic pipes that convey the water to its point of use, and there are opportunities for contamination of the water through cross-connection with impure water supplies and through *back-flow* [18] in plumbing systems.

The nature of the raw water in its relation to the required standards of water quality determines the method of treatment to be employed. Purification works in a public water-supply system must be selected and designed to deliver water that, if not already so, has been made (1) hygienically safe, (2) esthetically attractive and palatable, and (3) economically satisfactory for the uses to which it is to be put. The nature and sources of impurities have been briefly indicated in connection with the development of collecting works and with the sanitation of public water supplies. The most common classes of municipal water-purification works and their principal functions are:

1. Filtration plants [19] that remove objectionable color, turbidity, and bacteria as well as other potentially harmful organisms by filtration through sand after necessary preparation of the water by coagulation and sedimentation.

---

[17] Strictly speaking, rain water is collected from a surface source.

[18] *Back-flow* permits water that has been drawn into a fixture, tank, or similar device to flow back into the supply line by gravity or as a result of siphonage.

[19] In North America, there are many filtration plants, large and small, that incorporate the treatment processes sketched in Figure 2-5a. Among them are the filter plants of (1) Buffalo, N. Y., Cleveland, O., Detroit, Mich., and Mil-

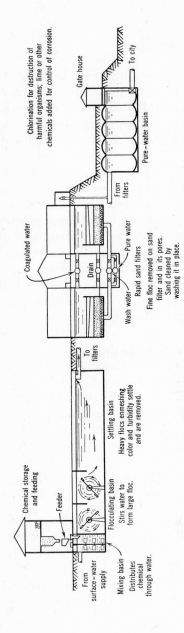

a. Filtration plant including coagulation, settling, filtration, chlorination, corrosion control, and pure-water storage.

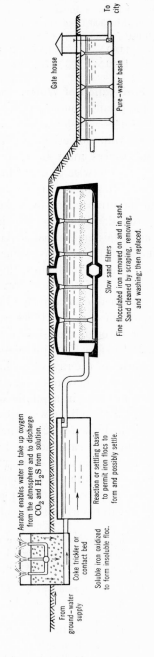

b. Deferrization plant including aeration, contact treatment, filtration, and pure-water storage.

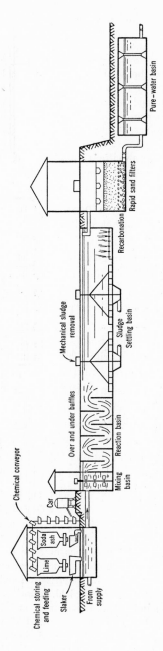

c. Softening plant including addition of softening chemicals, settling, recarbonation, filtration, and pure-water storage.

Figure 2-5. Common types of water-purification plants.

2. Deferrization and demanganization plants [19] that remove excessive amounts of iron and manganese by oxidizing the soluble ferrous and manganous compounds and converting them into insoluble ferric and manganic compounds which are removable by sedimentation and filtration.

3. Softening plants [19] that remove excessive amounts of scale-forming, soap-consuming compounds, chiefly the soluble bicarbonates, chlorides, and sulfates of calcium and magnesium (a) by the addition of lime and soda ash which precipitate calcium as a carbonate and magnesium as a hydrate, or (b) by passage of the water through cation-exchange media that exchange sodium for calcium and magnesium ions and are themselves regenerated by brine.

Diagrammatic sketches of purification plants of this kind are presented in Figure 2-5. Most water supplies, today, are chlorinated to assure their disinfection. Many waters are treated with lime or other chemicals to reduce their tendency to corrode iron and other metals with which they come into contact and so to maintain their quality during distribution as well as to insure longer life to the metallic portions of the water works. Waters containing odor- or taste-producing substances are treated with activated carbon that adsorbs most of these undesirable substances, or with taste-destroying doses of chlorine or chlorine dioxide. Numerous other treatment methods have been devised to meet special needs.

The design of water-purification plants is based (1) upon an understanding of the operation of the various treatment processes that bring about the removal or modification of the objectionable qualities of the water received (process design); (2) upon a knowledge of the factors affecting the flow of water through the various structures that constitute water-purification plants—namely, channels, pipes including perforated pipes, gates, measuring devices, basins, beds of sand and other granular materials, and pumps (hydraulic design); and (3) upon a comprehension of the behavior of these structures under load

waukee, Wis., on the Great Lakes; (2) Cincinnati, O., Louisville, Ky., Minneapolis and St. Paul, Minn., St. Louis, Mo., and New Orleans, La., in the drainage basin of the Mississippi River; and (3) Cambridge, Mass., Albany, N. Y., and Providence, R. I., which filter impounded upland supplies. Deferrization plants like that outlined in Figure 2-5b are numerous in New England, among them those at Lowell and Brookline, Mass., both of which treat ground waters. Slow sand filters not employed in connection with deferrization and, therefore, without coke prefilters are in operation (1) at Springfield, Mass., and Hartford, Conn., for impounded upland waters, and (2) at Philadelphia and Pittsburgh, Pa., and Washington, D. C., for the waters of large streams. Softening plants (Figure 2-5c) are found at Columbus, O. (Scioto River); Springfield, Ill. (impounded supply); Kansas City, Mo. (Missouri River); Los Angeles, Cal. (Colorado River); and numerous smaller places.

(structural design). Some conception of the size of the principal structures may be gained from the following normally applicable facts:

1. Mixing basins hold the water for a few minutes.
2. Flocculating and reaction basins hold about half an hour's flow.
3. Sedimentation basins hold the water for several hours and are rated at about 1 gpm per sq ft of water-surface area.
4. Slow sand filters pass water at a rate of about 3 mgad in simple filtration which is stepped up to about 10 mgad in deferrization and demanganization.
5. Rapid filters operate at a rate of about 125 mgad or 2 gpm per sq ft.
6. Coke tricklers are rated at about 75 mgad, or 1.5 gpm per sq ft.

Example 2-4. Estimate the capacity of the structural components of a filtration plant, such as that shown in Figure 2-5a, that is to deliver 10 mgd (6,940 gpm) of water to a city of 100,000 people.

a. Two mixing basins, 10 ft deep.
   1. Assumed detention period = 2 min.
   2. Volume = $2 \times 6{,}940/2 = 6{,}940$ gal = 928 cu ft each.
   3. Diameter = $\sqrt{92.8 \times 4/\pi} = 10.9$ ft.
b. Two flocculating and reaction basins, 10 ft deep.
   1. Assumed detention period = 30 min.
   2. Volume = $30 \times 6{,}940/2 = 104{,}000$ gal = 13,900 cu ft.
   3. Surface area = 1,390 sq ft (such as 35 ft by 40 ft).
c. Two settling basins, 10 ft deep, but allow for 2 ft of sludge.
   1. Assumed detention period = 2 hr.
   2. Effective volume = $120 \times 6{,}940/2 = 416{,}000$ gal = 55,700 cu ft.
   3. Surface area = $55{,}700/8 = 6{,}960$ sq ft (such as 35 ft by 200 ft).
   4. Surface rating = $6{,}940/6{,}960 = 1.0$ gpm per sq ft.
d. Ten rapid sand filters.
   1. Assumed rating = 2 gpm per sq ft.
   2. Area = $6{,}940/(10 \times 2) = 347$ sq ft (such as 15 ft by 24 ft).

2-8. Transportation of Water. Supply conduits, or aqueducts,[20] transport water from the source of supply to the community and so form the connecting link between the collection works and the distribution system. The location of the source determines whether the conduits are short or long, and whether the water is transported by gravity or by pumping. Depending upon topography and available materials, conduits are designed to carry the water in open-channel flow or under pressure. They may follow the hydraulic grade line as (1) canals dug through the ground, (2) flumes elevated above the

[20] The word *aqueduct* comes from the Latin *aqua,* water, and *ducere,* to lead or conduct. It describes all artificial channels that transport water. Use of the word is often confined by engineers to covered masonry conduits that are built in place. The great Roman aqueducts were constructed for the purpose of tapping high-lying clean sources of water and conveying it along the hydraulic gradient, because of the lack of pressure-resisting materials, to the city for distribution by gravity.

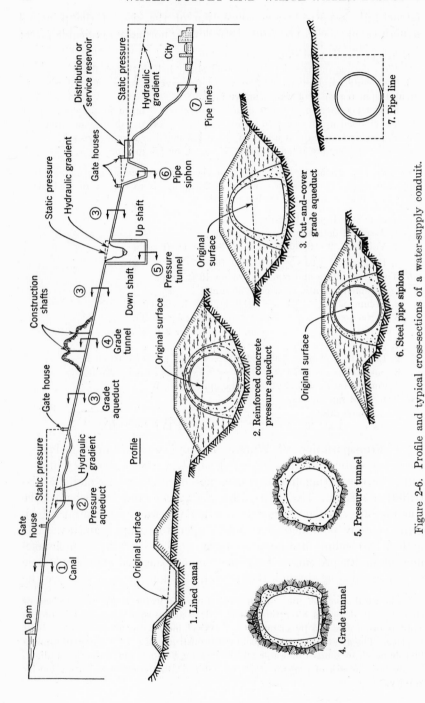

Figure 2-6. Profile and typical cross-sections of a water-supply conduit.

ground, (3) grade aqueducts laid in balanced cut and cover at the ground surface, and (4) grade tunnels penetrating hills; or they may depart from the hydraulic gradient as (5) pressure aqueducts laid in balanced cut and cover at the ground surface, (6) pressure tunnels dipping beneath valleys or hills, and (7) pipelines of fabricated materials following the ground surface, if necessary over hill and through

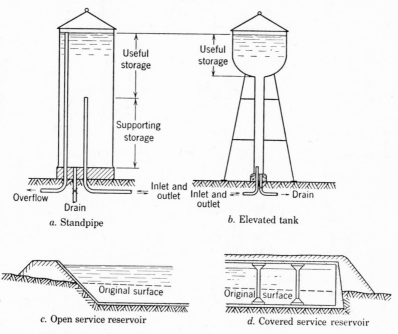

a. Standpipe

b. Elevated tank

c. Open service reservoir

d. Covered service reservoir

Figure 2-7. Four types of service, or distribution, reservoirs.

dale, sometimes rising even above the hydraulic grade line.[21] The profile of a supply conduit is shown in Figure 2-6 together with typical cross-sections of the conduit. The static pressures to which the conduits are exposed and their hydraulic grade lines are indicated.

Size and shape of supply conduits are determined by hydraulic, structural, and economic considerations. Velocities of flow are held

[21] The Colorado River Aqueduct of the Metropolitan Water District of Southern California is 242 miles long and includes 92 miles of grade tunnel, 63 miles of canal, 54 miles of grade aqueduct, 29 miles of inverted siphons, and 4 miles of force main. The Delaware Aqueduct of New York, N. Y., comprises 85 miles of pressure tunnel in three sections. Pressure tunnels 25 miles in length supply the metropolitan districts of Boston and San Francisco. The supply conduits of Springfield, Mass., are made of steel pipe and reinforced-concrete pipe; those of Albany, N. Y., of cast-iron pipe.

ordinarily between 3 and 5 fps. Requisite capacities depend upon the inclusion and size of *service*, or *distributing, reservoirs* in the supply system. If service reservoirs are designed to store enough water (1) to take care of the hourly variations in water consumption in excess of the rate of inflow, (2) to supply the water needed to fight a serious fire, and (3) to permit a shutdown of the supply conduit for inspection and minor repairs, the supply conduits leading to them (Figure 2-1) need only carry sufficient water to supply the use on the maximum day, about 50% in excess of the average daily rate of use. Ordinarily, required storage approximates a day's consumption. Distribution reservoirs are constructed as open or covered basins in balanced cut and fill, as standpipes, or as elevated tanks. The choice depends upon their size and their location with particular reference to available elevation above the area served by them (see Figure 2-7). A number of different reservoirs may be needed in large systems.

Example 2-5. Estimate roughly the size of a supply conduit leading to an adequate distributing reservoir serving a community of (1) 10,000 people, and (2) 500,000 people, and find the slope of its hydraulic gradient.

    a. Average daily water consumption at 100 gpcd:
        1. $10,000 \times 100/1,000,000 = 1.0$ mgd.
        2. $500,000 \times 100/1,000,000 = 50$ mgd.
    b. Maximum daily use 50% greater than the average:
        1. $1.0 \times 1.5 = 1.5$ mgd $= 2.32$ cfs.
        2. $50 \times 1.5 = 75$ mgd $= 116$ cfs.
    c. Diameter of circular conduit flowing at 4 fps:
        1. Diameter $= 12\sqrt{2.32/\pi} = 10$ in.
        2. Diameter $= 12\sqrt{116/\pi} = 73$ in.
    d. Slope of hydraulic gradient by the Hazen-Williams formula [22] for $C = 100$:
        1. Loss of head $= 10.8$ ft per 1,000.
        2. Loss of head $= 0.94$ ft per 1,000.
The higher loss of head of small conduits at equal velocities should be noted.

2-9. Distribution of Water. The system of conduits that conveys water to the points of use from the terminus of the supply conduit is known as the distribution system (see Figure 2-1). Street plan, topography, and location of supply works and distribution storage establish the type of distribution system and the character of flow through it. Depending upon the street plan, two distribution patterns predominate: (1) a branching pattern on the outskirts of the community, in which ribbon development follows the primary arteries of roads and streets (Figure 2-8a), and (2) a gridiron pattern within the

[22] See Section 12-2.

built-up portions of the community in which streets crisscross and
pipes are interconnected (Figures 2-8*b* and 2-8*c*). Hydraulically, the
gridiron system possesses the advantage of carrying water to any spot
from more than one direction; the branching system the disadvantage
of dead ends. The carrying capacity of the gridiron system is strengthened by providing, in place of a central feeder, a loop or belt of feeder
pipes that supplies water to the *congested,* or *high-value,* district from
at least two directions, thereby more or less doubling the delivery of
the grid (Figure 2-8*c*). In large systems, feeder conduits take the
form of pressure tunnels, pressure aqueducts, or steel pipes. In smaller

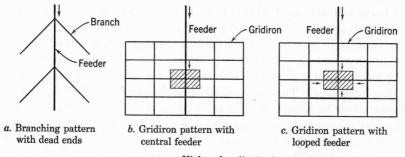

a. Branching pattern   *b.* Gridiron pattern with   *c.* Gridiron pattern with
    with dead ends   central feeder   looped feeder

High–value district is cross–hatched

Figure 2-8. Patterns of water-distribution systems.

communities, the entire distribution system is generally made up of
cast-iron pipes. Cast iron is the most common material for service
mains; steel and asbestos-cement pipes are less widely employed.

    a. High and Low Services. Sections of the community that lie at
too high an elevation to receive water at adequate pressure from the
principal, or *low-service,* works are generally incorporated in a separate distribution system possessing independent piping and service
storage. This *high-service* system is normally fed by pumps that take
suction from the main supply and boost its pressure by the requisite
amount. For areas of widely varying elevation, intermediate districts
may be required. The different systems are commonly interconnected,
for emergency use, by gated connections. Pressure-regulating valves
are sometimes installed for this purpose.

    b. Fire Supply. The congested central portion, or high-value dis-
trict, of large cities is suitably protected by an independent system of
pipes and hydrants that are capable of delivering large volumes of
water under high pressure for fire-fighting purposes. This high-pressure fire-supply normally takes water from the public supply and
raises its pressure by booster pumps whenever the alarm is given to

do so. For use in extreme emergency, rigorously protected connections may be established to an independent source of water: river, lake, or tidal estuary. Large industrial establishments, in which a large investment in plant, equipment, raw materials, and finished products is concentrated within a limited area, are generally provided with high-pressure fire supplies derived from private, sometimes questionable, sources. Some states or communities require rigid separation of such supplies from the public system. Others permit the use of protected cross-connections that are regularly inspected, but usually only on existing and not on new installations.

c. *Pressures.* For normal municipal uses, pressures of 60 to 75 psig in business blocks and 40 psig in residential areas are desirable. The need for higher pressures (100 psig or more) sufficient to deliver adequate amounts of water for fire fighting through hose attached directly to fire hydrants has been largely superseded by the development of the modern motor pumper which will deliver up to 1,500 gpm at adequate pressures. To supply their upper stories, tall buildings must boost water to tanks on their roofs or in their towers. In large industrial complexes, the water pressure may be raised during fires by fixed installations of fire pumps.

d. *Capacity.* The capacity of distribution systems is dictated by domestic, industrial, and other normal water uses and by the *stand-by* or *ready-to-serve* requirements for fire fighting. Pipes should be sufficiently large to carry the maximum *coincident* draft at velocities that are not so high that pressure drops and water hammer become excessive. Velocities of 2 to 4 fps are common and establish the sizes of water mains to be employed. The minimum diameter of pipe commonly installed today in North American municipalities is 6 in.

. **Example 2-6.** Estimate the number of people who can be supplied with water from (*a*) a 12-in. and (*b*) a 24-in. main (1) in the absence of fire service for a maximum draft of 200 gpcd, (2) with a residential fire-flow requirement of 500 gpm and a coincident draft of 150 gpcd. Also find the slope of the hydraulic gradient.

   A. Cross-sectional area of pipes: (*a*) 113 sq in. and (*b*) 452 sq in.

   B. Capacity of pipes at velocity of 3 fps: (*a*) $113 \times 3/144 = 2.35$ cfs and (*b*) 9.42 cfs.

   C. Flow available for domestic use:

   (1) With no fire service: (*a*) $2.35 \times 646,000 = 1,520,000$ gpd and (*b*) $9.42 \times 646,000 = 6,080,000$ gpd.

   (2) With fire service of 500 gpm = 720,000 gpd: (*a*) $(1,520,000 - 720,000) = 800,000$ gpd and (*b*) $(6,080,000 - 720,000) = 5,360,000$ gpd.

   D. Population served:

   (1) With no fire service, at rate of 200 gpcd: (*a*) $1,520,000/200 = 7,600$ people and (*b*) $6,080,000/200 = 30,400$ people.

(2) With fire service of 500 gpm, at rate of 150 gpcd: (*a*) 800,000/150 = 5,300 people, and (*b*) 5,360,000/150 = 36,000 people.

E. At velocity of 3 fps and for $C = 100$ in Hazen-Williams formula,[22] loss of head per 1,000 ft:

(*a*) 4.6 ft = 2.0 psi; (*b*) 2.0 ft = 0.9 psi.

e. Service to Premises. Water is conducted from the street mains through one or more services into the premises that are supplied by the system (see Chapter 14).

2-10. Management of Water Supplies. The development of water supplies from the ground up, or their improvement and extension, progresses from preliminary investigations through their financing, design, and construction to their operation, maintenance, and repair. All these steps involve political and financial activities as well as those of a more strictly engineering nature.

A concept of the magnitude of the engineering activity and responsibility involved in the design and construction of public water supplies is given by their cost. The per capita investment in physical plant depends upon many factors: the nature, proximity, and abundance of a suitable water source; the need for water treatment; the availability and cost of labor and materials; the size and requirements of the system; the habits of the people; and the characteristics of the area served. Because of wide differences in these factors, the first cost of water-supply systems varies considerably. For communities in excess of 10,000 population, costs in North America lie ordinarily between $50 and $200 per capita, with much of the investment in smaller communities chargeable to fire-protection needs. Of the various portions of the system, the collection and transportation works represent about a third of the cost, the distribution works slightly more than a half, and the purification works about a tenth, the remainder being invested in real estate. The first cost of water-filtration plants is about $100,000 per mgd capacity, and the cost of water treatment, excluding fixed charges, lies in the vicinity of $15 per mg (million gallons). Including interest and depreciation as well as charges against operation and management, water costs from $50 to $300 per mg and is charged for accordingly. As one of our most prized commodities, water is remarkably cheap. It sells for as low as 2 cents a ton delivered to the premises of large consumers and costs the small consumer as little as 4 cents a ton.

Example 2-7. Roughly, what is the replacement cost of the water works of a city of 100,000 people?

a. Assuming the per capita cost at $100, the total first cost is 100 × 100,000 = $10,000,000.

b. Assuming that 30% of this amount is invested in the collection works, 10% in the purification works, and 60% in the distribution works, the breakdown is as follows:

1. Collection works $0.3 \times 10,000,000 = \$3,000,000$.
2. Purification works $0.10 \times 10,000,000 = \$1,000,000$.
3. Distribution works $0.60 \times 10,000,000 = \$6,000,000$.

c. Assuming a water consumption of 100 gpcd, the total consumption is 10 mgd, and the cost of a filtration plant becomes $10 \times 100,000 = \$1,000,000$, which checks the previous estimate.

WASTE-WATER
DISPOSAL SYSTEMS

3-1. General Features of Waste-Water Disposal Systems. The disposal of waste waters requires the construction and operation of: (1) collection works and (2) disposal works. The latter are preceded by treatment works where needed. The complex of structures is called the *sewerage* or drainage system. The relative functions and positions of the component parts are outlined in Figure 3-1. If the collection works transport in the same conduits (1) waste matters from households and industries and (2) storm-water runoff, the conduits are called *combined sewers*[1] and form part of a *combined system* of sewerage. If the two kinds of waste waters are collected separately, the resulting *sanitary sewers* and *storm sewers* (or storm drains) create a *separate system* of sewerage. The water-carried wastes originating in households are *domestic sewage;* those coming from manufacturing establishments are *industrial wastes* or *trade wastes*. The addition of storm water creates *combined sewage*. *Municipal sewage* generally includes both domestic and industrial wastes. Combined sewerage systems are common in the older cities of the world[2] in which they evolved from the existing system of storm drains.

The collection works consist of one or more branching systems of conduits designed to remove the sewage or storm water by "free" flow as through the branches and stem of an underground river system. The main collector of many combined systems is, in fact, a stream that served originally as the receiving water and had to be covered when excessive pollution by tributary sewage made the stream unsightly, malodorous, and otherwise objectionable. Flow in sewers and drains is continuously downhill, except where pumping stations and force mains are interpolated in the system (1) in order to lift waste waters from a deep sewer to one near the ground surface and so to

---

[1] The word *sewer* is derived ultimately from the Latin words *ex*, out, and *aqua*, water. In the eighteenth and early nineteenth centuries, the common form of the word was *shor*.

[2] The sewerage systems of London, England; Paris, France; New York, N. Y.; and Boston, Mass.; are examples of this evolution.

avoid the construction of uneconomically deep conduits in flat country or bad ground; and (2) in order to transfer waste waters from one drainage area, or *sewer district,* to another. Sewers are laid below ground for reasons of convenience. They are not intended to flow under pressure. Otherwise, waste waters would have to be pumped into them through each individual building service and property drain; or it would be necessary to place the sewers far below cellar levels, in order to keep sewage from backing up into basements and spilling out of fixtures. Obviously, either arrangement would be impractical. Hydraulically, sewers are designed as "open channels," flowing partly full or, at most, just filled. Of the various formulas characterizing open-channel flow, American engineers commonly employ either the Chezy formula with Kutter's velocity coefficient or the Manning formula.[3] Vitrified-clay pipes are generally used for small sewers, and concrete or masonry pipes or conduits of special shapes for large ones.

Each branching system collects the sewage, storm runoff, or both from the area it is intended to serve and conducts it to the point of disposal. Here the collected waste waters are treated, if necessary. Ordinarily they are discharged into a water course that constitutes a natural drainage channel of the region or a natural receiver of drainage waters. This final emptying of waste waters into a *receiving body of water* is called disposal by *dilution.* In semiarid regions or places otherwise adapted for it, terminal discharge may be on land. This is called disposal by *irrigation.* Treatment of waste waters prior to final disposal aims at the removal of unsightly and putrescible matter from the carrying water and at the destruction of the disease-producing organisms that it may contain. The degree of treatment is predicated upon the economical conservation of the water and land resources of the region.

3-2. Sources and Nature of Waste Waters. *Sanitary sewage* is the spent water supply of the community. *Domestic sewage* is the waste water from kitchen, bathroom, lavatory, toilet, and laundry. In addition to the mineral and organic matter already in the water dispensed to the community, domestic sewage contains an imposed burden of human excrement, paper, soap, dirt, food wastes (garbage), and numerous other substances. Some of these waste matters are carried in suspension; others are taken into solution; still others are, or become, so finely divided that they possess the properties of colloidal (dispersed, ultramicroscopic) particles. A large portion of the waste matters is organic in nature and, because of its high energy value,

[3] See Section 15-3.

subject to attack by saprophytic microorganisms, i.e., organisms that feed upon dead organic matter. Domestic sewage, therefore, is unstable, decomposable, or putrescible; it may give rise to offensive odors, notably those of hydrogen sulfide, and other objectionable conditions associated with decomposition. Pathogenic organisms (1) discharged by persons harboring intestinal parasites or suffering from infectious diseases, particularly typhoid, paratyphoid, the dysenteries, and other gastrointestinal infections, or (2) excreted by carriers of these diseases, are always potentially present in domestic sewage and render it dangerous.

The nature of *industrial wastes* depends upon the industrial processes in which they originate. Industrial waste waters vary in nature from relatively clean rinse waters to waste liquors that are heavily laden with organic or mineral matter, or with corrosive, poisonous, inflammable, or explosive substances. Some industrial wastes are so objectionable that they should not be admitted to the public sewerage system; others contain so little and such unobjectionable foreign matter that it is safe to discharge them into a storm drain or directly into a natural body of water. Some industrial wastes adhere to sewers and clog them; acids and hydrogen sulfide destroy cement, concrete, and metals; hot wastes crack tile and concrete; poisonous chemicals, quite apart from their immediate danger to man, interfere with biological treatment processes and kill the organisms that normally populate receiving waters; inflammable or explosive substances, such as gasoline, endanger the structures through which sewage flows; and toxic gases or vapors create hazards to workmen and operators of sewage works. Industrial wastes become part of sanitary sewage when they are permitted to enter the public sewerage system.

All sewage contains some ground water that gains entrance into the sewers through their many joints.[4] In combined systems, storm runoff adds the washings from streets, roofs, gardens, parks, and yard areas. These are chiefly dirt, dust, sand, gravel, and other gritty substances that are heavy and inert. Leaves and other debris enter the system at certain seasons of the year. Storm drains receive, in addition to surface runoff from rain, ice, and snow, water that has been used to cleanse streets, fight fires, or flush the water distribution system through hydrants; sometimes, also, waste water from fountains, wading and swimming pools, and similar sources.

Sanitary sewage flows from the premises in which it originates through one or more service connections to the public sewer. The

---

[4] Clay sewer pipe, 8 to 24 in. in diameter, is 2, 2½, or 3 ft long; above that 2½ or 3 ft long. Concrete sewer pipe, 8 to 24 in. in diameter, is 2, 2½, 3, or 4 ft long.

service pipes are called *house* or *building drains* inside the building and *house* or *building sewers* outside. Storm water from roofs and paved areas, if taken into a *property drain,* is discharged into the street gutters or directly into the storm sewer. In combined systems of sewerage, roof water may be carried into the house drain and water from yard areas into the house sewer. Storm water that is not otherwise channeled travels over the ground until it reaches the street gutter along which it flows to a storm-water inlet or catch basin, whence it is piped to a manhole. In separate systems, connections to the wrong sewer, made by mistake or in violation of regulations, carry some storm water into sanitary sewers and some sewage into storm drains. The dry-weather flow in combined sewers is primarily sewage and ground water; the flow during and immediately following a heavy rainstorm is predominantly storm runoff.

3-3. Patterns of Collection Systems. The pattern of the collecting system is dictated by the following: (1) the type of system employed (whether separate or combined); (2) the street lines or rights of way to be followed; (3) the topography, hydrology, and geology of the area drained; (4) the political boundaries to be observed; and (5) the location and nature of the treatment and disposal works. Five different patterns are sketched in Figure 3-1.

Storm drains are naturally laid out to seek the shortest possible path to existing surface channels. This creates the *perpendicular pattern* of storm and combined sewerage shown in example *a* of Figure 3-1.[5] A combined system of this type pollutes the waters that wash the immediate shores of the community. It renders sewage treatment difficult because of the large number of outlets that are commonly constructed. If the sewage is to be carried to the outskirts of the community, or if it is to be treated at a central works, the sewage must be intercepted before it reaches the receiving water. An *intercepter pattern* results, as shown in example *b* of Figure 3-1.[5] If the area tributary to the intercepter is at all large, it is ordinarily necessary, for reasons of economy, to restrict the capacity of the intercepter to some small multiple of the average dry-weather flow or to the dry-weather flow plus the first flush of storm water which is most heavily

---

[5] Lower Manhattan Island in the City of New York offers an example of the perpendicular pattern. Intercepter and zone patterns are found in London, England; Boston, Mass.; Buffalo, N. Y.; Cleveland, O.; Chicago, Ill.; Milwaukee, Wis.; and many other places. The fan pattern is typified by the combined system of Vienna, Austria, where the Vienna River, covered in part to serve as a combined sewer, drains the lateral valley through which the city recedes from the banks of the Danube. The radial pattern is employed by Berlin, Germany, a radial city situated in flat country.

polluted. In North America, the capacity provided is seldom more than the maximum dry-weather flow. Sewage in excess of this amount is allowed to spill over into a natural water course through outlets that were in existence before interception, or through storm-water overflows otherwise constructed for this purpose. In order to reduce the amount of pumping commonly associated with water-front inter-cepters and to limit their size and minimize the difficulties of construction in low-lying and often bad ground, it may be possible to deal with the drainage area in a series of zones that differ in elevation and lend themselves to separate interception. The resulting *zone pattern* is shown in example *c* of Figure 3-1.[5] This pattern can be employed usefully also in connection with sanitary sewers. The *fan pattern* (see *d* in Figure 3-1 [5]) concentrates flows inward from the outskirts of the community and is readily served by a single outfall. The largest sewers, however, must ordinarily pass through the most congested districts of the community. This makes it difficult to increase the capacity of the system, for example, by building *relief sewers*, as the outlying suburbs in the water shed develop and add to the load on the works. In the *radial pattern* (see *e* in Figure 3-1 [5]), on the contrary, flow is outward from the heart of the city, as along the spokes of a wheel. The suburbs can then be served by relatively small and short lines of sewers that are added as needed. Radial flow, on the other hand, multiplies the number of disposal works.

3-4. Collection of Sanitary Sewage. Since about 70% of the water led into a community must be removed by its sewers, the average flow in sanitary sewers is about 70 gpcd. Daily and hourly variations in water use multiply this value about threefold. Illicit storm water and ground water further add to the required capacity, and a design value of about 300 gpcd is not unusual.

In order to hold in check the fouling of sanitary sewers by the deposition of waste matters, self-cleaning velocities (2 to 2.5 fps) are necessary. Except in unusually flat country, sewer grades are chosen so as to secure these velocities when the sewers are running reasonably full.[6] Some deposition of solids is bound to occur, however, and sewers must be made accessible for inspection and cleaning. In sewers that are not large enough to be entered, this is done by providing man-holes at all junctions of sewers, changes in direction, and changes in grade. The straight runs that can be rodded out between manholes are limited in length to 300 or 400 ft for sewers less than 24 in. in diameter. For larger sewers, they are up to 600 ft. Sewers so large

---

[6] Half full or more in circular sections, since the hydraulic radius of a semi-circle equals that of a circle.

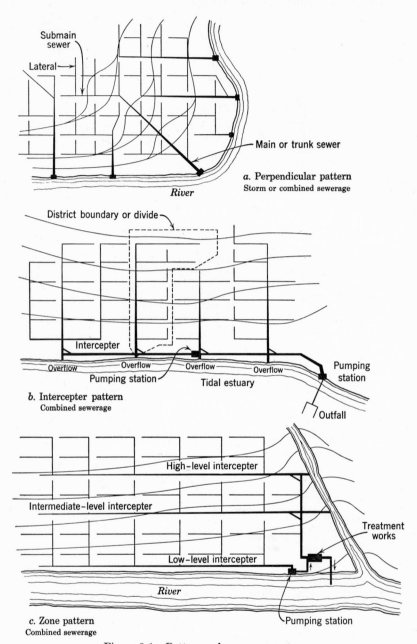

Figure 3-1. Patterns of sewerage systems.

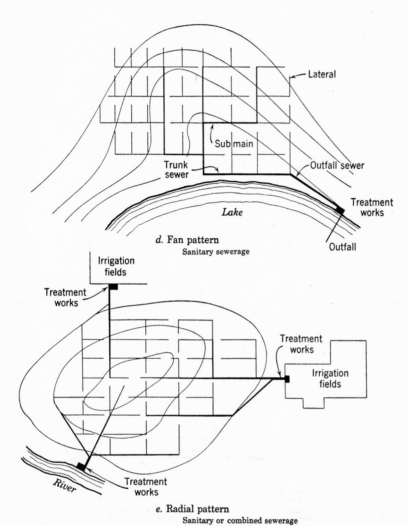

d. Fan pattern
Sanitary sewerage

e. Radial pattern
Sanitary or combined sewerage

Figure 3-1. (*Continued.*)

that they can be entered for inspection, cleaning, and repair are freed from these restrictions, and access manholes are placed quite far apart either symmetrically above the sewer or tangentially to one side. A plan and profile of a sanitary sewer and its laterals is shown in Figure 3-2, together with enlarged sections of sewer trenches and manholes. The use of lamp holes as substitutes for manholes on stubs of sewer lines or at breaks in grade or changes in direction between manholes is generally undesirable. Lamp holes usually consist of 8-in. clay pipes rising vertically from a tee in the sewer line. A lantern can be lowered into them for inspection of the run from the nearest manhole. The use of clean-outs on stubs is slightly more favorable. The clean-outs consist of 8-in. pipes that slope to the street surface from a Y in the sewer; this makes it possible to rod out the run. In very flat country and in other unusual circumstances, sewers must be laid on flat grades if very deep sewers are to be avoided and pumping is to be held to a minimum. Operating difficulties, however, are multiplied in such systems.

The minimum size of sewers in North American practice is 8 in. Smaller sewers clog too quickly and are harder to clean. The saving in cost effected by their use is not sufficient to offset operating troubles. Vitrified-clay pipes are commonly used for small sewers, and prefabricated concrete pipes for larger ones. In wet ground, sewers may be underdrained, or cast-iron pipes may be employed to reduce infiltration of ground water. Cast-iron pipes are greater in length and possess tighter joints than common sewer pipes. Clay pipes laid with open joints, or porous pipes of cinder concrete placed in a bed of gravel or broken stone beneath the sewer, will serve as underdrains for use either during construction or on a permanent basis. Free discharge of the underdrains into natural drainage channels should be sought. Consideration must be given to the fact that some sewage may seep into permanent underdrains and be discharged by them after the system has been placed in service. If the sewage contains grit or other abrading materials and the scouring of concrete is to be prevented, velocities in sewers must be held below 8 to 10 fps. Very large sewers are built in place, sometimes by tunneling operations. Hydraulically and structurally, they have much in common with the grade aqueducts used in water supplies and are given similar shapes.

Sewers are commonly laid at sufficient depth (1) to protect them against breakage or traffic shock, (2) to keep them from freezing, and (3) to permit them to drain the lowest fixture on the premises served by them. In fixing the depth of street sewers, due allowance must be made for the slope of the building sewer. Slopes of $\frac{1}{4}$ in. per ft or more are common.[7] In the northern United States, cellar depths generally range from 6 to 8 ft and frost depths from 4 to 6 ft. An earth cover of 2 ft will cushion most shocks. Sewage from deep basements may have to be ejected or pumped into the street sewer.

As shown in Figure 3-2, manholes are channeled so as to cause as little disturbance to flow as is possible in the circumstances. Drop manholes are used for a like purpose in connection with the entrance of high-lying laterals. Otherwise these laterals would have to be lowered over the length of their last run—a wasteful arrangement. The upper reaches of lateral sewers ordinarily receive so little sewage that self-cleaning velocities cannot be attained in 8-in. sewers. Such runs must be flushed out from time to time. This can be done (1) by damming up the flow at a lower manhole and releasing the stored waters after the sewer is almost full; (2) by suddenly discharging a large amount of water into a manhole; (3) by providing at the end of the line a *flushing manhole* that can be filled with water through fire hose attached to a nearby fire hydrant before a flap valve, shear gate, or similar quick-opening device leading to the sewer is opened; and (4) by installing an automatic flush tank that fills slowly and discharges suddenly. Possible back-flow from the sewer to the water supply is a bad feature of automatic flush tanks, in addition to cost and to maintenance difficulties.

Example 3-1. An 8-in. sewer is to flow full at a velocity of 2.5 fps. (1) What is its maximum capacity in cfs and gpd; (2) what is the minimum grade on which this sewer must be placed, if the coefficient of roughness is assumed to be 0.015; (3) how many people can it serve if the maximum per capita flow is 300 gpd; and (4) how many acres will it drain if the density of the population is 50 per acre?

1. Capacity $= [(\pi \times 64)/(4 \times 144)] \times 2.5 = 0.87$ cfs;   and $0.87 \times 646,000 = 560,000$ gpd.

2. By Manning's formula, minimum grade $= 0.007$ or 0.7%.

3. People served $= 560,000/300 = 1,870$.

4. Area drained $= 1,870/50 = 37.4$ acres.

3-5. Collection of Storm Water. In separate sewerage systems, much of the suspended load of solids carried by storm sewers or drains is heavy mineral matter that will settle out unless the velocity of flow is kept sufficiently high. Fine sand is ordinarily transported by water at velocities of 1 fps or more and gravel at 2 fps or more. Recommended minimum velocities, therefore, are 2.5 to 3 fps, or about 0.5 fps more than for sanitary sewers. Factors determining the ca-

---

[7] At this slope a 6-in. sewer flowing full will carry about 300 gpm or 40 cfm at a velocity of 3.5 fps.

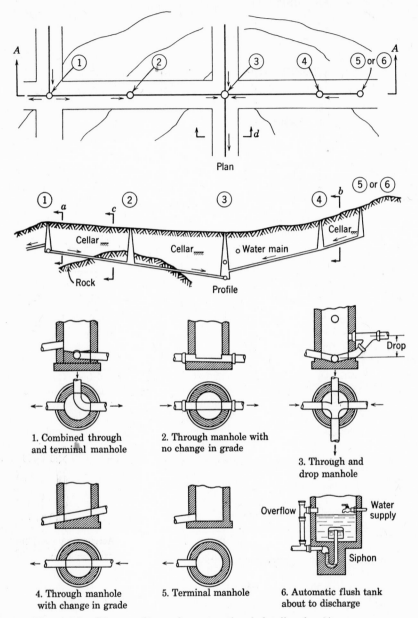

Figure 3-2. Plan, profile, and constructional details of sanitary sewers.

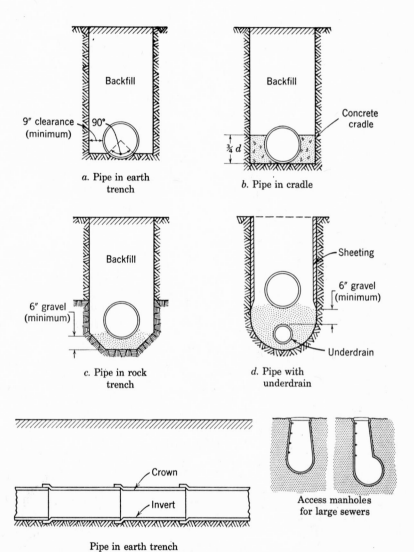

a. Pipe in earth trench

b. Pipe in cradle

c. Pipe in rock trench

d. Pipe with underdrain

Pipe in earth trench

Access manholes for large sewers

Figure 3-2. (Continued.)

pacity of storm drains are: (1) the intensity and duration of local rainfall, (2) the size and runoff characteristics of the tributary areas, and (3) the economy of design. Included in economic considerations are the characteristics of the district served and the opportunities for discharging the collected storm water into natural water courses or bodies of water. Waste waters other than storm runoff are ordinarily negligible quantities in the hydraulic design of storm drains, the primary function of which is to prevent (a) the inundation of streets, walks, and yard areas, and (b) the flooding of basements and other low-lying structures, together with the attendant inconvenience, disruption of traffic, and damage to property. In general, therefore, storm sewers are made large enough to drain away, sufficiently rapidly and without becoming surcharged, the runoff from storms that experience has shown to be of such magnitude and frequency as to be objectionable in the community under consideration or one like it. The heavier the storm, the greater is the potential inconvenience or damage, but the less frequent is its occurrence. The higher the property values, the greater is the damage that can be done in the absence of adequate sewer capacity. In a well-balanced system of storm drains, all these factors will have received recognition for each kind of area served: residential, mercantile, industrial, or mixed. The high-value mercantile district with basement stores, or stock rooms, for example, may be provided with sewers that will carry away surface runoff resulting from all but unusual storms, such as those estimated to occur only once in 5, 10, 20, 50, or even 100 years. Suburban residential districts may be given drains the capacity of which is exceeded by the 1-year or 2-year storm.

Until storm drains are installed in a given area and the area itself is fully developed, it is not possible to make runoff measurements. Normally, therefore, the design of storm sewers must proceed not through the analysis of recorded runoff but through: (1) the analysis of records of storm rainfalls—their intensity or rate of precipitation, duration, and frequency of occurrence; and (2) the estimation of runoff resulting from these rainfalls.

Although storm sewers are occasionally surcharged and subjected to pressures equal to their depth below street level, they are designed for open-channel flow and equipped with manholes in much the same manner as sanitary sewers. The minimum size of storm sewers commonly employed in North American practice, however, is 12 in. The greater size will help to prevent clogging of the drains by trash of one kind or another. The minimum depth is determined by structural requirements rather than the elevation of basement floors. Surface runoff is led into storm drains from street gutters through *street inlets* or *catch basins* (Figure 3-3) and through *property drains*. Street inlets are made large enough in size and number to prevent

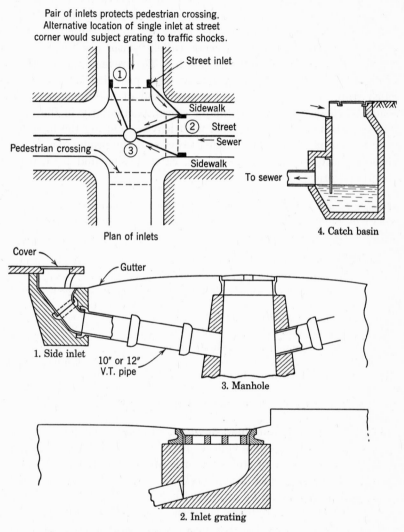

Figure 3-3. Street inlets and their connection to a manhole.

undue flooding of the traffic way. Their location and number are determined in part also by the desirability of keeping pedestrian crossings reasonably dry. Inlet pipes discharge preferably into manholes in order to permit inspection and cleaning of the pipes. Inlets that are enlarged and trapped constitute settling chambers in which the entering storm water will deposit some of the debris and heavy solids carried by it. They are then called catch basins. Historically, they antedate street inlets and were devised in connection with combined sewerage systems at a time when streets were largely unpaved and much sand and gravel was washed away by storm runoff. In those days, furthermore, the air in sewers, called "sewer gas," was erroneously considered dangerous to health. To prevent the escape of sewer air through catch basins, they were provided with a water-sealed trap. Catch basins need a good deal of maintenance. They should be cleaned after every major storm, particularly in the fall of the year when they become filled with leaves. During the mosquito-breeding season, they must be oiled to prevent the production of large crops of mosquitoes. On the whole, catch basins find little use in modern sewerage systems.

Example 3-2. A storm sewer is to drain an area of 37.4 acres (the area drained by an 8-in. sanitary sewer in Example 3-1). How large must this sewer be in order to carry away rain falling at a rate of 2 in. per hr during 30 min, the time needed for the entire drainage area to become tributary to the sewer? The required velocity of flow is to be 3 fps, and the ratio of the peak rate of runoff to the rate of rainfall on the area is assumed to be 0.6.

1. 1 in. per hr per acre = 1.0083 cfs = 1.0 cfs closely enough. This is a fact to remember.

2. Rate of runoff = $2 \times 0.6 \times 37.4 = 45$ cfs.

3. Cross-sectional area of drain = $45/3.0 = 15$ sq ft.

4. Diameter of drain = $12\sqrt{4 \times 15.0/\pi} = 53$ in.

5. Ratio of storm runoff to sanitary sewage (Example 3-1): $45.0:0.87 = 52:1$; i.e., sanitary sewage constitutes less than 2% of the combined flow.

6. Per capita storm runoff for a population density of 50 per acre = $2 \times 0.6 \times 646,000/50 = 15,500$ gpcd, against sanitary sewage of 300 gpcd.

3-6. Collection of Combined Sewage.

In combined sewerage systems, a single set of sewers collects both surface runoff and sanitary sewage. The quantity of storm water is often 50 to 100 times that of the sanitary sewage (see Example 3-2). Since the accuracy with which surface runoff can be estimated is generally of a lower order of magnitude than the difference between storm and combined sewage, combined sewers are designed essentially as storm drains. However, they are laid as deep as sanitary sewers since they must carry away the flows from building drains as well as street inlets or catch basins. Needless to say, the surcharging and overflowing of combined sewers is more objectionable than the backing-up of drains that carry only storm water.

The wide range of flows in combined sewers creates certain special problems. Among them are:

a. The choice of cross-section for the purpose of insuring self-cleaning velocities for the dry-weather flows of sanitary sewage.

b. The design of inverted siphons or depressed sewers which dip below the hydraulic grade line in order to carry sewage across a depression or below an obstruction, such as a stream or subway. Depressed sewers flow full and under pressure. If a single conduit were retained, variations in velocity would be much greater than those in open-channel flow. For this reason the flow is generally distributed between two or more parallel depressed sewers.

c. Provision of storm-water overflows in connection with the intercepters that will generally have to be introduced in the course of time if receiving waters are to be given reasonable protection against pollution.

a. Sections. Departures from circular cross-sections are generally prompted by structural or economic rather than hydraulic considera-

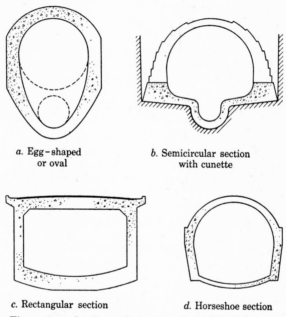

a. Egg–shaped   b. Semicircular section
   or oval   with cunette

c. Rectangular section   d. Horseshoe section

Figure 3-4. Sections of storm and combined sewers.

tions. To secure reasonably good hydraulic performance at dry-weather flows, however, some combined sewers have been given special shapes. Examples are the *egg-shaped* sewer and the *cunette* illustrated in Figure 3-4. The egg-shaped section is, in essence, an integration of two circular sewers: an underlying sanitary sewer and an overlying storm drain. An attempt is made to keep the hydraulic radius constant at all depths. The cunette [8] forms a trough dimensioned to carry the dry-weather flow, or sanitary sewage. The *rectangular section* is easy to construct and makes for an economical trench with low head-room requirements. The *horseshoe section* is structurally very satisfactory.

b. *Inverted Siphons.* The spread between dry-weather flows and storm flows through inverted siphons, or suppressed sewers, is cared

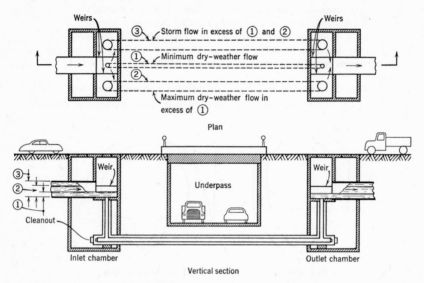

Figure 3-5. Inverted siphon or suppressed sewer for combined sewage.

for by installing a sufficient number of pipes to carry characteristic flows through the siphon at self-cleaning velocities. A simple example is shown in Figure 3-5. Low dry-weather flows of sanitary sewage are carried by the central siphon. High dry-weather flows spill over a weir into a lateral siphon to the right. Storm flows discharge over a weir into a lateral siphon to the left. The combined capacity of the three siphons equals that of the approach sewer. Weir heights are fixed by the depth to which the three characteristic flows fill the approach sewer and inlet structure. Flows are reunited in the outlet chamber. Large outfall sewers have been built as pressure tunnels.

[8] The main drains of Paris, France, made famous by Victor Hugo's references to them in *Les Misérables*, were constructed from 1833 onward. They were made sufficiently large (6 ft high and at least 2 ft 6 in. wide) to permit laborers to work in comfort. Their conversion from 1880 onward into combined sewers necessitated the addition of *cunettes*.

Example 3-3. A siphon is to carry a minimum dry-weather flow of 1.0 cfs, a maximum dry-weather flow of 3.0 cfs, and a storm flow of 45.0 cfs in three pipes. Select the proper diameters to assure velocities of 3.0 fps in all pipes.

1. For minimum dry-weather flow of 1.0 cfs, the nearest standard diameter of

pipe is $12\sqrt{\dfrac{4 \times 1.0}{\pi \times 3.0}} = 8$ in.; actual capacity $= \dfrac{\pi \times (8)^2}{4 \times 144} \times 3 = 1.05$ cfs.

2. For maximum dry-weather flow in excess of the minimum, namely, $3.0 - 1.05$

$= 1.95$ cfs, the nearest standard diameter of pipe is $12\sqrt{\dfrac{4 \times 1.95}{\pi \times 3.0}} = 12$ in.; actual

capacity $= \dfrac{\pi \times 1}{4} \times 3 = 2.36$ cfs.

3. For storm flows in excess of the maximum dry-weather flows, namely, $45 -$

$(2.36 + 1.05) = 41.6$ cfs, the next lowest standard diameter of pipe is $12\sqrt{\dfrac{4 \times 41.6}{\pi \times 3.0}}$

$= 48$ in., which will have to flow at a velocity of $\dfrac{41.6 \times 4}{\pi \times (4)^2} = 3.3$ fps.

c. Intercepters. Intercepting sewers are generally intended to carry the maximum dry-weather flow or, since maximum dry-weather flow and storms do not necessarily coincide, to bleed off as much combined sewage as is warranted by hygienic, esthetic, and economic considerations. Where rainfalls are intense and of short duration, as in most parts of the North American continent, it is not possible to discharge a substantial amount of storm water through intercepters that are reasonably proportioned, and intercepters are commonly designed to carry only 2 to 3 times the average dry-weather flow, or from 250 to 600 gpcd. A more informative measure of the capacity of intercepters in excess of the average dry-weather flow is the amount of rainfall or runoff that they can carry, expressed, for example, in inches per hour. Since the first flush of storm water is likely to move most of the accumulated sewer deposits, its interception is particularly important. Most of the storm water carried by the collector tributary to the intercepter must be allowed to overflow into the body of water that the intercepter is designed to protect. This overflow contains a proportionate share of the sanitary sewage that enters the combined system during the period of storm runoff. As a result, the total amount of polluting material reaching the "protected" body of water in the course of a year is usually a significant though small fraction of the total annual volume of sanitary sewage. For this reason, health authorities generally frown upon the installation or extension of sewerage systems that are built on the combined plan. Just how much sewage goes overboard is a function of the intensity and duration of rainfall and the relation of resulting storm runoff to the capacity of the intercepter. The amount can be calculated for a given locality.

Relative losses equaling 1% or more of the annual volume of sanitary sewage are not unusual.

d. Storm Stand-by Tanks. Interception is improved by installing storm-water stand-by tanks at the junction of the submain with the intercepter. These tanks, until they are filled, store the flows in excess of intercepter capacity; after that, they continue to function as settling

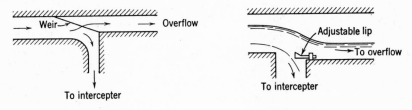

a. Diverting weir—plan

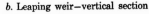

b. Leaping weir—vertical section

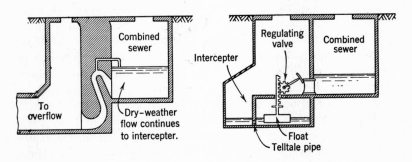

c. Siphon spillway—vertical section

d. Mechanical diverter, or regulator—vertical section; actual mechanisms are more complicated.

Figure 3-6. Regulation of storm-water overflow.

basins and remove much of the gross and unsightly settleable matter from the overflowing storm water, even when the detention period becomes as short as 15 minutes. The tank contents, together with the settled solids, are eventually flushed into the intercepter after the storm subsides. The operating range of tanks lies between the dry-weather flowline of the intercepter and the crown of the combined sewer. Where appreciable quantities of storm water are carried as far as the treatment works, the location of storm-water stand-by tanks may be shifted to the treatment plant.

e. Overflows. The amount of water entering the intercepter at the junctions of the submains of the combined system with it must be controlled by admitting only as much water to the intercepter as the capacity of its various reaches permits. All water in excess of this value must be diverted into storm-water overflows. Admission and diversion can be regulated hydraulically or mechanically, as shown in Figure 3-6.

Hydraulic separation of excess flows from dry-weather flows is accomplished by the following devices:

1. Diverting weirs in the form of side spillways. The crest level and length are chosen to spill excess flows, which, figuratively speaking, override the dry-weather flows, into the overflow. Dry-weather flows continue along their normal path to the intercepter. (See Figure 3-6a.)

2. Leaping weirs consisting essentially of gaps in the floor of the channel. Excess flows leap over these gaps under their own momentum. Dry-weather flows tumble through the gap into the intercepter. (See Figure 3-6b.)

3. Siphon spillways. Flows in excess of intercepter capacity are siphoned off into the overflow channel. (See Figure 3-6c).

Mechanical diversion of storm-water flows is generally regulated by a float-operated valve which controls the admission of water to the intercepter. (See Figure 3-6d.)

3-7. Choice of Collecting System. The combined system of sewerage, apart from questions of economy, is at best a compromise between the two wholly different functions that it attempts to perform: namely, water carriage of wastes, and removal of flooding runoff. In the life of growing communities, economies that are initially effected by the use of combined sewers will generally be offset in the long run (1) by undesirable pollution of natural water courses through necessary storm-water spills and consequent nuisance or, at least, ineffective utilization of the esthetic and recreational values of these bodies of water; (2) by increased cost of eventual sewage treatment or pumping associated with disposal of intercepted sewage; and (3) by greater nuisance caused by the occasional overflowing or backing-up of combined sewage rather than storm water. Many small streams, around which parks and other recreational areas could have been developed, have been forced into combined sewerage systems that, in the course of their evolution, degraded these streams into open sewers. A separate system of sewerage can utilize natural water courses hydraulically to the fullest possible extent by discharging storm water into them through short runs of storm drains. This will not pollute them, but it may necessitate their being channelized in order to improve their carrying capacity and control their flooding.

3-8. Disposal of Sewage. Whereas the water-carriage system of sewerage provides a simple and economical means for transporting unsightly, putrescible, and dangerous waste matters away from their place of origin in household and industry, it concentrates potential nuisances and dangers at the terminus of the collecting system. If sewage matters are to be kept, in whole or in part, out of rivers and canals, ponds, and lakes, or tidal estuaries and coastal waters, they must be "unloaded" from the transporting water prior to its disposal by dilution. This unloading operation is assigned to sewage-treatment plants. As previously stated, this is done in order that the receiving waters may be protected against damage in one or more of the following forms: (1) contamination of water supplies, bathing places, shell-fish layings, and ice supplies; (2) pollution sufficient in concentration to render the receiving waters unsightly or malodorous; (3) destruction of food fish and other valuable aquatic life; and (4) other impairment of the usefulness of natural waters for recreation, commerce, or industry. The required degree of treatment before such disposal of sewage depends (a) upon the nature and relative volume of the receiving water and (b) upon the purposes the water is to serve in the water economy of the region.

Treatment of sewage before its disposal by irrigation looks towards the full recovery of the "water value" of sewage and such recovery of the "fertilizing value" of sewage as is consistent: (1) with the avoidance of the spread of disease by crops grown on sewage-irrigated lands; (2) with the prevention of nuisance due to unsightliness or bad odors in the vicinity of the disposal areas; and (3) with the economic maintenance of disposal and agricultural activities. In sewage disposal by irrigation, the required degree of treatment must take into consideration the nature and size of the disposal area and the purposes it is to serve in the land economy of the region.

Raw sewage is still discharged into the great streams, lakes, and tidal waters of North America, and there are many irrigation areas that receive untreated sewage.

The daily load of solids imposed upon domestic sewage amounts to about half a pound per person per day. The resulting mixture of water and waste substances is very dilute—about 0.1% of solid matter by weight when the water consumption is 100 gpcd. Industrial wastes, however, may be far more concentrated. Floating matter, suspended solids, oil, and grease render sewage and its receiving waters unsightly; settling solids form sludge banks; organic solids render sewage and its receiving waters putrescible; pathogenic bacteria and other organisms make them dangerous.

a. Methods of Sewage Treatment. Removal of the load of waste matters from sewage is accomplished in a number of different ways, among which the following are common:

1. Bulky floating and suspended matter is strained out by passing the sewage through screens from which the collected solids are removed: *racks and screens.*

2. Oil and grease are allowed to rise to the surface of stilling chambers whence they are skimmed: *skimming tanks.*

3. Heavy and coarse suspended matters are allowed to settle to the bottom of stilling chambers, whence the accumulated solids or sludge are withdrawn: *grit chambers, detritus tanks, settling tanks,* or *sedimentation basins.*

4. More finely divided matter is removed by filtration through soil, sand, or other granular materials: *irrigation areas, intermittent sand filters,* and *rapid filters.*

5. Much of the non-settleable suspended matter and some of the dissolved solids are converted into settleable solids and rendered amenable to sedimentation by flocculation and precipitation with chemicals in much the same manner as in the coagulation of water: *chemical precipitation tanks.*

6. Even more of the colloidal and dissolved matter is converted into settleable solids by biological growths or slimes. The hosts of living cells that populate these slimes utilize some of the waste matters for growth and energy and create interfaces of relatively enormous extent at which adsorption, absorption, diffusion, and other interfacial forces or contact phenomena bring about movements of dissolved and particulate substances from the liquid to the slime. These biological slimes must be supplied with air. To this end, they are either supported on a bed of granular material, such as sand, gravel, and broken stone, through which the sewage flows intermittently or over which it trickles, or they are added to the flowing sewage and kept in suspension by agitating the mixed liquor with air or mechanical stirring devices: *trickling filters* and *activated-sludge tanks.*

7. Many of the pathogenic bacteria and other organisms are removed from sewage along with the solids in which they are imbedded or to which they are attached. Others die because the imposed environment is unfavorable to their continued existence. More direct destruction is accomplished by applying chemical disinfecting agents: *chlorination units.*

b. Methods of Sludge Treatment and Disposal. The unloaded solids still contain a large amount of water [9] and most of the organic matter. This makes them both bulky and putrescible. Sludge treatment, therefore, involves the removal of water and the destruction or stabilization of the organic matter in one of the following ways:

1. Destruction of organic matter by having it serve as food for bacteria: *sludge-digestion tanks.*

---

[9] Sludge settling from sewage by plain sedimentation contains about 95% water; activated sludge, 98% or more. If the daily volume of sewage is millions of gallons, the daily volume of sludge will be thousands of gallons.

2. Partial dewatering of sludge (usually digested sludge) by air-drying on sand beds: *sludge-drying beds.*

3. Partial dewatering of chemically coagulated sludge by filtration through cloth: *vacuum filters.*

4. Heat-drying of partially dewatered sludge: *flash driers.*

5. Destruction of organic matter by using partially or fully dewatered sludge as a fuel: *incinerators.*

Sludge digestion yields useful combustible gas of high fuel value, principally marsh gas or methane. After digestion, sewage solids are no longer recognizable as such and drain rapidly in the air when run out onto sand beds. Heat-dried sludge is stable. The final product of incineration is ash. All methods of sludge treatment reduce the number of pathogenic organisms concentrated in the sludge. Heat-drying renders sludge essentially sterile.

Under suitable conditions, sludge may be used as a fertilizer and soil builder. If not, it may be dumped at sea or into inland waters or used to fill low-lying lands. If sludge is used for agricultural purposes, attention must be paid to the possible contamination of food crops by all but heat-dried sludge.

Diagrammatic sketches of sewage-treatment plants are presented in Figure 3-7. Numerous other methods or combinations of methods are in use.[10] The plants shown in Figure 3-7 involve complete treatment of sewage and sludge. Partial treatment of either or both is often adequate to satisfy local needs. Seasonal operation of plants or parts of plants to secure a higher degree of treatment at critical times of the year is sometimes sufficient, for example, during periods of low runoff and high recreational use of the receiving water: bathing, boating, etc.

The works shown can be operated to remove from 80 to 95% or more of the suspended solids, putrescible matter, and bacteria. Chlorination of the effluent can increase the destruction of bacteria to 99% or more. Partial treatment reduces the removal values to between 40 and 70%.

[10] The combination of sedimentation and sludge digestion in a two-storied tank or in separate settling and digestion tanks, followed by biological treatment of the clarified sewage on a trickling filter (examples *a* and *b* in Figure 3-7), has found wide favor in North America, particularly in cities of moderate size: Fitchburg and Worcester, Mass.; Reading, Pa.; Schenectady, N. Y.; Trenton, N. J.; and Atlanta, Ga. Plain sedimentation followed by activated-sludge treatment with or without separate sludge digestion has found widest use in large treatment works (example *c* in Figure 3-7): the Tallman's Island, Bowery Bay, and Jamaica Bay plants of New York, N. Y.; the North Side and Southwest Side plants of Chicago, Ill.; the Easterly Works of Cleveland, O.; and many smaller places.

c. Design of Sewage-Treatment Works. The design of sewage-treatment works is based (1) upon an understanding of the operation of the various treatment processes and devices; (2) upon a knowledge of the factors affecting the flow of sewage, sludge, and often air, through the various structures employed; and (3) upon a comprehension of the behavior of these structures and mechanisms under load. Some conception of the size of the principal structures is obtained from the following facts (normally applicable to domestic sewage):

1. Primary tanks hold the sewage for about 2 hr and are rated at about 900 gpd per sq ft of water surface.
2. Secondary settling tanks, following biological treatment, have a detention period of about 1½ hr and a surface loading of up to 1,800 gpd per sq ft.
3. Sludge-digestion tanks, in the northern United States, have a capacity of about 2 cu ft per capita.
4. Trickling filters in low-rate operation are rated at about 3 mgad.
5. Activated-sludge tanks aerate the sewage and returned activated sludge, which equals about 25% of the volume of the sewage, for about 6 hr.
6. Drying beds for digested sludge provide an area of about 1 sq ft per capita in the northern United States.

Example 3-4. Estimate the capacity of the structural components of a trickling-filter plant, such as that shown in Figure 3-7a, that is to treat 8 mgd of domestic sewage from 100,000 people.

1. Settling compartments in 4 Imhoff tanks, averaging 10 ft in depth.
   a. Assumed detention period = 2 hr.
   b. Effective volume = $8{,}000{,}000 \times (2/24)/4 = 167{,}000$ gal = 22,300 cu ft.
   c. Surface area = $22{,}300/10 = 2{,}230$ sq ft (such as 25 ft by 89 ft).
   d. Surface rating = $(8{,}000{,}000/4)/2{,}230 = 900$ gpd per sq ft.
2. Sludge-digestion compartments in 4 Imhoff tanks:
   a. Assumed storage requirement = 2 cu ft per capita.
   b. Effective volume $2 \times 100{,}000/4 = 50{,}000$ cu ft.
   c. Depth below settling compartment = $50{,}000/2{,}230 = 22.5$ ft (with 1.5 ft additional to keep sludge clear of slots).
3. Sludge-drying beds, 10 in number.
   a. Assumed area requirement = 1 sq ft per capita.
   b. Effective area $1 \times 100{,}000/10 = 10{,}000$ sq ft (such as 16 ft by 62.5 ft).
4. Trickling filters, 2 in number.
   a. Assumed loading = 3 mgad.
   b. Effective area = $(8/2)/3 = 1.33$ acres.

d. Sewage Disposal by Dilution. The outfall pipes that carry sewage into receiving waters should terminate well below the low-water mark and there disperse the sewage or effluent as quickly and uniformly as possible. Dispersal is aided by providing a number of different outlets (1) spaced sufficiently far apart to prevent interference

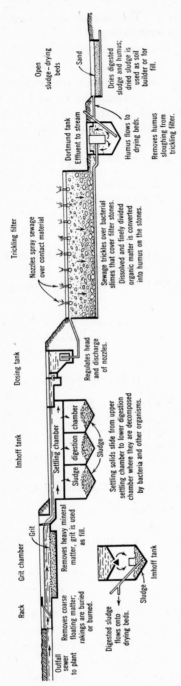

a. Trickling filter including coarse screening, grit removal, plain sedimentation, contact treatment, final settling, and sludge drying.

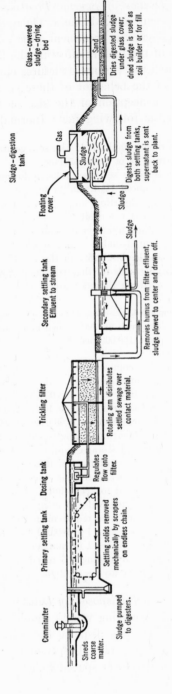

b. Trickling filter including comminution, plain sedimentation, contact treatment, final settling, and digestion and drying of sludge.

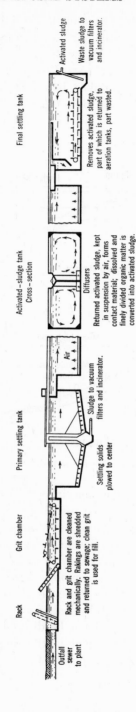

Rack

Grit chamber

Primary settling tank

Activated–sludge tank
Cross–section

Final settling tank

Outfall
sewer
to plant

Rack and grit chamber are cleaned
mechanically. Rakings are shredded
and returned to sewage; clean grit
is used for fill.

Settling solids
plowed to center

Sludge to vacuum
filters and incinerator.

Air

Diffusers

Returned activated sludge, kept
in suspension by air, forms
contact material; dissolved and
finely divided organic matter is
converted into activated sludge.

Removes activated sludge,
part of which is returned to
aeration tanks, part wasted.

Activated sludge

Waste sludge to
vacuum filters
and incinerator.

c. Activated–sludge plant including coarse screening, grit removal, plain sedimentation, contact treatment,
and final settling. Sludge is partly dewatered on vacuum filters and then incinerated.

Figure 3-7. Common types of sewage–treatment plants.

and (2) situated at or near the bottom of the receiving water in order to keep the generally warmer and lighter [11] sewage from overriding the dilution water in a thin layer (see Figure 3-8).

Outfalls must be located with due regard to prevailing currents and their bearing upon water-works intakes, bathing places, shellfish layings, and the like. No matter what the relative dilution, the forces of

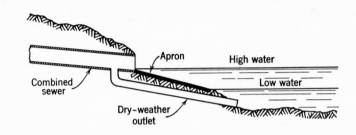

a. Outfall of combined sewer into a stream.

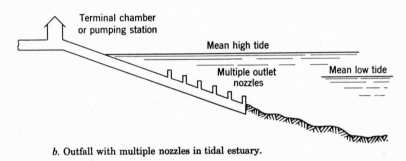

b. Outfall with multiple nozzles in tidal estuary.

Figure 3-8. Sewage outfalls.

natural purification, or self-purification, inherent in natural bodies of water will, in the course of time and associated distance, return the receiving water to its original state of cleanliness. These forces are essentially similar to those called upon in the controlled treatment of sewage by most of the methods presently in use. If dilution is sufficient, natural purification will be accomplished without nuisance, because conditions relatively close to those prevailing in clean waters will obtain and the complicated physical, chemical, and biological balance of the receiving water will not be disturbed. If dilution is insufficient, decomposition of putrescible matter may proceed at such a pace as to upset the normal balance of the receiving water and

[11] Especially when discharge is into sea water.

create, for a time at least, a black, unsightly, and malodorous body of water whose normal flora and fauna are completely destroyed.

A rule of thumb formulated by engineers for large American streams and giving a rough estimate of the required dilution is that untreated, combined sewage may be discharged safely (1) into swift streams that carry 2.5 cfs of water per 1,000 persons contributing sewage and (2) into sluggish streams that carry 10 cfs per 1,000 persons contributing sewage. The average value is 6 cfs per 1,000 persons. For domestic sewage, treated sewage, and industrial wastes, these figures can be apportioned to the relative amount of putrescible matter present.[12] Where the emphasis is on water supply, recreational use of water, and preservation of fish and other useful aquatic life, rather than on the avoidance of nuisance, dilution requirements become very much larger. If available dilution is inadequate, the sewage must be treated before disposal by dilution.

Example 3-5. The low-water flow of a normally rapid stream draining 2,000 sq miles is 0.1 cfs per sq mile. Estimate the extent to which the domestic sewage from a city of 100,000 people must be treated before discharge into this stream if nuisance is to be avoided; also the dilution ratio of sewage to stream water that will obtain. Assume a per capita flow of sewage of 80 gpd.

a. Low-water flow = $0.1 \times 2,000 = 200$ cfs.

b. Required flow for disposal of domestic sewage untreated = $6 \times 100/1.4 = 430$ cfs.

c. Per cent removal of pollutional load needed = $[(430 - 200)/430] \times 100 = 54\%$.

d. Dilution ratio = $(100,000 \times 80):(200 \times 646,000) = 1:16$.

e. Sewage Disposal by Irrigation. The terminal discharge of sewage onto land or into the soil rather than into water has as its objectives (1) the safe disposal of the sewage and (2), where possible, its utilization in the raising of crops. As a municipal treatment process, sewage irrigation cannot compete economically with other treatment methods in North America unless the water resources of the region are poor and large tracts of cheap, but suitable, land are available. Whether sewage should be treated before disposal on land depends upon the conditions encountered and the hygienic factors involved. There is an obvious hazard of contaminating food products which must receive careful consideration. The discharge of settled sewage into the ground through agricultural tile pipes in the disposal of sewage from isolated dwellings is known as subsurface irrigation and is widely employed.

[12] Combined sewage averages about 40% stronger than domestic sewage. Industrial wastes may be weaker or very strong indeed.

Example 3-6. The annual depth of water employed in the irrigation of crops is 10 in. Estimate the daily volume of sewage that can be disposed of on an acre of land and the land area required to dispose of the domestic sewage from a community of 10,000 people:

a. Rate of irrigation = $[(10/12) \times 7.5 \times 43,560]/365 = 750$ gpad.

b. Area for 10,000 people and a sewage flow of 80 gpcd = $10,000 \times 80/750 = 1,100$ acres = 1.7 sq miles.

3-9. Disposal of Industrial Waste Waters.

Under normal conditions, the waste waters of industry may be safely added to municipal sewage for disposal. Some wastes, however, are of such nature and strength that they will damage the collection system, interfere with or overload treatment facilities, and interfere with or overload the purifying power of receiving waters. Preparatory treatment of the wastes before their discharge into the collection system, or their complete separation from this system, is then mandatory. In either event, the requisite degree of treatment depends upon the composition, concentration, and condition of the wastes, the nature and capacity of the treatment works, and the nature and capacity of the receiving waters. Shock loads of industrial wastes, created by the sudden release of batches of wastes, are especially objectionable. They can be dampened by apportioning the discharge of the wastes to available treatment-plant and receiving-water capacities. Holding or storage basins are needed for this purpose.

Overloading is exemplified by wastes that, like domestic sewage, are rich in carbohydrates, proteins, or fats. Some industrial wastes are equivalent to the sewage of a very large number of people. The putrescible matter and suspended matter contained in the combined wastes from a distillery that processes 1,000 bushels of grain per day, for example, are equivalent to the sewage from 3,500 and 2,300 people respectively.

Interference with sewage treatment and natural purification in receiving waters is exemplified by copper wastes. At high concentrations, these wastes inhibit the anaerobic digestion of settled solids and destroy the biological slimes in trickling filters and activated-sludge plants. On the other hand, it is possible to habituate biological slimes, especially those of trickling filters, to certain organic chemicals, such as phenols and formaldehyde, that otherwise possess strong disinfecting powers. A slime flora can be developed that is not only inured to them but that will in fact use them as food.

Guiding principles in the solution of industrial-wastes problems are, in order of preference: (1) recovery of useful materials from wastes; (2) improvements in plant operation that will reduce the amount of waste matter to be disposed of; and (3) development of economic methods of treatment. Recovery of useful materials is generally most successful when these substances are similar in nature to the primary products of manufacture and so can be sold through the existing organization. Improvements in plant operation may make possible the safe discharge of the resulting waste matters into the public sewers. Satisfactory processes of treatment have been elaborated for a wide variety of industrial wastes. Most of them are quite like sewage-treatment methods. But there are chemical wastes that require a quite different approach. Cyanides from the plating industry, for example, are most conveniently oxidized to cyanates; chromates, also from the plating industry, are most conveniently reduced to chromic compounds; and acids and alkalies from various industries are most conveniently neutralized.

3-10. Management of Waste-Water Disposal Systems. As is true for water works, the development, improvement, or extension of sewerage systems progresses from preliminary studies through their financing, design, and construction to their operation, maintenance, and repair. The per capita investment in sewerage systems varies with the type of system; the topography, hydrology, and geology of the area served; the nature and proximity of receiving waters; the need for sewage treatment; the availability and cost of labor and materials; and the size and characteristics of the community.

The first cost of sanitary sewers lies ordinarily between $20 and $60 per capita in North American communities. The cost of storm drains and combined sewers, depending upon local conditions, is about three times as great. The first cost of sewage-treatment plants varies with the degree of treatment provided. Primary treatment works cost about $60,000, and complete treatment works about $200,000, per mgd capacity. Plants handling combined sewage are about one-third more expensive than those treating domestic sewage alone. The cost of treatment, excluding fixed charges, is close to $12 per mg for primary treatment and about twice that amount for complete treatment. Including interest and depreciation, as well as charges against operation and management, the removal of domestic sewage and its safe disposal costs from $30 to $60 per mg. Comparisons with the cost of water supply will show that complete sewage treatment works are relatively twice as expensive as water purification works, whereas collection systems for domestic sewage are about half as expensive as distribution systems for water. Sewer rentals, corresponding to charges for water, are employed when it is desired to place the cost of sewerage upon a "value received" basis. Rentals may cover part or all of the cost of the service rendered and are generally related to the water bill.

Example 3-7. Roughly, how much money is invested in the sanitary sewerage system of a city of 100,000 people?

1. Assuming the per capita cost at $50, the total first cost is $50 × 100,000 = $5,000,000.

2. Assuming that the flow of domestic sewage is 80 gpcd and that complete treatment works cost $200,000 per mgd capacity, the cost of the treatment works = (80 × 100,000/1,000,000) × 200,000 = $1,600,000, or about a third of the total cost.

No general values can be assigned to the cost of separate treatment of industrial waste waters. When they are discharged into municipal sewerage systems, the cost of their treatment can be estimated in terms of the load that they impose on the municipal works, as measured by the suspended solids, the putrescible matter, or a combination of these two with the volume of waste water.

4 _____ STATISTICAL ANALYSIS OF QUANTITATIVE INFORMATION

4-1. Types of Information and Analyses. The information underlying many of the decisions that must be reached by the designer and operator of water works and waste-water disposal systems consists of collections of numerical observations or measurements that can be made to tell their full story in significant and understandable terms only if they are subjected to suitable statistical analysis. Among collections to be analyzed are: (1) vital records of population changes; (2) measurements of water consumption and sewage flow; (3) observations of hydrological phenomena; (4) results of water and sewage analyses; (5) records of plant performance; and (6) cost data of all kinds.

Collection of the numerical facts pertaining to these and similar subjects is the first step in their scientific evaluation. The second step is the classification of the collected (raw) data, i.e. the sorting out of the observations—depending upon the information sought—according to their order of occurrence, magnitude, position in space, or qualitative difference. The final step is a generalization of the classified information. Determination of an average value for a number of observations of different magnitudes is a simple example of generalization drilled into us from childhood. Fitting a mathematical equation to the data is a more complicated but also a more complete and, often, more rewarding method of generalization.

As used here the word generalization does not mean the drawing of broad, ill-defined conclusions from the data in hand. Instead, the word is used in the stricter sense of deriving from limited data the principles, conceptions, or laws that describe the particular phenomenon being investigated. This type of generalization always involves the assumption that the limited data available constitute a representative sample, and that future behavior, or other like samples, or what is termed "the *total population*" (could it be observed), would display similar relationships. Determination of the reliability of generalizations made from samples comprising a limited number of observations is an important obligation of statistical analysis.

TABLE 4-1. Straight-Line Functions of Certain Equations

No.	Type of equation	Shape of curve on arithmetic paper for positive values of constants	Equation in straight-line form	Ordinate Variable	Ordinate Scale	Abscissa Variable	Abscissa Scale
4-1	$y = a + bx$	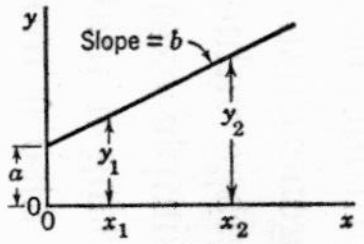	$y = a + bx$	y	arith.	x	arith.
4-2	$y = ae^{bx}$	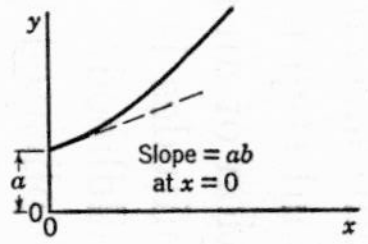	$(\log y) = (\log a) + (b \log e)x$	y	log.	x	arith.
4-3	$y = ax^b$	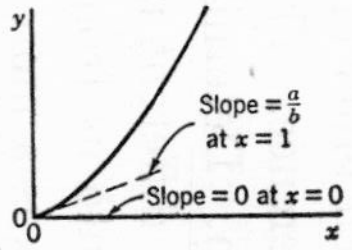	$(\log y) = (\log a) + b(\log x)$	y	log.	x	log
4-4	$y = a + \dfrac{b}{x}$	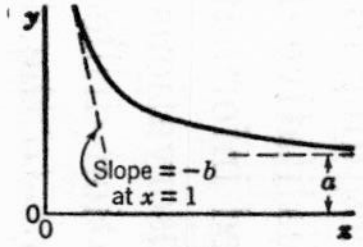	$y = a + b\left(\dfrac{1}{x}\right)$	y	arith.	$\left(\dfrac{1}{x}\right)$	arith.

Functional plotting (columns above, spanning Ordinate and Abscissa)

4-5 $y = \dfrac{x}{a + bx}$

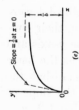

(e)

$\left(\dfrac{x}{y}\right) = a + bx$

$\left(\dfrac{x}{y}\right)$ arith. x arith.

4-6 $y = \dfrac{a}{b + cx}$

(f)

$\left(\dfrac{1}{y}\right) = \left(\dfrac{b}{a}\right) + \left(\dfrac{c}{a}\right)x$

$\left(\dfrac{1}{y}\right)$ arith. x arith.

4-7 $y = c + be^{ax}$

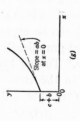

(g)

$\left(\log \dfrac{dy}{dx}\right) = (\log ab) + (a \log e)x$

$\left(\dfrac{\Delta y}{\Delta x}\right)$ log. x arith.

4-8 $y = c + ax^b$

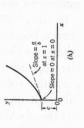

(h)

$\left(\log \dfrac{dy}{dx}\right) = (\log ab) + (b - 1)\log x$

$\left(\dfrac{\Delta y}{\Delta x}\right)$ log. x log.

4-2. Curve Fitting. A number of simple equations are found to fit different collections of numerical observations or measurements encountered in studies of water supply and waste-water disposal. Some of these equations are discussed later in this chapter; others, later in this book. Certain simple, more or less fundamental, and recurrent equations are brought together in Table 4-1. Methods for fitting these relationships to observed values are outlined briefly below.

The first and most difficult step in curve fitting is the selection of the most suitable equation. Sometimes this can be done on a rational basis. Often, however, the approach must be purely empirical. Plotting the data on arithmetic scales (ordinary graph paper) and drawing a smooth curve to fit the plotted points will indicate the general type of equation (see sketches in Table 4-1). The selection made can then be tested by plotting the straight-line function of the data. This should yield an approximately straight line. Instead of plotting the selected function of the observations, the observations themselves can be plotted on functional paper: semilog, log-log, arithmetic-probability, or logarithmic-probability paper, for example.

The second step in curve fitting is the evaluation of the constants of the equations shown in Table 4-1. This can be done approximately from the straight line of best fit drawn by eye through the observed points (graphical method). For more precise results, however, an analytical method must be used. Among such methods, the method of least squares is most satisfactory.

a. Graphical Method. Since the equations shown in Table 4-1 were chosen because they can be expressed in straight-line form, their constants are determined graphically from the intercept on the y-axis and the slope of the line. Taking Equation 4-1, $y = a + bx$, as the basic example, reference to the thumbnail sketch will show (1) that the intercept on the y-axis at $x = 0$ is $y = a$, and (2) that the slope of the line $dy/dx = (y_2 - y_1)/(x_2 - x_1) = b$. Using Equation 4-2, $y = ae^{bx}$ or $(\log y) = (\log a) + (b \log e)x$, as the functional example, it follows (1) that the intercept on the y-axis at $x = 0$ is $\log y = \log a$, or $y = a$, and (2) that the slope of the line $d(\log y)/dx = (\log y_2 - \log y_1)/(x_2 - x_1) = b \log e$. The remaining equations are dealt with in similar fashion.

A useful habit to acquire in curve fitting is to choose as y the variable that is to be found from different magnitudes of x. Another useful habit is to pass the straight line of best fit through the intersection of the arithmetic means, M_x and M_y, of the observed values of x and y, or their respective straight-line functions. This intersection is the most probable value of the x and y relationship. A simple computation of M_x and M_y, therefore, fixes the position of the fitted line. Then the only decision left to the eye is to select the slope of the line. The fit obtained should be fairer than it would be if both position and slope of line had to be selected by eye.

b. Method of Least Squares. This method is based upon the law of chance or random sampling that is discussed later in this chapter. It is called the method of least squares because it is designed to make the sum of the squares of the differences, or residuals, between observed and calculated values a minimum.[1]

If R_k represents the residual for the kth pair, of observations, y_k and x_k, that are to be fitted by the equation $y = a + bx$, then $R_k = (a + bx_k) - y_k$, where $(a + bx_k)$ is the value of y *calculated* to be paired with x_k, and y_k is its *observed* magnitude. The parameters a and b are to be so determined that the sum of the squares of the residuals will be a minimum, or: $\Sigma R^2 = \Sigma [(a + bx) - y]^2 =$ a minimum. To meet this requirement, the first derivatives of ΣR^2 with respect to a and b are set equal to zero, or;

$$\frac{\partial(\Sigma R^2)}{\partial a} = 2\Sigma \left[R\left(\frac{\partial R}{\partial a}\right) \right] = 2\Sigma(a + bx - y) = 0$$

$$\frac{\partial(\Sigma R^2)}{\partial b} = 2\Sigma \left[R\left(\frac{\partial R}{\partial b}\right) \right] = 2\Sigma(a + bx - y)x = 0$$

For n pairs of observed values of y and x, therefore, the following two simultaneous equations are found:

I. $\qquad \Sigma(a + bx - y) = na + b\Sigma x - \Sigma y = 0$

II. $\qquad \Sigma(a + bx - y)x = a\Sigma x + b\Sigma x^2 - \Sigma xy = 0$

---

[1] The theory behind the method of least squares may be outlined briefly as follows:

The probability of occurrence of a deviation x in a normal series of n observations is given by Equation 4-18 as:

$$\frac{y}{n} = \frac{1}{\sigma\sqrt{2\pi}} e^{-\frac{1}{2}(x/\sigma)^2} = ke^{-c^2 x^2}$$

Therefore the probability of deviations x_1, x_2, etc., is $y_1/n = ke^{-c^2 x_1^2}$, $y_2/n = ke^{-c^2 x_2^2}$, etc. Since the probability, P, of all deviations occurring at one time is the product of the individual probabilities, or

$$P = (1/n^n)(y_1 y_2 y_3 \cdots) = k^n e^{-c^2 \Sigma x^2}$$

the most probable system is that in which P is a maximum, or the exponent of e is a minimum. The latter becomes true when Σx^2 is a minimum, i.e., when the squares of the deviations are least.

Dividing these equations by n, or the second equation by Σx, we obtain the two *normal* equations:

I. $$a + b\left(\frac{\Sigma x}{n}\right) - \left(\frac{\Sigma y}{n}\right) = 0 \qquad\qquad 4\text{-}9$$

II. $$a\left(\frac{\Sigma x}{n}\right) + b\left(\frac{\Sigma x^2}{n}\right) - \left(\frac{\Sigma xy}{n}\right) = 0$$

or

$$a + b\left(\frac{\Sigma x^2}{\Sigma x}\right) - \left(\frac{\Sigma xy}{\Sigma x}\right) = 0 \qquad\qquad 4\text{-}10$$

These equations give the most precise values for a and b. Necessary calculations involve only the determination of the sums or arithmetic means of x, x^2, y, and xy. The number of normal equations equals the number of constants in the equation to be fitted to the data.

The method of least squares can be applied to non-linear equations either by direct differentiation of the equation or by differentiation of its straight-line transform. However, the results obtained are not necessarily identical.

Example 4-1. Find, by the method of least squares, the straight-line relationship between mean annual rainfall and altitude above sea level for the pairs of values [2] listed in Table 4-2.

TABLE 4-2. Least-Squares Calculations for Example 4-1

Mean annual rainfall—in. Observed y	Elevation above sea level—1,000 ft Observed x	x^2	xy	Calculated y
44	5.3	28.1	233	39.0
20	3.5	12.3	70.0	27.6
24	3.0	9.0	72.0	24.5
14	1.2	1.44	16.8	13.2
12	0.48	0.23	5.8	8.6
3	−0.26	0.07	−0.8	4.0
Sums 117	13.22	51.14	396.8	116.9
Means 19.5	2.20	8.52	66.1	19.5

The normal equations are:

I. $a + 2.20b - 19.5 = 0$.

II. $2.20a + 8.52b - 66.1 = 0$, or $a + 3.87b - 30.0 = 0$. It follows that $a = 5.64$ and $b = 6.30$ and that the completed equation is $y = 5.64 + 6.30x$.

---

[2] These values are rounded figures for San Diego County, Calif. See D. W. Mead, *Hydrology*, McGraw-Hill Book Co., New York, p. 294, 1919.

The line of best fit is plotted in Figure 4-1 together with the observed values. If this line had been drawn by eye through the intersections of the mean rainfall and mean altitude, a would have been read as the intercept on the y-axis and b as the slope of the line. This graphical determination of a and b is also indicated in Figure 4-1. The example illustrates the analysis of a series giving a location in space. Hydrologically it indicates the greater yield of water at higher elevations that are exposed to rain-bearing winds.

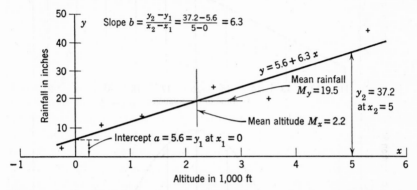

Figure 4-1. Graphical derivation of a straight-line equation for an observed relationship between mean annual rainfall and altitude above sea level.

4-3. Time Series. Observations arranged in order of occurrence are called *time series*. A study of the changing magnitudes of successive observations will discover (1) trends, (2) cycles or periodicities, and (3) fluctuations. Trends are tendencies of the observations to increase or decrease in magnitude with time. Cycles or periodicities are tendencies to form successive maxima and minima like the crests and troughs of water waves. Fluctuations are tendencies of the observations to change their magnitude explosively from time interval to time interval. Numerical examples of three time series, idealized to exhibit these three specific tendencies, are given in Table 4-3 and illustrated in Figure 4-2.

TABLE 4-3. Examples of Time Series

Time of observation	11	12	13	14	15	16	17	18	19	20	21
Magnitude of observation											
Series A (trend)	2	4	6	8	10	12	14	16	18	20	22
Series B (cycle)	6	4	6	12	18	20	18	12	6	4	6
Series C (fluctuation)	18	12	14	6	16	2	10	22	4	20	8

Series A exhibits a perfect arithmetic trend. The magnitudes of successive observations, which are taken at equal time intervals, increase uniformly from 2 to 22. Series B records a simple cyclical variation or periodicity. The magnitudes of the observation move up and

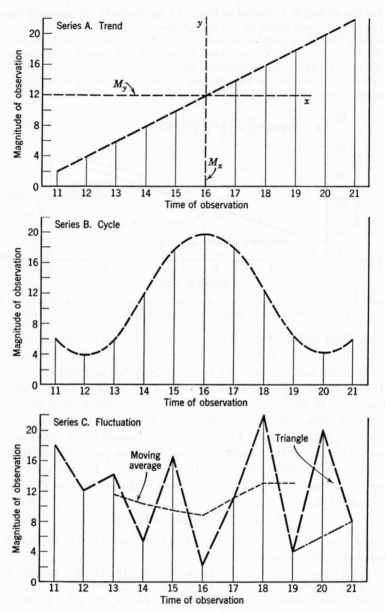

Fig. 4-2. Time series illustrating trends, cycles, and fluctuation; Series A, B, and C.

down systematically from a low value of 4 to a high value of 20 to trace a sine-like wave. In Series C, the magnitudes of the observations fluctuate from time interval to time interval between 2 and 22 with no apparent rhyme or reason.

The graphical representation of these three time series gives the observer a good general impression of their nature, but it does not express their story in numbers. For that we must turn either to a determination of the equations of the curves traced by the series or to an identification of suitable yardsticks, or parameters.

4-4. Trends, Cycles, and Periodicities. The tendencies of observations to change in magnitude may be simple or complex. The function of the statistician is to discover the inherent regularity, if such exists, and to express it in numbers. The regularity of change in magnitude with time, inherent in Series A, is easily recognized. The observations increase in magnitude by 2 units during each interval of time. Mathematically, this is a measure of the slope of the straight line that traces the changing magnitudes or fits them best. The slope, therefore, is an acceptable measure of the *generalized trend* of this arithmetic series. If we place the origin of the coordinate system at the intersection of the arithmetic mean of the time with that of the magnitudes of the observations—because this intersection, as previously stated, is the most probable value of the x and y relationship —the equation of the straight line that we are seeking will contain but one constant, the slope b. The equation will then read: $y' = bx'$, where x', and y' are the deviations of the magnitudes of the individual observations from the mean magnitudes. This single constant can be evaluated by least squares from the second normal equation for a straight line, Equation 4-10.[3] For $a = 0$, this equation becomes:

$$b\frac{\Sigma(x')^2}{n} - \frac{\Sigma x'y'}{n} = 0 \qquad \text{or} \qquad b = \frac{\Sigma x'y'}{\Sigma(x')^2} \qquad \text{4-11}$$

which is in itself a simple expression for the trend. If the observations are made at regular time intervals this expression can be further simplified by substituting the *order of the observations in time* (1, 2, 3, etc.) for the *time* itself. For n observations, the mean is then the $\frac{n+1}{2}$ th observation, and there may be substituted for the deviation x_k' of the kth observation the value $\left(k - \frac{n+1}{2}\right)$. Doing this in Equation 4-11

[3] Equation 4-9 cannot be used because $\Sigma x'$ and $\Sigma y'$ are each equal to zero when the origin is at the intersection of the means M_x and M_y.

gives the following result:[4]

$$
b = \frac{\Sigma \left(k - \dfrac{n+1}{2} \right) y'}{\Sigma \left(k - \dfrac{n+1}{2} \right)^2} = \frac{12}{n(n^2-1)} \Sigma \left(k - \frac{n+1}{2} \right) y' \qquad 4\text{-}12
$$

Example 4-2. Calculate the trend for Series A (see Table 4-4). By Equation 4-12:

$$
b = \frac{12}{11(121-1)} \, 220 = +2
$$

The trend, therefore, is +2 per unit interval of time, as noted before.

TABLE 4-4. Calculation of Trend (Example 4-2)

Observed time	11	12	13	14	15	16	17	18	19	20	21
Order $-k$	1	2	3	4	5	6	7	8	9	10	11
$\left(k - \dfrac{n+1}{2} \right) = (k-6)$	−5	−4	−3	−2	−1	0	+1	+2	+3	+4	+5
Observed magnitude	2	4	6	8	10	12	14	16	18	20	22
Deviation from mean $-y'$	−10	−8	−6	−4	−2	0	+2	+4	+6	+8	+10
$\left(k - \dfrac{n+1}{2} \right) y'$	50	32	18	8	2	0	2	8	18	32	50

Trends are not necessarily arithmetic. Geometric trends are quite common. For example, the reductions in the death rates from typhoid fever, tuberculosis, and many other diseases in North America are distinctly geometric. If, in accordance with Equation 4-2, the value of $(b \log e)$ is established as the trend of a geometric time series, the percentage change per unit of time is $100(y_{k+1}' - y_k')/y_k' = 100(e^b - 1)$ for a positive trend (magnitudes increasing with time) and $100(y_k' - y_{k+1}')/y_k' = 100(1 - e^b)$ for a negative trend (magnitudes decreasing with time). The subscripts $(k+1)$ and k denote observations a unit interval of time apart.

4-5. Moving Averages. Most water-supply and waste-water data do not extend over a period sufficiently long to assure the reliable identification of cycles or periodicities that have lengths of many years. A rough measure of possible periods is obtained, however, from an examination of plotted time series. Irregularities, due to ran-

[4] Because $\displaystyle\sum_{1}^{n} \left(k - \frac{n+1}{2} \right)^2 = \sum_{1}^{n} k^2 - (n+1)\sum_{1}^{n} k + \left(\frac{n+1}{2} \right)^2 n$

and $\displaystyle\sum_{1}^{n} k = \frac{n(n+1)}{2}$

and $\displaystyle\sum_{1}^{n} k^2 = \frac{n(n+1)(2n+1)}{6}$

dom sampling, that obscure both actual trends and periods can be suppressed in such plots by introducing a *moving average* of the magnitudes of the observations. Moving averages are averages (simple or weighted) of a convenient number of successive terms. Usually an odd number of items is taken, so that the average will coincide with the middle item. If the moving average is weighted, the middle item is customarily given greatest weight. Calling the observed magnitudes a, b, c, etc., examples of weighted moving averages are:

$$M_b = \frac{a + 2b + c}{4} \qquad M_c = \frac{b + 2c + d}{4} \qquad \text{etc.} \qquad \text{4-13}$$

or

$$M_c = \frac{a + 4b + 6c + 4d + e}{16} \qquad M_d = \frac{b + 4c + 6d + 4e + f}{16} \quad \text{etc.} \qquad \text{4-14}$$

The magnitudes of the weighting coefficients are arbitrary. Those shown in equations 4-13 and 4-14 are widely used because they lend themselves to systematic computations. This is shown in Table 4-5.

TABLE 4-5. Development of Weighted Moving Averages

Order (1)	Magnitude (2)	First reduction			Second reduction		
		(3)	(4)	(5)	(6)	(7)	(8)
1	a						
		$a+b$					
2	b		$a+2b+c$	$\dfrac{a+2b+c}{4}$			
					$\dfrac{a+3b+3c+d}{4}$		
		$b+c$					
3	c		$b+2c+d$	$\dfrac{b+2c+d}{4}$		$\dfrac{a+4b+6c+4d+e}{4}$	$\dfrac{a+4b+6c+4d+e}{16}$
		$c+d$			$\dfrac{b+3c+3d+e}{4}$		
4	d		$c+2d+e$	$\dfrac{c+2d+e}{4}$		$\dfrac{b+4c+6d+4e+f}{4}$	$\dfrac{b+4c+6d+4e+f}{16}$
		$d+e$			$\dfrac{c+3d+3e+f}{4}$		
5	e		$d+2e+f$	$\dfrac{d+2e+f}{4}$		$\dfrac{c+4d+6e+4f+g}{4}$	$\dfrac{c+4d+6e+4f+g}{16}$

The values in Columns 3, 4, 6, and 7 are obtained by summing successive pairs of items in the Columns preceding; the values in Columns 5 and 8 by dividing the items in the preceding columns by four. Column 5 yields a moving average of type 4-13; Column 8 of type 4-14.

Example 4-3. Calculate moving averages of types 4-13 and 4-14 for Series C. See Table 4-6. Columns 5 and 6 give the results; those of the second reduction are plotted in Figure 4-2C. The smoothing effect is marked.

TABLE 4-6. Calculation of Moving Averages (Example 4-3)

Time	Magnitude	First reduction			Second reduction		
(1)	(2)	(3)	(4)	(5)	(6)	(7)	(8)
11	18						
12	12	30					
13	14	26	56	14.0			
14	6	20	46	11.5	25.5		
15	16	22	42	10.5	22.0	47.5	11.9
16	2	18	40	10.0	20.5	42.5	10.6
17	10	12	30	7.5	17.5	38.0	9.5
18	22	32	44	11.0	18.5	36.0	9.0
19	4	26	58	14.5	25.5	44.0	11.0
20	20	24	50	12.5	27.0	52.5	13.1
21	8	28	52	13.0	25.5	52.5	13.1

4-6. Fluctuation. The magnitudes of the observations included in Series A and C (Figure 4-2) are the same. Their order of occurrence, however, is very different. In Series A the order is such that the magnitudes progress smoothly from low to high; in Series C the order is such that the magnitudes fluctuate violently. Among the measures of fluctuations that have been suggested, the *standard fluctuation* [5] and *coefficient of fluctuation* possess the qualities of good parameters. They are defined as follows:

$$\text{Standard fluctuation } F = \sqrt{\Sigma(\Delta'')^2/(n-2)} \qquad 4\text{-}15$$

$$\text{Coefficient of fluctuation } C_F = F/M \qquad 4\text{-}16$$

Here Δ'' is the second difference in magnitudes of successive observations, n is the number of observations, and M is the arithmetic mean of the observations.

The standard fluctuation is a measure of the area of the triangle formed by three successive observations (see Figure 4-2). [6] The larger this area, the greater is the degree of fluctuation. In the absence of a triangle, there may be change, but there can be no fluctuation, as in Series A. The coefficient of fluctuation makes possible comparisons between series of different magnitudes.

[5] W. L. Crum, "A Measure of Dispersion for Ordered Series," *Quarterly Publications of the American Statistical Association, 17,* 969 (1921).

[6] If we call y_1, y_2, and y_3 the magnitudes of the last three observations in Series C, the area of the triangle formed by these observations at unit time intervals is: $\frac{1}{2}(y_1 + y_2) + \frac{1}{2}(y_2 + y_3) - \frac{3}{2}(y_1 + y_3) = \frac{1}{2}[(y_2 - y_1) - (y_3 - y_2)] = \frac{1}{2}(\text{second-order difference})$.

Example 4-4. Calculate the standard fluctuation and coefficient of fluctuation for Series A and C.

a. In Series A, the first differences, Δ', all equal $+2$; the second differences, Δ'', therefore, all equal zero; and F as well as C_F equals zero.

b. In Series C, the story is different. See Table 4-7.

TABLE 4-7. Calculation of Fluctuation (Example 4-4)

Magnitude	18		12		14		6		16		2		10		22		4		20		8
First difference Δ'		-6		$+2$		-8		$+10$		-14		$+8$		$+12$		-18		$+16$		-12	
Second difference Δ''			$+8$		-10		$+18$		-24		$+22$		$+4$		-30		$+34$		-28		
$(\Delta'')^2$			64		100		324		576		484		16		900		1156		784		

1. By Equation 4-15, the standard fluctuation is: $F = \sqrt{4404/9} = 22.1$.
2. The arithmetic mean magnitude is: $M = 12$.
3. By Equation 4-16, the coefficient of fluctuation is: $C_F = 22.1/12 = 1.84$, or 184%.

4-7. Frequency Distributions. Observations arranged in order of magnitude form an array. If the magnitudes of the observations are the whole numbers 1, 2, 3, etc., the array will consist of a varying number of 1's, 2's, 3's, etc. In a given sample, these varying numbers record how often, or frequently, each particular magnitude is observed. In the array of observed magnitudes: 1, 1, 2, 3, 3, 3, for example, the magnitude 1 occurs twice, the magnitude 2 once, and the magnitude 3 three times. The number of times each magnitude is observed establishes the frequency distribution of the observations.

Numerical examples of two frequency distributions are given in Table 4-8 and plotted in Figure 4-3 as Series D and E. The total number of observations in each sample is 200, and the relative frequency of observations of individual magnitudes is generalized as a percentage [7] of the total number.

TABLE 4-8. Examples of Frequency Distributions

Magnitude of observation	1	2	3	4	5	6	7	8	9	10	11	*Total* ...
Number of observations												
Series D (symmetrical)	2	6	12	24	36	40	36	24	12	6	2	200
Series E (asymmetrical)	2	40	66	38	30	10	6	4	2	1	1	200
Percentage of observations												
Series D (symmetrical)	1	3	6	12	18	20	18	12	6	3	1	100
Series E (asymmetrical)	1	20	33	19	15	5	3	2	1	0.5	0.5	100

Series D and E are plotted in Figure 4-3 as histograms or step diagrams and are generalized as frequency curves. Series D yields a symmetrical and, as we shall see, *normal* curve; Series E is asymmetrical, or *skewed*.

[7] Use of percentages or ratios as a means for generalization and comparison is another habit worth acquiring.

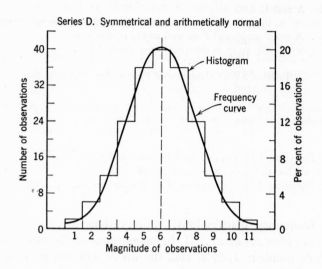

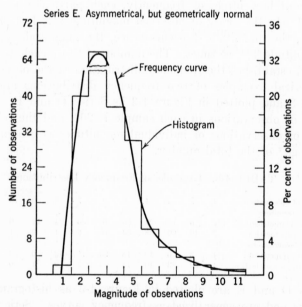

Figure 4-3.   Frequency distributions: Series D and E.

The data collected in practice seldom consist of values that are as discrete, integral, and simple in magnitude as those listed in Series D and E. Observations of about equal magnitude are recurrent, however, and can be grouped in such manner as to simplify computations without sacrificing their precision or usefulness. Data that are suitably grouped will bring out the nature of the frequency distribution when they are plotted as a histogram.

There are certain simple rules for the selection of groups that will assure their usefulness:

1. The number of groups should be 12 to 30; not too low to lose precision nor too high to become unwieldy.

2. The range in magnitude of each group, called the class interval i, should be so chosen that the midvalue of the group is a rounded (preferably integral) number. This simplifies computations. For a class interval $i = 1$, for example, values ranging from 46.50 to 47.49 have a midpoint at 47.00 and are readily identified as belonging in the group of average magnitude 47.

3. The number of observations in successive groups should not fluctuate violently. There should be as gradual an advance and recession as can be obtained by shifting the starting point of the first group.

The magnitude of the class interval selected to obey rules (1) and (2) is the nearest rounded number generally below the value found by dividing the range in observations by 12. If, for example, the highest value in a series is 97.6 and the lowest 54.4, $(97.6 - 54.4)/12 = 3.6$, and i is selected as equal to 3. The starting point, to obey rule (3), can then be placed at 51.5, 52.5, or 53.5, whichever will create the smoothest transition from group to group. Talley sheets or punched cards will assist in grouping the data.

4-8. Natural, or Normal, Frequency. It is a curious and important fact that the arrays of many types of observations and measurements trace a bell-shaped curve like that of Series D. The mathematical explanation for this fact is found in the following characteristics of such collections of data: (1) the largest number of observations occupies the center of the array; (2) smaller and smaller numbers of observations differ from the central magnitude by larger and larger amounts; and (3) values greater than the central magnitude occur about as often as values that are smaller.

If the y-axis is made to coincide with the axis of symmetry, the bell-shaped curve is seen to reach a maximum at $x = 0$ and to become asymptotic to the x-axis at $x = \pm \infty$. The slope of the curve dy/dx, therefore, must equal zero at both $x = 0$ and $y = 0$. This it does in the relationship:

$$dy/dx = -cxy \qquad \text{4-17}$$

Integration and evaluation of the constants of this equation establish
the equation of the *normal frequency curve*. This curve is also called
the Gaussian or normal probability curve. Probability is synonymous
with relative frequency. It is the ratio of the number of observations
of given magnitude to the total number of observations in the collection. The normal equation reads as follows:

$$y = \frac{n}{\sigma\sqrt{2\pi}}\, e^{-\frac{1}{2}(x/\sigma)^2} \qquad\qquad 4\text{-}18$$

where y is the number or frequency of observations of magnitude X;
x is the deviation of any magnitude, X, from the central, or arithmetic
mean, magnitude M, i.e. $x = X - M$;[8] n is the total number of observations; $\pi = 3.14159$; $\sqrt{2\pi} = 2.50663$; $1/\sqrt{2\pi} = 0.398942$; $e =$
2.71828; $\log e = 0.434295$; and $\sigma = \sqrt{\Sigma x^2/(n-1)}$ is the standard deviation from the mean, as measured by the distance from the arith-
metic mean to the points of inflection of the curve.

As derived from Equation 4-18, $\sigma = \sqrt{\Sigma x^2/n}$. This presupposes
that the origin of the curve is at the true mean rather than at the calculated mean. However, it can be shown that $\sigma = \sqrt{\Sigma x^2/(n-1)}$
yields a more probable value when deviations are measured from the
calculated mean. As n becomes large there is little difference between
the two expressions.

Examination of Equation 4-18 shows that a normal frequency distribution of n observations is described completely by the arithmetic
mean M and the standard deviation σ. To the statistically initiate,
therefore, the arithmetic mean and standard deviations are parameters
that completely generalize the collection of numerical data analyzed.

At first glance, Equation 4-18 looks complicated, and the calculations involved in its use look time-consuming. However, if we apply
the useful principle of generalizing relationships in terms of ratios, we
can transform Equation 4-18 to read as follows:

$$y/y_0 = e^{-\frac{1}{2}(x/\sigma)^2} = e^{-c^2 x^2} \qquad\qquad 4\text{-}19$$

where $y_0 = n/(\sigma\sqrt{2\pi})$ = the maximum frequency y or middle ordinate, at $x = 0$; and $c^2 = 1/(2\sigma^2)$. Next we can make this generalization the basis of a table of ordinates (Table 4-9) of the normal frequency distribution. Once determined, this table is applicable to any
set of data and permits rapid calculation of the ordinate, or frequency,

---

[8] Since the curve is symmetrical, the central magnitude must equal the arithmetic mean of all the observations ($M = \Sigma x/n$), and the sum of the deviations
from the mean must equal zero ($\Sigma x = 0$).

of any observation. Fitting a normal frequency curve to an observed series then becomes a simple matter indeed.

TABLE 4-9. Short Table of Ordinates of the Normal Frequency Curve. Values of y/y_0 for stated values of x/σ

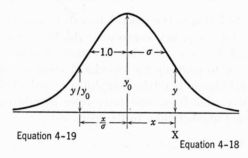

Equation 4-19   X
                                 Equation 4-18

x/σ	0.0	0.1	0.2	0.3	0.4	0.5	0.6	0.7	0.8	0.9
±0	1.000	.995	.980	.956	.923	.883	.835	.783	.726	.667
±1	0.607	.546	.487	.430	.375	.325	.278	.236	.198	.164
±2	0.135	.110	.089	.071	.056	.044	.034	.026	.020	.015

For $x/\sigma = \pm3$, $y/y_0 = 0.011$; for $x/\sigma = \pm4$, $y/y_0 = 0.003$.

Example 4-5. For Series D, determine the constants of the arithmetically normal frequency curve of best fit and the ordinates needed to plot this curve in Figure 4-3. The necessary calculations are systematized in Table 4-10.

TABLE 4-10. Calculation of Parameters and Ordinates of an Arithmetically Normal Frequency Distribution (Example 4-5)

Magnitude of observations X (1)	Number of observations, or frequency f (2)	$fX =$ (1) × (2) (3)	Deviation from mean $x = X - M$ (2) × (4) (4)	$fx =$ (2) × (4) (5)	$fx^2 =$ (4) × (5) (6)	x/σ (7)	y/y_0 from Table 4-2 (8)	Calculated ordinate $y = (8)iy_0$ (9)
1	2	2	−5	−10	50	−2.55	0.039	1.6
2	6	12	−4	−24	96	−2.04	0.125	3.1
3	12	36	−3	−36	108	−1.53	0.310	12.5
4	24	96	−2	−48	96	−1.02	0.594	24.0
5	36	180	−1	−36	36	−0.51	0.878	35.5
6	40	240	0	0	0	0	1.000	40.4
7	36	252	+1	+36	36	+0.51	0.878	35.5
8	24	192	+2	+48	96	+1.02	0.594	24.0
9	12	108	+3	+36	108	+1.53	0.310	12.5
10	6	60	+4	+24	96	+2.04	0.125	3.1
11	2	22	+5	+10	50	+2.55	0.039	1.6
Sums ..	200	1,200	...	....	772	......	.....	....

Arithmetic mean $M = \Sigma fX/n = 1{,}200/200 = 6$

Standard deviation $\sigma = \sqrt{\Sigma fx^2/(n-1)} = \sqrt{772/199} = 1.97$

Middle ordinate $y_0 = n/(\sigma\sqrt{2\pi}) = 200/(1.97 \times 2.51) = 40.4$

If the group range $i \neq 1$, the arithmetic may be simplified by expressing deviations from the mean in terms of group intervals. The standard deviation is then

$$\sigma = i\sqrt{\Sigma fx^2/(n-1)} \qquad 4\text{-}20$$

where x is the deviation of the group intervals in numerical order.

For plotting the frequency curve over the histogram or for comparing f and y, it is necessary either to express deviations in terms of group intervals or to multiply the calculated value of y by the group range i. The arithmetic is further simplified by calculating the mean and standard deviation from departures from an arbitrary origin assumed at a round number close to the mean as:

$$M = X_a + \Sigma fd/n \qquad 4\text{-}21$$

and

$$\sigma = \sqrt{\Sigma fd^2/(n-1) - (\Sigma fd)^2/[n(n-1)]} \qquad 4\text{-}22$$

where X_a is the value of X at the arbitrary origin and $d = X - X_a$. If d is expressed in group intervals, the summation term in the equation for M and the right-hand member of the equation for σ are multiplied by i. The algebraic operations that lead to these equations are:

$$x = X - M = X - (X_a + \Sigma fd/n) = d - \Sigma fd/n$$

or

$$x^2 = d^2 - 2d\Sigma fd/n + (\Sigma fd/n)^2$$

whence

$$\Sigma fx^2 = \Sigma fd^2 - 2(\Sigma fd)^2/n + n(\Sigma fd/n)^2 = \Sigma fd^2 - (\Sigma fd)^2/n$$

4-9. The Probability Integral. In Figure 4-3, the horizontal axis is labeled "magnitude of observations"; the vertical axis, "number of observations" and "per cent of observations." More strictly, the horizontal axis gives "magnitudes of group centers in each class interval"; the vertical axis, "number, or per cent, of observations per class interval." The boundaries of class intervals lie halfway between group centers. The horizontal scale, therefore, is "class intervals per inch" and the vertical scale "number, or per cent, of observations per class interval per inch." It follows that the area under each step of the histogram is: Number, or per cent, of observations per class interval per inch × Class intervals per inch = Number, or per cent, of observations. In other words, the number, or per cent, of observations is not measured by the height of each step but by the area under it. As a consequence, the total area under the histogram measures "the total number of observations or 100%." The ratio of any portion of the area bounded by vertical lines under the curve to the total area, therefore, measures the relative frequency or *probability* of occurrence of values lying between the values at which the vertical lines are erected. This is a very important property of the histogram. It is shared also by the frequency curve that generalizes the histogram. The number of observations represented by 1 sq in. of area is ba/i, where a equals units of magnitude of observations per inch of abscissa, b equals number, or per cent, of observations per inch of ordinate, and i equals units of magnitude of observations per class interval.

With this property in mind, the suggestion presents itself to deal with the area under the frequency curve instead of the curve itself, i.e. to determine the integral of Equation 4-18, called the *probability integral*. This is a procedure favored by engineers.

As shown in the sketch above Table 4-11, the area A under the normal frequency curve is measured from the center out. Therefore:

$$A = \int_0^x y\,dx \qquad \text{where} \quad y = \frac{n}{\sigma\sqrt{2\pi}}\,e^{-\frac{1}{2}(x/\sigma)^2}$$

For purposes of integration, $e^{-\frac{1}{2}(x/\sigma)^2}$ is replaced by the convergent series:

$$1 - \left(\frac{x}{\sigma\sqrt{2}}\right)^2 + \frac{1}{2!}\left(\frac{x}{\sigma\sqrt{2}}\right)^4 - \frac{1}{3!}\left(\frac{x}{\sigma\sqrt{2}}\right)^6 + \cdots$$

whence

$$\frac{A}{n} = \frac{1}{\sqrt{\pi}}\left[\left(\frac{x}{\sigma\sqrt{2}}\right) - \frac{1}{3}\left(\frac{x}{\sigma\sqrt{2}}\right)^3 + \frac{1}{5 \times 2!}\left(\frac{x}{\sigma\sqrt{2}}\right)^5 - \cdots\right] \qquad \text{4-23}$$

Since the partial area A is expressed in terms of the total area n and since x is expressed in terms of the standard deviation σ, Equation 4-23 presents a generalized solution that permits calculating a generalized table of the areas under the normal frequency distribution (Table 4-11) analogous to the table of ordinates (Table 4-9).

Since 0.5 or 50% of the area lies to either side of the center, the area B/n under the tail of the curve equals $(0.5 - A/n)$.

The integrated normal frequency curve, or summation curve, as shown in Figure 4-4, is a symmetrical S-shaped curve with a point of inflection in the center. The areas recorded by the ordinates to this summation curve are measured from the extreme left of the frequency curve to the right; therefore, as tail areas: $B/n = 0.5 - A/n$, to the left of the center and $B/n = 0.5 + A/n$ to the right of the center.

TABLE 4-11.   Short Table of Areas of the Normal Frequency Curve.   Values
of A/n from the center out to stated values of x/σ

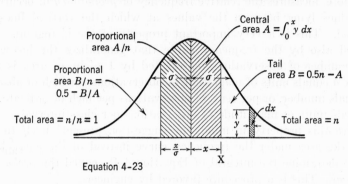

Equation 4-23

x/σ	0.0	0.1	0.2	0.3	0.4	0.5	0.6	0.7	0.8	0.9
±0	.000	.040	.079	.118	.155	.192	.226	.258	.288	.316
±1	.341	.364	.385	.403	.419	.433	.445	.455	.464	.471
±2	.477	.482	.486	.489	.492	.494	.495	.496	.497	.498

For $x/\sigma = \pm3$, $A/n = 0.49865$; for $x/\sigma = \pm4$, $A/n = 0.49997$.

Deviations from the mean smaller than $\pm\sigma$ are expected in $2 \times 0.341 \times 100 = 68.2\%$ of the observations; deviations greater than $\pm\sigma$ in $(100 - 68.2) = 31.8\%$ of the observations. In other words, about two-thirds of the observations fall within $\pm\sigma$ of the mean, and only about one-third lie outside this range. Deviations from the mean greater than $\pm3\sigma$ are expected to occur only in $2 \times (0.50000 - 0.49865) \times 100 = 0.27\%$ of the observations, or once in 370 observations, i.e. very rarely.

Example 4-6. For Series D determine the actual and calculated per cent of observations equal to or less than the observed magnitudes. Assume that Series D was developed for a class interval $i = 1$ which extends to the halfway mark between magnitudes. Assume also a uniform distribution of observations within the class interval. In accordance with Example 4-5, $M = 6.0$ and $\sigma = 1.97$. The necessary calculations are systematized in Table 4-12.

When a series contains so few observations that no labor is saved by grouping them, the cumulative percentage of observations equal to or less than the observed magnitudes is determined as $100 \sum_{1}^{k} f/(n + 1)$. By this means recognition is given to the fact that both higher and lower values than the observed maximum and minimum are expected to occur. For example, if a series consists of 20 observations, the percentage occurrence of values equal to or less than the smallest observa-

TABLE 4-12. Calculation of Arithmetically Normal Frequencies (Example 4-6)

No. of group (1)	Magnitude of grouped observations as class mean, X (2)	Number of observations in class interval, f (3)	Observations equal to or less than class mean		x/σ from Example 4-5 (6)	A/n from Table 4-11 (7)	Per cent of area $100(0.5 - A/n)$ or $100(0.5 + A/n)$ (8)
			Number (see note) (4)	Per cent $100 \times (4)/200$ (5)			
1	1	2	1	0.5	-2.55	0.495	0.5
2	2	6	5	2.5	-2.04	0.479	2.1
3	3	12	14	7.0	-1.53	0.437	6.3
4	4	24	32	16.0	-1.02	0.346	15.4
5	5	36	62	31.0	-0.51	0.195	30.5
6	6	40	100	50.0	0	0.000	50.0
7	7	36	138	69.0	$+0.51$	0.195	69.5
8	8	24	168	84.0	$+1.02$	0.346	84.6
9	9	12	186	93.0	$+1.53$	0.437	93.7
10	10	6	195	97.5	$+2.04$	0.479	97.9
11	11	2	199	99.5	$+2.55$	0.495	99.5

Note: Column 4, on the assumption that half the observations lie to either side of the class mean, is calculated as the sum of the observations below the class interval plus one-half the observations in the class interval. For any group k, therefore, the number of observations equal to or less than the class mean is: $\sum\limits_{1}^{k-1} f + \frac{1}{2}f_k$. For the 6th group, for example, $\sum\limits_{1}^{5} f + \frac{1}{2}f_6 = 80 + 20 = 100$. Column 8 in comparison with Column 5 records the goodness of fit of the calculated, or generalized, values or goodness of fit of the summation curve.

tion is not assumed to be $100 \times \frac{1}{20} = 5\%$, but $100 \times \frac{1}{21} = 4.8\%$; similarly, the percentage occurrence of values equal to or less than the largest observation is not taken as $100 \times \frac{20}{20} = 100\%$ but as $100 \times \frac{20}{21} = 95.2\%$.

4-10. Probability Paper. Although it is possible to express the normal summation curve or probability integral in straight-line form, it is simpler and more useful to develop a system of coordinates on which frequency distributions that are normal will plot as straight lines. How this is done is indicated in Figure 4-4. Here the origin of the coordinate system is placed at the halfway mark of the summation curve, and the horizontal scale of magnitudes is kept arithmetic. The vertical, originally arithmetic, scale is then compressed so that the distances h_1 and h_2 to the percentages P_1 and P_2 on the S-shaped summation curve are reduced to h_1' and h_2'. These compressed distances identify the position of the percentages P_1' and P_2' on a new scale—called the probability scale—which converts the S-shaped curve into a straight line. As shown in Figure 4-4, the relative magnitudes of h_1' and h_2' are given by the ratios: $h_1':h_2' = (x_1/\sigma):$ $(x_2/\sigma) = x_1:x_2$. A sample calculation will illustrate the development of the probability scale.

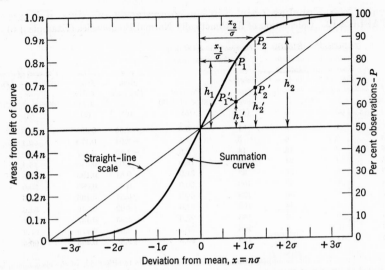

Figure 4-4. Probability integral curve or summation curve of normal frequency and its translation into a straight line.

Example 4-7. Determine the position of the 10% and 90% markings on a probability scale 10 in. long with end markings of 0.01% and 99.99%.

a. Place the 50% mark halfway from either end.

b. For 0.01% and 99.99% (each 49.99% from the center): $x/\sigma = \pm 3.72$ from Table 4-11.

c. For 10% and 90% (each 40% from the center): $x/\sigma = \pm 1.28$ from Table 4-11.

d. $h_1'/h_2' = (x_1/\sigma)/(x_2/\sigma)$, or $h_1' = h_2'(x_1/\sigma)/(x_2/\sigma)$. For $h_2' = 5$ in., $x_2/\sigma = \pm 3.72$, and $x_1/\sigma = \pm 1.28$; or $h_1' = 5 \times 1.28/3.72 = 1.72$ in.

Therefore place the 10% and 90% marks 1.72 in. to either side of the center of the scale.

The development and use of coordinate paper that incorporates a probability scale was first suggested by Hazen.[9] Any series of observations that is arithmetically normal will plot as a straight line on coordinate paper with arithmetic-scale abscissa and probability-scale ordinate. This paper is called arithmetic-probability paper,[10] and is widely employed by engineers and statisticians to record and study frequency distributions.

A straight-line plot of Series D is shown in Figure 4-5. The values for the observed magnitudes, or class means, and the per cent frequencies of observations equal to or less than the class means are

[9] A. Hazen, "Storage to Be Provided in Impounding Reservoirs," *Trans. Am. Soc. Civil Engrs.*, 77, 1539 (1914).

[10] This paper, as well as logarithmic-probability paper, is available on the market.

taken from Columns 2 and 5 in the computation schedule of Example
4-6 (Table 4-12). For comparison, the skewed frequency distribution, Series E, is also plotted on Figure 4-5.

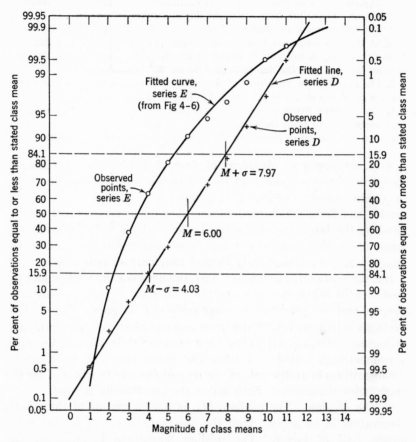

Figure 4-5. Straight-line summation plot of a frequency distribution on arithmetic probability paper; Series D. (Series E is added for comparison; see Figure 4-6.)

The position of the straight line of best fit for an arithmetically
normal distribution is defined by the following requirements:

1. It must pass through the intersection of the arithmetic mean M with the
50% frequency, since half the observations must lie to either side of the mean.

2. It must pass through the intersection of $M \pm \sigma$ with the 84.1% and 15.9%
frequency respectively, since, in accordance with Table 4-11, 34.1% of the observations must lie within $x/\sigma = 1$ of the mean and $50 \pm 34.1 = 84.1\%$ and 15.9%
respectively. For Series D, $M = 6.00$, and $M \pm \sigma = 6.00 \pm 1.97 = 7.97$ and 4.03
respectively.

Plotting data on arithmetic-probability paper will give the following information:

1. Approach to a straight line indicates arithmetic normality of the frequency distribution. Departure from a straight line is a sign of skewness.

2. The approximate magnitude of the arithmetic mean of the series can be read at the 50% frequency from a straight line plotted by eye. As pointed out before, however, it will pay to calculate the mean as one point on the fitted straight line and pass the line through it at the 50% frequency.

3. The approximate magnitude of the standard deviation can be found from a reading of $M \pm \sigma$ at the 84.1% and 15.9% frequencies respectively.

4. The expected frequency of any observation of a given magnitude (and vice versa) can be read from the plot.

5. Two or more series plotted to the same scale are readily compared.

4-11. Averages or Measures of Central Tendency. Averages are measures of central tendency: they state the magnitude of that value in a series of observations about which most of the values tend to cluster and from which observations deviate in smaller and smaller numbers the larger the deviations become. How well the *arithmetic mean* meets this requirement has been amply demonstrated in the analysis of the arithmetically normal frequency distribution.

But there are other averages [11] too, among them the *median* and the *mode.* Still other averages are the *geometric mean* or logarithmic average and the *harmonic mean* or reciprocal average. Use of these averages is indicated when the frequency distribution is geometrically, or harmonically, normal rather than arithmetically normal, i.e. when a symmetrical, bell-shaped frequency curve does not result unless the logarithms or reciprocals of the magnitudes are substituted for the magnitudes themselves. Such series are functionally normal.

a. The Median. The median, M_d, is the magnitude of the middle observation of an array. Half the observations are of smaller magnitude, half of larger. The median magnitude is given by the $[(n + 1)/2]$th observation in the array. In a histogram or frequency distribution, therefore, the ordinate erected at the median magnitude divides the area under the steps or curve into two equal parts. In a summation curve, the median magnitude is indicated by a frequency of 50%; $M_d = P_{50}$, the 50 percentile. As a general concept, the median value is "the magnitude of the average observation," whereas the mean is "the average magnitude of the observations." Strictly speaking, the arithmetic mean of a frequency distribution is a significant average only when the series is arithmetically normal. The median

[11] The use of the term *average* as synonymous with the term *arithmetic mean* should be avoided in statistical work.

remains significant no matter what type of variation is encountered. In an arithmetically normal frequency distribution the mean and median coincide. As a general rule, the median is not used as widely as it should be. The arithmetic mean, on the other hand, is often employed to generalize data for which it is an inadequate measure of central tendency.

If we assume that the observations in each group are uniformly spaced between its class boundaries, the magnitude of the median is given by the relation:

$$M_d = v + \frac{i}{f}\left(\frac{n}{2} - \sum_0^v f\right) \qquad 4\text{-}24$$

Here v is the lower class boundary of the median class, and $\sum_0^v f$ is the number of observations below the median class.

b. The Mode. The mode M_o is the magnitude of the most frequent and hence most probable value. It is the magnitude corresponding to the maximum of the frequency curve of best fit. For this reason it can be determined neither as quickly nor as directly as the mean or median. An important example of the use of the mode is the determination of the *most probable number* (better called the *modal number*) of coliform bacteria in water analysis. In an arithmetically normal frequency distribution, mean, median, and mode coincide.

Example 4-8. Find the means, medians, and modes of Series D and E, both of which contain 200 observations.

a. Series D. 1. $M = \Sigma f X/n = 1{,}200/200 = 6.0$.

2. The median observation is the $(n+1)/2 = 201/2 = 100.5$th observation, and lies in the group with class mean of 6.0. By Equation 4-24: $M_d = 5.5 + \frac{1}{40}(100 - 80) = 6.0$.

3. Of the 200 observations, 40 have a magnitude of 6. The mode, therefore, also falls into the group with class mean of 6.0. Actually the mode can only be identified closely from the frequency curve of best fit. For Series D, the mode coincides with the median and mean. This coincidence of M, M_d, and M_o is an indication of arithmetic normality.

b. Series E. 1. $M = \Sigma f X/n = 755/200 = 3.78$.

2. The median observation is the 100.5th observation and lies in the group with class mean of 3.0. Hence: $M_d = 2.5 + \frac{1}{66}(100 - 42) = 3.4$.

3. Of the 200 observations, 66 have a magnitude of 3. The mode, therefore, lies also in the group with class mean of 3.0. For Series E, the mode coincides with the median. The difference between the magnitudes of M and that of M_d and M_o is an indication of *skewness*.

4-12. Ranges or Measures of Dispersion. Ranges are measures of dispersion, deviation, variation, or scatter. They state how widely the observations differ in magnitude, and they share the dimensions of the observations. So far, we have encountered but one measure of dispersion: the standard deviation σ. Its importance in the analysis of the arithmetically normal frequency curve has been discussed. Strictly speaking, σ should be called the arithmetic standard deviation. As we shall see, there is also a geometric standard deviation, σ_g, which is a key parameter of geometrically normal frequency distributions. There are other ranges or measures of dispersion, as shown in Table 4-13. Most of them express a difference in the magnitudes of observations between certain percentage frequencies, i.e. at certain percentiles.[12] All of them can be expressed in terms of the standard deviation when the series is arithmetically normal. In these circumstances, therefore, there is little to be gained by their use in place of σ. See Table 4-13.

TABLE 4-13. Common Measures of Dispersion

Measure of dispersion	Magnitude	Normal relation to σ
Decentile range, D	$P_{90} - P_{10}$	2.563σ
Semi-interquartile range, Q	$\frac{1}{2}(P_{75} - P_{25})$	0.6745σ
Probable, or median, deviation, PE *	$0.6745\sqrt{\Sigma x^2/(n-1)}$	0.6745σ
Average deviation, AD	$\Sigma\lvert x \rvert/n$ (regardless of sign)	0.7979σ

* This measure is generally called the *probable error*, because it was first used in the precision of measurements.

In this schedule x is the deviation from the mean, n is the number of observations, and P is the percentile (with subscript denoting the percentage). The normal relation to σ follows from the probability integral. At $x/\sigma = 0.6745$, for example, the value of A/n is 0.25 as shown in Table 4-11. This means that half the area to either side of the mean, or half the total area under the curve, lies within a range of 0.6745σ from the mean. This range is called the probable, or median, deviation because half the deviations are smaller and half larger. There is, therefore, an equal chance that it will not be reached and that it will be exceeded. Departures from the normal relations listed in the schedule indicate skewness.

Although the average deviation is calculated more quickly than the standard deviation, it is not widely used because it is a less reliable parameter and does not enter directly into the equation of the normal frequency curve.

[12] The terms *quantiles* and *fractiles* are used to describe quantile or fractile frequencies.

For purposes of comparison, each one of the common measures of dispersion can be divided by the mean. The ratio of the standard deviation to the mean, σ/M, is called the coefficient of variation, c_v. Percentiles are read from the summation curve or calculated from arrayed or grouped data as follows:

$$P = v + \frac{i}{f}\left(\frac{Pn}{100} - \sum_0^v f\right) \qquad 4\text{-}25$$

Here P is any percentile, v the lower boundary of the group in which the percentile lies, i the class interval, f the number of observations in the group, and $\sum_0^v f$ the number of observations below the group.

4-13. Skew Frequency. The arithmetically normal frequency curve becomes asymptotic to the abscissa at infinity; it has no measurable upper or lower limit. Many collections of observations, however, are constrained in one or both directions. The lower limit for example may be zero. This restraint of the left portion of the frequency curve, the right portion being unconfined, leads to a sharper rise toward the maximum, or mode, of the curve and a subsequent flatter drop. The curve is said to be skewed to the right, because the mean falls to the right of the mode. The degree of skewness is measured in various ways. Readily understandable is Pearson's measure: [13]

$$\text{Skewness} = (M - M_o)/\sigma \qquad 4\text{-}26$$

The larger this generalized difference, the greater is the skewness. Pearson [13] has identified a large number of frequency curves to fit the many types of data encountered in statistical work. One of them, Type III, has found particularly useful application in hydrology and will be referred to in that connection. Somewhat different in concept is the functionally normal frequency distribution, of which the geometrically normal distribution is a useful example.

4-14. Geometrically Normal Frequency. Since the differences between logarithms of numbers decrease steadily as the numbers rise, a curve limited at its lower end by zero and unrestrained in its upper values is sometimes rendered symmetrical, or "functionally normal," by dealing with the logarithms of the observations instead of with their magnitudes.

A geometrically normal series of observations is completely definable in terms of the geometric mean M_g and the geometric standard

[13] See W. P. Elderton, *Frequency Curves and Correlation*, C. and E. Layton, London, 1906.

deviation σ_g. By analogy to the arithmetically normal series (Equation 4-18):

$$\log x_g = \log X - \log M_g \quad \text{or} \quad x_g = X/M_g \qquad \text{4-27}$$

$$\log M_g = (\Sigma \log X)/n \qquad \text{4-28}$$

$$\log \sigma_g = \sqrt{\frac{\Sigma \log^2 x_g}{n-1}} = \sqrt{\frac{\Sigma \log^2 X}{n-1} - \frac{n}{n-1} \log^2 M_g} \qquad \text{4-29}$$

$$y = \frac{n}{\log \sigma_g \sqrt{2\pi}} \, e^{-\frac{1}{2}\left(\frac{\log x_g}{\log \sigma_g}\right)^2} \qquad \text{4-30}$$

Since all deviations x_g are expressed in terms of the geometric mean, the geometric standard deviation is inherently a ratio to the geometric mean and incorporates the concept of the coefficient of variation.

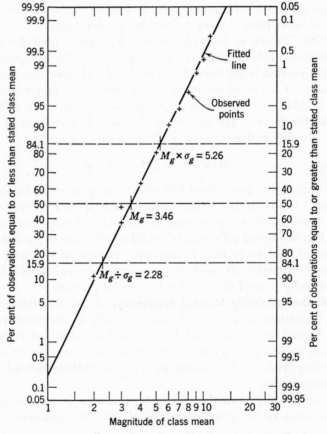

Figure 4-6. Straight-line summation plot of a frequency distribution on logarithmic probability paper; Series E.

Analysis of geometrically normal distributions, like that of arithmetic series, is simplified by the use of probability paper. A logarithmic scale of magnitudes replaces the arithmetic one. On logarithmic-probability paper, the straight line of best fit passes (1) through the intersection of the geometric mean with the 50% frequency, and (2) through the intersection of $M_g \times \sigma_g$ with the 84.1% or M_g/σ_g with the 15.9% frequency respectively. The geometric mean and the median, therefore, coincide, and $P_{84.1}/M_g = M_g/P_{15.9} = \sigma_g$.

Example 4-9. For Series E, determine the constants of the geometrically normal frequency curve of best fit and the points necessary to plot the straight line of best fit on log-probability paper (Figure 4-6). The necessary calculations are systematized in Table 4-14.

TABLE 4-14. Calculation of Geometrically Normal Frequencies (Example 4-9)

Magnitude of observation X (1)	Number of observations f (2)	Per cent of observations $100f/n$ (3)	$\log X$ $\log (1)$ (4)	$(100f/n) \log X$ $(3) \times (4)$ (5)	$\log x_g =$ $\log X - \log M_g$ $(4) - \log M_g$ (6)	$\log^2 x_g$ $(6)^2$ (7)	$(100f/n) \times$ $\log^2 x_g$ $(3) \times (7)$ (8)
1	2	1	0.0000	0.0000	−0.5390	0.2905	0.2905
2	40	20	0.3010	6.0200	−0.2380	0.0566	1.1320
3	66	33	0.4771	15.7443	−0.0619	0.0038	0.1254
4	38	19	0.6021	11.4399	+0.0631	0.0040	0.0760
5	30	15	0.6990	10.4850	+0.1600	0.0256	0.3840
6	10	5	0.7782	3.8910	+0.2392	0.0572	0.2860
7	6	3	0.8451	2.5353	+0.3061	0.0937	0.2811
8	4	2	0.9031	1.8062	+0.3641	0.1326	0.2652
9	2	1	0.9542	0.9542	+0.4152	0.1724	0.1720
10	1	0.5	1.0000	0.5000	+0.4610	0.2125	0.1063
11	1	0.5	1.0414	0.5207	+0.5024	0.2711	0.1356
Sums ..	$n = 200$	100.0	......	53.8966	....	......	3.2541
Means ..	..	.....	......	0.5390	....	....	......

$\log M_g = 0.539$; $M_g = 3.46$.

$\log \sigma_g = \sqrt{3.2541 \times 2/199} = 0.181$; $\sigma_g = 1.52$.

$M_g \times \sigma_g = 3.46 \times 1.52 = 5.26$. Plot at 84.1%.

$M_g/\sigma_g = 3.46/1.52 = 2.28$. Plot at 15.9%.

Reference to Example 4-8 shows that M_g (3.46) is smaller than M (3.78) but that it equals M_d and M_o. The coincidence of M_g and M_d is an indication of geometric normality.

4-15. Reliability of Statistical Results. In the interpretation of the results obtained by the statistical analysis of quantitative information, it is important to know how much reliability can be placed upon these results. Assuming that the measurements or observations are properly made and that the sample or collection of data is representative, it is obvious that, the larger the collection is, the more reliable must be the results of its analysis.

To find the degree of reliability of a measure such as the arithmetic mean, for example, it is necessary to determine how a number of equally good means (i.e. similarly derived) distribute themselves. It is generally true that they, too, form an arithmetically normal distribution for which the central tendency and dispersion can be found. The reliability of the means is then indicated by a measure such as the standard deviation of the distribution of these means, σ_M. This can be shown to be related to the standard deviation σ of the individual samples as follows: [14]

$$\sigma_M = \sigma/\sqrt{n} \qquad 4\text{-}31$$

This measure tells us, according to the probability integral, that the chances are $2 \times 34.1 = 68.2\%$ that a mean determined from a similar collection of data will lie within $\pm \sigma_M$ of the first mean. The reliability of other measures of central tendency and of measures of dispersion is indicated similarly by the standard deviation of distributions of these measures. We may list the measures and their standard deviations as in Table 4-15 for arithmetically normal distributions.

TABLE 4-15.   Standard Deviations of Common Statistical Parameters for Arithmetically Normal Frequency Distributions

Measure	Standard deviation of measure
$M = \Sigma X/n$	$\sigma_M = \sigma/\sqrt{n}$
$M_d = v + \dfrac{i}{f}\left(\dfrac{n}{2} - \sum\limits_0^v f\right)$	$\sigma_{M_d} = 1.2533\sigma/\sqrt{n}$
$\sigma = \sqrt{\Sigma x^2/(n-1)}$	$\sigma_\sigma = \sigma/\sqrt{2n} = 0.7071\sigma/\sqrt{n}$
$c_v = \sigma/M$	$\sigma_{c_v} = c_v\sqrt{1 + 2c_v^2}/\sqrt{2n} = \sqrt{1 + 2c_v^2}/\sqrt{2n}$
$PE = 0.6745\sqrt{\Sigma x^2/(n-1)}$	$\sigma_{PE} = 0.6745\sigma/\sqrt{2n} = 0.7071PE/\sqrt{n}$
$Q = \frac{1}{2}(P_{75} - P_{25})$	$\sigma_Q = 0.7867\sigma/\sqrt{n} = 1.166Q/\sqrt{n}$
$D = (P_{90} - P_{10})$	$\sigma_D = 2.792\sigma/\sqrt{n} = 0.8892D/\sqrt{n}$
$AD = \Sigma|\,x\,|/n$ (regardless of sign)	$\sigma_{AD} = 0.6028\sigma/\sqrt{n} = 0.7555AD/\sqrt{n}$

It is evident that the median, which is less well determined than the mean, is also less reliable, although it is not less significant as a

[14] For m sets of n measures each, where m and n are both large, the mean of the mn measures becomes the true mean, M. If M_s is a submean of n measures, $M_s - M = (1/n)(\Sigma X) - M = (1/n)(\Sigma X - nM) = (1/n)\Sigma(X - M) = (1/n)\Sigma x$. The square of the standard deviation, σ_M, of the submeans from the true mean is then: $\sigma_M^2 = (1/m)\Sigma(M_s - M)^2 = (1/m)\Sigma(1/n\Sigma x)^2 = (1/mn^2)\Sigma(x_1^2 + x_2^2 + \cdots x_n^2 + 2x_1x_2$

parameter of central tendency. For arithmetic normality, the standard deviation σ, and its variate, the probable error PE, are the most reliable measures of dispersion with the average deviation AD, decentile range D, and semi-interquartile range Q, following in that order. As shown in the schedule, comparisons may be had by expressing the standard deviation of these measures in terms of their own magnitudes.

Example 4-10. Determine the reliability of the mean, median, standard deviation, and coefficient of variation of Series D:

As derived in Examples 4-5 and 4-8, $M = 6.0$, $M_d = 6.0$, $\sigma = 1.97$, and $c_v = 0.33$. Hence for $n = 200$:

a. $\sigma_M = 1.97/\sqrt{200} = \pm 0.14$, for $M = 6.0$.

b. $\sigma_{M_d} = 1.25 \times 0.14 = \pm 0.17$, for $M_d = 6.0$.

c. $\sigma_\sigma = 1.97/20 = \pm 0.10$, for $\sigma = 1.97$.

d. $\sigma_{c_v} = 0.33\sqrt{1 + 2 \times (0.33)^2}/20 = \pm 0.02$, for $c_v = 0.33$.

The standard deviations of the geometric mean and the geometric standard deviation are shown in Table 4-16 for geometrically normal

TABLE 4-16. Standard Deviations of Common Statistical Parameters for Geometrically Normal Frequency Distributions

Measure	Standard deviation of measure
$\log M_g = (\Sigma \log X)/n$	$\log \sigma_g$ of $M_g = (\log \sigma_g)/\sqrt{n}$
$\log \sigma_g = \sqrt{(\Sigma \log^2 x_g)/(n-1)}$	$\log \sigma_g$ of $\sigma_g = (\log \sigma_g)/\sqrt{2n}$

series. Various ways for testing the "goodness of fit" of calculated frequencies and magnitudes of observations are elaborated in statistical treatises.

$+ 2x_1x_3 + \cdots 2x_1x_n + 2x_2x_3 \cdots 2x_{n-1}x_n)$. But $(1/mn)\Sigma(x_1^2 + x_2^2 + \cdots x_n^2) = \sigma^2$ where σ is the standard deviation of all observations from the true mean; also, $2x_1x_2 + 2x_1x_3 \cdots 2x_1x_n + 2x_2x_3 \cdots 2x_{n-1}x_n = 0$ (closely), because $x_1x_2 + x_1x_3 + \cdots x_1x_n = x_1S_1x$, and $x_2x_1 + x_2x_3 + \cdots x_2x_n = x_2S_2x$, etc., the sums of all the deviations from the true mean excepting the values of x_1, x_2, etc., respectively, are each closely equal to zero and are compensating values in any case. It follows, therefore, that $mn^2\sigma_M^2 = mn\sigma^2$, or $\sigma_M = \sigma/\sqrt{n}$.

5 — QUANTITIES OF WATER AND WASTE WATER

5-1. General Considerations. Both management and design of water-supply and waste-water disposal systems require a knowledge of the quantities of water needed and waste water produced and their relation to the population served. The water supplied and the waste water discharged, depending upon the use to which the figures are to be put, are often recorded in one of the following ways:

a. Total annual quantity in gallons (gal) or million gallons (mg).

b. Average daily quantity in gallons per day (gpd) or million gallons per day (mgd) = (a)/(365 or 366).

c. Average daily quantity in gallons per capita per day (gpcd) = (b)/(midyear population or tributary population).

d. Average daily quantity in gallons per person [1] connected to the system = (b)/(connected midyear population or tributary population).

e. Average daily quantity in gallons per service [2] = (b)/(number of services, active or total).

Fluctuations in flow are generally expressed as percentage ratios of the maximum or minimum daily and hourly values to the average daily and hourly values respectively. Per capita figures generalize the experience. They are useful in comparing the records of different communities and in estimating the future needs of a growing community or area. Forecasts of the midyear (July 1) population or tributary population are needed. These estimates also underlie the determination of the vital rates of the community, among which death and sickness rates due to water-borne diseases are of immediate concern to the water-supply and sewerage authorities.

Because of the nature of the work involved, water-supply and waste-water disposal systems, at the time of their construction, are made large enough to satisfy the needs of the community for a reasonable number of years in the future without requiring important additions or changes. Determination of this initial or design capacity

[1] Or "consumer" in water supply.
[2] Or "tap" in water supply.

116

calls for the exercise of skill in the interpretation of social and economic trends, as well as the use of sound judgment in the analysis of past experience for the purpose of predicting future requirements. Among the estimates to be made by the designer are the following:

1. The number of years during which the proposed system and its component structures and equipment are to be adequate. This is called the *period of design*.
2. The number of people to be served as determined by forecasts of population and expansion of service.
3. The rate of water use and sewage flow as reflected by estimates of future per capita water consumption and sewage discharge as well as industrial and commercial requirements.
4. For storm and combined sewerage, in particular, the area to be served and the allowances to be made for rainfall and runoff.[3]

5-2. Period of Design. In fixing upon a period of design, consideration is given to the following factors:

1. The useful life of the structures and equipment employed, taking into account obsolescence as well as wear and tear.
2. The ease, or difficulty, of extending or increasing the works, including a consideration of their location.
3. The anticipated rate of growth of the population, with due regard to increases in industrial and commercial needs.
4. The rate of interest that must be paid on bonded indebtedness.
5. The change in the purchasing power of money during the period of retirement of indebtedness.
6. The performance of the works during their early years when they are not loaded to capacity.

TABLE 5-1. Design Periods for Water-Supply and Sewerage Structures

Type of structure	Special characteristics	Design period—yr
Water supply		
Large dams and conduits	Hard and costly to enlarge	25–50
Wells, distribution systems, and filter plants	Easy to extend	
	When growth and interest rates are low *	20–25
	When growth and interest rates are high *	10–15
Pipes more than 12 in. in diameter	Replacement of smaller pipes is more costly in long run	20–25
Laterals and secondary mains less than 12 in. in diameter	Requirements may change fast in a limited area	Full development
Sewerage		
Laterals and submains less than 15 in. in diameter	Requirements may change fast in a limited area	Full development
Main sewers, outfalls, and intercepters	Hard and costly to enlarge	40–50
Treatment works	When growth and interest rates are low *	20–25
	When growth and interest rates are high *	10–15

* The dividing line is in the vicinity of 3% per annum.

[3] This aspect of the problem is considered in a separate chapter.

The longer the useful life (1), the greater the difficulty of extensions (2), the smaller the rate of growth (3), the lower the rate of interest (4), the greater the likelihood of inflation (5), and the better the early performance (6), the farther into the future can the design be projected with economic justification. The lengths of design periods often employed in practice are indicated in Table 5-1.

Population Estimates

5-3. Population Data. The best source of information on the population living in a given community or area at a designated time is an official census or enumeration. The government of the United States has made a decennial census since 1790. Additional data are sometimes available through state censuses, usually authorized for years ending in 5, and through special surveys conducted by public authorities or private agencies for governmental, social, or commercial purposes. The dates of the U. S. Census and the intervals between them are given in Table 5-2.

TABLE 5-2.   Dates of U. S. Census

Year	Date *	Census interval—years
1790–1820	First Monday in August	Approximately 10
1830–1900	1 June	Exactly 10, except 1820–1830
1910	15 April	9.875
1920	1 January	9.708
1930	1 April	10.250
1940, 1950	1 April	Exactly 10

* Changed in attempts to find a time when most people are in their home communities and accessible to the enumerator.

Census data are published by the Bureau of the Census in the Department of Commerce. The subdivisions for which population data are made available include states, counties, metropolitan districts, cities, and towns, wards, and census tracts. Summary tables are published for cities having at the time of the last census 100,000 inhabitants or more (from 1790 onward), also for smaller communities for a shorter range of time. Census-tract data offer the most complete breakdown of information and are made available for many cities.

5-4. Population Growth. Populations are increased by births, decreased by deaths, increased or decreased by migration, and increased by annexation. If the sum of these changes is positive, a gain is registered; if it is negative, a loss occurs. All four elements are influenced by social and economic factors some of which are inherent in the community concerned while others are country wide and even world wide in scope. Changes in birth and death rates in the United States since the First World War [4] must be interpreted in terms of (1) immigration restrictions that have decreased the proportion of young adults; (2) advances in maternal and child hygiene which have reduced infant mortality and the infectious diseases of childhood; (3) improvements in nutrition which have lowered the incidence of tuberculosis and deficiency diseases; (4) new discoveries in medicine which have decreased the fatality of many infectious diseases; and (5) variations in the national economy which have lowered or raised the birth rate. Other factors such as wars must also be considered. Recognizing that there are certain stable values toward which birth and death rates will move, and that annexations or extensions of services can be accounted for by following the development of the individual population groups, the most important and least predictable element of population change is the commercial and industrial activity of an individual community. This element may produce sharp rises, slow growth, stationary conditions, or even marked declines in population.[5]

Were it not for these manifold and varying influences, populations would trace the growth curve that is characteristic of all forms of life within a limited space. This curve is S-shaped (Figure 5-1), early growth taking place at an increasing rate, late growth at a decreasing rate as a saturation value or upper limit is approached. What the future holds for a given population depends upon the point that has been reached on the growth curve.

5-5. Methods of Estimating Population. As previously stated, two types of population estimates are needed in the management and design of sanitary works: (a) estimates of the midyear populations

[4] Birth and death rates in the United States per 1,000 population are recorded as follows:

	1915	1920	1925	1930	1935	1940	1945	1950
Birth rate	30	28	25	21	19	19	20	24
Death rate	13	13	12	11	11	11	11	10
Rate of natural increase	16	15	13	10	8	9	10	15

[5] Examples are furnished by the growth of Detroit, Mich. (automobile industry), the decline of Lowell, Mass. (textile industry), and the growth of Miami, Fla. (recreation).

Census year	1910	1920	1930	1940	1950
Population of Detroit	466,000	994,000	1,560,000	1,623,000	1,839,000
Population of Lowell	106,000	113,000	100,000	101,000	97,000
Population of Miami	5,500	30,000	111,000	172,000	247,000

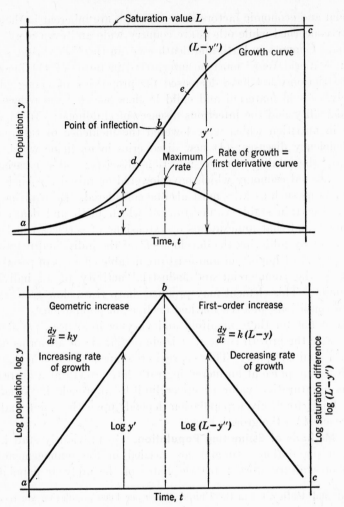

Figure 5-1. Curve of population growth. Note geometric increase from a to b; straight-line increase from d to e (approximately); and first-order increase from b to c.

for current years and the recent past, and (b) forecasts of population for the period of design.

    a. Estimates for Current and Past Years. These are either inter-censal estimates for the years between two censuses or postcensal estimates for the years since the last census. Mathematically, the mid-year values are readily interpolated, or extrapolated, on the basis of arithmetic or geometric change. Growth is *arithmetic* if the population increase dy in the time interval dt is a constant amount k_a, irrespective of the size of the population; i.e., $dy/dt = k_a$. Growth is *geometric* if the population increase dy in the time interval dt is proportional to the size of the population y; i.e., $dy/dt = k_g y$, where k_g is the proportionality factor. Integration of these relationships between the limits y_e (the population of the earlier census) and y_l (the population of the later census) and the limits t_e (the date of the earlier census) and t_l (the date of the later census) yields the values of k_a and k_g:

$$k_a = (y_l - y_e)/(t_l - t_e) \quad \text{for arithmetic growth} \qquad 5\text{-}1$$

$$k_g = (\log_e y_l - \log_e y_e)/(t_l - t_e) \quad \text{for geometric growth} \qquad 5\text{-}2$$

Integration between the limits y_m (the desired midyear population) and y_e or y_l, and between the limits t_m (the desired date) and t_e or t_l, gives the midyear population as follows:

Arithmetic estimate

Intercensal

$$y_m = y_e + (y_l - y_e)(t_m - t_e)/(t_l - t_e) \qquad 5\text{-}3$$

Postcensal

$$y_m = y_l + (y_l - y_e)(t_m - t_l)/(t_l - t_e) \qquad 5\text{-}4$$

Geometric estimate

Intercensal

$$\log y_m = \log y_e + (\log y_l - \log y_e)(t_m - t_e)/(t_l - t_e) \qquad 5\text{-}5$$

Postcensal

$$\log y_m = \log y_l + (\log y_l - \log y_e)(t_m - t_l)/(t_l - t_e) \qquad 5\text{-}6$$

It will be noted that the geometric estimate uses the logarithms of the populations in the same way the populations themselves are used in the arithmetic estimate; also, that arithmetic increase is analogous to growth by simple interest, geometric increase to growth by compound interest. The lower portion of the S-shaped growth curve (Figure 5-1) is approximated by geometric increase (concave upward) and the central portion by arithmetic increase (straight line). The upper portion is concave downward. It is analogous to a *first-order* chemical reaction.[6] Choice of method is best determined by an examination of the population curve that is obtained when all available census figures are plotted on arithmetic-coordinate paper.

[6] The first-order reaction is formulated in Section 18-15. Its application to population data is indicated in Figure 5-1 and involves an estimate of the limiting population, or saturation value L.

Example 5-1. A city [7] recorded a population of 111,000 in the earlier decennial census and 171,000 in the later one. Estimate the midyear (1 July) populations (a) for the fifth intercensal year and (b) for the ninth postcensal year by the arithmetic-increase method and the geometric-increase method. Assume a census date of 1 April.

a. Intercensal estimate for fifth year. $t_m - t_e = 5.25$ yr; $t_l - t_e = 10.00$ yr; and $(t_m - t_e)/(t_l - t_e) = 5.25/10.00 = 0.525$.

<table>
<tr><td colspan="2" align="center">Arithmetic</td><td colspan="2" align="center">Geometric</td></tr>
</table>

$y_l = 171,000$	$\log y_l = 5.23300$
$y_e = 111,000$	$\log y_e = 5.04532$
$y_l - y_e = 60,000$	$\log y_l - \log y_e = 0.18768$
$0.525(y_l - y_e) = 31,500$	$0.525(\log y_l - \log y_e) = 0.09853$
$y_m = 142,500$	$\log y_m = 5.14385$
	$y_m = 139,300$

b. Postcensal estimate for ninth year. $t_m - t_l = 9.25$ yr; $t_l - t_e = 10.00$ yr; and $(t_m - t_l)/(t_l - t_e) = 9.25/10.00 = 0.925$.

<table>
<tr><td colspan="2" align="center">Arithmetic</td><td colspan="2" align="center">Geometric</td></tr>
</table>

From (a) $y_l - y_e = 60,000$	$\log y_l - \log y_e = 0.18768$
$0.925(y_l - y_e) = 55,500$	$0.925(\log y_l - \log y_e) = 0.17360$
$y_l = 171,000$	$\log y_l = 5.23300$
$y_m = 226,500$	$\log y_m = 5.40660$
	$y_m = 255,000$

Note that the geometric estimates are higher for postcensal years and lower for intercensal years.

It is possible to arrive at supporting current estimates of populations by multiplying school enrollment and numbers of services of different utilities by suitable factors that have been derived from a study of the ratio of the population, known for the census dates for example, to these numbers. Since ratios of this kind vary locally and in time they must be chosen with care. No general values obtain. Their order of magnitude in North American communities approaches the following:

Population:school enrollment = 5:1.
Population:number of water, gas, or electric services = 3:1.
Population:number of telephone services = 4:1.

Current estimates of the nation's population are made by the Bureau of the Census by adding the differences between births and deaths [8] and between immigration and emigration to the last census population. For states and other large population groups, current (postcensal)

[7] The figures used are rounded values for Miami, Fla., 1930 and 1940.

[8] The Bureau of the Census estimates that 92% of all births are recorded and 98% of all deaths. Adjustments are made for this incomplete registration.

estimates are made in various ways that may be formulated as follows if we let y equal the local population and Y the national population and remember the subscripts employed in developing Equations 5-1 to 5-6.

1. The *apportionment method* makes the local increase equal to the national increase times the ratio of the local to the national intercensal increase:

$$y_m - y_l = (Y_m - Y_l)(y_l - y_e)/(Y_l - Y_e) \qquad 5\text{-}7$$

2. The *formula method* makes the local increase equal to its intercensal increase times the ratio of the national postcensal increase to the national intercensal increase. Algebraically the result is identical with that obtained by the apportionment method.

3. The *scaling-down method* modifies the local arithmetic increase $(y_m' - y_l)$ in proportion to the ratio of the average national postcensal increase to the average national intercensal increase:

$$y_m \doteq y_l + (y_m' - y_l)\left(\frac{Y_m - Y_l}{t_m - t_l}\right)\Big/\left(\frac{Y_l - Y_e}{t_l - t_e}\right) \qquad 5\text{-}8$$

Where a loss in population has been registered during the last decade, the Bureau of the Census recommends using the last census figure rather than estimating postcensal decreases.

b. Forecasts for the Period of Design. Long-range forecasts of population differ appreciably from postcensal estimates in their method of attacking the problem. Instead of dealing with the results of the last two censuses only, the full record of population growth is quite generally employed, in order to identify the long-term swing rather than short-term fluctuations. Forecasting methods include especially (1) mathematical curve fitting, and (2) graphical studies.

S-shaped curves, like the growth curve, can be described by a number of different equations that seek a rational biological basis for their selection. One of the best known is the *logistic* curve of Verhulst,[9] which is analogous to the curve of chemical *autocatalysis*.[10] Ordinarily, mathematical curve fitting is of most value in the study of large population groups, or nations.

Plots of population against time generally exhibit trends that are readily sketched in by eye. In the hands of a skilled interpreter of population growth this extension of the population curve will yield forecasts that are reasonably close to actual experience. For this reason, graphical forecasts are much used by engineers. In extending the population curve, judgment is sometimes aided by sketching in

[9] See Raymond Pearl, *Medical Biometry and Statistics,* W. B. Saunders Co., Philadelphia, Chapter 18, 1940.

[10] The autocatalytic curve is discussed in Section 19-6.

the growth experience of similar, but larger, communities that have reached the last census figure of the population under consideration in the not too distant past (see Figure 5-2).[11] It should be realized, however, that the historical periods involved in such a comparison are

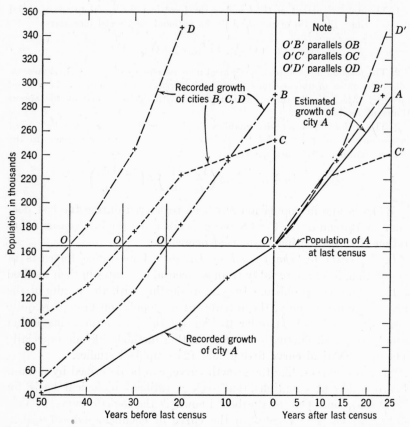

Figure 5-2. Graphical estimation of growth of a city by comparison with past growth of similar but larger cities.

quite unlike and that the future development of a community of a given size may be very different from the past development of a like community of similar size.

A somewhat different method for forecasting population involves the projection into the future, not of the growth curve, but of its first derivative, the rate-of-growth curve. For convenience the rate of

[11] The populations recorded in Figure 5-2 are those of A, Hartford, Conn.; B, Columbus, O.; C, Providence, R. I.; and D, Newark, N. J.; all prior to 1930.

growth is then generally expressed as the intercensal percentage increase in population, adjusted if necessary to account for variations in census dates. Comparisons can again be made with the rate of growth of other, larger populations. Plotting rate of growth against population density provides additional information.

Arithmetic scales are most generally useful in plotting population data. A logarithmic (geometric) scale for the population or rate of growth, however, often straightens out the curve and aids in its projection.

Example 5-2. The design period for the sanitary works of a community of 164,000 at the time of the last census is 25 years beyond the census. Estimate, from a study of its past rate of growth, what the design population will be, assuming (a) an arithmetic trend, (b) a geometric trend, in rate of growth. The recorded decadal populations of the community [12] and rates of growth prior to the last census are given in Table 5-3 together with the necessary calculations to fit trends to the rates by the method of least squares.

TABLE 5-3. Least Squares Calculations for Example 5-2

Population, x, in thousands	Decadal rate of growth, y, %	log y	x^2	xy	x log y
42.0	26.7	1.4265	1,764	1,121	59.91
53.2	50.2	1.7007	2,830	2,671	90.48
79.9	23.8	1.3766	6,384	1,901	109.99
98.9	39.6	1.5977	9,781	3,916	158.01
138.0	18.8	1.2742	19,044	2,595	175.84
Sums 412.0	159.1	7.3757	39,803	12,204	594.23
Means 82.4	31.8	1.4751	7,961	2,441	118.85

1. Calculate the trends in rate by Equations 4-9 and 4-10.
a. Arithmetic trend in rate: $y = 44.2 - 0.150x$.
b. Geometric trend in rate:

$$\log y = 1.6638 - 0.00211x \quad \text{or} \quad y = 46.1e^{-0.00527x}$$

2. Plot the observations and fitted trends in Figure 5-3.
3. Estimate the population from the decadal rates of growth read from Figure 5-3 or calculated from the fitted equations. The results are shown in Table 5-4. Here decadal increase = per cent growth $\times$ population/100; and population = preceding population + increase, except for the last value, where half the increase only is added.

---

[12] Rounded values for Hartford, Conn., from 1880 to 1930.

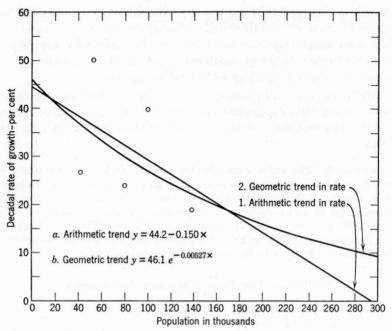

Figure 5-3. Population forecast from rate of growth. Trend lines are fitted by least squares.

TABLE 5-4. Calculation of Estimated Populations (Example 5-2)

Years after last census	Population in thousands		Decadal growth			
			Rate, %		Increase	
	a	b	a	b	a	b
0	164	164	19.6	19.4	32	32
10	196	196	14.8	16.4	29	32
20	225	228	10.5	13.9	21	32
25	236	244	....	....	..	..

5-6. Population Distribution or Density. Estimates of the total population of a community or area are used in the design and management of water works and sewerage systems as a whole. Distribution of water and collection of sewage within the community require, in addition, estimates of the density of the population and the nature of occupancy or the use of the different types of areas that compose the community. For these purposes, population density is generally expressed as the number of persons per acre. A classification of areas and expected population densities is shown in Table 5-5.

TABLE 5-5. Common Population Densities

	Persons per acre
1. Residential areas	
a. Single-family dwellings, large lots	5-15
b. Single-family dwellings, small lots	15-35
c. Multiple-family dwellings	35-100
d. Apartment or tenement houses	100-1,000
2. Mercantile and commercial areas	15-30
3. Industrial areas	5-15
4. Total, exclusive of parks, playgrounds, and cemeteries	10-50

Values of this kind are determined by an analysis of the present and possible future subdivision of typical blocks. Small lots, 50 ft by 150 ft, facing a 60-ft street in a block 600 ft long and 300 ft wide, for example, run 24 to the block and $43,560/(660 \times 360/24) = 4.4$ to the acre. If these lots are occupied by single-family dwellings, the resulting population density is $4.4 \times 5 = 22$ persons per acre, assuming 5 persons per dwelling unit. Much can be learned in this connection from building counts based on fire-insurance maps, aerial maps, and field surveys.

Census data on population distribution within communities may be had for the larger cities of the United States from an analysis of census tract reports; for the smaller cities, from an analysis of ward reports. From existing or collectable information, changes in occupancy or use must be forecast, as well as changes in population density or saturation. Zoning ordinances, which define the nature of occupancy as well as the bulk of the buildings allowed to be erected, are of assistance in arriving at reasonable design values. Unfortunately such ordinances are subject to repeal or to unreasonable as well as reasonable change.

Usually, therefore, allowances for possible changes are made. The smaller the district and the lower the density of population, the greater is the possible departure from the average. This is exemplified in Equation 5-9, which approximates graphical values proposed by Greeley and Stanley.[13]

$$D_{max}/D = (2.90 \times 1.026^D - \log p)/(1.026^D)^2 \qquad 5-9$$

Here D_{max} is the probable maximum number of persons per acre in a district containing p per cent of the population, and D is the average number of persons per acre. For $D = 20$ and $p = 10$, for example, $D_{max}/D = 1.4$ and $D_{max} = 28$ persons per acre.

[13] Calvin Davis, *Handbook of Applied Hydraulics*, McGraw-Hill Book Co., New York, p. 1017, 1952.

Water Consumption

5-7. Uses and Averages. Service pipes deliver water to dwellings, mercantile or commercial properties, industrial establishments, and public buildings. The water used is classified accordingly. The quantities delivered in North American communities approximate the values shown in Table 5-6, with wide variations to be expected be-

TABLE 5-6. Normal Water Consumption

	Quantity, gpcd	
Class of consumption	Normal range	Average
Domestic	15–70	35
Commercial and industrial	10–100	30
Public	5–20	10
Water unaccounted for	10–40	25
Total	40–230	100

cause of differences in (1) climate, (2) standard of living, (3) extent of sewerage, (4) type of mercantile, commercial, and industrial activity, (5) cost of water, (6) availability of private water supplies, (7) quality of water for domestic, industrial, and other uses, (8) pressure in the distribution system, (9) completeness of meterage, and (10) management of the system.

Water rates are generally classified, according to the annual consumption per service, as follows:

Domestic rate	less than 300,000 gal
Intermediate rate	300,000 to 3,000,000 gal
Manufacturing rate	more than 3,000,000 gal

The domestic rate permits about 24 persons to draw water at a rate of 35 gpcd through a single service.

5-8. Factors Affecting Consumption. *a. Domestic Consumption.* Extremes of heat and cold increase water consumption: hot and arid climates by more bathing, air conditioning, and irrigation; cold climates by water being bled through faucets in order to keep service pipes and building distribution systems from freezing. Higher standards of cleanliness, larger numbers of plumbing fixtures, and more lawn and garden sprinkling, car washing, and air conditioning, associated with greater wealth, result in heavier use of water.

Where extension of sewers has not kept pace with the growth of the water distribution system, difficulties of private sewage disposal will generally impose restrictions on water use.

b. Commercial and Industrial Consumption. Certain commercial enterprises, like hotels and restaurants, use more water than others; so do industrial establishments [14] like breweries, canneries, laundries, paper mills, railroad yards, and steel mills.

The lower the cost of water, the higher, ordinarily, is its consumption, particularly for industrial purposes. Rough rules based upon an analysis of North American experience are (1) that consumption varies inversely as the water rate for manufacturing purposes and (2) that an increase in rates reduces consumption by about one-half the percentage increase in rates. An abundant source of ground water underlying a community or accessibility of other suitable sources of water may lead large users to develop these supplies and restrict their draft from the public supply, for example for air conditioning, condensing, and other industrial processes.

c. Consumption in General. Use of the public supply is encouraged when the water delivered is clean, palatable, and of unquestioned safety for drinking and culinary uses; when it is soft for washing and cool for condensing purposes; and when it meets the quality standards of industry. Poor water drives consumers to private, sometimes dangerous, sources. The flow of water through faucets and similar outlets, as well as through leaks in mains and faulty plumbing, is akin to flow through an orifice and so varies about as the square root of the pressure head. In distribution systems, therefore, high pressures result (1) in rapid discharge of fixtures and increased waste of water, and (2) in increased leakage. Operating pressures in excess of about 60 psig are no longer as important for fire fighting as they were before the advent of the motor pumper.

Introduction of meterage encourages thrift and normalizes the demand. Meter consciousness, however, may depress domestic use abnormally immediately after meters are first installed. In a study of the effects of meterage, a distinction must be made between the "per cent of services" metered and the "per cent of consumption" metered. Large consumers are, understandably, provided with meters first. These initial installations, therefore, produce a greater per capita reduction in consumption than do those last installations that make meterage complete. Ordinarily, meterage should establish consumption at a value that is in keeping with the size and type of the community. The cost of metering water, including the reading and repair of the meter, is substantial. The cost of meterage, therefore, must be balanced against the value of the water made available by

[14] Industrial water requirements are discussed in Chapter 29.

reduction of waste. In some instances this reduction may permit the postponement of otherwise needed extension of, or addition to, the existing supply.

There is some leakage from all distribution systems. Where the main supply is measured by a Venturi meter or other measuring device, and the water delivered to consumers or used in other ways (for example, in the washing of filters and the flushing of streets, mains, and sewers) is metered or otherwise measured, about 85% of the supply should reasonably be accounted for. If allowance is made for the water used in fighting fires, this figure may be raised to 90%. The relative amount of water not accounted for is expressed more logically in gallons daily per capita, since leakage is independent of use. Leakage from new cast-iron water mains is estimated at 100 to 500 gpd per mile of pipe per inch diameter. Since there are close to 500 people per mile of pipe in North American cities, and the average diameter of pipe is about 8 in., leakage from this source alone lies between $100 \times 8/500 = 2$ gpcd and $500 \times 8/500 = 8$ gpcd. By comparison, a leaky water-closet tank will waste 300 gpd and a dripping faucet 60 gpd.

In a well-managed system, leakage is checked carefully and continuously. Controllable leakage is detected in various ways: (1) observation of water running in gutters, moist pavement, persistent seepage, excessive flow in sewers, abnormal drop in pressure, and unusually green vegetation (in dry climates); (2) use of sounding rods driven into the ground to test for moist earth; (3) employment of devices that report the sound of running water; (4) inspection of premises for leaky plumbing; and (5) water-waste surveys that involve isolating comparatively small sections of the system by closing valves on mains that supply these sections and measuring the water flowing to them, usually through a single connection and at night, by means of (a) Pitot tubes, (b) by-pass meters around the controlling valves, or (c) meters on one or more hose lines between hydrants that straddle a closed valve.

d. *Future Consumption.* As North American cities grow, their per capita use of water commonly increases by about one-tenth the percentage increase in population. If a city increases its population by 50%, therefore, water consumption per person is expected to rise by 5%. Water uses for summer air conditioning will undoubtedly mount in the future. With full employment of evaporative condensers, or cooling towers, however, the different structures cooled need not exert a demand in excess of 5 to 35 gpcd at maximum rate during the summer season nor an average annual demand greater than 0.5 to 4.5

gpcd. The expanding use of dishwashers, automatic home laundries, and garbage grinders will produce further increases in the per capita rate of consumption.

5-9. Variations in Demand. Water consumption changes with the seasons, with the days of the week, and with the hours of the day. There is a major seasonal peak during summer heat and drought when large volumes of water are drawn to refresh man and beast, water lawns and gardens, and feed the washers or cool the condensers of air-conditioning installations. There is a minor seasonal peak during extremely cold weather when water is allowed to run to waste and when leakage is greatest from the joints of metallic pipes because they are contracted by cold. In addition, there are seasonal uses of water in industry, such as the processing of agricultural products in the fall, and the alternating use of private ground-water supplies in the summer and of the public surface-water supply in the winter so as to gain the benefits of lower water temperatures. There are variations from day to day during the week that reflect household and industrial activity: Sundays for rest and Mondays for washing. Finally there are fluctuations from hour to hour, with a peak close to noon and an extreme minimum in the small hours of the morning. These normal variations in water use must be known if supply pipes, service reservoirs, and distributing pipes are to be properly proportioned. Quite different from these normal variations in demand are the sudden, heavy, and unpredictable drafts of water to fight fires. Although the volume of water used in quenching fires is relatively small, the rate at which it must be supplied is of determining influence in the design of the distribution systems of North American communities.

a. Normal Variations. The smaller the community, the greater, in general, is the variation in its demand for water. The shorter the period of flow, furthermore, the greater is the departure from the average. For purposes of comparison, these variations are expressed as ratios to the average demand. Large differences must be expected, depending upon the balance of factors concerned in different communities. The following values are indicated by experience:

Ratio	Normal range	Average
Maximum day:average day	(From 1.2 to 2.0):1	1.5:1
Maximum hour:average hour	(From 2.0 to 3.0):1	2.5:1

b. Fire Demand. The rate at which water should be supplied to extinguish fires and prevent conflagrations is determined by factors such as the bulk, congestion, fire resistance, and content of buildings. So far as the high-value, congested district in the heart of North

American communities is concerned, the character of this area, as reflected by these factors, is a function of the size of the community. The fire demand of this district, therefore, has long been represented by an equation that relates fire flow to population. For the residential districts outside of the central portion of the community, fire-flow estimates are based upon the type and congestion of the buildings. Industrial and commercial properties have requirements of their own which are accounted for in part by the provision of private fire supplies, storage, and pumps.

In North America, the protection of property against fire is the purpose of the National Board of Fire Underwriters, a fact-finding organization supported by fire-insurance companies. Among many other activities, this board grades public water supplies on adequacy for fire protection.[15] Careful and continuing analyses of water demands experienced during fires have led this organization to formulate general standards from which the designer should depart only after careful study and for good and sufficient reasons. Standard fire flows take into account probable loss of water from connections that are broken during a large fire. The general requirements of the National Board are summarized below.[16]

1. Within the central, congested, high-value district, the rate Q in gpm [17] at which water must be made available in order to check a serious conflagration varies with the population P in thousands in accordance with the following relationship for communities of 200,000 people or less:

$$Q = 1{,}020\sqrt{P}\,(1 - 0.01\sqrt{P}) \qquad 5\text{-}10$$

2. The central portion of communities with populations in excess of 200,000 requires capacities of 12,000 gpm and from 2,000 to 8,000 gpm in addition for a second fire.

3. For residential districts the required fire flow varies from 500 gpm to 6,000 gpm.

As previously stated, the actual volume of water used in fighting fires in the course of a year, however, is almost negligibly small.

c. Coincident Draft. It is hardly conceivable that the maximum rate of draft of water for general community purposes will be exerted at the same time as a serious conflagration is being fought. For this reason the coincident draft caused by those portions of the system that are called upon to provide water for both normal and fire-fighting

[15] *Standard Schedule for Grading Cities and Towns of the United States,* National Board of Fire Underwriters, New York, 1942.

[16] A more detailed statement is deferred until Chapter 13.

[17] This is the customary unit; 1,000 gpm = 1.44 mgd.

purposes need not be assumed to equal the maximum hourly rate. A value in excess of the average daily rate, such as the maximum daily rate (150% of the average), appears to be reasonable.

Example 5-3. The four typical water-works systems shown in Figure 5-4 serve a community with an estimated future population of 100,000. Determine the

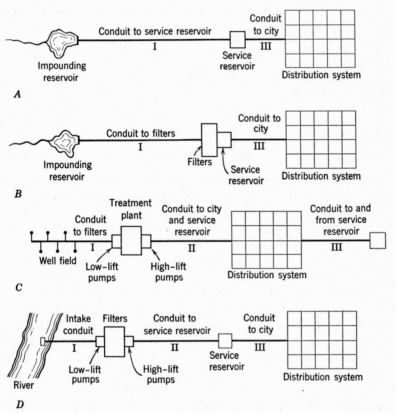

Figure 5-4. Capacity requirements for the constituent structures of four typical water-works systems. The service reservoir is assumed to take care of hourly fluctuations, fire drafts, and emergency reserve.

		Capacity of system, mgd			
Structure	Required capacity	A	B	C	D
1. River or well field	Maximum day	....	....	15.0	15.0
2. Conduit I	Maximum day	15.0	15.0	15.0	15.0
3. Conduit II	Maximum day	....	....	15.0	15.0
4. Conduit III	Coincident draft and fire	28.2	28.2	28.2	28.2
5. Low-lift pumps	Maximum day plus reserve	....	....	20.0	20.0
6. High-lift pumps	Maximum day plus reserve	....	....	30.0	30.0
7. Filters or treatment plant	Maximum day plus reserve	....	16.0	16.0	16.0
8. Distribution system to high-value district	Coincident draft and fire	28.2	28.2	28.2	28.2

required capacities of their constituent structures for an average water consumption of 100 gpcd and a distributing reservoir so sized that it can provide enough water to care for differences between hourly and daily flows, fire demands, and emergency water requirements. Fundamental calculations are:

  a. Average daily draft = 100 × 100,000/1,000,000 = 10 mgd.

  b. Maximum daily draft = coincident draft = 1.5 × 10 = 15 mgd.

  c. Maximum hourly draft = 2.5 × 10 = 25 mgd.

  d. Fire flow to high-value district = $1,020\sqrt{100}\,(1 - 0.01\sqrt{100}) = 9,180$ gpm, or $9.180 \times 1.44 = 13.2$ mgd.

  e. Coincident draft plus fire flow = 15.0 + 13.2 = 28.2 mgd > (c).

  f. Provisions for breakdowns and repairs of pumps, and water purification units by installing at least one reserve unit give the following capacities:

Low-lift pumps: 2 × average daily draft = 2.0 × 10 = 20 mgd.

High-lift pumps: 3 × average daily draft = 3.0 × 10 = 30 mgd.

Filters and the like: 1.6 × average daily draft = 1.6 × 10 = 16 mgd.

The resulting capacities of the four systems shown in Figure 5-4 are summarized below that figure.

Waste-Water Flows

5-10. Sources of Flow and Averages. The flow in sewers includes one or more of the following: the spent water of the community, ground-water seepage,[18] and storm-water runoff.

  a. *Spent Water.* The spent water of the community is that portion of the public supply which is discharged into sewers from the collecting systems of all types of buildings. Water drawn from private water sources for air conditioning, industrial processes, and similar uses may also become spent water. Ordinarily, from 60 to 70% of the total water supplied becomes waste water. The balance is used up in watering lawns and gardens, flushing streets, fighting fires, generating steam, and satisfying miscellaneous household, commercial, and industrial needs. Commercial areas may be assumed to discharge about 25,000 gpd per acre. Industrial waste waters vary widely in quantity.

  b. *Ground Water.* Water enters street and building sewers from the ground through joints and manholes that are not water-tight and through cracks in the pipes. The amount of seepage depends upon the height of the ground-water table above the invert of the sewers, the permeability of the soil, and the workmanship exercised in the construction of manholes and sewers as well as their connections to buildings. Seepage rates are stated in various ways to suit the convenience of the designer. Common allowances are:

A: 500 to 5,000 gpd per acre; average 2,000.

B: 5,000 to 100,000 gpd per mile of sewer; average 30,000.

---

18 Also called infiltration but generally identified as seepage in this book.

C: 500 to 5,000 gpd per mile of sewer per inch diameter (average 2,500) plus 100 gpd per manhole.

These allowances can be explained in terms of rainfall, infiltration into the ground, and area drained. Values rise and fall with precipitation and infiltration as well as with the magnitude of the true, in contrast to the apparent, area drained. Conversion from A to B follows from the length of sewers per acre in North American communities (namely 115 ft for average development and 300 ft for full development), the diameter of the sewer (normally about 12 in.), and the spacing of manholes (generally less than 400 ft).

Example 5-4. Find A, B, and C for an annual rainfall of 48 in., one-half of which filters into the ground and eventually reaches the sewers.

$A = 48 \times \frac{1}{2} \times \frac{1}{12} \times 43{,}560 \times 7.5/365 = 1{,}800$ gpd per acre.

$B = 1{,}800 \times 5{,}280/300 = 32{,}000$ gpd per mile for full development.

For a 12-in. sewer and $5{,}280/350 = 15$ manholes per mile, $C = (32{,}000 - 15 \times 100)/12 = 2{,}500$ gpd per mile per inch diameter.

No allowance is made for seepage when sewers are provided with underdrains that have a free outlet. The amount of seepage is determined by gaging sewers in the early morning hours and making an allowance for the small quantities of spent water received at that time. The initial tightness of the system is established by gagings made before properties are connected to the sewers.

c. Storm Water. Runoff from precipitation is intended to be discharged into storm drains or combined sewers. The amounts received are large and, as previously mentioned, overshadow the flow of sanitary sewage in combined systems. Separate sanitary sewers should be free of storm water but are not. Illicit connections and manhole covers that are not tight permit entrance of some runoff. Amounts vary with the degree of enforcement of regulations and the effectiveness of countermeasures. Rates up to 70 gpcd and averaging 30 gpcd are reported.

Example 5-5. What is the degree of separation of storm water from roof leaders of houses 20 ft by 30 ft occupied by 5 persons when the rainfall intensity is 1 in. per hr and the storm-water flow in the sewers is 50 gpcd?

a. Storm runoff $= 20 \times 30 \times 1 \times 646{,}000/(43{,}560 \times 5) = 1{,}780$ gpcd (since 1 in. per hr per acre $= 1$ cfs, and 1 cfs $= 646{,}000$ gpd).

b. Per cent non-enforcement $= 100 \times 50/1{,}780 = 3\%$.

Gagings of flows in sanitary sewers will record illicit storm water as the difference between the normal dry-weather flow and the discharge immediately following intense rains.

5-11. Variations in Flow. The rate of flow in storm and combined sewers is determined by the rate of runoff from precipitation. In sanitary sewers, flow varies with water consumption, but fluctuations are smaller for the following reasons: (a) only a portion of the sewage is derived from the water supply; (b) fluctuations of this portion are damped by the seepage of a relatively steady amount of ground water; and (c) open-channel flow in sewers creates further damping effects. Rising waters are stored and falling waters are supplemented by release of stored water. The instantaneous flow at a given point, finally, is a composite of upstream waters that were discharged at time intervals increasing with the distance from the given point. The resulting *time of concentration* produces an averaging of peak discharges analogous to that associated with flood flows in rivers and storm sewers. Hence some formulations of expected variations in flow are like flood-flow formulas. The Maryland Department of Health, for example, has proposed design flows for sanitary sewers of:

$$Q = 3.2 Q_{ave}^{5/6} \qquad \text{5-11}$$

where Q is the design flow and Q_{ave} the average flow (1 to 16 mgd). For $Q_{ave} = 10$ mgd this gives a ratio of 2.2:1.

Wider variations in flow are expected, therefore, from small areas or small numbers of people than from large ones. Harmon [19] has generalized North American experience as follows:

$$Q_{max}/Q_{ave} = (18 + \sqrt{P})/(4 + \sqrt{P}) \qquad \text{5-12}$$

where Q_{max} is the maximum rate of flow of domestic sewage, Q_{ave} is the average rate of flow of domestic sewage, and P is the population in thousands. For 100,000 people, for example, the ratio is 2:1. Where ground-water seepage or the discharge of industrial wastes is considerable, the ratio must be modified to meet local conditions.

Other ratios, frequently used for the flow of domestic sewage from small areas, are:

Maximum daily flow = 2 $\times$ average daily flow.

Maximum hourly flow = 1.5 $\times$ maximum daily flow = 3 $\times$ average daily flow.

Example 5-6. Estimate the average and peak rates of flow in a district sanitary sewer serving 9,000 people in a community of 45,000 with an average water consumption of 100 gpcd and draining an area of 600 acres.

---

[19] W. G. Harmon, "Forecasting Sewage Discharge at Toledo," *Eng. News-Rec.*, *80*, 1235 (1918).

a. Spent water: $0.7 \times 100 = 70$ gpcd.

b. Maximum hour: $3 \times 70 = 210$ gpcd.

By Equation 5-12, $Q_{max} = 70[(18 + \sqrt{9})/(4 + \sqrt{9})] = 210$.

c. Proportion of total population served: $100 \times 9{,}000/45{,}000 = 20\%$.

d. Average population density: $9{,}000/600 = 15$ persons per acre.

By Equation 5-9, maximum population density:

$$D_{max} = 15 \left[\frac{2.90}{1.026^{15}} - \frac{\log 20}{(1.026^{15})^2} \right] = 15 \times 1.4_4 = 21 \text{ persons per acre}$$

e. Storm water: 30 gpcd (assumed).

f. Infiltration: 2,000 gpd per acre (assumed).

g. Average rate of flow: $21(70 + 30) + 2{,}000 = 4{,}100$ gpd per acre, if storm water is included.

h. Peak rate of flow: $21(210 + 30) + 2{,}000 = 7{,}040$ gpd per acre.

In sanitary and combined sewers, the minimum flow is fully as significant as the maximum flow, because velocities are decreased as flows drop off and the sewers may then be unable to meet their main responsibility: the removal of waste matters without nuisance due to the deposition and decomposition of suspended solids and the clogging of the system. Expressed as ratios to the average, minimum hourly flows may be expected to be about as follows:

Minimum daily flow = $\frac{2}{3} \times$ average daily flow.

Minimum hourly flow = $\frac{1}{2} \times$ minimum daily flow = $\frac{1}{3} \times$ average daily flow.

6-1. Definitions. Hydrology [1] is the science or classified body of knowledge pertaining to the properties, distribution, and behavior of water in nature. As such, it is a basic science for many branches of civil engineering, and hydrologic studies underlie the reasonable solution of problems of water supply and sewerage, drainage and irrigation, navigation and river regulation, and water power and flood control.

The study of hydrology may be divided into three branches that treat of water in its different forms of existence above, on, and below the earth's surface: (1) atmospheric water, (2) surface water, and (3) subsurface water.

a. Atmospheric Water. In its relation to the atmosphere, hydrology is concerned with rainfall and other forms of precipitation—their causes, origin, occurrence, magnitude, distribution, and variation. The study of atmospheric water is more particularly a part of the broad science of meteorology, which covers all atmospheric phenomena. The term hydrometeorology is applied to those phases of the study of water in which hydrology and meteorology overlap.

b. Surface Water. The hydrology of surface waters deals with the following: runoff as flood flow, normal flow, and dry-weather flow; storage in ponds, lakes, and reservoirs; physical features of river systems; and the origin and behavior of surface waters in general. This branch of hydrology is called hydrography and includes: (1) rheology [2]—the study of flowing waters such as brooks and rivers; (2) limnology [3]—the study of standing bodies of fresh water such as ponds, lakes, and reservoirs; and (3) oceanography—the study of the oceans. Use of the term "limnology" is often broadened to include the study of all bodies of fresh water, whether they stand or flow.

[1] From the Greek words *hydor,* water, and *logos,* science.
[2] From the Greek *rhein,* to flow; also called potamology from the Greek *potamos,* a river.
[3] From the Greek *limne,* a lake.

c. Subsurface Water. The hydrology of subsurface water, commonly called ground water, considers the origin, nature, and occurrence of subsurface water, the infiltration of water into the ground, its passage or percolation through the ground, and its seepage out of the ground.

Many parts of hydrology have no immediate application in water-supply and waste-water engineering. Most of these are omitted from this book or are touched upon only briefly in this and later chapters. The student of water-supply and waste-water engineering, however, is urged to widen his acquaintance with hydrological phenomena in order that, as an educated man, he may possess a broader background in hydrology than is required for the mere use of the tools of his profession.

6-2. Sources of Hydrological Data. In the United States, the chief sources of hydrological information bearing upon water supply are the records and publications of the Water Resources Branch of the U. S. Geological Survey.[4] In Canada the corresponding agency is the Water-Power and Reclamation Branch of the Department of the Interior. Additional important sources of hydrological data are found in the records of the Corps of Engineers, U. S. Army, the Soil Conservation Service, the Forrestry Service, and the former National Resources Planning Board. Of less direct bearing upon water supply but of importance in storm-sewerage design and the protection of water-supply and sewerage structures against floods is the work of the U. S. Weather Bureau.[5]

Besides these federal agencies, there are state, municipal, and private organizations that collect hydrological data. State agencies are gen-

[4] The U. S. Geological Survey maintains more than 6,000 stream-gaging stations and carries on special investigations of ground-water resources. The information obtained is published in *Water Supply Papers,* 1896 to date. Unpublished data may be obtained from the District Engineer's Office of the Water Resources Branch. The close to 1,200 *Water Supply Papers* are numbered consecutively. Those containing stream-flow records are published annually in twelve parts. In each annual part are printed a list of the river basins in the twelve subdivisions and a table indicating the serial number of *Water Supply Papers* that contain earlier data on the streams of the basins. Other *Water Supply Papers* record special hydrological studies.

[5] This agency maintains some ten thousand stations at which rainfall and other meteorological observations are recorded. The statistical information collected at these stations is published in *Reports of the Chief of the Weather Bureau* from 1891 to 1934, the *Meteorological Yearbook* from 1935 to 1942, the *Monthly Weather Review* since 1872, and *Climatological Data* since 1914. Certain of the "regular" Weather Bureau stations publish in addition their own more detailed reports, and access may be had to their unpublished records.

erally public works departments; conservation, water supply, water resources, irrigation, and drainage commissions; and geological, natural history, and forestry surveys. Municipal agencies are commonly the public works, water works, and sewage works departments of cities and towns. Private agencies are water-power, water-supply, drainage, and irrigation companies.

6-3. The Cycle of Water. Precipitation, percolation, runoff, and evaporation are stages in the cycle of water, which is without beginning

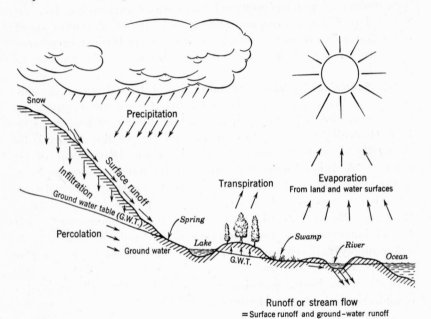

Figure 6-1. The water cycle.

or end. Of the water precipitating upon the earth, part falls directly upon water surfaces; part flows over the surface of the ground and finds its way into brooks and rivers, and into ponds, lakes, and reservoirs, or into the ocean; part is immediately returned to the atmosphere by evaporation from water surfaces, land surfaces, and vegetation; and part percolates into the ground.

Of the water that soaks into the ground, part is held by capillarity near the surface, some of it ultimately evaporating directly from the ground into the atmosphere, and some being taken up by vegetation to be returned in large measure to the atmosphere by transpiration.[6]

---

[6] Transpiration is evaporation or exhalation of water or water vapor from plant cells, such as leaf cells. It corresponds to perspiration in animals.

The remainder of the infiltering water passes through the soil until it meets and forms part of the underlying ground water. Most of the ground water is eventually discharged at the surface of the earth as springs or seepage outcrops, or passes, at or below the water line, into streams and standing bodies of water, including the oceans.

The water flowing in brooks and rivers is known as *runoff*. It is derived either directly from precipitation as surface runoff or indirectly as dry-weather flow from the lowering of lakes, ponds, and reservoirs, and from ground-water seepage.

Figure 6-1 shows diagrammatically the various phases of the cycle of water. Evaporation and precipitation are the driving forces in the cycle of water, with solar radiation as the source of energy. Runoff and percolation shift the scene of evaporation, or upward motion of water, laterally along the earth's surface. Atmospheric circulation accomplishes a similar shift for precipitation.

6-4. Precipitation. Atmospheric moisture reaches the earth's surface chiefly in the form of precipitation as rain, snow, hail, or sleet. The most important causes of precipitation are external and dynamic cooling. By dynamic cooling is meant the reduction in temperature accompanying the expansion of air when it rises or is driven to higher altitudes.

The observed decrease in temperature of the atmosphere with altitude is called the *lapse rate*. Up to 7 miles above the earth's surface (within the troposphere) in the middle latitudes, the lapse rate is normally about 3 F in 1,000 ft. However, within the first 2 or 3 miles the lapse rate is quite variable and may at times be negative. An increase in temperature with altitude (or negative lapse rate) is called an *inversion*. Rising air cools by adiabatic expansion at a rate of about 5.5 F in 1,000 ft if no precipitation of moisture occurs. When external and dynamic cooling reduce the temperature to the dew point, precipitation releases the latent heat of vaporization and retards the rate of adiabatic cooling. The *retarded* or *wet adiabatic* rate of cooling is about 3.2 F in 1,000 ft.

Air is *stable*, i.e., will not rise by convection, whenever the lapse rate is smaller than both the wet and the dry adiabatic rates. Stable air cannot rise, for, were it to do so, its temperature would be less and its density greater than that of the surrounding air at the higher altitude. If the lapse rate is greater than the dry adiabatic rate, rising air becomes warmer and thus lighter than the air surrounding its upward path. Hence it continues to rise and is *unstable*. If the lapse rate lies between the wet and dry adiabatic rates, the air will be stable if moisture is not condensing, but the air becomes unstable when precipitation begins. This situation of *conditional instability* is one of the requirements for successful rain making. In modern rain-making operations, Dry Ice or silver iodide crystals provide the nuclei that trigger precipitation and convert stable air into unstable air.

The upward movement of moist air essential to precipitation is brought about in three principal ways: (1) by convective currents which cause *convective* rainfalls; (2) by hills and mountain ranges which produce *orographic* rainfall; and (3) by cyclonic circulation which is responsible for *cyclonic* rainfall.

a. Convective Precipitation. Convective precipitation is exemplified by the so-called tropical rainstorm. In the tropics, the air near the surface of the earth is heated during the day, expands while absorbing heat, and is consequently reduced in weight. At the same time it takes up increasing quantities of water vapor which possesses a specific gravity of about 0.6 relative to dry air. This also causes the air to become lighter. When the warm, moisture-laden air becomes unstable, almost exclusively vertical currents are induced. As these progress toward higher altitudes, the air is exposed to lower temperatures and expands under reduced pressures; external and dynamic cooling take place; water vapor is condensed; and precipitation is induced.

b. Orographic Precipitation. Orographic precipitation is encountered when horizontal currents of moist air strike hills or mountain ranges that deflect the currents upwards. In North America, the rainfalls of the Pacific Northwest and the Southern Appalachian Mountains furnish examples of this type of precipitation.

Example 6-1. Air on the coast at sea level with a temperature of 60 F and a dew point of 54 F is forced over a mountain range that rises 4,000 ft above sea level. The air then descends to a plain 3,000 ft below. If the dew point falls at a rate of 1.1 F per 1,000 ft, find (a) the height at which condensation will begin; (b) the temperature at the mountain top; (c) the temperature on the plain beyond the mountain if the condensed moisture precipitates before the air starts downward.

a. If H_c is the elevation at which condensation begins and T_c and D_c are respectively the air and dew-point temperatures at this elevation, $T_c = D_c$ when condensation starts, and $T_c = 60 - 5.5 \times 10^{-3}H_c = D_c = 54 - 1.1 \times 10^{-3}H_c$. Hence $H_c = 1,360$ ft. Air cools at the dry adiabatic rate below this elevation and at the retarded adiabatic rate above it.

b. The temperature at the top of the mountain is: $60 - 1,360 \times 5.5 \times 10^{-3} - (4,000 - 1,360)3.2 \times 10^{-3} = 44$ F.

c. If the descending air warms at the dry adiabatic rate, the temperature on the plain will be: $44 + 3,000 \times 5.5 \times 10^{-3} = 60.5$ F.

c. Cyclonic Precipitation. Cyclonic precipitation is associated with the unequal heating of the earth's surface and the creation of pressure differences that cause air to flow from points of higher pressure to points of lower pressure. There are two major temperature effects: (1) the difference in temperature between the equator and the poles, which produces so-called planetary circulation; and (2) the unequal heating of land and water masses, which results in the formation of secondary areas of high and low pressure on sea or land and consequent atmospheric circulation.

The difference in relative rotary speed between the equator and the poles deflects to the east tropical air currents moving towards the poles. This is responsible for the general easterly direction of cyclonic disturbances over the North American continent as well as for the rotary or cyclonic motion of the horizontal air currents that converge at points of low pressure.

In the continuous planetary circulation of the atmosphere between the equator and the poles, warm, moisture-laden, tropical air masses travel towards the poles, are cooled, precipitate their moisture, and are ultimately transformed into cold, dry, polar air. A return movement carries heavy, polar air masses towards the equator. Heaviest precipitation takes place when tropical air masses collide with polar air masses. The light, warm, tropical air is forced up and over the colder air, cools, and precipitates its moisture. Collisions between tropical and polar air masses normally produce the protracted general rainfalls and the accompanying floods of the central and eastern United States. When, for unknown reasons, polar air does not move southward in the usual manner, serious droughts may occur.

The Bjerkness cyclone model, Figure 6-2, shows graphically the movements of warm and cold air masses in the usual type of cyclonic storm. Precipitation is indicated on the plan by shading. The cross-sections show the manner in which warm air is forced upward by the cold air masses. At the *cold front,* the colder air pushes below the mass of warm air and usually advances southward and eastward in the northern hemisphere. At the *warm front,* the warm air is forced over the retreating wedge of cold air and advances usually northward and eastward in the northern hemisphere. When there is little or no movement at the boundary of the air masses, the front is called *stationary.* When the cold front overtakes the warm front and lifts all the warmer air above the surface, the front is said to be *occluded.*

Cyclonic storms are eddies in the vast planetary circulation between the equator and the poles. They are generally several hundred miles in diameter, and their rotational and lateral motion are both relatively slow. The cyclone is a distinctly different phenomenon from the violent whirlwind of a tornado or hurricane. In the central or low-pressure portion of the cyclonic disturbance, moisture is precipitated from the rising air, while fair weather usually prevails in high-pressure areas that surround the cyclone.

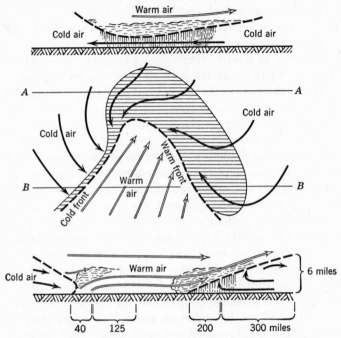

Figure 6-2. Bjerkness cyclone model. After *Engineering News-Record, 119,* 198 (1937).

The central part of the figure shows the wind distribution in the horizontal found in any well-organized disturbance. The double arrows represent warm air currents, and the single arrows cold currents. The upper portion of the figure shows a vertical section through *AA* of the central figure; the lower portion shows a vertical section through *BB*. The vertically hatched areas indicate precipitation.

The storms of most importance on the North American continent as a whole originate in the Pacific Ocean and strike the coast of the northern United States or Canada. They then swing south and east over the central or northern United States and generally escape through the St. Lawrence Valley to the Atlantic Ocean. Storms originating in the Gulf of Mexico drift northward over the continent and out to sea.

Commonly the three types of precipitation—convective, orographic, and cyclonic—do not occur independently. Most precipitation in the temperate regions of the earth is due to the combined activity of two or more causative agents. For example, the rainfall on the Pacific slopes is due to cyclonic storms that are forced upward by the Rocky Mountains; and local thunderstorms are due partly to convective and partly to cyclonic motion of the air.

About one-fourth to one-third of the water that falls on continental areas reaches the oceans as runoff. The balance is returned to the air by evaporation and transpiration. Of this vaporized water, a small part is reprecipitated, but the major part is carried away to the oceans. The streamflow from continents, therefore, represents the net water loss from the circulating air masses as they precipitate and re-evaporate moisture in their course across the continents.

6-5. Droughts. Droughts are of particular importance in water-supply engineering because they impose a critical demand upon works designed to furnish continuously an ample amount of water. Droughts are defined as periods when crops fail to mature owing to lack of precipitation, or when precipitation is insufficient to meet the needs of established human activity. Drought conditions may exist when there is a deficiency in annual rainfall, or a poor seasonal distribution of rainfall; or they may occur when the annual precipitation is concentrated into a few very heavy rainfalls that drain away rapidly.

The cause of droughts is not well understood. As mentioned earlier in this chapter, the failure of polar air masses to travel southward across the North American continent has been responsible for protracted droughts in the United States and Canada. Statistical studies of past droughts indicate that they have a strong tendency to perpetuate themselves. Many droughts are broken ultimately only by a change in the seasons.

6-6. Measurement of Precipitation. Of the many thousands of stations of the U. S. Weather Bureau, all but a few hundred are "cooperative observer" stations at which only limited records are kept. At these stations, rainfall is measured in cylindrical can gages, 2 ft high and 8 in. in diameter (see Figure 6-3). A funnel-shaped receiver concentrates the catch in a measuring tube which is so proportioned that a depth of 1 in. on a measuring stick inserted in the tube equals 0.1 in. of rainfall.

At the official Weather Bureau stations, recording gages are used. These register rainfall rates during short intervals of time, as well as daily quantities of precipitation. Rainfall rates need to be known in the design of storm sewerage systems, and continuous rainfall records are essential in forecasting flood stages on streams. The two types of continuous-recording gages shown in Figure 6-3 are in common use. They are: (1) the *tipping-bucket gage,* in which a two-compartment bucket is supported in such a way that when one compartment is filled it tips and empties while the other compartment is moved under the funnel that collects the rain; and (2) the *weighing gage,* which contains a can, supported on scales that weigh the rain

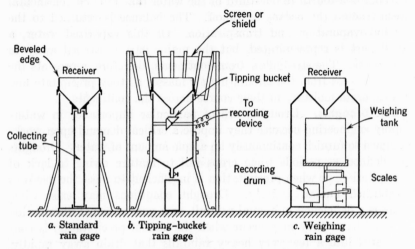

a. Standard   *b.* Tipping–bucket   *c.* Weighing
rain gage   rain gage   rain gage

Figure 6-3. Rain gages: (*a*) Standard rain gage; (*b*) Tipping-bucket gage; (*c*) Weighing gage.

collected in an exposed funnel. In both gages, the measurement is converted to movement of a pen that traces the rainfall on a clock-operated chart.

Snowfall is measured with the standard rain gage by removing the receiving funnel and using the can after the fashion of a "cookie cutter" to collect samples of snow from undrifted areas. The snow is melted by the addition of a known amount of warm water, and the quantity of precipitation is recorded in inches of water. The water equivalent of snow varies greatly. On an average 10 in. of snow equal 1 in. of water.

Since snowfall increases rapidly with elevation, the measurements of snow at ordinary rain-gaging stations, most of which are at relatively low altitudes, do not provide records from which average snowfalls in mountainous areas can be computed. Therefore, in regions where melting of the winter's accumulation of snow produces a major part of the annual runoff, or where spring thaws may cause serious floods, more accurate methods for determining the snowfall on a water shed are desirable. Two methods have been developed. The older one is to select representative sampling stations along a snow course laid out across the drainage area. An observer walks the course periodically and samples the snow blanket at each station with a hollow-tube collector. The water content of the sample is determined by weighing it or by melting the snow. In the newer methods, batteries of shielded snow gages are used. Four or five of these gages are spaced some 200 or 300 ft apart in a location that is typical of average conditions on the water shed. The water equivalent of the snowfall between periods of observation is computed from the increment in weight of the container.

The precipitation of a region is often shown by plotting the station record on a map of the region and interpolating lines of equal rainfall, called *isohyetal* lines, between stations. The United States is divided into two distinct climatological regions by the 20-in. isohyetal line which roughly follows the 100th meridian. In the humid east, rainfall is sufficient for normal agricultural and water-supply purposes. In the arid west the amount of water that can be collected and stored for use during the dry season limits the extent to which this area can be usefully developed.

Measurement of precipitation is subject to a number of errors:

1. Wind eddy currents sweep rain over the gage. All rain gages except those with the funnel set flush with the ground, therefore, catch less than the true ground-surface rainfall. Shields for standard rain gages have been devised by Hall and by Nipher. These increase the catch of rainfall almost to that obtained by setting the rim of the gage flush with the ground. However, such shields are not used as widely as they might be.

2. Obstructions such as trees, bushes, fences, and buildings interfere with accurate collections. Gages should be placed away from obstructions, preferably at a distance greater than the height of the obstructions. Gages should be located on the ground. If they are placed on the roofs of buildings, they should be situated in the center of a flat space.

3. Snow measurements, as ordinarily made, are quite inaccurate. From the standpoint of the water-supply engineer, snowfall is generally more significant than rainfall that occurs during the growing season. Where melting snow fields constitute an important source of water supply, as they do in the higher mountains, snow surveys and the use of special gages are called for.

The limitations of precipitation records must be clearly recognized. Considering the errors involved in measurement and the areal variations in precipitation (even over relatively small stretches of country), the record of a single gage is far from being representative of average conditions even for local rainfall.

6-7. Evaporation. Evaporation is the process by which water passes from the liquid or solid [7] state into the vapor state. By evaporation, water is lost from water surfaces and moist earth surfaces. This is of importance in determining the storage requirements for impounding reservoirs and in estimating the losses of water from lakes, ponds, and open reservoirs, and from swamp areas.

a. Evaporation from Water Surfaces. The factors influencing the rate of evaporation from water surfaces are: (1) vapor pressure, (2) temperature, (3) wind movements, (4) barometric pressure, and (5) water quality. Individual effects, however, are not clear cut because the factors involved are by no means independent.

1. If the difference is great between the maximum vapor pressure [8] corresponding to the temperature of the water surface and the actual pressure of aqueous vapor in the air overlying the water, evaporation will be rapid; if small, evaporation will be slow; and if negative, condensation will take place.

2. The vapor pressure of water is given in Section 17-3. Within the normal range of natural water temperatures the vapor pressure is almost doubled for every rise of 20 F. Hence temperature affects evaporation profoundly. The slow warming and cooling of deep bodies of water makes for more even evaporation.

3. If the air above a water surface is quiescent, it soon becomes saturated with moisture, and evaporation practically ceases. Within limits, wind increases evaporation by carrying away the moisture-laden air and bringing new volumes of relatively dry air into contact with the water surface.

4. Evaporation increases with decreasing pressure. Changes in altitude, however, probably exert but little effect upon evaporation because of the accompanying and counterbalancing changes in temperature. Increased rates of evaporation, if observed at high altitudes, are probably due, in large measure, to the greater wind velocities there encountered.

5. Dissolved salts decrease the rate of evaporation slightly.

Attempts have been made to formulate the factors affecting evaporation. Most of the equations developed take somewhat the following form: [9]

$$E = C(V - v)[1 + (w/K)] \qquad 6\text{-}1$$

---

[7] Passage of a substance from its solid state into its vapor state without intermediate melting is more specifically termed *sublimation.*

[8] The vapor pressure or vapor tension of water is the maximum gaseous pressure exerted at any temperature by the water vapor in contact with the water surface. The pressure of water vapor in air that is not saturated with aqueous vapor equals the vapor pressure of water at the dew-point temperature of the air, i.e., the temperature at which the air would be saturated by the moisture actually in it. In other words, vapor pressure is the partial pressure exerted by the water vapor in the air.

[9] There is a second type of equation which relates evaporation to the difference between incoming solar radiation and heat accounted for as back radiation, heat storage in the water, and heat lost in other ways.

where E is the evaporation in a given interval of time; V is the vapor pressure at the water temperature; v is the vapor pressure at the dew-point temperature of the air; w is the wind velocity; and C and K are constants.

In Meyer's formula, based upon common observations at nearby stations of the Weather Bureau, E is inches per 30-day month; V is inches of mercury of vapor pressure at the mean temperature of large or deep bodies of water or at the monthly mean air temperature for small ponds and surface moisture; v is inches of mercury of actual vapor pressure at the monthly mean air temperature and relative humidity; w is miles per hour of wind velocity about 30 ft above the general level of the surrounding country or roofs of city buildings; K has a magnitude of 10; and C has a magnitude of 15 for small, shallow ponds and for moisture on grass and leaves, and of 11 for large or deep bodies of water.

Example 6-2. Estimate the evaporation for a month during which the following averages obtain: water temperature = 60 F; maximum vapor pressure V = 0.52 in.; air temperature = 80 F; relative humidity = 40%; vapor pressure v = 1.03 × 0.40 = 0.41 in.; and wind velocity w = 8 mph.

By Equation 6-1, $E = 15(0.52 - 0.41)(1 + 0.8) = 3.0$ in.

Evaporation from surfaces of snow and ice proceeds much as it does from water surfaces. At temperatures below freezing, the wind factor seems to be particularly important.

b. Evaporation from Land Surfaces. Evaporation from land surfaces is of two types: (1) rapid evaporation from recently wetted surfaces and (2) relatively slow evaporation from moist soil.

1. Surface evaporation is the evaporation of rain water that has been caught upon the surface of vegetation or has collected as moist films, pools, or puddles upon the top of the ground, upon roofs, or upon paved surfaces. Surface evaporation, immediately following a rainstorm, approximates the rate of loss from shallow water. As the free moisture on exposed surfaces disappears, the rate of evaporation gradually drops off.

2. Soil evaporation is evaporation of water that has seeped into the soil and that is evaporated internally or drawn to the surface by capillarity and there evaporated. Soil evaporation varies greatly with the characteristics of the soil and the depth to the ground-water table. Where the water table is 3 ft or more below the surface, soil evaporation is negligible after the moisture held in the pores of the surface layers has dried out. Evaporation from cultivated soils is less than from uncultivated soils, hence the practice of loosening soils for the purpose of conserving moisture.

c. Transpiration. Transpiration is the vaporization of water from the breathing pores of leaf and other plant surfaces. The amount of water returned to the atmosphere by transpiration depends upon the nature of the vegetation, the conditions of soil moisture, and the meteorological conditions that affect evaporation. Where vegetative activity is high, transpiration losses are also high.

Much larger volumes of water are returned to the atmosphere over continents by transpiration than by evaporation. There are two reasons for this: (1) the exposed surface area of plant leaves is tremendous as compared with the ground surface and free water surfaces, and (2) plants have the ability to draw water from considerable depths within the soil and yield it to the atmosphere by transpiration.

The effect of vegetation, particularly forest cover, upon the water cycle is the subject of much argument. Such factual data as have been gathered indicate that the effects of different types of vegetal cover, such as grass, brush and forests, are much the same and that, depending upon the circumstances, the water losses to the atmosphere from barren areas may or may not be greater than losses from growth-covered areas. The beneficial effect of vegetal cover in reducing soil erosion is not necessarily related to the effect that growing plants exert upon the water cycle, and the two should not be confused.

The factors influencing transpiration and evaporation from land surfaces are so many that it is difficult to estimate, with any degree of accuracy, the amount of water returned to the air by these processes. Studies of evaporation from land surfaces and of transpiration are of interest as explaining the disposition of precipitation and the loss of subsurface water.

6-8. Measurement of Evaporation and Transpiration. Measurements of evaporation from water surfaces, a matter of importance in water-supply studies, are commonly made by exposing pans of water to the air and recording the evaporation losses by systematic observations or by means of self-registering devices. Both floating pans and land pans have been used. The standard equipment adopted by the Weather Bureau consists of a 4-ft galvanized iron pan, 10 in. in depth, exposed on an open platform of spaced 2-in. by 4-in. timbers, raised slightly above ground for circulation of air all around the pan. A stilling well and hook gage are provided and, nearby, a shelter with maximum and minimum thermometers, rain gage, and anemometer. The anemometer is exposed beside and just above the tank. An exposed land pan of this type probably does not give results as nearly correct as those that might be obtained from floating pans of larger dimensions. Typical land and floating pans are illustrated in Figure 6-4. Results are affected by the location of the pan, its area, depth, color, and material. In the greater part of the United States, the mean annual evaporation from water surfaces generally equals or exceeds the mean annual rainfall.

Transpiration and evaporation from land surfaces, called *consumptive use*, have been studied quantitatively by agriculturists. Two types of measurement have generally been made: one, in which evaporation losses are determined as the difference between the amount of rain falling on a plot of ground and the amount of water collected from underdrains in the ground; the other, in which the water level has been kept constant relative to the surface of a tank filled with

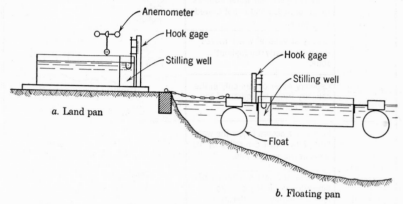

Figure 6-4. Evaporating pans.

representative soils in which representative plants are grown. If the tank has a pervious bottom, it becomes a *lysimeter*. In such a tank, consumptive use equals the difference between the amount of water falling on or applied to the surface and that draining through the bottom, adjustments being made for the changes in soil moisture content. Such data are of limited value because of the complex conditions that control the rate of plant growth in nature.

6-9. Percolation. The term percolation describes the passage of water into, through, and out of the ground. The term *infiltration* is frequently used to describe the entrance of water into the ground and its vertical movement down to the ground-water table, while the terms *percolation* or *ground-water flow* are applied to the movement of water after it has reached the water table. Water below the surface of the earth is known as subsurface water and is encountered in various conditions shown in Figures 2-4 and 6-5.

Of the different kinds of subsurface water, only ground water, i.e., water in the saturated zone, is available for the development of water supplies from subsurface sources provided that this water will flow in adequate quantities into collection works that are economically justified. The penetration of ground water into sewerage systems is an element of sewerage design. Soil water is the primary interest of the agronomist since it is available to growing plants.

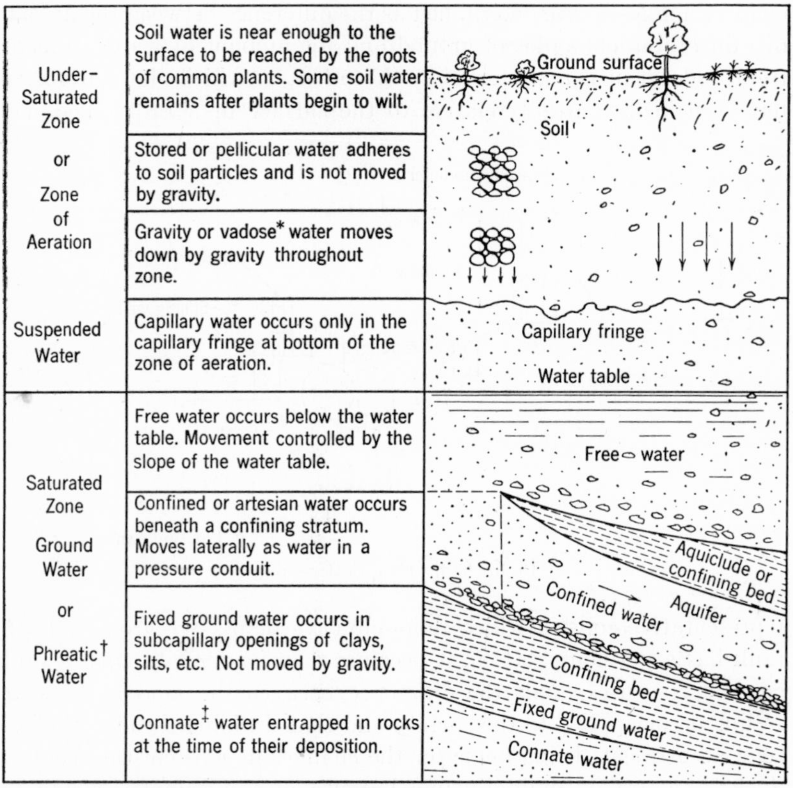
Under-Saturated Zone or Zone of Aeration
Soil water is near enough to the surface to be reached by the roots of common plants. Some soil water remains after plants begin to wilt.
Stored or pellicular water adheres to soil particles and is not moved by gravity.
Gravity or vadose* water moves down by gravity throughout zone.
Suspended Water
Capillary water occurs only in the capillary fringe at bottom of the zone of aeration.
Saturated Zone Ground Water or Phreatic† Water
Free water occurs below the water table. Movement controlled by the slope of the water table.
Confined or artesian water occurs beneath a confining stratum. Moves laterally as water in a pressure conduit.
Fixed ground water occurs in subcapillary openings of clays, silts, etc. Not moved by gravity.
Connate‡ water entrapped in rocks at the time of their deposition.
Ground surface
Soil
Capillary fringe
Water table
Free water
Aquiclude or confining bed
Confined water
Aquifer
Confining bed
Fixed ground water
Connate water

* From the Latin *vadosus* full of something going.
† From the Greek *phreas* a well. ‡ From the Latin *connatus* born together.

Figure 6-5. Occurrence and distribution of subsurface water. After C. F. Tolman, *Ground Water,* McGraw-Hill Book Co., New York, 1937.

Ground water is derived from two sources: (1) precipitation that filters into the ground, or seeps through cracks or solution passages into rock formations, and penetrates deep enough to reach the ground-water table; and (2) surface water from streams, swamps, ponds, lakes, and reservoirs that filters into the ground when the soil is permeable and the elevation of the ground-water table is lower than that of the free water surface. Where ground water is recharged by infiltration from a stream, the stream is known as an *influent* stream in contrast to the more common passage of ground water from the soil into the channel of an *effluent* stream.

The water table is the upper limit of the zone of saturation. It is overlain by the capillary fringe in which the water is held by capillary action. The depth of the fringe varies from a foot or so in sand to as much as 10 ft in clay. The capillary fringe rises and falls with the water table but lags behind to become thicker above a falling water table and thinner above a rising one. The fringe is of importance in lifting water to, or close to, the surface. It may be significant in relieving ground water of pollution that spreads out along the water table and is lifted into the fringe, where it is trapped and destroyed. When a water-bearing stratum dips below an impervious stratum, there is no water table, except immediately below the intake area where the water is still free. A piezometric surface is created instead.

The amount of rainfall that enters the ground and penetrates to the ground-water table is influenced by a great many factors, some of which are listed below, together with a statement of the ways in which they affect percolation.

1. Hydraulic permeability of the ground, as affecting the rate at which infiltration takes place and is transmitted to the ground-water table. When the ground freezes during the winter, its permeability is reduced, and this renders infiltration relatively small.

2. Turbidity of water. Suspended matter picked up by erosion in one area often tends to clog the pores of the soil in other more permeable areas where infiltration would normally occur.

3. Nature of rainfall and wetness of the soil at the time of rainfall. When a light rain falls, wetness of the soil reduces storage of water on the surface of the ground and in the root zone. Infiltration downward to the water table is increased thereby. During heavy rainfalls, the effect is the opposite: time is not sufficient for the slow process of infiltration to take effect, and a major part of the rainwater flows away over the wet ground as surface runoff. Heavy rains, furthermore, compact the soil and reduce its surface openings, and prolonged rains cause the soil to swell. This closes surface openings. Escape of displaced air from the soil also opposes entrance of water. Dry ground, on the other hand, will absorb a heavy rainfall. This water may then be released gradually to join the water table. During the summer, the ground is not only dry, but the surface is also broken by sun cracks and penetrated by biological channels. Rates of absorption are then particularly high.

4. Nature and growth of vegetation. These affect runoff and evaporation from the soil surface, and retention and use of soil water. Obviously the effects are greatest during the growing season.

5. Geology of the area. An example is the presence of lenses of impervious materials which intercept incoming water and keep it from reaching the general

ground-water table. An independent zone of saturation is thereby created. The water in this zone is called *perched* water. A second example is the presence of confining layers of impervious material. These create *artesian* water.

6. Slope of the ground. Steep slopes increase surface runoff and reduce infiltration.

The maximum depths to which subsurface water can penetrate in the earth's crust is set by the depth of porous rock. This is estimated at 2 to 8 miles. Below this depth, the pressures are so great that plastic flow closes the interstices.

6-10. Measurement of Infiltration and Ground-Water Flow. Experiments have been made to determine the amount of infiltration into various types of soil supporting different kinds of vegetation. The variables entering into the problem are so many, however, that ground-water flow and yield cannot be predicated upon observations of rainfall. Values in the vicinity of 50% of the rainfall are common. Annual percolation is best expressed in inches, just as rainfall is. The methods available for measuring infiltration and the flow of ground water are discussed in Chapter 9.

6-11. Discharge and Storage of Subsurface Water. In nature, subsurface water is discharged from the ground in two ways: (1) by hydraulic discharge through springs or seepage outcrops; and (2) by evaporative discharge from soil or through vegetation.

Hydraulic discharge takes place whenever the water table intersects the land surface. Numerous geologic and hydraulic conditions force the return of ground water in the form of springs. Important among them are: (1) the outcropping of an impervious stratum overlain by pervious soil or other water-bearing formations; (2) overflow of a subterranean basin in limestone or lava; (3) leakage from artesian systems through faults that obstruct flow; and (4) steep surface slopes that cut into the water table. Seepage into streams ordinarily occurs throughout their length in humid regions.

Evaporative discharge from soil occurs in much the same way as does evaporation from water surfaces. It is commonly confined to the belt of soil water, but it affects ground water when the capillary fringe reaches the land surface. Transpiration takes place either from the belt of soil water, or from the capillary fringe and, therefore, from ground water when the roots of plants are able to penetrate to them. Trees and so-called *phreatophytes* (deep-rooted, water-loving plants) do this. The *xerophytes* draw water only from the zone of aeration. The methods of natural discharge of subsurface water are illustrated in Figures 6-1 and 2-4. The depth of soil water that contributes to evaporation varies from a few feet in humid climates to about 20 ft in arid regions. The depth to which phreatophytes may send their roots in arid regions may be as great as 50 ft.

The difference between the ratio of recharge and discharge is reflected in the amount of water stored in the zone of saturation. During wet weather, the water table rises; during dry weather it recedes. Since the dry-weather flow of streams is supported by the discharge of ground water, good correlation often obtains between this kind of stream flow and observations of ground-water levels. Observed correlations may be applied to the prediction of ground storage.

Removal of ground water by pumping upsets the natural regimen of subsurface waters. A new balance between recharge, discharge, and storage must then be created. Lowering the water table by artificial discharge may decrease or completely stop natural discharge. At the same time, it may increase the rate of recharge to some extent. Increases occur especially in areas adjacent to surface streams. The extent to which water can be salvaged by lowering the water table through pumping may be limited by the cost of lifting water from increased depths. To keep the water table at a desired level, the average rate of withdrawal must, of course, equal the average rate of recharge under the newly established conditions.

There are, in addition to differences between rates of recharge and discharge, other influences upon the water-table level that must be understood if observed fluctuations are to be used for hydrological studies. These include: (1) differences in rate of recharge and discharge resulting from alternating wet and dry weather; (2) seasonal changes in evaporation and transpiration; (3) diurnal variations in transpiration; (4) changes in barometric pressure; (5) passage of trains or other moving loads over artesian formations; (6) land tides; (7) ocean tides; (8) earthquakes; and (9) removal of water by pumping.

The actual fluctuations registered by a continuous, level-recording gage on an observation well are seldom due to individual forces. Careful analysis of the records is essential if measured fluctuations are fully to reflect the underground hydrological cycle.

6-12. Runoff. The runoff, or stream flow, is the water that is gathered into rivulets, brooks, and rivers. The water that is derived directly from precipitation and passes over the ground into water courses is known as the *surface, storm,* or *flood runoff*. The surface runoff then consists of the precipitation less the losses from infiltration, evaporation, and the like. The water that flows in streams during dry spells, or when precipitation takes the form of snow that remains on the ground without melting, is known as the *dry-weather* *flow* or *runoff*. It is made up of surface water that is discharged gradually from lakes, ponds, swamps, and other backwaters, in which it has accumulated during wet weather, and of ground water that seeps out of the soil into stream beds when the water level of the stream drops below the level of the ground-water table. The dry-weather yield of streams from surface sources comes from *natural storage;* that from the soil, from *ground-water storage*. In some river basins with headwaters at high altitudes, the summer runoff is augmented by waters from melting snowfields. These, then, constitute an additional variety of natural storage. Unless the snow melt, or surface storage, provides water during droughts, streams lying above the ground-water table at all stages of flow are *ephemeral* (short-lived), whereas those lying above the summer ground-water level are *intermittent*.

The volume and variation of runoff are influenced chiefly by the rainfall and its distribution, by the size, shape, cover, and general topography of the catchment area, and by the nature and condition of the ground. In general, conditions that tend to produce high surface runoff—such as high rates of rainfall, steep slopes, frozen or bare and heavy soils, and lack of surface storage—are also the conditions that tend to decrease dry-weather flow.

Runoff studies form the basis for the investigation of surface-water supplies, storm and combined sewerage systems, and waste-water disposal by dilution.

6-13. Measurement of Runoff. Stream-flow data are obtained by various methods of stream gaging, based upon measurements by current meters, floats, weirs, chemical methods, and slope methods. It is not an easy matter to obtain accurate measurements of stream flow. The limitations of the various methods and the records obtained by their use must be appreciated if existing information is to be employed intelligently and to best purpose.

6-14. Use of Hydrological Records. Records of the magnitude of past hydrological phenomena, particularly records of precipitation and of the resulting stream flows and ground-water flows, provide the information without which it would be impossible to design and operate safe and economical works for the development of water supply and the drainage of communities. The collection of exact and continuous records is the primary bookkeeping of hydrology. It should be encouraged and extended at every opportunity.[10]

[10] "It must not be imagined for a single instant that these long lists of figures are dead things. In the hands of competent and original-minded engineers, they have within them as great a potency of life as the fabled dragon's teeth, and,

Although precipitation is the ultimate source of all water supplies, it must be understood at the start that studies for water supplies should be based, whenever possible, on direct measurements of water yield, such as runoff records for surface-water supplies and the results of ground-water explorations for ground-water supplies. There are certain relations between rainfall and runoff and likewise between rainfall and infiltration, but their quantitative determination remains a challenging problem in engineering. The unreliability of estimating the magnitude of the various hydrological phenomena that form the links in the chain of hydrological sequences has been pointed out repeatedly in the preceding paragraphs.

Although the engineer should not depend on rainfall records for a reliable determination of the yield of a given source of water supply, he may well consult precipitation records for the following reasons:

1. Records of precipitation extend over longer periods of time than runoff records.[11] For this reason rainfall records are of use in the business of water supply and drainage by giving a wider conception of the variations that must be expected. They give a better idea, for example, of the drought that comes but once in 100 years or of the storm that occurs but once in 20 years. They may also be studied for cycles and trends, and, if such are found, the likelihood of future cycles and trends in runoff may be inferred.

2. Records of precipitation are more numerous than runoff records. They permit studies of rainfall distribution at different elevations and at different distances from the sea coast, thereby giving us a notion, in a general way, of runoff from similar areas. Records of storm rainfall are employed in the design of sewerage systems that are to carry away the storm-water runoff of communities. Such estimates are useful, too, in the study of flood flows.

6-15. Estimating Runoff from Rainfall for Water Supply. In the past, attempts have been made to estimate runoff from rainfall in order to build up an artificial record in place of an actual one. Such trials have not been too successful. In recent years, the number of runoff records has increased greatly, so that the necessity for using rainfall records in water-supply studies is not so great as formerly.

In the absence of runoff records, some inference as to runoff condi-

when sown up and down, may chance to spring up armed men. Without them, no grasp can ever be had of the behavior of the Upper Nile and its tributaries." Wilcox and Craig, *Egyptian Irrigation,* E. & F. N. Spon, Ltd., London, 3rd ed., 1913.

[11] The longest runoff record in the United States is that of the Croton River, one of the sources of water supply of New York City, measurements being available since 1868. The longest continuous rainfall record is that of New Bedford, Mass., which has been kept since 1814.

tions may be drawn from a study of rainfall characteristics. An example follows:

If the rainfall on the Croton catchment area is 49 in. and the runoff is 23 in., while the precipitation records for a neighboring area show a rainfall of 46 in.—there being no runoff records for that area—then, if the areas have similar characteristics, it may be presumed that the runoff would be less for the neighboring area than the measured runoff for the Croton area. It must not be assumed, however, that the reduction will be the same as the reduction in rainfall. In a general way, the reduction in runoff may be expected to be 80% or 85% of the reduction in rainfall; but this cannot be expected to follow closely.

Reasoning such as this can well be applied in order to obtain a first, rough estimate of the yield of a given catchment area for which runoff records are not available; but actual measurements of runoff should be instituted at once if development of the area for water-supply purposes is seriously contemplated. Comparison can then be had between the short-term runoff observations of the area under investigation and the longer records of neighboring areas. These conversions can be made in a variety of ways. If long rainfall records are available in both watersheds, correlation of ratios of rainfall with ratios of runoff, for the period of stream flow record in both basins, provides a reasonable basis for extending the shorter record. Correlation by any method may be poor because of the variability of rainfall distribution and water-shed characteristics within each basin, as well as between them.

In general, comparative studies of hydrographs or duration curves are more reliable than studies based upon precipitation and other hydrological characteristics.

The fact that, in the United States, precipitation records are kept for the calendar year while runoff records are assembled for the water year, October 1 to September 30, should be accounted for in comparing rainfall and runoff. The U. S. water year has been adopted for runoff records because September 30 is, in a very rough and general way, the average yearly low point in the natural storage of ground-water and surface flows.

6-16. Estimating Runoff from Rainfall for Storm-Water Drainage and Flood Flows. Records of the intermittent runoff from small areas that are yet to be drained by storm sewers are not numerous. Such records, furthermore, are of little use because the velocity of flow from an area is completely changed by installation of the drainage system. Moreover, storm drains are designed for surface runoff conditions that will exist in the future when municipal development becomes complete. Continuous rainfall records are, therefore, used extensively to estimate the amount of runoff that must be carried by storm-water drainage systems.

Flows are measured in existing sewers in order to obtain information concerning actual amounts of runoff as against expected amounts. However, this information is difficult to interpret and apply to design of other sewers unless they are situated in similar, normally nearby, drainage areas.

In the study of flood flows, the engineer is interested in the unusual as well as the normal experience. In order to extend the range and number of useful observations, he must resort to all available hydrological information, especially measurements of rainfall.

6-17. The Laws of Hydrology. The object of seeking to establish the laws underlying a science is to enable the investigator to predict what will happen as well as to explain what has happened. Hydrology is a young science. Its laws have not been formulated, as have the laws of astronomy, physics, or chemistry. Further reason for this rests in the complexity of hydrologic phenomena. The driving forces and the resistances they meet are many, so many indeed that it has not yet been possible to isolate and evaluate satisfactorily even the most important of them, a step essential to the establishing of laws.

Appreciating the present status of hydrology, it is evident that exact solutions cannot be found for hydrological problems. The best we can do is to estimate future behavior on the basis of past experience. This requires familiarity with statistical methods, i.e., "methods specially adapted to the elucidation of quantitative data affected by a multiplicity of causes." [12] It is an important reason why the elements of these methods have been presented in Chapter 4.

[12] G. U. Yule and M. G. Kendall, *Theory of Statistics*, J. B. Lippincott Co., London, p. 3, 1940.

7-1. Reasons for Engineering Analysis. The designer of water-supply and waste-water disposal systems is concerned, in particular, with two types of rainfall and runoff records: (1) records of the amounts of water collected by a given water shed in fixed calendar periods, such as days, weeks, months, and years, and (2) records of the intensities and durations of rainstorms and flood flows in a given drainage area. Studies of the yield of water in different calendar periods underlie the safe and economic development of surface-water supplies by continuous draft and by storage. They cast some light, too, upon the possible production of ground water and are needed in gaging the pollutional load that can safely be imposed upon a body of water into which sewage and industrial wastes are discharged. Studies of rainfall intensities and flood runoff are the starting points for the design of storm and combined sewers and their appurtenances. They provide, too, the information needed for the proper dimensioning of spillways and diversion conduits for dams and similar structures, for the location and protection of water and waste-water works that lie in the flood plains of streams, and for the proper proportioning of works that collect rain water.

In favorable circumstances, the needed hydrological information is available to the engineer at the site of the structure he wishes to develop or protect. More often, information is either incomplete or obtainable only for points or areas some distance away. All manner of available data must then be collated in order to arrive at a reasonable estimate of the rainfall or runoff to be expected.

7-2. Annual Rainfall and Runoff. The analysis of annual rainfall and runoff records for trends and cycles, although of general interest, is seldom directly profitable in studies of water supply and sewerage. Ordinarily, available records are not sufficiently long to distinguish periodic from random variations. The analysis of arrayed observations, on the other hand, yields results that are useful in comparative hydrology.

Both rainfall and runoff form frequency distributions that are skewed to the right. Skewness is induced by the constraint imposed by a lower limit of annual rainfall or runoff. This limit is generally greater than zero but smaller than the recorded minimum. It stands to reason that there must be an upper limit as well, but its value is less circumscribed than that of the lower limit and, from the standpoint of water supply, also less important. In spite of these acknowledged facts, most records of rainfall and runoff can be generalized with fair success as arithmetically normal series and somewhat better as geometrically normal series. Reasonably accurate comparisons can be had, therefore, in terms of the arithmetic mean M and standard deviation σ or the geometric mean M_g and standard deviation σ_g. Still closer fits between observed and calculated values can be secured by including a parameter of skewness, as indicated in Section 7-8 in connection with flood flows. For ordinary purposes, however, mean annual values and coefficients of variation, $c_v = \sigma/M$, will indicate the comparative safe yields of water supplies that are developed with and without storage. Draft is then best expressed for comparative purposes in terms of the mean annual rainfall or runoff, whatever the basis of measurement happens to be.

a. Rainfall. In those portions of the North American continent in which municipal development has taken place on a significant scale, mean annual rainfalls generally exceed 10 in. They range thence to almost 80 in. For the well-watered regions, the coefficient of variation is as low as 0.1; for the arid regions it is as high as 0.5. This means that a deficiency as great as half the mean annual rainfall is expected to occur in the arid regions as often as a deficiency of only one-tenth the mean annual rainfall, or less, in the well-watered ones.[1] High values of c_v, therefore, signify reduced maintainable drafts or increased storage requirements.

Within a given region, the coefficient of variation established for different rainfall stations is substantially uniform. Excessive differences can generally be traced to improper location of gages or to false readings and therefore offer a check on the records.

b. Runoff. Losses by evaporation and transpiration, together with unrecovered infiltration, reduce the magnitude of annual runoff below that of annual rainfall. So much depends upon the seasonal distribu-

---

[1] Reference to the probability integral, Table 4-11, will show that deficiencies, or negative deviations from the mean, equal to or greater than $c_v M = \sigma$ are to be expected $50.0 - 34.7 = 15.9\%$ of the time or $1/0.159 =$ once in 6.3 years since $x/\sigma = 1.0$. These calculations, however, are only approximately true because normality is assumed where skewness exists.

tion of rainfall, however, that it is impossible to establish a direct and reliable relationship between the two. There is likewise no direct relationship between their variability. On the North American continent, the mean annual runoff from catchment areas that contribute flow to water supplies ranges from about 5 to 40 in., and the coefficients of variation lie between 0.15 and 0.75. The fact that the mean annual runoff is usually less than half the mean annual rainfall, whereas the variation in stream flow is about half again as great as the variation in precipitation, militates against the establishment of direct runoff-rainfall ratios.

Example 7-1. Analyze the 26-year record of a stream[2] in the northeastern United States and of a rain gage[2] situated in a neighboring valley and covering the identical period of observation (Table 7-1).

TABLE 7-1. Record of Annual Rainfall and Runoff (Example 7-1)

Order of occurrence	Rainfall, in.	Runoff, in.	Order of occurrence	Rainfall, in.	Runoff, in.
1	43.6	26.5	14	48.9	25.4
2	53.8	35.5	15	66.3 (max.)	39.9
3	40.6	28.3	16	42.5	23.3
4	45.3	25.5	17	47.0	26.4
5	38.9 (min.)	21.4	18	48.0	29.4
6	46.6	25.3	19	41.3	25.5
7	46.6	30.1	20	48.0	23.7
8	46.1	22.7	21	45.5	23.7
9	41.8	20.4	22	59.8	41.9 (max.)
10	51.0	27.6	23	48.7	32.9
11	47.1	27.5	24	43.3	27.7
12	49.4	21.9	25	41.8	16.5 (min.)
13	40.2	20.1	26	45.7	23.7

a. The arrayed data produce the results shown in Table 7-2.

TABLE 7-2. Statistical Parameters of Rainfall and Runoff (Example 7-1)

	Rainfall	Runoff	Runoff-rainfall ratio, %
1. Length of record, n, yr	26	26	...
2. Arithmetic mean, M, in.	46.8 ± 1.2	26.6 ± 1.1	57
3. Median, M_d, in.	46.3 ± 1.5	25.5 ± 1.4	55
4. Geometric mean, M_g, in.	46.5 $\times$ 1.02	26.1 $\times$ 1.04	56
5. Arithmetic standard deviation, σ, in.	6.0 ± 0.8	5.8 ± 0.8	97
6. Coefficient of variation, c_v, %	12.9 ± 1.8	21.8 ± 3.2	169
7. Geometric standard deviation, σ_g	1.13 $\overset{\times}{\div}$ 1.02	1.24 $\overset{\times}{\div}$ 1.03	110

[2] The Westfield Little River which supplies water to the city of Springfield, Mass., the rain gage being situated at the West Parish filtration plant. The years of record are 1906 to 1931 (Table 7-1).

To test the reliability of the different parameters, their standard deviations are appended. The chances are 68.2% (namely, 2×34.1) that the magnitudes of the individual parameters will not vary by more than the stated deviation.

b. Each year of record covers $100/26 = 3.85\%$ of the experience. The values in each array, because they are not grouped, are plotted on probability paper at $100k/(n+1) = 100k/27\%$ in Figure 7-1. This method of plotting locates

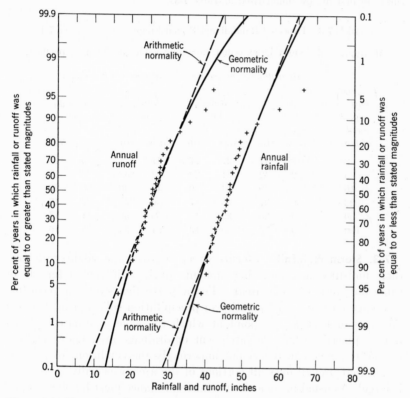

Figure 7-1. Frequency distribution of annual rainfall and runoff plotted on arithmetic-probability paper.

identical points whether the left-hand or right-hand scales of the probability paper are employed. Only an arithmetic plot is shown. On it, the arithmetically normal curve of best fit is a straight line, the geometrically normal curve a curved line. The straight line passes through the intersection of the mean with the 50% frequency and through that of $M \pm \sigma$ with the 84.1% or 15.9% value. The curve of geometric normality is traced by values read from a similar straight line of best fit passing through M_g at 50% and through $M_g \times \sigma_g$ at 84.1% and M_g/σ_g at 15.9% on logarithmic-probability paper.

c. Examination of the results and the plot (Figure 7-1) shows the following:

1. Both records are fitted approximately by an arithmetically normal distribution and somewhat better by a geometrically normal distribution.

2. A little over half the annual rainfall appears as stream flow. The range of recovery is from 39 to 70%.

3. Runoff is more variable than rainfall; about 1.7 times as much, as measured by c_v.

4. The probable lower limits of rainfall and runoff are fairly well defined by the plot, namely 30 in. for rainfall and 10 in. for runoff.

5. The magnitudes of maximum and minimum yields expected once in 2, 5, 10, 20, 50, and 100 years, i.e. 50, 20, 10, 5, 2, and 1% of the time, as read from the curves of best fit, are summarized in Table 7-3.

TABLE 7-3. Expected Rainfall and Runoff Frequencies (Example 7-1)

Maximum values may be exceeded, minimum values may not be reached.

Frequency, once in stated number of years	By arithmetic normality				By geometric normality			
	Rainfall, in.		Runoff, in.		Rainfall, in.		Runoff, in.	
	Max.	Min.	Max.	Min.	Max.	Min.	Max.	Min.
2	47	47	27	27	47	47	26	26
5	52	42	31	22	52	42	32	22
10	54	39	34	19	54	40	35	20
20	56	37	35	17	56	38	37	18
50	59	35	39	15	59	36	41	17
100	60	33	40	13	61	35	43	16

7-3. Storm Rainfall. Storms sweeping over the country deposit their moisture in fluctuating amounts during different intervals of time and over varying areas. For a particular storm, a recording rain gage measures the quantity of precipitation collected in specified intervals of time at the point at which the gage is situated. Even if it is placed within the catchment or drainage area under investigation, the gage can reflect but imperfectly the conditions of precipitation that prevail over all portions of the area, especially if the area is large. As usual in such circumstances, reliance must be placed upon the statistical averaging of experience to offset individual departures from the norm. Given the records of one or more recording rain gages within or reasonably near the area studied, it is found that rainfall varies in intensity (1) during the course or duration of individual storms; (2) throughout the area covered by individual storms; and (3) from storm to storm. These variations establish respectively: (1) the time-intensity, or intensity-duration relationship of individual storms; (2) the areal distribution of individual storms; and (3) the frequency of storms of specified intensity and duration.

7-4. Intensity of Storms. The intensity, or rate, of rainfall is conveniently expressed in inches per hour; and it happens that an inch of water distributed over an acre in an hour equals closely a cubic foot per second. The most intense rainfall frequently occurs near the beginning of the storm; but it may be experienced at any time during the progress of the storm. By convention, the storm intensity is expressed as the arithmetic mean rate of precipitation during a specified period. This makes it a progressive mean covering increasing periods of time. The intensity is highest for short periods and declines steadily with the length of the period to which the mean is applied. Analysis of time-intensity relationships is illustrated in Example 7-2.

Example 7-2. Given a rain-gage record for successive periods of a storm,[3] find the arithmetic mean rate, or intensity, of precipitation for various durations. The gage record is shown in Columns 1 and 2 of Table 7-4. The necessary calculations are added in Columns 3 to 7. It should be noted that Columns 5 to 7 are independent of the preceding Columns.

TABLE 7-4. Time and Intensity of a Storm Rainfall (Example 7-2)

Rain-gage record				Time-intensity relationship		
Time from beginning of storm min (1)	Cumulative rainfall, in. (2)	Time interval, min (3)	Rainfall during interval, in. (4)	Duration of rainfall, min (5)	Maximum total rainfall, in. (6)	Arithmetic mean intensity, in. per hr (7)
5	0.31	5	0.31	5	0.54	6.48
10	0.62	5	0.31	10	1.07	6.42
15	0.88	5	0.26	15	1.54	6.16
20	1.35	5	0.47	20	1.82	5.46
25	1.63	5	0.28	30	2.55	5.10
30	2.10	5	0.47	45	3.40	4.53
35	2.64	5	0.54	60	3.83	3.83
40	3.17	5	0.53	80	4.15	3.11
45	3.40	5	0.23	100	4.41	2.65
50	3.66	5	0.26	120	4.59	2.30
60	3.83	10	0.17	Column 6 records maximum rainfall in stated consecutive periods. The magnitudes are obtained from Column 4 by finding the value, or combination of consecutive values, that produces the largest rainfall for the indicated period. Column 7 = Column 6 × 60/Column 5.		
80	4.15	20	0.32			
100	4.41	20	0.26			
120	4.59	20	0.18			

In this example the maximum rate of rainfall was experienced during the 5-min interval between the 30th and 35th minute.

---

[3] Storm of October 27-28, 1908, at Jupiter, Fla.

7-5. Frequency of Intense Storms. The greater the intensity of storms, the rarer is their occurrence or the smaller their frequency. Roughly, the highest intensity of specified duration that is reported in a station record of n years has a frequency of once in n years and is called the n-year storm. The next highest value has a frequency of twice in n years or once in $n/2$ years and is called the $n/2$-year storm.

This approach, however, does not allow for chance variations in the observed magnitudes. If m equally reliable records of n years were available, the value of the average largest magnitude would be the median of the m largest observed magnitudes in each record of n years. Reasoning in this way leads to the conclusion that the highest intensity associated with a given duration in a single record of n years will probably be exceeded as an average only once in $n/(1 - 0.5) = 2n$ years and the next highest intensity once in $n/(2 - 0.5) = 0.67n$ years. In general terms, therefore, the observation of kth largest magnitude in an array is likely to be reached or exceeded but once in $n/(k - 0.5)$ years. Here k is the number of observations which reach or exceed that magnitude in the arrayed record. This method of calculating frequencies is statistically logical; but the results obtained are less conservative than when n is divided by k as in the first-described approach. The second method is identical with that given in Section 7-8 for calculating average recurrence intervals for floods (Equation 7-8). Use of a third method has been suggested in Section 2 of this chapter. In accordance with it, the frequency of occurrence of the kth magnitude is calculated to be once in $(n + 1)/k$ intervals of time.

By pooling all observations irrespective of their association with individual storm records, a generalized intensity-duration-frequency relationship is obtained. Some effort can be saved in the preparation of records of storm rainfall for analysis if, at the outset, storms of low intensity are eliminated from consideration. The following empirical relationships are useful in indicating the lower limits of the intensities that should ordinarily be included in the analysis of North American station records:

$$i = 0.6 + 12/t \qquad \text{for the northern United States} \qquad 7\text{-}1$$

$$i = 1.2 + 18/t \qquad \text{for the southern United States} \qquad 7\text{-}2$$

Here i is the intensity of rainfall in inches per hour and t is its duration in minutes. For a duration of 10 min, for example, intensities below 3 in. per hr in the southern states need not receive attention. The storm recorded in Example 7-2 exhibits double this intensity.

There are many different patterns of storm-rainfall analysis. All procedures start, however, from a summary of experience such as that shown in Example 7-3. The data included in such a summary may then be used directly, or after smoothing (generally graphical) operations that generalize the experience. The developed intensity-duration-frequency relationships may be expressed in tabular or graphical form or as equations.

Example 7-3. The number of storms of varying intensity and duration recorded by a rain gage [4] in 45 years are listed in Table 7-5. Determine the time-intensity values for the 5-year storm.

TABLE 7-5. Record of Intense Rainfalls (Example 7-3)

Duration, min	Number of storms of stated intensity (inches per hour) or more												
	1.0	1.25	1.5	1.75	2.0	2.5	3.0	4.0	5.0	6.0	7.0	8.0	9.0
5							123	47	22	14	4	2	1
10					122	78	48	15	7	4	2	1	
15				100	83	46	21	10	3	2	1	1	
20			98	64	44	18	13	5	2	2			
30	99	72	51	30	21	8	6	3	2				
40	69	50	27	14	11	5	3	1					
50	52	28	17	10	8	4	3						
60	41	19	14	6	4	4	2						
80	18	13	4	2	2	1							
100	13	4	1	1									
120	8	2											

If it is assumed that the 5-year storm is equaled or exceeded in intensity $45/5 = 9$ times in 45 years; the generalized time-intensity values may be interpolated from the summary by finding (a) for each specified intensity the duration that is equaled or exceeded by 9 storms and (b) for each specified duration the intensity that is equaled or exceeded by 9 storms. Interpolation proceeds along the broken diagonal line both vertically and horizontally with the results shown in Table 7-6. These values are plotted in Figure 7-2. A smooth curve drawn

TABLE 7-6. Calculation of Storm Frequencies (Example 7-3)

a. Duration, min	5	10	15	20	30	40	50	60	80	100
a. Intensity, in. per hr	6.50	4.75	4.14	3.50	2.46	2.17	1.88	1.66	1.36	1.11
b. Intensity, in. per hr	1.0	1.25	1.5	1.75	2.0	2.5	3.0	4.0	5.0	6.0
b. Duration, min	116.0	89.9	70.0	52.5	46.7	29.0	25.7	16.0	9.3	7.5

through them traces the course of the 5-year storm rainfall. Similar calculations for the 1-, 2-, and 10-year rainfalls yield the remaining members of the family of curves included in Figure 7-2.

----

[4] Record for New York City from 1869 to 1913.

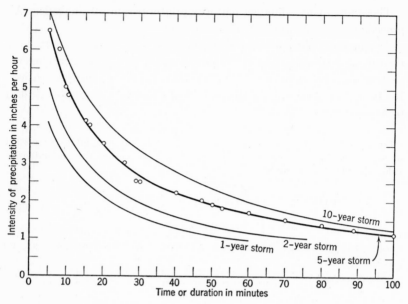

Figure 7-2. Intensity-duration-frequency of intense rainfalls.

7-6. Formulation of Intensity-Duration-Frequency Relationships.

Time-intensity curves like those in Figure 7-2 for different frequencies of occurrence are immediately useful in the design of storm-drainage or collection systems and in flood-flow analysis. Instead of preserving and communicating them as graphical records, the curves can be formulated (1) in individual equations that express the time-intensity relationships for specific frequencies only or (2) in a single equation that generalizes the intensity-duration-frequency relationships as a whole.

Good fits to observed data are usually obtained by an equation of the form

$$i = cT^m/(t + d)^n \qquad\qquad 7\text{-}3$$

where i is the intensity in inches per hour, t is the duration in minutes, T is the frequency of occurrence in years, and c, d, m, and n are co-efficients and exponents varying regionally in magnitude according to prevailing hydrological conditions. The order of magnitude of the coefficients and exponents is about as follows in North American experience: $c = 5$ to 50; $d = 0$ to 30; $m = 0.1$ to 0.5; and $n = 0.4$ to 1.0.

The problem of fitting Equation 7-3 to a station record can be tackled in a number of different ways, either graphically or by least-squares treatment. For storms of specified frequency, Equation 7-3 reduces to $i = A(t + d)^{-n}$, where $A = cT^m$.

a. *Graphical Fitting.* Since the equation $i = A(t + d)^{-n}$ may be transformed to read: $[\log i] = \log A - n[\log (t + d)]$, a direct plotting of i against t on log-log paper for the various frequencies produces curves that can be converted into straight lines through the addition of trial values of d to the observed values of t. A single value of d must be found that will place the resultant values of $(t + d)$ along a family of straight lines having the same slope for all frequencies. This slope establishes the value of n. Values of A can then be calculated, or they can be read as ordinates at $(t + d) = 1$ if this point appears on the plot. To determine c and m, the derived values of A are plotted on log-log paper against T for the frequencies studied. Since $[\log A] = \log c + m[\log T]$, the slope of the resulting straight line of best fit gives the values of m, and the value of c is read on the ordinate at $T = 1$.

b. *Least-Squares, or Graphical, Fitting.* For least-squares fitting, the equation $A = cT^m$ presents no difficulty when it is written in straight-line form. A fitting, either least-squares or graphical, of the equation $i = A(t + d)^{-n}$ is somewhat more taxing.

The straight-line form of this equation is

$$[\log (-di/dt)] = \log n - (1/n) \log A + (1 + 1/n)[\log i] \qquad 7\text{-}4$$

If the storm intensities are recorded at uniform intervals of time, the slopes $(-di/dt)$ of the intensity-duration curves at i_{k+1} are closely approximated by the relation

$$-di/dt = (i_k - i_{k+2})/(t_{k+2} - t_k) \qquad 7\text{-}5$$

where the subscripts k, $k + 1$, and $k + 2$ denote the sequence of the pairs of observations in the series. It is common experience that a better fit is obtained if the data below 60 min are separated for analysis from the data for longer durations. Example 7-4 is therefore restricted to this maximum duration.

Example 7-4. Fit Equation 7-3, $i = cT^m/(t + d)^n$, to the 60-min record of intense rainfalls presented in Example 7-3.

a. Find the coordinates of the straight-line plot in terms of Equation 7-4,

$$[\log (-di/dt)] = \log n - (1/n) \log A + (1 + 1/n)[\log i]$$

as shown in Table 7-7.

TABLE 7-7.　Calculations for Example 7-4.　First Step

Duration, t min	Intensity of rainfall, i, in. per hr For storms of stated frequency				Slope $(-di/dt) = (i_k - i_{k+2})/(t_{k+2} - t_k)$ For storms of stated frequency			
	1-yr	2-yr	5-yr	10-yr	1-yr	2-yr	5-yr	10-yr
10	3.09	3.77	4.75	5.83				
20	1.99	2.41	3.50	4.17	0.076	0.0905	0.1145	0.1167
30	1.57	1.96	2.46	3.50	0.0345	0.0410	0.0665	0.0770
40	1.30	1.59	2.17	2.63	0.0250	0.0290	0.0290	0.0503
50	1.07	1.38	1.88	2.44	0.0180	0.0190	0.0251	0.0345
60	0.94	1.21	1.66	1.94				

b. Plot these values on double log paper as shown in Figure 7-3. The points are seen to approximate straight lines of equal slope. These may be drawn in

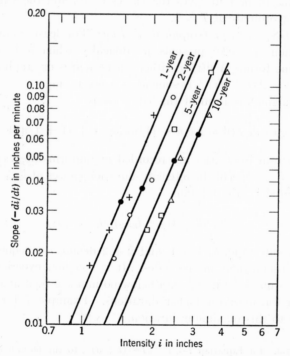

Figure 7-3.　Straight-line plot of $-di/dt$ against i to establish the constants of the equation $[\log (-di/dt)] = \log n - (1/n) \log A + (1 + 1/n) [\log i]$.

by eye or calculated by least squares. In both methods the lines should pass through the geometric means M_y and M_x of the ordinates and abscissas respectively. These are calculated in Table 7-8.

TABLE 7-8. Calculations for Example 7-4. Second Step

	$y = \log(-di/dt)$				$x = \log i$		
1-yr	2-yr	5-yr	10-yr	1-yr	2-yr	5-yr	10-yr
−1.1192	−1.0434	−0.9412	−0.9329	0.2989	0.3820	0.5441	0.6201
−1.4622	−1.3872	−1.1772	−1.1135	0.1959	0.2923	0.3909	0.5441
−1.6021	−1.5376	−1.5376	−1.2984	0.1139	0.2014	0.3365	0.4200
−1.7447	−1.7212	−1.6003	−1.4622	0.0294	0.1399	0.2742	0.3874

Sums	−5.9282	−5.6894	−5.2563	−4.8070	0.6381	1.0156	1.5457	1.9716
Means	−1.4821	−1.4224	−1.3141	−1.2018	0.1595	0.2539	0.3864	0.4929
Antilogs	0.0330	0.0378	0.0485	0.0628	1.44	1.79	2.43	3.11

The antilogs are the geometric mean slopes (M_x) and intensities (M_y).

c. To find the straight lines of best fit by least squares, calculate Σx^2 and Σxy (Table 7-9).

TABLE 7-9. Calculations for Example 7-4. Third Step

	$x^2 = \log^2 i$				$xy = \log i \log(-di/dt)$		
1-yr	2-yr	5-yr	10-yr	1-yr	2-yr	5-yr	10-yr
0.08934	0.14592	0.29604	0.38452	−0.3345	−0.3986	−0.5121	−0.5785
0.03838	0.08543	0.15280	0.29604	−0.2864	−0.4055	−0.4602	−0.6058
0.01297	0.04056	0.11323	0.17640	−0.1825	−0.3097	−0.5174	−0.5453
0.00086	0.01957	0.07519	0.15008	−0.0513	−0.2408	−0.4388	−0.5665

Sums	0.14155	0.29148	0.63726	1.00704	−0.8547	−1.3546	−1.9285	−2.2961
Means	0.03539	0.07287	0.15932	0.25176	−0.2137	−0.3387	−0.4821	−0.5740

The normal equations take the form

I. $n'a + b\Sigma x - \Sigma y = 0$.

II. $a\Sigma x + b\Sigma x^2 - \Sigma xy = 0$, where $a = (\log n) - (1/n)(\log A)$, and $b = (1 + 1/n)$.

Solution of the four pairs of normal equations gives the following results:

1-year	$0.0624b = 0.1423$	or	$n = 0.781$
2-year	$0.0331b = 0.0884$	or	$n = 0.599$
5-year	$0.0259b = 0.0664$	or	$n = 0.639$
10-year	$0.0179b = 0.0373$	or	$n = 0.923$

It is seen that the values for n vary from 0.60 to 0.92.

Since n is to be the same for the four frequencies, find its best value by averaging the solutions for b and n to obtain $0.1393b = 0.3344$, or $b = 2.399$ and $n = 0.714$. We have now progressed to a point where we can write Equation 7-3 as $i = A/(t + d)^{0.714}$ and must still find the values of A and d.

d. The straight lines of slope b must pass through the intersections of the geometric means M_y and M_x of log $(-di/dt)$ and log i respectively. The intercept $a = (\log n)$ − $(1/n)(\log A)$, or the ordinate at $i = 1.0$ (or log $i = 0$), is thereby determined for each frequency. With n fixed, the value of a is given by the slope

$$\tan \alpha = b = (\log M_y - a)/(\log M_x - \log 1.0)$$

whence

$$a = \log M_y - b \log M_x.$$

e. Calculate a for each frequency

1-year	$a = -1.4821 - 2.399 \times 0.1595 = -1.8647$
2-year	$a = -1.4224 - 2.399 \times 0.2539 = -2.0315$
5-year	$a = -1.3141 - 2.399 \times 0.3864 = -2.2411$
10-year	$a = -1.2018 - 2.399 \times 0.4929 = -2.3843$

f. Determine the values of A from the relation $a = \log n - (1/n)(\log A)$ as

$$\log A = n(\log n - a)$$

1-year	$\log A = 0.714(-0.1463 + 1.8647) = 1.2269$	or	$A = 16.9$
2-year	$\log A = 0.714(-0.1463 + 2.0315) = 1.3460$	or	$A = 22.2$
5-year	$\log A = 0.714(-0.1463 + 2.2411) = 1.4957$	or	$A = 31.3$
10-year	$\log A = 0.714(-0.1463 + 2.3843) = 1.5979$	or	$A = 39.6$

g. Find the values of c and m in the relation $A = cT^m$ or $\log A = \log c + m \log T$ by least squares (Table 7-10). Plot this relation on double log paper as shown in Figure 7-4.

TABLE 7-10.   Calculations for Example 7-4.   Last Step

T	$\log T$	A	$\log A$	$\log^2 T$	$\log T \log A$	Calculated A
1	0.0000	16.9	1.2269	0.0000	0.0000	17.0
2	0.3010	22.2	1.3460	0.0906	0.4051	22.0
5	0.6990	31.3	1.4957	0.4886	1.0455	30.9
10	1.0000	39.6	1.5979	1.0000	1.5979	40.0
Sums	2.0000	110.0	5.6665	1.5792	3.0485	
Means	0.5000	27.5	1.4166	0.3948	0.7621	

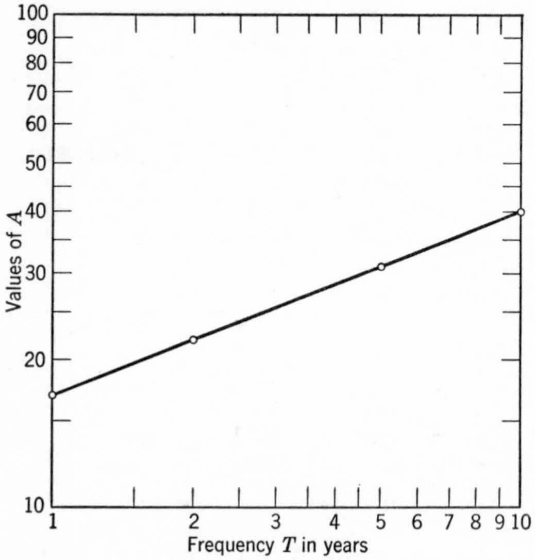

Figure 7-4.   Straight-line plot of A against T to establish the constants of the equation $A = cT^m$.

The normal equations for the straight line of best fit are:

I. $a' + 0.5000b' - 1.4166 = 0$.
II. $0.5000a' + 0.3948b' - 0.7621 = 0$. Whence

$$b' = 0.3716 = m \qquad a' = 1.2308 = \log c \qquad \text{and} \qquad c = 17.0$$

We can now write Equation 7-3 as $i = 17.0T^{0.372}/(t + d)^{0.714}$ and must still find the value of d.

h. From the relation $i = A(t + d)^{-n}$ determine the best value of d. In straight-line form this relation is $(A/i)^{1/n} = d + t$. The slope of the line, or coefficient of t, is fixed at 1.0, and the line must pass through the intersection of the means M_y and M_x of the coordinates $y = (A/i)^{1/n}$ and $x = t$ respectively. Since $\tan \alpha = 1.0 = (M_y - d)/(M_x - 0)$, $d = M_y - M_x$.

The values of i and t are taken from (a) as observed magnitudes. The values of n and A are taken as fitted magnitudes from (c) and (g). Values of $(A/i)^{1/n} = (A/i)^{1.40}$ calculated on this basis, and specified values of t, are shown in Table 7-11. Hence $d = M_y - M_x = 36.0 - 35.0 = 1.0$.

TABLE 7-11. Observed and Calculated Values of Rainfall Intensity (Example 7-4)

	Observed	Calculated		Calculated
$x = t$	i	A	$y = (A/i)^{1.40}$	i
10	3.09	17.0	10.9	3.1
10	3.77	22.0	11.8	4.0
10	4.75	30.9	13.7	5.6
10	5.83	40.0	14.8	7.2
20	1.99	17.0	20.2	1.9
20	2.41	22.0	22.2	2.5
20	3.50	30.9	21.2	3.5
20	4.17	40.0	23.7	4.5
30	1.57	17.0	28.2	1.5
30	1.96	22.0	29.5	1.9
30	2.46	30.9	34.6	2.7
30	3.50	40.0	30.2	3.4
40	1.30	17.0	36.5	1.2
40	1.59	22.0	39.5	1.5
40	2.17	30.9	41.2	2.2
40	2.63	40.0	45.3	2.8
50	1.07	17.0	47.9	1.0
50	1.38	22.0	48.0	1.3
50	1.88	30.9	50.3	1.9
50	2.44	40.0	50.0	2.4
60	0.94	17.0	57.4	0.9
60	1.21	22.0	58.2	1.2
60	1.66	30.9	60.0	1.6
60	1.94	40.0	69.2	2.1
Sums 840	....	....	864.5	...
Means 35.0	....	....	36.0	...

Substitution of the calculated values of c, d, m, and n in Equation 7-3 gives the solution of the problem as $i = 17.0T^{0.372}/(t + 1)^{0.714}$.

To show the goodness of fit, values of i calculated by means of this equation are included in Table 7-11.

7-7. Storm Runoff or Flood Flows. The flood waters that descend the water courses of a drainage basin or that are collected by the storm drains or combined sewers of a municipal drainage district are derived from the rains that fall upon the tributary water shed. In their partial conversion to runoff, however, storm rainfalls are modified by many influences. These must be clearly recognized in the interpretation of flood experience and especially in attempts to derive runoff from rainfall or to compare returns from different areas. It should be noted that, hydrologically, there is no difference between the flood flows of a stream and the rates of discharge of a system of storm sewers. The two terms are, therefore, used more or less interchangeably in this chapter.

As previously stated, the highest rates of discharge ordinarily prevail at a specified point in the drainage system by the time storm runoff begins to reach it from the entire tributary area. This time is called the *time of concentration*. Since rainfall decreases in intensity with duration, the shorter the time of concentration the higher is the rate of discharge per unit area. The time is shortest for small, broad, steep areas with rapidly shedding surfaces. It is increased by dry soil, surface inequalities or indentations, vegetal cover, and storage in water courses and adjacent areas.

The volume of runoff associated with a given storm is reduced by infiltration, freezing, and storage. It is increased by thawing of ice and snow, and by the release of water from storage on purpose, or as the result of the failure of dams or the collapse of log, ice, or debris jams. Velocity and direction of storms affect the rate of discharge appreciably. Maximum rates obtain when storms move down stream at velocities that will carry them to the point of discharge in about the time of concentration. The runoff resulting from the most intense rainfall will then reach the point of discharge from all parts of the water shed at nearly the same instant to produce the maximum possible flood crest.

Many ways have been devised for estimating the storm runoff, or flood flow, that is to be provided for in engineering designs. They may be classified as follows:

1. Statistical analyses based upon observed records of adequate length. Obviously these present the most direct answer. Unfortunately the records available for analysis seldom permit the determination of critical magnitudes by generaliza-

tion within the actual experience. Resort must then be had to extrapolation, a practice always fraught with danger. The record of one or more adjacent, similar basins may serve in the absence of a record for the basin itself.

2. "Rational" estimates relating runoff to rainfall; as far as possible, with the benefit of at least brief records of actual runoff measurements. This is the preferred procedure in calculating runoff from sewered areas that are to be developed as part of a municipal drainage scheme.

3. Calculations based upon empirical formulations that are applicable to existing water-shed conditions. These formulations are varied in structure and must be selected with full appreciation of the limitations of their derivation. At best, they should be applied as checks of statistical or rational methods.

For the protection of large engineering structures, the failure of which will entail great damage or loss of life, every bit of available hydrological information should be adduced to arrive at economical but safe design values. In this connection, hydraulic models of the water shed may be studied to good purpose.

7-8. Statistical Analysis of Runoff Records. Records of maximum daily, weekly, monthly, or annual runoff form frequency distributions that are skewed to the right. They can be generalized roughly as geometrically normal series but are fitted better by equations containing a larger number of coefficients. Type III in the Pearsonian family of frequency curves has been used to good advantage in hydrological studies and may serve as an example. The equation of this curve is

$$y = y_0 e^{-\gamma(x+d)} \left(1 + \frac{x + d}{a} \right)^{\gamma a} \qquad 7\text{-}6$$

This curve has a lower limit at $x + d = -a$ $(y = 0)$ but no upper limit. For the origin at the mean see sketch in Table 7-12. The notation is as follows:

y = the ordinate or frequency of runoff of specified magnitude.
x = the abscissa or deviation in magnitude of runoff from the mean runoff.
y_0 = the modal ordinate or frequency of the modal runoff.
e = the Napierian base of logarithms.
a = the deviation of the lower limit from the mode.
d = the difference between the mode and the mean magnitude.
γ = a measure of both variability and skewness.

The fitting of Equation 7-6 to flood flows involves the determination of the coefficients a, d, and γ. It can be accomplished by direct mathematical methods. Calculations are greatly simplified, however, by the use of a table of areas which is similar in concept to that developed for the normal frequency curve.[5] Such a table must include measures

[5] Table 4-11.

TABLE 7-12. Short Table of Areas of Pearson's Type III Skew Frequency Curve

Values of $x/\sigma = (X - M)/\sigma$ for stated values of $100A/n$ from the lower limit for stated skewness $d/\sigma = (M - M_0)/\sigma$

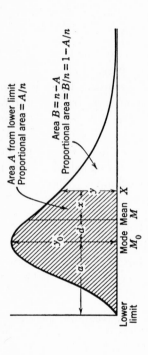

Deviation $x/\sigma = (X - M)/\sigma$ for stated skewness $d/\sigma = (M - M_0)/\sigma$

Values of $100A/n$ from the lower limit	0.0	0.1	0.2	0.3	0.4	0.5	0.6	0.7	0.8	0.9	1.0	1.2	1.4
0.01	−3.73	−3.32	−2.92	−2.53	−2.18	−1.88	−1.63	−1.42	−1.25	−1.11	−1.00	......	......
0.1	−3.09	−2.81	−2.54	−2.28	−2.03	−1.80	−1.59	−1.40	−1.24	−1.11	−1.00	......	......
1.0	−2.33	−2.18	−2.03	−1.88	−1.74	−1.59	−1.45	−1.32	−1.19	−1.08	−0.99	−0.83	−0.71
5	−1.65	−1.58	−1.51	−1.45	−1.38	−1.31	−1.25	−1.18	−1.11	−1.04	−0.97	−0.82	−0.71
10	−1.28	−1.25	−1.22	−1.19	−1.16	−1.12	−1.08	−1.05	−1.00	−0.95	−0.90	−0.79	−0.70
20	−0.84	−0.85	−0.85	−0.86	−0.86	−0.86	−0.85	−0.84	−0.82	−0.80	−0.78	−0.71	−0.65
50	−0.00	−0.03	−0.06	−0.09	−0.13	−0.16	−0.19	−0.22	−0.25	−0.28	−0.30	−0.35	−0.38
80	+0.84	+0.83	+0.82	+0.80	+0.78	+0.76	+0.74	+0.71	+0.68	+0.64	+0.61	+0.54	+0.47
90	+1.28	+1.30	+1.32	+1.33	+1.34	+1.34	+1.35	+1.34	+1.33	+1.32	+1.30	+1.25	+1.20
95	+1.65	+1.69	+1.74	+1.79	+1.83	+1.87	+1.90	+1.93	+1.96	+1.98	+2.00	+2.01	+2.02
99	+2.33	+2.48	+2.62	+2.77	+2.90	+3.03	+3.15	+3.28	+3.40	+3.50	+3.60	+3.78	+3.95
99.9	+3.09	+3.38	+3.67	+3.96	+4.25	+4.54	+4.82	+5.11	+5.39	+5.66	+5.91	+6.47	+6.99
99.99	+3.73	+4.16	+4.60	+5.04	+5.48	+5.92	+6.37	+6.82	+7.28	+7.75	+8.21	......	......
99.999	+4.27	+4.84	+5.42	+6.01	+6.61	+7.22	+7.85	+8.50	+9.17	+9.84	+10.51	......	......
99.9999	+4.76	+5.48	+6.24	+7.02	+7.82	+8.63	+9.45	+10.28	+11.12	+11.96	+12.81	......	......

of skewness as well as variability and so becomes somewhat more extensive than it is for the special case of normality, i.e. skewness equals zero. Table 7-12 is a short table of areas based upon Foster's calculations.[6] By Pearson's definition [7] skewness equals $(M - M_o)/\sigma$. For Type III curve,

$$\frac{M - M_o}{\sigma} = \frac{\Sigma x^3}{2\sigma\Sigma x^2} = \frac{d}{\sigma} \qquad 7\text{-}7$$

where M is the arithmetic mean, M_o is the mode, σ is the standard deviation $\sqrt{x^2/(n-1)}$, x is the deviation from the mean, d is $M - M_o$ (see sketch in Table 7-12), and n is the number of observations in the series. Finding the skewness for Pearson's Type III curve involves, therefore, calculation of Σx^3 as well as Σx^2. The reliability of the parameter of skewness, like that of other statistical parameters, is a function of the number of observations. The numerical value of skewness is affected, in addition, in its own magnitude by the number of observations. Hazen [8] has suggested that this be taken into account in the analysis of runoff records by multiplying the calculated skewness by the factor $(1 + 8.5/n)$. The calculations necessary to fit Type III curve to observed flood flows are illustrated in Example 7-5.

Example 7-5. Given the 20-year record of flood runoff of a stream draining 48.5 square miles of hilly country in the northeastern United States,[9] plot Pearson's Type III curve of best fit and determine the magnitude of the flood that is expected to be equaled or exceeded once in 50, 100, 200, and 1,000 years.

a. The observed flood flows are recorded in Table 7-13 together with the calculations necessary to determine the arithmetic mean M, the standard deviation σ, and the skewness d/σ.

Number of observations $n = 20$; arithmetic mean $M = 910/20 = 45.5$; variation $\sigma = \sqrt{\Sigma x^2/(n-1)} = \sqrt{12,676/19} = 25.9$; coefficient of variation $c_v = 25.9/45.5 = 0.57$; skewness $\dfrac{d}{\sigma} = \dfrac{\Sigma x^3}{2\sigma\Sigma x^2} = \dfrac{551,400}{2 \times 25.9 \times 12,700} = 0.838$; adjusted skewness $(d'/\sigma) = 0.838\,(1 + 8.5/20) = 1.20$.

It should be noted that the coefficient of variation of the flood flows is more than twice as large as the coefficient of variation in annual flows (see Section 7-2).

---

[6] H. A. Foster, "Theoretical Frequency Curves," *Trans. Am. Soc. Civil Engrs.*, *87*, 142 (1924).

[7] The Pearsonian definition of skewness is used here rather than that of Hazen, who defines the coefficient of skewness as twice the Pearsonian skewness for Type III curve.

[8] Allen Hazen, *Flood Flows*, John Wiley & Sons, New York, 1930.

[9] The Westfield Little River in Massachusetts for the years from 1910 to 1929.

TABLE 7-13. Observed Flood Flows and Calculation of Statistical Parameters (Example 7-5)

Maximum annual flood flow csm (1)	Deviation from mean x (2)	x^2 (3)	x^3 (4)	Per cent of years flood is not exceeded (5)
17	−28.5	812	− 23,100	4.8
18	−27.5	756	− 20,800	9.5
24	−21.5	462	− 9,900	14.3
24	−21.5	462	− 9,900	19.0
31	−14.5	210	− 3,000	23.8
31	−14.5	210	− 3,000	28.6
34	−11.5	132	− 1,500	33.3
35	−10.5	110	− 1,200	38.1
36	− 9.5	90	− 900	42.8
36	− 9.5	90	− 900	47.6
38	− 7.5	56	− 400	52.4
43	− 2.5	6	0	57.2
46	+ 0.5	0	0	61.9
47	+ 1.5	2	0	66.7
51	+ 5.5	30	+ 200	71.5
59	+13.5	182	+ 2,500	76.3
60	+14.5	210	+ 3,000	81.0
63	+17.5	306	+ 5,400	85.8
91	+45.5	2,070	+ 94,200	90.5
126	+80.5	6,480	+521,700	95.2
Sums 910	......	12,676	+551,400	....

b. The coordinates necessary to plot the summation curve of best fit are obtained with the assistance of Table 7-12 as shown in Table 7-14.

TABLE 7-14. Calculated Frequency of Flood Flows (Example 7-5)

Per cent of time $100A/n$ in Table 7-12 (1)	x/σ from Table 7-12 (2)	x $25.9 \times$ (2) (3)	Flood flow $X = x + M$ (3) + 45.5 csm (4)
1	−0.83	− 21.5	24.0
5	−0.82	− 21.2	24.3
10	−0.79	− 20.5	25.0
20	−0.71	− 18.4	27.1
50	−0.35	− 9.1	36.4
80	+0.54	+ 14.0	59.5
90	+1.25	+ 31.3	76.8
95	+2.01	+ 52.1	97.6
99	+3.78	+ 97.9	143.4
99.9	+6.47	+167.5	213.0

c. Observed points and the curve of best fit are plotted in Figure 7-5 on arithmetic-probability paper. The fit is seen to be good. It would be still better, especially in the lower though less important reaches, if maximum monthly, weekly, or daily values had been analyzed instead of yearly ones. Probability paper is selected in this instance only for convenience in plotting. A logarithmic time scale might have been employed in place of the probability scale. The runoff scale could have been logarithmic instead of arithmetic in either case.

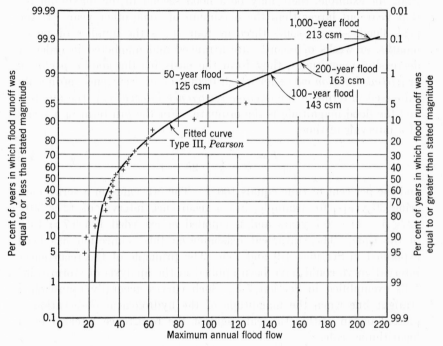

Figure 7-5. Frequency distribution of annual flood flows plotted on arithmetic-probability paper and fitted by Pearson's Type III curve.

d. The magnitudes of the floods that are expected to be equaled or exceeded once in 50, 100, 200, and 1,000 years are

50-year flood $=$ 125 csm read at 98% or 2%
100-year flood $=$ 143 csm read at 99% or 1%
200-year flood $=$ 163 csm read at 99.5% or 0.05%
1,000-year flood $=$ 213 csm read at 99.9% or 0.01%

Physically, the maximum flood that can occur on a given stream is limited by the size of the drainage area and the maximum rate at which atmospheric water can be transported over the area. Long records of floods indicate that this limit is approached once in 50 to 200 years. Uncertainty of estimate by extrapolation suggests the use of 1,000-year or even 100,000-year values in the design of major structures.

Some engineers prefer to avoid the implications of probability analysis and to rely entirely on graphical or purely empirical methods of attack. A much-used method involves the analysis of the peak floods irrespective of the time interval in which they occur. In any one year, for example, there may be a flood second to the maximum for that year but larger than the maximum of some other year. If the peak floods—up to some three or four times the number of years, months, or weeks of record—are arranged and numbered in order of decreasing magnitudes, they form the basis for the *flood-expectancy* or *partial duration curve* for which frequency of occurrence, ordinarily expressed in terms of the *average recurrence interval I,* is the abscissa and the flood magnitude is the ordinate. For the kth term in a series of n intervals of time,

$$I = \frac{n}{k - \frac{1}{2}} = \frac{2n}{2k - 1} \qquad\qquad 7\text{-}8$$

and the per cent of time equals $100/I$. The 5th value in a series covering 30 years, for example, has a recurrence interval of $(2 \times 30)/(2 \times 5 - 1) = 6.7$ years and is equaled or exceeded $100/6.7 = 15\%$ of the time. The statistical reasoning in this connection has been explained in Sections 4-9 and 7-5. The principle of the recurrence-interval curve could have been applied in the analysis of storm rainfalls exemplified in Section 7-5. Such curves generally approach a straight line when the magnitude of the hydrological observation is plotted on an arithmetic scale against the recurrence interval on a logarithmic scale.

7-9. Rational Estimates of Runoff from Rainfall. There are two general ways of estimating runoff from rainfall. One is called the *rational* method; the other, the *unit hydrograph* method.

a. The Rational Method. This method postulates that

$$Q = cia \qquad\qquad 7\text{-}9$$

where Q is the rate of runoff at a specified point and time, a is the drainage area tributary to the specified point at the specified time, i is the average intensity of rainfall over the tributary drainage area for the specified time, and c is the coefficient of runoff or ratio of rate of runoff to rate of rainfall applicable to the particular situation.

The time normally specified is the time that will make Q a maximum. Ordinarily this can be shown to be the time of concentration because $i = A/(t + d)^n$ (Section 7-6), where d is greater than zero and n is less than one, whereas $a = kt^2$ if the velocity of travel towards the point is considered to be uniform, i.e., a increases faster than i decreases. Since for i in inches per hour and a in acres, Q is closely cubic feet per second; $Q = 640cia$ when the tributary area is large and a is more conveniently expressed in square miles. Only when the area drained by the headwaters of the system is long and narrow does the time of concentration increase more rapidly than the area. In these circumstances, the maximum drainage may occur when only part of the area is tributary.

Of the three factors included in Equation 7-9, a is ascertained from a map of the region or specific water shed, i is determined by means outlined in Sections 3 to 6 of this chapter, and c is estimated from the characteristics of the catchment area. The time of concentration involved in the determination of i is found (1) for flood discharge by estimating the average velocities of flow obtaining in the principal drainage channels of the tributary area and calculating elapsed time from the quotient of length and velocity; and (2) for runoff from sewered areas by estimating the time required for runoff to enter the sewerage system from adjacent surfaces (called the *inlet time*) and adding to it the time of flow in the sewers or storm drains proper. Since rapid inflow from tributaries creates flood waves in the main stem of a river system, flood velocities are assumed to be from 30 to 50% higher than normal rates of flow.

The selection of suitable values for c in estimating runoff from sewered areas is discussed more fully in connection with the design of storm drains and combined sewers (Chapter 16). In the translation of rainfall into flood flows, c varies seasonally, regionally, and locally. For the eastern United States, Bernard[10] has suggested limiting values, c_{max}, varying approximately from 0.3 to 1.5, the highest values applying to the northern portion of the country where melting snow and ice may contribute to the immediate runoff from spring rains. Bernard has further suggested reducing the limiting coefficient to that of the selected flood frequency in accordance with the relation

$$c = c_{max} (T/100)^m \qquad 7\text{-}10$$

on the assumption that the limiting coefficient has a frequency of once in 100 years. In Equation 7-10, T is the frequency of occurrence in years and m a coefficient, both in accordance with their significance in Equation 7-3.

[10] M. Bernard, "Modified Rational Method of Estimating Flood Flows," Appendix A of *Low Dams*, National Resources Committee, Washington, 1938.

Example 7-6. For the region studied in Example 7-3, estimate the 1-year and 10-year flood runoff from an area of 1 sq mile on the assumption that c_{max} is 1.0 and the time of concentration t is 60 min.

a. From Equation 7-3

$$1\text{-year intensity } i = 17.0/61^{0.714} = 0.9 \text{ in. per hr}$$
$$10\text{-year intensity } i = (17.0 \times 10^{0.372})/61^{0.714} = 2.1 \text{ in. per hr}$$

b. From Equation 7-10

$$1\text{-year magnitude } c = 1.0 \ (0.01)^{0.37} = 0.18$$
$$10\text{-year magnitude } c = 1.0 \ (0.1)^{0.37} = 0.43$$

c. From Equation 7-9

$$1\text{-year runoff } Q = 0.18 \times 0.9 \times 1.0 \times 640 = 104 \text{ cfs}$$
$$10\text{-year runoff } Q = 0.43 \times 2.1 \times 1.0 \times 640 = 580 \text{ cfs}$$

b. The Unit Hydrograph. In dry weather, or when precipitation is frozen, the residual hydrograph or base flow of a stream is traced by

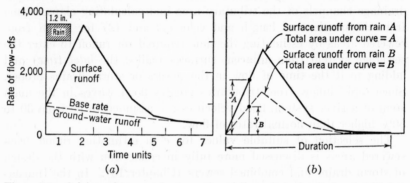

(a)   (b)

Figure 7-6. Origin and geometric properties of the unit hydrograph. (a) Hydrograph resulting from unit-time rain. See Example 7-7. (b) Distribution graph showing geometric properties of unit hydrograph; $y_A : A = y_B : B$; base duration is constant.

water released from storage in the ground or in ponds, lakes, reservoirs, and backwaters of the stream. Immediately after a rainstorm, the rate of discharge rises above base flow by the amount of surface runoff reaching the drainage system. That portion of the hydrograph which rises above the base flow and can be isolated from it is a measure of the true surface runoff (see Figure 7-6). The *unit hydrograph* method is an outcome of investigations into the geometric properties of the surface-runoff portion of the hydrograph in their relation to an *effective rain* that has fallen during a *unit* of time such as a day or an hour. An effective rain is one that actually produces surface runoff.

The important geometric properties of the unit hydrograph of surface runoff are illustrated in Figure 7-6 as follows:

1. The length of abscissa, which measures time duration above base flow, is substantially constant for all unit-time rains.

2. The ordinates, which measure rates of discharge above base flow at the end of each time unit in a sequence of such units, are proportional to the total runoff resulting from unit-time rains irrespective of the individual magnitudes of these rains.

3. The ratios to the total area under the hydrograph of individual areas— which ratios measure the amount of water discharged in a given interval of time—are constant for all unit hydrographs of the same drainage area. These distribution ratios are generally referred to as the *distribution graph,* even when they are not presented in graphical form.

4. Rainstorms extending over several units of time, with or without interruption, create a hydrograph composed of a series of unit hydrographs superimposed in such manner as to distribute the runoff from each unit-time rain in accordance with the successive distribution ratios derived from unit-time rainfalls.

These geometric properties do not apply when runoff originates in melting snow or ice, or when the speed of flood waves in the stream is changed appreciably if the river stage is varied by fluctuating flows. Time is an important element of the procedure, and the method requires that rainfall data be available for unit times that are shorter than the time of concentration of the drainage area. Unit times of a day can be employed successfully only for large water sheds (1,000 sq miles or more). For sheds of 100 to 1,000 sq miles, Sherman [11] suggests values of 6 to 12 hr; for sheds of 20 sq miles, 2 hr; and for very small areas ¼ to ⅓ of the time of concentration. The unit hydrograph method is illustrated in Example 7-7.

Example 7-7. *a.* Given the rainfall and runoff records of a drainage area of 620 sq miles, determine the generalized distribution of runoff (the distribution graph) from isolated unit-time rainfalls. This involves first of all a search for records of isolated rainfalls and for records of the resulting surface runoff. The

TABLE 7-15. Observations and Calculations for Unit Hydrograph (Example 7-7)

Sequence of time units (1)	Observed rainfall, in. (2)	Runoff, cfs		Estimated distribution of surface runoff		Average distribution ratio for 10 storms, % (7)
		Observed total (3)	Estimated base flow (4)	cfs (5) = (3) − (4)	% (6) = 100(5)/6200	
1	1.20	1,830	870	960	15.5	16
2	0.03	3,590	800	2,790	45.0	46
3	0.00	2,370	690	1,680	27.1	26
4	0.00	1,220	600	620	10.0	10
5	0.00	640	510	130	2.1	1
6	0.00	430	410	20	0.3	1
7	0.00	350	350	0	0.0	0
Totals	....	.....	...	6,200	100.0	100

[11] O. E. Meinzer, *Hydrology,* McGraw-Hill Book Co., New York, p. 524, 1942.

basic data for a typical storm are shown in Table 7-15 together with the necessary calculations. The development of this table is straightforward, with the exception of Column 4, which records the estimated base flow. This can be derived only from a study of the general hydrograph of the stream in connection with all related hydrological observations of the region.

b. Apply the average estimate of runoff distribution to the observed rainfall sequence that is presented in Table 7-16.

TABLE 7-16. Application of Unit Hydrograph Method (Example 7-7)

Sequence of time units (1)	Rainfall, in. Observed (2)	Rainfall, in. Estimated loss (3)	Net (4) = (2) − (3)	Average runoff distribution ratio, % (5)	Distributed runoff for stated time units, in. 1st (6)	2nd (7)	3rd (8)	5th (9)	Compounded runoff in. (10)	cfs * (11)
1	1.8	1.3	0.5	16	0.08	....	....	....	0.08	1,300
2	2.7	1.6	1.1	46	0.23	0.18	....	....	0.41	6,900
3	1.6	1.1	0.5	26	0.13	0.50	0.08	....	0.71	11,900
4	0.0	0.0	0.0	10	0.05	0.29	0.23	....	0.57	9,500
5	1.1	0.2	0.9	1	0.01	0.11	0.13	0.14	0.39	6,500
6	0.0	0.0	0.0	1	0.00	0.01	0.05	0.42	0.48	8,000
7	0.0	0.0	0.0	0	0.00	0.01	0.01	0.23	0.25	4,200
8	0.0	0.0	0.0	0	0.00	0.00	0.00	0.09	0.09	1,500

* Rate of runoff in cubic feet per second = inches × 26.88 × 620 sq miles = 16,700 cfs if the time unit is a day. For other time units multiply by reciprocal ratio of length of time to length of day.

The calculations in Table 7-16 need little explanation except Column 3, the estimated loss of rainfall due principally to infiltration. This estimate is made on the basis of all available information for the region. It is discussed in principle in Section 7-9 and in Chapter 9. Column 5 is identical with Column 7 of Table 7-15. Column 6 is the net rain of 0.5 in. during the first time unit multiplied by the distribution ratio of Column 5. Columns 7, 8, and 9 are similarly derived for the net rains during the subsequent time units. Column 10 gives the sums of Columns 6 to 9, and Column 11 converts these sums from inches to cubic feet per second. If the base flow is estimated and added to the surface runoff shown in Column 11 the complete hydrograph is constructed.

The unit hydrograph method is useful in estimating the magnitudes of unusual flood flows, in forecasting flood crests during storms, and in the manipulation of storage on large river systems. It has the important property of tracing the full hydrograph resulting from a storm rather than being confined to a determination of the peak flow alone. For small drainage areas, the method depends upon the availability of the readings of a recording rain gage. Many refinements in procedure and aids to the rationalization of the various steps are being developed by hydrologists and engineers.

7-10. Flood-Flow Formulas. The basis of flood-flow formulas is an empirical evaluation of drainage-basin characteristics and hydrological factors which must rationally fall within the framework of the relation $Q = cia$ (Equation 7-9). In most of the formulas used by engineers, frequency relations are implied even if they are not expressed in exact terms. Variation of rainfall intensities with time of concentration, furthermore, is often introduced indirectly as a function of the size of area drained. Equation 7-9 is thereby reduced to the expression $Q = Ca^m$, where m is less than 1. This follows from what has been said before (Section 7-9) about relative changes in i and a with t; namely, $i = A/(t + d)^n$ and $a = kt^2$. For d close to zero, therefore, $i = \text{constant}/(a^{n/2})$, and, substituting i in Equation 7-9, $Q = \text{constant } a^{1-n/2} = Ca^m$, where $m = 1 - n/2$. Since n varies from 0.4 to 1.0 (Section 7-6), m must and does vary in different formulations from 0.8 to 0.5. The value of C comprehends the initial rate of rainfall, the runoff-rainfall ratio of the particular water shed, and the frequency factor. An example is the Fanning formula which is listed in Table 7-17 together with other flood-flow formulas in which certain of the component variables or their influence upon runoff are individualized.

TABLE 7-17. Examples of Flood-Flow Formulas

Individualized variable	Author and region	Formula
None	Fanning, New England	$Q = Ca^{5/6}$, where $C = 200$ for a in sq miles
Rainfall intensity and slope of water shed	McMath, St. Louis, Mo.	$Q = cia^{4/5}s^{1/5}$, where s = slope in ft per 1,000 and $c = 0.75$ for a in acres
Shape of water shed	Dredge or Burge, India	$Q = Ca/l^{2/3}$, where l = length of area in miles and $C = 1,300$ for a in sq miles
Shape, slope, and surface storage	Kinnison and Colby, New England	$Q = (0.000036h^{2.4} + 124)a^{0.95}/(rl^{0.7})$, where h = median altitude of drainage basin in ft above the outlet; r = % of lake, pond, and reservoir area; l = average distance in miles to outlet; and a = sq miles
Frequency of flood	Fuller, U.S.A.	$Q = Ca^{0.8}(1 + 0.8 \log T)(1 + 2a^{-0.3})$, where T = number of years in the period considered, and C varies from 25 to 2,000 for a in sq miles

These examples are presented for the purpose of showing the form that flood-flow formulas may take. They are not necessarily the best of their type or widely applicable.

It is customary to rate or identify the flood-flow characteristics of different drainage basins by means of the modified formula of Myer,

$$Q = 100p\sqrt{a} \qquad \text{7-11}$$

where Q is the extreme peak flow in cfs; p is the percentage ratio of Q to the ultimate maximum flood flow for all streams, $Q_u = 10,000\sqrt{a}$; and a is the drainage area, which must be 4 sq miles or more. In the eastern United States, Myer's ratings of 50% are seldom exceeded.

Fuller's formula is of particular interest because it incorporates a frequency factor and is country-wide in scope. It was developed in sequence as follows:

1. The average annual 24-hr flood:

$$Q_{\text{ave}} = Ca^{0.8} \qquad \text{7-12}$$

2. The most probable maximum 24-hr flood in T years:

$$Q_{\text{max}} = Q_{\text{ave}}(1 + 0.8 \log T) \qquad \text{7-13}$$

3. The most probable peak discharge in T years:

$$Q = Q_{\text{max}}(1 + 2a^{-0.3}) \qquad \text{7-14}$$

Inspection of these equations suggests the nature of their graphical derivation from observed flood flows. For the United States C varies from 25 to 200. It should be noted that the maximum flood in T years

TABLE 7-18.   Fuller's Flood Frequency Values

Type of structure	Damage in case of failure	Values of $(1 + 0.8 \log T)$
Temporary works during construction	Slight	1.5–2
Minor permanent structures	Slight	2–3
Temporary works	Considerable	2–3
Major permanent structures	Material	3–5
Major permanent structures	Material and disastrous	5–6

is the most probable value to occur in that period rather than the value that is equaled or exceeded once in that period. Since Fuller assumes that the most probable value is the arithmetic mean of the group of "exceeding" values, flood flows calculated by his formula are generally higher than those determined by common statistical procedures for equal periods. Thomas [12] has indicated that Fuller's fre-

12 Unpublished study by H. A. Thomas, Jr.

quency factor $(1 + 0.8 \log T)$ has a rational basis, and is more completely expressed as $(1 - 0.45c_v + 1.80c_v \log T)$. The variability in runoff of different streams is thereby related to c_v, the coefficient of variability. Fuller[13] recommends using the values of the frequency factor $(1 + 0.8 \log T)$ shown in Table 7-18.

Example 7-8. For the New England Drainage Area of 48.5 sq miles in Example 7-5, calculate (a) the Myer rating and (b) the magnitude of the maximum peak flood to be expected in 100 years by Fuller's formula.

a. Example 7-5 gives the 200-year flood as 163 csm or $163 \times 48.5 = 7,900$ cfs. Assuming that the 200-year value is the maximum, $p = 7,900/(100\sqrt{48.5}) = 11.3\%$. This is a reasonable value for the region.

b. Example 7-5 gives the arithmetic mean peak flood as 45.5 csm; hence

$$C = \frac{Q}{a^{0.8}(1 + 2a^{-0.3})} = \frac{45.5 \times 48.5}{48.5^{0.8}(1 + 2 \times 48.5^{-0.3})} = 61$$

This, too, is a reasonable value for the region. For a normal value of $C = 60$,

$$Q = 60 \times 48.5^{0.8}(1 + 0.8 \log 100)(1 + 2 \times 48.5^{-0.3})$$

$$= 60 \times 22.3 \times 2.6 \times 1.624 = 5,700 \text{ cfs} \quad \text{or} \quad 5,700/48.5 = 118 \text{ csm}$$

The value of the flood flow to be equaled or exceeded once in 100 years is given in Example 7-5 as 143 csm. Fuller's empirical 100-year frequency factor is $(1 + 0.8 \log T) = 2.6$. Thomas's rational 100-year frequency factor for $c_v = 0.57$ (Example 7-5) is $(1 - 0.45c_v + 1.8c_v \log T) = (1 - 0.45 \times 0.57 + 1.8 \times 0.57 \times 2) = 2.8$.

[13] W. E. Fuller, "Flood Flows," *Trans. Am. Soc. Civil Engrs.*, 77, 564 (1914).

8-1. Importance in Water Supply and Waste-Water Disposal. In nature, the runoff from drainage areas is stored to a varying extent in lakes and ponds and in the backwaters and channels of streams. There is some storage, too, in the ground adjacent to water courses. This is called *bank storage*. During periods of drought, the stored waters are released and reduce the severity of low-water stages. In times of flood, the water lost from storage is replenished. This lowers flood peaks and decreases the total discharge during high-water stages. Both low-water and high-water effects are important in the regional conservation of water.

In the absence of adequate natural storage, engineers resort to the construction of impounding reservoirs or, more rarely, to the excavation of storage basins in lands adjacent to streams. Natural storage, too, can be regulated or developed. This is done by the construction of control works (gates and weirs) on the outlets of lakes and ponds.

Some storage works are designed to serve a single purpose, such as water supply; others are planned to include a number of different functions in serving the broader economy of natural resources—among them:

1. Water supply for household, farm, and industry.
2. Disposal of sewage and other municipal and industrial wastes.
3. Irrigation of arable lands.
4. Harnessing of water power.
5. Low-water regulation for navigation.
6. Preservation and cultivation of useful aquatic life.
7. Recreation—fishing, boating, and bathing.
8. Control of destructive floods.

As a matter of wise planning, the multipurpose development of storage works should receive consideration in connection with all storage projects. A judicious combination of reservoir functions will secure the greatest over-all benefit at least cost.

In water supply, surface storage is provided when the low-water flows of streams are inadequate in quantity or when they are rendered unsatisfactory in quality by heavy concentration of pollution. Release of stored waters increases flows and dilutes pollution. Storage, itself, also affects the quality of the waters impounded. Recognition of the conditions responsible for the changes produced, which may be both desirable and undesirable, calls for familiarity with the principles commonly embodied in the study of *limnology*, the science of lakes or, more broadly, of inland waters.

In the disposal of waste waters—principally municipal sewage and industrial process waters—regulation of stream flow permits adjusting the flow to the pollutional load that is imposed upon the receiving waters. Low-water regulation, as such, is accomplished by storage of water upstream from the points of waste-water discharge. Reservoirs constructed below these points aid dilution, but they also play an active part in the natural purification of river systems by themselves becoming part of the water course. The results may be beneficial or adverse, depending upon the nature of the waste matters introduced and the regimen of the stream that is developed.

8-2. Safe Yield of Streams. As previously indicated, the safe yield of a river system, in the absence of storage, is its lowest dry-weather flow, whereas, with full development of storage, the safe yield approaches the mean annual flow. The economical yield of a given water shed generally lies between these limits. The yield that is attainable by storage is modified in a number of different ways, including: (1) loss of water from storage by evaporation; (2) gain in water by its storage in the ground adjacent to impounding reservoirs; (3) loss of water from storage by seepage out of the catchment area; and (4) reduction in storage volume, in the course of time, by silting.

The relations between yield and storage are illustrated in this chapter by the calculations that are made in determining the storage that must be provided in impounding reservoirs for water supply; but the principles involved are applicable also to the other purposes and uses of storage.

8-3. Storage as a Function of Draft and Runoff. A dam thrown across a river valley impounds the waters of the stream. Once the impounding reservoir has filled, the water drawn from it is eventually replenished by the stream, provided that a proper balance has been struck between runoff, storage, and draft. There are a number of different ways of calculating the storage from draft and runoff relationships in long-term records of stream flow. To be of use, these records should include at least the average monthly rates of discharge. Storage is determined either by analytical or by graphical methods.

Assuming that the reservoir is full at the beginning of the dry season, or dry period, the maximum amount of water S that must be

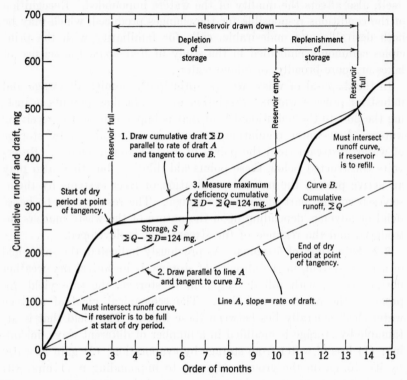

Figure 8-1. Mass-diagram or Rippl method for the determination of storage required in impounding reservoirs.

drawn from storage to maintain a draft or flow D equals the maximum cumulative difference between the draft and runoff Q subsequent to the beginning of the dry period, or:

$$S = \text{maximum value of } \Sigma(D - Q) \qquad 8\text{-}1$$

To find S, therefore, $\Sigma(D - Q)$ is calculated arithmetically or determined graphically. The last is done as a most convincing and useful demonstration by finding $\Sigma(D - Q) = \Sigma D - \Sigma Q$ by the mass-diagram or Rippl [1] method illustrated in Figure 8-1. The shorter the interval of time for which runoff is recorded, the more exact is the result. As

[1] W. Rippl, "The Capacity of Storage Reservoirs for Water Supply," *Proc. Inst. Civil Engrs.*, **71**, 270 (1883).

the maximum value is approached, therefore, it may be worth while to shift to short intervals of time: from monthly values to daily values, for example. The additional storage indicated by such a shift may equal as much as 10 days of draft.

Example 8-1. Find the storage required to maintain a constant draft of 750,000 gpd per sq mile from a stream [2] with the following record of monthly mean runoff values:

Order of month	1	2	3	4	5	6	7	8	9	10	11	12	13	14	15
Observed runoff, mg per sq mile	94	122	45	5	5	2	0	2	16	7	72	92	21	55	33

a. The necessary calculations for the arithmetic and graphical solution of this problem are shown in Table 8-1, all volumes of water being stated in million gallons per square mile.

TABLE 8-1. Calculation of Required Storage (Example 8-1)

Order of months (1)	Recorded runoff, Q (2)	Estimated draft, D (3)	Cumulative runoff, ΣQ (4) = $\Sigma(2)$	Deficiency, $D - Q$ (5) = (3) − (2)	Cumulative deficiency, $\Sigma(D - Q)$ (6) = $\Sigma(5)$	Remarks (7)
1	94	23	94	−71	0 (192)	
2	122	23	216	−99	0 (121)	
3	45	23	261	−22	0 (22)	Reservoir full at begin-
4	5	23	266	18	18	ning of dry period;
5	5	23	271	18	36	reservoir empties
6	2	23	273	21	57	
7	0	23	273	23	80	
8	2	23	275	21	101	
9	16	23	291	7	108	
10	7	23	298	16	124	Maximum deficiency at
11	72	23	370	−49	75	end of dry period
12	92	23	462	−69	6	
13	21	23	483	2	8	
14	55	23	538	−32	0 (24)	Reservoir refilled
15	33	23	571	−10	0 (34)	

Column 3: 750,000 gpd per sq mile = 0.75 × 30.4 = 23 mg per sq mile for an average month of 30.4 days.

Column 5: A negative value indicates a surplus rather than a deficiency.

Column 6: Negative values are not included in $\Sigma(D - Q)$ until the beginning of the dry period, i.e. until all water is lost from storage, and there is room to store incoming flows. The surplus preceding the dry period, however, must equal or exceed the preceding maximum deficiency; otherwise, the reservoir will not be full at the beginning of the dry period. The cumulative surplus, calculated backwards from the beginning of the dry period, is shown in parentheses in Column 6 and is seen to exceed 124 mg.

b. The schedule gives the maximum cumulative deficiency, or required storage, as 124 mg per sq mile. This equals 124/0.75 = 165 days of draft; i.e., enough water must be stored to supply the community for 165 days (almost half a year).

c. Column 4 furnishes the data for the mass diagram shown in Figure 8-1. The graphical method parallels the arithmetic calculations and checks the calculated storage.

---

[2] The Westfield Little River near Springfield, Mass., for March, 1914, to May, 1915. In New England, a yield of 750,000 gpd per sq mile can generally be assured with economical storage.

For drafts that are not constant and for the inclusion of varying allowances for evaporation from the water surface that is created by the impoundage, the analytical method possesses distinct advantages over the graphical method. The principal value of the Rippl method, indeed, is not in connection with the estimation of storage requirements but in the determination of the yield of catchment areas upon which storage reservoirs are already established. This use of the Rippl principle is illustrated in Figure 8-2. In order to simplify graphical

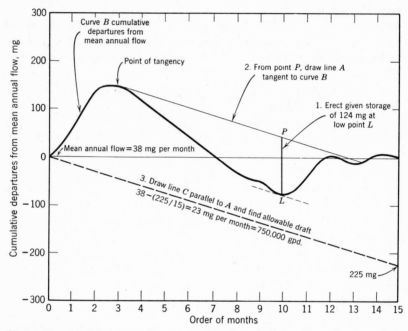

Figure 8-2. Modified mass-diagram or Rippl method for determination of the yield of impounding reservoirs.

presentation, the cumulative departures from the mean annual flow, rather than the cumulative flows themselves, are plotted in this figure. The resulting curve of flows hugs the horizontal reference line that represents the mean annual flow. Lines parallel to it and tangent to the curve establish the storage needed for full, or maximum possible, development of the stream. Partial utilization is indicated by lines that slope downward from left to right.

8-4. Design Storage. Except for occasional series of dry years, only seasonal storage is required in the well-watered regions of North America. Water is plentiful, and stream flows do not vary greatly from year to year. Under these conditions, it does not pay to go in for high or complete development of catchment areas, and reservoirs generally refill within the annual hydrologic cycle. In semiarid regions, on the other hand, water is scarce, hence more valuable, and stream flows fluctuate widely from year to year. High developments are then warranted, and the runoff of wet years must often be conserved for use during subsequent dry years. Given a series of storage values for the years of record, the engineer must decide which value he will use. Shall it be the highest value on record, or the second, third, or fourth highest? Obviously the choice depends upon the degree of protection that is to be afforded against water shortage. This must be fitted into the drought experience, which is a function of the length of record. In order to arrive at a reasonable and uniform basis of design, it is best to resort to a statistical analysis of the arrayed storage values and to select as the design storage a value of some reasonable frequency, such as the storage requirement that is equaled or exceeded but once in 20, 50, or 100 years, i.e., 5, 2, and 1% of the time. For water supply, Hazen [3] has suggested that the 5% value be employed in ordinary circumstances. In other words, design storage should be adequate to compensate for a drought of such severity that it is not expected to occur oftener than once in 20 years. In still drier years, it may be necessary to curtail the use of water somewhat by limiting, or prohibiting, lawn sprinkling, car washing, and similar practices.

Curtailing the use of water results in economic loss, is a nuisance to the public, and constitutes a poor business method of operating a public utility. As a practical matter, curtailment of use for conservation of stored water must be started well in advance of anticipated exhaustion of the impounded supply. The most logical approach is to decide not only on the allowable frequency of curtailment but also on the depletion at which conservation measures should be instituted. In practice, the reserve remaining when conservation is begun generally lies between 20% and 50% of the total volume of water stored. Requiring a 25% reserve for the drought that occurs about once in 20 years is reasonable. During a drought that equals or exceeds the once-in-20-years magnitude, curtailment will ordinarily be instituted and will diminish the draft to a point at which the chance of exhausting the last 25% will vanish. Instead of making a reserve allowance, storage provisions may be based on the drought to be expected once in 100 years. In general, this gives a total reservoir

[3] Allen Hazen, "Storage to be Provided in Impounding Reservoirs," *Trans. Am. Soc. Civil Engrs.*, 77, 1539 (1914).

volume less than but close to that derived from estimates based on a once-in-20-years risk combined with a 25% reserve.

In undeveloped areas, there are few records even as long as 20 years. Estimation of the 5, 2, and 1% frequencies, or of recurrence intervals of 20, 50, and 100 years, requires extrapolation from available data. Probability plots are well adapted to this purpose. However, such plots must be prepared and used with considerable thought. Where severe droughts in the record extend over several years and require annual rather than seasonal storages, the resulting series of storage values becomes non-homogeneous and is no longer strictly subject to ordinary statistical interpretations. They can be made reasonably homogeneous by including, besides all truly seasonal storages, not only all truly annual storages but also those seasonal storages that would have been identified within the periods of annual storage if the drought of the preceding year or years had not been measured. Plots of recurrence intervals should include minor storages as well as major ones. The results of these statistical analyses are conveniently reduced to a set of draft-storage-frequency curves.

Example 8-2. Examination of the 25-year record runoff from an eastern stream [4] shows that the storages listed in Table 8-2 are needed in successive years to maintain a draft of 750,000 gpd per sq mile.

TABLE 8-2. Storage Requirements (Example 8-2)

Order of year	1	2	3	4	5	6	7	8	9	10	11	12	13
Calculated storage, mg	47	39	104	110	115	35	74	81	124	29	37	82	78

Order of year	14	15	16	17	18	19	20	21	22	23	24	25
Calculated storage, mg	72	10	117	51	61	8	102	65	73	20	53	88

Estimate the design storage requirement that is probably reached or exceeded but once in 20, 50, and 100 years.

a. The 25 calculated storage values arrayed in order of magnitude are plotted on arithmetic-probability paper in Figure 8-3. The arrayed storages are plotted at $100k/26 = 3.8\%$, 7.7%, 11.5%, etc. The straight line of best fit is identified by the arithmetic mean storage $M = 67$ mg and the standard deviation $\sigma = 33$ mg.

b. The storage requirements that are reached or exceeded once in 20, 50, and 100 years, or 5, 2, and 1% of the time, are found to be 123, 137, and 146 mg respectively. Use is made of probability paper because it offers a rational basis for projecting the information beyond the period of experience. The once-in-20-years requirement with 25% reserve suggests a design storage of $123/0.75 = 164$ mg per sq mile of drainage area.

---

[4] The Westfield Little River near Springfield, Mass., for the years 1906 to 1930.

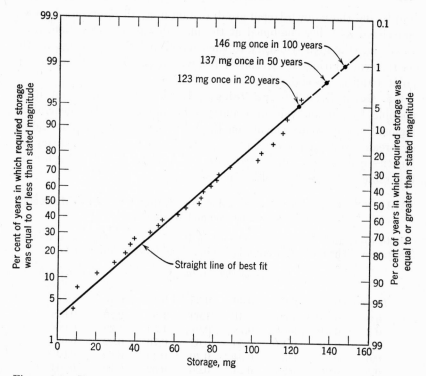

Figure 8-3. Frequency distribution of required storage plotted on arithmetic-probability paper.

c. It should be noted that the coefficient of variation of the calculated storage $c_v = 100 \times 33/67 = 50\%$ is more than twice as great as the variability of runoff ($c_v = 22\%$) for closely the same period of observation (see Example 7-1).

d. For comparison with other river records, the draft and storage may be expressed in terms of the mean annual flow (MAF) and the storage also in terms of daily draft. For a mean annual flow of 26.6 in., or $26.6 \times 0.0477 = 1.27$ mgd per sq mile (Example 7-1):

1. Draft = 750,000 gpd per sq mile = $100 \times 0.750/1.27 = 59\%$ of MAF.

2. Storage requirement equaled or exceeded once in 20 years = 123 mg per sq mile, or $(100 \times 123)/(1.27 \times 365) = 27\%$ of MAF.

3. Storage requirement = $123/0.750 = 164$ days of draft, or nearly half a year if 10 days are added to compensate for the use of monthly average runoffs in place of daily stream discharge.

When more than one reservoir is developed on a stream, the overflow from each impoundage becomes available to the reservoir next below in the valley together with the runoff from the intervening water shed. The amount of overflow is determined from the storage analysis for each year or for the critical year. If the reservoirs are operated jointly and those downstream are drawn on first, all reservoirs may be considered as being combined at the most-downstream location, provided that the area tributary to each reservoir is large enough to fill its reservoir during the season of heavy runoff. The last-mentioned point requires special study.

8-5. Generalized Storage Values. Hazen [5] has shown that it is possible by an analysis of country-wide information to generalize regional storage requirements on the basis of the mean annual flows of streams and their coefficients of variation. A partial summary of Hazen's generalized storage values is given in Table 8-3. The use of this table is illustrated in Example 8-3.

TABLE 8-3.   Generalized Storage Values for Streams East of the Mississippi River, or in Oregon and Washington

Both draft and storage are expressed in terms of the mean annual flow of the stream. The coefficient of variation in annual flows is designated c_v

	Storage for stated values of c_v						Deduction for 30 days'
Draft	0.20	0.25	0.30	0.35	0.40	0.45	ground storage
0.9	0.85	1.05	1.31	1.60	1.88	2.20	0.074
0.8	0.54	0.64	0.78	0.97	1.19	1.39	0.066
0.7	0.39	0.43	0.50	0.62	0.76	0.92	0.058
0.6	0.31	0.32	0.34	0.40	0.49	0.60	0.049
0.5	0.23	0.23	0.24	0.26	0.32	0.39	0.041

Example 8-3. For the eastern stream dealt with in Examples 8-1 and 8-2, find the generalized storage for a draft of 750,000 gpd per sq mile on the assumption that the coefficient of variation in annual flow is 0.22 and the mean annual flow 1.27 mgd (Example 7-1).

a. The draft is 59% of MAF as shown in Example 8-2.

b. For 59% and $c_v = 0.22$, Table 8-3 gives a storage of 0.30 MAF or 0.30 × 1.27 × 365 = 139 mg per sq mile.

c. For 30 days' ground storage, deduct, according to Table 8-3, 0.048 from 0.30, making it 0.25 MAF or 0.25 × 1.27 × 365 = 116 mg per sq mile.

The agreement between the results obtained by normal analytical procedures and by the use of Hazen's generalized storage values is good.

8-6. Loss by Evaporation, Seepage, and Silting. Construction of an impounding reservoir alters the hydrology of that portion of the water shed which is inundated by the reservoir. The original land surface is replaced by a fluctuating water surface which loses water by evaporation and gains water by direct reception of rainfall. This may be called the water-surface effect. The rising water alters the

[5] Allen Hazen, *American Civil Engineers' Handbook,* John Wiley & Sons, New York, p. 1446, 1930.

pattern of ground-water flow, and seepage from the reservoir may discharge through permeable soils into neighboring catchment areas. The quiescence created by the impoundage, finally, reduces the carrying power of the stream and causes the subsidence of settleable solids or silting of the reservoir.

a. *Water-Surface Effect.* The effect of introducing a new water surface includes:

1. *Loss:* (a) runoff from land area flooded by the reservoir = QW (closely), where Q is the rate of runoff per unit area of original water shed, and W is the area of water surface of the reservoir; and (b) evaporation from the water surface = EW, where E is the rate of evaporation per unit area of reservoir.

2. *Gain:* rainfall on the water surface = RW, where R is the rate of rainfall per unit area of reservoir.

Hence the net rate of loss or gain for the portion of the water shed in question = $[R - (Q + E)]W$. A negative value records a net loss and a positive value a net gain.

All the factors involved in the change vary within the hydrologic cycle and from year to year. They can be measured. Preparation of exact calculations, however, is commonly handicapped by inadequate data on evaporation. Wherever possible, the information on evaporation should be derived from local or nearby observations. The area of the water surface involved is determined most concisely from a contour map of the reservoir site. The mean annual water surface is sometimes substituted to simplify calculations. It is normally about 90% of the area at spillway level.

To make for convenience in calculation, the water-surface effect is accounted for in one of the following ways:

1. *Revised runoff.* If A is the total catchment area and Q_r is the revised rate of runoff per unit area,

$$Q_r = Q - (Q + E - R)(W/A) \qquad 8\text{-}2$$

The revised values of runoff are then used in recalculating the storage requirements.

2. *Equivalent draft.* If D_e is the draft equivalent of the difference in yield between the water and land area,

$$D_e = (Q + E - R)(W/A) \qquad \text{on a unit area basis} \qquad 8\text{-}3$$

The sum of the drafts D and draft equivalents D_e, or the effective draft $(D + D_e)$, is then used in calculating the storage requirements.

Since, in the eastern United States, the seasonal decline in runoff is roughly equal to the seasonal increase in evaporation, the sum $(Q + E)$ remains fairly constant throughout the year. The monthly rainfall is also constant, and D_e

can, therefore, be considered a uniform draft which in dry years may amount to 1 or 2 in. per month over the effective water surface.

For concise results methods 1 and 2 call for complete hydrologic data on rainfall and evaporation as well as runoff. They can then be applied to any available element of time. Coarser adjustments are made when information is incomplete.

3. *Equivalent land area.* The water surface is expressed in terms of the equivalent land area W_e by the relation

$$W_e = W(R - E)/Q \qquad\qquad 8\text{-}4$$

and the effective catchment area A_e is then considered to be

$$A_e = A - W + W_e = A - W[1 - (R - E)/Q] \qquad\qquad 8\text{-}5$$

This adjustment is generally based on average annual values.

4. *Adjusted flowline.* The flowline elevation of the impounding reservoir is changed by an amount equal to $Q + E - R$, all factors being stated in a unit such as inches or feet yearly. This unit, converted from the mean annual water surface to the reservoir area at spillway level, is then added to the flowline elevation. As a rough approximation, an increase in the height of the spillway level by a foot or two is sometimes employed.

Example 8-4. A mean draft of 30.0 mgd is to be developed from a catchment area of 40.0 sq miles. First calculations give a reservoir area of 1,500 acres at flowline. The mean annual rainfall is 47.0 in.; the mean annual runoff is 27.0 in.; and the mean annual evaporation is 40.0 in. Find (1) the revised mean annual runoff, (2) the equivalent mean draft, (3) the equivalent land area, and (4) the adjusted flowline.

1. By Equation 8-2: $Q_r = 27.0 - (27.0 + 40.0 - 47.0)0.9 \times 1,500/(640 \times 40.0)$ $= 27.0 - 1.1 = 25.9$ in.

2. By Equation 8-3: $D_e = 1.1$ in., or 52,000 gpd per sq mile, and the effective draft is $30.0 + 40.0 \times 0.052 = 32.1$ mgd.

3. By Equation 8-5: $A_e = 40.0 - \dfrac{0.9 \times 1,500}{640}\left(1 - \dfrac{47.0 - 40.0}{27.0}\right) = 40.0 - 1.6$ $= 38.4$ sq miles.

4. $Q + E - R = 27.0 + 40.0 - 47.0 = 20$ in.
At spillway level this equals $20 \times 0.9 = 18$ in.

b. Seepage. If the valley that encloses a reservoir is underlain by porous strata, there may be considerable loss of water by seepage. Only a subsurface exploration can tell how great the expected loss will be. Seepage is not confined to the dam site proper. It occurs wherever the sides and bottom of the reservoir are sufficiently permeable to permit entrance of water and its discharge through the ground beneath the surrounding hills.

c. Silting. The silting of reservoirs is the result of soil erosion on the water shed. Both are undesirable. Erosion destroys arable lands. Silting destroys useful storage. How bad conditions are in a given catchment area depends principally upon the type of soil and rock in the water shed, the slope of the ground surface, the vegetal cover, the methods of cultivation employed, and the occurrence and intensity of storm rainfalls.

Silt accumulated in reservoirs by sedimentation of eroded soil cannot be removed economically by any means so far devised. Dredging is expensive, and attempts to flush out the silt deposits by opening scour valves in dams are fruitless. They only produce gullies in the silt. In favorable circumstances, however, much of the heaviest load of suspended silt can be passed through the reservoir by opening large sluices that are installed for this purpose. Flood flows are thereby selected for storage in accordance with their quality as well as their volume.

Reduction of soil erosion is a long-range undertaking, the magnitude of which is determined by the size of the catchment area. Involved are: proper farming methods, such as contour plowing; terracing; reforestation or afforestation; the cultivation of permanent pastures; and the prevention of gully formation through the construction of check dams or debris barriers.

In the design of reservoirs that impound silt-bearing streams, suitable allowances must be made for loss of capacity by silting. The rate of silt deposition appears to be greatest for reservoirs on small catchment areas. Measured rates of the order of magnitude shown in Table 8-4 have been reported for the southwestern United States.[6]

TABLE 8-4. Rate of Silting of Reservoirs in the Southwestern United States

Size of drainage area, sq miles	10	100	1,000	10,000
Annual deposition, acre-ft per sq mile				
High	2.5	1.7	1.2	0.80
Average	1.0	0.60	0.35	0.20
Low	0.30	0.15	0.09	0.05

These figures can be approximated by the equation

$$V_s = cA^{0.77} \qquad \text{8-6}$$

Here V_s is the volume of silt deposited annually (acre-ft), A is the size of the drainage area (sq miles), and c is a coefficient that equals 0.43, 1.7, and 4.8 for low, average, and high deposition respectively. The similarity of this empirical relationship to a flood-flow formula is not surprising. However, no direct value attaches to the stated magnitudes of c. Every impoundage must be considered by itself in

[6] For basic information see H. M. Eakin, "Silting of Reservoirs," *U. S. Dept. Agr. Tech. Bull.*, 524, 1939.

the light of information available for reservoirs on nearby water sheds of similar character. The rate of silting is often fast when the reservoir is first placed in service and may reach a state of equilibrium as time goes on. A silting rate of 1.0 acre-ft per sq mile per year corresponds roughly to a reduction in storage of 0.3 mg per sq mile per annum, because an acre 3 ft deep is closely 1 mg.

8-7. Area and Volume of Reservoirs. The surface areas and volumes of water associated with given flowline elevations are determined from a contour map of the site that is flooded by the reservoir. The areas enclosed by each contour line are planimetered, and volumes between contour lines are calculated ordinarily by the *average-end-area method*. This is generally good enough for the attainable precision of measurements.

For uniform contour intervals h and successive contour areas a_0, a_1, $\cdots a_n$, the volume V of water stored up to the nth contour is

$$V = h \left(\frac{a_0 + a_1}{2} + \frac{a_1 + a_2}{2} + \cdots \frac{a_{n-1} + a_n}{2} \right)$$

$$= \left(\frac{a_0 + a_n}{2} + \sum_1^{n-1} a \right) h \qquad \text{8-7}$$

Surface areas and volumes that do not coincide with mapped contour lines are interpolated most satisfactorily from curves obtained by plotting the measured contour-line areas and calculated volumes against the contour elevations. Figure 8-4 shows such curves.[7] It should be noted that volumes can be determined from the surface-area curve in this figure by planimetering the area enclosed between this curve and its abscissa. For impounding reservoirs, the volume curve is approximated mathematically by the equation

$$V = cH^m \qquad \text{8-8}$$

where H is the height of water at the dam and c and m are constants for a given reservoir site. The area curve, consequently, is approximated by the first derivative of this equation, i.e. by

$$A = cmH^{m-1} \qquad \text{8-9}$$

Plotted on double log paper, both curves approximate straight lines from which the values of c and m are determined. The indicated magnitude of m is about 3.

[7] The vertical scale implied by elevations generally leads engineers to plot elevations as ordinates. Figure 8-4, however, is kept consistent with the injunction to plot as the ordinate the variable that is to be found.

In reservoir operation, *useful storage* generally excludes a small amount of water that lies below the invert of the reservoir outlet or that, being the dregs of the impounding, is objectionable in quality. This water should be so identified. The reduction in storage represented by it is offset in general by bank storage that is released from the soil when the reservoir is drawn down.

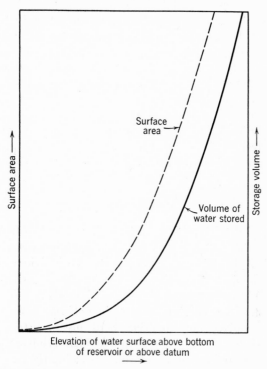

Figure 8-4. Surface area of a reservoir and volume of water stored.

A knowledge of surface areas and volumes of reservoirs is needed not only in the solution of hydrological problems but also in the control of algae by the addition of copper sulfate and in other questions relating to the quality of stored waters.

8-8. Spillway Capacity and Flood Routing. Impounding reservoirs must be provided with spillways capable of discharging the maximum peak flood that the storage works are expected to pass. To be on the safe side in designing the spillway, it is assumed that the entrant flood may occur when the reservoir is full. Before the maximum head on the spillway can be developed, however, the flood waters must back up in the reservoir and fill the space between spillway level and flood level. This storage above spillway level retains some of the entering flood waters and reduces the flood peak—often by enough to lower the required discharge capacity of the spillway by a significant amount. Of opposite effect upon spillway flows is the amount of water that overflowed into the flood plain of the stream within the reservoir site before the storage works were built. Construction of the reservoir deprives the stream of this valley storage, and allowance may have to be made for it in studies of flood routing that are based on the analysis of stream-flow records.

Apart from valley storage, the retardation of floods by storage above spillway level is a function of the rate of inflow I into the reservoir, the available storage S above spillway level, and the rate of outflow Q from the reservoir. All these factors are variable during the course of the flood and not sufficiently regular to be generalized mathematically. Analytical procedures, therefore, are usually based upon a stepwise analysis of the various hydraulic occurrences: varying inflow, changing water level, and varying outflow. For a specified interval of time, Δt,

$$Q \, \Delta t = I \, \Delta t - \Delta S \qquad\qquad 8\text{-}10$$

If it is assumed that the average rates of inflow and outflow are closely equal to the arithmetic means of the rates obtaining at the beginning and the end of short intervals of time Δt, the individual steps in the proposed mechanical integration are: $Q \, \Delta t = \Delta t(Q_k + Q_{k+1})/2$; $I \, \Delta t = \Delta t(I_k + I_{k+1})/2$; and $\Delta S = (S_{k+1} - S_k)$. Here the subscripts k and $(k + 1)$ denote successive intervals of time of length Δt. Substitution of these expressions in Equation 8-10 gives $\Delta t(Q_k + Q_{k+1})/2 = [\Delta t(I_k + I_{k+1})/2] - (S_{k+1} - S_k)$. In this relationship outflow and storage are both related to spillway head.[8] Bringing the associated terms together,

$$\left(\frac{S_{k+1}}{\Delta t} + \frac{Q_{k+1}}{2}\right) = \left(\frac{S_k}{\Delta t} - \frac{Q_k}{2}\right) + \left(\frac{I_k + I_{k+1}}{2}\right) \qquad 8\text{-}11$$

This equation provides a means for determining the outflow pattern that is produced by a given pattern of inflow into an impounding reservoir. The process of calculation is known as *flood routing*. The method of flood routing based on Equation 8-11 is best explained by

[8] Spillway discharge $Q_1 = CL(H_1 - H_0)^{3/2}$ by the common weir formula, while storage $S_1 = V_1 - V_0 = c(H_1{}^m - H_0{}^m)$ as indicated in Equation 8-8. Here H_0 is the depth of water at spillway level, $H_1 - H_0$ is the head on the spillway, and L is the length of weir.

an example (Example 8-5). There are numerous other approaches to this problem.

Example 8-5. From the predicted hydrograph of a stream in flood (Figure 8-5), construct the outflow hydrograph to be expected from a reservoir of known storage characteristics impounding the stream under the assumed conditions of runoff prevailing during the flood.

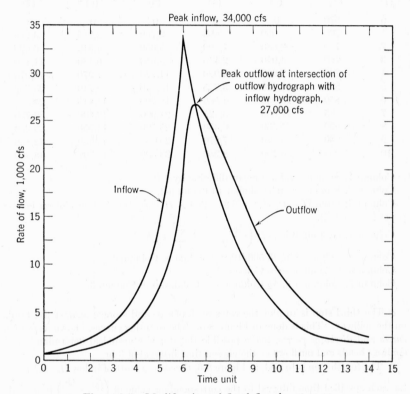

Figure 8-5. Modification of flood flow by storage.

The following assumptions are made: length of spillway tentatively selected $L = 250$ ft; appropriate weir coefficient $C = 3.8$; and time interval $\Delta t = 3$ hr $= 10{,}800$ sec.

a. The first step in the solution of this problem is to determine, for increasing heads H, the outflow Q and storage S above spillway level. To do this, the surface area A of the reservoir must be found from a curve of the type shown in Figure 8-4.

b. The second step is to calculate the corresponding functional rates of storage values $\dfrac{S}{\Delta t}$, $\left(\dfrac{S}{\Delta t} - \dfrac{Q}{2}\right)$, and $\left(\dfrac{S}{\Delta t} + \dfrac{Q}{2}\right)$. These steps are carried out in Table 8-5.

TABLE 8-5. Calculation of Functional Rates of Storage (Example 8-5)

Head on spillway H, ft	Reservoir area A, acres	Calculated outflow Q, cfs	Calculated storage S above spillway level, acre-ft	$\dfrac{S}{\Delta t}$ cfs	$\left(\dfrac{S}{\Delta t} - \dfrac{Q}{2}\right)$ cfs	$\left(\dfrac{S}{\Delta t} + \dfrac{Q}{2}\right)$ cfs
(1)	(2)	(3)	(4)	(5)	(6)	(7)
0	670	0	0	0	0	0
1	700	950	685	2,760	2,285	3,235
2	730	2,680	1,400	5,650	4,310	6,990
3	760	4,940	2,145	8,650	6,180	11,120
4	790	7,600	2,920	11,770	7,970	15,570
5	820	10,620	3,725	15,020	9,710	20,330
6	850	13,950	4,560	18,390	11,415	25,365
7	885	17,600	5,425	21,900	13,100	30,700
8	920	21,500	6,330	25,500	14,750	36,250
9	960	25,700	7,270	29,300	16,450	42,150
10	1,000	30,100	8,250	33,300	18,300	48,400

Column 1: Assumed values; heads differing by 1 ft.

Column 2: From area curve similar to Figure 8-4.

Column 3: From $Q = CLH^{3/2} = 3.8 \times 250 \times H^{3/2}$ or straight-line plot on log-log paper (Figure 8-6).

Column 4: By Equation 8-7: $\left(\dfrac{A_0 + A_n}{2} + \sum_1^{n-1} A\right) h.$

Column 5: Column 4 $\times$ 43,560/10,800 = 4.03 $\times$ Column 4.

Column 6: Column 5 $-$ ½ Column 3.

Column 7: Column 5 $+$ ½ Column 3 = Column 6 $+$ Column 3.

c. The third step is to plot the rates of discharge and storage against the heads on the spillway. This is done in Figure 8-6. The resulting curves, known as *routing curves* and *discharge curves*, make possible the stepwise graphical determination of spillway heads and outflows at the chosen time interval of 3 hr.

d. The fourth step is to add, in Figure 8-6, the average rate of inflow $(I_k + I_{k+1})/2$ for each specified time interval to the corresponding value of $\left(\dfrac{S_k}{\Delta t} - \dfrac{Q_k}{2}\right)$ in accordance with Equation 8-11 and to find at the resulting magnitude of $\left(\dfrac{S_{k+1}}{\Delta t} + \dfrac{Q_{k+1}}{2}\right)$ the spillway head and discharge that must obtain in order to satisfy these relationships. To establish a starting point, it is assumed that the reservoir is in equilibrium at the initial rate of inflow of 700 cfs shown in Figure 8-5, the head on the spillway being $H = \left(\dfrac{Q}{CL}\right)^{2/3} = \left(\dfrac{700}{3.8 \times 250}\right)^{2/3} = 0.82$ ft.

The necessary calculations are presented in Table 8-6.

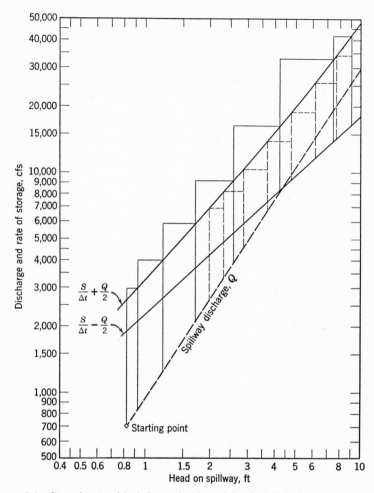

Figure 8-6. Stepwise graphical determination of head and discharge relationships in routing a flood through an impounding reservoir.

TABLE 8-6. Calculation of Reservoir Outflows (Example 8-5)

Time number (1)	Observed inflow I, cfs (2)	Average inflow cfs (3)	$\dfrac{S}{\Delta t} - \dfrac{Q}{2}$ At beginning of time interval (4)	$\dfrac{S}{\Delta t} + \dfrac{Q}{2}$ At end of time interval (5)	Head on spillway ft (6)	Out-flow Q cfs (7)
0	700	......	......	......	0.817	700
1	1,400	1,050	1,900	2,950	0.920	840
2	2,400	1,900	2,100	4,000	1.20	1,250
3	4,000	3,200	2,700	5,900	1.70	2,100
4	7,000	5,500	3,700	9,200	2.55	3,870
5	15,000	11,000	5,400	16,400	4.20	8,170
6	34,000	24,500	8,300	32,800	7.40	19,100
7	22,000	28,000	13,700	41,700	8.95	25,400
8	14,000	18,000	16,200	34,200	7.65	20,010
9	9,000	11,500	14,200	25,700	6.10	14,300
10	6,000	7,500	11,500	19,000	4.70	9,680
11	3,400	4,700	9,300	14,000	3.70	6,760
12	2,500	2,950	7,400	10,350	2.85	4,570
13	2,200	2,350	5,900	8,250	2.30	3,310
14	2,000	2,100	4,850	6,950	1.95	2,590

Column 1: Each time interval is 3 hours.

Column 2: The observed inflow is taken from the chosen flood hydrograph of the stream before impoundage. See Figure 8-5.

Column 3: Average of successive values in Column 2.

Column 4: Value of $\left(\dfrac{S}{\Delta t} - \dfrac{Q}{2}\right)$ at beginning of time interval read during construction of Figure 8-6.

Column 5: Value of $\left(\dfrac{S}{\Delta t} + \dfrac{Q}{2}\right)$ at end of time interval = Column 4 + Column 3 in accordance with Equation 8-11.

Columns 6 and 7: Read from Figure 8-6 with exception of the initial values: 0.82 ft and 700 cfs. These identify the starting point of the step integration.

e. The last step is to plot the calculated outflow hydrograph against the observed inflow hydrograph. This is done in Figure 8-5. It is seen that storage above spillway level lowers the peak flow from 34,000 cfs to 27,000 cfs, i.e. to 80% of its uncontrolled magnitude. The head on the spillway, therefore, is 9.2 ft (Figure 8-6).

The principles involved in this method of flood routing can be employed also in studies of the effect upon flood flows of channel storage, detention or retardation basins, and other types of storage.

A rough determination of whether calculations such as these are worth while can be had from generalized estimates suggested by

Fuller[9] (Table 8-7). If the outflow is reduced to 90% or less of the inflow, more accurate calculations are justified.

TABLE 8-7. Generalized Estimates of Reservoir Outflows

Ratio of storage above spillway level to flood flow in 24 hours, %	5	10	20	30	40	50	60	70
Ratio of peak outflow to peak inflow, %	99	97	93	86	77	65	53	40

Example 8-6. The flood flows presented in Example 8-5 will produce a maximum 24-hr flood of 27,600 acre-ft. If the maximum allowable head on the spillway is assumed to be 10 ft, the storage available above spillway level is 8,250 acre-ft. The ratio of peak outflow to peak inflow is then found as follows from Fuller's values (Table 8-7):

a. Ratio of storage above spillway level to 24-hr flood 100 × 8,250/27,600 = 30%.

b. From Fuller's values, ratio of peak outflow to peak inflow = 86%.

c. The value ascertained in Example 8-5 was 80%, the maximum head on the spillway being 9.2 ft.

Since Fuller's outflow ratio is less than 90%, making the more accurate determination is warranted.

The principles presented in the preceding sections of this chapter are applicable also to the storage and regulation of storm-water runoff collected by combined municipal drainage schemes. The storm-water stand-by tanks used for this purpose may be incorporated in the collecting system itself or become auxiliary units in sewage-treatment works (Section 3-6).

[9] W. E. Fuller, "Flood Flows," *Trans. Am. Soc. Civil Engrs.*, 70, 564 (1914).

9-1. Matters to Be Considered. The hydrology of ground water has been discussed in Sections 6-9, 6-10, and 6-11, and brief reference has been made to the development of ground-water supplies in Section 2-6. It is the purpose of the present chapter to deal primarily with the evaluation of those matters—hydrologic, geologic, and hydraulic— that are of concern to the engineer in the capturing of ground-water sources. As presently indicated, some of these matters also have a bearing on surface storage and runoff and on the loss of water from conduits or drains or its entrance into them.

The factors governing the recharge of ground water by precipitation or by seepage from surface sources, the storage of ground water, its flow through the ground, and its discharge from the ground are more complex and more difficult of measurement than are many of the corresponding factors pertaining to surface waters. Hence the statistical information that can reasonably be made available for the quantitative study of ground water is often meager and fragmentary. Indirect evidence, generally of a geologic nature, must be adduced in order to arrive at useful conclusions. For major developments, the services of a competent geologist are essential.

In the study of a particular ground-water source, its hydrologic, geologic, and hydraulic system must first of all be isolated. Surface collection areas and underground conduits and reservoirs can then be identified, and the hydraulic characteristics of the system discovered. An estimate of the safe yield of the source will require evaluation of the following factors: (1) the quantities of water added to the formation by infiltration of rain, melting snow and ice, and surface waters; (2) the volume of water stored within the isolated system as measured by the porosity, thickness, and areal extent of the water-bearing soil or rock formation; (3) the rate at which the water moves through the ground and can be withdrawn from it, which is a function of its permeability and the available hydraulic gradients; and (4) the amount of water lost from the ground by evaporation and transpiration, by effluent seepage into streams and other surface bodies of water, by flow from springs, and by underground routes of escape. At the same time, the effect of pumping, or other induced withdrawal of water from the ground, must be taken into account because the natural hydrologic and hydraulic balance is upset by such withdrawal: water levels fall, directions of movement change, return of water to the surface or to the atmosphere by natural processes may be reduced, and infiltration may be increased. If these varied effects are not anticipated, the supply of water that is to be developed may not remain adequate, or its exploitation may become uneconomical in the course of time as water has to be lifted from greater and greater depths.

Geologic Aspects

9-2. The Earth's Crust. The wide variation in the texture and stratigraphy of the earth's crust is reflected in the manner of occurrence of both free and confined ground water. The water table may lie at or near the earth's surface as in streams and swamps, or it may be several thousand feet down. Ground water may flow through caverns, crevices, and solution passages at velocities comparable to those of turbulent surface streams (1 or more feet per second), or it may move in laminar flow through the capillary interstices of soils and rocks at velocities of only a few feet a year. Aquifers may be thick and isotropic [1] as well as homogeneous, or they may consist of a wide variety of layers, lenses, and tortuous bands of varying materials. The conditions of storage and flow, therefore, depend in large measure upon the geologic origin and history of the water-bearing formations.

From a geological standpoint the earth's crust is made up of rocks and soils. The rocks are igneous, sedimentary, and metamorphic in origin. Briefly, rocks are classified as follows: [2]

1. *Igneous.* Resulting from the cooling and solidification of molten materials from the earth's interior. Depending upon the place and manner of solidification there are two types:

a. *Intrusive.* Solidifying beneath the earth's surface with prolonged cooling. Examples are: granite, rhyolite, diorite, andesite, basalt, and diabase.

b. *Extrusive.* Cooling rapidly at the earth's surface with liberation of steam during the period of volcanic activity. Examples are: lava and volcanic ash.

---

[1] Possessing the same properties in all directions.

[2] *Hydrology Handbook,* American Society of Civil Engineers, *Manuals of Engineering Practice,* **28** (1949).

   2. *Sedimentary.* Formed by the consolidation of materials laid down in water
   after:
      a. Precipitation from solution. Examples are: flint, vein quartz, caliche,
      gypsum, common salt, and some limestones.
      b. Sedimentation and deposition of suspended particles, including: (1) The
      remains of animals and plants. Examples are: limestone, chalk, marl, and
      coal. (2) Particles weathered from older rocks. Examples are: sandstone
      and shale.
   3. *Metamorphic.* Created by the transformation of the structure of igneous and
   sedimentary rocks, chiefly by the action of water, heat, and pressure. Examples are: quartzite, slate, marble, schist, and gneiss.

The soils result from the weathering of the rocks and include, separately or mixed, all loose and unconsolidated clays, silts, sands, gravels,
and boulders.

9-3. Water-Bearing Rocks. The *intrusive* igneous rocks are dense
in texture and would be barren of water, were it not for the occurrence
in them of fissures and cracks. But their width is generally small
(seldom more than 1 mm), and they die out with depth. The numbers
of inclined joints that can be intersected by wells decreases rapidly
(from about 4 per 100 ft down to the 100-ft level to less than 1 per
100 ft below the 400-ft level). Therefore, such water as can be captured is derived from depths that generally do not exceed 300 ft. Of
the intrusive rocks, basalt is a good aquifer, rhyolite a poor one.
Weathering of the granites produces the silica sands and gravels that,
after transportation, abrasion, and sorting by wind and water, form
the most productive water-bearing soils. The *extrusive* igneous rocks
may be very porous and may contain cracks, holes, and extensive
caverns. As a result, some lava formations [3] yield water in abundance.

Of the four common varieties of sedimentary rocks (limestones and
related calcareous rocks, shales, sandstones, and conglomerates), the
limestones are usually dense and impervious. However, they are the
most soluble of all rocks, and, where they have been subjected to the
leaching action of water that contains dissolving carbon dioxide or
organic acids, they are honeycombed by solution passages and caverns.
Underground streams and lakes are formed in the course of time, and
these may overflow at the surface to create large springs.[4] *Shales,*
which result from the consolidation of clays, are generally impervious
and act as aquicludes. *Sandstones,* on the other hand, may be very
pervious. Their water-bearing capacity depends upon the extent to
which the pores of the sand grains are filled with cementing materials.

---

[3] For example, in the northwestern United States and the Hawaiian Islands.
[4] Examples are numerous, particularly in Florida and in the Ozarks of Missouri
and Arkansas.

Quartzites, constituted of silica sands that are completely filled with cementing siliceous materials, are comparable to granites in density and imperviousness, whereas loosely cemented sandstones are among the most productive aquifers. The water-bearing capacity of the consolidated or cemented heterogeneous mixtures of materials that constitute *conglomerates* varies considerably. As a rule, however, they are quite tight. Good aquifers are sometimes encountered in limestone and sandstone at depths in excess of a mile. However, most ground-water developments are less than 2,000 ft deep.

None of the metamorphic rocks is an important water producer. *Marble*, like the limestone from which it is created, is soluble and may yield water from solution channels. *Slates* and *schists*, which originate in shales, are both relatively impervious, but they transmit some water along joints, cleavage cracks, and fractures. *Gneiss* resembles, in its structural and water-bearing properties, the intrusive granites from which it is generally derived.

In North America, the important water-bearing rock formations lie at considerable depths below the earth's surface and generally carry water under artesian pressure.[5] The supplies obtained from cavernous limestones near the surface are an exception.

9.4. Water-Bearing Soils. Although the water-bearing rocks of the United States are important sources of water, the areas served by them are small within the country as a whole. Greater yields of water are actually derived from the soils of the overburden in which free and artesian conditions of flow exist.

The size classification of soil particles developed by the Bureau of Chemistry and Soils of the U. S. Department of Agriculture and by the International Society of Soil Science is shown in Table 9-1.

Sands and *gravels* are by far the most important water-bearing materials. They have high specific yield and permeability [6] and are ordinarily so situated that replenishment is rapid. Uniform or well-

[5] The great artesian systems of the United States are: (1) the extensive Paleozoic system of the east-central region, where shales confine water in sandstones and limestones, e.g., the well-known Potsdam sandstone in Wisconsin and northern Illinois; (2) the Roswell system in New Mexico, where a cavernous Permian limestone furnishes large quantities of water used for irrigation; (3) the Atlantic and Gulf coastal plain systems, in which dipping formations of pervious Cretaceous and Tertiary sands and gravels or sandstones and limestones are interbedded with clays or shales; and (4) the Cretaceous artesian systems of the Great Plains, in which water is confined under great pressure in extensive sandstones that lie below thick, dense shales, e.g., the productive Dakota sandstone that underlies parts of Wyoming, Colorado, North and South Dakota, Nebraska, and Minnesota.

[6] For a definition of these terms, see Sections 9-10 and 9-11.

TABLE 9-1. Size Classification of Soil Grains

Diameter of grain, cm

Soil	U. S. Dept. of Agriculture	International Society of Soil Science
Fine gravel (grit)	2×10^{-1} to 10^{-1}	
Coarse sand	10^{-1} to 5×10^{-2}	2×10^{-1} to 2×10^{-2}
Medium sand	5×10^{-2} to 2.5×10^{-2}	
Fine sand	2.5×10^{-2} to 10^{-2}	2×10^{-2} to 2×10^{-3}
Very fine sand	10^{-2} to 5×10^{-3}	
Silt	5×10^{-3} to 5×10^{-4}	2×10^{-3} to 2×10^{-4}
Clay	5×10^{-4} or less	2×10^{-4} or less

sorted sands and gravels are the most productive, while mixed materials containing clay are least so, for example, boulder clay deposited beneath ice sheets. Transported material is generally more permeable than that in immediate contact with the mother rock. Most sand and gravel beds have been deposited in shallow, active water: (1) in seas, lakes, or river beds as alluvial deposits; (2) at the mouth of canyons as outwash cones; or (3) along the edge of retreating ice sheets as outwash plains. Since the origin of these materials and the depth and motion of the transporting water varied in time, the deposits generally include alternating layers of material of varying size and grading. Beds deposited in lakes and seas are often extensive, whereas outwash cones or river channels usually contain relatively small lenses of sand and gravel confined between layers of less pervious material.[7]

Clays and *silts*, although porous, are generally quite impervious. They are poor aquifers and are significant only (1) when they confine or interfere with the movement of water through the more pervious soils and (2) when they supply water to permeable formations by consolidation.

9-5. Interrelationships. Where the rock outcrops at the surface, the rate of water intake is likely to be small. Where the rock is overlain by porous and permeable soils, on the other hand, the rate of infiltration is good, and the overburden becomes a reservoir from which water is steadily fed into the underlying rock. The thicker the water-bearing mantle, the greater, in general, is the safe yield from rocks as well as from the soil itself. Topography, or surface relief,

[7] The largest supplies of ground water in the United States come from the following sand and gravel deposits: (1) glacial outwash plains north of the Ohio and Missouri rivers and in New England; (2) valley fill in the western mountain region; (3) Tertiary and Quaternary deposits in the Quaternary terrace and lowland deposits in the Atlantic and Gulf coastal plains.

also enters into the problem. The steeper the slope, the more effectively does it shed rainfall and runoff from melting snow. Valleys not only accumulate the heaviest overburden but are, ordinarily, areas of least slope. In mountainous country they are rivaled in flatness only by broad hills, plateaus, and upland plains. Slope and cover combine, therefore, to make for high or low yield of ground water. The stratigraphy of the earth's crust, as previously indicated, is responsible for the occurrence of ground water as perched, free, or artesian water. It also affects the yield of artesian waters by the compression of both aquicludes and aquifers.

9-6. Geological and Geophysical Exploration. A detailed knowledge of the geology of ground-water areas is essential, if the capacity of water-bearing formations is to be fully established. Surface geology and exposures due to mining, quarrying, and related operations must be supplemented by *well logs*. These are records of the nature and depth of the various strata that were encountered in sinking existing wells.[8] When they are combined with measurements of the capacity of wells, the logs furnish the most important information that can be had without the aid of test wells or geophysical reconnaissance.

Geological formations differ in their gravitational, magnetic, seismic, acoustic, and radioactive properties. These can be identified by suitable means. The measurements obtained are then translated into geological terms from the known behavior of similar formations. This is called geophysical exploration or prospecting. Some of the methods can be applied from the surface or in existing wells, others only in the latter. Measurement of variations of gravity and of the earth's magnetic field are made with the aid of the torsion balance and the magnetometer. Although these instruments do not determine the presence of water itself, they suggest the location of geological structures that may be favorable water carriers. Acoustic and seismic methods measure the speed of travel of sound and shock waves through the underground formations. Dependence of wave velocity upon the density of the materials through which it passes makes possible a geophysical analysis of the test area. The presence of water makes itself felt, too. Wave reflection is measured when interest is centered on deep strata, wave refraction when the water-bearing formation is near the surface of the earth (see Figure 9-1a).[9]

[8] Many states require the keeping of well logs and their filing with a state authority or with the U. S. Geological Survey.

[9] Daniel Linehan and Scott Keith, "Seismic Reconnaissance for Ground-Water Development," *J. New Eng. Water Works Assoc., 63,* 76 (1949).

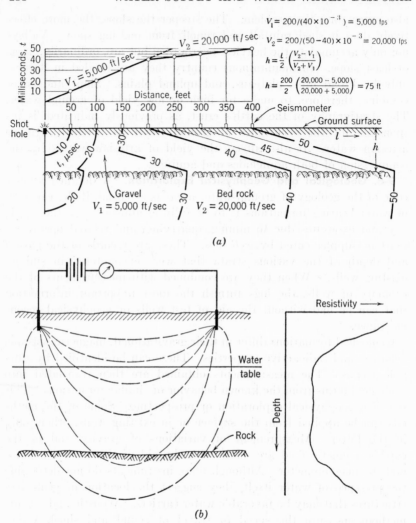

Figure 9-1. Identification of water-bearing strata by geophysical prospecting. (a) Seismic refraction. *After Linehan and Keith.* (b) Electric resistivity. *After Jakosky and Wilson.*

The resistance of the ground and its contained water is determined by impressing a current on electrodes inserted in the ground. As shown in Figure 9-1b, the presence of water is shown by a drop in resistance within the water-bearing strata, the depth of penetration of the current being approximately equal to the electrode spacing.[10]

[10] J. J. Jakosky and C. H. Wilson, "Geophysical Studies in Placer and Water Supply Problems," *Am. Inst. Mining Met. Engrs. Tech. Pub.*, 515 (1933).

Hydrologic Aspects

9-7. The General Hydrologic Equation. Hydrological equilibrium is expressed by the following equation:

$$\Sigma R = \Sigma D + \Delta S \qquad\qquad 9\text{-}1$$

where ΣR denotes the various hydrological factors of recharge, and ΣD those of discharge, while ΔS is the associated change in storage volume. More specifically, the recharge is composed of the following:

1. Natural infiltration derived from rainfall and snow melt.
2. Infiltration from surface bodies of water.
3. Underflow.
4. Leakage through confining layers, or water displaced from them by compression.
5. Water derived from diffusion, charging, and water-spreading operations.

Conversely, the discharge includes:

1. Evaporation and transpiration.
2. Seepage into surface bodies of water.
3. Underflow.
4. Leakage through confining layers or absorbed by them by the reduction of compression.
5. Water withdrawn through wells and infiltration galleries or basins.

As shown by Equation 9-1, determination of the safe yield of an aquifer is quite analogous to finding the permissible draft from a surface supply. A complete hydrological inventory of a water-producing area includes, in addition to the evaluation of the three terms in Equation 9-1, a consideration of rainfall and surface runoff. The larger the area, the greater are the difficulties of obtaining accurate measurements or estimates of the components of an inventory.[11]

9-8. Evaluation of Recharge. When the bulk of the water received by an aquifer is derived by infiltration from surface streams, the progressive reduction in surface flow along the water course is the principal measure of recharge.[12] The amount of intake of rain and melting snow is much more difficult of determination, since it requires a knowledge of losses by evaporation and transpiration, and of the water needed to satisfy the field-moisture capacity or specific retention of the soil. Needed information is obtained by the study of

---

[11] In the United States, experimental stations for the intensive study of ground-water hydrology are maintained by the Soil Conservation Service and the Forest Service. The publications of these services hold much of interest.

[12] This is true, for example, in some parts of the western United States.

representative experimental plots, *lysimeter* studies, and water-table fluctuations, a record being kept also of soil-water deficiencies in different portions of the intake area (see also Section 6-8). Underflow is measured in terms of the behavior of the water-bearing formations as conduits (Section 9-13). Leakage through aquicludes and displacement of water from them by compression must be kept in mind where the geology of the area indicates artesian or perched-water conditions. Leakage will be reflected by decreases in the amounts of water stored in or flowing through the ground beyond the aquiclude. Although the confining formation may be relatively impervious, the differences in head existing between the free and artesian waters may be sufficiently large to create a considerable amount of leakage in the direction of the pressure drop. The amount of water that enters the ground from diffusion, charging, and water-spreading arrangements is generally a matter of record, or it is readily made so.

9-9. Evaluation of Discharge. The measurement of evaporation and transpiration, called the consumptive use, is discussed in Section 6-8. Discharge of ground water by these means is restricted to areas in which the capillary fringe reaches the root zone or the surface, or in which phreatophytes are prevalent. Since transpiration is more or less confined to the hours of daylight, diurnal fluctuations in water-table elevations are a measure of discharge by this phenomenon. Discharge of ground water by seepage into surface bodies of water is the counterpart of recharge from these sources and is determined by similar methods. Since escaping ground water constitutes the dry-weather flow of streams, subtraction of surface runoff and water released from channel storage will establish the magnitude of the dry-weather flow. It is of interest, in this connection, that a determination of the seasonal relationships between the elevation of the ground-water table and the dry-weather flow of streams will furnish an estimate of the amount of water the escape of which can be purposefully prevented by means of a controlled lowering of the ground-water table. For the determination of the amount of underflow passing out of gathering grounds, reference is made to Sections 6-11 and 9-11. Measurement of discharge leakage through confining layers is determined in the same manner as recharge leakage through these formations. The amount of water withdrawn through ground-water works, finally, is assessed through records of draft.

9-10. Evaluation of Storage. The volume of water within a saturated formation of rock or soil equals its pore space. This is generalized in terms of the *porosity*, or ratio f of pore, void, or interstitial volume to total volume of rock or soil. The *voids ratio* or ratio of pore volume to solid volume, $e = f/(1 - f)$, is also a useful concept in ground-water hydraulics and soil mechanics. As shown in Figure 9-2, there are two limiting arrangements, or packings, of spherical particles of uniform diameter that are in contact with each other: the orthogonal, or cubic, and the rhombic, or rhombohedral. In accordance with its geometry, orthogonal packing creates a porosity of 47.64%; rhombic packing, one of 25.95%; both irrespective of the magnitude of the spheres themselves. When large spheres are interspersed with smaller ones, however, the porosity of the mass may be

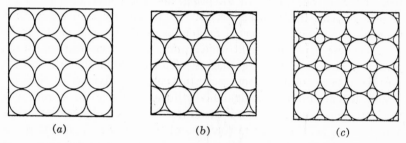

(a) (b) (c)

Figure 9-2. Effect of arrangement and size variation of grains upon porosity. (a) Orthogonal packing; porosity = 47.64%. (b) Rhombic packing; porosity = 25.95%. (c) Two sizes, orthogonal; porosity = 43.92%.

greatly reduced. Irregularity in particle shape generally increases porosity; cementing substances decrease it. Freshly deposited silt may possess a very high porosity (up to 80%). A common porosity of natural sands and gravels is 40%. The value for sandstones is more nearly 20%. Porosity is a static quality of rocks and soils. It is not of itself a measure of perviousness or permeability. These are dynamic qualities that have no meaning in the absence of flow (see Section 9-11).

Not all the water stored in a geological formation can be withdrawn by normal engineering operations. There is, therefore, a difference between total storage and useful storage. The quantity that will drain off by gravity is called the *specific yield;* its counterpart is the *specific retention.* Specific yields vary from zero for plastic clays to values close to the magnitude of the porosity for coarse sands and gravels.

Specific yield may be determined in a number of different ways, including the following: (1) saturation of samples of rock or soil with water followed by their drainage by gravity or centrifugal force (in field measurements, saturation must be confined to the material above the capillary fringe); (2) drainage of samples taken from just above

the capillary fringe after the water table has fallen (specific retention); (3) determination of the volume of ground drained by removing a measured volume of water through pumping operations; and
(4) measurement of the particle size and porosity of a sample and
estimation of its specific yield from known values of similar materials.

The factor of specific yield can be eliminated from an inventory of
ground-water yield by starting and ending the hydrological inventory at identical values of ground-water storage.   In North America,
the period of accumulation of water in the ground, like that in surface
reservoirs, extends from fall to spring, and the period of depletion is
associated with the growing season.   As previously stated, the U. S.
Geological Survey has selected September 30 as the end of the *water
year*, because it is the date at which annual depletion of ground water
generally stops and recharge begins.   To the extent that the storage
on this date is constant from year to year, this division of time enhances the accuracy of annual inventories.   Changes in storage volume are based on records of the water levels in observation wells.
Volumes are calculated from contours of the water table or the piezometric surface.

The variation in the storage of an artesian basin is generally small.
It is sometimes expressed in terms of the *storage coefficient* or ratio
of the volume of water released from the full depth of the aquifer
through a unit area of its base when the piezometric surface of the
basin drops a unit of height.   The range of values is reported to lie
between 5×10^{-5} and 5×10^{-3}.   As is true for leakage through aquicludes, the relative magnitudes are small, but the associated absolute
values may be appreciable when the areas and pressure differences
are great.   Storage coefficients and specific yields become substantially
identical when ground-water conditions are free.

Ground storage is relatively large, and deficits may be extended
over many years.   Ultimately, of course, they must be offset by recharge if the source is not to fail.

Hydraulic Aspects

9-11. Ground-Water Flow.   Water filtering into the ground moves
downward to the zone of saturation before it percolates laterally in
the direction of greatest slope of the ground-water table or piezometric surface.   This slope is the hydraulic gradient of underground
flow.   Like the hydraulic gradient of open channels and pipes, it is a
measure of the frictional resistance to flow, the energy lost being
dissipated as heat.   Since recharge, discharge, and storage fluctuate,

flow is both unsteady and non-uniform, and the hydraulic gradient is not stationary. During replenishment, the water table rises, the gradient steepens, and flow increases. During dry spells, the opposite occurs. Ordinarily, the hydraulic gradient slopes in the direction of the ground surface, but the degree of slope is not necessarily the same. Flow may be free as in an open channel or confined as in a pipe. Flow may be laminar when pores or crevices and associated velocities or Reynolds numbers are small, or turbulent when cracks or solution passages and associated velocities or Reynolds numbers are large.

An aquifer that offers little resistance to flow is called *pervious* or *permeable;* conversely, one that offers much resistance is called *impervious* or *impermeable.* The nature of the system of pores, rather than their relative volume, determines resistance to flow at a given velocity. Hence permeability and porosity are not synonymous terms. Clays with porosities of 50%, for example, are quite impervious, whereas sandstones with porosities of 15% or less are quite pervious.

In nature, the rate of ground-water movement and slope of the ground-water table, or piezometric surface, are not large. In aquifers of high yield, velocities of 5 to 60 ft a day are associated with hydraulic gradients of 10 to 20 ft per mile. Underflow through gravel deposits may reach several hundred feet per day, but flows as low as a few feet per year may also be economically useful.

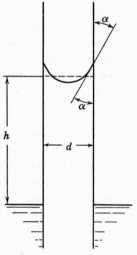

9-12. Capillary Rise. Water is held above the true water table by capillary action and thereby forms a capillary fringe. If the interstices are small, the quantity of water held in this partially saturated layer of soil may be significant.

Surface tension, or intermolecular cohesion, determines the height to which water will rise in the capillary channels of fine-grained soils and porous rocks. As shown in Figure 9-3, the capillary rise h of water of specific weight γ in contact with air of specific weight γ_a in a tube of diameter d establishes a weight of

Figure 9-3. Capillary rise of a liquid in a tube.

water $\frac{1}{4}\pi d^2(\gamma - \gamma_a)h$ that must be supported by a force produced by the surface tension σ of the water being exerted along the line of contact of the water surface with the tube and forming a contact angle α

with its vertical walls. The magnitude of this supporting force is $\pi d\sigma \cos \alpha$. Equating the weight of water to the supporting force and solving for the capillary rise,

$$h = \frac{4\sigma \cos \alpha}{d(\gamma - \gamma_a)} \qquad 9\text{-}2$$

For an air-water interface, a contact angle of zero degrees, which obtains in a glass tube that has been cleaned and moistened, and σ in dynes per centimeter,

$$h = \frac{4\sigma}{gd(\gamma - \gamma_a)} = \frac{\sigma}{245d} \text{ cm} \qquad 9\text{-}3$$

because the specific weight of air (1.25×10^{-3} gm/cm^3 at 10 C) is so small and the specific weight of water is so close to unity.

Example 9-1. How high will water at a temperature of 10 C rise in a capillary tube 0.1 mm in diameter?

From Equation 9-3 and for a surface tension of 74.2 dynes/cm (Table 17-4):

$$h = 74.2/(245 \times 0.01) = 30.3 \text{ cm} = 1 \text{ ft}$$

9-13. Darcy's Law. Although Hagen[13] and Poiseuille[14] were the first to propose that the velocity of flow of water and other liquids through capillary tubes is proportional to the first power of the slope of the hydraulic gradient, credit for the verification of this observation and for its application to the flow of water through the ground, or, more specifically, its filtration through sand, must go to Henri Darcy.[15] The relationship is known as Darcy's law and may be written

$$v = Ks \qquad 9\text{-}4$$

where v is the face or approach velocity, or the quantity of water flowing per unit, gross, cross-sectional area; s is the slope of the hydraulic gradient, or the loss of head per unit length of flow path; and K is the coefficient of permeability or the proportionality constant for water of a given temperature flowing through a given material. Since s is a dimensionless ratio, K has the dimensions of velocity and is in fact the velocity of flow that is associated with a hydraulic gradient of unity. Because the value of K varies inversely as the kinematic vis-

[13] G. Hagen, "Über die Bewegung des Wassers in engen cylindrischen Röhren," *Ann. Physik und Chemie, 46,* 423 (1839).

[14] G. L. M. Poiseuille, "Recherches expérimentales sur le mouvement des liquides dans les tubes de très petit diamètre," *Roy. Acad. Sci. Inst. France Math. Phys. Sci. Mem., 9,* 433 (1846).

[15] *Les fontaines publiques de la Ville de Dijon,* Paris, 1856.

cosity ν of the flowing liquid (Section 17-2), measurements of K are generally referred to a standard water temperature such as 60 F or 10 C. The ratio of the viscosity at the standard temperature to the observed temperature is the necessary correction factor, or

$$K_1/K_2 = \nu_2/\nu_1 \qquad\qquad 9\text{-}5$$

The upper limit of Darcy's law [16] is reached at Reynolds numbers between 1 and 10. This limit is generally reached as water approaches the face of wells in coarse-grained sandy soils. In practice, no lower limit has been observed even at vanishingly small hydraulic gradients such as a few inches a mile.

The value of K is expressed in various units, depending upon the interests of the investigator and the system of measurements employed. The U. S. Geological Survey has adopted as its *standard*

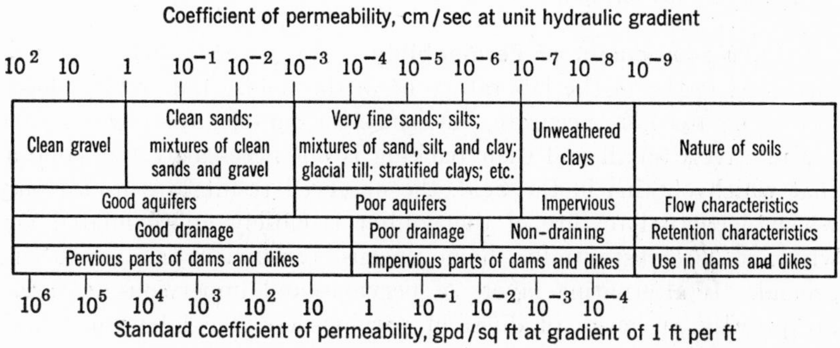

Coefficient of permeability, cm/sec at unit hydraulic gradient

10^2	10	1	10^{-1}	10^{-2}	10^{-3}	10^{-4}	10^{-5}	10^{-6}	10^{-7}	10^{-8}	10^{-9}

Clean gravel	Clean sands; mixtures of clean sands and gravel	Very fine sands; silts; mixtures of sand, silt, and clay; glacial till; stratified clays; etc.	Unweathered clays	Nature of soils
Good aquifers		Poor aquifers	Impervious	Flow characteristics
Good drainage		Poor drainage	Non–draining	Retention characteristics
Pervious parts of dams and dikes		Impervious parts of dams and dikes		Use in dams and dikes

10^6	10^5	10^4	10^3	10^2	10	1	10^{-1}	10^{-2}	10^{-3}	10^{-4}

Standard coefficient of permeability, gpd/sq ft at gradient of 1 ft per ft

Figure 9-4. Magnitude of the coefficient of permeability for different classes of soils. *After Arthur Casagrande.*

coefficient of permeability the gallons per day of water at 60 F flowing through 1 sq ft of cross-section under a gradient of 1 ft per ft (100%). In the *field coefficient of permeability,* flow is related to the prevailing temperature, a cross-section 1 mile in width and 1 ft in depth, and a hydraulic gradient of 1 ft per mile. At a ground-water temperature of 60 F, the field coefficient and the standard coefficient are identical. The *coefficient of transmissibility* is obtained by multiplying the standard coefficient of permeability by the full saturated height, or depth, of the aquifer.

The range in magnitude of the coefficient of permeability for various classes of soils is shown in Figure 9-4. Individual values may be determined (1) by laboratory experiment or field test or (2), for

[16] As determined by the evaluation of the constituent terms proposed in Section 24-6.

granular deposits, by calculations that are based upon measurable characteristics of the soil and water. The second method is of particular importance in connection with the filtration of water and is discussed in Chapter 24.

Example 9-2. (*a*) Estimate the velocity of flow in feet per day and the discharge in gallons per day through an aquifer of very coarse sand 1,000 ft wide and 50 ft deep when the slope of the ground-water table is 20 ft per mile. (*b*) Find the standard coefficient of permeability and the coefficient of transmissibility on the assumption that the temperature of the ground water is 60 F.

a. From Figure 9-4 choose a coefficient of permeability of

$$K = 1.0 \text{ cm per sec } [17] = 2,835 \text{ ft per day}$$

Since $s = 20/5,280$, Equation 9-4 states that $v = 2,835 \times 20/5,280 = 11$ ft per day and $Q = 11 \times 1,000 \times 50 \times 7.5 \times 10^{-6} = 4.1$ mgd.

b. The standard coefficient of permeability is $2,835 \times 7.5 = 2.13 \times 10^4$, and the coefficient of transmissibility becomes $2.13 \times 10^4 \times 50 = 1.06 \times 10^6$.

9-14. Measurement of Permeability. The permeability of soils is measured either in the laboratory or in the field. Laboratory determinations are more accurate, but, since the samples that can be used are relatively small and their packing is not necessarily the same as that which obtains in the field, the observed results are useful only when the actual texture of the aquifer is closely approximated and when it is substantially homogeneous throughout the gathering ground. If alternating layers of pervious and impervious materials are present, or lenses of different perviousness, the laboratory findings are meaningless.

a. Laboratory Measurements. Four common types of permeameters are shown in Figure 9-5 and described below.

1. The *constant-head permeameter* discharges water upward through the sample to be tested. It operates at a fixed rate Q under a constant head h and collects a volume V in the time t from a bed of cross-section A and depth l. The value of the coefficient of permeability is given by the following equation:

$$K = \frac{Vl}{Ath} \frac{\nu}{\nu_0} \qquad 9\text{-}6$$

Here ν is the kinematic viscosity at the observed water temperature, and ν_0 the kinematic viscosity at the reference temperature. The resulting value of K, it must be repeated, applies only to the material as placed in the permeameter. If the soil is cohesive, an undisturbed sample should be used. When cohesionless sands are tested, the degree of compaction in the permeameter should be that of the material in place. Upward flow displaces air from the sample when the permeameter is set in operation.

---

[17] 1 cm/sec $= 3.28 \times 10^{-2}$ fps $= 2,835$ ft per day.

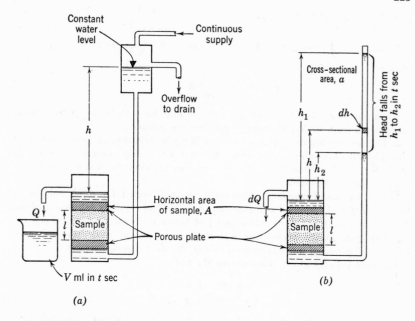

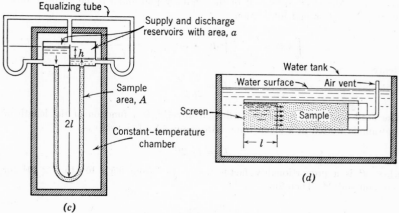

Figure 9-5. Permeameters: (a) Constant head; (b) Falling head; (c) Non-discharging; (d) Horizontal capillary.

2. The *falling-head permeameter* is more generally used for materials of low permeability. For heads h_1 and h_2 at the beginning and end of a time interval t and for a cross-sectional area a of the standpipe, the differential equation for the rate of flow d under a head h in the time dt is

$$dQ = -\frac{a\,dh}{dt} = K\frac{h}{l}A\frac{\nu_0}{\nu}$$

Transformation and integration give

$$\int_0^t dt = \frac{al}{KA} \frac{\nu}{\nu_0} \int_{h_1}^{h_2} -\frac{dh}{h} \quad \text{or} \quad t = \frac{al}{KA} \frac{\nu}{\nu_0} \log_e \frac{h_1}{h_2}$$

whence

$$K = \frac{al}{tA} \frac{\nu}{\nu_0} \log_e \frac{h_1}{h_2} \qquad 9\text{-}7$$

When the time of test is long, precautions may have to be taken to prevent evaporation from the liquid surface and from the sample.

3. The *non-discharging permeameter* is like the falling-head permeameter in principle but eliminates evaporation. Because a test may continue over a considerable period of time, special means for maintaining the water at constant temperature are desirable.

4. The *horizontal capillary permeameter* is well suited for rapid field tests. Permeability is determined as a function of the rate of capillary saturation of the dry soil in a sample that is submerged just below the water surface. Since the capillary pull on the percolating water remains constant while the resistance increases, the rate of movement decreases as the wetted zone lengthens.

The pore velocity at any time during the test is

$$\frac{v}{f} = \frac{dl}{dt} = \frac{K h_0}{f} \frac{\nu_0}{l} \frac{\nu_0}{\nu}$$

where h_0 is the head equivalent of the capillary pull and f is the porosity ratio. By transformation and integration

$$\int_0^l l \, dl = \frac{K h_0}{f} \frac{\nu_0}{\nu} \int_0^t dt \quad \text{or} \quad \frac{l^2}{2} = \frac{K h_0}{f} \frac{\nu_0}{\nu} t$$

Hence

$$K = \frac{l^2 f}{2 h_0 t} \frac{\nu}{\nu_0}$$

The head h_0, which cannot be evaluated directly, is a function of the length of the sample wetted in a given time. An empirical relationship is

$$h_0 = Ft/2l^2$$

where F is a proportionality factor that varies from 3.5×10^4 to 2×10^5 for common soils.[18] Therefore,

$$K = \frac{l^4 f}{t^2 F} \frac{\nu}{\nu_0} \qquad 9\text{-}8$$

For a given type of soil, the value of F is calculated from direct measurement of K by means of permeameters a, b, or c. For most calculations, it is sufficient to assume a value of $F = 10^5$.

b. Field Measurements. Permeability is ordinarily determined in the field in one of two ways: (1) by measurement of the hydraulic gradient and velocity of water movement in the ground; and (2) by

[18] D. W. Taylor, *Fundamentals of Soil Mechanics,* John Wiley & Sons, New York, 1948.

determination of the discharge and drawdown of pumped wells. The principle underlying the second method is described in Section 11-10.

As we shall see, the velocity observed in field measurements is the true average rate of motion through the interstices of the aquifer, whereas the velocity over the full cross-section is made part of Equations 9-4 and 9-6. In Equation 9-8, the average velocity of flow in granular materials is expressed as v/f. Since not all the interstices are effective in carrying water, however, the average interstitial velocity v_f should be expressed as $v/(k_f f)$, where k_f is the proportion of effective pore space. The effective porosity probably lies somewhere between the gross porosity and the specific yield. Its determination has not received attention commensurate with its importance.

On the basis of effective porosity, effective velocity, and hydraulic gradient,

$$K = \frac{k_f f v_f}{s} \frac{v}{v_0} \qquad 9\text{-}9$$

The effective or true average velocity of ground-water flow can be measured in terms of the time required for a salt, dye, or radioactive substance to pass from an injection well to an observation well that lies in the direction of water movement. The time of arrival of a salt solution is determined by consecutive chemical titrations or by electrical means, that of a dye by visual observation or colorimetric methods, and that of a radioactive tracer by means of a Geiger or similar counter. The time required for half the recovered substance to have been received divided by the distance between the test wells gives the effective, or median, velocity. Similar methods can be employed in investigations of ground-water pollution. Among the dyes available for this purpose, uranin, a sodium salt of fluorescein, is visible in dilution of $1:4 \times 10^7$ without a fluoroscope and in dilution of $1:10^{10}$ with one.

9-15. Patterns of Flow (Flow Nets). The equation of continuity requires that for a given element of time the volume of water entering an elemental mass of soil from one or more directions must equal the volume of water leaving it in one or more directions, provided that there is no change in the mass or its void space. For two-dimensional flow, the equation formulating this statement, as illustrated in Figure 9-6, is

$$v_x \, dy + v_y \, dx = \left(v_x + \frac{\partial v_x}{\partial x} \, dx \right) dy + \left(v_y + \frac{\partial v_y}{\partial y} \, dy \right) dx \qquad 9\text{-}10$$

whence

$$\frac{\partial v_x}{\partial x} + \frac{\partial v_y}{\partial y} = 0 \qquad 9\text{-}11$$

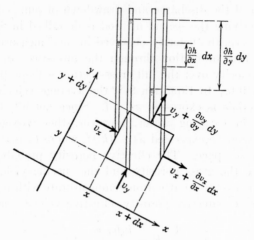

Figure 9-6. Two-dimensional flow in isotropic materials.

For the three-dimensional case, therefore, continuity requires that

$$\frac{\partial v_x}{\partial x} + \frac{\partial v_y}{\partial y} + \frac{\partial v_z}{\partial z} = 0 \qquad\qquad 9\text{-}12$$

and since in accordance with Darcy's law

$$v_x = K\frac{\partial h}{\partial x} \qquad v_y = K\frac{\partial h}{\partial y} \quad \text{and} \quad v_z = K\frac{\partial h}{\partial z} \qquad 9\text{-}13$$

it follows that

$$\frac{\partial^2 h}{\partial x^2} + \frac{\partial^2 h}{\partial y^2} + \frac{\partial^2 h}{\partial x^2} = 0 \qquad\qquad 9\text{-}14$$

This is a Laplace differential equation.

a. One-Dimensional Flow. For unidirectional flow, all terms in the series but one drop out, and $d^2h/dx^2 = 0$. If x measures the length of path in the direction of flow, d^2h/dx^2 becomes the derivative of the Darcy equation, $dh/dx = v/K$, where v is constant and independent of x. The unidirectional flow pattern through a confined aquifer, shown in Figure 9-7a, is an example. If the aquifer has a width b and thickness m

$$dh/dx = Q/(Kbm) \qquad\qquad 9\text{-}15$$

and the head decreases uniformly at the rate v/K or $Q/(Kbm)$.

If the flowlines in the aquifer, both in any horizontal section and any vertical section (in the direction of flow), are so spaced that the quantity ΔQ encompassed by adjacent paths distant Δb or Δm from

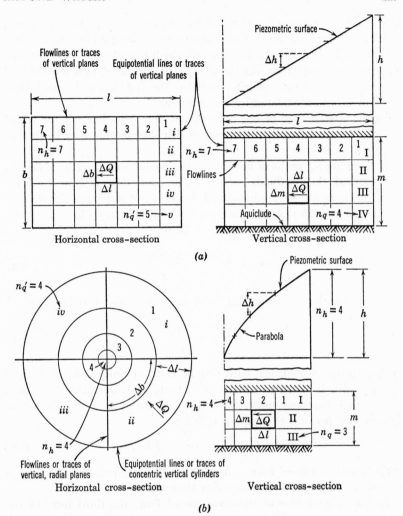

Figure 9-7. Idealized flow nets for confined parallel and radial flow. (*a*) Parallel flow: for constant Δh, Δl is constant. (*b*) Radial flow: for constant Δh, Δl varies as the radius of the flow net.

each other respectively is the same, and the head lost in the distance Δl along the line of flow is Δh, then

$$\frac{\Delta h}{\Delta l} = \frac{\Delta Q}{K\,\Delta b\,\Delta m} \quad \text{or} \quad \frac{\Delta Q}{\Delta h} = K\,\frac{\Delta b\,\Delta m}{\Delta l} \qquad 9\text{-}16$$

If ΔQ and Δh are to be the same through the aquifer, the ratio $\Delta b\,\Delta m/\Delta l$ must be constant, provided that the value of K does not change. All blocks must therefore be identical in size and shape. In this special case of uniform flow, Δb, Δm, and Δl may be made equal for convenience. A flow net is then created, the lines of which bound cubes of equal size. The unidirectional case has thereby been translated into a simplified three-dimensional case which elucidates the fundamental principle of the flow net, first explored by Forchheimer.[19]

In the special case of one-dimensional flow, the flow net for which ΔQ and Δh are constant throughout the field of motion may be further analyzed as follows:

If there are n_q' paths of flow in the horizontal and n_q paths of flow in the vertical (longitudinal) sections, the total flow is $Q = n_q n_q' \Delta Q$. Also, if there are n_h equipotential drops, the total potential drop is $h = n_h \Delta h$ and $\Delta h = h/n_h$. In accordance with Darcy's law, therefore, $v = K \Delta h/\Delta l$ and $\Delta Q = \Delta b \, \Delta m K \, \Delta h/\Delta l$, or

$$Q = Kh \frac{n_q n_q'}{n_h} \frac{\Delta b \, \Delta m}{\Delta l} \qquad \text{9-17}$$

In the particular case where $\Delta l = \Delta b \, \Delta m$, this equation reduces to

$$Q = Kh \frac{n_q n_q'}{n_h} \qquad \text{9-18}$$

Ordinarily one would deal with a unit width or unit depth of aquifer. If the width is taken as unity, $\Delta b = 1$, $n_q' = 1$, and $\Delta l = \Delta m$; or if the depth is taken as unity, $\Delta m = 1$, $n_q = 1$, and $\Delta l = \Delta b$. If the resultant flow per unit thickness is called q,

$$q = Khn_q/n_h \qquad \text{or} \qquad Khn_q'/n_h \qquad \text{9-19}$$

b. *Two-Dimensional Flow.* As previously indicated, uniform flow of ground water is the exception rather than the rule.

In the general case of two-dimensional flow, the third term of the series in Equation 9-14 drops out, and the equation describes two families of curves that intersect at right angles. The geometrical properties of these curves afford a graphical solution for almost every two-dimensional seepage problem. Confined radial flow into a well, for example, is non-uniform in a horizontal plane, as idealized in Figure 9-7b. Equation 9-19 applies, but the velocity $v = \Delta Q/(\Delta b \, \Delta m)$ is not constant, and Δl changes in proportion to Δb for a constant value of $\Delta h = h/n_h$. Since Δb varies as the radius or diameter, Δl varies in the same manner. The blocks of the flow net are no longer equal, but they are orthogonal solids, similar in two dimensions and equal in the third. The trace of

---

[19] Philip Forchheimer, *Hydraulik*, B. Teubner, Leipzig, 1930.

the piezometric surface is a parabola with its apex at the center of the circular flow net.

Conformance of the network to Equation 9-19 requires that there be but one ratio of n_q/n_h. Had twice as many potential drops been assumed in Figure 9-7, the number of radial flow paths would have had to be doubled.

c. Boundary Conditions. The entrance, discharge, and transfer conditions that govern the line of seepage, or uppermost flowline, as identified by Casagrande,[20] are illustrated in Figure 9-8. These

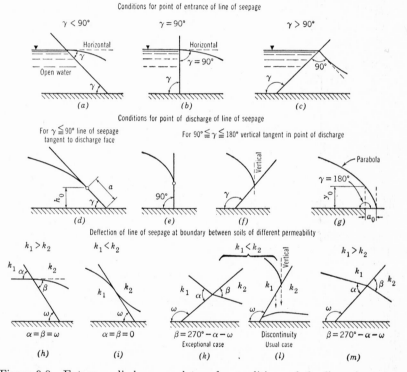

Figure 9-8. Entrance, discharge, and transfer conditions of the line of seepage. *After Arthur Casagrande.*

boundary conditions must be superimposed upon the general requirements laid down by Forchheimer if the flow net is to reflect the conditions that actually obtain.

The results secured by the construction of flow nets can be verified (1) by hydraulic models in which the paths traced by injected dyes

[20] Arthur Casagrande, "Seepage through Dams," *J. New Eng. Water Works Assoc., 51*, 139 (1937).

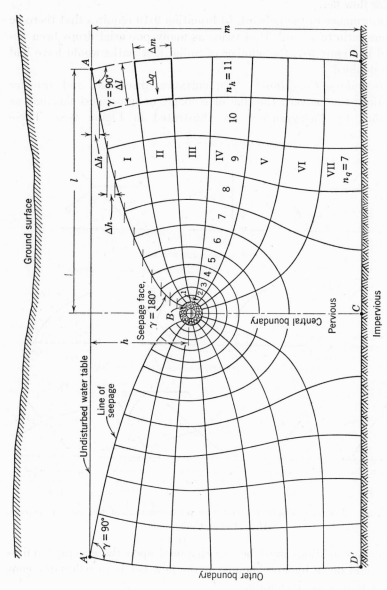

Figure 9-9. Equipotential net for the flow of water into a drain.

can be observed through transparent sides, or (2) by electrical analogies that identify the location of the equipotential lines.

Where the permeability of the ground is not uniform, the analysis of flow nets becomes more difficult. However, it is possible, as explained in Section 11-8, to obtain useful results by suitable modification of the orthogonal system.

Example 9-3. Figure 9-9 illustrates the construction of a flow net for a horizontal drain or collecting pipe in an unconfined aquifer. If the drain is fairly long and the area serving it is correspondingly large, two-dimensional non-uniform flow can be assumed to exist. Total flow then equals the discharge through a cross-section of unit width multiplied by the length of the collector. Preparation of the flow net involves the following stepwise procedure:

1. Draw a cross-section of the collector and aquifer to a convenient scale.

2. Locate the outer boundaries AD and $A'D'$. (For convenience these are assumed to be symmetrical in Figure 9-9.)

3. Locate the central or inner boundary BC. In constructing a flow net that has a free surface, as this one does, one should proceed upstream in sketching the flow net.

4. Divide AD and $A'D'$ into a convenient number of equal parts Δm. Beginners should not use too many subdivisions.

5. Sketch in a system of orthogonal flowlines that fulfill (a) the boundary conditions of Figure 9-8 for entrance and discharge and (b) the requirement that the quantity Δq encompassed by adjacent lines is the same throughout the system. The appearance of the entire flow net should be kept in mind. Details should not be attended to until the entire net is approximately right.

6. Divide the uppermost flowline, or line of seepage, into a whole number of parts Δh. The number to be chosen is indicated in this instance by the requirements (a) that the central boundary BC must contain the same number of divisions, by the creation of squares, as the line of seepage and (b) that Δl must equal Δm both at the central boundary and at the outer boundary.

On completion of a satisfactory orthogonal system, the flow into the collector can be calculated by Equation 9-19. If $h = 4.8$ ft, $m = 13.4$ ft, and $K = 10^{-1}$ cm/sec = 3.28×10^{-3} fps for clean sand and gravel (see Figure 9-4), the seepage from each direction per foot of collector is: $q = 3.28 \times 10^{-3} \times 4.8 \times 7/11$, because $n_q = 7$ and $n_h = 11$. Hence $q = 1.0 \times 10^{-2}$ cfs per ft, and $Q = 2 \times 1.0 \times 10^{-2} \times 10^2 =$ 2.0 cfs per 100 ft from both sides.

Other flow-net problems are considered in Chapter 11.

10-1. General Considerations. As shown in Chapters 1 and 2, the development of surface-water supplies depends upon the nature of their source and involves: (1) the selection, preparation, and control of catchment areas; (2) the choice and treatment of reservoir sites as well as the operation of reservoirs; and (3) the design, construction, and maintenance of dams and dikes, and of intake and outlet structures. The engineering problems encountered lie within the purview of hydrology, hydraulics, soil mechanics, structural mechanics, and sanitation.

Among the hydrological matters, those relating to the yield of catchment areas, storage to be provided in reservoirs, and routing of floods through diversion conduits and over spillways have been discussed in Chapters 7 and 8. These matters are quantitative and statistical. There are others of a different kind. Among them are studies relating to limnology—the physics, chemistry, and biology of lakes and other inland waters—and concerned, in particular, with the sanitary quality of surface-water supplies. These are dealt with in Chapters 17 to 21. For the sake of completeness, however, some reference must be made to limnological matters also in the present chapter.

The structural mechanics, soil physics, and foundation problems of earth and masonry dams cannot be treated adequately within the space that can be allotted to them in this book. However, there are certain features of these structures that concern the over-all planning of water-supply developments. These, together with their associated hydraulic problems, will receive attention here.

Catchment Areas and Reservoir Sites

10-2. The Catchment Area. The gathering grounds for public water supplies vary in extent from a few square miles to thousands of square miles; in characteristics, from uninhabited uplands to densely populated and highly industrialized river valleys. The smaller they are and the less developed, the better do they lend themselves to the kind of exploitation that will provide a maximum yield of water of good quality.

a. Upland Areas. In the most favorable circumstances, it is possible for the water utility to acquire possession of the entire water shed and to manage the area solely for the purposes of water supply. Exclusion of habitations and industries insures the production of a safe water. Elimination of cultivated lands prevents wasteful runoff and keeps the waters clear of turbidity. Drainage of swamps increases yield by reducing evaporation and eliminates an important source of color and, frequently also, of algal growths. Afforestation and reforestation may cause winter snows and storm runoffs to be shed more slowly and thus to preserve stream flow.

As needed quantities of water and required areas increase in size, it is seldom possible to extend the holdings of the utility beyond the marginal lands of lakes, reservoirs, and streams. In the vicinity of the water intake, however, large holdings are justified. Sanitation of habitations, diversion or treatment of sewage, control of industrial wastes, drainage of swamps, and prevention of soil erosion—by contour plowing, construction of check dams, bank protection, and forest management—will generally produce worthwhile results.

These are the situations that are commonly encountered in the development of upland sources by impoundage of the waters of small streams traversing sparsely inhabited areas of relatively small size. Some such water sheds, however, are large enough to satisfy the water needs of great cities.

b. Lowland Areas. When water is drawn from large lakes and great rivers, which, without additional storage, provide an abundant supply of water, management of the catchment area ordinarily becomes of concern to more than one community; sometimes to more than a single state and even to a single country. Regional authorities are then needed to protect the water resources. Since such catchment areas must generally serve the manifold purposes of agriculture, industry, and other human activity, the quality of the raw water is hardly ever satisfactory, and purification works must be provided. Much can be accomplished, however, by sanitary authorities in preventing unnecessary degradation of regional sources of water supply. They may be called upon to regulate the discharge of wastes into the water courses, to require the treatment of sewage and industrial wastes, and to exercise such control over land use as is conducive to water cleanliness without interfering with desirable agricultural, industrial, and residential development. Multipurpose planning of the water resources then becomes a particularly important element in the regional water economy.

c. Sanitary Control. In order to protect water quality, lands owned by the water utility can be fenced in and posted, water sheds of reasonable size can be patrolled, and areas near water-works intakes on larger bodies of water can be zoned as to use so that the supply will not become unsafe. The policing of catchment areas is an expensive undertaking which may outweigh the cost of water purification. If, as is true in many instances, the water development represents an important addition to the scenic and recreational assets of the region, it behooves the water authority to encourage the enjoyment of this asset without endangering its safety. This can often be accomplished by provision of recreational areas that are suitably located, properly supervised, and adequately equipped with sanitary facilities.

d. Swamp Drainage. Three types of swamps are encountered on catchment areas: (1) rain-water swamps formed by the accumulation of rain water on flat lands or by the overflowing of streams during floods; (2) backwater swamps or areas of shallow flowage produced in sluggish—particularly, meandering—streams at bends or other obstructions to flow; and (3) seepage-outcrop swamps created where hillsides meet the plain and sand or gravel are underlain by clay or other impervious material. Rain-water swamps can be drained by ditches within the flood plain of the stream. Backwater swamps can be eliminated by channel regulation. Seepage-outcrop swamps require marginal drains along the hillside to intercept the seepage water and, in addition, central-surface or subsurface drains to lead it away.

10-3. Selection of Reservoir Sites. In the absence of natural ponds and lakes, intensive utilization of upland water sources requires the construction of impounding reservoirs. The selection of a suitable site for a reservoir depends upon a number of interrelated factors that establish the adequacy, economy, safety, and palatability of the supply. Among desirable factors are the following:

1. The surface topography should be such as to create a high ratio of water storage to dam volume; i.e., a broad and branching valley for the reservoir should impinge upon a narrow gorge for the dam. The topography should also present a favorable site for an adequate spillway and a suitable route for an aqueduct or pipeline.

2. The subsurface geology should be such as to provide useful materials for the construction of the dam and appurtenant structures, safe foundations for the dam and spillway, and tightness against seepage of the impounded waters beneath the dam and through its abutments.

3. The reservoir area, i.e., the area to be flooded, should be sparsely inhabited, not heavily wooded, and not traversed by important roads or by railroads. It should contain little marshland. The area, furthermore, should constitute a reservoir (*a*) of such shape as not to favor short-circuiting of the incoming waters to the intake, and (*b*) of such depth, especially around its margins, as not to create large areas of shallow flowage. Purification of water by storage is an important asset of impounding reservoirs. Narrow reservoirs with their major axis in the direction of prevailing winds are especially subject to short-circuiting. Areas of shallow flowage often support a heavy growth of aquatic vegetation, when they are submerged, and of land plants, when they are uncovered by the lowering of the water surface. Decaying vegetation imparts odors and tastes to the water, supports algal growths, and liberates color.

4. The reservoir should interfere as little as possible with existing water rights; the intake should be as close as possible to the community it is to serve; and the development should preferably be at such elevation as to supply its waters by gravity.

10-4. Preparation of Reservoir Sites. In the development of large reservoirs, the sites of whole villages—with their dwellings, stores, churches, and other meeting houses; their manufacturing establishments, stables, barns, and outhouses; their gardens, playgrounds, and graveyards—as well as the agricultural and wood lands of the valley are inundated. Although the area can be seized by right of eminent domain, a wise water authority will attempt to create as much good will as possible within the region in which it is to operate. This it will do by offering to transport dwellings and other wanted buildings to new locations outside of the reservoir area, by establishing a new cemetery and offering to remove bodies and headstones to it or to one selected by relatives, and by contributing as far as it can to a reconstitution of regional economy.

a. Rate of Stabilization. When the reservoir area is flooded, the vegetation dies, and the organic matter released to the water from this source, as well as from the topsoil, undergoes decomposition. Algae and other microorganisms flourish. Odors, taste, and color are imparted to the water, and 10 to 15 years must elapse before decomposition of the putrescible substances within the reservoir area has been substantially completed and the reservoir has been stabilized. A state of equilibrium is reached when the water within the reservoir takes its quality from the incoming water. The progressive reduction in the color of the water and in the growths of microscopic organisms supported by it is illustrated in Figure 10-1. The rate of improvement, when referred to conditions of equilibrium, is approximately 14% annually, which implies 90% improvement in about 14 years.

Since the bettering of water quality, after impounding reservoirs are filled, is due to the gradual stabilization of the organic matter

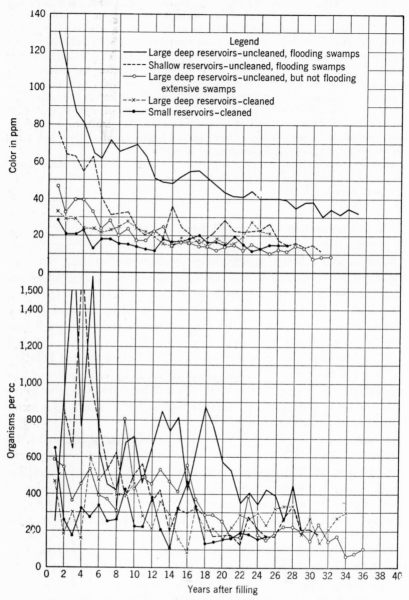

Figure 10-1.   Progressive reduction in color and microscopic organisms in impounding reservoirs subsequent to their filling.   (From *Microscopy of Drinking Water*, Whipple, Fair, and Whipple, John Wiley & Sons, Fourth Edition, 1927.)

permeable fill to either side
the additional weight needed
ers. The common features of
llustrated in Figure 2-3. Earth
hat will render them impervious
h materials, concrete-core walls
rs are intended to drain readily
rom the borrow pits, are ideally
to the core to coarse material at
s. Within the range of destructive
protected against erosion, by waves
e paving or riprap, or by a concrete
y placed at the foot of the protected
stream face may receive similar treat-
storm-water runoff. More commonly,
or planted with covering vines such as
lgare). The slope is broken by berms
am face into smaller drainage areas and
for mowing the grass and for other mainte-
ms slope inward to gutters which intercept
and conduct it safely down the face of the
surface or subsurface drains leading to the

s are constructed either as rolled fills or as
fills are built by spreading and rolling succes-
thicknesses of 4 to 9 in. Sheep's-foot rollers as
h-conveying and earth-moving vehicles used in
nstructions compact the soil. Parts of the em-
ot be reached by the rollers are carefully com-
y power tampers. Fills adjacent to concrete-core
its, and the wingwalls of spillway sections are

fill method creates an embankment in which the
th is graded from the coarsest grain sizes at the face
he finest in the core. The method includes several
are determined by the ways employed for securing
ng the fill material. In the most completely hydraulic
oil is washed from sidehill borrow pits by jets of water
nozzles called "giants" or "monitors." The washings are
d for removal of debris and large stones by passage
orizontal rack or "grizzly" at the entrance to sluiceways
et transport the suspended soil to the shoulders of the dam.

within the flooded area, the improvement is a manifestation of the natural purification of polluted waters and closely analogous to the stabilization of bottom deposits (Chapter 28). The relationships illustrated in Figure 10-1 can, therefore, be formulated in much the same way as the relationships that obtain in the self-purification of streams.

Taking the first year after filling as the starting point for the time axis t, and the conditions of equilibrium, $y = L$, as the reference axis for color, algal growths, and other suitable measures of improvement, we can write the equation

$$dy/dt = -k(y - L) \qquad \text{10-1}$$

whence, by integration between the limits $y = y_1$ and $y = y$, and $t = 1$ and $t = t$,

$$y = L + (y_1 - L)e^{-k(t-1)} \qquad \text{10-2}$$

Here y is the color intensity or microscopic count of the reservoir (with a 1-year value of $y = y_1$ and an ultimate, or equilibrium, value of $y = L$), t is the time after filling, and k is the rate constant of improvement.

Example 10-1. During the 15 years after filling, the waters in the large deep reservoirs of Figure 10-1 that flooded extensive swamps and were not stripped possessed the gross color intensities, color intensities due to decomposition (on the basis of an equilibrium value of 32 ppm), and percentage colors listed in Table 10-1.

TABLE 10-1. Stabilization of Reservoirs (Example 10-1)

Years after filling, t	1	2	4	6	8	10	12	14	15
Color, ppm, y	130	108	80	62	66	69	51	48	52
Color due to decomposition, $y - L$	98	76	48	30	34	37	19	16	20
Percentage color due to decomposition, $100(y - L)/(y_1 - L)$	100	78	49	31	35	38	19	16	20

Find (a) the rate of stabilization, (b) the time required for 90% completion, and (c) the annual percentage stabilization.

a. The percentage values are plotted logarithmically against time in Figure 10-2. The straight line fitted by eye has a slope $k \log e = -0.0677$. Hence the rate constant k is -0.156 per annum and Equation 10-2 becomes

$$y = 32 + (130 - 32)e^{-0.156(t-1)}$$

b. For 90% stabilization $(y - L)/(y_1 - L) = 0.1 = e^{-0.156(t-1)}$ and the elapsed time $t = 13.8$ years.

c. For any one year, the percentage stabilization accomplished is given by

$$100(y - L)/(y_1 - L) = 100(1 - e^{-k}) = 14.4\%$$

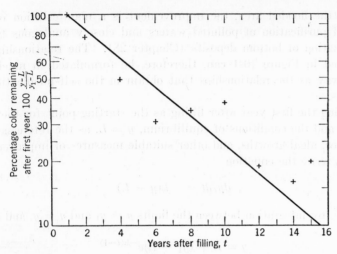

Figure 10-2. Natural rate of color reduction in large deep reservoirs flooding extensive swamps.

b. Treatment Methods. Preparation of the reservoir site to insure reasonable cleanliness of the area to be flooded and provide satisfactory operating conditions includes the following:

1. For the entire reservoir area:
   a. Removing or otherwise destroying dwellings and other structures.
   b. Cleaning barnyards, privies, and cesspools.
   c. Removing manure piles.
   d. Cutting trees and brush close to the ground and removing usable timber from the area to be flooded.
   e. Burning slash, weeds, and grass.
   f. Removing as much muck as possible from swamps that will be submerged, and covering residual muck with clean gravel and sand.
   g. Cutting channels to pockets within the reservoir bottom to make them self-draining when the water level is lowered.
2. For a marginal strip extending from the high-water mark reached by wave action down to a vertical depth of about 20 ft:
   a. Removing all stumps, roots, and topsoil.
   b. Draining all marginal swamps.
   c. Creating, if possible, a shore-water depth of at least 8 ft during a considerable part of the growing season of aquatic plants. This can be done by excavation or fill, or by the construction of auxiliary dams on the upper reaches of the reservoir.

The removal from the reservoir site of all topsoil that contains more than 1 or 2% organic matter, a practice called *soil stripping*, is not included in this list. This radical preparatory operation is generally more expensive than water treatment and will provide a less satis-

There, the earth-water mixture is discharged inward to form beaches and a central pool (see Figure 10-3). As the water gushes from the pipe ends, it spreads and is differentially relieved of its imposed burden. The coarser materials drop out first and the finest last. Core material settles within the central pool, whence water is wasted or repumped to the borrow area. By regulating the width of the pool and the time of detention within it, a core of desired dimensions and grain size is created, provided that the borrow area contains the wanted materials. In practice, the pool is often held to a width equal to the height of the structure remaining to be completed.

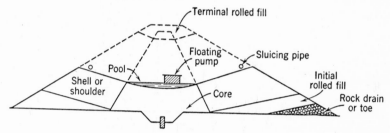

Figure 10-3. Construction of earth dam by hydraulic fill method.

Proper control of pool materials produces a core that is substantially impervious as soon as it is formed. However, the core material is usually unstable to begin with and consolidates but slowly by releasing the water filling its voids. Drainage takes place through the surrounding shell. Generally speaking, hydraulic placement of material by washing dumped earth into place does not give as good grading as does full hydraulic fill or the discharge from a hog box. If the fill is more conveniently transported to the dam site by trucks, tractors, trains, or belt conveyors, it is either deposited along the shoulders of the dam and washed into place by monitors that may be supplied with water from the core pool, or it is dumped into a suspending chamber or "hog box" supplied with water. The box empties into sluiceways or pipes which convey the material to the shoulders, beaches, and pool of the dam. Because the poor initial stability of hydraulic-fill dams has produced numerous failures of such structures, and because the use of modern earth-moving equipment produces a stable structure and has overcome the economic advantage of hydraulic placement, rolled fills are commonly constructed in preference to hydraulic fills.

The methods of constructing earth dams have been outlined because they determine the composition of the embankment and its stability.

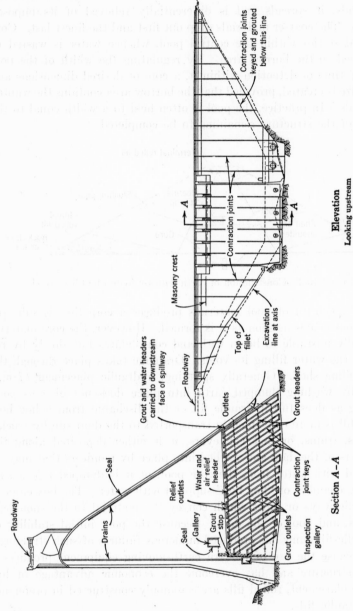

Elevation
Looking upstream

Section A–A

Figure 10-4. Gravity masonry dam. After C. E. Pearce, "Design of Hiwassee Dam," *Civil Engineering, 10*, 433 (1940).

The principles involved in the selection, transportation, and deposition of hydraulic fills need not be discussed here because they are shared with some of the important processes of water and waste-water treatment and are described in connection with them in later sections of this book.

b. *Masonry and Other Dams.* As shown in Figures 10-4 and 10-5, masonry dams are built as gravity, arched, or reinforced structures. They may include their own spillway by permitting passage of water

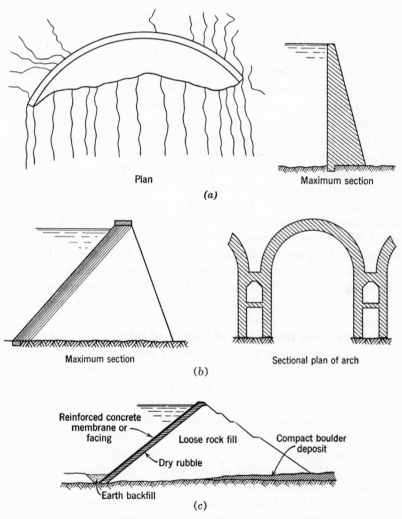

Figure 10-5. Arched masonry dams and rock-fill dam. (a) Arched dam; (b) multiple arch (buttress) dam; (c) rock-fill dam.

over their full length or part of it, or they may be of the "non-over-flow" variety which is protected by a separate spillway. Constructions of cyclopean masonry and mass concrete embedding large stones have, in the course of time, generally given way to the use of poured concrete.

Gravity dams are designed to be in compression under all conditions of loading and can be made to fit almost any location that offers a suitable foundation. Arched dams depend upon arch action to transmit the water thrust laterally to both sides of the valley. For this reason, they are adapted to use only in narrow valleys with strong sides. Structurally, arch dams act as cantilevers in a vertical direction and as arches in a horizontal direction. If more than one arch is to be employed, the contact points of the arches must be supported by heavy buttresses. Such structures are also called buttress dams. Reinforced-concrete dams are commonly composed of flat slabs that face upstream and lie on a framework of heavy beams and columns. Sometimes they, too, incorporate a spillway section.

Availability or lack of materials may dictate the construction of timber, rock fill, or steel dams (Figure 10-5). Timber dams are built as cribs that are packed with rocks for weight and sheathed on their upstream face for water tightness. These dams are generally confined to low heights. Rock-fill dams, by contrast, have been built of great size. Where rock outcrops on canyon walls and can be blasted into the stream bed, rock fill becomes particularly economical. Providing rock fills with a water-tight upstream face or membrane that will not break up as the fill settles is difficult. Steel dams resemble reinforced-concrete dams. Rolled-steel sections, however, replace the concrete slabs, beams, and columns.

10-7. Common Dimensions of Dams and Dikes. A first step in the investigation of impounding reservoirs is a comparative study of available dam and reservoir sites. Involved in particular are the determination of the quantities and characteristics of the dam materials that can be provided and of their cost in place. With the aid of maps, a field reconnaissance, and acceptance of the common dimensionings of different dam types, it is possible to confine detailed designs to the most promising locations, often even to a single site. Needless to say, the exact dimensioning of structures as important as dams and dikes can be made only on the basis of (1) exhaustive studies of the materials available at or near the site or otherwise economically procurable; (2) careful surveys of site topography; (3) adequate geological exploration of the area with special reference to abutments and foundations for the required structures; (4) development of probable seepage patterns and estimate of seepage rates; and (5) detailed structural analyses.

a. Freeboard. All dams of the "non-overflow" variety must rise a safe distance above the maximum storage level in order not to be overtopped by waters that rise above the spillway crest in times of storm. This distance is called the *freeboard*. A safe distance is particularly critical for earth dams and dikes. The requisite value is a composite of a number of different factors:

1. Head of water on the spillway crest at maximum rate of discharge.
2. Wind set-up, or increase in elevation of reservoir surface by the drag exerted in the direction of persistent winds (see Section 17-8).
3. Wave height (trough to crest).
4. Wave run-up, or ride-up on sloping surfaces.
5. Depth of frost (for earth dams only).

Determination of the head on the spillway involves the routing of floods through reservoirs, a matter that has been discussed in Section 8-8. The head itself is normally calculated from a weir formula that is suited to the form of crest that is to be employed. The remaining factors are best determined by observation of similar situations; but there are general formulations that will establish approximate magnitudes.

In studies for the dams and dikes for the Zuider Zee in Holland, *wind set-up* was found to be approximated by the relationship

$$h_s = \frac{w^2 F}{1,400d} \cos \alpha \qquad \text{10-3}$$

where h_s is the wind set-up above pool level in feet, w is the wind velocity in miles per hour, F is the fetch (or maximum clean sweep of the wind towards the dam or dike) in miles, d is the mean depth of water in feet, and α is the angle between the wind direction and a normal to the structure or shore line. After the wind subsides, the water at the leeward shore falls while that at the windward shore rises. This rhythmic rising and falling repeats itself and is called a *seiche* (pronounced sāsh). It may be produced also by differences in barometric pressures at opposite shores.

Wave height, as shown by Stevenson,[1] is related to the fetch. His formulation, $h_w = 1.5\sqrt{F_N} + (2.5 - \sqrt[4]{F_N})$, where F_N is the fetch in

[1] Thomas Stevenson, *Design and Construction of Harbours,* 2nd ed., A. J. Black, Edinburgh, 1874.

nautical miles, has been modified by Molitor [2] to include the wind velocity as follows:

$$h_w = 0.17\sqrt{wF} + (2.5 - \sqrt[4]{F})$$ 10-4

When the fetch exceeds 20 miles, the right-hand term of this equation is omitted. Wave height depends also on the duration of the blow. Maximum wave height may be estimated from the following equation, which approximates the values given by a dimensionless relationship established by Sverdrup and Munk: [3]

$$h_w = 0.047w\sqrt{F}$$ 10-5

The rise of the wave crest above the pool level is approximately three-quarters of the wave height.

In deep water (depth > ½ wave length), *wave velocities* will eventually equal the velocity of the wind and may indeed exceed it. For wave heights between 1 and 7 ft, the wave velocity v in feet per second is approximated by the relationship:

$$v = 7 + 2h_w$$ 10-6

The run-up of waves on the face of a dam or dike approaches the velocity head of the waves. The height of wave action h_a is a combination of wave height and run-up. It may be approximated as $1.5h_w$, or as

$$h_a = 0.75h_w + v^2/2g$$ 10-7

Earth dams and dikes must be given a freeboard height above maximum pool level at least equal to the regional depth of frost. Otherwise the material exposed to wetting may freeze and crack. Depth of frost action is discussed in Section 12-7 in reference to the required depth of cover for water conduits.

Example 10-2. Estimate the height of set-up and wave action for an impoundage with an average depth of 40 ft and a fetch of 25 miles exposed to winds with velocities of 49 mph that strike the dam at an angle of 30° to the normal.

1. By Equation 10-3: $h_s = \dfrac{(49)^2 \times 25}{1,400 \times 40} 0.866 = 0.93$ ft.
2. By Equation 10-4: $h_w = 0.17\sqrt{49 \times 25} = 5.95$ ft.
3. By Equation 10-6: $v = 7 + 2 \times 5.95 = 18.9$ fps; or $v^2/2g = 5.55$ ft.
4. By Equation 10-7: $h_a = 0.75 \times 5.95 + 5.55 = 10.0$ ft.

---

[2] D. A. Molitor, "Wave Pressures on Sea-Walls and Breakwaters," *Trans. Am. Soc. Civil Engrs.*, *100*, 984 (1935).

[3] H. V. Sverdrup and W. H. Munk, "Wind, Sea, and Swell," *Hydrographic Office, U. S. Navy*, Publ., 601 (1947).

The total freeboard includes, in addition to the allowance for wave action (10.0 ft), the head on the spillway and the set-up (0.93 ft). Since frost depths commonly do not exceed 5 ft in the United States, no allowance for frost action need be made.

b. Earth Dams and Dikes. Experience in the design, construction, and maintenance of earth dams has produced certain common dimensions and rules of thumb that can form a working basis for the limited objective of this section, namely, arrival at a first estimate of the size of a particular structure. These dimensions and rules of thumb are shown in Figure 10-6.

The slopes of earth dams that are constructed of cohesionless materials, such as sand, may be made uniform from top to bottom. The slope must be less than the angle of internal friction of the grains, a factor of safety of 1.3 to 1.5 in terms of the tangent of the angle commonly being provided. If cohesive materials such as clay are included, the slopes must become progressively flatter. Sand and other cohesionless materials depend for their stability almost entirely on the friction between their grains. If the structure of the fill is loose, i.e., if the voids are large and the points of contact between grains are few, internal friction is small. Vibration or other disturbance will cause such a structure to seek a more stable, denser form. The *critical density* is reached when the grains are so interlocked by compaction that further movement within the material can be accomplished only by expansion as the particles roll over one another. The critical density may, therefore, be defined as the maximum density of a cohesionless material undergoing shear failure.

If the sand pores are full of water, the water must be displaced when the void space is reduced. There is, therefore, a period between the start of any collapsing movement of the grains and the escape of the water during which the sand grains are suspended in the water that filled their voids and are thereby deprived of their resistance to shear. The entire mass will then flow almost like a liquid.

The importance of compacting cohesionless materials in earth dams to a density greater than the critical is obvious. In a rolled-fill dam, a dense structure can be assured by rolling and compacting the layers of earth. In hydraulic fill, attainment of a density greater than the critical is less certain. The core material, in fact, is often quite loose and depends for its stability primarily on the cohesive force of molecular attraction. If the core does not drain, the shoulders of hydraulic-fill dams must indeed be heavy enough to resist the fluid pressure of the core as well as that of the stored water. The unit weight of a fluid core is taken as about 110 lb per cu ft.

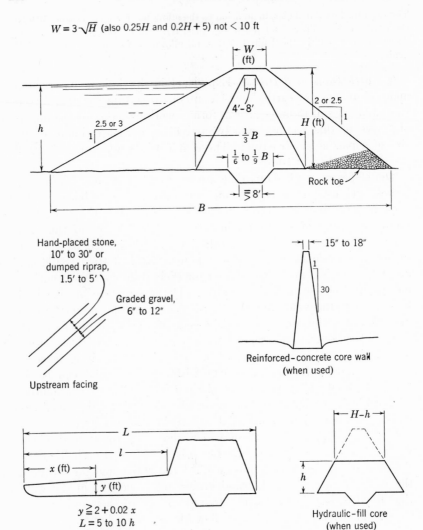

$W = 3\sqrt{H}$ (also $0.25H$ and $0.2H + 5$) not < 10 ft

Figure 10-6.   Common dimensions of earth dams.

Upstream slope 2.5 on 1, downstream slope 2 on 1 for: (1) homogeneous well-graded material; (2) homogeneous silty clay, or clay, when $H \gtreqless 50$ ft; and (3) sand, or sand and gravel, with reinforced-concrete wall.

Upstream slope 3 on 1, downstream slope 2.5 on 1 for: (1) homogeneous coarse silt; (2) homogeneous silty clay, or clay, when $H > 50$ ft; and (3) sand, or sand and gravel, with clay core.

Dams that can be given dimensions of the order of magnitude indicated in Figure 10-6 will effect the storage of 1 mg of water with about 100 cu yd of earth when the site is good. The relative yardage needed at unusually favorable sites is often half this value, sometimes even less. Justification of a large yardage ratio may be given by the high regional value of water.

Embankments may consolidate and shrink in volume under their own weight, the change taking place over an extended period of time

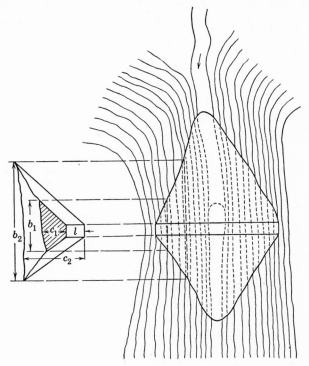

Figure 10-7. Plan and sections of earth dam for earthwork computations.

and requiring the addition of the displaced volumes of earth. Ordinarily, rolled fill can be fully consolidated during the period of construction. Nevertheless the dam may have to be given additional height to allow for the slow consolidation of the foundation.

The volume of the dam as a whole and of its constituent portions is computed in accordance with common earthwork practice by "average end areas" or "prismoidal formula," or by a combination of the two. Computation by average end areas with prismoidal correction is based on the equation:

$$V = \tfrac{1}{2}l[(a_1 + a_2) - \tfrac{1}{6}(c_1 - c_2)(b_1 - b_2)] \qquad \text{10-8}$$

where V is the volume of earthwork between two parallel cross-sections of the dam, l is the distance between these sections, and a_1 and a_2 are the end areas with center heights c_1 and c_2 and base widths b_1 and b_2 (Figure 10-7). For computation of the volume of water stored, see Section 8-7.

The upstream shoulder of earth dams, because of the buoyant and lubricating effect of the saturating water, is less stable than the downstream shoulder. Hence the upstream slope is generally made flatter. If outward hydrostatic pressure and sloughing of the upstream face are to be avoided when the reservoir is being drawn down rapidly, the shoulder material should drain rapidly. In dams on impervious foundations, water escaping into the downstream shoulder can be safely led away through a broken stone drain at the toe of the structure (Figure 2-3). Entrance to the drain should be through a graded filter. In dams on pervious foundations, underflow is held to a minimum either by placing an impervious blanket between the heel and core of the dam (Figure 10-6) or by carrying the concrete-core wall to bed rock or driving sheet piling to it. The purpose is not so much the prevention of loss of water as the checking of velocities that will carry dam material or subsoil away and cause the dam to fail.

The berms and gutters of the downstream face are placed at vertical intervals of about 30 ft. Design of gutters and drains parallels, in all respects, that of storm-drainage systems for municipal areas (Chapter 16).

c. Gravity Masonry Dams. The forces acting on a gravity masonry dam are readily identified and evaluated as to magnitude, distribution, and direction. The structural analysis of such dams, therefore, is straightforward. It need not be detailed in this book because it is commonly covered both in textbooks on hydraulics and in textbooks on structural mechanics. However, a brief consideration of the forces that must be taken into account is of interest. These forces include (1) the weight of the structure; (2) the fluid pressure of water and silt on the face of the dam; (3) the hydrostatic pressure on the base of the structure; (4) ice pressure on the face of the dam at the water line; (5) inertia forces due to earthquakes; and (6) the foundation reaction. Common assumptions are: (1) a unit weight of concrete of 150 lb per cu ft; (2) a unit weight of silt of 90 lb per cu ft; (3) full hydrostatic pressure acting on two-thirds of the area of the base; (4) ice pressures of 20,000 to 50,000 lb per linear foot of dam; and (5) seismic acceleration equaling $0.1g$ to $0.2g$, where g is the acceleration due to gravity.

Ice pressure can be exerted only when the ice sheet is restrained, i.e., when the ice cannot buckle or slide up the face of the dam or the banks of the reservoir. Maximum ice pressure is a function of the crushing strength of the ice (from 100 to 1,000 psi) and of the thickness of the sheet. Buckling is expected to occur when the distance from the dam to the shore exceeds 200 times the thickness of

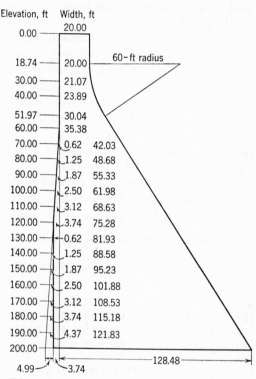

Figure 10-8. Dimensions of masonry dams; Wegman's Practical Type 2.

the ice sheet. Ice pressure can be neutralized by using steam or compressed air to maintain a narrow channel of open water at the face of the dam.

Seepage through and beneath masonry dams is obstructed by building metal water stops into the contraction joints and by grouting the foundation beneath the heel of the dam. Uplift on the base of the dam and within it is reduced by installing vertical drains in all contraction joints and in the foundation on the downstream side of the water stops and grout curtain (Figure 10-4). These drains lead to an inspection gallery running the length of the dam just above tail-water height, whence the seepage water is discharged to openings in the downstream face of the structure. The heat released by setting of the concrete is sometimes removed during construction of large dams by circulating a coolant through an extensive built-in piping system. When the structure is cool, the construction joints are sealed by forcing grout into them through another piping system installed for this purpose.

Structural analysis of a gravity section to meet a given set of conditions, including the provision of a roadway over the dam, produces a specific profile. First estimates of the amount of masonry needed at a given site may be had, without detailed computation, by reference to a "practical profile" developed for this purpose on the basis of common assumptions. Such a profile is shown in Figure 10-8. Known as "Wegmann's Practical Type No. 2," [4] this cross-section was developed for zero uplift, masonry weighing 145.8 lb per cu ft, and zero ice pressure except that the top width was made 20 ft. If this width is retained, the profile of a lower dam is obtained by cutting off the unwanted lower portion. If a smaller top width is to be used, every dimension shown in Figure 10-8 must be reduced in the ratio of the desired width to 20 ft. The proper height is then obtained, as before, by cutting off the unwanted lower portion of the modified structure.

Example 10-3. Estimate the salient dimensions of a dam 120 ft high with top width of 16 ft.

Calculated from Wegmann's Practical Type No. 2 for a ratio of $160/200 = 0.8$, the dimensions are:

Upstream face
(a) vertical for $60 \times 0.8 = 48$ ft
(b) sloping outward for $60 \times 0.8 = 48$ ft by $3.74 \times 0.8 = 2.99$ ft
(c) vertical for $120 - 96 = 24$ ft
Downstream face
(a) vertical for $18.74 \times 0.8 = 14.99$ ft
(b) curved to depth of $51.97 \times 0.8 = 41.58$ ft
(c) radius of curvature $60 \times 0.8 = 48$ ft
Base
(a) width under upstream slope $3.74 \times 0.8 = 2.99$ ft
(b) intersection of upstream slope
    and base at distance of $1.87 \times 0.8 = 1.50$ ft from heel
(c) remaining width of base $95.23 \times 0.8 = 76.18$ ft

Height of 120 ft corresponds to height of 0.8×150 in the profile.

10-8. Seepage through Dams and Their Foundations. The embankments of earth dams and the foundations of all dams are seldom, if ever, perfectly tight. Depending upon the type of the embankment

[4] W. W. Wegmann, *The Design and Construction of Dams*, New York, John Wiley & Sons, 1927.

and foundation materials, seepage flows are small or large. Whether or not this seepage will endanger the structure depends upon the circumstances.

a. Dangers of Seepage. Earth dams will fail when seepage water escapes at the downstream face of the embankment in sufficient volume to erode the surface or cause it to slough. Sloughing of the upstream face will occur when the water filling the pores of the upstream pervious shell of a dam does not drain away sufficiently fast to relieve the pore-water pressure while the water surface of the reservoir is being lowered rapidly. The safety of all dams is endangered when water escapes from the embankment or foundation material with sufficient velocity to dislodge and carry soil grains with it. This it will do in increasing amounts as a passage, or *pipe*, is worn through the material. The resulting phenomenon is called *piping*. It is observed whenever the drag force of the upward flow exceeds the weight in water of the sand grains. If we call the hydraulic gradient through the soil s, the specific weight of the soil γ_s (or its specific gravity s_s), and its porosity f, it follows that, for a soil volume of unit cross-sectional area and water of density γ, existence of the relationship

$$\gamma s > (1 - f)(\gamma_s - \gamma) \quad \text{or} \quad s > (1 - f)(s_s - 1) \quad \text{(closely)} \quad 10\text{-}9$$

will produce piping (see Section 15-2*b*). The associated velocity of flow must exceed the settling velocity of the soil grains that are washed away by upward flow at the toe of the dam (see Section 22-2).

Example 10-4. Find the hydraulic gradient and seepage velocity at which grains of specific gravity 2.64 (quartz) in soil with a porosity of 39% are subject to removal by piping.

From Equation 10-9, $s = (1 - 0.39)(2.64 - 1) = 1.00$. Since, according to Darcy's law (Equation 9-4: $v = Ks$), $v = K$, for $s = 1.00$, the critical seepage velocity equals the coefficient of permeability of the material in this case.

It is important, therefore, to be able to predict (1) the position of the free water surface within an earth dam and (2) the intensity of seepage and pore-water pressure in earth embankments and foundations. As shown in Figure 10-9, seepage can be deflected from the face of a dam by the proper use of an earth or masonry core, a cutoff, a filter blanket, or a rock toe. Rock toes, in addition to providing drainage, weight down the foundation. In order that the soil may not be washed into them by the escaping waters, rock toes must grade into the embankment and foundation through a transitional filter layer. The principles of filtration enunciated in Chapter 24 apply in this connection. Seepage through pervious earth foundations is

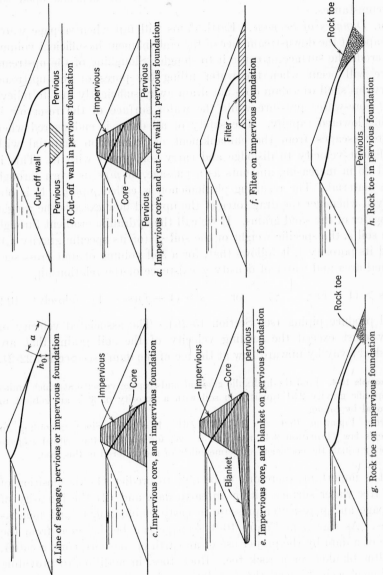

Figure 10-9. Modification of lines of seepage through earth dams.

a. Line of seepage, pervious or impervious foundation

b. Cut-off wall in pervious foundation

c. Impervious core, and impervious foundation

d. Impervious core, and cut-off wall in pervious foundation

e. Impervious core, and blanket on pervious foundation

f. Filter on impervious foundation

g. Rock toe on impervious foundation

h. Rock toe in pervious foundation

controlled by the use of clay blankets, cutoffs, filter blankets, and rock toes.

The length l (Figure 10-6) of a clay blanket beneath the upstream shell of an earth dam is governed by the permissible seepage. If the blanket itself is to offer, within its own thickness y (Figure 10-6), as much resistance to seepage as a depth d of the foundation material underlying the blanket, it follows from Darcy's law that

$$Q = K_1(h/l)d = K_2(h/y)x$$

and that

$$(y/x) = (K_2/K_1)(l/d) \qquad\qquad 10\text{-}10$$

Here Q is the rate of seepage, h is the frictional resistance in terms of lost head, and K_1 and K_2 are the coefficients of permeability of the foundation medium and the clay blanket respectively. As shown in Figure 10-6, y is given a minimum thickness $(2 + 0.02x$ ft) for practical reasons of construction, and the total length of blanket and core material is made equal to 5 or 10 times the head of water in the reservoir in order to insure safety against piping.

b. Flow Nets and Flow Calculations. When water flows through an embankment or a dam foundation of homogeneous material, the cross-sectional area through which flow takes place decreases because the water surface drops. The rate of flow, however, remains constant. Hence flow is non-uniform, and the line of seepage can be determined by analytical methods only if the boundary conditions can be closely established. This can be done in certain simple cases. Graphical methods (flow-net construction), models (using dyes to trace flowlines in a thin section between glass plates), and electrical analogies are employed to identify the potential net in most circumstances. Flow nets are sketched for a foundation and for a dam in Figures 10-10 and 10-11 in accordance with the principles laid down in Section 9-15.

Figure 10-10 presents Forchheimer's classical solution [5] of a flow-net problem in a foundation. This solution is used here because the boundary conditions of the problem are fully established. The ground surface to either side of the sheet piling is the locus of horizontal equipotential lines; the pressure on the water side equals the head of water h above the ground surface; the pressure on the opposite side is zero; and the bottom of the pervious stratum and the sides of the sheet piling constitute the boundaries of the flowlines. The flow net of Figure 10-10 includes $n_h = 18$ equal drops in head Δh or fields, and $n_q = 9$ flow channels. If we call the average dimension of any one

---

[5] Philip Forchheimer, *Hydraulik*, B. Teubner, Leipzig, 1930.

of the four-sided figures within the network a, the hydraulic gradient $s = \Delta h/a$, where $\Delta h = h/n_h$. Hence the quantity of water flowing through the foundation, in accordance with Equation 9-19, becomes

$$q = Khn_q/n_h \qquad\qquad 9\text{-}19$$

In nature, soils are seldom isotropic; i.e., they do not possess the same properties in all directions. Materials that have been laid down

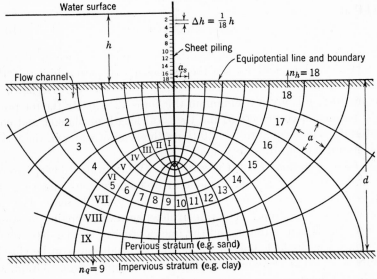

Figure 10-10. Seepage under sheet piling. *After Forchheimer.*

in water, for example, are generally stratified horizontally and present more resistance to flow in a vertical direction $(K = K_{min})$ than in a horizontal direction $(K = K_{max})$. The flow net for an anisotropic medium can be developed from a transformed cross-section in which all dimensions in the direction of maximum permeability, K_{max}, are multiplied by the factor $\sqrt{K_{min}/K_{max}}$. The flow net for the transformed cross-section is then projected back into the true cross-section by multiplying all dimensions, including those of the flow net, by the reciprocal of the factor that was previously applied (see Figure 10-11). In computing the quantity of seepage, the geometric mean of the maximum and minimum permeabilities, i.e., $\sqrt{K_{max} \times K_{min}}$, is substituted for K in Equation 9-19.

The seepage pressure at any point within the soil is tangent to the flowline through the point and equal to $s\gamma$. The head remaining within

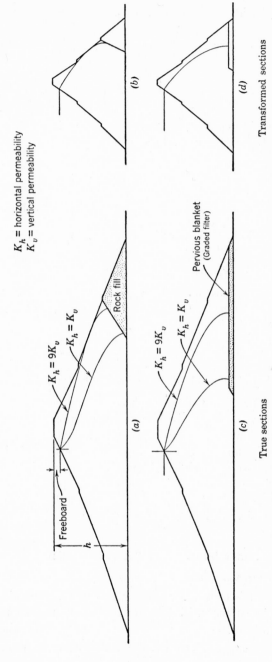

K_h = horizontal permeability
K_v = vertical permeability

Rock fill

$K_h = 9K_v$

$K_h = K_v$

Freeboard

h

(a)

(b)

Pervious blanket
(Graded filter)

$K_h = 9K_v$

$K_h = K_v$

(c)

(d)

True sections

Transformed sections

Figure 10-11. Seepage through stratified dam sections. *After Arthur Casagrande.*

the soil at any point such as the kth equipotential line is $\dfrac{n_h - k}{n_h} h$ or $\left(1 - \dfrac{k}{n_h}\right) h$, and the excess hydrostatic pressure p is

$$p = \left(1 - \frac{k}{n_h}\right) h\gamma \qquad\qquad 10\text{-}11$$

Example 10-5. If the height of water in Figure 10-10 is 40 ft and the foundation material has a coefficient of permeability $K = 2 \times 10^{-3}$ cm/sec, what are (a) the seepage through each foot of width of the foundation, (b) the intensity of the excess hydrostatic pressure on the upstream side of the bottom of the sheet piling, and (c) the maximum hydraulic gradient and its relation to the coefficient of permeability?

a. From Equation 9-19, $q = 2 \times 10^{-3} \times 3.28 \times 10^{-2} \times 40 \times \tfrac{9}{18} = 1.31 \times 10^{-3}$ cfs. This equals $1.31 \times 10^{-3} \times 6.47 \times 10^{5} = 850$ gpd per ft of width.

b. From Equation 10-11, $p = (1 - \tfrac{8}{18})40 \times 0.433 = 9.62$ psig.

c. The maximum hydraulic gradient occurs in the flow channel adjacent to the piling. If this measures 9 ft at the ground surface,

$$s = \Delta h/a_s = 40/(18 \times 9) = 0.25$$

In accordance with Example 10-4, therefore, there is no danger of piping if the medium has a porosity close to 40% and a specific gravity of 2.65. The associated velocity v equals Ks; or it is found from (a) as

$$\frac{q}{n_q a_s} = \frac{1.31 \times 10^{-3}}{9 \times 9} = 1.62 \times 10^{-5}\text{ fps} \quad\text{or}\quad \frac{1.62 \times 10^{-5}}{3.28 \times 10^{-2}} = 4.94 \times 10^{-4}\text{ cm/sec}$$

Hence $v/K = 4.94 \times 10^{-4}/(2 \times 10^{-3}) = 0.25$, as is to be expected.

To trace the line of seepage through an embankment, one boundary condition, namely, the point, or line, of intersection of the free water surface with the downstream face, with a filter or rock toe, or with the foundation itself remains to be established. An exact solution of this problem is not always possible. Approximations can be made, however, and, in view of the normal variation in the permeability of soils from point to point, such approximations generally fall within the limits of error inherent in stating the problem.[6]

Water Intakes and Reservoir Outlets

10-9. Water Intakes. Depending upon the size and nature of the installation, water is drawn from rivers, lakes, and reservoirs through relatively simple, submerged intakes or through more elaborate structures that rise above the water surface and may include, in addition

[6] For numerous solutions, see Arthur Casagrande, "Seepage through Dams," *J., New Eng. Water Works Assoc., 51*, 131 (1937).

to gates, mechanical screens, chlorinators, and living quarters for the operating personnel (see Figure 2-2). Intakes should be so placed and designed as to draw water that is as clean and palatable as the source of supply can provide.

a. River Intakes. These are constructed well upstream from points of discharge of the community's sewage and industrial wastes. They are so placed within the river channel as to take advantage of deep

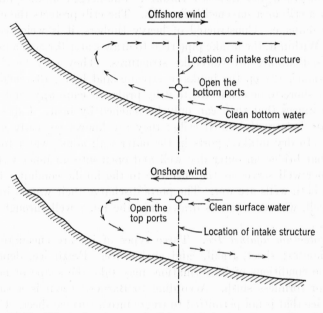

Figure 10-12. Effect of onshore and offshore winds on water quality at intake.

water, a stable bottom, and differential water quality (if pollution hugs one shore of the stream, for example), all with due reference to protection against floods, debris, ice, and river traffic. In small streams, an intake or diversion dam may be needed to keep the intake submerged and preclude the entraining of air. The intake pool, furthermore, acts as a settling basin and allows sheet ice to form in winter (see *d* in this section).

b. Lake and Reservoir Intakes. Lake intakes avoid shore waters where possible and are placed with due reference to sources of pollution, prevailing winds, surface and subsurface currents, and shipping lanes. As shown in Figure 10-12, provisions for shifting the depth of draft make it possible to seek the clean bottom water that streams toward lake intakes when the wind is offshore and conversely to open surface ports when onshore winds drive clean surface water to the intake structure. The intake should be placed in water of such depth that bottom sediments are not stirred up by wave action and that ice troubles are minimized.

Reservoir intakes are similar in concept to lake intakes. They are generally placed closer to shore and are often incorporated in the dam that creates the reservoir (see Figure 2-3).

c. *Submerged and Exposed Intakes.* Submerged intakes take the form of a crib or a screened bellmouth. The crib protects the conduit against damage. Constructed of heavy timbers, it is weighted with rocks. Within it, the intake pipe rises to draw water through a grating.

Exposed intakes are towerlike structures. They may be situated (1) in dams, (2) on the banks of streams and lakes, (3) sufficiently near the shore to be connected to it by bridge or causeway, and (4) at such distances that they can only be reached by boat. Exposed intakes are incorrectly called cribs; they are known correctly as gate houses. In dry intakes, ports in the outer wall admit water to gated pipes that bridge an outer dry well and open into an inner wet well. The inner well serves as the entrance to the intake conduit. In wet intakes both wells are wet. The ports discharge their waters into the outer well, whence water is drawn into the inner well through gated openings.

d. *Protection against Ice.* Three types of ice are encountered in cold climates: sheet, frazil,[7] and anchor ice. Frazil ice, depending upon the conditions of its formation, may take the shape of needles, flakes, or formless slush. According to Barnes,[8] frazil is a surface-formed ice that is not permitted to freeze into a surface sheet. Carried to intakes or produced in them from supercooled water, frazil ice attaches itself to metallic racks, screens, conduits, and pumps. Anchor ice behaves like frazil ice but is derived from ice crystals that have developed on the bottom and on submerged objects in much the same way that frost forms on vegetation during a clear night. Neither frazil nor anchor ice is normally encountered below sheet ice, which thus offers some protection against their occurrence. Difficulties can also be prevented by heating metallic surfaces or raising the temperature of supercooled water by about 0.1 F, the common order of magnitude of maximum supercooling. Compressed air, backflushing, and light explosives ($\frac{1}{4}$ lb of 60% dynamite) have also been used successfully to free ice-clogged intakes. Telltale chains hung in front

[7] A French-Canadian term derived from the French for the forge cinders that fine, spicular frazil ice resembles.

[8] H. T. Barnes, *Ice Formation,* John Wiley & Sons, New York, 1906.

of ports will give warning of impending ice-clogging troubles (see Section 17-7).

e. Intake Velocities and Depths. Ice troubles are reduced in frequency if intake ports are placed as deep as 25 ft below the water surface and if entrance velocities are kept between 3 and 4 in. per sec. Low velocities also will not transport ice and will hold the entraining of leaves and debris to a minimum. At low velocities, too, fish can escape from the intake current. Bottom sediments are kept out of the intake if entrance ports are raised 4 to 6 ft above the lake or reservoir floor. Ports should be provided at numerous other levels as well, in order to permit shifting the draft to optimum water quality. A vertical interval of 15 ft is often chosen. Wet wells should include a blowoff gate. Submerged gratings are given openings of 2 to 3 in. Screens are commonly 2 to 8 meshes to the inch and have face velocities of 3 to 4 in. per sec. Screens are discussed further in Sections 15-11 and 21-9.

f. Intake Conduits and Pumping Stations. Constructed as pipes (often with flexible joints) or as tunnels, intake conduits are designed to carry water to the shore at self-cleansing velocities of 3 to 4 fps. Pipelines are generally laid in trenches that are dredged and backfilled. Where they reach the shore line, the pipes must be well protected against disturbance by waves and ice. Conduits on earth foundations beneath dams are subjected to high loads and to the stresses incident to the consolidation of the foundation.

Pumps that draw water through intake conduits are generally placed in a well on shore. Since the suction lift, including friction, should not exceed 15 to 20 ft, pump wells are often quite deep in order to be of service when river, lake, or reservoir levels are lowered appreciably in times of drought. This creates problems of hydrostatic uplift and seepage in times of flood. Large pumping units are generally placed in dry wells.

10-10. Reservoir Outlets. The outlet works of water-supply reservoirs normally include stream-diversion conduits and spillways. Where reservoirs serve more than this single purpose, outlets may be provided in addition for low-water regulation (compensating water), development of hydroelectric power, and flood control. Navigation locks and fish ladders or fish elevators complete the list of possible control works.

a. Control Conduits. Depending upon the geology and topography of the area, stream-diversion conduits are passed through the dam site or around it. After fulfilling their purpose of by-passing the stream and protecting the dam and valley during construction, they are often incorporated in the intake or outlet system for water supply

(Figure 2-3), power development, and stream control (Figure 10-14). Their capacity is determined by flood-flow requirements (Section 7-10), including a consideration of the effects of variations in head and volumes of flood water impounded behind the dam as it rises during construction (Section 8-8). Diversion conduits are built as grade aqueducts and tunnels, or as pressure conduits and tunnels. However, no conduit passing through an earth dam can safely be placed under pressure. Gates should, therefore, be installed only at the inlet end of the conduit. If the conduit must work under pressure, consideration should be given to laying it within a larger access conduit. Conduits laid in earth dams or in earth foundations are often equipped with projecting fins or collars which discourage seepage along the outside of the conduit. The projections are designed to increase the path of seepage by 20% or more and to change the direction of seepage to include that of minimum permeability. At its terminus in the toe of the dam, a conduit traversing the dam should be surrounded with rock that, like a rock toe, will permit seepage waters to escape safely.

Flow into the outlet works is controlled by gates that are managed from gate houses. Control structures may also include racks and screens, diversion openings provided with stop logs, Venturi meters, water wheels, and electric generators.

b. Spillways. Spillways may be incorporated into the dam structure or they may be separated from it by a considerable distance.

The spillway section of masonry dams and of earth dams with a masonry spillway is designed as a masonry dam. In cross-section it commonly follows an ogee curve. This curved surface has a high coefficient of discharge. The water is delivered to the stream channel from an apron or stilling device. Ogee weirs have a coefficient of discharge of $C = 3.5$ to 4.0 based on the common weir formula

$$Q = Clh^{3/2} \qquad\qquad 10\text{-}12$$

where Q is the rate of discharge, l is the length adjusted for contraction, and h is the head. Reduction in length due to contractions is generally estimated at $0.1h$ for each sharp corner and at $0.05h$ for each rounded corner.

Separate spillways take the form of saddle, side-channel, and drop-inlet or shaft structures. Spillways placed in a saddle at some distance from the dam are particularly attractive because they divert flow away from the dam. The spillway may be an open channel that discharges into a natural flood way leading back to the stream below the dam, or it may be a low overflow weir in advance of the flood way. For the latter an ogee weir is common. If an open channel is used,

it must be proportioned to provide adequate inlet and channel capacity. In accordance with Figure 10-13, the inlet creates a transition from substantial quiescence to full channel velocity. Maximum
discharge will be reached, therefore, when the entrance is smooth and
flow is at critical depth (see Section 15-6). The velocity head h_v at

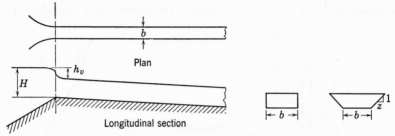

Figure 10-13. Channel spillway.

the entrance then equals one-third the height H of the reservoir level
above the channel bottom at the entrance, and the rate of discharge
through a rectangular channel becomes

$$Q = 3.087CbH^{3/2} \qquad \text{10-13}$$

where b is the width of the channel and C is an entrance coefficient
varying from 1.0 for a smooth entrance to 0.8 for an abrupt one. In
line with Section 15-6, a trapezoidal channel with side slopes of z
(horizontal to vertical) discharges

$$Q = 8.03Ch_v^{1/2}(H - h_v)[b + z(H - h_v)] \qquad \text{10-14}$$

where

$$h_v = \frac{3(2zH + b) - \sqrt{16z^2H^2 + 16zbH + 9b^2}}{10z} \qquad \text{10-15}$$

In accordance with well-known hydraulic principles, best hydraulic
efficiency is obtained when a semicircle can be inscribed in the cross-
section. Greatest hydraulic efficiency, however, does not necessarily
coincide with best economy of construction.

Flow will be uniform below the entrance if frictional resistance is
balanced by channel slope. Otherwise non-uniform flow is established.
Channel sections are then adjusted to the changing conditions of flow.
A weir within the channel produces a backwater curve.

Side-channel spillways are economical of space within the valley
of the impounded stream. The crest of the spillway is placed along
one hillside next to the dam, and the channel into which the spillway
discharges is carried around the end of the dam and safely past its

toe. The channel is preferably blasted out of rock. Failing this, it is lined with concrete. The hydraulic principles of design are those incorporated in the dimensioning of wash-water gutters for water filters. These principles are discussed in Section 24-10.

Shaft or drop-inlet spillways, as shown in Figure 10-14, consist of an overflow lip supported on a riser that discharges into an outlet conduit, which is often the original stream-diversion conduit. The

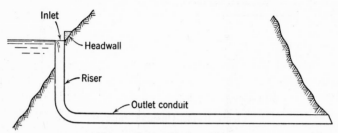

Figure 10-14. Shaft spillway.

lip is given any desired configuration. A circular lip and trumpet-like transition to the shaft creates a "morning-glory" spillway that must be placed at adequate distance from the shore if it is to be fully effective. A three-sided or semicircular lip is more accessible and can be in contact with the hillside. The capacity of shaft spillways is governed by that of its constituent parts and by the conditions of flow, including the effects of entrained air. Best hydraulic efficiency, as well as maximum flow capacity, is attained when the conduit and riser are flowing full. Model tests are much used to reach a design that will function properly.

Flashboards and gates are added to spillways to take advantage of storage above crest level, but only when their use will not endanger the structure.

11-1. General Considerations. The collection of ground waters and their protection, as indicated in Chapters 1, 2, 6, and 9, must be based upon an adequate knowledge and understanding of the geology, hydrology, and general hydraulics of the ground-water area that is to be developed. As with surface supplies, the control of the catchment area of the ground-water collecting system is an important sanitary responsibility. Where infiltration takes place at no great distance from the ground-water works, many of the principles of watershed control laid down in Chapter 10 are valid. Where water is drawn from great depths, however, the gathering ground may lie far away. Sanitary control is then directed, more particularly, to the collecting system itself and to its immediate surroundings. Contrary to popular belief, the water drawn from the ground is not necessarily safe. Serious outbreaks of water-borne diseases have, in the past, been traced to ground-water supplies. Although the suspected source of contamination has generally been discovered in the immediate vicinity of the collection works, water derived from the solution passages of limestone and related formations has, upon occasion, transported infection over long distances. As previously stated, flow through such passages is like that in a surface stream. It does not include the natural filtration associated with fine-grained soils and rocks.

In reference to the yield of ground-water developments, their history is often one of great ingenuity in obtaining the supplies and of thoughtless failure to conserve them. Since many ground waters come from unseen depths, their origin, behavior, and volume have too long been the subject of unfounded and optimistic conjecture. Superstitions about ground water are hard to combat. Most persistent, undoubtedly, is an unwarranted faith in water dowsing. The divining rod, generally a forked twig, is grasped firmly at its free ends by the water dowser but is, nevertheless, held in delicate equilibrium. This is upset by the slightest movement of the wrists of the dowser and causes the fork to tilt sharply downward, supposedly attracted by subterranean waters.

Too often the drilling of wells is considered a panacea for municipal water-supply needs, regardless of the adequacy and economy of such projects. Much money is wasted, too, on private wells drilled deep into dense Archean rocks in the hope of striking so-called artesian water. The belief that supplies, once found, are inexhaustible has been all too prevalent. As a result, the rate of pumping is often excessive, until the supply starts to fail or has been seriously damaged by overdraft or by encroachment of salt water. The importance of applying the hydrological principles discussed in Chapter 9 *before*, not *after*, the development of ground-water resources has taken place cannot be stressed too much.

In spite of attendant difficulties, the ground often affords a naturally purer and more satisfactory supply than surface sources, particularly when water supplies are individualistic and drafts are relatively small. The water supplies of farms and isolated dwellings are examples.

It is the purpose of the present chapter to discuss the constructional features of ground-water developments, the hydraulics induced by the draft of water, and the means for the maintenance and care of the collecting works.

Collection Works

11-2. Common Features of Collection Works. Ground water must generally be raised from aquifers by pumping. To insure satisfactory performance, the suction lift including entrance and pipe losses is commonly held below 25 ft. Where the water table lies below the allowable suction depth, the collecting piping or conduit leading to the pump and the pumping unit itself must be placed below ground level, or deep-well pumps must be installed in individual wells. In favorable circumstances, air-lift pumps can be substituted for deep-well pumps. Infiltration galleries can discharge by gravity into pump wells, whence the water is lifted into force mains that lead to purification works or directly to the community. Full gravity flow, comparable to that from upland surface sources, is obtained but rarely: from springs at the base of mountains, from tunnels driven into hillsides, and from flowing artesian wells that lie sufficiently high above the community to provide the necessary head. Both suction and gravity conduits, but particularly the former, must be guarded against pollution from sources in their immediate surroundings.

Water drawn from the ground by suction or discharged by air lifts must be passed through an air-separating tank that collects the gases contributed by the air lifts or released from the water as its pressure drops below atmospheric. The collected gases are removed by a vacuum or air pump. Where sand or other soil granules are pulled into the water from the aquifer, sand separators must be employed if pumps and piping are to be protected against abrasion.

The sinking of wells is a highly specialized art that has evolved along many, more or less regional, lines. In the United States, it is common practice to allow the well driller considerable latitude in the choice of suitable methods. He undertakes to sink a well of specified minimum size at a fixed price per foot. Ordinarily, therefore, the engineer is not directly concerned with drilling operations themselves but with the adequacy, suitability, and economy of proposed developments and with the best location of the works from the standpoint of hydrology and sanitary protection. However, he is called on to select the size, number, and arrangement of wells, to specify the pumping equipment, to see that a reliable contractor is employed, to supervise the testing and development of completed wells, to see that they are properly disinfected before being placed in service, and to make certain that necessary precautions are taken to prevent contamination of the operating supply from both surface and underground sources of pollution.

The size, number, and arrangement of wells are determined by the amount and depth of water to be developed, the hydrology and hydraulics of the available aquifers, and the methods of pumping to be used.

Large *dug wells*, 6 ft or more in diameter, are generally sunk only where ground water is shallow and storage within the well is needed to care for fluctuations in the rate of pumping. Where the permeability of the ground is too low to keep a single well supplied with enough water, several small wells must be substituted.

Groups of shallow wells can be pumped simultaneously by connecting them to suction lines that lead to a single pumping-station. To make this scheme work, the well strainers, or bottom of the drop pipes, must remain submerged at all times, and all suction lines must be airtight. The principal disadvantage of this arrangement is that the wells must usually be spaced so closely (50 to 200 ft on centers) that the cones of depression or circles of influence overlap too much for good efficiency. Only the water filtering into the surface of the field or flowing laterally into it is collected. Pumping an entire field of closely spaced wells has frequently been shown to be no more productive of water than pumping a selected group of adequately spaced wells. The spacing by which interference or overlapping of cones of depression is avoided increases as the rate of draft rises and the rate of natural flow falls.

Because of their expense, *deep wells* must be pumped at high rates. They must be spaced relatively far apart as a consequence. Although no fixed rule can apply, a spacing of 1,000 ft or more is usually found to be desirable.

The effect of well diameter upon yield is discussed in Section 11-9. Although the size should be such that drawdown and yield are not adversely affected, the method of sinking the well and the space requirements for pumping machinery govern the choice more often than do hydraulic considerations. Strainers or screens and riser pipes should be sized to keep entrance losses and frictional resistances to flow within reasonable magnitudes at maximum pumping rates. Riser-pipe velocities are commonly held to 2 or 3 fps. Entering sand will clog and damage well casings and pumps. Sand will not be sucked in if strainers and casings are properly proportioned and entrance velocities are held down. In other respects, deep wells are made as small as drilling equipment permits.

Construction methods depend primarily on the nature of the ground or rock to be penetrated and on cost. In addition to size, depth, and design, the cost of construction depends on the equipment and experience of the drillers who operate in the area. Designs improve and costs decline as regional information concerning aquifers and their overlying formations accumulates. *Well logs* should, therefore, be kept. They should give an accurate description of all formations encountered, rates of drill penetration, amounts of water tapped, and other pertinent data for the various depths reached. On completion of the well, the driller's log may be supplemented by caliper, electric, and radioactivity measurements.

11-3. Infiltration Galleries. Infiltration galleries are suitably constructed (1) as marginal drains along hillsides; (2) at right angles to the underflow of valleys; and (3) parallel to streams toward which upland flow is traveling, and from which water may be drawn by seepage, if this is desired. Unwanted seepage from streams is excluded by blanking off the stream side of the gallery and, if necessary, placing clay or a cutoff wall on that side.

For maximum yield, galleries should be placed at the full depth of the aquifer. Large galleries are constructed of masonry or concrete with numerous openings. They are built in open trenches or are driven by tunneling methods. Surrounding them with gravel will increase their intake, which is generally large. Tile drains laid with open joints and surrounded with gravel are used to collect smaller quantities of water. They are sometimes placed radially around springs and dug wells to increase their yield.

The capacity of galleries that are built across a valley is increased by sinking a cutoff wall of concrete into the ground to dam up the underflow and force its entrance into the upstream collecting system.

11-4. Unconfined Steady Flow into a Gallery. In the most favorable circumstances, steady flow into a blanked-off infiltration gallery situated in an unconfined aquifer is non-uniform in but two dimensions. The approximate amount of water drawn into such a gallery can, therefore, be determined by the flow-net principles outlined in Section 9-15. If the water table is relatively flat and the bottom of the gallery rests on a horizontal impervious sole, as shown in Figure 11-1, it becomes possible to deal with the situation in more direct

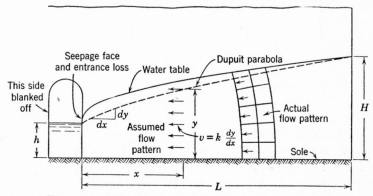

Figure 11-1. Flow into a blanked-off infiltration gallery.

mathematical terms. As proposed by Dupuit,[1] the following simplifying assumptions must be made: (1) that the soil is isotropic and incompressible; (2) that the tangent of the angle of inclination of the water table, i.e., its slope, is substantially equal to its sine; and (3) that the flow is uniform and horizontal throughout the depth of the aquifer.

In accordance with Darcy's law, and the notation of Figure 11-1, the discharge per unit length of gallery then becomes

$$q = Ky \, dy/dx \qquad 11\text{-}1$$

where $y \times 1$ is the area of unit width through which the water flows with velocity $K \, dy/dx$. By integration

$$qx = \tfrac{1}{2}Ky^2 + c \qquad 11\text{-}2$$

[1] Jules Dupuit, *Études théoriques et pratiques sur le mouvement des eaux,* Paris, 2nd ed., 1863.

If $y = H$ at $x = L$, and it is assumed that $y = h$ at $x = 0$,

$$q = \tfrac{1}{2}K(H^2 - h^2)/L \qquad\qquad 11\text{-}3$$

Equation 11-3 traces a parabolic water table that departs, often significantly, from the true water table and continues to rise beyond any finite boundary. What the line of seepage should be, in order to meet the requirements at entrance and discharge that are laid down in Figure 9-8, is indicated in Figure 11-1. The capillary fringe is not taken into account. The greater the ratio of L/H, the closer is the agreement between the calculated and true flow systems, except at the discharge face.

Example 11-1. A stratum of clean sand and gravel 20 ft deep has a coefficient of permeability $K = 10^{-1}$ cm/sec (3.28×10^{-3} fps) and is supplied with water from a diffusion ditch that penetrates to the bottom of the stratum. If the water surface in an infiltration gallery lies 2 ft above the sole of the stratum, and its distance to the diffusion ditch is 30 ft, what is the flow into a foot of gallery?

In accordance with Equation 11-3,

$$q = \tfrac{1}{2}(3.28 \times 10^{-3})(20^2 - 2^2)/30$$

$$= 2.2 \times 10^{-2} \text{ cfs} \qquad \text{or} \qquad 14{,}000 \text{ gpd}$$

11-5. Construction of Wells. A brief description of the methods commonly used for sinking wells will identify the different kinds of wells.

a. Dug Wells. Small dug wells are generally excavated by hand. In loose overburden, wells are cribbed with timber, lined with brick, rubble, or concrete, or cased with large-diameter vitrified tile or concrete pipe. Wells in rock are commonly left unlined. Excavation is continued until water enters more rapidly than it can be bailed out (see Figure 11-2a).

Large and deep dug wells are often constructed by sinking their liners as excavation proceeds. The leading ring is equipped with a steel cutting edge, and new sections are added as excavation progresses. After striking water, caisson methods may be employed (see Figure 11-2b).

b. Driven Wells. The use of driven wells is confined to relatively shallow sand formations. As shown in Figure 11-3, a driving point is attached to a strainer or perforated section of drive pipe. Driving friction is reduced by making the point somewhat larger than the casing. The driving weight is commonly suspended from a block attached to a tripod. Where the ground is hard, a cylindrical shoe equipped with water jets will loosen the soil and wash it to the surface.

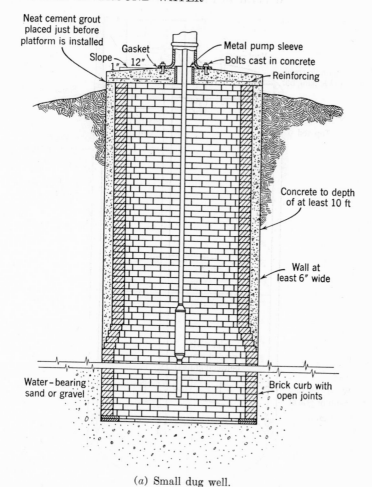

Neat cement grout placed just before platform is installed

Gasket

Slope

Metal pump sleeve

Bolts cast in concrete

Reinforcing

Concrete to depth of at least 10 ft

Wall at least 6" wide

Water-bearing sand or gravel

Brick curb with open joints

(a) Small dug well.

Figure 11-2. Dug wells and their sanitary protection. *After Iowa State Department of Health.*

c. *Bored Wells.* In soil that is sufficiently cohesive to prevent serious caving, wells are bored with augers by hand or machinery. The soil usually remains in the auger, which is raised and cleaned periodically. Below the water table, sand may wash out of the auger and have to be removed from the bore hole by a bailer or sand pump. As boring proceeds, sections of rod are added to the auger stem. Bits up to 20 in. in diameter have been used successfully, and wells have been enlarged in diameter up to 48 in. by reaming. A well casing is inserted in the hole and cemented in place. The strainer is then installed.

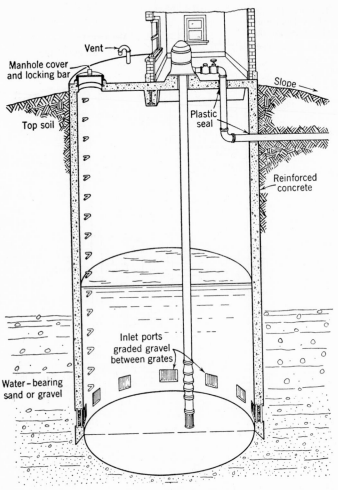

Vent

Manhole cover
and locking bar

Slope

Top soil

Plastic
seal

Reinforced
concrete

Inlet ports
graded gravel
between grates

Water-bearing
sand or gravel

(b) Large dug well.

Figure 11-2. (*Continued.*)

d. Drilled Wells. These wells are sunk either by percussion or rotary drilling. There are many methods, among which the following are most widely used.

Percussion drilling with cable tools is common in the United States. The string of tools includes a blunt or chisel-edged bit, a drill stem, jars, and a rope socket, all connected by tapered screw joints. The tools are alternately raised and dropped in a wet hole by a crank arm, a reciprocating pulley, or a walking beam. The drill rope must be slightly stretched when the bit strikes bottom. The return spring in the rope then prevents the bit from sticking or the tools from jamming.

As their name implies, the *jars* (two heavy, loose, chainlike links) help to loosen the bit by jarring it on the return stroke. The driller turns the bit and judges the performance of the tools by grasping the drill rope.

Blunt bits are used in soft material and chisel edges in hard rock. The drilling edge is somewhat larger than the shank to provide working clearance. The loosened material is removed by a bailer attached to a sand line. Water is

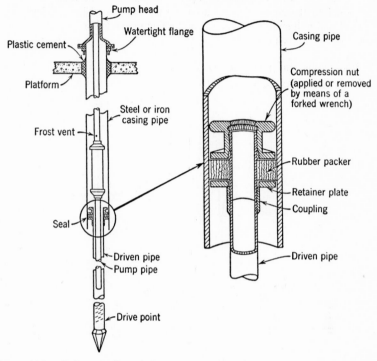

Figure 11-3. Driven well and its sanitary protection. *After Wisconsin State Board of Health.*

added if natural flow into the well is not adequate for drilling and bailing. If the hole caves, a casing is inserted, and the drilling is continued with a smaller bit.

The *California stovepipe method* was developed for use in the unconsolidated, water-bearing, alluvial deposits of the western United States. A mud scow which serves both as bit and bailer is substituted for the string of tools, and short joints of overlapping casing are forced down as drilling progresses. The cylindrical mud scow is equipped with a flap valve and a cutting shoe. The earth is chopped loose and worked into the drill by plunging it up and down. The filled scow is hauled up and emptied. The casing consists of sections of thin steel pipe that overlap by half their length. Joints are locked by denting the casing with a pick. The casing may be driven, a special driving head being used, or it may be forced down by hydraulic jacks anchored to timbers embedded in the soil. Slots to admit the water are cut at the level of permeable formations after the casing is in place.

Rotary drilling employs a fish-tail or similar bit, attached to a hollow drill rod, which is rotated rapidly by an engine-driven rotary table. A heavy suspension of colloidal clay is pumped into the drill pipe, flows through openings in the bit, and brings the loosened material to the surface. The drilling fluid is recirculated into the well after the suspended cuttings have been separated from it in a mud pit or settling lagoon. Rotary drilling was first used in the oil fields. Its application to water-well drilling was delayed by the fact that the thick drilling clay was forced into the aquifer and reduced the flow to the well. Development of the gravel-wall well and improvements in flushing methods have largely overcome these objections to rotary drilling.

Drilled wells should be *cemented* so as to cut off downward flow of possibly contaminated water into the well from outside, avoid erosion

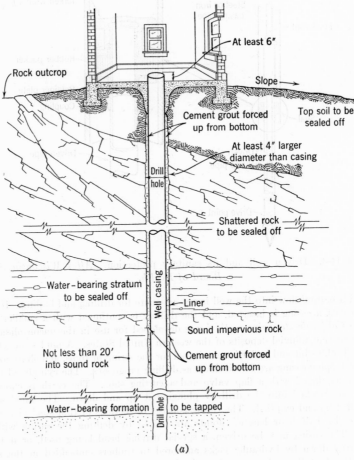

(a)

Figure 11-4. Drilled well and its sanitary protection. *After Iowa State Department of Health.*

of the soil outside the casing, protect the casing against exterior corrosion, and prevent leakage when the casing ultimately rusts through from within. Cementing involves filling the annular space between the casing and the wall of the drill hole with dense cement grout not less than 2 in. thick. Beginning at the top of the aquifer, the grout must be forced upward until it reaches the surface of the ground. Cementing is an important conservation and health-protection measure. See Figure 11-4.

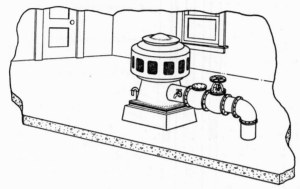

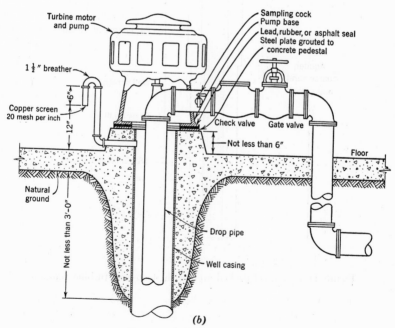

(b)

Figure 11-4. (Continued.)

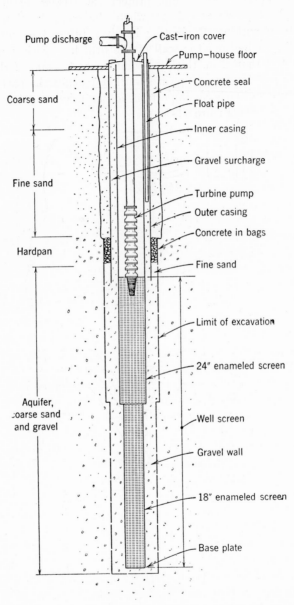

Pump discharge

Cast–iron cover

Pump–house floor

Concrete seal

Coarse sand

Float pipe

Inner casing

Gravel surcharge

Fine sand

Turbine pump

Outer casing

Concrete in bags

Hardpan

Fine sand

Limit of excavation

24″ enameled screen

Aquifer,
coarse sand
and gravel

Well screen

Gravel wall

18″ enameled screen

Base plate

Figure 11-5.   Gravel-packed well with deep-well turbine pump.

e. Gravel-Wall Wells. As shown in Figure 11-5, an envelope of gravel placed outside the well screen creates a gravel wall which increases the effective diameter of the well. A well hole is first drilled and reamed to the desired diameter (24 in. or more). An outer casing is then cemented in, and the aquifer is cleaned before a smaller inner casing carrying the well screen is inserted. After this, pea-sized gravel is fed down between the two casings against a slowly rising mud stream. The mud prevents the settling gravel from arching to leave cavities. The mud is thinned with water as the filling proceeds, and a plunger is operated rapidly up and down inside the casing to assist in compacting the gravel. The churning action of the plunger enlarges the hole in loose material, and the thinning water washes out the mud and fine sand. Gravel-wall wells may suck in sand when they are first placed in operation, and gravel may have to be added from time to time. The gravel wall not only improves the hydraulic characteristics of the well, but it also reduces greatly difficulties with sanding and underground caving.

11-6. Well Strainers. The openings in well strainers are constructed in such fashion as to keep unwanted sand out of the well while admitting water with the least possible friction. In fine, uniform material, the openings must be small enough to prevent the entrance of the constituent grains. Where the aquifer consists of particles that vary widely in size, however, the capacity of the well is improved by using strainer openings through which the finer particles are pulled into the well, while the coarser ones are left behind with increased void space. A graded filter is thereby created around the well. The finer two-thirds of the sand are generally withdrawn with the aid of back-flushing operations, or by high rates of pumping.

Well strainers commonly take the form of perforated casings or fabricated screens. Perforated casings are used in uncemented wells when relatively large openings are permissible. They may be machine-perforated at the factory, or they may be slotted after installation in the ground. Ripping the casing in place is common practice in the western United States.

In fabricated well screens, the beveled openings commonly enlarge inward to clear the slots of sand that might otherwise lodge in them. Screens made of corrosion-resistant materials are more durable than slotted casings, but they are also more expensive. The special metals suitable for well screens may be listed in the following order of preference: [2] Monel metal, supernickel, Everdur metal, silicon bronze, sili-

[2] Tentative Standard Specifications for Deep Wells, prepared by the American Water Works Association.

con brass, red brass, and stainless steel. Entrance velocities must not be large enough to move the particles that are to be left undisturbed.

11-7. Development of Wells. The operations of flushing, testing, and equipping wells before they are put into service are called *well development*. Temporary equipment is generally used for high-rate pumping and backflushing. When sand no longer enters the well, its *specific capacity*, or yield per foot of drawdown, is determined by pumping at different rates for a sufficient length of time to reach fairly stable water levels. Selection of permanent pumping equipment is based on the information obtained.

The pumping tests made in connection with the development of a well provide information on the hydraulic characteristics of the aquifer and the well. They do not indicate safe, long-time yields. To find these, one must turn to the hydrologic considerations discussed in Chapter 9.

11-8. Confined, Steady Flow into Wells. Steady flow into a well through a screen that is open to the full depth of an extensive confined aquifer of uniform thickness and permeability can be approximated mathematically in terms of Dupuit's principles (see Section 11-4). The flow toward the well is but two-dimensional in the plane of the aquifer. A graphical determination of its magnitude is, therefore, possible and will develop the flow pattern of artesian flow toward a well.

a. Mathematical Formulation of Artesian Flow. Formulation of the flow into an artesian well in accordance with the principles of Dupuit applies strictly only to steady radial flow from an outer circular boundary that is concentric with the well. For the conditions depicted in Figure 11-6,

$$Q = 2\pi Kxm \, dy/dx \qquad\qquad 11\text{-}4$$

Integrating over the limits $x = \frac{1}{2}d$ for $y = h$ and $x = \frac{1}{2}D$ for $y = H$,

$$Q = 2\pi Km \frac{H - h}{\log_e (D/d)} = 2.73 Km \frac{H - h}{\log (D/d)} \qquad 11\text{-}5$$

The discharge is seen to be directly proportional to the drawdown $H - h = p$. The yield per unit drawdown, or the *specific capacity* of the well, is generally expressed in gallons per minute per foot of drawdown. It has actually been observed to remain fairly constant at all reasonable values of drawdown.

b. Flow Net of a Single Artesian Well. As shown in Section 9-15, the flow net of an artesian well that draws water from an aquifer with level piezometric surface consists of radial flowlines and concentric equipotential circles. If, as is more usual, the natural piezometric surface is sloped, the radial flow net is superimposed upon the undisturbed rectangular flow net, and the pattern illustrated in Figure 11-7 is thereby evolved.

In the delineation of such a flow net the total number of linear flow paths, or channels, that are tributary to the well (16 in Figure 11-7) will equal the total number of radial flow paths towards it. The

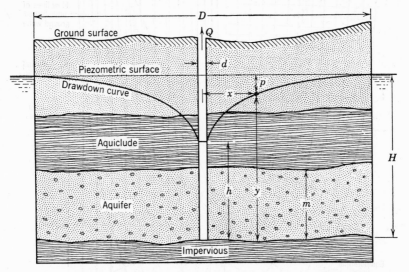

Figure 11-6. Artesian well with steady radial flow from a concentric circular boundary.

direction of flow is traced by the vector sum of the linear and radial components, as illustrated in the right-hand margin of Figure 11-7. The equipotential lines cross the flowlines at right angles. If they are given the same spacing as the flowlines, they form an orthogonal flow net. The apex of the limiting flowline in Figure 11-7 establishes the point of stagnation P. The line itself demarcates the divide between water drawn into and passing by the well. The flow pattern of this outer region, incidentally, is that past a solid object of the form traced by the limiting flowline.

For flow through a unit depth of aquifer, Equation 11-5 becomes

$$q = 2\pi K \frac{H - h}{\log_e (D/d)} \qquad \text{11-6}$$

whence

$$K(H - h) = \frac{q}{2\pi} \log_e \frac{D}{d} \qquad \text{11-7}$$

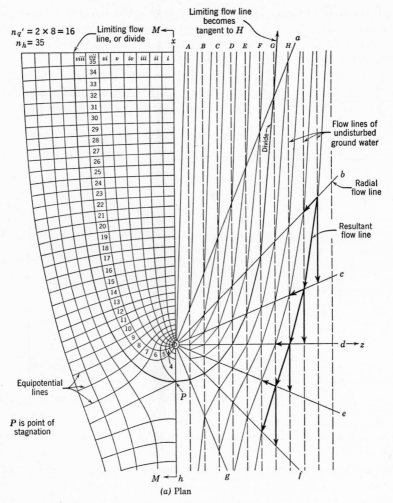

Figure 11-7. Flow net of a single artesian well.

This is the velocity potential ϕ_d for radial flow towards a well. For the radial system of Figure 11-7, $(\tfrac{1}{2}D)^2 = x^2 + z^2$. Hence

$$\phi_d = \frac{q}{2\pi} \log_e \frac{D}{d} = \frac{q}{4\pi} \log_e \frac{x^2 + z^2}{(\tfrac{1}{2}d)^2} \qquad 11\text{-}8$$

The velocity potential of the undisturbed ground-water flow in the x direction is $\phi_0 = v_0 x$ and that of the combined flow is the sum of the two, i.e., $\phi = \phi_0 + \phi_d$. The point of stagnation downstream from the well is found by equating the x component of the velocity to zero and solving for x:

$$v_x = \frac{\partial \phi}{\partial x} = v_0 + \frac{q}{2\pi} \frac{x}{x^2 + z^2} = 0 \qquad \text{11-9}$$

Since $z = 0$,

$$x = -\frac{q}{2\pi v_0} \qquad \text{11-10}$$

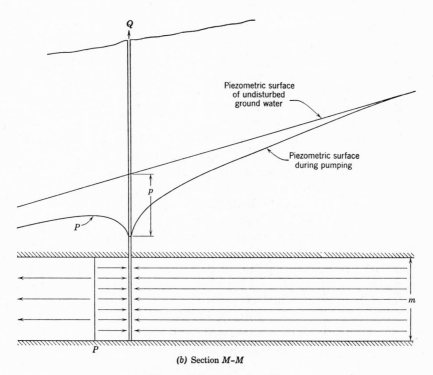

(b) Section *M-M*

Figure 11-7. (*Continued.*)

Example 11-2. If the well shown in Figure 11-7 penetrates an aquifer 40 ft thick and draws water laterally from a distance of 56 ft, the piezometric surface being lowered significantly for a distance of 140 ft upstream from the well by a drop in head of 30 ft at the well, what is the yield of the well if the coefficient of permeability of the aquifer is 3.28×10^{-4} fps and the piezometric slope of the undisturbed ground water is 40 ft in 140 ft; also what is the distance of the point of stagnation from the well?

a. Since the yield of the well must equal the rate of flow of the tributary ground water,

$$Q = Ksa = 3.28 \times 10^{-4} \times (40/140) \times 2 \times 56 \times 40$$

$$= 0.42 \text{ cfs} \quad \textbf{or} \quad 272{,}000 \text{ gpd}$$

b. In accordance with Equation 9-19,

$$Q = Kh(n_q'/n_h)m = 3.28 \times 10^{-4} \times (40 + 30) \times 2 \times (8/35) \times 40$$

$$= 0.42 \text{ cfs} \quad \text{or} \quad 272,000 \text{ gpd}$$

c. The point of stagnation is identified by Equation 11-10 as $x = -\dfrac{q}{2\pi v_0}$, in which

$q = 0.42/40 = 1.05 \times 10^{-2}$ cfs and $v_0 = Ks = 3.28 \times 10^{-4} \times 40/140 = 9.37 \times 10^{-5}$ fps.

Hence

$$x = \frac{1.05 \times 10^{-2}}{2\pi \times 9.37 \times 10^{-5}} = 17.8 \text{ ft}$$

c. Flow Net of a Field of Artesian Wells. In order to construct the flow net for a field of existing artesian wells, all available data pertaining to boundaries for a given set of conditions must be plotted on a map that shows the location of pumped wells or well groups. As large a number as possible of reasonably simultaneous observations of piezometric surface levels should be plotted. Each such observation establishes a boundary point. Construction of the net is aided by including on the map known outcrops and other formation boundaries that will limit flow.

As proposed by Robert Bennett,[3] the flow net is constructed by fitting equipotential lines to the observed piezometric elevations in a way analogous to the preparation of a contour map, while the flowlines are concurrently drawn in a manner to satisfy known fixed boundaries and to develop the system of squares. It should be recognized that each equipotential line that encompasses the field is in fact a complete external boundary.

An example of a flow net drawn in this manner is shown in Figure 11-8. The piezometric contour spacing is constant throughout the field. The value of this quantity is 10 ft in the example. Since the sketch identifies the value of n_q', the quantity pumped from each well or group of wells can be calculated if the transmissibility is known. Conversely, the transmissibility can be calculated if the pumping rates are known. If quantities and transmissibilities are both known, the comparison of the n_q' value for the flow net with that calculated from Equation 9-19 affords a check. If the two determinations of n_q' are not in agreement, the measured quantities, the measured transmissibilities, or the flow net must be in error.

Table 11-1 exemplifies the calculation of the coefficients of trans-

[3] R. R. Bennett and R. M. Meyer, "Geology and Ground Water Resources of the Baltimore Area," *Maryland Dept. Geology, Mines, and Water Resources, Bull.* **4** (1952).

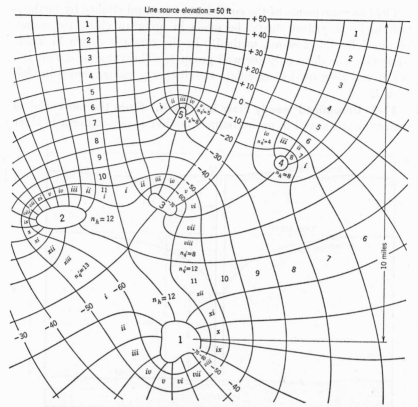

Figure 11-8. Flow net of a field of artesian wells. *After Bennett and Meyer.*

missibility for the well field shown in Figure 11-8. The high transmissibility obtained for well group 3 is of interest.

TABLE 11-1. Calculation of Transmissibility from Equipotential
Flow-Net Data

Well group no. (1)	Number of flow-lines, n_q' (2)	Measured rate of pumping, mgd (3)	Calculated discharge,* mgd (4)	Calculated coefficient of transmissibility, gpd per ft (5)
1	12	7.5	7.5	6.2×10^4
2	13	8.5	8.1	6.5×10^4
3	8	7.5	5.0	9.4×10^4
4	4	2.5	2.5	6.3×10^4
5	5	3.0	3.1	6.0×10^4

* Coefficient of transmissibility = 6.2×10^4 gpd per ft was measured only
for well group 1 but was assumed to apply to other well fields.

Field measurements of the coefficient of transmissibility by methods still to be described should be made in order to check the values obtained by the flow-net method. In the example shown in Table 11-1, this was done only for well group 1. The value of 62,000 gpd per ft was then used to calculate the discharge values shown in Column 4.

11-9. Unconfined Steady Flow into Wells. Since the movement of water toward a well in an unconfined aquifer is non-uniform in three

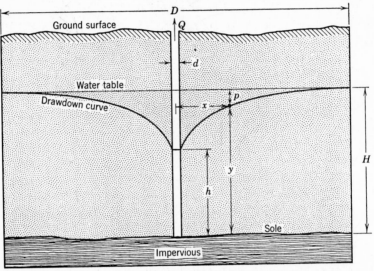

Figure 11-9. Water-table well in a ground-water reservoir.

dimensions, the graphical method described in Section 9-15 is not applicable. However, a useful differential equation for flow can be formulated and integrated in accordance with the principles laid down by Dupuit, provided that the well penetrates to the sole of the aquifer and flow is steady. The latter requirement implies prolonged pumping at a uniform rate until a state of equilibrium has been reached. For the unusual case of steady radial flow into a well from a concentric outer boundary, or circle of influence, illustrated in Figure 11-9, the following equation has been formulated by Dupuit:

$$Q = 2\pi Kxy \, dy/dx \qquad\qquad 11\text{-}11$$

where Q is the rate of flow into the well, and x and y are the coordinates of any point on the Dupuit cone of depression, or drawdown curve. The component factors are $2\pi xy$ the area through which flow takes place, and $K \, dx/dy$ the velocity. By integration

$$Q \log_e x = \pi K y^2 + c \qquad \text{11-12}$$

and for $y = h$ at $x = \frac{1}{2}d$ (d being the diameter of the well) and $y = H$ at $x = \frac{1}{2}D$ (D being the diameter of the circle of influence, or $\frac{1}{2}D$ being the distance of the outer boundary from the center of the well),

$$Q = \pi K \frac{H^2 - h^2}{\log_e (D/d)} = 1.36K \frac{H^2 - h^2}{\log (D/d)} \qquad \text{11-13}$$

The significance and limitations of this equation are similar to those discussed in Section 11-4 for the Dupuit formulation of steady flow into an infiltration gallery. The order of magnitude of D can be gaged by assuming that the normal ground-water flow within the circle of influence will enter the well. If the hydraulic slope of this flow is s,

$$Q = KsDH \qquad \text{11-14}$$

which equated to 11-13 gives

$$D = \frac{\pi(H^2 - h^2)}{sH \log_e (D/d)} = \frac{1.36(H^2 - h^2)}{sH \log (D/d)} \qquad \text{11-15}$$

Equation 11-15 is solved for D by trial.

If a well taps a ground-water reservoir from which there is little or no natural discharge, the circle of influence will extend to the limits of the basin. Pumping then lowers the general water table and will ultimately empty the reservoir. A steep hydraulic slope s, by contrast, reduces the circle of influence (Equation 11-15) and increases the yield (Equation 11-13). Further examination of Equation 11-13 shows the following changes in yield, as the drawdown, or the diameter of the well, is varied. Since H is constant, the quantity $(H^2 - h^2)$ increases at a decreasing rate as h is reduced. Thus successive increases in drawdown reduce the specific capacity of water-table wells. For a constant value of D the logarithmic ratio of the diameters of the circle of influence and diameter of the well and their inverse relation to the yield indicate that increasing the diameter of a well does not greatly increase its yield. For example, a 2-ft well will yield only 15 to 30% more water than a 3-in. well. Diameters, therefore, are ordinarily chosen to satisfy the methods used for drilling, developing, and pumping wells.

The principal value of the well formulas that have been presented in this and the preceding section is their indication of the general relations that obtain between rate of discharge and well diameter, circle of influence, slope and depth of undisturbed ground-water movement, and drawdown. The importance of the coefficient of permeability must not be overlooked. Its maximum value is many times greater than its minimum value in water-yielding formations.

11-10. Determination of Permeability under Conditions of Steady Flow. If we integrate Equation 11-4 between the limits x_1 and x_2 for y_1 and y_2 respectively and solve for K, we find that

$$K = \frac{Q}{2\pi m(y_2 - y_1)} \log_e \frac{x_2}{x_1} = \frac{0.367Q}{m(p_1 - p_2)} \log \frac{x_2}{x_1} \qquad 11\text{-}16$$

where p_1 and p_2 are drawdowns at the respective distances of x_1 and x_2 from the well.[4] Equation 11-16 offers a means of finding the value of the coefficient of permeability of an artesian aquifer by measuring the water level in two or more observation wells situated at different distances from a well that is discharging at a constant rate. Application of this formulation constitutes Thiem's method.[5]

Tests by Wenzel [6] indicate that consistent values for the coefficient of permeability can be obtained if the following procedures are used: (1) p_1 is taken as the average drawdown at two observation wells each of which is situated at a distance x_1 from the pumped well, but on opposite sides; (2) p_2 is similarly the average drawdown at the greater distance x_2 along the same radial line; (3) all test wells lie within the area where the drawdown has approximately reached stability, but they are situated outside the area immediately around the well where permeability has been changed by development of the well or where upward flow occurs because the well does not penetrate the aquifer in its entirety; and (4) more than two observation wells are used.

To establish the magnitude of K, all possible values of $(1/m)$ log (x_2/x_1) are plotted against corresponding values of $(p_1 - p_2)$. In accordance with Equation 11-16, the slope of the line of best fit multiplied by $0.367Q$ gives the best estimate of the coefficient of permeability. Goodness of fit of the straight line indicates the reliability of the method.

If the undisturbed water table or piezometric surface is flat, the cone of depression around a pumped well is symmetrical. The Darcy

---

[4] $p_1 = H - y_1$, and $p_2 = H - y_2$.

[5] Günther Thiem, *Hydrologische Methoden*, J. M. Gebhardt, Leipzig, 1906.

[6] L. K. Wenzel, "The Thiem Method of Determining Permeability of Water-Bearing Materials and Its Application to the Determination of Specific Yield," *U. S. Geol. Survey Water Supply Paper* 679-A (1936).

equation can then be used directly to compute the coefficient of permeability. For unconfined flow,

$$K = \frac{Q}{2\pi x y \, dy/dx}$$ 11-17

For confined flow,

$$K = \frac{Q}{2\pi x m \, dy/dx}$$ 11-18

The hydraulic gradient dy/dx at the distance x from the well is determined either from a profile of the cone of depression or from the differences in elevation of the water in observation wells.

If the undisturbed water table or piezometric surface has an appreciable slope, the average hydraulic gradient may be determined with a fair degree of accuracy by observing the elevation of the water table or piezometric surface during pumping in four wells that are placed $(x + a)$ ft and $(x - a)$ ft upstream and downstream from the well. A convenient value for a is 10 ft.

For both unconfined and confined flow, the geometry of the cone of depression approximates the average hydraulic slope along any line of flow as $1/(4a)$ times the sum of the differences in the water levels in the two upstream wells and the two downstream wells. This approximation rests on the fact that the cord of a parabolic curve is essentially parallel to the tangent to the curve midway between the two points joined by the cord.

11-11. Unsteady Flow into Wells. Theis [7] originated and Jacob,[8] Wenzel,[9] and Cooper and Jacob [10] have further developed equational relationships for the flow of water into wells in which the time from beginning or stopping of pumping is an added variable. This important advancement of the hydraulics of wells has eliminated the difficulty arising from the long time-lag before conditions of steady flow or equilibrium assumed in earlier formulations have actually been reached.

[7] C. V. Theis, "The Relation between the Lowering of the Piezometric Surface and the Rate and Duration of Discharge of a Well Using Ground-Water Storage," *Trans. Am. Geophys. Union, 16,* 519–524 (1935).

[8] C. E. Jacob, "On the Flow of Water in an Elastic Artesian Aquifer," *Trans. Am. Geophys. Union, 21,* 574–586 (1940).

[9] L. K. Wenzel, "Methods for Determining Permeability of Water-Bearing Materials," *U. S. Geol. Survey Water Supply Paper* 887, facing page 89 (1942).

[10] H. H. Cooper, Jr., and C. E. Jacob, "A Generalized Graphical Method for Evaluating Formation Constants and Summarizing Well-Field History," *Trans. Am. Geophys. Union, 27,* 526–534 (1946).

Since the gradual approach of the cone of depression towards a steady state is due primarily to the removal of water from storage as the cone deepens, a storage factor comes into play. This factor and that of permeability are called the *formation constants* of an aquifer.

The original development of the Theis equation was based on an analogy to the flow of heat toward a *sink* or point where heat is removed at a uniform rate. The existing mathematical solution of the heat-flow problem was transferred directly to the hydraulic problem, hydraulic pressure being analogous to temperature, pressure gradient to temperature gradient, permeability to thermal conductivity, and specific yield (or coefficient of storage) to specific heat.

The equation is

$$p = \frac{Q}{4\pi Km} \int_u^\infty \frac{e^{-u}\,du}{u} = \frac{Q}{4\pi Km} F(u) \qquad \text{11-19}$$

Here u is the lower limit of the integral which is defined as

$$u = \frac{x^2 S}{4Kmt} \qquad \text{11-20}$$

S being the *storage coefficient* and t the time during which the well has been pumped. For $Km = T$ the coefficient of transmissibility in gallons per day per foot of width, Q the uniform rate of pumping in gallons per minute, x the distance from the well in feet, t the time of pumping in days, and p the drawdown in feet,

$$p = \frac{114.6Q}{T} \int_u^\infty \frac{e^{-u}\,du}{u} = \frac{114.6Q}{T} F(u) \qquad \text{11-21}$$

and

$$u = \frac{1.87}{T} S \frac{x^2}{t} \qquad \text{11-22}$$

When flow is unconfined, the storage coefficient S equals the specific yield expressed as a decimal fraction. For an artesian aquifer, S equals the volume of water released, by virtue of compression, from storage within the column of the aquifer that underlies a unit surface area during a unit drawdown of the piezometric surface.

The integral in Equation 11-19 is called the *well function of u*, $F(u)$. It can be solved by expansion into the convergent series,

$$F(u) = 0.5772 - \log_e u + u - \frac{u^2}{2 \times 2!} + \frac{u^3}{3 \times 3!} - \cdots \qquad \text{11-23}$$

A series of values of $F(u)$ for values of u expressed as $N \times 10^n$ is given in Table 11-2.

TABLE 11-2. Values of the Well Function $F(u)$ for Various Values of u

From *U. S. Geological Survey Water Supply Paper* 887

u

N	$N \times 10^{-15}$	$N \times 10^{-14}$	$N \times 10^{-13}$	$N \times 10^{-12}$	$N \times 10^{-11}$	$N \times 10^{-10}$	$N \times 10^{-9}$	$N \times 10^{-8}$
1.0	33.96	31.66	29.36	27.05	24.75	22.45	20.15	17.84
1.5	33.56	31.25	28.95	26.65	24.35	22.04	19.74	17.44
2.0	33.27	30.97	28.66	26.36	24.06	21.76	19.45	17.15
2.5	33.05	30.74	28.44	26.14	23.83	21.53	19.23	16.93
3.0	32.86	30.56	28.26	25.96	23.65	21.35	19.05	16.75
3.5	32.71	30.41	28.10	25.80	23.50	21.20	18.89	16.59
4.0	32.57	30.27	27.97	25.67	23.36	21.06	18.76	16.46
4.5	32.46	30.15	27.85	25.55	23.25	20.94	18.64	16.34
5.0	32.35	30.05	27.75	25.44	23.14	20.84	18.54	16.23
5.5	32.26	29.95	27.65	25.35	23.05	20.74	18.44	16.14
6.0	32.17	29.87	27.56	25.26	22.96	20.66	18.35	16.05
6.5	32.09	29.79	27.48	25.18	22.88	20.58	18.27	15.97
7.0	32.02	29.71	27.41	25.11	22.81	20.50	18.20	15.90
7.5	31.95	29.64	27.34	25.04	22.74	20.43	18.13	15.83
8.0	31.88	29.58	27.28	24.97	22.67	20.37	18.07	15.76
8.5	31.82	29.52	27.22	24.91	22.61	20.31	18.01	15.70
9.0	31.76	29.46	27.16	24.86	22.55	20.25	17.95	15.65
9.5	31.71	29.41	27.11	24.80	22.50	20.20	17.89	15.59

u

N	$N \times 10^{-7}$	$N \times 10^{-6}$	$N \times 10^{-5}$	$N \times 10^{-4}$	$N \times 10^{-3}$	$N \times 10^{-2}$	$N \times 10^{-1}$	N
1.0	15.54	13.24	10.94	8.633	6.332	4.038	1.823	2.194×10^{-1}
1.5	15.14	12.83	10.53	8.228	5.927	3.637	1.465	1.000×10^{-1}
2.0	14.85	12.55	10.24	7.940	5.639	3.355	1.223	4.890×10^{-2}
2.5	14.62	12.32	10.02	7.717	5.417	3.137	1.044	2.491×10^{-2}
3.0	14.44	12.14	9.837	7.535	5.235	2.959	0.9057	1.305×10^{-2}
3.5	14.29	11.99	9.683	7.381	5.081	2.810	0.7942	6.970×10^{-3}
4.0	14.15	11.85	9.550	7.247	4.948	2.681	0.7024	3.779×10^{-3}
4.5	14.04	11.73	9.432	7.130	4.831	2.568	0.6253	2.073×10^{-3}
5.0	13.93	11.63	9.326	7.024	4.726	2.468	0.5598	1.148×10^{-3}
5.5	13.84	11.53	9.231	6.929	4.631	2.378	0.5034	6.409×10^{-4}
6.0	13.75	11.45	9.144	6.842	4.545	2.295	0.4544	3.601×10^{-4}
6.5	13.67	11.37	9.064	6.762	4.465	2.220	0.4115	2.034×10^{-4}
7.0	13.60	11.29	8.990	6.688	4.392	2.151	0.3738	1.155×10^{-4}
7.5	13.53	11.22	8.921	6.619	4.323	2.087	0.3403	6.583×10^{-5}
8.0	13.46	11.16	8.856	6.555	4.259	2.027	0.3106	3.767×10^{-5}
8.5	13.40	11.10	8.796	6.494	4.199	1.971	0.2840	2.162×10^{-5}
9.0	13.34	11.04	8.739	6.437	4.142	1.919	0.2602	1.245×10^{-5}
9.5	13.29	10.99	8.685	6.383	4.089	1.870	0.2387	7.185×10^{-6}

The magnitudes of the formation constants are found by measuring the drawdown in observation wells that accompanies the withdrawal of water from the well under study. If other drawdown values, or rates of flow, are to be calculated, the formation constants must be assumed to remain unchanged within the area of influence.

If, therefore, Q, S, and T are considered to be constant, the quantities $Q/(4\pi Km) = C_1$ and $x^2/(ut) = 4Km/S = C_2$ are also constant, and it follows from Equations 11-21 and 11-22 that

$$\log C_1 = \log p - \log F(u) \qquad \text{11-24}$$

and

$$\log C_2 = \log \frac{x^2}{t} - \log u \qquad \text{11-25}$$

The values of C_1 and C_2 are found from field observations as follows:

1. The measured values of p are plotted logarithmically as ordinates against measured values of x^2/t as abscissas.
2. Values of $F(u)$ taken from Table 11-2 are plotted as ordinates on the same diagram against values of u as abscissas.
3. Curves are drawn through the two sets of points, the curve through the second set of points being called the *type curve*.

It follows from the method of plotting and from Equations 11-24 and 11-25, that for every point on the p against x^2/t curve there is a corresponding point on the $F(u)$ against u curve which is displaced vertically by a fixed distance representing $\log C_1$ and horizontally by a fixed distance representing $\log C_2$. Therefore, a fixed amount of vertical and horizontal shift will bring the two curves into coincidence. See Figure 11-10.

If transparent paper is used for the plot of the observed data and it is placed over the type curve, to be shifted horizontally and vertically until a best fit of the plotted points to the type curve is obtained, then any matching point will identify the values of $F(u)$ and u that correspond to the values of p and x^2/t by which Equations 11-21 and 11-22 can be solved for T and S.

Example 11-3. For purposes of illustration, Figure 11-10 shows observed data fitted to the type curve as if a transparency of the observed data had been moved into place over the type curve.

a. Selecting the point $p = 5$, $x^2/t = 5 \times 10^6$, as the matching point, the formation constants T and S are computed for the observed values of $Q = 350$ gpm and $x = 225$ ft from the derived values of $u = 10^{-2}$ and $F(u) = 4.0$, as

$$T = 114.6Q\,\frac{F(u)}{p} = \frac{114.6 \times 350 \times 4}{5} = 3.2 \times 10^4 \text{ gpd per ft}$$

and

$$S = \frac{uT}{1.87x^2/t} = \frac{10^{-2}(3.2 \times 10^4)}{1.87(5 \times 10^6)} = 3.4 \times 10^{-5}$$

b. For 10 days of pumping at a rate of 700 gpm, Equation 11-22 states that

$$u = \frac{1.87}{3.2 \times 10^4}\,3.4 \times 10^{-5}\,\frac{(225)^2}{10} = 1.0 \times 10^{-5}$$

Reading the value of $F(u) = 10.9$ from Table 11-2, Equation 11-21 gives us

$$p = 114.6(7 \times 10^2)10.9/(3.2 \times 10^4) = 27 \text{ ft}$$

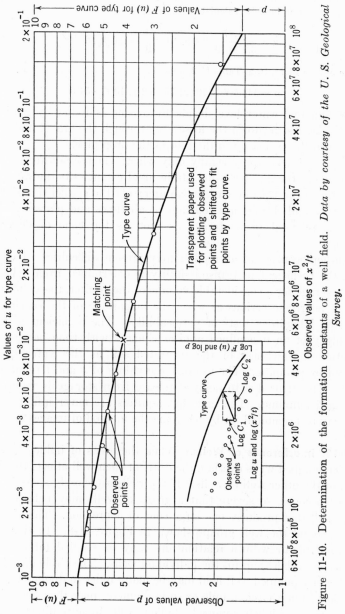

Figure 11-10. Determination of the formation constants of a well field. *Data by courtesy of the U. S. Geological Survey.*

c. If the well is gravel packed with an outside diameter of the gravel wall of 24 in., the drawdown at the well itself after 10 days of pumping at 700 gpm is given in similar fashion by calculation of

$$u = \frac{1.87}{3.2 \times 10^4} 3.4 \times 10^{-5} \frac{1}{10} = 2.0 \times 10^{-10}$$

whence $F(u) = 21.75$, from Table 11-2, and

$$p = 114.6(7 \times 10^2)21.75/(3.2 \times 10^4) = 54 \text{ ft}$$

The dynamic water level inside the casing is found by adding to the calculated drawdown the losses (a) through the gravel and screen and (b) in the casing up to the foot of the drop pipe.

These equations apply rigidly only when: (1) the aquifer is homogeneous; (2) the aquifer is infinite in areal extent; (3) the well penetrates the entire thickness of the aquifer; (4) the coefficients of transmissibility and storage are constant at all times and places; and (5) water is released from storage as soon as the cone of depression develops.

Non-homogeneity of an aquifer may present difficulties. However, when the coefficient of transmissibility is determined from field tests as an average for a considerable volume of the aquifer, these difficulties are not nearly so serious as when the magnitude of the coefficient is based on laboratory tests of permeability. The coefficient of transmissibility of an unconfined aquifer changes with time because of a reduction in thickness of the saturated soil as the water table is lowered by pumping. The use of large values of x and t reduces this effect. The error due to delayed release from storage is reduced by prolonged pumping. The fact that aquifers are never infinite in extent may be accounted for by applying the method of images described later.

11-12. Interference of Wells. When the areas of influence of two or more pumped wells overlap, the draft of each well affects the drawdown of the other well or wells. If the wells are closely spaced, interference becomes so severe that a group of wells may behave like a single well that produces one large cone of depression. This situation exists around the well groups shown in Figure 11-8. In this event, the discharge-drawdown relationships may be studied for the group as a whole rather than for the individual wells. The circle of influence of a heavily pumped well field may be many miles in diameter. Wells that lie within a circle a mile or so in diameter may then behave as a single group. Lightly pumped, shallow wells in unconfined aquifers, however, may provide no interference even when they are less than 100 ft apart.

The equations that have been developed for unsteady flow may be used to calculate for a single well the drawdown that is caused by the pumping of interfering wells. To the drawdown in the well, computed as if it were pumped by itself, is then added the drawdown due to the pumping of each of the interfering wells, one at a time.

Example 11-4. An example will illustrate the necessary calculations. If there are added to the well of Example 11-3 two other wells situated respectively 1,000 ft and 2,000 ft distant on a straight line, (a) what is the expected drawdown in each well when the first well is pumped at a rate of 700 gpm for 10 days, and (b) what are the drawdowns in each well when all three are pumped at a rate of 700 gpm for 10 days?

a. As shown in Example 11-3, the drawdown of the first well is 54 ft, while the drawdown of the well 1,000 ft away is calculated from

$$u = \frac{1.87}{3.2 \times 10^4} 3.4 \times 10^{-5} \frac{10^6}{10} = 2 \times 10^{-4} \quad \text{and} \quad F(u) = 7.94 \quad \text{(from Table 11-2)}$$

as

$$p = 114.6(7 \times 10^2)7.94/(3.2 \times 10^4) = 20 \text{ ft}$$

Similarly, the drawdown of the second well is given by

$$u = \frac{1.87}{3.2 \times 10^4} 3.4 \times 10^{-5} \frac{4 \times 10^6}{10} = 8 \times 10^{-4} \quad \text{and} \quad F(u) = 6.55$$

as

$$p = 114.6(7 \times 10^2)6.55/(3.2 \times 10^4) = 16 \text{ ft}$$

b. If all three wells are pumped at a rate of 700 gpm, the drawdown in the first and third wells will be their own drawdown plus the drawdown in one well 1,000 ft away and another well 2,000 ft away, or $(54 + 20 + 16) = 90$ ft, whereas the drawdown of the second or central well will be its own drawdown plus twice the drawdown in a well 1,000 ft away, or $(54 + 2 \times 20) = 94$ ft.

11-13. The Method of Images. In considering both steady and unsteady flow into wells, the aquifer was assumed to be unlimited in areal extent. Whether or not areal restriction is a matter of concern depends on the magnitude of the draft relative to the rate of replenishment. If, under conditions of equilibrium, the circle of influence does not extend to the bounds of the aquifer or to the source of replenishment, the assumption of an infinite aquifer introduces no difficulty. However, the assumption is often invalid: streams, outcrops, and topographic divides often lie within the radius of influence; formation boundaries, folds, and faults may limit the extent of the aquifer to a few miles; and water-bearing valley fills may be only 100 ft in breadth.

In order to deal with these limiting influences, the method of images developed by Lord Kelvin for analysis of electrostatic phenomena has

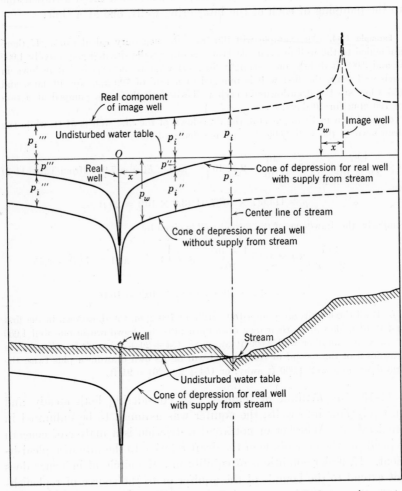

Figure 11-11. Application of the method of images to a well that receives water from a stream. *Idealized.*

been adapted to the solution of ground-water problems.[11,12] The method consists in imposing one or more image wells, i.e., the traces of identical wells at an equal distance beyond the boundary, in such manner that the superimposed effect of the image well produces the necessary limiting conditions at the boundary. The method provides solutions for a variety of boundary conditions.

Figure 11-11 illustrates the effect of a stream lying within the area of influence of a well. If percolation from the stream is sufficient to maintain saturation of the aquifer lying beneath its bed, the stream surface becomes an established equipotential line and is, therefore, a fixed boundary or limiting condition. In order to construct the cone of depression as modified by the stream, the cone for the well is developed as if the boundary did not exist. A doubly mirrored image of the well is then placed on the opposite side of the boundary and becomes the equivalent of a recharge well of the same capacity as the real well. In the nature of this construction, the rise in the water table of the real well due to the discharge of the image well will bring the cone of depression to the water surface of the stream. The reduction in drawdown of the real well is then given by the recharge line of the image well that lies above the real well. The addition of this line to the cone of depression of the real well satisfies the limit of the problem and is, therefore, a solution.

Figure 11-11 shows the drawdown and recharge of the real and image wells as solid lines in the real region and as dotted lines in the image region.

Example 11-5. If the well of Example 11-3 is 1,000 ft from a stream that can supply water to the ground at a rate that will hold the water table at the surface along the stream course, (a) find the drawdown in the well after 10 days of pumping at 700 gpm, and (b) sketch the profile of the intersection of the cone of depression with a vertical plane through the well normal to the stream.

a. As shown in Example 11-3, the drawdown without supply from the stream is 54 ft. The image recharge well is 2,000 ft distant and will, therefore, have a build-up of 16 ft as calculated for the drawdown at this distance in Example 11-4. Thus the resultant drawdown is $(54 - 16) = 38$ ft.

b. For $T = 3.2 \times 10^4$ gpd per ft, $S = 3.4 \times 10^{-5}$, and $Q = 700$ gpm, needed values of u are calculated from Equation 11-22 for various assumed values of x. Corresponding values of $F(u)$ are then found in Table 11-2, and values of p are calculated from Equation 11-21. The results are tabulated in Table 11-3 and plotted in Figure 11-11.

---

[11] C. V. Theis, "The Effect of a Well on the Flow in a Nearby Stream," *Trans. Am. Geophys. Union, 21*, 734–737 (1940).

[12] J. G. Ferris, "Ground-Water Hydraulics as a Geophysical Aid," *Michigan Dept. Conservation*, Lansing, Mich., *Tech. Rept.* 1 (1948).

TABLE 11-3. Calculation of Cone of Depression (Example 11-5)

Distance from real well $x,$ ft	Depression without supply from stream $p_u,$ ft	Build-up from image well $p_i,$ ft	Depression with supply from stream $p,$ ft
1,000 right	19.8	-19.8	0
500 right	23.4	-17.8	5.6
100 right	31.4	-16.7	14.7
10 right	43.0	-16.4	26.6
1 right and left	54.4	-16.4	38.0
10 left	43.0	-16.4	26.6
100 left	31.4	-16.2	15.2
500 left	23.4	-15.3	8.7
1,000 left	19.8	-14.4	5.4

A well penetrating valley fill, between rocky valley walls which constitute aquicludes that lie within the area of influence, offers another example of the type of problem that can be solved by the method of images. Since no flow can cross the boundary of the aquicludes, the cone of depression of the well must intersect at right angles the vertical planes that represent the average position of the boundaries. Mirrored images of the real well will provide the necessary limiting conditions. Exclusion of flow that would have been provided in the absence of the aquicludes makes it necessary to subtract from the cone of depression of the real well the depression of the water table represented by the cone of depression of the image wells. The solution of a problem is shown in Figure 11-12. Two image wells are not sufficient because the intersection at either boundary of the depression due to the image beyond the opposite valley wall leaves an unbalanced head potential. A second set of images at twice the distance from the real well eliminates this error but will leave, in turn, a reduced discrepancy at the opposite boundaries. Hence a series of images must be introduced on each side of the well. Other situations will suggest themselves to the reader.

11-14. Collection of Ground Water in Contact with Salt Water. Fresh water occurs in contact with salt water most frequently (1) in islands, peninsulas, spits, or bars that are surrounded by the sea or extend into it, and (2) in artesian aquifers that outcrop under the sea. The yield of fresh water under these conditions and the encroachment of salt water upon fresh-water sources are exemplified by the dynamics of fresh water in sand, volcanic, and coral islands in the sea.

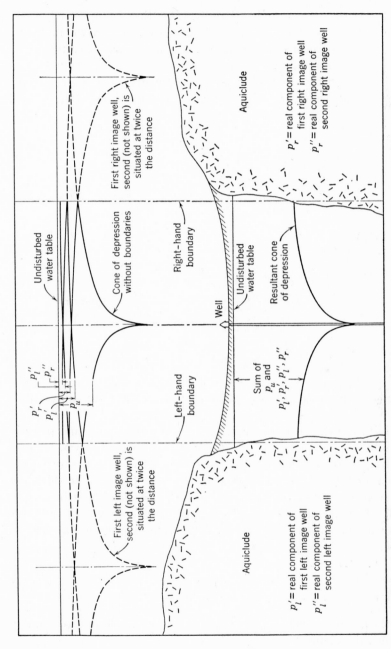

Figure 11-12. Application of the method of images to a well, flow to which is reduced by impervious outcrops.

Depending upon the nature of the subsoil, rain water percolates downward to join the body of fresh water that is supported, as an underground lens, upon the denser salt water. As shown in Figure 11-13, the movement of fresh water is downward and outward within this lens. During rainy seasons, the water table rises and the bottom of the lens sinks. In the fluctuating boundary of contact between fresh and salt water, there is a gradation of water from fresh, through

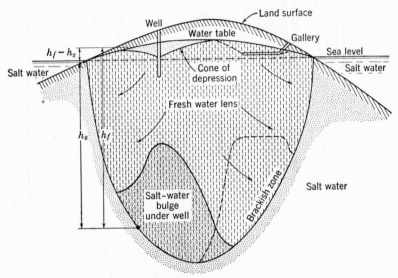

Figure 11-13. Dynamics of a fresh-water lens in contact with salt water.

brackish, to salt. The thickness of the lens at any time and place is controlled by the height of the water table above sea level, because the fresh-water column must balance the salt-water pressure at the bottom of the lens. If, as shown in Figure 11-13, h_f is the thickness of the lens in any vertical plane through the lens, h_s is its depth below sea level, and s_f and s_s are respectively the specific gravity of the fresh water and salt water, conditions of equilibrium require that $h_f s_f = h_s s_s$ or $(h_f - h_s)s_f + h_s s_f = h_s s_s$, whence

$$h_s = \frac{s_f}{s_s - s_f} (h_f - h_s) \qquad 11\text{-}26$$

For the normal specific gravities of salt water (1.025) and fresh water (1.000), therefore,

$$h_s = 40(h_f - h_s) \qquad 11\text{-}27$$

If, for example, the water table rises 4 ft above sea level, the theoretical depth of the fresh-water lens below sea level is $40 \times 4 = 160$ ft.

Pumping, conversely, reduces the thickness of the fresh-water lens below sea level by 40 times the drawdown in the ground-water table above it. As shown in Figure 11-13 there develops, therefore, beneath the cone of depression of a well a similar, but 40 times greater, upward bulge in the zone of contact between the fresh water and salt water. The volume of fresh water that can be withdrawn, before this bulge is completely established, equals the sum of (a) the volume of water stored between the original fresh-water table and the stable cone of depression, (b) the volume of fresh water displaced by salt water in forming the bulge in the bottom of the fresh-water lens, and (c) the volume of water percolating downward into the zone of influence around the well. Since the volume of fresh water displaced in forming the bulge is often very large, the water table may fall very slowly. Some years of pumping may be required before equilibrium conditions are actually established.

Because the fresh-water lens is flat in very permeable formations, such as coral and lava, the use of galleries constructed above sea level provides a more satisfactory means than wells for the collection of fresh water in geological formations of this kind.

12-1. Classification of Conduits. Water is transported from its source to the community by a number of different means. They may be classified as follows:

Free-flow conduits	*Pressure conduits*
a. Canals	e. Pressure aqueducts
b. Flumes	f. Pressure tunnels
c. Grade aqueducts	g. Pipelines and force mains
d. Grade tunnels	h. Depressed pipes or inverted siphons

Most of these conduits are illustrated in Figure 2-6. Free-flow conduits are laid on slopes that provide sufficient fall to create and maintain the flow of water. Their hydraulic gradient coincides with their free water surface or with the crown of the conduit if it is enclosed and just flowing full. Pressure conduits are laid up and down hill as needed (see Figure 12-6). They lie below the hydraulic gradient, except where unusual circumstances force them to rise a limited height above the gradient.

The design of outfall sewers that conduct the collected sewage of a community to a suitable point of disposal is governed by the same hydraulic, structural, and economic principles as is the design of water-supply conduits.

a. *Canals.* These open channels are formed, as far as possible, by balanced cut and fill. They may be lined or remain unlined depending upon the nature of the ground and the available slope. In suitable ground, they are cheap to construct, but they are subject to numerous drawbacks: loss of water by infiltration and evaporation, ice troubles, injury by cattle and by burrowing animals, pollution by surface wash and seepage, and deterioration of water quality by the growth of aquatic plants that impart unpleasant odors and tastes. Canals are generally trapezoidal in cross-section, but they may be rectangular when they are lined or are cut through rock.

b. Flumes. Constructed of wood, masonry, or metal, these open channels are supported on or above the ground in order to transport water over valleys and other depressions in the path of the conduit or along steep or rocky sidehill locations (bench flumes). Disadvantages in their use are: loss of water by leakage and evaporation, troubles due to extremes of temperature, difficulties of maintenance, and development of attached aquatic growths. Wood and masonry flumes are commonly rectangular in shape; metal and wood-stave flumes semicircular.

c. Grade Aqueducts. These structures, generally of large capacity, are intended to utilize locally available materials and to be laid in balanced cut and cover that will protect them against the elements and mechanical damage. Built formerly of brick or stone, they are constructed today mostly of concrete. Grade aqueducts will last almost indefinitely and retain their carrying capacity, if they are properly maintained. Objectionable features are that they must ordinarily be built to the full capacity of the supply and that their embankments form obstructions to natural drainage and normal development of the areas through which the aqueduct winds its way. Also, there remains the possibility of pollution entering the practically pressureless conduit by seepage through cracks or joints. The cross-section of grade aqueducts is generally horseshoe shaped. Steel reinforcement is usually confined to the floor, or invert, of those portions of the aqueduct that are constructed on deep fill and so exposed to unequal settlement. The stream-diversion conduits of dams in wide valleys are often short grade aqueducts.

d. Grade Tunnels. It is the purpose of grade tunnels (1) to shorten the route, conserve the head, or reduce the cost of aqueducts that traverse broken country; or (2) to carry conduits out of difficult terrain—deep gorges, for example—into more accessible or more convenient locations in neighboring valleys or water sheds. In stable rock, grade tunnels may be lined with concrete or other suitable materials to reduce friction and prevent entrance of undesired seepage water. In soils and unstable rock, lining is essential. The minimum size of tunnels is set, by working requirements, at a height of 6 to 7 ft and a width of about 5 ft for hand excavation and at 8 by 8 ft when machinery is to be employed. If the amount of water to be carried is much less than the tunnel capacity, the invert alone may be lined, or the entire section may be left unlined and a pipe laid through it. Like grade aqueducts, grade tunnels are generally horseshoe shaped. Grade tunnels also find use in the diversion of streams during the construction of dams in narrow valleys.

e. Pressure Aqueducts. Generally of reinforced concrete, these conduits are built in place in balanced cut and cover. Commonly they share the advantages and disadvantages of grade aqueducts, but they are not normally exposed to pollution by seepage waters. Pressure aqueducts are ordinarily circular in cross-section, though not necessarily circular in outer form.

f. Pressure Tunnels. Pressure tunnels are employed to cross rivers and valleys. In large works and suitable ground, they may compose the entire conduit, especially when it must traverse broken country and cross numerous divides. Pressure tunnels are used also in connection with large intake works in lakes, reservoirs, and rivers and as the main feeders of important distribution systems. Wherever possible, the weight of the rock, or other natural cover, is relied upon to resist the internal pressure. A circular cross-section is common. Like grade tunnels, pressure tunnels are normally lined. When cover is inadequate—near tunnel portals, for example—strength is secured by the use of steel cylinders or other reinforcing. Deep tunnels are often reached through down-take and up-take shafts.

g. Pipelines and Force Mains. Pipelines are pressure conduits that follow the profile of the ground surface over hill and through dale (Figure 12-6). They are circular in cross-section, and the materials used in their fabrication include cast iron and steel (formerly also wrought iron) with coatings of coal tar or protective linings of cement or bituminous enamel, and wood, asbestos cement, and precast or reinforced concrete. Force mains are pressure conduits or pipelines that carry water from a pumping station to the distribution system, or waste-water from one level to another.

h. Depressed Pipes or Inverted Siphons. These pressure conduits or pipelines connect two portions of a grade conduit (or of a pressure conduit at normal grade) when its direct path is crossed by a valley, stream, tidal estuary, or other depression in the earth's surface, or by some other obstruction.

12-2. Hydraulics of Conduits. The hydraulic design of supply conduits is concerned chiefly with the estimation of frictional resistances to flow and with the pressures that are maintained or created in the conduit. In long supply lines, changes in velocity heads and losses in transitions and appurtenances may be safely neglected. They are relatively much smaller in magnitude than the differences introduced by errors in estimating the friction or discharge coefficients of the conduit.

a. Formulation of Flow. The most nearly rational relationship between the velocity of flow and the head loss in a conduit, also one of the earliest, is that proposed by Darcy [1] and later modified by Weisbach and others. As now used for calculating the head loss in round pipes flowing full, it has the form:

$$h_f = f \frac{l}{d} \frac{v^2}{2g} \qquad\qquad 12\text{-}1$$

where h_f is the head loss, l is the length of the pipe, d is the diameter of the pipe, v is the mean velocity of flow, g is the gravity constant, and f is a dimensionless friction factor. Since Equation 12-1 is dimensionally homogeneous it applies for any consistent system of units. If the flow is laminar, $f = 64/R = 64\nu/(vd)$, where R is the Reynolds number and ν is the kinematic viscosity (Section 17-2).

As the Reynolds number rises, the flow ordinarily changes from laminar to turbulent between a value of $R = 2,000$ and $R = 4,000$. In this critical zone the head loss cannot be predicted with any certainty. As R continues to rise, a transition zone is reached in which turbulence predominates but the effects of viscosity are still discernible. In this zone, the friction factor f varies with both R and the relative roughness of the conduit.[2]

At the limit of the transition zone, the effect of viscosity is lost, and the flow is said to be completely turbulent. The friction factor then depends only on the relative roughness and is constant for all values of the Reynolds number ordinarily encountered in engineering practice.

Moody [3] has used the Colebrook [4] function and available experimental data to construct a diagram, called the Moody diagram, Figure 12-1, which shows the relationship between f and R. If the absolute roughness ϵ is known, values of f from this diagram can be used in Equation 12-1 to calculate the head loss in round pipes flowing full.[5]

[1] H. Darcy, *Recherches expérimentales relatives au mouvement de l'eau dans les tuyaux*, Paris, 1857.

[2] The relative roughness is the ratio of the absolute roughness to the pipe diameter ϵ/d.

[3] L. F. Moody, "Friction Factors for Pipe Flow," *Trans. Am. Soc. Mech. Engrs.*, *66*, 671 (1944).

[4] C. F. Colebrook, "Turbulent Flow in Pipes, with Particular Reference to the Transition Region Between the Smooth and Rough Pipe Laws," *J. Inst. Civil Engrs.*, *11*, 133 (1938–39).

[5] Equation 12-1 is one form of Equation 22-3, for the two are identities when, in Equation 22-3, F_D is $h\rho g$ times the cross-section of the pipe; A_c is the interior surface area of the pipe of length l and diameter d; v_s is the mean velocity in the pipe; and C_D equals $f/4$. Note the similarity between Figures 12-1 and 22-1.

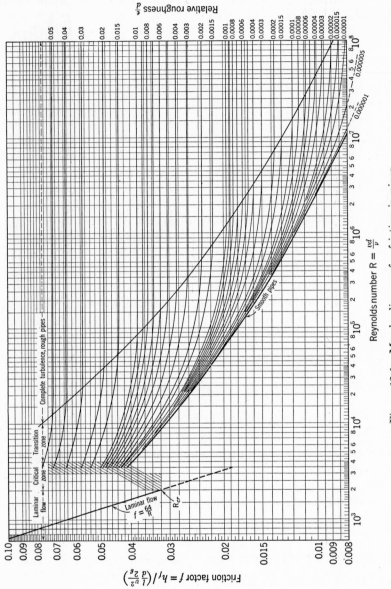

Figure 12-1. Moody diagram for friction in pipes.

Three difficulties attend the use of friction-factor diagrams and Equation 12-1 for finding the head losses in water and waste-water lines: (1) the coefficient of absolute roughness has not as yet been evaluated in terms of the commonly recognized types of surfaces;[6] (2) a special diagram must be prepared for each shape of conduit, and each such diagram is applicable only to the full conduit or to one operating at a single relative depth; and (3) considerable difficulty accompanies the use of these diagrams for solving problems that involve initially unknown depths of flow in partially filled conduits.

Because of these difficulties, engineers continue to make use of so-called exponential equations which relate loss of head to flow. Among them the Hazen-Williams formula is most widely used to express flow relations in pressure conduits, whereas the Manning formula is favored to express flow relations in free-flow conduits.

b. The Hazen-Williams Formula. The Hazen-Williams formula, which was proposed in 1905, will be discussed in this chapter as applying particularly to water-supply work. Discussion of the Manning formula is left to Chapter 15. The following notation is used:

Q = rate of discharge in mgd, gpd, gpm, or cfs as needed.
D = diameter of large circular conduits in ft.
d = diameter of small circular conduits, especially pipes, in in.
v = average velocity of flow in fps.
$a = \pi D^2/4 = \pi d^2/576$ = cross-sectional area of conduit in sq ft.
$r = a/(\text{wetted perimeter}) = D/4 = d/48$ = hydraulic radius in ft.
$s = h_f/l$ = slope of hydraulic gradient, or loss of head h_f in ft in a conduit of length l in ft.

The Hazen-Williams formula as written by its authors is

$$v = Cr^{0.63}s^{0.54} \times 0.001^{-0.04} \qquad 12\text{-}2$$

where C is a coefficient, known as the Hazen-Williams coefficient, and the factor $0.001^{-0.04} = 1.318$ makes C conform in general magnitude[7] with established values of a similar coefficient in the more-than-a-century-older Chezy formula.

For circular conduits:

$$v = 0.550CD^{0.63}s^{0.54} = 0.115Cd^{0.63}s^{0.54} \qquad 12\text{-}3$$

and

$$Q_{(mgd)} = 0.279CD^{2.63}s^{0.54} \qquad 12\text{-}4$$

or

$$Q_{(gpd)} = 405Cd^{2.63}s^{0.54} \qquad 12\text{-}5$$

[6] For evaluation of ϵ/d in large pipes see: J. N. Bradley and L. R. Thompson, "Friction Factors for Large Conduits Flowing Full," *Bur. Reclamation Eng. Monograph* 7, Denver (1951).

[7] Specifically for $r = 1$ ft and $s = 0.001$.

Solution of Equations 12-2 through 12-5 for Q, v, r, D, d, s, or C requires the use of logarithms, a log-log slide rule, and tables [8] or a diagram. Two types of diagrams lend themselves to this purpose: (1) a family of straight lines on logarithmic scales such as the diagram included at the end of this book, and (2) an alignment chart or nomogram.

The weakest element in the use of the Hazen-Williams formula is the estimate of the value of C when its magnitude has not been determined by actual measurements of loss of head and discharge or velocity. It should be noted that C is a measure of hydraulic capacity which is reciprocally related to the Darcy-Weissbach friction factor f.[9]

Values of C vary for different materials of construction and with the relative deterioration of these materials by length of service. They vary also somewhat with size and shape. The values listed in Table 12-1 reflect more or less general experience:

TABLE 12-1. Values of the Hazen-Williams Coefficient C for Different Conduit Materials and Age of Conduit

Conduit material	New	Uncertain
Cast-iron pipe, coated with coal tar	130	100
Cast-iron pipe, lined with cement or bituminous enamel	130 *	130 *
Steel, riveted joints, coated with coal tar	110	90
Steel, lock-bar joints, coated with coal tar	130	100
Steel, welded joints, coated with coal tar	140	100
Steel, welded joints, lined with cement or bituminous enamel	140 *	130 *
Concrete conduits	140	130
Wood-stave pipe	130	130

Age spans the New and Uncertain columns.

* For use with the nominal diameter, i.e., diameter of unlined pipe.

For purposes of comparison, the size of non-circular conduits is often stated in terms of the diameter of circular conduits of equal carrying capacity. A general relation is obtained by multiplying Equation 12-2 by the conduit area a in square feet and equating the resulting expression to Equation 12-4 converted from million gallons per day to cubic feet per second. For identical values of C and s,

$$D = 1.53a^{0.38}r^{0.24} \qquad \text{12-6}$$

[8] Gardner S. Williams and Allen Hazen, *Hydraulic Tables*, John Wiley & Sons, New York, 3d ed., 1952.

[9] Specifically $C = \text{constant}/(f^{0.5}d^{0.13}s^{0.04})$.

The variation in the hydraulic elements of circular and non-circular conduits with depth of flow is discussed in Chapter 15.

Example 12-1. The pipe-flow diagram at the end of this book establishes the numerical relationships between Q, v, d, and s for a value of $C = 100$. Conversion to other magnitudes of C is simple because both v and Q vary directly as C. Show the mathematical and graphical basis of this diagram.

a. Written in logarithmic form, Equation 12-5 is

$$\log Q = 4.61 + 2.63 \log d + 0.54 \log s$$

or

$$\log s = -8.54 - 4.87 \log d + 1.85 \log Q$$

A family of straight lines of equal slope results, therefore, when s is plotted against Q on double-log paper for specified diameters d. Two points define each line. Pairs of coordinates for a 12-in. pipe, for example, are:

$$Q = 100,000 \text{ gpd} \qquad s = 0.028 \text{ ft per } 1,000$$

and

$$Q = 1,000,000 \text{ gpd} \qquad s = 2.05 \text{ ft per } 1,000$$

b. Written in logarithmic form, Equation 12-3 is:

$$\log v = 1.0607 + 0.63 \log d + 0.54 \log s$$

If the diameter d is eliminated from the logarithmic transforms of Equations 12-5 and 12-3,

$$\log Q = 0.180 + 4.17 \log v - 1.71 \log s$$

or

$$\log s = 0.105 + 2.43 \log v - 0.585 \log Q$$

A family of straight lines of equal slope is obtained when s is plotted against Q on double-log paper for specified velocities v. Two points define each line. Pairs of coordinates for a velocity of 1 fps, for example, are:

$$Q = 100,000 \text{ gpd} \qquad s = 1.5 \text{ ft per } 1,000$$

and

$$Q = 10,000,000 \text{ gpd} \qquad s = 0.10 \text{ ft per } 1,000$$

c. If the discharge were read in cubic feet per second (instead of thousands of gallons per day), by what factor F would the diameter have to be multiplied if it were to be read in feet (instead of inches)?

From Equation 12-5, since 1 cfs = 646,000 gpd,

$$646Q = 405C(12FD)^{2.63}s^{0.54}$$

whence

$$(12F)^{2.63} = 646 \qquad \text{and} \qquad F = 0.976$$

To carry 1,000 cfs on a gradient of 5.0 ft per 1,000, for example, a circular conduit would have to be $10 \times 0.976 = 9.76$ ft in diameter.

Example 12-2. A tunnel of horseshoe shape has a cross-sectional area of 27.9 sq ft and a hydraulic radius of 1.36 ft. Find the diameter, hydraulic radius, and area of the hydraulically equivalent circular conduit.

a. By Equation 12-6, the diameter is $D = 1.53 \times (27.9)^{0.38} \times (1.36)^{0.24} = 5.85$ ft.

b. The hydraulic radius $r = D/4 = 1.46$ ft.

c. The area $a = (\pi D^2)/4 = 26.8$ sq ft.

It should be noted that neither the cross-sectional area nor the hydraulic radius of this equivalent circular conduit is the same as that of the horseshoe section proper.

c. Hydraulic Transients. Water transmission lines must withstand transient pressures caused by the opening and closing of valves or by the starting and stopping of pumps (see Section 12-6). The two important types of hydraulic transients [10] are known as water hammer and surge.

Water hammer is the pressure rise that accompanies a sudden change in velocity. When the velocity is decreased, energy of motion must be stored by elastic deformation of the system. The sequence of phenomena that follows sudden closure of a gate, for example, is closely analogous to that which would ensue if a long, rigid spring, traveling at uniform speed, were suddenly stopped and held stationary at its forward end. A pressure wave would travel back along the spring as it compressed against the point of stoppage. Kinetic energy would change to elastic energy. Then the spring would vibrate. In a pipe, compression of the water and distention of the pipe wall replace the simple compression of the spring. The behavior of the pressure wave and the motion of the spring and the water are identically described by the differential equations for one-dimensional waves. Both systems would vibrate indefinitely, were it not for the dissipation of energy by internal friction.

Water hammer is held within bounds in small pipelines by operating them at moderate velocities because the pressure rise in pounds per square inch cannot exceed about 50 times the velocity expressed in feet per second. In larger lines the pressure is held down by changing velocities at a sufficiently slow rate so that the relief wave returns to the point of control before excessive pressures are reached. If this is not practicable, pressure-relief or surge valves are used.

Very large lines, 6 ft or more in equivalent diameter, operate economically at relatively high velocities. Since the cost of designing such large conduits to withstand water hammer would ordinarily be prohibitive, the energy is dissipated slowly by employing surge tanks. In its simplest form, a surge tank is a standpipe placed at the end of the line next to the point of velocity control. If this control is a gate, the surge tank accepts water and builds up back pressure when velocities are regulated downward. When demand on the line increases,

[10] G. R. Rich, *Hydraulic Transients*, McGraw-Hill Book Co., New York, 1951.

the surge tank affords an immediate supply of water and, in so doing, generates the excess hydraulic gradient needed to accelerate the flow through the conduit. Following a change in the discharge rate, the water level in a surge tank oscillates slowly, till the excess energy is dissipated by hydraulic friction through the system.

12-3. Capacity and Size of Conduits. With the rate of water consumption and fire demand known, the capacity of supply conduits depends upon their position in the water-works system and upon the choice exerted by the designer between (1) a structure of full size and (2) duplicate lines that are staggered in time of construction.

Minimum workable size, as already stated, is one controlling factor in the design of tunnels. Otherwise, size is determined by hydraulic and economic considerations. The controlling hydraulic factors are the available heads and the allowable velocities. In finding the heads available, due allowance must be made for drawdown of reservoirs and for pressure requirements in the various parts of the community, under conditions of normal as well as fire demand. Heads greater than necessary to transport the water at normal velocities may be utilized to develop power when it is economical to do so.

Allowable velocities are determined by the characteristics of the water carried and by the need for protecting the conduit against excessive water hammer. For transportation of silt-bearing waters, there are both lower and upper limits; for clear waters, only an upper limit. The minimum velocity should prevent deposition of silt; this velocity lies in the vicinity of 2 to 2.5 fps. The maximum velocity should not cause erosion or scour, nor should it endanger the conduit by creating excessive water hammer when gates are closed rapidly. Velocities of 4 to 6 fps are common, but the upper limit lies between 10 and 20 fps for most materials of which supply conduits are normally constructed and for most types of water carried. Unlined canals impose greater restrictions. Limiting velocities in them may be estimated roughly from Kennedy's empirical equation for a condition of no silting, no scouring:

$$v = cd^{0.64} \qquad \text{12-7}$$

where v is the average velocity in feet per second, d is the depth in feet, and c is a coefficient varying from 0.6 to 1.0 for fine and coarse silts respectively. Silting and scouring are considered more fully in connection with maintaining self-cleansing velocities in sewers (Section 15-2) and with the design of grit chambers (Section 22-17). Some of the formulations advanced there are applicable to the problem discussed here.

The size of force mains and of gravity mains that include power generation is fixed by the relative cost or value of the conduit and the cost of pumping or power.

When aqueducts include more than one kind of conduit, the most economical distribution of the available head among the different classes of conduit is effected when the ratio of change in cost Δc to change in head Δh is the same for each component conduit. The proof for this statement is provided by Lagrange's method of undetermined multipliers. As shown, for example, by the Sokolnikoffs,[11] the maximum or minimum value of a function $u = f(x, y, z)$ that is connected by a relation $\phi(x, y, z) = 0$ can be evaluated from the following four equations:

$$\partial f/\partial x + \lambda\, \partial\phi/\partial x = 0 \qquad \partial f/\partial y + \lambda\, \partial\phi/\partial y = 0$$

$$\partial f/\partial z + \lambda\, \partial\phi/\partial z = 0 \qquad \text{and} \qquad \phi(x, y, z) = 0$$

Here λ is the undetermined multiplier.

For three conduits operating under an available head

$$H = h_1 + h_2 + h_3 \tag{12-8}$$

the cost of each conduit is a function of the head loss through it. The total cost, which is to be a minimum, is then given by the expression

$$C = c_1 + c_2 + c_3 = f_1(h_1) + f_2(h_2) + f_3(h_3) \tag{12-9}$$

In accordance with Lagrange's method, the imposed conditions are satisfied by Equation 12-8 and the relationships

$$\partial c_1/\partial h_1 + \lambda\, \partial H/\partial h_1 = 0 \qquad \partial c_2/\partial h_2 + \lambda\, \partial H/\partial h_2 = 0$$

$$\partial c_3/\partial h_3 + \lambda\, \partial H/\partial h_3 = 0$$

Since $\partial H/\partial h_1 = \partial H/\partial h_2 = \partial H/\partial h_3 = 1$, it follows that $\partial c_1/\partial h_1 + \lambda = 0$; $\partial c_2/\partial h_2 + \lambda = 0$; and $\partial c_3/\partial h_3 + \lambda = 0$, and that $\partial c_1/\partial h_1$, $\partial c_2/\partial h_2$, and $\partial c_3/\partial h_3$ must be the same. Approximately, therefore,

$$\Delta c_1/\Delta h_1 = \Delta c_2/\Delta h_2 = \Delta c_3/\Delta h_3 \tag{12-10}$$

and the minimum cost is incurred when $\Delta c/\Delta h$ is the same for each conduit and $H = \Sigma h$.

In Figure 12-2, the heads h_1, h_2, and h_3 lost in three sections of a conduit are plotted against the decrease in cost Δc per unit increase in loss of head Δh. The sums of the ordinates to the three curves ($h_1 + h_2 + h_3$), trace an over-all curve that measures the head H lost in the

[11] I. S. and E. S. Sokolnikoff, *Higher Mathematics for Engineers and Physicists,* McGraw-Hill Book Co., New York, p. 127, 1934.

system as a whole at particular values of $\Delta c/\Delta h$. If H' is the head available for the whole conduit, the ordinate to the over-all curve that equals H' determines the most economical distribution of head losses h_1', h_2', and h_3' in the three component parts of the conduit.

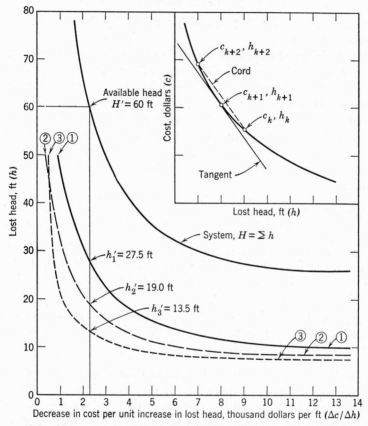

Figure 12-2. Most economical distribution of available head between different portions of a conduit.

Example 12-3. Given the head loss and cost relationships shown in Figure 12-2 for three sections of a conduit, find the most economical distribution of available head between the three sections when the available head is 60 ft.

This problem is solved by noting, on the system curve in Figure 12-2, the value $\Delta c/\Delta h = 2.3$ corresponding to a total head $H' = 60$ ft. The head losses available for the three sections at $\Delta c/\Delta h = 2.3$ are:

$$
\begin{array}{ll}
\text{Section 1.} & h_1' = 27.5 \text{ ft} \\
\text{Section 2.} & h_2' = 19.0 \text{ ft} \\
\text{Section 3.} & h_3' = 13.5 \text{ ft} \\
\hline
\text{Total} & H' = 60.0 \text{ ft}
\end{array}
$$

The values of $\Delta c/\Delta h$ can be determined from a plot of c against h. If values of c are read from these curves at regular intervals, the slope $\Delta c/\Delta h$ at c_{k+1} is closely approximated by the relation

$$\Delta c/\Delta h = (c_{k+2} - c_k)/(h_{k+2} - h_k) \qquad 12\text{-}11$$

where the subscripts k, $k + 1$, and $k + 2$ identify the pairs of observations in the series.

12-4. Number of Conduits. Analysis of the cost of construction of masonry aqueducts and tunnels shows ordinarily that it is cheapest to build them to the full, projected capacity of the system. Pipelines, however, are sometimes more economical if a first line of limited capacity is built to be followed by a second line that will round out the total requirements at the time at which the capacity of the first line has been reached. Multiple supply lines may be constructed simultaneously, however, under a number of special conditions, as follows:

a. When the size of a single line would exceed the maximum size of pipe that is, or can be, manufactured satisfactorily. Centrifugal cast-iron pipe, for example, is not manufactured in sizes greater than 36 in.

b. When the pipe is known to fail in such a way that much damage is done and that repairs cannot be made within a reasonable length of time. Cast-iron pipe, for example, has been known to fracture suddenly and to open up cracks that release enough water to wash out a number of lengths of pipe before the water can be shut off.

c. When the location of the line presents special hazards. River crossings, for example, are endangered by floods, ice, and ships' anchors; conduits in mining areas by cave-ins of the ground.

Twin lines cost from 30 to 50% more than a single line of equal capacity and of the same material. If they are laid sufficiently close together, twin lines should be interconnected at reasonable intervals, and the connecting conduits should be equipped with gates so that as much of the system as possible can be kept in operation at all times. Twin lines should not be laid in the same trench if there is danger of the failure of one destroying the other. To strengthen the distribution system by having water delivered to it at two, more or less opposite, points on its periphery, dual lines may be assigned to follow widely divergent routes.

12-5. Shape of Conduits. The shape of supply conduits is varied to insure their best hydraulic performance while respecting important structural needs. Since the discharge capacity of conduits is conveniently characterized by equations, such as the Hazen-Williams formula, $Q = C'ar^{0.63}s^{0.54}$, it follows that maximum capacity Q is associated, in a conduit of given cross-sectional area a and hydraulic slope s, with the maximum attainable hydraulic radius r. Because circle and half-circle possess the largest hydraulic radius, or smallest frictional surface per unit volume of conduit, a circular cross-section is adopted for closed conduits and a semicircular one for open conduits whenever structural conditions so permit. Next best are shapes in which circle or semicircle respectively can be inscribed.

The following shapes are common:

a. For canals in earth—trapezoids approaching half a hexagon as nearly as the maintainable side slopes permit.

b. For canals in rock—rectangles twice as wide as they are deep.

c. For flumes of masonry or wood—rectangles twice as wide as they are deep.

d. For flumes of wood staves or steel—semicircles.

e. For pressure aqueducts, pressure tunnels, and pipelines—circles.

f. For grade aqueducts and grade tunnels—horseshoe sections.

Internal pressures are best resisted by circular shapes of materials that are strong in tension. External earth and rock pressures that are

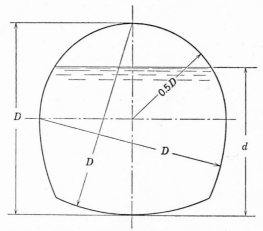

Figure 12-3. Common proportions for horseshoe sections.

not opposed by internal pressures are best resisted by horseshoe sections of materials that are strong in compression. The hydraulic properties of horseshoe sections are only slightly poorer than those of the circle, and the relatively flat invert is convenient for "mucking" [12] and other construction operations. Common proportions for horseshoe sections are shown in Figure 12-3.

[12] Mucking is the removal of debris resulting from blasting and other tunnel-driving operations.

12-6. Strength of Conduits. Structurally, closed conduits are called upon to resist a number of different forces singly or in combination:

a. Water pressure within the conduit equal to the full head of water to which the conduit can be subjected.

b. Water hammer or increased internal pressure due to sudden reduction in the velocity of the water; by the rapid closing of a gate, for example.

c. External loads in the form of backfill and traffic.

d. Expansion and contraction with changes in temperature that are normally confined to fluctuations in the temperature of the water carried in the conduit.

Internal pressure, including water hammer, creates transverse stress known as hoop tension. Bends and closures, including gates, are responsible for unbalanced pressures that produce longitudinal stress. External loads and foundation reactions (manner of support), including the weight of the conduit itself and the water it contains, as well as atmospheric pressure (when the conduit is under vacuum), result in flexural stresses. Variations in temperature, finally, produce longitudinal stresses if the conduit is not permitted to change its length.

For convenience of reference, the various equations that describe these relations are summarized here, using the following notation:

w = weight of unit volume of water in lb per cu ft.

g = acceleration of gravity in ft per sec^2.

P = total force in lb.

p = intensity of pressure in psi or psig.

d = diameter of conduit in in.

t = thickness of conduit shell in in.

s = allowable stress in psi.

E = modulus of elasticity of conduit shell in psi.

    = 29.4×10^6 for steel; 15×10^6 for cast iron; and 2.5×10^6 for concrete.

K = volume modulus of compression of water (294,000 psi).

v = velocity of flow in fps.

V = velocity of compression wave in fps; (velocity of sound in water is 4,700 fps).

l = length of conduit in ft.

T = time of closure of a gate at end of line in sec.

α = angular change in direction, or angle, of a bend.

θ = change in water temperature in F.

c = coefficient of expansion of conduit shell per deg F.

    = 6.5×10^{-6} for steel; 6.2×10^{-6} for cast iron; and 5.5×10^{-6} for concrete.

Δ = change in length of conduit in ft.

Hoop tension per linear inch of pipe:

$$P/2 = pd/2 \quad \text{and} \quad s = pd/2t \qquad \text{12-12}$$

Longitudinal tension: $P = (\pi/4)\, d^2 p$ and $s = pd/4t$ or, more exactly,

$$s = \frac{pd^2}{4t(d + t)} \qquad \text{12-13}$$

Velocity of compression wave:

$$V = \cfrac{1}{\sqrt{\cfrac{w}{g}\left(\cfrac{1}{K} + \cfrac{d}{Et}\right)}} = \cfrac{4{,}700}{\sqrt{1 + \cfrac{294{,}000}{E}\cfrac{d}{t}}} \qquad 12\text{-}14$$

where $[1/K + d/(Et)]^{-1}$ is the equivalent bulk modulus of elasticity of the water and pipe combined.

Critical time of closure, i.e., producing maximum water hammer:

$$T \gtreqless 2l/V \qquad 12\text{-}15$$

Maximum water-hammer pressure:

$$p = 62.4vV/32.2 = 1.94vV \qquad 12\text{-}16$$

The water hammer is maximum for any time of closure less than the critical time. If the actual time of closure is greater than the critical time, the actual water hammer is reduced approximately in proportion to the ratio of the critical to the actual time of closure.[13] Since the time of closure of gate valves varies inversely with the size of the line, small lines are most commonly subjected to large water-hammer pressures. To reduce the danger of rupture in small pipelines, they are often designed to carry water at lower velocities than are permitted in large lines. Common allowances for water hammer in cast-iron pipes are those suggested by Dexter Brackett (Table 12-2).

TABLE 12-2. Allowances for Water Hammer in Cast-Iron Pipes

Diameter, in.	4 to 10	12 and 14	16 and 18	20	24	30	36	42 to 60
Water hammer, psi	120	110	100	90	85	80	75	70

Unbalanced static pressure at bends:

$$P = \tfrac{1}{2}\pi d^2 p \sin \tfrac{1}{2}\alpha \qquad 12\text{-}17$$

Unbalanced dynamic pressure at bends (generally negligible):

$$P = \frac{1}{2}\pi d^2 \frac{62.4}{144 \times 32.2} v^2 \sin \frac{1}{2}\alpha = 0.021(dv)^2 \sin \frac{1}{2}\alpha \qquad 12\text{-}18$$

Change in length of conduit with change in temperature:

$$\Delta = c\theta l \qquad 12\text{-}19$$

---

[13] For calculations, see *J. Am. Water Works Assoc.*, *31*, 1835 (1939).

When expansion or contraction of the pipe is not possible, the longitudinal stress due to change in temperature is

$$s = c\theta E \qquad\qquad 12\text{-}20$$

and

$$P = \pi dts \qquad \text{or (more exactly)} \qquad \pi(d + t)ts \qquad\qquad 12\text{-}21$$

The magnitude of external loads imposed upon conduits that are laid in trench or otherwise surrounded with earth depends upon many factors, among them: the characteristics of the covering material, the nature of the bedding material, the method of supporting the conduit, the width and depth of the trench, the method of backfilling the trench, and the rigidity of the conduit. Marston,[14] Schlick,[15] and their coworkers have shown that the vertical external load on a conduit is approximated by the equations:

$W = cwD^2$ for pipes on, or projecting above, ground in cohesionless cover   12-22

$W = (c_0 - c')wBD$ for flexible pipes in trenches and thoroughly compacted side fills   12-23

$W = (c_0 - c')wD^2$ for rigid pipes in trenches, ordinary bedding and $B < 1.5D$ 12-24

Here W is the vertical external load (pounds per foot of pipe); c, c_0, and c' are experimental coefficients that depend upon the previously named factors; w is the unit weight of backfill (pounds per cubic foot); B is the width of the trench at the top of the pipe (feet); and D is the external diameter of the pipe.

Characteristic values of the experimental coefficients for different soils and methods of laying are presented in Figure 12-4. In all but narrow trenches some relief of stress is obtained by horizontal earth pressure. Ordinarily the horizontal pressure is 20 to 30% of the vertical pressure.

In pipes, such as cast-iron pipes with bell-and-spigot joints, the longitudinal stresses must either be resisted by the joints or relieved by motion. The magnitude of the resistance of lead and lead-substitute joints in bell-and-spigot cast-iron pipe to being pulled apart may

[14] Anson Marston, "The Theory of External Loads on Closed Conduits in the Light of the Latest Experiments," *Iowa State Coll. Eng. Exp. St. Bull.* 96 (1930).

[15] W. J. Schlick, "Loads on Pipes in Wide Trenches," *Iowa State Coll. Eng. Exp. St. Bull.* 108 (1932).

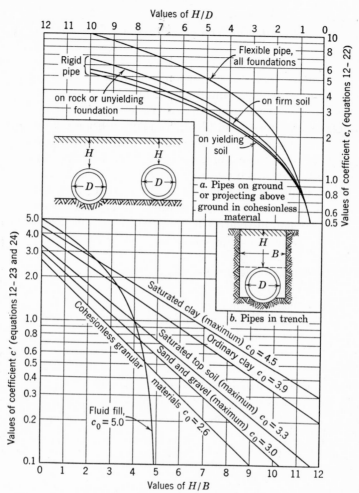

Figure 12-4. Determination of vertical external loads on circular conduits. *After Marston and Schlick.*

be estimated from Prior's observational formula: [16]

$$p = \frac{3,800}{d+6} - 40 \quad \text{or} \quad P = \frac{\pi d^2}{4}\, p = \left(\frac{3,000}{d+6} - 31\right) d^2 \qquad 12\text{-}25$$

Tables of normal thickness of cast-iron, steel, and reinforced-concrete pipe are found in professional manuals and manufacturers' publications.

[16] J. C. Prior, "Investigation of Bell-and-Spigot Joints in Cast-Iron Water Pipes," *Ohio State Univ. Eng. Exp. St. Bull.* 87 (1935).

12-7. Location of Conduits. The procedure of locating a supply conduit is similar to that employed in the location of railroads or highways.

a. Line and Grade. Grade aqueducts and tunnels are held rigidly to the hydraulic grade line. Cut and fill are utilized to greatest advantage in maintaining a uniform gradient. At the same time cut and cover are balanced to reduce haul. Valleys and rivers that would be bridged by railroads and highways may be bridged also by aqueducts. Such indeed was the practice of ancient Rome, but modern aqueducts no longer rise above valley, stream, and hamlet. Pressure conduits have taken the place of these lofty structures. Sometimes pressure conduits are incorporated in bridges that may be designed to serve the primary or ancillary purpose of carrying a highway; sometimes they are laid in trenches as inverted siphons, or depressed pipes, that pass beneath valleys and streams; sometimes they strike deep below the surface in pressure tunnels. For the location of such tunnels, geological exploration fixes both line and grade.

Pressure aqueducts and pipelines can move freely up and down slopes. For economy they should hug the hydraulic grade line as closely as possible while they pursue a relatively straight path between the points connected. Size and thickness of conduit and difficulty of construction must be balanced against length. The shortest route is not necessarily the cheapest.

True siphons are avoided wherever it is possible to do so. Air released from the water and trapped at high points reduces the available waterway, increases friction, and may even interrupt flow. An air ejector or vacuum pump must, therefore, be installed at summits that rise above the hydraulic grade line. If this rise is confined to less than 20 ft and the velocity is kept above 2 fps, operating troubles are held at a minimum. For best results the summit should be approached at a uniform and gradual slope and the conduit should then drop away rapidly.

Ordinarily the location of supply conduits is studied first by plotting the proposed line on available maps of the region, such as the topographic and geologic sheets of the U. S. Geological Survey. Route surveys are then carried into the field. Topography and geology are not the only features of importance. Rights of way, accessibility of the route and proposed conduit, and the nature of obstructions must be investigated too.

b. Curves. In long supply conduits, changes in direction and changes in grade are not made sharp in the ordinary course of design. Masonry conduits that are built in place may be brought to any desired degree of curvature by proper form work, although economic utilization of forms will often circumscribe the maximum. Cast-iron pipelines are limited in curvature by the maximum bend that can be made at the juncture of standard lengths of pipe. The desired curve is then built up gradually by repeated offsets from the tangent. If the pipes are shortened by cutting or special fabrication, sharper curves can be formed. Permissible angles vary with the type of pipe. If tightness and strength of joint are to be maintained in cast-iron, bell-and-spigot pipe, the angular deflection of successive lengths of pipe should not exceed the values listed in Table 12-3. Welded-steel

TABLE 12-3. Angular Deflections in Cast-Iron, Bell-and-Spigot Pipe

Diameter, in.	4	6	8	10	12	16	18	20	24	30	36	42	48
Angle													
deg	4	3	3	3	3	2	2	2	1	1	1	1	0
min	0	30	14	7	0	41	26	9	47	26	12	2	55

pipelines less than 15 in. in diameter are sufficiently flexible to be bent after several joints have been welded together in the field. Bends in larger steel pipe are made by cutting the end of the pipe at an angle. The maximum angle depends upon the type of transverse joint employed, the thickness of the steel plate, and the size of the pipe. For riveted field joints on steel pipe larger than 30 in. in diameter, the allowable angular deflection is approximately that shown in Table 12-4. The cutting and welding of short sections make it possible to build up almost any desired angle.

TABLE 12-4. Angular Deflections in Riveted-Steel Pipes Larger than 30 in. in Diameter

Thickness, of plate, in.	$\frac{1}{4}$	$\frac{5}{16}$	$\frac{3}{8}$	$\frac{7}{16}$	$\frac{1}{2}$
Angle of bend, deg	6	5	4	$3\frac{1}{2}$	3

Long-radius curves are made in precast-concrete pipe, asbestos-cement pipe, and machine-made wood-stave pipe by offsets from the tangent. The angle that can be made varies with the type of joint employed. Values similar in magnitude to those listed for cast-iron pipe with bell-and-spigot joints are attainable. Continuous-stave pipe is built in place on curves with a minimum radius about 50 times the diameter of the pipe.

For sharp curves, transitions, and branches, special fittings are built up of the same materials as the main conduit, or special castings are employed.

c. *Depth of Cover.* Conduits that follow the surface of the ground are generally laid below the frost line, although the thermal capacity and latent heat of water are so great that there is little danger of freezing so long as the water remains in motion. In order to reduce the external load on large conduits, only the lower half may be laid below the frost line. Along the forty-second parallel of latitude in the United States, which describes the southern boundaries of Massachusetts, upper New York, and Michigan, the frost seldom penetrates more than 5 ft beneath the surface. Along the forty-fifth parallel the depth of frost increases to 7 ft. The following equation approximates Shannon's [17] observations of the depth of the frost line:

$$d = 1.65F^{0.468} \qquad\qquad 12\text{-}26$$

where d is the depth of frozen soil in inches and F, the freezing index, is the algebraic difference between the maximum positive and negative

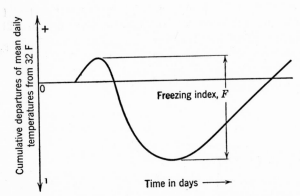

Figure 12-5. Determination of the freezing index of soils as the cumulative departure of the mean daily temperature from 32 F. *After Shannon.*

cumulative departures, $\Sigma(T_d - 32)$, of the daily mean temperatures (T_d) from 32 F. Accumulation, as shown in Figure 12-5, begins on the first day on which a freezing temperature is recorded. In concept, the freezing index is analogous to the term "degree days" which describes the heat requirements of buildings during the heating season. Where daily temperature readings are lacking, the value of F may be approximated, in North America, from the mean monthly temperatures as follows:

$$F = (32n - \Sigma T_m)30.2 \qquad\qquad 12\text{-}27$$

Here n is the number of months during which the temperature is less than 32 F, ΣT_m is the sum of the mean temperatures during each of

[17] W. L. Shannon, "Prediction of Frost Penetration," *J. New Eng. Water Works Assoc., 59,* 356 (1945).

these months, and 30.2 is the mean number of days in December, January, February, and March.

Protection of conduits against extremes of heat and against ordinary mechanical damage is secured at depths of 2 to 3 ft, but cover of 5 ft or more may be required in streets or roads that carry heavy vehicles.

Depth of cover, or allowable weight of backfill, is limited by the structural characteristics of the conduit. These characteristics vary for the different classes of material that are employed and may necessitate laying the conduit in open cut, i.e., cut in which the depth of backfill does not exceed the maximum allowable value.

12-8. Materials for Conduits. The materials employed in the construction of the various types of supply conduits have been listed in the first section of this chapter. The materials used in pipe lines, namely cast-iron, steel, wood-stave, precast reinforced-concrete, and asbestos-cement pipe, however, need further description. The broader aspects of the effect of the properties of these materials upon the choice of the type of pipe are considered below.

The selection of materials for pipelines and evaluation of their cost must take into consideration:

a. The initial carrying capacity of the pipe and its change with use, expressed, for example, in terms of the coefficient C in the Hazen-Williams formula (Section 12-2).

b. The strength of the pipe, i.e., its ability to resist internal pressures and external loads (Section 12-6).

c. The length of life or durability of the pipe, i.e., the resistance of cast-iron and steel pipe to corrosion; of wood-stave pipe to rotting and corrosion; and of concrete and asbestos-cement pipe to erosion and disintegration.

d. The ease or difficulty of transporting, handling, and laying the pipe under different conditions of topography and geology.

e. The safety, economy, and availability of manufactured sizes, a matter that has been mentioned in Section 12-4.

f. The availability of skilled labor for the construction of the pipeline.

g. The requirements of maintenance and repair, losses of water by leakage, and other matters of pipe behavior and suitability.

a. Carrying Capacity. The initial value of the Hazen-Williams coefficient C hovers about 140 for all types of well-laid pipelines, but the coefficient tends to be somewhat higher for reinforced-concrete and asbestos-cement lines and to sink to a normal value of about 130 for unlined cast-iron pipe unless the line is laid with extraordinary care. Double-riveted steel pipe loses about 20 points in addition, but riveted longitudinal joints are seldom used today. Their place has been taken in succession by lock-bar and welded joints. The riveted transverse joint, too, has made way for the welded joint or for mechanical couplings. Unlined, welded-steel pipe has an initial coefficient of C close to 140. Spiral-riveted pipe is seldom used in long lines; its coefficient is low. Cast-iron and steel pipes that are lined with cement or with bituminous enamel possess coefficients of 130 and over on the basis of their nominal diameter, because improved smoothness offsets the reduction in their cross-section.

The loss of capacity with age or, more strictly speaking, with service depends (1) upon the quality of the water carried and (2) upon the characteristics of the pipe. Modern methods of water treatment for the correction of aggressive properties (Chapter 23) give promise that the corrosion of metallic pipes as well as the disintegration of cement linings and reinforced concrete and of asbestos-cement pipe will be very largely, if not fully, controlled in the future.

In the present state of the art of corrective treatment of water, it is not possible to make satisfactory estimates of the reduction in the value of C with length of service. The results of information collected by a committee of the New England Water Works Association,[18] before corrective treatment was extensive, are presented in Table 12-5. Three observations are pertinent.

TABLE 12-5. Reduction in the Capacity of Pipes with Length of Service in Terms of the Hazen-Williams Coefficient C

Number and Material	Water quality	Diameter, in.	Age, years				
			0	10	20	30	40
1. Steel	Inactive	..	135	128	121	115	108
2. Steel	Eastern	..	135	125	115	106	97
3. Cast iron	Average, soft, unfil-	48	130	112	100	90	83
	tered river water	36	130	112	100	90	82
	(Hazen-Williams)	24	130	111	99	89	81
		12	130	110	96	86	77
		6	130	107	93	80	72
4. Cast iron (tar-coated)							
a. Supply lines, 9 cities		28 (ave)	135	106	93	85	..
b. Supply and distribution, 19 cities		25 (ave)	130	90	74	65	..
c. Distribution, 10 cities		6.85 (ave)	125	77	55	45	..

1. Loss of capacity is relatively more rapid for small than for large pipes. In iron and steel pipes, this is due to the interference of rust and deposits that restrict the waterway and increase the roughness of the pipe walls. In cement-lined pipes and asbestos-cement pipe the smooth surface of the walls is destroyed.

2. Before extensive corrective treatment was introduced, loss of capacity was often more pronounced in purified waters than in raw waters. As formerly practiced, water purification probably rendered the water more aggressive by removing slime-forming protective substances, adding oxygen and carbon dioxide, and otherwise affecting the physical and electrochemical properties of the water.

---

[18] *J. New Eng. Water Works Assoc.*, **49**, 241 (1935).

3. Discharge capacity is greater for supply lines than for distribution lines. This is due to losses at fittings, valves, and other appurtenances that are far greater in number in distribution lines.

Cement and bituminous-enamel linings and reinforced-concrete and asbestos-cement pipes do not, as a rule, show significant losses in capacity with service.

b. Strength. Steel pipe is best suited to resist high internal pressures, but the ability of large steel pipes to withstand external loads while empty or subjected to partial vacuum is very poor. Collapse must be guarded against by limiting the depth of cover or by surrounding the pipe with concrete. Cast-iron pipe and asbestos-cement pipe are good for moderately high water pressures and for appreciable external loads, provided that the pipes are properly laid. Reinforced-concrete pipe and wood-stave pipe are satisfactory under moderate water pressures. Reinforced-concrete pipe can carry high external loads.

c. Durability. Experience with all but tar-coated cast-iron pipe has been too short and changes in water treatment have been too numerous to permit the assigning of reliable values to the length of life of different pipe materials. In the past, engineers have employed values of the following approximate magnitude:

Cast-iron pipe, coated with coal tar	100 years or more
Steel pipe, coated with coal tar	25 to 50 years
Reinforced-concrete pipe	75 years or more
Wood-stave pipe	25 to 50 years

Wood-stave pipe must be kept under pressure if rotting of the wood is to be avoided. External corrosion (soil corrosion) and disintegration of pipe and electrolysis are important factors in the evaluation of durability. Acid soils, sea water, and cinder fills should be avoided where possible. Metal pipes and the banding of wood-stave pipe are commonly more corrodible than reinforced-concrete and asbestos-cement pipes. Metal pipes, too, are better conductors of electricity and so more exposed to destruction by electrolysis (Section 23-7). Cathodic protection is of some promise in this connection.

d. Transportation. Pipelines must frequently be constructed in rugged and normally inaccessible locations. Pipe dimensions and weights then become important. Cast-iron pipe is heavy in the larger sizes. Steel pipe is relatively much lighter though bulkier because of the longer sections ordinarily employed. The normal laying length of cast-iron pipe is 12 ft; [19] that of steel pipe is 20 to 30 ft. Wood-

[19] Lengths of 16 ft, 5 m (16.4 ft), 18 ft, and 20 ft are also available in different types of bell-and-spigot pipe.

stave pipe is "machine made or prefabricated" in sizes up to 24 in. and lengths up to 20 ft. Pipes of greater diameter are built in place from staves and bands. This simplifies transportation. Reinforced-concrete pipe is generally cast in the vicinity of the pipeline. The sections are ordinarily 12 and 16 ft long and are very heavy in the larger sizes. Sizes smaller than 24 in. are unusual. Asbestos-cement pipe comes in laying lengths of 18 ft. It weighs about one-quarter as much as cast-iron pipe of the same diameter.

e. Safety. Because of the suddenness and extensiveness of failure, breaks in cast-iron pipe are often quite destructive. Steel fails slowly, chiefly by corrosion. Perforations of the shell at scattered points create small leaks, and repairs are simple. Collapse of steel pipe under vacuum while the line is being drained is a possible but rare occurrence. Wood-stave pipe and reinforced-concrete pipe fail gradually. Asbestos-cement pipe fails much like cast-iron pipe.

f. Skilled Labor. Skill is required chiefly in connection with making the joints. Mechanical joints place the smallest demands upon labor, welded and poured joints the greatest.

g. Maintenance and Leakage. Large pipe that can be entered should be inspected regularly and maintained in good condition. All sizes of line must be watched for outward signs of failure, generally indicated by leakage and by loss of pressure. There is not much choice between materials in this respect. Repairs to precast concrete pipe are perhaps the most difficult to make but are seldom called for. Small cast-iron and welded-steel pipes can be cleaned by scraping machines and lined in place with cement.

All pipelines are tested for tightness during construction. The amount of leakage observed is often expressed in gallons per day per inch diameter (nominal) and mile of pipe, but gallons per day per foot of joint is a better generalization. The test pressure must naturally be stated. It is usually assumed, by reference to the behavior of orifices, that the loss varies as the square root of the pressure.

The allowable leakage of bell-and-spigot, cast-iron pipe that has been carefully laid and well tested during construction is given by the following empirical relationship:

$$Q = nd\sqrt{p}/1{,}850 \qquad\qquad 12\text{-}28$$

where Q is the leakage in gallons per hour, n is the number of joints in the length of pipe tested, d is the nominal diameter of pipe in inches, and p is the average pressure during test in pounds per square inch, gage. A mile of 24-in. cast-iron pipe laid in 12-ft lengths and tested under a pressure of 64 psig, for example, may be expected to show a leakage of $Q = (5,280/12) \times 24 \times \sqrt{64}/1,850 = 46$ gal per hr. Since a 24-in. pipe has a carrying capacity of 250,000 gal per hr at a velocity of 3fps, it is seen that leakage from joints is, relatively speaking, very small.

Steel pipe should be made tight by calking. When it is laid under water with mechanical couplings, it becomes difficult to find small leaks, and allowances as high as 6 gpd per ft of transverse joint may have to be made. The leakage to be expected from asbestos-cement pipe is of the same order of magnitude as that from cast-iron pipe, whereas that from precast-concrete pipe corresponds to the leakage from steel lines.

To make a leakage test, the pipe is isolated by closing gates and placing a temporary header or plug at the end of the section of line last completed. The pipe is then filled with water and placed under pressure, the amount of water needed to maintain the pressure being measured by an ordinary meter of the household type. In the absence of water, air may be employed. For disinfection, see Section 27-12.

12-9. Appurtenances for Conduits. In order to isolate and drain convenient sections of supply conduits for test, inspection, and repair, or for removal of silt and other deposits by scour, and in order to protect conduits in other ways, a number of appurtenances, or auxiliaries, may be needed (Figure 12-6).

a. Gates. In pressure conduits, gate valves are generally placed at the major summits, (1) because these define the sections of line that can be drained by gravity, and (2) because the pressure is least at these points, making for cheaper valves and easier operation. For the sake of economy, valves smaller in diameter than the conduit are used, where possible. They are connected to the pipe by means of reducers. Gates 8 or more inches in diameter generally include a 4-in. or 6-in. gated by-pass. When the larger gate is sealed against pressure, water can be admitted through the by-pass to the section of line behind the larger gate. The pressure on both sides is equalized, and the larger gate can then be lifted more easily.

Small gate valves are operated through gate boxes; large ones are placed in gate chambers or vaults, or they are buried in the ground. They must be protected against frost and against temperature stresses [see (*g*) of this section].

In gravity conduits, gate chambers are common. They are placed (1) at points strategic for the operation of the supply conduit, (2) at the beginning and end of depressed pipes and pressure tunnels, and (3) wherever it is convenient to drain the gravity sections. Sluice

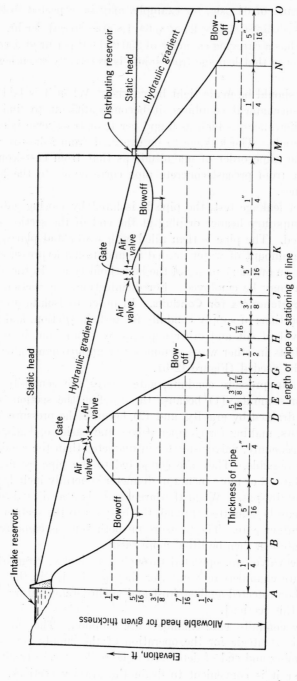

Figure 12-6. Profile of pipeline showing pipe thickness and location of gates, blowoffs, and air valves. *Not to scale, vertical scale magnified.*

gates are normally employed on conduits that are laid at grade, especially when they are large. Needle valves for fine control of flow in supply conduits, butterfly valves for ease of operation, and cone valves for regulating the time of closure may replace gate and sluice valves in special situations.

b. Blowoff Valves. In pressure conduits, small, gated take-offs are provided at low points in the line. The gates are known as blowoff or scour valves. They discharge into natural drainage channels or into a sump from which the water can be pumped to waste. There should be no direct connections to sewers. For safety in operation, two blowoff valves are normally placed in series. Their size depends upon local circumstances, especially upon the time in which the line drained by them is to be emptied. Due reference should be had to the velocities created in the conduit [see (*c*) of this section]. Calculations are based upon the discharge from an orifice under a falling head. This head equals the difference in elevation of the water surface in the conduit and the blowoff, minus the friction head due to flow. Frequency of use depends upon the quality of the water carried. The gate chambers of gravity conduits include drainage gates.

c. Air Valves. Cast-iron and other rigid pipes and pressure conduits require air valves at all high points for the purpose of automatically removing (1) air that is displaced during the filling of the line, and (2) air that is released from the flowing water if the pressure fluctuates appreciably and if the summit lies close to the hydraulic gradient. If the pressure at the summits is high, a manually operated cock or gate may be substituted because little, if any, air will accumulate and air removal is confined to filling operations.

Steel and other flexible conduits need air valves for the purpose of automatically admitting air to the line and preventing its collapse under vacuum. A vacuum may be created when the pipe is being drained on purpose or when water escapes accidentally from the line —as the result of a break at or near a low point, for example. Air-inlet valves must be placed on both sides of gates at summits in the line, on the downstream side of other gates, and at changes in grade to steeper slopes in sections of the line that are not otherwise protected by air valves.

The required size of valve is obviously related to the size of the conduit. The following ratios of diameter of air valve to diameter of conduit are common:

For release of air only   1:12 or 1 in. per ft

For admission as well as release of air   1:8 or 1½ in. per ft

A rough calculation will show that under a vacuum of 12 in. of water, an automatic air valve, acting as an injection orifice under a head of $1/(1.3 \times 10^{-3}) = 770$ ft of air of specific gravity 1.3×10^{-3}, may be expected to admit somewhat less than $\sqrt{2g \times 770} = 220$ cfs of air per sq ft of valve. If the ratio of diameters is 1:8, the displacement velocity in the conduit can then be as high as $220/64 = 3.5$ fps without exceeding a vacuum of 12 in. of water. A similar calculation will show the rate of release of air. The amounts of air that can be dissolved by water at atmospheric pressure are about 2.9% by volume at 32 F and 1.9% at 77 F. These amounts change in direct proportion to the pressure; e.g., they are doubled at two atmospheres or 14.7 psig.

An analysis of air-inlet valve requirements of steel pipelines by Sweeten,[20] which takes the compressibility of air into account and combines equations for safe differential pressures of cylindrical steel pipe, pipe flow, and air flow, yields the equation

$$\frac{d_a}{d} = \frac{ds^{0.25}}{210.5t^{0.75}} \qquad\qquad \text{12-29}$$

where d_a and d are respectively the diameter of the air orifice and pipe in inches, s is the slope of the hydraulic gradient of the conduit between the air valve and the break, and t is the thickness of the steel in inches. This equation holds for pressure differentials up to 6.94 psi, the critical pressure beyond which air flow cannot increase.

Example 12-4. In a 60-in. steel pipeline ⅜ in. thick leading from a reservoir, 2,000 ft of pipe with hydraulic slope of 40 per 1,000 are followed by 1,000 ft with a slope of 60 per 1,000. Find the size of air valve to be placed at the change in slope.

From Equation 12-29:

$$\frac{d_a}{d} = \frac{60 \times (0.06)^{0.25}}{210.5 \times (0.375)^{0.75}} = 0.295 \qquad \text{and} \qquad d_a = 60 \times 0.295 = 17.7 \text{ in.}$$

Instead of a single inlet 17.7 in. in diameter, a larger number of smaller "stock-item" valves—say three 10-in. valves—would probably be placed in a cluster on a manifold controlled by a single gate and taking off at the change in grade.

d. Manholes. To serve as access openings, manholes are spaced 1,000 to 2,000 ft apart on large conduits. They are helpful during the construction of the line and for its inspection and repair. Manholes are common on steel and concrete lines; less so on cast-iron and asbestos-cement lines.

[20] A. W. Sweeten, "Air-inlet Valve Design for Pipelines," *Eng. News-Rec., 97,* **294 (1926).**

e. Insulation Joints. Use of insulation joints is naturally confined to metallic pipes. Although their primary purpose is to introduce resistance to the flow of stray electric currents along the pipeline, they may be of assistance in the control of electrolysis. They are designed in many different ways. Modern insulation joints make use, very largely, of rubber-covered sections of pipe that are sufficiently long to introduce appreciable resistance.

f. Expansion Joints. The effect of temperature changes upon conduits has been formulated in Section 12-6. Expansion joints are not needed if the pipe joints themselves will take care of pipe movements. Steel pipe that is laid with rigid transverse joints must either be permitted to expand at definite points, or motion must be restrained by anchoring the line.

g. Anchorages. Anchorages are employed for one or more of the following reasons:

1. To resist the tendency of pipes to pull apart at bends and other points of unbalanced pressure when the resistance of their joints to longitudinal (shearing) stresses is exceeded.
2. To resist the tendency of pipes to pull apart when they are laid on steep gradients and the resistance of their joints to longitudinal (shearing) stresses is inadequate.
3. To restrain or direct the expansion and contraction of rigidly joined pipes under the influence of temperature changes.

The following examples will give some concept of the magnitude of the forces that must be resisted by anchorages.

Example 12-5. *a.* The unbalanced pressure created by a 90-deg bend in a 48-in. pipeline that carries water under a pressure of 100 psig is:

$$P = \tfrac{1}{2}\pi \times (48)^2 \times 100 \times 0.7071 = 256,000 \text{ lb or } 128 \text{ tons} \quad \text{(from Equation 12-17)}$$

the two component pressures in the direction of each pipe leg being $\tfrac{1}{4}\pi \times (48)^2 \times 100 = 182,000$ lb or 91 tons.

b. If the line is constructed of cast-iron pipe, the resistance offered by lead joints between pipe and bend (even before applying a factor of safety), namely,

$$P = [(3,000/54) - 31](48)^2 = 56,000 \text{ lb} \quad \text{or} \quad 28 \text{ tons} \quad \text{(from Equation 12-25)}$$

is inadequate, and the line must be tied together or suitably anchored.

c. If the line is constructed of butt-welded steel plates, ¼ in. thick, the temperature stress created by a possible range in water temperature from 32 to 75 or 80 F, i.e., a difference of about 46 F, is:

$$s = 6.5 \times 10^{-6} \times 46 \times 30 \times 10^6 = 9,000 \text{ psi} \quad \text{(from Equation 12-20)}$$

and

$$P = \pi \times 48 \times \tfrac{1}{4} \times 9,000 = 340,000 \text{ lb} \quad \text{or} \quad 170 \text{ tons} \quad \text{(from Equation 12-21)}$$

The magnitude of this stress may be halved by closing the pipeline at the average water temperature, say 55 F, instead of the highest or lowest temperatures. An anchorage that will resist a force of $\frac{1}{2} \times 170 = 85$ tons must, therefore, be provided.

d. The expansion and contraction of the steel line, if unrestrained, might be as great as

$$\Delta = 6.5 \times 10^{-6} \times 46 \times 1,000 = 0.3 \text{ ft per 1,000 ft of length}$$

from Equation 12-19.

Anchorages take many forms. For bends—both horizontal and vertical—they may be designed as concrete buttresses or "kick blocks" that resist the unbalanced pressure by their weight, in much the same manner as a gravity dam resists the pressure of the water that it impounds. The resistance offered by the pipe joints themselves, by the friction of the pipe exterior, and by the bearing value of the soil in which the block is buried may be taken into consideration if the cost of the block is to be held at a minimum. Steel straps attached to heavy boulders or to bed rock are used in place of buttresses where it is possible and convenient to do so. Cast-iron pipes and fittings can be cast with lugs through which tie rods are passed when it is desired to prevent movement of the pipe. In order to restrain the motion of steel pipe or force it to take place at expansion joints that have been inserted for that purpose, the pipe may be anchored in much the same way as described for bends. Due attention must be paid to the bonding of the pipe to the anchors. In the absence of expansion joints, steel pipe must be anchored at each side of gates and meters in order to prevent their destruction. Where gate chambers are used, they may be so designed of steel and concrete that they hold the two ends of the steel line rigidly in place. In the absence of anchors, flanged gates are sometimes bolted on one side to the pipe—usually the upstream side—and on the other side to a cast-iron nipple that is connected to the pipe by means of a sleeve or expansion joint.

h. *Other Appurtenances.* These may include: air-relief towers at the first summit of the line to remove air that is mechanically entrained as water is drawn into the entrance of the pipeline; surge tanks at the end of the line to reduce water hammer that is created by rapid closing of a valve at the end of the line; pressure-relief valves or overflow towers on one or more summits to keep the pressure in the line below a given value by causing water to flow to waste when the pressure builds up beyond the design value; check valves on force mains to prevent back-flow when pumps shut down; self-acting shut-off valves that will close when the velocity in the pipe exceeds a predetermined value in case of accident to the line; altitude-control valves that will shut off the inlet to service reservoirs, elevated tanks, and standpipes when overflow levels are reached; and Venturi meters to measure the flow.

12-10. Pumping Units. Pumping stations for water and waste water are generally equipped with centrifugal pumps, driven in most cases by electric motors, occasionally by steam turbines or internal-combustion engines.[21] The direction of flow through the impeller depends on the type of pump. Radial flow occurs in volute and turbine pumps, axial flow in propeller pumps, and diagonal flow in mixed-flow pumps. Strictly speaking, a propeller pump is not a centrifugal pump.

The selection of pumping units requires a knowledge of system-head and pump characteristics. The system head, which is the sum of the static and dynamic heads against the pump, varies (1) with the flow in the system, (2) with changes in storage and suction levels, and (3) with shifts in demand when a distribution system lies between the pump and the reservoir. The pump characteristics depend on the size, speed, and design of the pump. For a given speed N in revolutions per minute, they are defined by the relationships between the rate of discharge Q, usually in gallons per minute, and the head H in feet, the efficiency E in per cent, and the power input P in horsepower. A pump of given geometrical design is also characterized by its specific speed N_s. This is the hypothetical speed of an homologous (geometrically similar) pump with an impeller diameter D such that it will discharge 1 gpm against a 1-ft head. Since discharge varies as area multiplied by velocity and since velocity must vary as $H^{1/2}$, $Q \propto D^2 H^{1/2}$. But velocity varies also as $\pi D N / 60$. Hence $H^{1/2} \propto DN$, or $N \propto H^{3/4}/Q^{1/2}$, and the specific speed is given by the relation

$$N_s = NQ^{1/2}/H^{3/4} \qquad \text{12-30}$$

Generally speaking, the efficiencies of pumps increase with their size and capacity. Below specific speeds of 1,000 units, efficiencies drop off rapidly. Between specific speeds of 1,000 and 4,000 units, radial-flow pumps perform well. Mixed-flow pumps are efficient in the range of 4,000 to 7,500 units. After that axial-flow pumps have higher efficiencies. As shown by Equation 12-30, rising magnitudes of N_s at constant values of N are associated with increasing rates of discharge and decreasing heads. This explains why axial-flow pumps are often used in drainage and irrigation works, whereas radial-flow

[21] W. H. Sears, "Pumping Water—An Historical Review," *J. New Eng. Water Works Assoc.*, *49*, 119 (1935).

pumps are common in municipal water works. For double-suction pumps half the capacity establishes the specific speed.

Specific speed is an important criterion, too, for determining safety against cavitation. This phenomenon occurs on impeller surfaces when conversion of potential energy to kinetic energy reduces the absolute pressure below the vapor pressure of water at the prevailing temperature. The water then vaporizes to form pockets of vapor. The sudden collapse of these pockets, when they are swept to regions of higher pressure, results in vibration, noise, and rapid destruction of the impeller. Cavitation occurs beyond certain limiting inlet pressures or when the capacity or speed of rotation is increased without a compensating rise in inlet pressure. Lowering the elevation of a pump in relation to its water source, therefore, reduces cavitation. If we replace the head H in Equation 12-30 by H_{sv}, the net inlet head or difference between the total inlet head (including the velocity head in the inlet pipe) and the head corresponding to the vapor pressure of the water pumped, we obtain the *suction specific speed*

$$S = NQ^{1/2}/H_{sv}^{3/4} \qquad\qquad 12\text{-}31$$

for which certain general safe limits have been established by experiment.[22] The following are examples:

Single-suction pumps with overhung impellers	$S \leqq 8{,}000\text{--}12{,}000$
Single-stage pumps with shaft through eye of impeller	$S \leqq 7{,}000\text{--}11{,}000$
High-pressure, multistage pumps (single suction)	$S \leqq 5{,}500\text{--}\ 7{,}500$
High-pressure, multistage pumps with special first-stage impeller (single suction)	$S \leqq 7{,}500\text{--}10{,}000$

Interrelationships between the common performance characteristics of a centrifugal pump operating at constant speed are illustrated in Figure 12-7. Note that the shut-off head is a fixed limit and that the power consumption is minimum at shut-off. For this reason, centrifugal pumps are often started with the pump discharge valve closed. As the head falls past the point of maximum efficiency (point 1 in Figure 12-7) the power continues to rise. Care must be taken, therefore, not to operate a pump against too low a head, for this sometimes overloads the motor if it has been selected to operate the pump in a head range around maximum efficiency.

[22] G. F. Wislicensus, R. M. Watson, and I. J. Karassik, "Cavitation Characteristics of Centrifugal Pumps Described by Similarity Considerations," *Trans. Am. Soc. Mech. Engrs.*, *61*, 170 (1939); also G. F. Wislicensus, section on centrifugal pumps, *Mechanical Engineers' Handbook*, L. S. Marks, Editor, McGraw-Hill Book Co., New York, 1951.

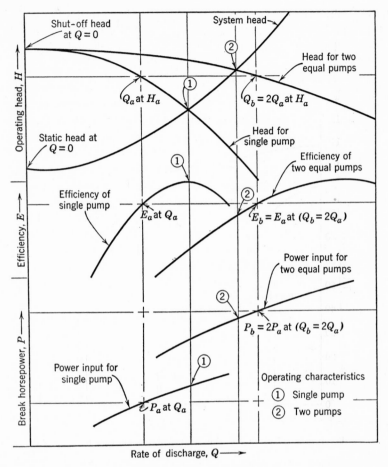

Figure 12-7. Performance characteristics of single and twin centrifugal pumps operating at constant speed.

The effects of using more than one pumping unit are also shown in Figure 12-7, and a curve for the system head is drawn in. It is obvious that pumping units can operate only at the point of intersection of their own head curves with the head curve of the system. In practice, the system head at a given discharge varies over a considerable range (see Figure 12-8). Where a distributing reservoir is part of a system, for example, and both the reservoir and the source of water fluctuate in water-surface elevation, there is (1) a lower curve that identifies head requirements when the reservoir is empty and the water surface of the source is high and (2) an upper curve that establishes the system head for a full reservoir and a low water level at the source. How the characteristic curves for twin-unit operation are developed is indicated in Figure 12-7. It should be noted that in this illustration the two identical pumping units have not been selected with an eye to highest efficiency of operation in parallel. Development of characteristic curves for other multiple units proceeds in the same way from the known curves of the individual units.

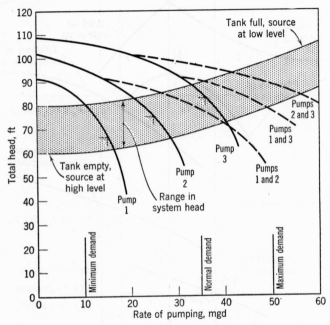

Figure 12-8. Pump selection for the water supply described in Example 12-6. *After Richard Hazen.*

Example 12-6. A mill supply is to draw relatively large quantities of water from a river and to deliver them at a fairly low head.[23] The minimum demand is 10 mgd, the normal demand 35 mgd, and the maximum demand 50 mgd. The river fluctuates in level by 5 ft, and the working range of a balancing tank is to be 15 ft. The vertical distance between the bottom of the tank and the surface of the river at high stage is 60 ft. The friction head in the pumping station and a 54-in. force main rises from a minimum of 1 ft at the 10-mgd rate to a maximum of nearly 20 ft at the 50-mgd rate. Make a study of suitable pumping units.

Hazen's solution of this problem is shown in Figure 12-8. Three pumps are provided: No. 1 with a capacity of 15 mgd at 66-ft head; No. 2 with 25 mgd at 78-ft head; and No. 3 with 37 mgd at 84-ft head. Each pump has an efficiency of 89% at the design point.

---

[23] See Richard Hazen, "Pumps and Pumping Stations," *J. New Eng. Water Works Assoc., 67,* 121 (1953).

The efficiencies at the top and bottom of the working range are listed in Table 12-6.

TABLE 12-6. Pumping Characteristics of System in Example 12-6

Pumps in service	Rate of pumping, mgd.	Head, ft.	Pump efficiency		
			No. 1	No. 2	No. 3
No. 1	10	81	80	..	..
	15	66	89	..	..
	16.5	62	88	..	..
No. 2	21	83	..	88	..
	25	78	..	89	..
	28.5	66	..	84	..
No. 3	33.5	88	..	..	88
	37	84	..	..	89
	40.5	73	..	..	86
No. 1 & No. 2	27	85	71	86	..
	34	80	82	88	..
	40	73	88	88	..
No. 1 & No. 3	36	90	35	..	87
	43.5	85	71	..	89
	49.5	79	83	..	88
No. 2 & No. 3	42	93	..	68	84
	49.5	89	..	79	87
	56.5	84	..	87	89

Centrifugal pumps are normally operated with discharge velocities of 5 to 15 fps. Therefore, the diameter (in inches) of the pump outlet, which is generally used to designate the size of the pump, is, on an average, $0.2\sqrt{Q}$, where Q is the capacity of the pump in gallons per minute.

13 ———————————— DISTRIBUTION OF WATER

13-1. Distribution Systems. Excepting scattered taps or take-offs along a main supply conduit itself, the distribution system of a public water supply may be said to start where the conduit attaches to the reticulated system of pipes that traverse the area served with water. As pointed out in Section 2-9, street plan, topography, and location of supply works and distribution storage establish the type of distribution system and the type of flow through it. Although service reservoirs may find their best place along the line of the supply conduit proper, where they may be of value in reducing the pressures on the conduit (Section 12-9), their main purpose is to take care of distribution needs. For this reason they are generally considered part of the distribution system.

a. One- and Two-Directional Flow. According to type of flow, we can distinguish the four systems illustrated in Figure 13-1. The hydraulic gradients of the systems and the residual pressures within the areas served, together with the volume of distribution storage, determine the sizes of pipe within the network. It is plain that flow from opposite directions will increase the capacity of the distribution system. Two-directional flow in the main arteries themselves is made possible by conducting the supply from pumps, or from a gravity-supply, or service, reservoir (1) to opposite ends of the distribution system; or (2) through the system to elevated storage in a reservoir, tank, or standpipe situated towards the far end of the area of greatest water demand. Selection of volume and location of distribution storage depend upon topography and water needs (see Section 13-7).

b. Types of Service. As explained in Section 2-9, different areas of a community, depending upon their elevation in relation to the main source of supply, may be supplied through separate, though commonly interconnected, distribution systems. High-lying areas are placed in the high-service system; low-lying areas in the low-service system. There may also be an area of intermediate elevation with its own system. Hydraulic analysis must take cognizance of the independence as well as the interdependence of such systems. High-service draft from low-service arteries deserves special recognition. Since high-service areas are commonly small in extent, the support that the low service may expect to receive from high-service storage, during a breakdown in the main supply, is generally disappointing.

Where an independent system of pipes within the high-value district of a large community constitutes a high-pressure fire supply

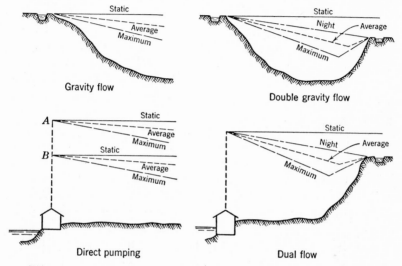

Figure 13-1. One- and two-directional flow in distribution systems.

(Section 2-9), it occupies, hydraulically, much the same status as a high-service supply. It is independent in its larger functions of water distribution but does draw upon the general water works for its supply. Such dependence may be greatly reduced by the provision of adequate storage from which the fire supply is fed. When the main supply fails in a catastrophe, resort must be had to other available sources of water, if conflagrations which are frequent companions of catastrophes are to be put under control.

13-2. Pipe Grids. Within the gridiron system of pipes that generally covers all but the outlying sections of a community (Figure 2-8), a choice must be made between the use of single mains and dual mains in individual streets. As outlined in Figure 13-2, a distribution system of single mains, customarily laid on the north and east sides of streets for protection against freezing, is provided with valves generally as follows: three at crosses, two at tees, and one on the single-hydrant branches. In a system of dual mains, *service headers* are

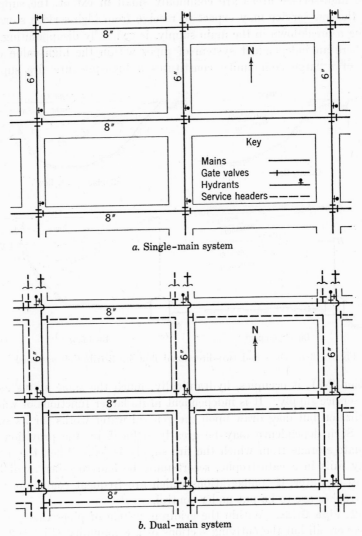

a. Single-main system

Key

Mains
Gate valves
Hydrants
Service headers

b. Dual-main system

Figure 13-2. Gridiron system of single and dual mains.

added on the south and west sides of streets, and piping is generally placed beneath the sidewalks. In a scheme suggested by Ballou,[1] valves are installed as follows: one on each main at intervals of two blocks, one at the junction of the service header with its main, and one on each of two branches to the hydrants. The operations necessitated and the conditions of service created by breakdowns are summarized in Table 13-1.

TABLE 13-1. Conditions Created by Breakdowns in Single-Main and Dual-Main Systems

Breakdown of	Single-main system	Dual-main system
(1) Hydrant	Close one hydrant valve.	Close two hydrant valves.
(2) East-west main	Close four valves on main. This dead-ends supply to one hydrant and cuts out intermediate service taps; it also dead-ends supply to eastern intersection.	Close two valves on main and one valve on each of the connected hydrants and service headers. Hydrants and service headers remain in commission; house service taps on main are placed out of commission; service headers are dead-ended.
(3) North-south main	Close two valves on main. One hydrant and intermediate house taps are placed out of commission.	Same as for east-west main.

Hydraulically, the advantages of dual-main systems over single-main systems are more or less local in extent, because service headers do not contribute to flow outside of their own block. The important fact is that breaks in mains do not impair the usefulness of hydrants and do not dead-end mains in dual-main systems.

13-3. Required Capacity and Pressure of Distribution Systems. The capacity of distribution systems must cover the *stand-by* or *ready-to-serve* requirements for fire fighting as well as domestic, industrial, and other normal water use. The capacity to serve cannot be expressed, however, merely in terms of the rate at which water can be drawn. The pressure at which this water is made available is equally important. The water must rise to the upper stories of buildings of normal height, and it must flow from hydrants, directly or through

[1] A. F. Ballou, "Hydrant Connections and the Control of Dual Mains." *J.. New Eng. Water Works Assoc., 52,* 81 (1938).

pumpers, to form the fire streams issuing from the nozzles of fire hose that is long enough to reach the scene of conflagration.

a. Capacity. If there was no fire hazard, the hydraulic capacity of the distribution system would have to equal the maximum demand for domestic, industrial, and other general uses. For absolute safety, the fire demand would be added to this figure. Ordinarily this is not done: (1) because it would be most unusual for the maximum draft to coincide with a serious conflagration; and (2) because systems are dimensioned for the future and new construction is generally completed, in a reasonably foresighted community, before the designed capacity of the original system has been reached. In the absence of unusual hazards, such as inflammable structures or storage of inflammable raw or manufactured materials, a draft of 40 gpcd in excess of the average annual consumption may ordinarily be assumed to coincide with the requisite fire flow. In the presence of unusual hazards, higher allowances should be made. Determination of the requisite capacity of the distribution system within different areas of the community is aided greatly if the municipality has been "zoned" and the ordinances are well drawn to regulate both the *use* to which properties may be put in different zones and the *bulk* that the buildings to be erected may occupy.

The general requirements of the National Board of Fire Underwriters governing the fire-fighting capacity of distribution systems have been stated in Section 5-9. In part they are briefed, in part elaborated, in the following schedule.

a. Within the central, congested, or high-value, district of North American communities:

1. For communities of 200,000 people or less,

$$Q = 1,020\sqrt{P}\,(1 - 0.01\sqrt{P}\,) \qquad \text{5-8}$$

where Q is the fire draft in gpm and P is the population in thousands.

2. For populations in excess of 200,000, $Q = 12,000$ gpm with from 2,000 to 8,000 gpm in addition for a second fire.

b. For residential districts with

1. Small, low buildings—⅓ of lots in block built upon, $Q = 500$ gpm.

2. Larger or higher buildings, $Q = 1,000$ gpm.

3. Buildings approaching dimensions of hotels or high-value residences, $Q = 1,500$ to 3,000 gpm.

4. Three-story buildings in densely built-up sections, $Q = $ up to 6,000 gpm.

c. Proportion or amount of the estimated flow to be concentrated, if necessary, on one block or one very large building:

1. In the high-value district, ⅔.

2. In compact residential areas, ¼ to ½.

3. For detached buildings, 500 to 750 gpm.

Table 13-2 is based upon Equation 5-8 and shows the relatively large stand-by capacity needed.

TABLE 13-2. Required Fire Flow, Fire Reserve, and Hydrant Spacing Recommended by the National Board of Fire Underwriters

| Population | Fire flow | | Fire reserve | Area per hydrant, sq ft | |
	gpm	mgd	mg	Engine streams	Hydrant streams
1,000	1,000	1.5	0.3	120,000	100,000
2,000	1,500	2.0	0.4	....	90,000
4,000	2,000	3.0	1.2	110,000	85,000
6,000	2,500	3.5	1.5	....	78,000
10,000	3,000	4.5	1.9	100,000	70,000
13,000	3,500	5.0	2.1	....	....
17,000	4,000	6.0	2.4	90,000	55,000
22,000	4,500	6.5	2.7	....	....
28,000	5,000	7.5	3.0	85,000	40,000 †
40,000	6,000	8.5	3.6	80,000	....
60,000	7,000	10.5	4.4	70,000	....
80,000	8,000	12.0	5.0	60,000	....
100,000	9,000	13.0	5.5	55,000	....
125,000	10,000	14.5	6.1	48,000	....
150,000	11,000	16.0	6.7	43,000	....
200,000 *	12,000	18.5	7.6	40,000	....

* For populations over 200,000 and local concentration of streams, see outline of National Board Requirements.
† For fire flows of 5,000 gpm and over.

b. *Pressure.* For normal drafts, the pressure at the street line must be at least 20 psig (46 ft of water) in order to permit water to rise three stories and overcome the frictional resistance of the house-distribution system (Section 14-4); but 40 psig is a more desirable pressure. Business blocks are supplied more satisfactorily at pressures of 60 to 75 psig. To supply their upper stories, tall buildings boost water to tanks on their roofs or in their towers.

Fire demand is commonly gaged in terms of the *standard fire stream:* 250 gpm issuing from a 1⅛-in. nozzle and requiring a pressure at the base of the tip of 45 psig. When this amount of water flows through 2½-in. rubber-lined hose, the frictional resistance is about 15 psi per 100 ft of hose. Adding to this hydraulic loss the hydrant resistance and the required nozzle pressure of 45 psig gives the pressure needs at the hydrant shown in Table 13-3. A standard fire stream is effective to a height of 70 ft and has a horizontal carry of 63 ft.

TABLE 13-3. Hydrant Pressures for Different Lengths of Fire Hose [2]

Length of hose, ft	100	200	300	400	500	600
Required pressure, psig	63	77	92	106	121	135

Hydrants are normally planned to cover areas within a radius of 200 ft. Hence it is evident that, for direct attachment of fire hose to hydrants (hydrant streams), the required residual pressure at the hydrant must be about 75 psig. To maintain this pressure at times of fire, normal pressures must approach 100 psig. Disadvantages of pressures as high as this are that leakage and waste of water mount approximately in proportion to the square root of the pressure. The minimum pressure for hydrant streams is commonly set at 50 psig. Such streams, however, will not approach standard magnitudes after passing through hose as short as 50 ft.

Modern motor pumpers will deliver up to 1,500 gpm at adequate pressures, and large cities use single streams discharging as much as 1,000 gpm from a 2-in. nozzle. In order that domestic and industrial draft may be maintained and the system safeguarded against pollution by seepage and by failure under a vacuum, fire engines are not expected to pull down the pressure in the mains below 20 psig. For large hydrant outlets, this limit is sometimes lowered to 10 psig. In a sense, modern fire-fighting equipment has done away with the necessity for pressures much in excess of 60 psig except for small towns that cannot afford a full-time, well-equipped fire department. The additional pressure drop through the system made available by the use of pumpers increases the fire-fighting capacity in the ratio of $\sqrt{p-20}/\sqrt{p-75}$, where p is the normal dynamic pressure of the system.

13-4. Structural Components of Distributing Systems. The basic elements of the reticulation system are its pipes, gates, and hydrants. The dimensioning and spacing of these components rest upon a background of experience that is normally sufficiently precise in its minimum standards to permit roughing in all but the main arteries and

[2] J. R. Freeman, "Experiments Relating to Hydraulics of Fire Streams," *Trans. Am. Soc. Civil Engrs.*, *21*, 303 (1889).

feeders of most distribution systems. Common standards include the following:

Pipes

Smallest pipes in gridiron	6-in.
Smallest branching pipes (dead ends)	8-in.
Largest spacing of 6-in. grid (8-in. pipe used beyond this value)	600 ft
Smallest pipes in high-value district	8-in.
Smallest pipes on principal streets in central district	12-in.
Largest spacing of supply mains or feeders	2,000 ft

Gates

Spacing in single- and dual-main systems	(See preceding discussion.)
Largest spacing on long branches	800 ft
Largest spacing in high-value district	500 ft

Hydrants

Areas protected by hydrants	(See Table 13-2.)
Largest spacing when fire flow exceeds 5,000 gpm	200 ft
Largest spacing when fire flow is as low as 1,000 gpm	300 ft

Pipe sizes in excess of the minimum are determined by the occupancy of the properties along the lines (whether residential, commercial, or industrial) and by the water uses of each, together with the fire risks involved.

The "hydrant areas" shown in Table 13-2 are based upon a single fire stream being effective within a radius of 200 ft from the hydrant. The area of the resulting circle is 120,000 sq ft. In order to attack a fire from all sides, or at least from two hydrants, a minimum of four streams (1,000 gpm) must be brought to play upon this area. As communities increase in size, buildings grow in bulk, and the area served by each hydrant must be reduced. Hydrant streams tax the distribution system more than do engine streams and have less leeway when pressures drop. Allowance is made for this by reducing the size of the area to be served by each hydrant. In all these standards, experience with conflagrations underlies the recommended values.

13-5. Field Studies of Distribution Systems. The hydraulic performance of existing distribution systems is determined most directly and expeditiously by pressure surveys and hydrant-flow tests. There is no limit to the extent of such tests. They should cover all typical portions of the community: the high-value district, residential neighborhoods of different kinds, industrial areas, the outskirts, and high-service zones. If need be, they can be extended into every block. The results obtained will establish available pressures and flows and existing deficiencies. These can then be made the basis of hydraulic calculations for extensions, reinforcements, and new gridiron layouts. Subsequent tests can be conducted to show how nearly the desired changes have been accomplished.

a. Pressure Surveys. These yield the most rudimentary information about the network. If they are conducted both at night (minimum flow) and during the day (normal demand), they will indicate

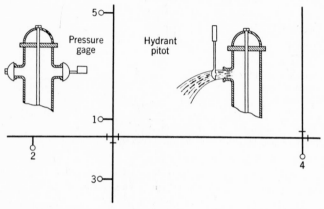

Figure 13-3. Location of pipes and hydrants in flow test and use of hydrant Pitot and pressure gage. See Table 13-4 and Figure 13-4.

the hydraulic efficiency of the system in meeting common requirements. The information presented, however, is not sufficient to establish the probable behavior of the system under conditions of stress, such as are produced by a serious conflagration.

b. Hydrant-Flow Tests. As commonly performed, hydrant-flow tests include (1) observation of the pressure at a centrally situated hydrant during the conduct of the test; and (2) measurement of the flow from a group of neighboring hydrants. Hydrant Pitot tubes are employed to record the velocity heads in the jets issuing from the hydrants. If the tests are to be significant, the following precautions should be observed:

1. The hydrants tested should form a group such as might be called into play in fighting a serious fire in the district under study.

2. Water should be drawn at a sufficient rate to create a drop in pressure so great that its value is not measurably affected by normal fluctuations in draft within the system.

3. The time of test should coincide with drafts (domestic, industrial, etc.) in the remainder of the system, reasonably close to expected values.

The requirements of the National Board of Fire Underwriters that have already been outlined are valuable aids in planning hydrant-flow tests. The layout of pipes and hydrants in a typical flow test is shown in Figure 13-3, and the observed values are summarized in Table 13-4.

TABLE 13-4. Record of a Typical Hydrant-Flow Test

All pressures are expressed in psig

Conditions of test	Observed pressure at hydrant 1	Observed discharge pressure (p) (velocity head)	Calculated flow (Q), gpm	Remarks
All hydrants closed	74	....	...	All hydrant outlets are 2½
Hydrant 2 opened, 1 outlet	..	13.2	610	in. in diameter.
Hydrant 3 opened, 2 outlets	..	9.6	2 × 520	Total Q = 2,980 gpm.
Hydrant 4 opened, 1 outlet	..	16.8	690	Calculated engine streams
Hydrant 5 opened, 1 outlet	46	14.5	640	= 4,200 gpm.
All hydrants closed	74	....	...	

This table is more or less self-explanatory. The initial and residual pressure was read from a Bourdon gage at hydrant 1. Hydrants 2, 3, 4, and 5 were opened in quick succession, and their rates of discharge were measured simultaneously by means of hydrant Pitots. A test such as this does not consume more than 5 min, if it is conducted by a well-trained crew.

c. Hydrant-Flow Calculations. The necessary calculations may be outlined as follows for the flow test recorded in Table 13-4.

Example 13-1. 1. For outlets of diameter d in., the discharge Q in gpm is: $Q = 29.82cd^2\sqrt{p}$, where p is the Pitot reading in psig and c is the coefficient of hydrant discharge.[3] For smooth, well-rounded 2½-in. outlets, $c = 0.9$ and $Q = 168.2\sqrt{p}$.

2. The total discharge is 2,980 gpm for a pressure drop of $(74 - 46) = 28$ psi.

3. For engine streams the pressure drop is $(74 - 20) = 54$ psi and the approximate, expected discharge $Q_2 = Q_1\sqrt{p_2/p_1} = 2,980\sqrt{54/28} = 4,150$ gpm.

4. Since most of the loss occurs in the piping rather than the hydrant outlet, the expected discharge is calculated more closely from the Hazen-Williams formula, or $Q_2 = 2,980 (54/28)^{0.54} = 4,250$ gpm. This value can be read directly from the Hazen-Williams diagram (see Appendix).

5. If the required fire flow in this district is estimated to be 6,000 gpm, the deficiency is $(6,000 - 4,200) = 1,800$ gpm and must be supplied by the addition of suitable piping.

---

[3] Since $Q = cav$ where c is the coefficient of hydrant discharge, a is the area of the hydrant outlet, and v is the velocity of discharge $(2.308p = v^2/2g)$. Here Q is measured in cfs, a in sq ft, and v in fps. The value of c varies from 0.9 for well-rounded, smooth outlets to 0.7 for sharp outlets projecting into the barrel.

The pressure-discharge relations established in this test are illustrated in Figure 13-4. If the true static pressure is known, a more exact calculation than that here proposed is possible, although the results seldom justify the additional labor involved. If a pressure gage is inserted in a hydrant in exact juxtaposition to the hydrant

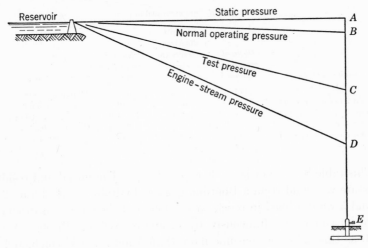

Figure 13-4. Pressure and discharge relations established by hydrant-flow test. See Figure 13-3 and Table 13-4.

A: Static water table.

B: No hydrant discharge. Pressure = 74 psig; pressure drop p_0 due to coincident draft Q.

C: Hydrant discharge. Pressure = 46 psig; pressure drop $p_1 = (74 - 46) = 28$ psi accompanies discharge of $Q_1 = 2,980$ gpm.

D: Engine streams. Pressure = 20 psig; pressure drop $p_2 = (74 - 20) = 54$ psi accompanies discharge $Q_2 = 4,200$ gpm.

E: Hydrant 1, recording residual pressure of hydrant groups shown in Figure 13-3.

outlet that is to be opened, the pressure recorded will equal the discharge pressure in accordance with the common hydraulic analysis of Borda's mouthpiece. Difficulty of centering such a gage generally makes the use of a hydrant Pitot more satisfactory and reliable.

Hydrant tests are sometimes made for the purpose of ascertaining the capacity of individual hydrants and advertising it to firemen (particularly to engine companies summoned from neighboring towns) by painting the bonnet a suitable color. The New England Water Works Association has recommended that all hydrant barrels be painted chrome yellow for visibility and that the bonnets be given the following distinguishing colors:

Color	Rated Capacity
Red	less than 500 gpm
Yellow	500 to 1,000 gpm
Green	more than 1,000 gpm

The weakness of this system lies in the restriction of flow measurements to single hydrants. In fire fighting, groups of hydrants are normally brought into action. Hydrant tests of individual hydrants are of limited value only. They may be quite misleading.

13-6. Office Studies of Distribution Systems. No matter how energetically the study of distribution systems is pursued in the field, hydraulic investigations of extensions, reinforcements, and new networks can be brought to satisfactory conclusion only in the office. The necessary analysis presupposes some familiarity with certain processes of hydraulic computation. Although, at first glance, some of these processes may appear to be complicated, closer scrutiny will show that the best of them can be so systematized as to make their application a matter of simple arithmetic calculations in addition to the use of a pipe-flow table or diagram, or a slide rule.

Three methods of analysis will be found to be particularly useful. These will be defined as: (1) the method of sections; (2) the Hardy Cross method; and (3) the method of equivalent pipes which may be applied alone or in conjunction with the Hardy Cross method.

a. Method of Sections. This is an approximate method, simple in concept and application, and widely useful provided that its limitations are clearly acknowledged and allowed for. The method of sections was employed by Allen Hazen as a quick check of distribution systems. Pardoe's method [4] is somewhat like it but is more involved. Of similar concept, too, is the circle method described in most textbooks on water supply but confined in its application to the cutting by a circle of the system of pipes tributary to a central fire-hydrant or group of hydrants (see Example 13-3).

Use of the method of sections is illustrated in Figure 13-5 and Example 13-2. The various steps involved may be outlined as follows:

1. Cut the network by a series of lines, not necessarily straight or regularly spaced but chosen with due regard to the varying sequence of pipe sizes and the characteristics of district. A first series of lines may well be chosen so as to cut the distribution piping substantially at right angles to the general direction of flow, i.e., perpendicular to a line drawn from the supply conduit to the high-

---

[4] W. S. Pardoe, *Eng. News-Rec., 93,* 516 (1924).

value district (see Figure 13-5). Further series may be oriented in some other critical direction; for example, horizontally and vertically in Figure 13-5. If there is more than one supply conduit, the sections may be curved to intercept the flow from each.

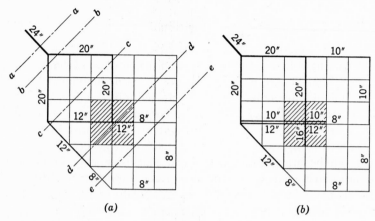

Figure 13-5. Plan of network analyzed by method of sections. See Example 13-2.

a. Existing system.

b. Recommended system. When pipe size is not indicated, the pipe diameter is 6 in. The cross-hatched area is the high-value district.

2. Estimate the water that must be supplied to the areas *beyond* each section. Estimates are based on a knowledge of the population density and the general characteristics of the zone: residential, commercial, and industrial. The water requirements comprise (*a*) the normal, coincident draft, here called the domestic draft; and (*b*) the fire demand (see Table 13-2). Whereas domestic use decreases progressively from section to section, as population or industry is left behind, the fire demand remains the same until the high-value district has been passed; then it drops to the figure that applies to the type of outskirt area encountered.

3. Estimate the capacity of the distribution system at each section across the piping. To do this:

a. Tabulate the number of pipes of each size cut. Count only those pipes that deliver water in the general direction of flow that is being studied.

b. Determine the average available hydraulic gradient or frictional resistance. This depends (1) upon the pressure to be maintained in the system and (2) upon the allowable pipe velocity.[5] Hydraulic gradients lie, ordinarily, between 1 and 3 ft per 1,000, and velocities range from 2 to 4 fps.

---

[5] To illustrate, assume a level region, a distance of 25,000 ft from the junction of the supply conduit with the network to the high-value district, a pressure of 70 psig at the junction, an available pressure drop down to 20 psig for engine streams, a requisite capacity of the system of 17 mgd, and a variation in pipe sizes from 6 in. to 24 in. Since the available hydraulic gradient is $(70 - 20) \times 2.308/25 = 4.6$ ft per 1,000, the carrying capacity of the system is equivalent to

4. On the basis of the available, or desirable, hydraulic gradient, determine the capacity of the existing pipes and sum them to obtain the total capacity.

5. Calculate the deficiency as the difference between the required and the existing capacity.

6. On the basis of the available, or desirable, hydraulic gradient, select the pipes to be added to the system in order to offset the deficiency. General familiarity with the community as well as studies of the network plan will aid judgment. Removal of existing small pipes to make way for larger mains must be taken into account.

7. Determine the size of pipe equivalent to the reinforced systems and calculate the velocity of flow through the system. Excessive velocities, and the dangerous water hammer that may accompany them, should be avoided, if necessary, by lowering the hydraulic gradient actually called into play.

8. Check important pressure requirements against the plan developed for the network.

The method of sections is particularly useful (1) in the study of large and complicated distribution systems; (2) as a check upon other methods of hydraulic analysis; and (3) as a basis for further investigation of the system by more exact calculations.

Example 13-2. Analyze the network shown in Figure 13-5 by the method of sections. The hydraulic gradient available within the network proper is estimated to lie close to 2 ft per 1,000, and the value of C in the Hazen-Williams formula is taken to be 100. The domestic (coincident) draft is assumed to be 140 gpcd. The fire demand is taken from Table 13-2.

1. Section a–a. Population 16,000   mgd
   a. Demands:

Domestic	= 2.2
Fire	= 5.6
Total	= 7.8

   b. Existing pipes: 1, 24-in.   Capacity   = 6.0
   c.   Deficiency = 1.8
   d. If no pipes are added, the 24-in. pipe must carry 7.8 mgd. This it will do with a loss of head of 3.2 ft per 1,000 at a velocity of 3.8 fps (see Hazen-Williams diagram).

2. Section b–b. Population and flow as in a–a.   mgd
   a.   Total demand = 7.8
   b. Existing pipes: 2, 20-in.   Capacity   = 7.4
   c.   Deficiency   = 0.4
   d. If no pipes are added, existing pipes will carry 7.8 mgd with a loss of head of 2.2 ft per 1,000 at a velocity of 2.8 fps.

that of a 30-in. pipe, and the velocities in the system lie between 1.9 fps for 6-in. pipes and 4.7 fps for 24-in. pipes. If the velocity in 24-in. pipes is to be reduced to 3 fps, the hydraulic gradient must be lowered to 2 ft per 1,000. To accomplish this, the network must be strengthened by the addition of pipes, and the reinforced network must possess a capacity equivalent to that of a 35-in. pipe.

3. Section *c–c*. Population 14,000   mgd
    a. Demands: Domestic   = 2.0
                                                  Fire   = 5.6
                                                  Total   = 7.6
    b. Existing pipes: 1, 20-in.   Capacity   = 3.7
                      2, 12-in.   Capacity   = 2.0
                      5, 6-in.   Capacity   = 0.8
                                              Total   = 6.5
    c.   Deficiency = 1.1
    d. Pipes added: 2, 10-in.   Capacity   = 1.2
        Pipes removed: 1, 6-in.   Capacity   = 0.2
                                      Net added capacity = 1.0
    e.   Reinforced capacity = 7.5

The reinforced system (equivalent pipe,[6] 26.0 in.) will carry 7.6 mgd with a loss of head of 2.1 ft per 1,000 at a velocity of 3.2 fps.

4. Section *d–d*. Population 8,000   mgd
    a. Demands   Domestic   = 1.1
                                                      Fire   = 5.6
                                                     Total   = 6.7
    b. Existing pipes: 2, 12-in.   Capacity   = 2.0
                      8, 6-in.   Capacity   = 1.3
                                            Total   = 3.3
    c.   Deficiency = 3.4
    d. Pipes added: 1, 16-in.   Capacity   = 2.1
                      2, 10-in.   Capacity   = 1.2
        Pipes removed: 1, 6-in.   Capacity   = 0.2
                                      Net added capacity = 3.1
    e.   Reinforced capacity = 6.4

The reinforced system (equivalent pipe = 24.6 in.) will carry 6.7 mgd with a loss of head of 2.2 ft per 1,000 at a velocity of 3.1 fps.

5. Section *e–e*. Population 3,000   mgd
    a. Demands: Domestic   = 0.5
                                                    Fire   = 1.5
                                                    Total   = 2.0
    b. Existing pipes: 2, 8-in.   Capacity   = 0.7
                      6, 6-in.   Capacity   = 0.9
                                          Total   = 1.6
    c.   Deficiency = 0.4
    d. Pipes added: 1, 10-in.   Capacity   = 0.6
        Pipes removed: 1, 6-in.   Capacity   = 0.2
                                      Net added capacity = 0.4
    e.   Reinforced capacity = 2.0

The reinforced system (equivalent pipe = 15.8 in.) will carry 2 mgd with a loss of head of 2.0 ft per 1,000 at a velocity of 2.3 fps.

---

[6] The equivalent pipe is one that will carry 7.5 mgd on a hydraulic gradient of 2 ft per 1,000.

Example 13-3. Assuming that water is to be delivered to a fire through not more than 500 ft of hose; find, by the circle method, the water available at the circumference of a 500-ft circle in the center of the network shown in Figure 13-6 in which the pressure in the 12-in. feeders is 40 psig and the residual hydrant pressure is to be not less than 20 psig.

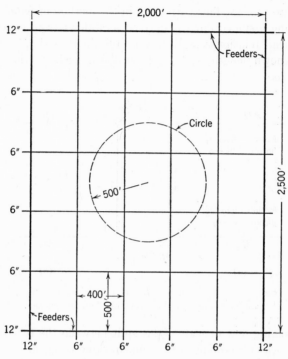

Figure 13-6. Plan of network analyzed by circle method. See Example 13-3.

a. The pipes cut by the circle, the average length of these pipes from their feeder pipes to the hydrants within the circle, and the hydraulic gradient of these pipes are as follows:

Horizontally: 4, 6-in., $[1,000 - \frac{1}{2}(500)] = \quad 750$ ft, $(40 - 20) \times 2.308/0.75 = 61.6\%_0$

Vertically: $\quad$ 4, 6-in., $[1,250 - \frac{1}{2}(500)] = 1,000$ ft, $(40 - 20) \times 2.308/1.00 = 46.2\%_0$

b. The carrying capacity of these pipes, assuming $C = 100$, is:

$$\text{Horizontally: } 4 \times 700 = 2,800 \text{ gpm}$$
$$\text{Vertically: } \quad 4 \times 600 = 2,400 \text{ gpm}$$
$$\overline{\text{Total} = 5,200 \text{ gpm}}$$

Number of Standard Fire Streams $= 5,200/250 = 20.8$

b. Hardy Cross Method.[7] This is a method of relaxation, or controlled trial and error, by which systematic corrections are applied (1) to an initial set of assumed flows, or (2) to an initial set of assumed heads, until the network is balanced hydraulically.

1. *Method of Balancing Heads by Correcting Assumed Flows.* The basic equation for the flow correction in the method of *balancing heads* by correcting assumed flows is derived as follows from a study of the flow and head relationships that must obtain in a simple network of pipes of known length, size, and condition such as that shown in Figure 13-7a.

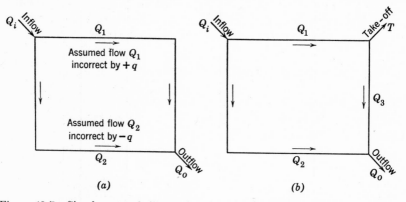

Figure 13-7. Simple network illustrating (*a*) the derivation of the Hardy Cross method and (*b*) the effect of changing flows.

The incoming flow of water Q_i is split between the two branches so that the clockwise flow has an assumed value of Q_1 and the counterclockwise flow an assumed value of $Q_2 = Q_i - Q_1$. Calculation of the loss of head in the two branches by some convenient pipe-flow formula will then yield a loss of head H_1 due to the clockwise flow Q_1 and a loss of head H_2 due to the counterclockwise flow Q_2. In accordance with any one of the commonly used exponential formulas for the flow of water in pipes, the loss of head is $H = kQ^n$, where k is a numerical constant for a particular pipe and n is a constant for all pipes.[8] If Q_1 and Q_2 have been so chosen that the system is balanced hydraulically, $H_1 = k_1Q_1{}^n$ must equal $H_2 = k_2Q_2{}^n$, or $H_1 - H_2 = 0$. If, as may be expected, $H_1 - H_2$ is not zero, the initially assumed values of Q_1 and Q_2 are in error. For Q_1 too small by an amount q, Q_2 must be too large by the same amount q. Making the

[7] Hardy Cross, *Univ. Illinois Bull.* 286 (1936).

[8] In the Hazen-Williams formula, $Q = 405Cd^{2.63}s^{0.54}$, or (for given values C, d, and l or $s = H/l$) $H = kQ^{1.85}$, where k is a constant for the given values.[7]

necessary corrections, the true flows become $Q_1' = (Q_1 + q)$ and $Q_2' = (Q_2 - q)$, and the associated losses of head become H_1' and H_2' respectively, where $H_1' - H_2' = 0$ because the frictional resistances through both branches are the same. It follows that:

$$H_1' - H_2' = k_1(Q_1 + q)^n - k_2(Q_2 - q)^n = 0$$

Expanding the binomials,

$$k_1(Q_1^n + nqQ_1^{n-1} + \cdots) - k_2(Q_2^n - nqQ_2^{n-1} + \cdots) = 0$$

If the first estimate of flow distribution has been reasonable, q will be small and the terms in the expansion that include powers of q greater than unity will be so small as to be safely neglected. We may then write

$$k_1Q_1^n + nk_1qQ_1^{n-1} - k_2Q_2^n + nk_2qQ_2^{n-1} = 0$$

But $k_1Q_1^n = H_1$ and $k_2Q_2^n = H_2$; also $k_1Q_1^{n-1} = k_1Q_1^n/Q_1 = H_1/Q_1$ and $k_2Q_2^{n-1} = H_2/Q_2$. Here Q_1 and Q_2 as well as H_1 and H_2 are given positive or negative signs for clockwise or counterclockwise flow respectively, in order to make the formulations algebraically consistent. Substitution of the derived expressions evaluates the necessary flow correction or, more exactly, the first approximation of the flow correction

$$q = - \frac{H_1 - H_2}{n(H_1/Q_1 + H_2/Q_2)}$$

Since the numerator of the right-hand term in this equation represents the sum of the losses of head and its denominator is n times the sum of the head-flow ratios, we obtain as the basic equation for successive flow corrections:

$$q = - \frac{\Sigma H}{n\Sigma H/Q} = - \frac{\Sigma H}{1.85\Sigma H/Q} \qquad \text{13-1}$$

It follows from the derivation of Equation 13-1 that a network is seldom balanced by a single correction. The number of corrections that must be made depends upon the closeness of the first estimate of flow distribution.

If the total flow through the network is changed, the distribution of flows between individual pipes will be changed in the same proportion, provided that the take-off flows are also altered in the same ratio. The losses of head that accompany such changes vary as the 1.85 power (or approximately as the square) of the ratio of the change.

As shown in Figure 13-7b, $Q_i = Q_1 + Q_2$. If Q_i is changed to rQ_i, where r is the ratio of the new to the old flow,

$$rQ_i = rQ_1 + rQ_2$$

also

$$rQ_o = rQ_3 + rQ_2 = r(Q_1 - T) + rQ_2$$

or

$$rQ_o = rQ_1 + rQ_2 - rT \qquad \text{13-2}$$

Since

$$H_1 = k_1 Q_1{}^n \qquad \text{and} \qquad H_1' = k_1 (rQ_1)^n$$

$$H_1'/H_1 = r^n = r^{1.85} \qquad \text{13-3}$$

2. *Method of Balancing Flows by Correcting Assumed Heads.* As pointed out by Cross, the method of balancing heads is directly applicable when the quantities of water entering and leaving the network are known. When the quantities are unknown and there are several inlets, the distribution of flow among them can be determined by a *method of balancing flows.* In this method, the heads at inlets and outlets must be known. Heads at junctions and associated, between-junction, friction losses are then assumed, and use is made of the fact that the sum of the flows at a junction must be zero if flows towards the junction and away from it are given opposite signs.

For any pipe, the assumed head is $H = kQ^n$ and the corrected head becomes

$$H + h = k(Q + q)^n = k(Q^n + nqQ^{n-1} + \cdots)$$

where h is the necessary head correction. Substituting H for kQ^n, H/Q for kQ^{n-1}, and neglecting the terms in the expansion that include powers of q greater than unity, we then find the head and flow corrections:

$$h = nq(H/Q) \qquad \text{and} \qquad q = (h/n)(Q/H)$$

At each junction, excepting inlet and outlet junctions at which flow to and from the junction is provided solely by the inlet or outlet respectively, the sum of the corrected flows must equal zero, i.e.,

$$\Sigma(Q + q) = 0 \qquad \text{or} \qquad \Sigma Q = -\Sigma q$$

But, since $\Sigma q = \dfrac{h}{n} \Sigma \dfrac{Q}{H}$, the unbalanced flow becomes $Q = -\dfrac{h}{n} \Sigma \dfrac{Q}{H}$, and

$$h = -\frac{n\Sigma Q}{\Sigma Q/H} \qquad \text{13-4}$$

The systematic application of Equations 13-1 or 13-4 permits the solution of complex networks by the use of a table or diagram of the Hazen-Williams formula and by the simple arithmetic processes of addition, subtraction, multiplication, and division.

The corrections q and h are only approximate. After they have been applied once to the assumed flows, the network will be more nearly in balance than it was at the beginning. The process of correction can then be repeated as often as it is necessary to perfect the balancing operations. The work involved is straightforward, but it is greatly facilitated by a satisfactory scheme of bookkeeping such as that outlined for the method of balancing heads in Example 13-4 for the network sketched in Figure 13-8.

The calculating system employed in Examples 13-4 and 13-5 appears to be the most generally useful one. As the analyst becomes familiar with the method, he will discover a number of different shortcuts, some of which have been described in the literature. He is warned, however, against the danger of employing shortcuts too early in the stepwise corrections, because that will inevitably lead to faulty results. As a matter of fact, shortcuts are ordinarily applicable only after successive corrections have balanced the network so closely that further correction, no matter how elegant and expeditious, lies well within the fundamental uncertainty introduced by the choice of such factors as the Hazen-Williams coefficient C.

In spite of the simplicity of the system used in Example 13-4, the network cannot be solved conveniently by algebraic methods, because it contains two interfering hydraulic constituents: (1) a cross-over (pipe 4) or pipe that operates in more than one circuit; and (2) a series of take-offs representing water used along the lines of pipe, fire flows drawn off through hydrants, or supplies through pipes to neighboring circuits.

Example 13-4. Balance the network shown in Figure 13-8 by applying the Hardy Cross method of balancing heads. The schedule of calculations shown in Table 13-5 includes the following:

Columns 1–4 identify the position of the pipes in the network and record their length and diameter. There are two circuits and seven pipes. Pipe 4 is shared by both circuits. To indicate this, one star is used in connection with Circuit I, and two stars in connection with Circuit II. The dual function of this pipe must not be overlooked.

Columns 5–9 deal with the assumed flows and the derived flow correction. For purposes of identification the hydraulic elements Q, s, H, and q are given a subscript zero.

Column 5 lists the assumed flows Q_0 in mgd. They are preceded by positive signs if they are clockwise in direction and by negative signs if they are counterclockwise in direction. The distribution of flows has been purposely misjudged in order to highlight the balancing operation. At each junction the total flow remaining in the system must be accounted for.

Column 6 gives the friction losses s_0 in ft per 1,000 ft when the pipe is carrying the quantities Q_0 shown in Column 5. The values of s_0 can be obtained directly from tables or diagrams of the Hazen-Williams formula.

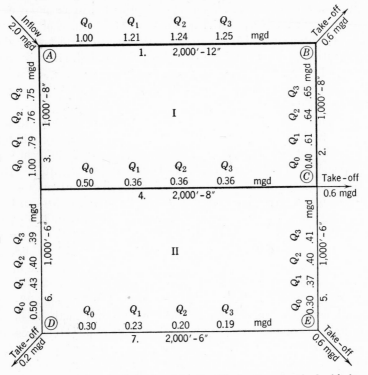

Figure 13-8. Plan of network analyzed by the Hardy Cross method of balancing heads. See Example 13-4.

Column 7 is obtained by multiplying the friction loss per 1,000 ft of pipe (s_0) by the length of the pipe in 1,000 ft; i.e., Column 7 = Column 6 $\times$ (Column 3 $\div$ 1,000). The head losses H_0 obtained are preceded by a positive sign if the flow is clockwise and by a negative sign if the flow is counterclockwise. The values in Column 7 are added up for each circuit, with due regard to signs, in order to obtain ΣH in the flow-correction formula.

Column 8 is found by dividing Column 7 by Column 5. Division makes all signs of H/Q positive. This column is added up for each circuit in order to obtain $\Sigma H/Q$ in the flow-correction formula.

Column 9 contains the calculated flow correction q. The computations necessary to obtain

$$q = -\Sigma H \div (1.85 \times \Sigma H/Q)$$

are performed after the two summing operations that have been described in

TABLE 13-5. Analysis of the Network of Figure 13-8, Example 13-4, by the Hardy Cross Method of Balancing Heads

Circuit No. (1)	Pipe No. (2)	Length, ft (3)	Diameter, in. (4)	Q₀, mgd (5)	s₀, ‰ (6)	H₀, ft (7)	H₀/Q₀ (8)	q₀, mgd (9)	Q₁, mgd (10)	s₁, ‰ (11)	H₁, ft (12)	H₁/Q₁ (13)	q₁, mgd (14)
I	1	2,000	12	+1.0	2.1	+4.2	4.2	+0.21	+1.21	3.0	+6.0	5.0	+0.03
	2	1,000	8	+0.4	2.8	+2.8	7.0	+0.21	+0.61	6.1	+6.1	10.0	+0.03
	3 *	1,000	8	−1.0	15.1	−15.1	15.1	+0.21	−0.79	9.8	−9.8	12.4	+0.03
	4 *	2,000	8	−0.5	4.2	−8.4	16.8	+0.21 −0.07 †	−0.36	2.3	−4.6	12.8	+0.03 −0.03 †
						−16.5 ÷	43.1 ×	1.85) = −0.21			−2.3 ÷	40.2 ×	1.85) = −0.03
II	4 **	2,000	8	+0.5	4.2	+8.4	16.8	+0.07 −0.21 †	+0.36	2.3	+4.6	12.8	+0.03
	5	1,000	6	+0.3	6.6	+6.6	22.0	+0.07	+0.37	9.8	+9.8	26.5	+0.03
	6	1,000	6	−0.5	16.9	−16.9	33.8	+0.07	−0.43	12.9	−12.9	30.0	+0.03
	7	2,000	6	−0.3	6.6	−13.2	44.0	+0.07	−0.23	4.1	−8.2	35.6	+0.03 −0.03 †
						−15.1 ÷	116.6 ×	1.85) = −0.07			−6.7 ÷	104.9 ×	1.85) = −0.03

Circuit No. (1)	Pipe No. (2)	Length, ft (3)	Diameter, in. (4)	Q₂, mgd (15)	s₂, ‰ (16)	H₂, ft (17)	H₂/Q₂ (18)	q₂, mgd (19)	Q₃, mgd (20)	s₃, ‰ (21)	H₃, ft (22)	Loss of Head A–E (23)
I	1	2,000	12	+1.24	3.1	+6.2	5.0	+0.01	+1.25	3.2	+6.4	1. Via pipes 1, 2, 5, 25.0 ft
	2	1,000	8	+0.64	6.6	+6.6	10.3	+0.01	+0.65	6.8	+6.8	2. Via pipes 3, 4, 5, 25.3 ft
	3 *	1,000	8	−0.76	9.1	−9.1	12.0	+0.01	−0.75	8.9	−8.9	3. Via pipes 3, 6, 7, 25.5 ft
	4 *	2,000	8	−0.36	2.3	−4.6	12.8	+0.01 −0.01 †	−0.36	2.3	−4.6	
						−1.1 ÷	40.1 ×	1.85) = −0.01			−0.3	
II	4 **	2,000	8	+0.36	2.3	+4.6	12.8	+0.01 −0.01 †	+0.36	2.6	+4.6	
	5	1,000	6	+0.40	11.3	+11.3	28.2	+0.01	+0.41	11.8	+11.8	
	6	1,000	6	−0.40	11.3	−11.3	28.2	+0.01	−0.39	10.8	−10.8	
	7	2,000	6	−0.20	3.1	−6.2	31.0	+0.01	−0.19	2.9	−5.8	
						−1.6 ÷	100.2 ×	1.85) = −0.01			−0.2	

* Pipe serves more than one circuit; first consideration of this pipe.

** Second consideration of this pipe.

† Corrections in this column are those calculated for the same pipe in the companion circuit; they are of opposite sign.

Q = flow in mgd; s = slope of hydraulic gradient or friction loss in ft per 1,000 (‰) by the Hazen-Williams formula for $C = 100$. H = head lost in pipe (ft).

q = flow correction in mgd; $q = -\dfrac{\Sigma H}{1.85\,\Sigma H/Q}$. $Q_1 = Q_0 + q_0$; $Q_2 = Q_1 + q_1$; $Q_3 = Q_2 + q_2 = Q_2 + q_2$.

connection with Columns 7 and 8. For example: in Circuit I, $\Sigma H = -16.5$, $\Sigma H/Q = 43.1$; and $(-16.5) \div (1.85 \times 43.1) = -0.21$; or $q = +0.21$. Since pipe 4 operates in both circuits, it draws a correction from each circuit. The second correction, however, is of opposite sign to that applied to the companion circuit. As a part of Circuit I, for example, pipe 4 receives a correction of $q = -0.07$ from Circuit II in addition to its basic correction of $q = +0.21$ from Circuit I.

Columns 10–14 cover the once-corrected flows. The hydraulic elements (Q, s, H, and q) are, therefore, given the subscript one. Column 10 is obtained by adding, with due regard to sign, Columns 5 and 9. Columns 11, 12, 13, and 14 are then found in the same manner as Columns 6, 7, 8, and 9.

Columns 15–19 record the twice-corrected flows, and the hydraulic elements (Q, s, H, and q) carry the subscript two. These columns are otherwise like Columns 10 to 14.

Columns 20–23 present the final result, Columns 20 to 22 corresponding to Columns 15 to 18 or 10 to 12. No further flow corrections are developed because the second flow corrections are of the order of 10,000 gpd for a minimum flow of 200,000 gpd, or at most 5%. To test the balance obtained, the losses of head between points A and D in Figure 13-8 via the three possible routes are given in Column 23. The losses vary from 25.0 to 25.5 ft. The average loss is 25.3 ft, and the variation is about 1%.

In accordance with the principles set forth in Equation 13-2, doubling or halving the inflow (or changing it in any other ratio) will double or halve the flow in each pipe and at each take-off (or change it in corresponding ratio). The accompanying loss of head through the system will be altered as the 1.85 power [9] (or approximately as the square) of the ratio, as shown in Equation 13-3. If the inflow is increased from 2.0 mgd to 3.0 mgd, for example, the loss of head from A to D will become $25.3 \times 1.5^{1.85} = 54$ ft (approximately $25.3 \times 1.5^2 = 57$ ft). If the take-off flow is not changed in proportion to the inflow, the system must be balanced anew from the beginning.

Example 13-5. Balance the network shown in Figure 13-9 by applying the Hardy Cross method of balancing flows. The necessary calculations are given in Table 13-6.

The schedule of calculations used in Example 13-5 includes the following:

Columns 1 to 5 identify the pipes at the three "free" junctions.

Columns 6 and 7 give the assumed head loss and the derived hydraulic gradient which determines the rate of flow shown in Column 8 and the flow-head ratio recorded in Column 9 = (Column 8 ÷ Column 6).

Column 10 contains the head correction h_0 as the negative value of 1.85 times the sum of Column 8 divided by the sum of Column 9, for each junction in accordance with Equation 13-4. A subsidiary head correction is made for "shared" pipes as in Example 13-4.

Column 11 gives the corrected head $H_1 = H_0 + h_0$ and provides the basis for the second flow correction by determining s_1, Q_1, and Q_1/H_1 in that order.

---

[9] A simple way of finding the answer graphically from the Hazen-Williams diagram is illustrated in connection with this diagram in the Appendix to this book.

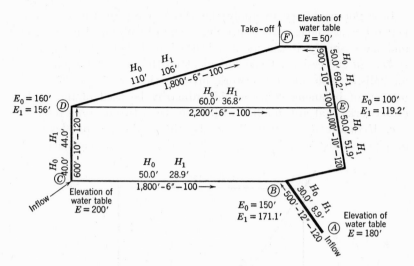

Figure 13-9. Plan of network analyzed by the Hardy Cross method of balancing flows. See Example 13-5.

TABLE 13-6. Analysis of the Network of Figure 13-9 by the Hardy Cross Method of Balancing Flows *

Only the first head correction is calculated for purposes of illustration

Junction letter (1)	Pipe (2)	Length, ft (3)	Diameter, in. (4)	C (5)	H_0, ft (6)	s_0, ‰ (7)	Q_0, mgd (8)	Q_0/H_0 (9)	h_0, ft (10)	H_1, ft (11)
B	AB	500	12	120	+30	60.0	+7.33	0.244	−21.1	+8 9
	BE	1,000 †	10	120	−50	50.0	−4.12	0.082	−21.1 + 19.2	−51.9
	CB	1,800	6	100	+50	27.8	+0.66	0.013	−21.1	+38.9
							1.85(+3.87) ÷ 0.339 = +21.1			
D	CD	600	10	120	+40	66.7	+4.8	0.120	+4.01	+44.0
	DE	2,200 ‡	8	100	−60	27.3	−1.37	0.023	+4.01 + 19.2	−36.8
	DF	1,800	10	100	−110	61.1	−3.82	0.037	+4.01	−106.0
							1.85(−0.39) ÷ 0.180 = −4.01			
E	BE	1,000 §	10	120	+50	50.0	+4.12	0.082	−19.2 + 21.1	+51.9
	DE	2,200 ‖	8	100	+60	27.3	+1.37	0.023	−19.2 − 4.01	+36.8
	EF	900	10	100	−50	55.6	−3.64	0.073	−19.2	−69.2
							1.85(+1.85) ÷ 0.178 = +19.2			

* The basic data for this illustrative example are the same as those used by C. E. Carter and Scott Keith, *J. New Eng. Water Works Assoc., 59*, 273 (1945).
† First consideration of pipe BE.
‡ First consideration of pipe DE.
§ Second consideration of pipe BE.
‖ Second consideration of pipe DE.

It is not necessary to apply the Hardy Cross method to a large network as a whole. Much information can be obtained more quickly and more simply if the method is used to balance portions of the system in succession. Good judgment on the part of the analysts is an indispensable aid to network investigations such as these. The method of balancing flows would ordinarily be used in the analysis of networks that are supplied with water from two or more reservoirs.

c. Method of Equivalent Pipes. By this method, a complex system of pipes is replaced by a single line of equivalent capacity. The

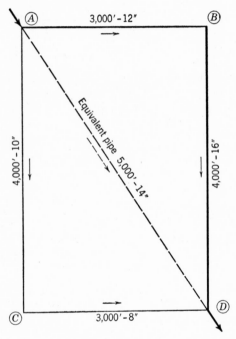

Figure 13-10. Plan of network analyzed by the method of equivalent pipes. See Example 13-6.

method cannot be applied directly to a system of pipes that contains cross-overs or take-offs. It is frequently possible, however, by judicious skeletonizing of the system to obtain significant information on the quantity and pressure of water available at important points in the network. In paring down the system to a workable skeleton, the analyst can be guided by the fact that the following pipes contribute little to flow: (1) small pipes, 6 in. and under in most systems and as large as 8 or 10 in. in more extensive systems; and (2) pipes at right angles to the direction of flow for which no appreciable pressure differential is established between their junctions in the system. The method of equivalent pipes is useful in simplifying networks that are to be analyzed by the Hardy Cross method. Scattered through most networks there are often combinations of pipes that can be replaced by hydraulically equivalent pipes. These reduce to advantage the number of units that must be handled in the Hardy Cross method.

The method of equivalent pipes, even as the method of Hardy Cross, makes use of two hydraulic axioms: (1) that the loss of head due to the flow of a given quantity of water through pipes in series, such as pipes AB and BD in Figure 13-10, is additive; and (2) that the quantities of water flowing through pipes in parallel, such as pipes ABD and ACD in Figure 13-10, must be such that the loss of head through each line is the same.

Example 13-6. Analyze the network of Figure 13-10 by the method of equivalent pipes. Express Q in mgd; s in ft per 1,000; H in ft; and assume a Hazen-Williams coefficient C of 100.

1. *Line ABD.* Assume $Q = 1$ mgd   ft
   a. Pipe AB, 3,000 ft, 12 in.; $s = 2.1$; $H = 2.1 \times 3 =$ 6.3
   b. Pipe BD, 4,000 ft, 16 in.; $s = 0.52$; $H = 0.52 \times 4 =$ 2.1
   c.   Total $H =$ 8.4
   d. Equivalent length of 12-in. pipe: $1,000 \times 8.4/2.1 = 4,000$ ft

2. *Line ACD.* Assume $Q = 0.5$ mgd   ft
   a. Pipe AC, 4,000 ft, 10 in.; $s = 1.42$; $H = 1.42 \times 4 =$ 5.7
   b. Pipe CD, 3,000 ft,   8 in.; $s = 4.2$; $H = 4.2 \ \times 3 = 12.6$
   c.   Total $H = 18.3$
   d. Equivalent length of 8-in. pipe: $1,000 \times 18.3/4.2 = 4,360$ ft

3. *Equivalent line AD.* Assume $H = 8.4$ ft   mgd
   a. Line ABD, 4,000 ft, 12 in.; $s = 8.4/4.00 = 2.1$; $Q = 1.00$
   b. Line ACD, 4,360 ft,   8 in.; $s = 8.4/4.36 = 1.92$; $Q = 0.33$
   c.   Total $Q = 1.33$
   d. Equivalent length of 14-in. pipe: $Q = 1.33$, $s = 1.68$, $1,000 \times 8.4/1.68 =$ 5,000 ft.
   e. Result: 5,000 ft of 14-in. pipe.

The calculations involved in Example 13-6 may be outlined as follows:

1. Since line ABD consists of two pipes in series, the losses of head created by a given flow of water are additive. Find, therefore, from the Hazen-Williams diagram the frictional resistance s for some reasonable flow (1 mgd), (a) in pipe AB and (b) in pipe BD. Multiply these resistances by the length of pipe to obtain the loss of head H. Add the two losses to find the total loss $H = 8.4$ ft. Line ABD, therefore, must carry 1 mgd with a total loss of head of 8.4 ft. Any pipe that will do this is an equivalent pipe. Since a 12-in. pipe has a resistance $s = 2.1$ ft per 1,000 when it carries 1 mgd of water, a 12-in. pipe, to be an equivalent pipe, must be $1,000 \times 8.4/2.1 = 4,000$ ft long.

2. Proceed for line ACD in the same general way as for line ABD and find the length of the equivalent 8-in. pipe to be 4,360 ft.

3. Since ABD and ACD together constitute two lines in parallel, the flows through them for a given loss of head are additive. If some convenient loss is assumed, such as the loss already calculated for one of the lines, the missing, companion flow can be found from the Hazen-Williams diagram. Assuming a loss of 8.4 ft, which is associated with a flow through ABD of 1 mgd,[10] it is only necessary to find from the diagram that the quantity of water that will flow through the equivalent pipe ACD, when the loss of head is 8.4 ft (or $s = 8.4/4.36 = 1.92$ ft per 1,000), amounts to 0.33 mgd. Add this quantity to the flow through line ABD (1.0 mgd) and obtain 1.33 mgd. Line AD, therefore, must carry 1.33 mgd with a loss of head of 8.4 ft. If the equivalent pipe is assumed to be 14 in. in diameter, it will discharge 1.33 mgd with a frictional resistance $s = 1.68$ ft per 1,000, and its length must be $1,000 \times 8.4/1.68 = 5,000$ ft. We can therefore replace the network shown in Figure 13-10 by a single 14-in. pipe 5,000 ft long.

No matter what the original assumptions for quantity, diameter, and loss of head may be, the calculated equivalent pipe will always perform hydraulically in the same way as the network that it replaces.

d. *Other Methods of Analysis.* There are a number of other methods for studying the hydraulics of networks. Among them should be mentioned in particular Freeman's graphical method as expanded by Howland [11] and the use of electric analyzers. Camp and Hazen [12] built the first electric analyzer designed specifically for the hydraulic analysis of water distribution systems. McIlroy [13] has continued this approach to network analysis and has developed an analyzer that is manufactured commercially. Electric analyzers use non-linear resistors to simulate the resistance of pipes. For each branch of the system, the pipe equation,[8] $H = kQ^{1.85}$, is thus replaced by an electrical equation, $V = K_e I^{1.85}$, where V is the voltage drop in the branch, I is the current, and K_e is the non-linear-resistor coefficient whose value is suited to the pipe coefficient k for the selected voltage-head loss and the amperage-water flow scale ratios. If the current inputs and take-offs are made proportional to the water flowing into and out of the system, the head losses will be proportional to the measured voltage drops.

[10] It was, therefore, really unnecessary to specify the length and diameter of the equivalent pipe ABD.

[11] W. E. Howland, "Expansion of the Freeman Method for the Solution of Pipe Flow Problems," *J., New Eng. Water Works Assoc., 48,* 408 (1934).

[12] T. R. Camp and H. L. Hazen, "Hydraulic Analysis of Water Distribution Systems by Means of an Electric Network Analyzer," *J. New Eng. Water Works Assoc., 48,* 383 (1934).

[13] M. S. McIlroy, "Direct-Reading Electric Analyzer for Pipeline Networks," *J., Am. Water Works Assoc., 42,* 347 (1950).

13-7. Service Storage. As stated before, service, or distribution, reservoirs are hydraulically an integral part of the distribution system, and the supply conduits leading to them are generally so proportioned that they can deliver water at a rate sufficiently high to meet the 24-hr demand of the maximum day. Hourly demands in excess of this rate are supplied from storage. To this must be added the water reserves needed in a serious conflagration. Depending upon the nature of the supply works and particularly upon the characteristics of the supply conduits—number, length, and material, and the presence of special hazards such as river crossings and unstable ground—further volumes of water must be stored to allow for the interruption of supply for repairs to conduits and other works. The three major components of service storage, therefore, are: (1) equalizing, or operating, storage; (2) fire reserve; and (3) emergency reserve.

a. Equalizing, or Operating, Storage. If the planned rate of supply and the fluctuation in the rate of demand are known, the equalizing, or operating, storage that should be provided may be ascertained from a rate curve or, more satisfactorily, from a mass diagram similar to the Rippl diagram (Section 8-3). As shown in Figure 13-11 for the simple conditions of steady inflow, during 12 and 24 hr respectively, the amount of equalizing, or operating, storage is the sum of the maximum ordinates between the demand and supply lines. To construct a mass diagram proceed as follows:

1. From past measurements of flow, determine the draft during each hour of the day and night for typical days (maximum, average, and minimum).
2. Calculate the amounts of water that are drawn up to certain times, i.e., the cumulative draft.
3. Plot the cumulative draft against time, as shown in Figure 13-11.
4. For steady supply during 24 hr, draw a straight line diagonally across the diagram, as in Figure 13-11a. The ordinates between the draft and the supply line measure the difference between demand and supply.
5. For steady supply during 12 hr, by pumping, for example, draw a straight line diagonally from the beginning of the pumping period to its end (from 6 AM to 6 PM in Figure 13-11b).

Steady supply at the rate of maximum daily use will ordinarily require an equalizing storage close to 15% of the average day's consumption. Limitation of supply to 12 hr may be expected to raise the operating storage to 50% of the average day's consumption.

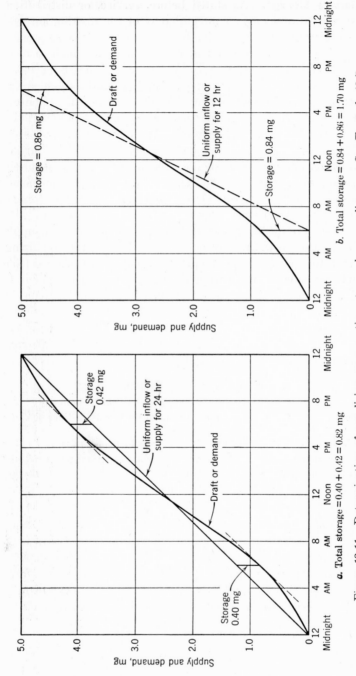

Figure 13-11. Determination of equalizing, or operating, storage by mass diagram. See Example 13-7.

a. Uniform inflow, or supply, extending over 24 hr.
b. Uniform inflow, or supply, confined to 12 hr.

Example 13-7. Determine the equalizing, or operating, storage for the drafts of water shown in Table 13-7 (*a*) when inflow is uniform during 24 hr; (*b*) when flow is confined to the 12 hr from 6 AM to 6 PM.

TABLE 13-7. Observed Drafts (Example 13-7)

4-hr periods lapsing at

		4 AM	8 AM	noon	4 PM	8 PM	midnight
a.	Time	4 AM	8 AM	noon	4 PM	8 PM	midnight
b.	Draft, mg	0.484	0.874	1.216	1.102	0.818	0.506
c.	Cumulative draft, mg	0.484	1.358	2.574	3.676	4.495	5.000

a. For steady supply during 24 hr, the draft plotted in Figure 13-11*a* exceeds the demand by 0.40 mg by 6 AM. If this excess is stored, it is used up by 11 AM. In the afternoon, the demand exceeds the supply by 0.42 mg by 6 PM and must be drawn from storage that is replenished by midnight. Hence the required storage is the sum of the morning excess and afternoon deficiency, or 0.82 mg. This equals 16.4% of the daily draft.

b. For steady supply during the 12-hr period from 6 AM to 6 PM, the draft plotted in Figure 13-11*b* exceeds the supply by 0.84 mg between midnight and 6 AM and must be drawn from storage. In the afternoon, the supply exceeds the demand by 0.86 mg by 6 PM, but this excess is required to furnish water from storage between 6 PM and midnight. Total storage, therefore, is 1.70 mg, or 34% of the day's consumption.

b. Fire Reserve. Based upon the durations of serious conflagrations that have been experienced in the past, the National Board of Fire Underwriters recommends that distributing reservoirs be made large enough to supply water for fighting a serious conflagration for 10 hr in communities of more than 2,500 people and for 5 hr in smaller ones. The resulting fire reserve is shown in Table 13-2. These amounts may not always be economically attainable, and design values may have to be adjusted downward to meet local financial abilities.

c. Emergency Reserve. The magnitude of this component of storage depends (1) upon the danger of interruption of reservoir inflow by failure of supply works; and (2) upon the time needed to make repairs. If the shutdown of the supply is confined to the time necessary for routine inspections and these are relegated to the hours of minimum draft, the emergency reserve is sometimes taken as equal to 25% of the total storage capacity, i.e., the reservoir is assumed to be drawn down by $\frac{1}{4}$ its average depth. If supply lines or equipment are expected to be out of operation for longer periods of time, suitable allowances must be made. The National Board of Fire Underwriters bases its rating system on an emergency storage of 5 days at maximum flow.

d. Total Storage. The total amount of storage is desirably equal to the sum of the component requirements. In each instance, economic

considerations determine the final choice. In pumped supplies, cost
of storage must be balanced against cost of pumping. Particular attention must be paid to the economies that can be effected by more
uniform operation of pumps and by restricting pumping to a portion
of the day. In all supplies, cost of storage must be balanced against
cost of supply lines, increased fire protection, and more uniform pressures in the distribution system.

Example 13-8. For a steady gravity supply equal to the maximum daily demand,
a 10-hr fire supply, and no particular hazard to the supply works, find the storage
to be provided for a city of 50,000 people using an average of 5 mgd of water.

$$\begin{array}{lr} & \text{mg} \\ \text{Equalizing storage} = 15\% \text{ of 5 mg} & 0.75 \\ \text{Fire reserve (Table 13-2)} & 4.00 \\ \hline \text{Subtotal} & 4.75 \end{array}$$

Emergency reserve = $\frac{1}{4}$ of total storage.
Therefore subtotal is $\frac{3}{4}$ of total storage,
and total storage = 4.75/0.75   6.33

If we assume that the maximum daily use is 150% of the average, the emergency storage suggested by the National Board would approximate $5 \times 5 \times 1.5 =$
38 mg, instead of $6.33 - 4.75 = 1.58$ mg.

e. Location of Storage. As shown in Section 13-1 and Figure 13-1,
location as well as capacity of service storage is an important factor
in the control of distribution systems. A million gallons of elevated
fire reserve, suitably situated with reference to the area that is to be
protected, is equivalent, for example, to the addition of a 12-in. supply
main. If this volume of water is drawn in a 10-hr fire, flow would be
provided at a rate of $(24/10) \times 1 = 2.4$ mgd. This is the amount
of water that a 12-in. pipe can carry at a velocity of less than 5 fps.
That this must be neighborhood storage is evidenced by the high
frictional resistance of more than 10 ft per 1,000 that accompanies
such use.

13-8. Distributing Reservoirs. Where topography and geology permit, the water stored for distribution is held in reservoirs that are
formed by impoundage, by balanced excavation and embankment, or
by masonry construction (see Figure 2-7). In order to protect the
water against chance contamination and against deterioration, particularly by the growth of algae under the influence of sunlight, distributing reservoirs should be covered. Roofs need not be watertight
if the reservoir is properly fenced. Open reservoirs should always be
fenced, and, where they are so placed that surface runoff can be car-

ried into them, a marginal intercepting drain should be provided for their protection. Circulation through reservoirs may be controlled by suitable baffles.

Earthen reservoirs, their bottom sealed by a blanket of clay or rubble masonry and their sides by core walls, were widely employed at one time. Lining with concrete slabs is more common today. Wood roofs and concrete roofs of beam and girder, flat-slab, arch, and groined-arch construction are used. Concrete roofs are commonly covered with earth for the protection of roof and water against extremes of temperature. Gunite, a sand-cement-water mixture, discharged from a nozzle or gun through and onto a mat of reinforcing steel, has been employed to line or reline the invert and sides of reservoirs.

Inlets, outlets, and overflows are suitable placed in a gate house. Circulation (1) to insure more or less continuous displacement of the water, or (2) to provide proper detention of water after chlorination, may be controlled by baffles or subdivisions. The capacity of the overflow should equal the maximum rate of inflow. Altitude-control valves on reservoir inlets will automatically shut off inflow when maximum water level is reached. An arrangement that does not interfere with draft from the reservoir includes a by-pass with a swing check valve seating against the inflow.

Where natural elevation is inadequate, elevated storage is obtained in standpipes and elevated tanks that are constructed of wood, concrete, or steel. In cold climates, steel is found most suitable. Unless the steel is prestressed in reinforced-concrete tanks, vertical cracks are formed, and leakage and freezing cause rapid deterioration of the structure. Wood has been employed almost wholly for railroad and industrial supplies.

The useful capacity of standpipes and elevated tanks is confined to the volume of water stored above the elevation at which adequate pressure is created in the connected distribution system. In elevated tanks this elevation generally coincides with the bottom of the water tank proper; in standpipes it may lie much higher. For steel tanks, both welded and riveted construction are employed. Structural design and erection of steel tanks has become the specialized activity of a number of manufacturers.

The function of elevated tanks and spheroidal tanks can be expressed to esthetic advantage in their architecture without resorting to ornamentation. Standpipes are simple cylinders. They generally require the use of a veneer or an outer shell of concrete or masonry to render them attractive.

13-9. Management of Distribution Systems. Intelligent management of distribution storage requires information as to the level of the water in the reservoir. Where this cannot be observed directly, gages, floats, or electrically operated indicators and recorders must be installed to meet the particular requirements of the system.

Well-kept records and maps of the pipes and appurtenances of distribution systems are essential to their proper operation and maintenance. In order to avoid the occasional discharge of roiled water, the distribution system should be flushed systematically through its hydrants. Dead ends, in particular, need flushing; a bleeder on the dead end will counteract the effects of too sluggish water movement. The disinfection of newly laid pipe or pipe that has been repaired is discussed in Section 27-12. The control of pipe corrosion and the cleaning and relining of water mains are dealt with in Section 23-7.

The thawing of frozen pipes is discussed in Section 14-2. If pipes are placed at proper depth and adequate flow is maintained through them, they should not freeze. Pipes that are deprived of adequate cover due to the regrading of streets, or that are subjected to protracted and exceptionally cold spells, may be protected by bleeding water from them through services. Pipes that are exposed on bridges or similar crossings should be insulated. Provision is sometimes made to heat large and important lines where exposure is severe. In very cold climates, water and sewer pipes may be laid in a heated boxlike conduit, known as a *utilidor*.

Loss of water by leakage from distribution systems and connected consumer premises should be kept under control by leakage surveys (see Section 5-8).

14

WATER SUPPLY AND DRAINAGE OF BUILDINGS

14-1. Functions and Controls. Within dwellings, commercial or public buildings, and industrial establishments, water supply and drainage combine to form the plumbing [1] system of the buildings they serve. Plumbing systems thereby become the link through which public water-supply systems are connected with public waste-water disposal systems. The plumbing system begins at the point where water enters the building from the public water main through the *service pipe* of the building. The plumbing system ends where drainage water leaves the building to be discharged into the public sewer through the *building sewer*. Within the building, water distribution terminates and drainage begins at the various plumbing fixtures or at the manufacturing units of industrial establishments. Fire-sprinkler systems and swimming pools are specialized parts of plumbing systems.

The design and construction of plumbing systems, as a whole, are the responsibility of architects and industrial engineers rather than water-supply and sewerage engineers. However, an understanding of the underlying principles is essential to the proper servicing and supervision of these systems. In a broad sense, plumbing systems are an integral part of public water-supply and waste-water disposal systems, individually small but collectively large and important.

The regulation of plumbing systems is an exercise of the police power in the interest of public health. Promulgation and administration of the necessary codes is vested in state or local health authorities, building departments, or special plumbing boards. Plumbing codes specify in particular (1) materials, fittings, and sizes for water piping, drains, stacks, vents, and certain fixtures; (2) grades for drains; (3) methods of venting fixture drains; (4) required air gaps between fixture inlets and water levels; (5) needed back-flow preventers; and (6) inspection and tests. Most codes aim at simplification as well as

---

[1] The word *plumbing* comes from the Latin *plumbum*, lead. Early water-supply and drainage pipes of buildings were constructed very largely of lead.

standardization of requirements. Much of the factual material contained in this chapter is taken, of necessity, from existing codes and manuals.[2]

Water Supply

14-2. Water Piping. That portion of the water supply of a building which lies between the public main and the take-offs to the various plumbing fixtures or other points of use of water is illustrated in Figure 14-1. It includes the service pipe,[3] its fittings, and accessories.

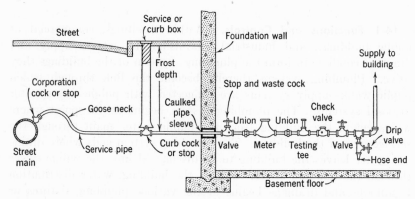

Figure 14-1. Service pipe, fittings, and accessories. There are many possible modifications, both inside and outside the building. In moderate climates, the meter is often placed in a vault outside the building.

It begins with the corporation [4] cock and ends with the stop-and-waste cock or with the water meter inside the building. The remainder of the system consists of vertical risers, horizontal runs, and necessary fittings (Figure 14-2).

a. Service Pipes. The service pipe is also called the building main. It is either connected rigidly to the street main, or a flexible *gooseneck* is interposed in order to avoid breakage of the service pipe by settlement of the street main or by traffic shock. The materials that have been used in small services include lead, galvanized iron, or steel,

---

[2] "Plumbing Manual," National Bureau of Standards *Report* BMS 66, 1940; "The Uniform Plumbing Code for Housing," Housing and Home Finance Agency *Technical Paper* 6 (1948); "Report of the Uniform Plumbing Code Committee," U. S. Government Printing Office, 1949; and "American Standard Plumbing Code," American Standards Association A 40.7 (1949).

[3] The term *service pipe* is sometimes restricted to that portion of the building main that is under the jurisdiction of the water department or water company.

[4] So named after the body politic, or corporate, that owns the water-supply system.

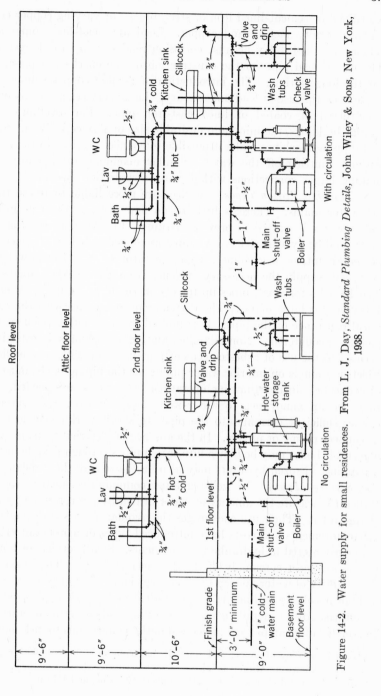

Figure 14-2. Water supply for small residences. From L. J. Day, *Standard Plumbing Details*, John Wiley & Sons, New York, 1938.

lead-lined or cement-lined iron or steel, brass [5] of varying copper content, admiralty metal,[6] and copper. Lead and lead-lined pipes are seldom installed today because corrosion renders their use dangerous. The use of lead pipe for the construction of goosenecks has persisted for the longest time. The introduction of flexible copper tubing has made even this use of lead unnecessary. Large services are commonly constructed of coated or lined cast-iron pipe. For dwellings and similar buildings, the minimum desirable size of service is ¾ in. Special tapping machines make it possible to connect services to the main without shutting off the water. Similar machines are also used in making larger connections within water-distribution systems.

b. *Thawing Frozen Pipes.* Services are more liable to freeze than are water mains. There is little or no flow through them at night, unless water is wasted to prevent freezing. Frozen pipes are thawed most readily by electricity. A transformer connected to the electric power circuit, or a gasoline-driven generator of the electric-welding type, will supply the necessary current: from 100 to 200 amperes at 3 to 10 volts for small pipes up to several thousand amperes at 55 or 110 volts for large mains. The current required varies with the electrical resistance of the pipe. It is limited by the melting point of the metals encountered. Non-metallic jointing compounds in cast-iron mains and the use of asbestos-cement pipe interfere with current flow. Electric grounds on interior water piping, or the piping itself, must be disconnected during thawing operations. Grounds are needed, but they are an annoyance to water-works operators when the ground carries sufficient current into the pipes to shock workmen who must disconnect piping or meters. In the absence of electricity, steam from a portable boiler may be blown into frozen pipes through flexible block-tin tubing. Frozen hydrants may also be thawed by these means.

c. *Service Meters.* In well-regulated communities, meters are installed to measure the amount of water drawn by the consumer and to charge for it. Their use encourages the avoidance of waste. Operating requirements and costs have introduced types of meters not otherwise encountered in hydraulic measurements. Small service, or house, meters are most commonly of the displacement type. They measure the quantity of water flowing by recording the number of times a space of known volume within the meter is filled and emptied. A rotating, or nutating, disk generally controls the filling and emptying operations. In North American practice, inlet and outlet connections to disk meters

[5] Brass is an alloy of copper and zinc. It may contain as little as 60% copper and is then known as Muntz metal.

[6] Admiralty metal contains about 71% copper, 28% zinc, and 1% tin.

have diameters varying from ⅝ in. to 6 in. for flows rated normally at 10 to 500 gpm. For heavy flows and high pressures, current or velocity meters are employed. In these a calibrated propeller or water wheel constitutes the measuring element. Displacement and velocity meters are used singly and in various combinations with themselves or with a free waterway, in which a friction ring creates proportional flow through the by-pass on which the meter is mounted. Such combinations are known as proportional-flow, compound, and fire-flow meters.

d. *Distributing Pipes.* The pipe materials employed to distribute water through buildings are the same as for service pipes. In poorly proportioned distributing systems or systems in which iron rust or other products of corrosion have restricted the water way, the pressure may become so low that water will not reach fixtures in upper stories when water is being drawn at one or more fixtures in lower stories. A vacuum may then be created in parts of the system and cause contaminated or polluted water to enter the water-supply system from fixtures that are not protected against back-flow (see Figure 14-3). A vacuum may be produced also when a street main breaks or is emptied for inspection and repairs, or when water is pumped at too high a rate from the main during a fire. To prevent this type of vacuum, which may also collapse hot-water boilers, the distribution system of buildings is sometimes provided with a check valve at or near the terminus of the service pipe on the house side of the water meter (see Figure 14-1).

The pressure in street mains, ranging between 20 psig in residential areas and 100 psig or more in commercial districts, is not sufficient to furnish water to the upper stories of tall buildings. Such structures are equipped with pumps that boost the municipal pressure within the building. The pumps are generally thrown in and out of operation by float-operated switches connected to storage tanks. They serve zones of 10 to 15 stories and are situated at least two stories above the top floor of their respective zones. The piping of the building may be unified if valves, including pressure-regulating valves, are inserted in the risers at the levels that separate the zones.

e. *Hot-Water Supply.* Gravity systems in which an open, float-fed storage tank in the attic or on the roof supplies water to a low-pressure heater, such as the water back of a coal or wood stove, and to a hot-water storage tank are safe. But the low pressures developed limit the rate of drawing water, and attic tanks often become foul. In modern dwellings and large hot-water supplies, therefore, pressure systems (Figure 14-2) are employed instead. The danger of explosion due to overheating the water is guarded against by attaching a three-purpose valve to the storage tank. This valve opens (1) when a vacuum is created in the tank; (2) when the temperature of the hot

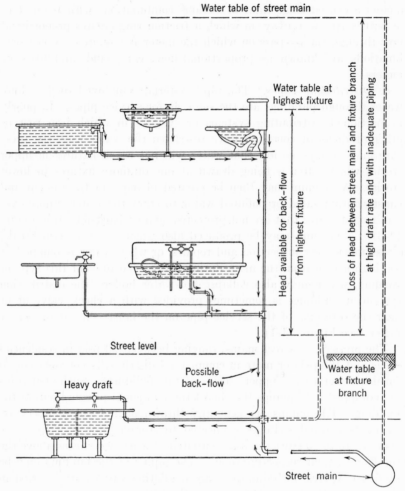

Figure 14-3. Hydraulics of back-flow, and common back-flow hazards in dwellings.

water rises above a certain limit, generally 212 F; and (3) when the working pressure of the tank is exceeded. Hot water is prevented from backing into the supply main and from ruining the hard rubber disk of displacement meters by installing a check valve on the building side of the meter. The material used for hot-water piping must be carefully selected because corrosion, like most chemical reactions, is accelerated at elevated temperatures. Circulation of hot water by installing return piping permits drawing water of suitable temperature more or less instantaneously. Hot-water tanks should be placed near the bottom of the system—in the basement or on the lowest floor in the zone, therefore. Desirable water temperatures range from 120 to 160 F. Temperatures approaching 160 F are needed for mechanical dishwashers and washing machines. All-metal meters are used to measure hot water.

f. Drinking Fountains and Refrigerated-Water Supplies. A sanitary drinking fountain discharges an inclined jet of water. Water that has come in contact with the mouth of the user cannot then fall back on the bubbler and contaminate it. The orifice is shielded to keep it from being touched inadvertently by hands or lips, and its lower edge rises a sufficient distance (¾ in. or more) above the flood-level rim of the receptor to keep it from being inundated. The jet is strong enough to carry the water away from the orifice. Examination of poorly constructed, vertical-jet fountains has shown that hemolytic streptococci [7] can be recovered both from the surface of the bubbler and from the drinking water issuing from it.

The drinking-water supply of buildings is sometimes cooled in individual coolers or in a central refrigerating system. For physiological reasons, the water should not be too cold (not less than 40 F). In order to prevent waste of water that has become warm in the pipes, the cooled water may be recirculated. If the drinking water is stored in a tank, it must be protected against chance contamination.[8]

g. Testing for Tightness. Plumbing regulations generally require that the completed water-supply systems of buildings be tested for tightness before they are approved. The entire system is filled with water under a pressure of 100 psig or more and examined for leaks. An air test at a minimum pressure of 35 psig may be substituted in special circumstances.

14-3. Design of Water Piping. Hydraulic calculations for water piping are straightforward. Matters to be determined by the designer are: (1) the demand load on the system; (2) the allowable friction loss in the piping; and (3) the friction actually created in tentative and final layouts.

---

[7] A group of bacteria commonly present in the mouth, nose, and throat of man. Some members of this group are responsible for infections such as scarlet fever, septic sore throat, pneumonia, and rheumatic fever.

[8] Leakage from drainage lines passing over a storage tank was one of the sources of pollution suspected of being responsible for a severe outbreak of amebic dysentery in Chicago in 1933.

Because of its resistance to corrosion, copper is generally the best material for small water-piping systems. The zinc coating on galvanized-iron and galvanized-steel pipe is corroded away in a few years unless the water is unusually non-corrosive. Accumulations of iron rust then reduce the free cross-section of the waterway and increase the frictional resistance to flow. For this reason, iron and steel pipes, or galvanized-iron and galvanized-steel pipes, are generally given a somewhat larger inside diameter than copper pipes that are to be used for the same purpose. An excess internal diameter of ⅛ in. to ¼ in. for ferrous pipes ¾ in. and smaller in size, and an excess of ¼ in. to ½ in. for ferrous pipes of larger size normally constitute reasonable allowances.

a. Demand Load. The demand load of a building depends (1) upon the number and kinds of fixtures installed and (2) on the probable simultaneous use of these fixtures. The rates at which water is desirably drawn into different types of fixtures are known. These rates become whole numbers of small size when they are expressed in cubic feet per minute (cfm). This unit has, therefore, been adopted as a matter of convenience of expression. A rate of 1 cfm is called a *fixture unit*. The demand rates of common fixtures are shown in Table 14-1

TABLE 14-1.   Rate of Water Supply of Common Fixtures and Minimum Sizes of Fixture Branches

Fixture and type of supply control	*Number of fixture units (cfm)*		*Minimum nominal size of fixture branches, in.*
	Private building	*Public or office building*	
Wash basin, faucet	1	2	⅜
Water closet			
flush tank	3	5	⅜
flush valve	6	10	1
Urinal			
(stall or wall), flush tank	..	3	⅜
(stall or wall), flush valve	..	5	½
(pedestal), flush valve	..	10	1
Bathtub or shower, faucet or mixing valve	2	4	½
Bathroom group			
flush tank for closet	6	..	...
flush valve for closet	8	..	...
separate shower head	2	..	...
Kitchen sink, faucet	2	4	½
Laundry trays (1 to 3), faucet	3	..	½
Combination fixture, faucet	3	..	½
Service sink, faucet (hotel or restaurant)	..	3	½

together with the minimum desirable sizes of branch piping leading to these fixtures.[9]

Since all the fixtures in a given layout are not expected to be in operation at the same time, the total rate at which water will probably flow in main supply branches need not equal the sum of the requirements of the individual fixtures. A probability study made by

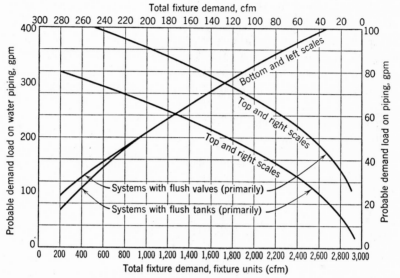

Figure 14-4. Demand load on water piping. *After Hunter.*

Hunter [10] suggests the relationships shown in Figure 14-4. In making use of these curves special allowances are made as follows:

1. Demands for service sinks are ignored in calculating the total fixture demand.

2. Demands of supply outlets, such as sill cocks, hose connections, and air conditioners, through which water flows more or less continuously over a considerable length of time, must be added to the probable flow rather than the fixture demand. Sill cocks discharge at a rate of about 5 gpm and should be supplied, at the least, through a ½-in. branch.

3. Fixtures supplied with both hot and cold water exert reduced demands upon main hot-water and cold-water branches (not fixture branches). An allowance of ¾ of the demand shown in Table 14-1 for individual fixtures is suggested.

[9] A calculation will show that the velocities created in the fixture branches range upward from about 12.5 fps with friction losses of about 2 ft per foot of pipe.

[10] Roy B. Hunter, "Methods of Estimating Loads in Plumbing Systems," National Bureau of Standards, *Report* BMS 65 (1940). See also Housing and Home Finance Agency, *Housing Research Paper* 15 (1951).

b. Allowable Friction Loss. The allowable friction loss in the piping is determined by the following variables:

1. The minimum daily service pressure in the street main.
2. The elevation of the highest fixture or group of fixtures above the street main.
3. The minimum satisfactory operating pressure at the highest fixture or group of fixtures: 15 psig for flush valves and 8 to 10 psig for faucets or flush tanks.
4. The friction loss through appurtenances such as water meters and hot-water heaters.

The allowable friction loss equals the difference between the first variable and the sum of the remaining variables, expressed in common units (psi or ft). Not all the allowable loss will necessarily be used up. Line noises are avoided if the maximum velocity of flow is held below 10 fps.

c. Calculated Friction. Pressure losses in water piping fall into the following general categories:

1. Pipe friction. This is determined by one of the common pipe-flow formulas. The actual diameter of pipe (see manufacturers' catalogues), rather than the nominal diameter, must be employed, and allowance must be made for corrosion of piping and consequent obstruction to flow. In the Hazen-Williams formula (Section 12-2) a coefficient of 100 is employed in ordinary circumstances.
2. Pressure loss in service meters. The loss in disk meters is approximated by the following equation:

$$\Delta p = 0.01 Q^2/d^{3.33} \qquad\qquad 14\text{-}1$$

where Δp is the pressure drop through the meter in psi, Q is the flow in gpm, and d is the nominal size of meter in inches.

The flow characteristics of service meters are shown in Table 14-2. At the normal test flows shown in this table, meters are generally required to register

TABLE 14-2. Flow Characteristics of Service Meters

Nominal Size, in.	Normal test and operating flows, gpm	Minimum test flows, gpm
⅝	1– 20	¼
¾	2– 34	½
1	3– 53	¾
1½	5– 100	1½
2	8– 160	2
3	16– 315	4
4	28– 500	7
6	48–1,000	12

100% ± 2% of the water passing through them; at the minimum test flows, at least 90% of the water passing through them. At the upper limit of normal flow, the pressure drop must not exceed 25 psi. According to Equation 14-1, the pressure drop through service meters is about 7 psi at average operating flows. Fire-service meters of the compound type from 3 to 12 in. in diameter will discharge from 400 to 6,400 gpm respectively at a loss of head of 4 psi.

3. Friction loss in valves and fittings. This loss is generally expressed either in terms of velocity heads or of equivalent lengths of straight pipe. The value of k in the expression $h = kv^2/2g$ (where h is the loss of head in ft, and $v^2/2g$ is the velocity head in ft) is about as follows:

	Value of k			Value of k
Elbows, 90°	1.0	Valves (open), Gate	0.2
45°	0.6	Globe	8
		Angle	4
Tee, 90° takeoff	1.5		
Straight run	0.3	Coupling	0.3

The equivalent length of pipe for various fittings is shown in Table 14-3.

TABLE 14-3. Equivalent Length of Pipe for Friction Losses in Valves and Threaded Fittings (non-recessed) *

Nominal diameter of fitting, in.	Length of pipe, ft						
	Elbow		Tee		Valve (open)		
	90°	45°	Take-off	Straight run †	Gate	Globe ‡	Angle
⅜	1	0.6	1.5	0.3	0.2	8	4
½	2	1.2	3	0.6	0.4	15	8
¾	2.5	1.5	4	0.8	0.5	20	12
1	3	1.8	5	0.9	0.6	25	15
1¼	4	2.4	6	1.2	0.8	35	18
1½	5	3	7	1.5	1.0	45	22
2	7	4	10	2	1.3	55	28
2½	8	5	12	2.5	1.6	65	34
3	10	6	15	3	2	80	40
3½	12	7	18	3.6	2.4	100	50
4	14	8	21	4	2.7	125	55
5	17	10	25	5	3.3	140	70
6	20	12	30	6	4	165	80

* For recessed, threaded fittings and streamlined, soldered fittings, divide tabular values by 2.

† Also for coupling.

‡ Also for faucets, sill cocks, shower valves, shower heads, and flushometer valves.

Example 14-1. A two-story dwelling contains the following fixtures: 2 bathroom groups, 1 additional water closet, 1 additional wash basin, 1 kitchen sink, 1 laundry tray, and 1 sill cock. All water closets are served by flush tanks; the highest fixture lies 30 ft above the street main; the maximum developed length of water pipe is 100 ft; [11] the minimum daily pressure of the street main is 40 psig; and a disk meter measures the water. Find: (a) the demand load, (b) the required size of meter, (c) the allowable friction loss, and (d) the required size of pipe.

a. Demand load: From Table 14-1:

Fixture
units

2 bathroom groups @ 6 =	12
1 water closet	@ 3 =	3
1 wash basin	@ 1 =	1
1 kitchen sink	@ 2 =	2
1 laundry tray	@ 3 =	3
		—
Total		21

From Figure 14-4, the probable flow in the building main will be 15 gpm plus 5 gpm for the sill cock, or a total of 20 gpm.

b. Size of service meter for 20 gpm: From Table 14-2, the choice of meters lies between a ¾-in. meter with a range of flow of 2 to 34 gpm and a 1-in. meter with a range of flow of 3 to 53 gpm.

c. Allowable friction loss for 20 gpm:

	psig
Pressure in street main	= 40.0
Elevation of highest fixture above main = 30 ft, or	
30 × 0.433	= 13.0
Difference	= 27.0

1. Loss of pressure in ¾-in. meter. By Equation 14-1:   psi

$$\Delta p = 0.01(20)^2/(0.75)^{3.33} \qquad = 10.4$$

Allowable friction loss with ¾-in. meter (27.0 − 10.4) = 16.6

2. Loss of pressure in 1-in. meter   = 4.0

Allowable friction loss with 1-in. meter (27.0 − 4.0)   = 23.0

d. Size of main piping: The Hazen-Williams formula gives the following losses of head for $C = 100$ and $Q = 20$ gpm:

	s(ft/ft)
¾-in. pipe (actual diameter 0.82 in.)	1.36
1-in. pipe (actual diameter 1.05 in.)	0.420
1¼-in. pipe (actual diameter 1.38 in.)	0.111

---

[11] The maximum developed length is the sum of (1) the lengths of all pipe runs from the street main to the farthest fixture or the fixture to which the loss is greatest plus (2) the equivalent lengths of all fittings along this line, excepting the meter.

1. Allowable system loss with ¾-in. meter = 16.6 psi, or 16.6/0.433 = 38.4 ft. Since the developed length of the piping is 100 ft, the friction loss per unit length = 38.4/100 = 0.384 = s. Therefore, a 1¼-in. pipe is needed with a ¾-in. meter, and the pipe velocity is 4.3 fps.

2. Allowable system loss with 1-in. meter = 23.0 psi, or 23.0/0.433 = 53.2 ft, and $s = 0.532$. Therefore, a 1-in. pipe is needed with a 1-in. meter, and the pipe velocity is 7.4 fps.

14-4. Back-Flow. When the pipe supplying water to a fixture, tank, or similar unit terminates below or too near the water or liquid level of that unit, there is danger of back-flow or siphonage. A number of common back-flow hazards are illustrated in Figure 14-3. Similar conditions occur in almost infinite variety in the distribution systems of existing buildings. Their sanitary significance has been widely appreciated only since the outbreak of amebic dysentery in Chicago in 1933.

To protect the water supply against pollution by back-flow, one of the following conditions must obtain: (1) a sufficient air gap must intervene between the water-supply outlet and the maximum possible water or liquid level; or (2) the supply pipe must be equipped with a suitable vacuum breaker, or back-siphonage preventer. Water will not back-siphon across an air gap that is three times the diameter of the smallest waterway in the fitting.

Vacuum breakers or back-siphonage preventers admit air to the supply pipe whenever a vacuum is created within it. To offer adequate protection, these devices must function satisfactorily under a vacuum as high as 15 in. of mercury.

The hazard of back-flow justifies the interest and activity of health authorities in the regulation of plumbing systems.

14-5. Supplementary Water Supplies. In addition to a supply of water from the public distribution system, some (usually industrial) buildings and yard areas secure water from a supplementary source for one or more of the following reasons: (1) to obtain softer, cooler, more palatable, or otherwise more suitable water for washing, drinking, air conditioning, industrial processing, and other uses; (2) to secure cheaper water for air conditioning and industrial purposes; and (3) to provide additional quantities of water for fire-fighting purposes, particularly in large industrial establishments with high fire risks. The supplementary sources may be: (a) rain-water cisterns that store soft water; (b) wells that, in comparison with the public supply, yield colder water in summer, more palatable water, or cheaper water; and (c) streams or ponds from which are drawn independent supplies of water for use in manufacturing processes or to quench fires.

a. Cross-Connections. Unless the quality of supplementary water supplies is equal or superior to that of the public supply and unless it is so maintained at all times, a direct cross-connection between the two should not be tolerated. How the two sources can be divorced without losing altogether the protective benefit of a dual supply is illustrated in Figure 14-5. Ground-level storage may be substituted but is less advantageous for fire protection.

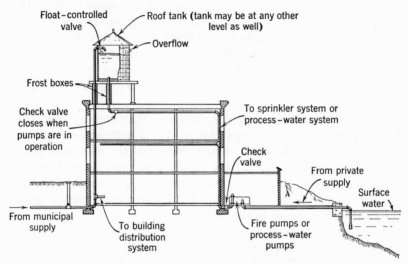

Figure 14-5. Use of private water supply without cross-connection. *After Minnesota State Board of Health.*

Existing cross-connections that it is not expedient to remove should be equipped with approved double check-valves installed in vaults accessible for inspection and provided with the necessary valves, gages, and bleeders (see Figure 14-6). The connection should be tested at regular intervals by water and health authorities. There is no record of water-borne disease traceable to an approved and properly supervised, protected cross-connection. Such installations can be further safeguarded by automatic chlorination of the auxiliary supply.

b. Interconnections. The term cross-connection is generally applied to a physical connection between a public and private source of water. The term interconnection applies to any physical connection or arrangement of pipes between two otherwise separate water-piping systems whereby water can flow from one to the other. The use of interconnections should be avoided except where the water is of the same origin or of equally good quality.

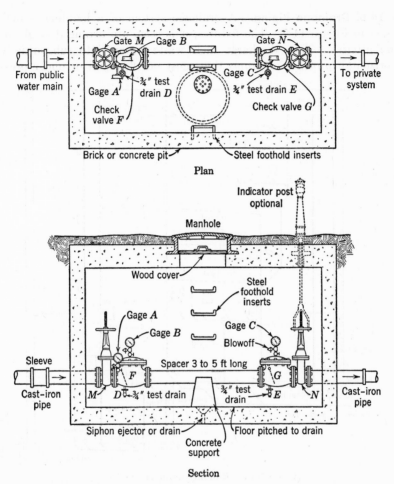

Plan

Section

Figure 14-6. Cross-connection between municipal water supply and private (industrial) water supply protected by double check-valve installation. To test installation: (1) close gates M and N; (2) open test drain D, and observe gages A and B; (3) open test drain E, and observe gage C. If check valves F and G are tight, gage A will drop to zero; gages B and C will drop only slightly owing to compression of rubber gaskets on check valves F and G.

Drainage

14-6. Drainage Piping. A drainage system of a building is outlined in Figure 14-7. The fixtures, it is seen, are arranged singly or in batteries. They discharge their waste waters into substantially horizontal *branches* or *drains* that must not flow full or under pres-

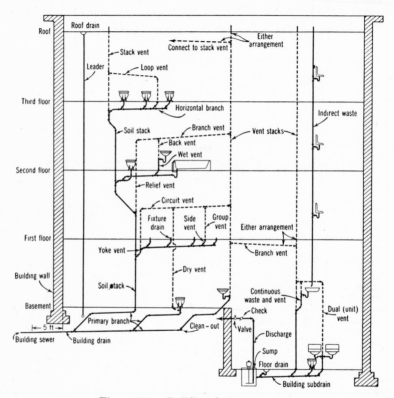

Figure 14-7. Building drainage system.

sure. Otherwise, tributary fixtures would not discharge freely, and their protecting *traps* might become unsealed. The horizontal drains empty into substantially vertical *stacks*. These, too, must not flow full, if waste waters are not to back up into fixtures on the lower floors. The drainage stacks discharge into the *building drain* which, 5 ft outside of the building, becomes the *building sewer* (or *house sewer*) and empties into the street sewer (see Figures 14-8 and 14-9). Drains and stacks that convey human excreta (with or without other wastes) are called *soil pipes* and *soil stacks* respectively. If they carry other wastes only, they are called *waste pipes* and *waste stacks* instead. Waste pipes with air gaps, called indirect wastes (Figure 14-7), are employed to protect refrigerators, stills, sterilizers, and similar equipment against back-flow from the drainage system.

Traps form part of the drainage piping or are built into fixtures, such as water closets. The traps hold a water seal that obstructs, and essentially prevents, the passage of foul odors and noxious gases, as well as insects and other vermin, from the drainage pipes and

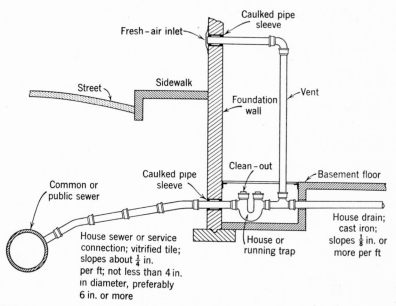

Figure 14-8. Connecting building drainage system to sewer. House, or running, trap may be installed or omitted.

sewers into the building. Discharge of fixtures sends water rushing into the drains and tumbling down the stacks. Air is dragged along by the water, and air pressures above or below atmospheric would be created within the system and might unseal the traps were it not for the provision of *vents*. These lead from the traps to the atmosphere and allow the air pressures in the drainage pipes to become equalized.

Various trap designs are shown in Figure 14-10. They include fixture traps in which resistance to siphonage is created not by venting but by one or more of the following: (1) mechanical devices similar to check valves; (2) tortuous passages; (3) large volumes of water; and (4) increased depths of seal. In most of these traps, grease and solids quickly render mechanisms inoperative or clog waterways and obstruct flow. Vent arrangements are shown in Figure 14-7. Ordi-

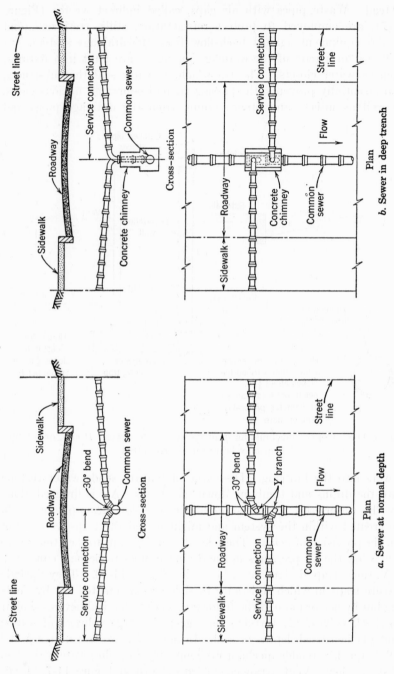

Figure 14-9. Service connections to public sewer.

a. Sewer at normal depth

b. Sewer in deep trench

narily, public authorities do not permit the use of unvented fixture traps, except in situations in which vents are impractical and the unsealing of the trap is neither probable nor seriously objectionable. The *building trap* shown in Figure 14-8 separates the drainage system

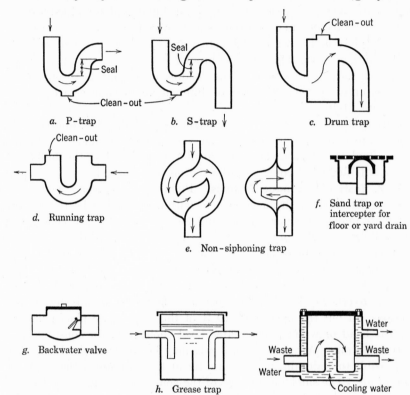

a. P-trap   *b.* S-trap ↓   *c.* Drum trap

d. Running trap   *e.* Non-siphoning trap   *f.* Sand trap or intercepter for floor or yard drain

g. Backwater valve   *h.* Grease trap or intercepter   *i.* Water-cooled grease trap or intercepter

Figure 14-10.   Traps and intercepters.

as a whole from the sewerage system proper.   Its use is generally confined to cold climates.

The waste water from fixtures and floor drains that lie below the level of the public sewer must be lifted by ejectors or pumps (see Figure 14-7).   Sumps or receiving tanks facilitate automatic operation.   Sand and other solids from cellars or yards are kept out of the drainage system by *sand intercepters,* grease by *grease intercepters,* and oil by *oil intercepters.*   These devices are also called separators or traps.   They take the form of small settling, skimming, or holding tanks.   The use of grease intercepters below kitchen sinks is confined, today, largely to hotels, camps, and institutions. Cooling the intercepter aids grease separation. Public authorities may require the installation of oil intercepters in garages, machine shops, cleaning and dyeing establishments, and similar enterprises. The substances intercepted are always objectionable and often inflammable and explosive. It is wise to keep them out of sewers and away from sewage-treatment works and receiving waters. Waste waters from toilets and urinals should not be permitted to pass through intercepters for grease and oil. *Backwater valves* prevent the flooding of basements through the backing up of sewage. Sketches of different appurtenances are shown in Figure 14-10.

Cast iron, galvanized steel or wrought iron, lead, brass, and copper piping are employed for drains and vents above ground. Building drains laid below ground are made of cast iron. For the building sewer, vitrified-clay, concrete, or cast-iron pipe is used.

14-7. Tests of Drainage Systems. Plumbing regulations generally require (1) that the drainage system within a building be tested for tightness under water or air pressure before the pipes are concealed or the fixtures are set in place and (2) that the combined drainage and vent system be subjected to a smoke test, or air-pressure test, after the fixture traps have been connected. The water test is applied by closing all but the highest opening and filling the system with water until it overflows through this opening. If the system is tested in sections, all but the uppermost 10 ft of the system are placed under a 10-ft head of water. The water level should remain constant for at least 15 min. Air pressure of 5 psig may be substituted. It should be possible to maintain this pressure for at least 15 min without addition of air. The smoke or air test of the completed drainage and vent piping is conducted under a pressure of 1 in. of water after all trap seals have been filled with water. The smoke is produced by burning oily waste, tar paper, or similar material in the combustion chamber of a "smoke machine." Chemical smokes are not satisfactory.

14-8. Design of Drainage Pipes. Hydraulically, the design of the drainage pipes of a plumbing system is not as straightforward and exact as that of the water-supply pipes. Flow is seldom uniform and steady, and the presence of air within the piping introduces complicating pneumatic problems. Questions to be answered by the designer relate to (*a*) drainage load or rate of flow, (*b*) capacity of horizontal branches or drains, (*c*) capacity of vertical stacks, and (*d*) capacity of vents.

a. Drainage Load. If flooding of fixtures is to be avoided, the rate of discharge of fixtures must equal the rate at which water is supplied to them. In the operation of water closets, flush tanks fill slowly; but their rate of discharge equals that of flush valves. The rates of discharge of common fixtures are assembled in Table 14-4 together

TABLE 14-4. Rate of Discharge of Common Fixtures and Minimum Sizes of Traps and Fixture Drains

Fixture	Number of fixture units, cfm Private	Public	Minimum size of trap and drain, in.
Wash basin	1	2	1¼
Water closet	6	10	. . .
Urinal			
wall or stall	. .	5	2
pedestal	. .	10	2
Bathtub	2	4	1½
Shower head	2	4	2
Bathroom group	8	. .	. . .
(with separate shower stall)	10	. .	. . .
Kitchen sink *	2	. .	1½
Laundry trays, 2 or 3 with single			
trap *	3	. .	1½
Service sink	. .	3	2
Combination sink and laundry tray *	3	. .	1½

* These fixtures may be omitted in determining total flow tributary to soil pipes but not to separate waste lines.

Use drains no smaller than the outlet of traps integral with the fixture.

Use 2-in. trap and drain for floor drains, hotel or public sinks, service sinks, and trough urinals.

Use 1½-in. trap and drain for dishwasher sink.

Use 1¼-in. trap and drain for drinking fountain and for small sink in pantry or bar.

For sewage ejector or sump pump allow 50 fixture units for each 25 gpm.

with the minimum sizes of traps and fixture drains necessary to empty the fixtures at the stated rate.

As is true for the water-supply demand, the drainage load placed on different parts of the system does not equal the sum of the rates of discharge of the individual fixtures. Not all of them will discharge at the same instant or in such manner as to concentrate the full flow at a given point in the system. The larger the system, the smaller becomes the intensity of flow relative to the total fixture discharge and the steadier is that flow. Building-drainage systems, in this respect, behave, on a small scale, like sewerage systems. The time factor complicates the estimation of a reasonable load for a given number of fixtures. It is affected by the distribution of fixtures within the system as well as the arrangement of piping. Probable loads are greater for an individual horizontal branch than for the stack into which it discharges. Similarly, these loads are also greater for an individual stack than for the building drain in which it ends. Therefore, allowable ratios of fixture load to design load are relatively small for horizontal drains, larger for stacks, and greatest for building drains. All these complicating factors make it impossible to show the relation between fixture discharge and drainage load by simple curves similar to those presented for water supply in Figure 14-4.

b. *Capacity of Drains.* Hydraulically, horizontal branches are open channels. Although flow through them may be non-uniform and unsteady, performance requirements and costs are generally not so stringent as to require consideration of this possibility in their design. Flow may safely be formulated in simple terms by Manning's formula ($n = 0.012$), for example. Velocities should be self-cleaning ones— in the neighborhood of 2 fps, therefore; but velocities in excess of 3 fps and above 4 fps are advisable for greasy wastes. A 4-in. drain is the minimum size ordinarily permitted when water-closet discharges are to be carried. Its capacity when laid on a slope of $\frac{1}{8}$ in. per ft is 160 fixture units.

Lateral drains and stacks may contribute head to main drains, such as the building drain, and increase their velocity of flow. Bends and running traps slow down the flow and may cause drains to fill. This produces back pressure and fills vents with waste water. To prevent clogging, no main pipe should be smaller than any of its tributaries.

c. *Capacity of Stacks.* The flow pattern of stacks is made up of a sheet of water that hugs the wall of the stack in a ring of fairly uniform thickness. The falling water drags air along, and a maximum velocity of both air and water is reached when the weight of falling water equals the frictional resistance encountered, i.e., when the loss of head per unit length is unity. The following equation is based upon the interpretation by Dawson and Kalinske [12] of experimental findings. In terms of Manning's formula,

$$v_{\max} = 8.7(Q/d)^{2/5} \qquad\qquad 14\text{-}2$$

where $v_{\max}$ is the maximum velocity in feet per second, Q is the rate of discharge in cubic feet per minute or fixture units, and d is the diameter of stack in inches.

This equation may be derived by substituting $n = 0.006$, $r = \dfrac{Q/v}{\pi d}$,

[12] "Hydraulics and Pneumatics of the Plumbing Drainage System," *Univ. Iowa Studies in Eng. Bull.* 10 (1937).

and $s = 1$ in Manning's formula and solving for v. The ratio Q/v is a measure of the area of the ring of water within the stack. In the calculation of stack velocities and capacities, it is generally assumed that the falling water will occupy $\frac{1}{4}$ the cross-section. At this ratio maximum air flow through vent openings has been recorded.[12] Limiting the flow to that which fills $\frac{1}{4}$ the cross-section controls noise and keeps the building drain from flowing full. The permissible loadings recommended by the National Bureau of Standards for a 4-in. stack are 240 fixture units for buildings of one or two stories (one or two branch intervals) and 600 fixture units for buildings three or more stories in height (three or more branch intervals). For a 3-in. drain, the corresponding values are but 30 and 80 fixture units.

The rush of water from upper floors and the carrying away of air that is dragged along reduce the pressure in the upper portion of a stack below atmospheric. The subsequent piling up of this air at the foot of the stack raises the pressure above atmospheric in the lower portion. If the system is unvented, pressure differentials of 30 in. or more of water may be produced. These differentials are increased still more if the house drain flows full.

Drains entering a stack through which water from higher floors is flowing at high velocity must either discharge their drainage waters through the established sheet of water in the stack, or they must deflect this sheet. A back pressure must be built up to do so. It may be sufficiently great to back up drainage waters into fixtures such as shower stalls or bathtubs and to fill vents.

d. Capacity of Vents. As previously indicated, the air carried along by waste waters in drainage piping must be supplied and removed through a system of vents without creating negative or positive pressures in excess of (and preferably about half as great as) the depth of the water seals in the fixture traps, i.e., about 1 in. Air and water velocities are almost equal. The air flow that must be supplied by vents is actually somewhat smaller than the total air flowing down the stack (ordinarily 3 times the rate of stack discharge), because some air enters through the top of the stack. The length of vent that will supply or remove this flow of air with a drop in pressure of 1 in. of water may be determined from formulas for air flow that are discussed in Section 25-14. Because of the small pressure differential, it is reasonable to assume that the air is incompressible and that the length of vent is given sufficiently closely by the following modification of the Darcy-Weisbach formula:

$$l = \frac{40}{f} \frac{d^5}{Q^2} \qquad 14\text{-}3$$

where l is the length of vent in feet causing a drop in pressure of 1 in. of water; d is the diameter of vent in inches; Q is the rate of air flow in cubic feet per minute, or approximately 3 times the rate of waste discharge; [13] and f is the friction factor (approximately 0.01 for rough pipe and 0.005 for smooth pipe).

The National Bureau of Standards recommends (1) that vent stacks or main vents have a diameter at least ½ that of the soil or waste stack served by them and (2) that their size be increased if their length is appreciable and the stack load is great.

Example 14-2. If the two-story dwelling of Example 14-1 has its two bathroom groups on the second floor and its additional water closet and wash basin, kitchen sink, and laundry tray on the first floor, find (a) the drainage load, (b) the diameter of the house drain, (c) the diameter of the soil stack, and (d) the diameter of the vent stack.

a. Drainage load (From Table 14-4):

		Fixture units
3 water closets	@ 6 =	18
3 wash basins	@ 1 =	3
3 bathtubs	@ 2 =	6
1 kitchen sink	@ 2 =	2
1 laundry tray	@ 3 =	3
Total		32

b. Diameter of house drain: Use a 4-in. drain; capacity, 160 fixture units. A smaller drain cannot be used because water-closet discharge is carried.

c. Diameter of soil stack: Use a 4-in. stack.

d. Diameter of main vent: The minimum diameter must equal half the diameter of the soil stack, or ½ × 4 = 2 in. From Equation 14-3, a 2-in. main vent may be 30 ft long, a 2½-in. main vent 95 ft long.

14-9. Storm Drainage. If there is a separate system of sanitary sewers, the storm water that falls upon roofs and paved areas is carried away through separate storm drains into the public storm-drainage system or into the public gutter. Where the combined system of sewerage is used, roof and yard drains may be led into the building drain or building sewer through a Y-fitting at least 10 ft downstream from any primary branch. Separation of the two systems, however, is preferable.

The amount of storm runoff depends upon local hydrological conditions. Rates of rainfall and runoff of 3 or 4 in. per hr are often accepted as a basis for calculations of runoff. A drained area of 240

[13] More exactly, $Q_{\text{air}} = 60(\pi d^2/576 - 60Q_{\text{water}}/v_{\text{max}})v_{\text{max}}$, where v_{max} is obtained from Equation 14-2.

or 180 sq ft respectively then delivers 1 cfm or a fixture unit. Allowance should be made for intercepted, slanting rain water that strikes walls projecting above the roof.

Hydraulically, roof gutters are open channels to which water is being added in proportion to the roof area tributary to them. Rates of discharge, therefore, are not the same throughout the length of the gutter. Flow conditions are described most precisely in the terms later shown to apply to lateral spillway channels or to wash-water gutters of rapid sand filters (Section 24-10). Manning's formula ($n = 0.012$) yields the values shown in Table 14-5, for steady flow in semicircular gutters, with a fall of $\frac{1}{16}$ in. per ft, draining roof areas upon which rain is falling at a rate of 4 in. per hr.

TABLE 14-5. Gutter Diameter and Roof Area Drained

Diameter of gutter, in.	3	4	5	6	7	8	10	12
Maximum roof area, sq ft	170	360	625	960	1,380	1,990	3,600	6,800

For slopes s greater than $\frac{1}{16}$ in. per ft these areas must be multiplied by the square root of the ratio of s to $\frac{1}{16}$, i.e., by $\sqrt{16s}$. Slopes much less than $\frac{1}{16}$ in. per ft should not be used. Roof gutters are made of metal, wood, or other suitable material.

Leaders that are placed in the walls of buildings or in service shafts are made of the same material as the sanitary drainage piping. Outside leaders are generally constructed of sheet metal. They should discharge into the drainage system through a cast-iron pipe extending 1 ft or more above ground level.

Leaders or connecting pipes laid on a slope of $\frac{1}{2}$ in. per ft or more should be able to drain $2 \times \sqrt{16} \times \frac{1}{2} = 5.7$ times as much roof area as a semicircular gutter of the same diameter. Calculated areas and allowable areas suggested by the National Bureau of Standards are presented in Table 14-6.

TABLE 14-6. Leader Diameter and Roof Area Drained

Diameter, in.	2	2½	3	4	5	6	8
Calculated area, sq ft	330	640	1,000	2,000	3,600	5,500	11,300
Allowable area, sq ft	500	960	1,500	3,100	5,400	8,400	17,400

Example 14-3. A roof area of 1,000 sq ft is tributary to a gutter laid on a slope of $\frac{1}{8}$ in. per ft served by a single vertical leader. Find the required size of gutter and leader for a maximum rainfall of 3 in. per hr.

a. A 3-in. rain on 1,000 sq ft is equivalent to a 4-in. rain on $\frac{3}{4} \times 1,000 = 750$ sq ft.

b. A gutter laid on a slope of $\frac{1}{8}$ in. per ft will drain a roof area $\sqrt{16 \times \frac{1}{8}} = 1.414$ times as large as a gutter laid on a slope of $\frac{1}{16}$ in. per ft. Hence the equivalent roof area is $750/1.414 = 530$ sq ft.

c. An equivalent area of 530 sq ft is safely drained by a half-round gutter 5 in. in diameter.

d. An equivalent area of 750 sq ft is safely served by a leader $2\frac{1}{2}$ in. in diameter.

The collection of rain water from roof areas for purposes of water supply is discussed in Sections 2-4, 30-4, and 30-5.

15-1. General Considerations. A general description of sewerage systems has been presented in Chapter 3, and the quantities of sewage and storm water to be dealt with have been discussed in Sections 5-10 and 5-11 and in Chapter 7 respectively. It is the purpose of the present chapter to consider in greater detail those hydraulic elements of sewers and their appurtenances that are of significance in the design of both separate and combined sewerage systems.

Hydraulically, a waste-water disposal system differs from a water-supply system in three essentials: (1) the conduits employed are almost exclusively of the free-flow type; (2) the flow of waste water is almost without exception unsteady and non-uniform; and (3) relatively large amounts of floating and suspended matter are impressed upon the flowing waters. Sewers accordingly are designed (1) for open-channel flow; (2) to satisfy the requirements of unsteady and non-uniform flow; and (3) to transport the waste materials in such fashion that their deposition and decomposition will be avoided or kept within reason.

As shown in Section 5-2, the design period for the main collectors, outfalls, and intercepters of a sewerage system, because of the cost and difficulty of enlargement or supplementation, is as much as 50 yr. Rates of flow, therefore, are subject not merely to the seasonal, daily, and hourly fluctuations that are normal to any one year but also to the changes imposed by expansion of the system and growth of population from the time when the system is first placed in operation to the end of the design period. Systems that include storm drainage are subject, furthermore, to the chance variations of runoff from rainfall and melting snow and ice. Although sanitary sewerage systems share their changing capacity requirements with water-distribution systems, the hydraulic balance of the latter is less delicate. They do not need to maintain self-cleansing velocities but can, with relative impunity, vary their velocities over a wide range of values and adjust their hydraulic gradients to the passage of time. The hydraulic gradients of sewers, by contrast, are, in essence, set once and for all when the sewers are built.

15-2. Limiting Velocities of Flow. Fecal solids, kitchen refuse, and other household wastes are flushed into sanitary sewers. Sand, gravel, and the debris of streets enter storm sewers through curb inlets. Combined sewers carry the gross solids received from both of these sources. The heaviest materials are swept along the sewer invert and constitute the "bed load" of the channel. The lightest materials float along the water surface. If the velocity of flow is too low, the heaviest solids are deposited on the bottom and the lightest are left stranded at the water's edge. If the velocity is too high, the invert is eroded. Both deposition and erosion are functions of the tractive force of the moving stream of sewage or storm water.

The average intensity of tractive force exerted by flowing water on its channel or on deposits within it equals the weight of water per unit surface area of channel (or deposit) times the loss of head per unit length.[1] Since the volume of water per unit surface area of channel equals the hydraulic radius of the channel, we may write

$$\tau = \gamma r s \qquad\qquad 15\text{-}1$$

where τ is the intensity of tractive force, γ is the specific weight of water at the temperature of the sewage or storm water; r is the hydraulic radius of the filled section; and s is the slope of the invert or loss of head per unit length of channel when flow is uniform and the water surface parallels the invert.

a. Damaging Velocities. Since the velocity of flow in a sewer is a function of r and s, we may replace these terms in Equation 15-1 by a velocity term. Using the Chezy formula, $v = c\sqrt{rs}$, for example,

$$\tau = \gamma(v/c)^2 \qquad\qquad 15\text{-}2$$

Here v is the velocity and c is the Chezy coefficient. The intensity of tractive force is seen to vary as the square of the velocity. In order to avoid erosion of the sewer invert, an effort is generally made to hold velocities below 12 fps for tile sewers and 8 fps for concrete drains. Assuming a value of $c = 100$, the intensity of tractive force of water flowing at a velocity of 8 fps is about 0.4 lb per sq ft; at 12 fps it becomes almost 1 lb per sq ft.

---

[1] This tractive force is analogous, in a sense, to the friction of a body sliding down an inclined plane, the sine of small angles being equal to their tangents.

Of the ceramic materials used in sewer construction, vitrified tile and glazed brick are very resistant to wear. Building brick, on the other hand, is easily eroded. Concrete, too, is subject to abrasion. The inverts of large concrete or brick sewers are, therefore, often protected by vitrified-tile liners, glazed or paving brick, or granite blocks. Because of the greater content of abrading materials in storm-water runoff, storm drains and combined sewers are more subject to damage than are sanitary sewers.

b. Transporting Velocities. If sewers and their appurtenances are to be self-cleansing, they must flow at velocities that will transport the solid matter discharged into them. The required velocities can be derived from Equation 15-1 as follows:

If the tractive force is sufficient to bring about a general movement of the bed material, it must at least equal the resistance to motion of the particles constituting the bottom deposits. In the absence of friction between particles, the intensity of resistance would be proportional to the effective weight (or weight in water) of the particles per unit surface area of the particles. If γ_s is the unit weight of particles of volume V, surface area A, and diameter d, the intensity of resistance to motion would be $(\gamma_s - \gamma)V/A = k(\gamma_s - \gamma)d$. For a sphere, the value of V/A is $\frac{1}{6}d$; for particles of irregular shape, V/A may be set equal to kd. Here k is fundamentally a measure of shape. But it will suit our convenience to let it include also the cohesiveness of the particles and the effectiveness of scour. In this sense, $\gamma rs = (\gamma_s - \gamma)kd$, or $rs = \dfrac{\gamma_s - \gamma}{\gamma} kd$. If follows that the invert slope at which a sewer will be self-cleansing is

$$ s = \frac{k}{r}\frac{\gamma_s - \gamma}{\gamma} d \qquad 15\text{-}3 $$

In accordance with the Chezy formula, furthermore, the velocity v of a stream that will transport the particles is given by the equation

$$ v = c\sqrt{k\frac{\gamma_s - \gamma}{\gamma} d} \qquad 15\text{-}4 $$

Here, the value of c for the conduit or stream must be chosen with due regard to the presence of deposited solids. If the Kutter coefficient of roughness n is to be introduced into Equation 15-4, the pertinent expressions for c in the Kutter or Manning formulas (Equations 15-7 and 15-8) are substituted. In terms of the Manning formula, for example,

$$v = \frac{1.486}{n} r^{\frac{1}{6}} \sqrt{k \frac{\gamma_s - \gamma}{\gamma} d} \qquad 15\text{-}5$$

Substitution of the Darcy-Weisbach friction factor f on the basis of $c = \sqrt{8g/f}$, yields a formula derived by Camp from studies by Shields:

$$v = \sqrt{\frac{8k}{f} g \frac{\gamma_s - \gamma}{\gamma} d} = \sqrt{\frac{8k}{f} g(s_s - 1)d} \qquad 15\text{-}6$$

Here s_s is the specific gravity of the particles and $(s_s - 1) = (\gamma_s - \gamma)/\gamma$ closely. As indicated for c, the values of f and n, too, must reflect the roughness of the fouled, rather than the clean, channel.

The magnitude of the sediment characteristic k must be determined by experiment. Values reported by Shields range from 0.04 for the initiation of scour to 0.8 or more for adequate cleansing.

Example 15-1. Find the minimum velocity and gradient required to transport coarse sand through a sewer 12 in. in diameter.

Coarse sand has a diameter of 0.1 cm (0.1/30.48 ft) and a specific gravity of 2.65.

Neglecting changes in the density of water with temperature and assuming values of $k = 0.04$ and $n = 0.012$:

By Equation 15-5:

$$v = \frac{1.486}{0.012} \left(\frac{1}{4}\right)^{\frac{1}{6}} \sqrt{0.04 \frac{(2.65 - 1.00)}{1.00} \frac{0.1}{30.48}} = 1.45 \text{ fps}$$

By Equation 15-3:

$$s = \frac{0.04}{0.25} \frac{2.65 - 1.00}{1.00} \frac{0.1}{30.48} = 0.00087$$

As shown in Section 3-4, sanitary sewers are generally given a minimum velocity of 2 fps, and storm sewers one of 2.5 fps. Since the diameter of particles transported varies as the square of the velocity, it may be assumed from Example 15-1 that under the conditions there stated the diameters of the particles moved by these velocities would be 0.19 cm (fine gravel) and 0.30 cm (medium gravel) respectively. The fact that the velocity required for adequate cleansing may have to be about 4.5 times as great is of interest in connection with the flushing of sewers for cleansing purposes.

15-3. Flow in Filled Sewers. In the absence of precise information on the roughness factors that attach to theoretical formulations of the flow in open channels, engineers continue to base the hydraulic design of sewers, like that of water conduits flowing under pressure (Section 12-2), upon suitable empirical formulas. Two such formulas are in common use in North America: the Kutter formula which dates back to 1869 and the Manning formula of 1890. Both of them evaluate the velocity or discharge coefficient c in the Chezy formula and include a coefficient of roughness n which is of identical magnitude.

Using the same notation that was employed for the Hazen-Williams formula (Section 12-2), the two expressions for c may be written as follows: according to Kutter,

$$c = \frac{41.65 + \dfrac{0.00281}{s} + \dfrac{1.811}{n}}{1 + \left(41.65 + \dfrac{0.00281}{s}\right)\dfrac{n}{\sqrt{r}}} \qquad 15\text{-}7$$

according to Manning,

$$c = \frac{1.486}{n} r^{1/6} \qquad 15\text{-}8$$

Manning's value satisfies experimental findings just as well as the clumsier formulation of Kutter and Ganguillet, and it lends itself more satisfactorily to mathematical manipulation, arithmetic computations, and graphic representation. Manning's formula is, therefore, used by preference within these pages in all matters relating to open-channel flow. An example of this use has already been given in the preceding section of this chapter.

In its complete form, Manning's formula reads as follows:

$$v = \frac{1.486}{n} r^{2/3} s^{1/2} \qquad 15\text{-}9$$

It is seen to be akin to the Hazen-Williams formula in concept and, similarly, is readily adapted to flow in circular conduits and evaluation of rates of discharge.

Calculation of the velocity of flow and rate of discharge of standard circular sewers by the Manning formula is simplified by using the values for $1.486R^{2/3}$ and $1.486AR^{2/3}$ shown in Table 15-1.[2]

---

[2] Capital letters are employed in this book to identify the hydraulic elements of sewers that flow full; lower-case letters for partially filled sewers.

TABLE 15-1. Velocity and Discharge of Circular Sewers Flowing Full

$S^{1/2}/N = 1$ in the Manning Formula.

Diameter, D, in.	Area, A, sq ft	Velocity, V_0, fps	Discharge, Q_0, cfs
6	0.1963	0.3715	0.07293
8	0.3491	0.4500	0.1571
10	0.5455	0.5222	0.2848
12	0.7854	0.5897	0.4632
15	1.2272	0.6843	0.8398
18	1.7671	0.7728	1.366
21	2.4053	0.8564	2.060
24	3.1416	0.9361	2.941
27	3.9761	1.0116	4.026
30	4.9087	1.0863	5.332
36	7.0686	1.2267	8.671
42	9.6211	1.3594	13.08
48	12.5664	1.4860	18.67
54	15.9043	1.6074	25.56
60	19.6350	1.7244	33.86

For given values of S and N multiply velocity V_0 and discharge Q_0 by $S^{1/2}/N$ in order to obtain V and Q respectively.

Like the selection of C in the Hazen-Williams formula, the choice of a suitable value of the roughness factor N is of utmost importance but must usually be left to the judgment of the designer. Of assistance in this connection can be the values in Table 15-2 which are taken from a list compiled by Horton[3] from reliable experimental data.

TABLE 15-2. Values of the Kutter Coefficient of Friction N for Different Conduit Materials (after Horton)

| Conduit material | Condition of interior surface | | | |
	Best	Good	Fair	Bad
Tile pipe, vitrified (glazed)	0.010	0.012	0.014	0.017
unglazed	0.011	0.013	0.015	0.017
Concrete pipe	0.012	0.013	0.015	0.016
Cast-iron pipe, coated	0.011	0.012	0.013	.....
Brick sewers, glazed	0.011	0.012	0.013	0.015
unglazed	0.012	0.013	0.015	0.017
Steel pipe, welded	0.010	0.011	0.013	.....
riveted	0.013	0.015	0.017	.....
Concrete-lined channels	0.012	0.014	0.016	0.018

[3] R. E. Horton, "Some Better Kutter's Formula Coefficients," *Eng. News, 75,* 373 (1916).

The values listed for fair conditions of the interior surface are widely employed as the basis of design for sewers flowing partially full as well as full. Studies by Wilcox [4] on 8-in. sewer pipe and by Yarnell and Woodward [5] on clay and concrete drain tile 4 to 12 in. in diameter have recorded values of $N = 0.0095$ to 0.011 in Manning's formula when the pipes were clean and flowing full. For partially filled sections, however, n was observed to increase by as much as 25% when the depth of flow dropped to 0.4 of the full depth. In the absence of actual measurements of discharge of substantially identical pipes, a design value [6] of $N = 0.012$ is suggested for the filled sections of tile and concrete sewers 6 to 24 in. in diameter. For larger sizes, the value of N may be dropped to 0.011.

The minimum grades S and capacities Q of sewers up to 24 in. in diameter flowing full at velocities V of 2.0, 2.5, and 3.0 fps are shown in Table 15-3 for a coefficient of roughness of 0.012.

TABLE 15-3. Minimum Grades and Capacities of Circular Sewers
Flowing Full

$N = 0.012$ in the Manning Formula.

Diameter, in.	6	8	10	12	15	18	21	24
				$V = 2.0$ fps				
$S \times 10^3$	4.18	2.85	2.12	1.66	1.23	0.969	0.788	0.657
Q, cfs	0.393	0.698	1.09	1.57	2.45	3.53	4.81	6.28
				$V = 2.5$ fps				
$S \times 10^3$	6.51	4.44	3.30	2.58	1.93	1.51	1.23	1.02
Q, cfs	0.491	0.873	1.36	1.96	3.07	4.42	6.01	7.85
				$V = 3.0$ fps				
$S \times 10^3$	9.20	6.27	4.77	3.73	2.78	2.17	1.78	1.48
Q, cfs	0.589	1.05	1.64	2.36	3.68	5.30	7.22	9.42

15-4. Flow in Partially Filled Sewers. The upper reaches of sanitary sewers generally flow at shallow depths, because the pipe size employed is relatively large whereas the number of houses served is relatively small. Other portions of the system are planned to flow full only towards the end of their design period and then but spasmodically at times of maximum flow. Discharge ratios varying from 4:1 to as

[4] E. R. Wilcox, *Univ. Wash. Eng. Exp. Sta. Ser. Bull.* 27 (1924).

[5] D. L. Yarnell and S. M. Woodward, *U. S. Dept. Agr. Bull.* 854 (1920).

[6] "Report of Committee to Study Limiting Velocities of Flow in Sewers," *J. Boston Soc. Civil Engrs.*, *29*, 286 (1942)

high as 18:1 are thereby established for sanitary sewers. For this reason, the upper reaches of sanitary sewers are often designed on a basis of flowing full at a velocity of 3.0 fps rather than 2.5 or 2.0 fps. Even greater variations in requisite capacity are registered by combined and storm sewers. The design of sewerage systems, therefore, is concerned with the hydraulic performance of partially filled as well

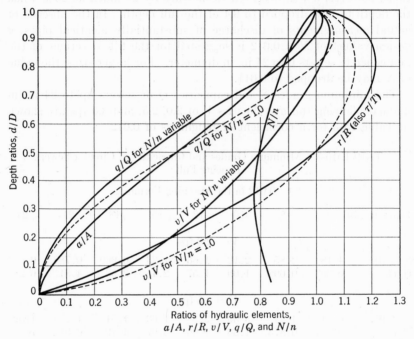

Figure 15-1. Basic hydraulic elements of circular sewers for all values of roughness and slope.

as filled sections and with the maintenance, insofar as practicable, of self-cleansing velocities throughout the range of expected flows.

A flow formula such as Manning's has within it the following variables: Q or v, r or a/p (p = wetted perimeter), s or h/l, and n. Together these variables constitute the hydraulic elements of a conduit of given shape. For any one shape and for a fixed coefficient of roughness and invert slope, these elements vary in individual magnitude with the depth d of the filled section. For purposes of generalization, this variation is conveniently expressed in terms of the ratio of each element of the filled section (indicated by a lower-case letter) to the corresponding element of the full section (indicated by a capital letter). This is done for a sewer of circular cross-section in Figure 15-1, the variation of n with depth suggested by Camp[7] being plotted as the reciprocal of n/N for convenience of calculation.

Of the elements shown in Figure 15-1, those of area and hydraulic radius are static, or elements of shape, and those of roughness, velocity, and discharge are dynamic, or elements of flow. The basis for the computation of both groups of elements, with the exception of n, is shown in Table 15-4. The geometric elements of circular sewers are solely functions of the angle θ or through it of the depth ratio d/D. The dynamic elements are also functions of roughness and invert slope. If flows and velocities are calculated from the Manning formula, the slope factor cancels out of the ratios and the roughness factor appears as the reciprocal of n/N. Since definitive values of the variation of n with depth are yet to be determined, the roughness ratio is presented as a separate item in Table 15-4 as well as in Figure 15-1. In order to

TABLE 15-4. Hydraulic Elements of a Sewer of Circular Cross-Section

(Uncorrected for variations in roughness with depth.)

Central angle: $\cos \tfrac{1}{2}\theta = 1 - 2d/D$; $\sin \tfrac{1}{2}\theta = 2d/D$

Area: $\dfrac{D^2}{4}\left(\dfrac{\pi\theta}{360} - \dfrac{\sin\theta}{2}\right)$

Wetted perimeter: $\pi D\theta/360$

Hydraulic radius: $\dfrac{D}{4}\left(1 - \dfrac{360\sin\theta}{2\pi\theta}\right)$

Velocity: $\dfrac{1.486}{n} r^{\frac{2}{3}} s^{\frac{1}{2}}$

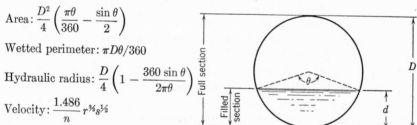

Depth	Area	Hydraulic radius			Velocity	Discharge	Rough-
					v/V	q/Q	ness
d/D	a/A	r/R	R/r	$(r/R)^{\frac{1}{6}}$	for $N/n = 1.0$		N/n
(1)	(2)	(3)	(4)	(5)	(6)	(7)	(8)
1.000	1.000	1.000	1.000	1.000	1.000	1.000	1.000
0.900	0.949	1.192	0.839	1.030	1.124	1.066	0.93
0.800	0.858	1.217	0.822	1.033	1.140	0.988	0.89
0.700	0.748	1.185	0.843	1.029	1.120	0.988	0.85
0.600	0.626	1.110	0.900	1.018	1.072	0.838	0.82
0.500	0.500	1.000	1.00	1.000	1.000	0.671	0.80
0.400	0.373	0.857	1.17	0.975	0.902	0.500	0.79
0.300	0.252	0.684	1.46	0.939	0.776	0.337	0.78
0.200	0.143	0.482	2.07	0.886	0.615	0.196	0.79
0.100	0.052	0.254	3.94	0.796	0.401	0.088	0.81
0.000	0.000	.....	.....	.....	.....	0.021	.....
						0.000	

[7] T. R. Camp, "Design of Sewers to Facilitate Flow," *Sewage Works J.*, 18. 3 (1946).

facilitate calculations that allow for roughness changing with depth, curves of v/V and q/Q for values of N/n that change with depth have been made the principal lines of reference in Figure 15-1.

As related to the depth ratio d/D, the calculated ratios shown in Table 15-4 and plotted in Figure 15-1 are:

Column 2: $\dfrac{a}{A} = \dfrac{\theta}{360} - \dfrac{\sin \theta}{2\pi}$.

Column 3: $\dfrac{r}{R} = 1 - \dfrac{360 \sin \theta}{2\pi\theta}$.

Column 6: $\dfrac{v}{V} = \dfrac{N}{n} \left(\dfrac{r}{R}\right)^{\frac{2}{3}} \left(\dfrac{s}{S}\right)^{\frac{1}{2}}$, or $\left(\dfrac{r}{R}\right)^{\frac{2}{3}}$ for $n = N$ and $s = S$.

Column 7: $\dfrac{q}{Q} = \dfrac{N}{n}\dfrac{a}{A} \left(\dfrac{r}{R}\right)^{\frac{2}{3}} \left(\dfrac{s}{S}\right)^{\frac{1}{2}}$, or $\dfrac{a}{A} \left(\dfrac{r}{R}\right)^{\frac{2}{3}}$ for $n = N$ and $s = S$.

As shown in Table 15-4 and Figure 15-1, the velocity of flow in the partially filled, circular section will equal or exceed that in the full section whenever the sewer flows more than half full provided that there is no increase in roughness at lowered depth. Where there is such an increase, velocities equal to, or greater than, the velocity at full depth are restricted, in accordance with Camp's values of n, to the upper 20% of the depth only. This does not imply that sewers flowing at depths between 0.5 and 0.8 full must be placed on steeper grades if they are to be as self-cleaning as sewers flowing full. The grade actually required and the associated velocity and discharge are functions of the intensity of the tractive force. This involves the coefficient of friction as well as the velocity of flow. The needed hydraulic elements can be computed from Equation 15-1 on the assumption that sewers flowing at partial depth will remain as self-cleaning as sewers flowing full if the intensity of the tractive force on sewer deposits remains the same at all depths of flow, or

$$\tau = T = \gamma rs = \gamma RS$$

Hence

$$\frac{s}{S} = \frac{R}{r} \quad \text{or} \quad s = \frac{R}{r}S \qquad\qquad 15\text{-}10$$

and the induced self-cleaning velocity v_s and rate of flow q_s are determined by the Manning formula as:

$$\frac{v_s}{V} = \frac{N}{n}\left(\frac{r}{R}\right)^{\frac{2}{3}}\left(\frac{s}{S}\right)^{\frac{1}{2}} \qquad\qquad 15\text{-}11$$

or from Equation 15-10:

$$\frac{v_s}{V} = \frac{N}{n}\left(\frac{r}{R}\right)^{\frac{1}{6}}$$

15-12

and

$$\frac{q_s}{Q} = \frac{N}{n}\frac{a}{A}\left(\frac{r}{R}\right)^{\frac{1}{6}}$$

15-13

The significance of these equations is shown in the following example.

Example 15-2. An 8-in. sewer is to flow at 0.3 depth on a grade that will insure a degree of self-cleaning equivalent to that obtaining at full depth for a velocity of 2.5 fps. Find the required grades and associated velocities and rates of discharge at full depth and 0.3 depth. Assume $N = 0.012$ at full depth.

a. From Table 15-3, find for full depth of flow and $V = 2.5$ fps, $Q = 0.873$ cfs and $S = 4.44$ ft per 1,000.

b. From Figure 15-1 or Table 15-4, find for 0.3 depth, $a/A = 0.252$, $r/R = 0.684$ (or $R/r = 1.46$), $v/V = 0.776$, $q/Q = 0.196$, and $N/n = 0.78$; and from Table 15-4, find $(r/R)^{\frac{1}{6}} = 0.939$.

Hence at 0.3 depth and a grade of 4.44 ft per 1,000, $v = 0.776 \times 2.5 = 1.94$ fps for $n = N$, or 1.51 fps for $N/n = 0.78$, and $q = 0.196 \times 0.873 = 0.171$ cfs for $n = N$, or 0.133 cfs for $N/n = 0.78$.

c. For self-cleaning flow, however, $s = 1.46 \times 4.44 = 6.5$ ft per 1,000, by Equation 15-10; $v_s = 0.939 \times 2.5 = 2.35$ for $n = N$, or $0.78 \times 2.35 = 1.83$ fps for $N/n = 0.78$, by Equation 15-12; and $q_s = 0.252 \times 0.939 \times 0.873 = 0.207$ cfs for $n = N$, or $0.78 \times 0.207 = 0.161$ cfs for $N/n = 0.78$, by Equation 15-13.

To facilitate findings such as these, the implications of the variation of n with depth and of Equations 15-10 to 15-13 can be incorporated in a diagram of the hydraulic elements that are associated with a sewer that will flow, at all depths, at velocities equal in self-cleaning action to the velocity of the full section. This has been done in Figure 15-2 which shows, among other matters, that no change in slope need be made when a sewer flows more than half full but that the slope must be doubled when the depth of flow drops to 0.2 full and quadrupled at 0.1 depth.

It is evident that Equations 15-12 and 15-13 could have been derived equally well from Equation 15-5; also that, in accordance with Equation 15-6, they can be expressed in terms of the Darcy-Weisbach friction factor as

$$v_s/V = \sqrt{F/f}$$

15-14

and

$$q_s/Q = (a/A)\sqrt{F/f}$$

15-15

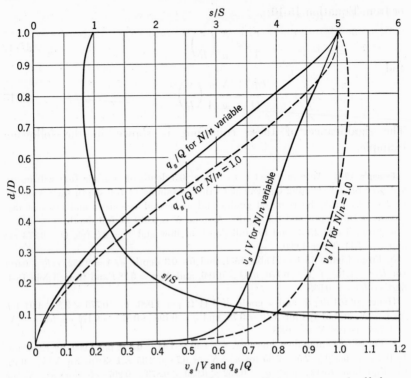

Figure 15-2. Hydraulic elements of circular sewers that possess equal self-cleansing properties at all depths.

Example 15-3. An 8-in. sewer is to discharge 0.161 cfs at a velocity equivalent in self-cleaning action to that of a sewer flowing full at 2.5 fps. Find the depth and velocity of flow and the required slope.

a. From Example 15-2, $Q = 0.873$ cfs and $S = 4.44$ ft per 1,000. Hence $q_s/Q = 0.161/0.873 = 0.185$.

b. From Figure 15-2, for $N = n$ and $q_s/Q = 0.185$, $d_s/D = 0.25$, $v_s/V = 0.91$, and $s/S = 1.70$. Hence $v_s = 0.91 \times 2.5 = 2.28$ fps, and $s = 1.70 \times 4.44 = 7.5$ ft per 1,000.

c. From Figure 15-2, for N/n variable and $q_s/Q = 0.185$, $d_s/D = 0.30$, $v_s/V = 0.732$, and $s/S = 1.46$. Hence $v_s = 0.732 \times 2.5 = 1.83$ fps, and $s = 1.46 \times 4.44 = 6.5$ ft per 1,000.

The increase in the coefficient of roughness is seen to be an aid to the cleansing action of flow and to allow lower velocities and slopes.

Egg-shaped sewers and cunettes, as indicated in Section 3-6, attempt to provide adequate velocities for the dry-weather flow of combined sewers. The hydraulic elements of these sewers, as well as of horseshoe-shaped and box sewers, can be charted in exactly the same manner as that demonstrated for circular sections.

15-5. Flow in Sewer Transitions. The flow in sewers, as has been stated, is both unsteady (changing in rate of discharge) and non-uniform (changing in velocity and depth). Since it is not practicable to identify with needed accuracy the variation in flow with time for all reaches of the sewerage system and since the system is designed for the maximum expected flow, the design flow is assumed to be steady except in unusual circumstances. In sewer transitions, however, non-uniformity of the flow must be taken into account if a rational and economical design of the system is to be attained.

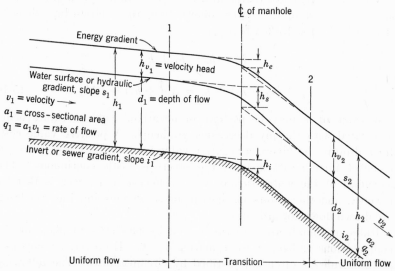

Figure 15-3. Changes in hydraulic and energy gradients at a transition in size or grade of sewer.

Sewer transitions include (1) changes in size, grade, and volume of flow; (2) free and submerged discharge at the end of the line; (3) passage through measuring and diversion devices; and (4) junctions. The most common form of sewer transition occurs at a change in size or grade. The influence of such a change upon the shape of the water surface and energy gradient is shown, greatly foreshortened, in Figure 15-3. Here h_e is the loss in energy or head lost in the transition; h_s is the drop in water surface; and h_i is the required drop in the invert within the transition. By assuming that these changes are concentrated at the center of the transition, the sizes and elevations of the sewers can be fixed. The detailing of the transition can then be completed. The energy loss h_e is usually small. In the absence of exact information, it is generally assumed to be proportional to the difference, or change, in velocity heads, i.e., $h_e = k(h_{v_2} - h_{v_1})$. According to Hinds,[8] the proportionality factor k may have a value as low as 0.1 for increasing velocities and as low as 0.2 for decreasing velocities, provided that flow is in the "upper alternate stage." For flow in the "lower alternate stage," the value of k may be expected to increase approximately as the square of the velocity ratios. Camp [7] has suggested allowing a minimum value of 0.02 ft for the loss of head in a transition of this kind. If a curve is included in the transition, the loss of head will be greater.

With the energy loss placed at a reasonable value, the requisite drop h_i in the invert of the sewer follows from the relationships demonstrated in Figure 15-3, where

$$h_2 + h_e = h_1 + h_i$$

or

$$h_i = (h_2 - h_1) + h_e = \Delta(d + h_v) + k\Delta h_v \qquad 15\text{-}16$$

The value of h_i may be positive or negative, negative values being associated with sharply decreasing gradients. A positive value calls for a drop in the invert, a negative value for a rise. A rise, however, is never introduced; instead, the invert is made continuous. The elevation of the water surface in the downstream sewer is thereby lowered, and the waters in the run of sewer entering the transition are drawn down towards it.

Rules of thumb are sometimes used by engineers in place of the computations called for by Equation 15-16. However, employment of these rules is often not justified by circumstances. The following rules for drops in manholes at changes in size are examples:

a. $h_i = \frac{1}{2}(d_2 - d_1)$ for sewers smaller than 24 in. $h_i = \frac{3}{4}(d_2 - d_1)$ for 24-in. sewers and larger.

b. Keeping the $0.8d$ line continuous on the principle that it represents the line of maximum velocity.

c. Basing flow calculations on a roughness factor greater than that obtaining in straight runs; $N = 0.015$, for example, instead of $N = 0.012$.

d. Allowing a drop of 0.1 ft in a through manhole; 0.2 ft in the presence of one lateral or bend; and 0.3 ft for two laterals.

Example 15-4. Two 8-in. sanitary sewers, each flowing full and carrying 0.7 cfs at a velocity of 2 fps on minimum grade, discharge into a steeper sewer that is to pick up 0.01 cfs in the course of its next run. The lower sewer can be laid on a grade as low as 10 per 1,000 and as high as 13 per 1,000. Find the required slope of the lower sewer and the invert drop in the transition.

---

[8] Julian Hinds, "The Hydraulic Design of Flume and Siphon Transitions," *Trans. Am. Soc. Civil Engrs., 92,* 1423 (1928).

a. From Table 15-1, an 8-in. sewer flowing full will carry 1.41 cfs on a slope of 11.6 per 1,000 with a velocity of 4.05 fps if $N = 0.012$. Pertinent information is, therefore, as follows:

$$d_1 = 0.67 \text{ ft}, \quad v_1 = 2.00 \text{ fps}, \quad h_{v_1} = 0.062 \text{ ft}, \quad d_1 + h_{v_1} = 0.73 \text{ ft}$$

$$d_2 = 0.67 \text{ ft}, \quad v_2 = 4.05 \text{ fps}, \quad h_{v_2} = 0.255 \text{ ft}, \quad d_2 + h_{v_2} = 0.92 \text{ ft}$$

$$\Delta h_v = 0.19 \text{ ft}, \quad \Delta(d + h_v) = 0.19 \text{ ft}$$

Assuming a loss of head of $h_e = 0.2\Delta h_v = 0.038$ ft, Equation 15-16 gives the required drop in invert,

$$h_i = 0.19 + 0.04 = 0.23 \text{ ft}$$

b. A 10-in. sewer laid on a grade of 10 per 1,000 has a capacity of 2.37 cfs and velocity of 4.35 fps when flowing full. From Figure 15-1, for $N/n \times q/Q = 0.595$, $d/D = 0.63$, and $N/n \times v/V = 0.905$, or $d = 6.3$ in., and $v = 3.94$ fps. Hence, the upper sewers remaining unchanged,

$$d_2 = 0.525 \text{ ft}, \quad v_2 = 3.94 \text{ fps}, \quad h_{v_2} = 0.24 \text{ ft}, \quad d_2 + h_{v_2} = 0.77 \text{ ft}$$

$$\Delta h_v = 0.18 \text{ ft}, \quad \Delta(d + h_v) = 0.04 \text{ ft}$$

Assuming a loss of head $h_e = 0.2\Delta h_v = 0.036$ ft, we find

$$h_i = 0.04 + 0.04 = 0.08 \text{ ft}$$

15-6. Alternate Stages and Critical Depth of Flow. For a full analysis of transitions, the designer must be able to identify the alternate stages of open-channel flow and the special case of flow at critical depth. Taking the elevation of the sewer invert as the datum, the energy gradient, as shown in Figure 15-3, is situated at a height

$$h = d + h_v = d + v^2/2g = d + q^2/(2ga^2) \qquad \text{15-17}$$

above this datum.[9] Since the cross-sectional area of the conduit is a function of its depth, Equation 15-17 is a cubic equation in terms of the depth. Two roots of this equation are positive and represent the two alternate stages at which a given rate of discharge q will be maintained for a given energy head h. The two stages fuse into a single "critical stage" for conditions of maximum discharge. For uniform flow, the slope of the water surface parallels that of the invert ($s = i$) and determines the stage. Critical flow is unstable and should be avoided in design if uncertainties and fluctuations in depth of flow are not to be introduced. Depths of flow within 10% of the critical depth are also likely to be unstable.

[9] If v is the mean velocity of flow, the kinetic energy head is actually greater than $v^2/2g$ by 10 to 20%, depending upon the shape and roughness of the channel. But this fact is not ordinarily taken into account in hydraulic computations.[7]

Equation 15-17 may be generalized by expressing its three terms as dimensionless ratios. A family of curves or a nomogram can then be prepared to facilitate the determination of the alternate stages and critical depth of flow in a conduit of given cross-section. Bringing the term containing the rate of discharge q to one side of the equation and multiplying both sides of the resulting equation by $\dfrac{1}{D}\left(\dfrac{a}{A}\right)^2$, we obtain the following straight-line relationship:

$$\left(\frac{q}{A\sqrt{gD}}\right)^2 = 2\left(\frac{a}{A}\right)^2\left(\frac{h}{D} - \frac{d}{D}\right) \qquad \text{15-18}$$

Again, the capital letters in this equation denote the hydraulic elements of the full section, and the lower-case letters those of the partially filled section of the conduit.

A plot of Equation 15-18 for circular conduits is shown in Figure 15-4. It will be noted that the family of straight lines for particular values of d/D spontaneously generates a curve for the critical depth, thus avoiding calculations that are somewhat tedious when the conduit is irregular in cross-section.

Maximum rate of discharge obtains at the critical depth d_c. Hence this element is determined analytically [10] by differentiating Equation 15-18 with respect to d and equating the result to 0.

The following relation is obtained for a circular cross-section:

$$\frac{h}{D} = \frac{1}{8}\left[\left(10\frac{d_c}{D} - 1\right) + \frac{\dfrac{1}{4}\pi + \dfrac{1}{2}\sin^{-1}\left(2\dfrac{d_c}{D} - 1\right)}{\sqrt{\dfrac{d_c}{D}\left(1 - \dfrac{d_c}{D}\right)}}\right] \qquad \text{15-19}$$

Substitution into Equation 15-19 of values of d_c/D varying by tenths from

[10] For a circular cross-section the area a of the partially filled section is related to the depth as follows:

$$a = \frac{1}{2}\pi\frac{D^2}{4} + 2\int_{y=0}^{y=y} x\, dy$$

where x and y are the coordinates of a point on the circle referred to axes passing through the center of the circle. Expressed in terms of y and of D and d,

$$2\int_{y=0}^{y=y} x\, dy = 2\int_{y=0}^{y=y}\sqrt{(D^2/4 - y^2)}\, dy = 2\int_{d=D/2}^{d=d}\sqrt{d(D-d)}\, dd$$

$$= \left(d - \frac{D}{2}\right)\sqrt{d(D-d)} + \frac{D^2}{4}\sin^{-1}\left(2\frac{d}{D} - 1\right)$$

Introduction of these quantities into Equation 15-18 and differentiation yield Equation 15-19.

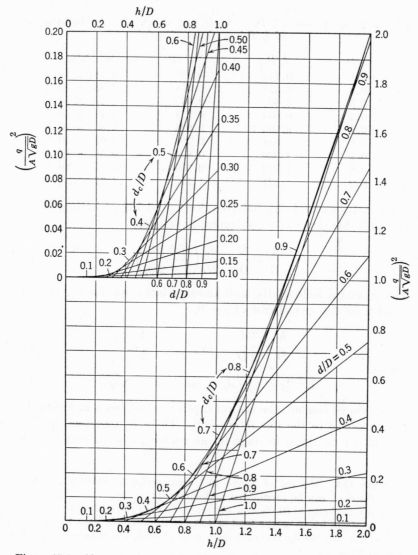

Figure 15-4. Alternate stages and critical depths of flow in circular conduits.

0.1 to 0.9 yields the numerical results for h/D, $\dfrac{v_c}{\sqrt{gD}}$, and $\left(\dfrac{q}{A\sqrt{gD}}\right)^2$, shown in Table 15-5. Within the range shown, the relationship between depth and rate of discharge is closely approximated by the equation

$$\frac{d_c}{D} = 0.9\left(\frac{q}{A\sqrt{gD}}\right)^{0.514} \qquad\qquad 15\text{-}20$$

TABLE 15-5. Values of h/D, $v_c/\sqrt{gD}$, and $(q/A\sqrt{gD})^2$ for Varying Values of d_c/D in a Circular Conduit

d_c/D	h/D	$v_c/\sqrt{gD}$	$(q/A\sqrt{gD})^2$
0.1	0.134	0.261	1.184×10^{-4}
0.2	0.270	0.378	2.86×10^{-3}
0.3	0.408	0.465	1.37×10^{-2}
0.4	0.550	0.553	4.18×10^{-2}
0.5	0.696	0.626	9.80×10^{-2}
0·6	0.851	0.709	1.97×10^{-1}
0.7	1.020	0.800	3.58×10^{-1}
0.8	1.222	0.919	6.23×10^{-1}
0.9	1.521	1.11	1.12

For a trapezoidal channel (see Section 10-10) of bottom width b and with side slopes of z (horizontal to vertical)

$$\frac{h}{D} = \frac{d_c}{D} + \frac{d_c}{2D}\left(\frac{b + zd_c}{b + 2zd_c}\right) \qquad 15\text{-}21$$

This equation includes the well-known relationship for a rectangular channel for the special case of $z = 0$,

$$\frac{h}{D} = \frac{3}{2}\frac{d_c}{D} \quad \text{or} \quad h = \frac{3}{2}d_c \qquad 15\text{-}22$$

whence

$$v_c^2/2g = h - d_c \quad \text{or} \quad v_c = \sqrt{gd_c} \qquad 15\text{-}23$$

In a closed conduit, the critical depth line, as shown in Figure 15-4, is asymptotic to the line $d/D = 1.0$. There is, therefore, neither a critical nor an alternate stage for an enclosed conduit that is flowing full.

Example 15-5. The use of Figure 15-4, construction of which is simple and straightforward, can be exemplified as follows:

Given a discharge of 60 cfs in a 4-ft sewer, find (a) the critical depth, (b) the alternate stages for an energy head of 4 ft, (c) the alternate stage for an energy head of 6 ft, and (d) the lower alternate stage associated with an upper alternate stage at 0.8 depth.

a. For $q = 60$ cfs and $D = 4$ ft, $\left(\dfrac{q}{A\sqrt{gD}}\right)^2 = \left(\dfrac{60 \times 4}{\pi \times 16\sqrt{4g}}\right)^2 = 0.177$. From Figure 15-4, read $d_c/D = 0.59$. Hence $d_c = 0.59 \times 4 = 2.36$ ft.

b. For $h = 4.0$, $h/D = 1.0$, and $\left(\dfrac{q}{A\sqrt{gD}}\right)^2 = 0.177$ as in (a), read, from Figure 15-4, $d/D = 0.42$ and 0.90, or $d_l = 0.42 \times 4 = 1.7$ ft, and $d_u = 0.90 \times 4 = 3.6$ ft.

c. For $h = 6.0$, $h/D = 1.5$, and $\left(\dfrac{q}{A\sqrt{gD}}\right)^2 = 0.177$ as in (a), read, from Figure

15-4, $d/D = 0.32$, whence $d_l = 0.32 \times 4 = 1.3$ ft. There is no upper stage since the conduit flows full when h/D equals or exceeds 1.09 (at intersection of $d/D = 1.0$ and ordinate of 0.177). Hence the conduit is placed under a pressure of $(1.5 - 1.09 = 0.41) \times 4 = 1.6$ ft.

d. For $\left(\dfrac{q}{A \sqrt{gD}} \right)^2 = 0.177$ as in (a) and $d_u/D = 0.8$, or $d_u = 3.2$ ft, read, from Figure 15-4, $d_l/D = 0.45$, or $d_l = 1.8$ ft.

15-7. Length of Transitions. Transition from one to the other alternate stage carries the flow through the critical depth. Passage from the upper alternate stage (a) to the critical depth, or (b) through it, to the lower alternate stage or to free fall produces non-uniform (accelerating) flow and a drawdown curve in the water surface. Passage from the lower to the upper alternate stage creates the hydraulic jump. Reduction in velocity of flow, (a) by discharge into relatively quiet water or (b) by weirs and other obstructions to flow, dams up the water and induces non-uniform (decelerating) flow and a backwater curve in the water surface. Economy of design requires that the size of conduit be adapted to the conditions of flow within the range of changing depths associated with non-uniformity in flow. If the depths of flow at both ends of the transition are known, the energy and hydraulic gradients of transition can be traced by stepwise calculations or by integration (graphical [11] or analytical [12]). Both methods are based upon the consideration that the change in the height of the energy gradient h above a given datum per unit length l of conduit must equal the sum of the changes in (1) the height of the invert z above the datum, (2) the depth of flow d, and (3) the velocity head h_v, all per unit length, or,

$$\frac{\partial h}{\partial l} = \frac{\partial z}{\partial l} + \frac{\partial d}{\partial l} + \frac{\partial h_v}{\partial l}$$

Since $\partial h/\partial l$ closely equals the slope s of the water surface and $\partial z/\partial l$ is the slope i of the invert,

$$s - i = \frac{\partial(d + h_v)}{\partial l} \qquad \text{or} \qquad \partial l = \frac{\partial(d + h_v)}{s - i} \qquad \text{15-24}$$

For stepwise calculations of the reach of conduit extending between cross-sections of given depth,

$$\Delta l = \frac{\Delta(d + h_v)}{s - i} \qquad \text{15-25}$$

[11] H. A. Thomas, *Hydraulics of Flood Movement,* Carnegie Institute of Technology, 1934.

[12] M. E. von Seggern, "Integrating the Equation of Non-uniform Flow," *Proc. Am. Soc. Civil Engrs.,* **75**, 105 (1949).

Flow being steady, the rate of discharge is constant, and the velocity of flow at any depth is fully determined. The invert slope i is likewise known. Therefore, only the value of s needs to be calculated. This is done by means of a flow formula, such as the Manning formula, for the average hydraulic elements of each conduit reach. The average hydraulic elements are ordinarily arithmetic mean values. The geometric mean or the harmonic mean will yield closely the same results. The necessary calculations are shown in Example 15-6 for a backwater curve and in Example 15-7 for a drawdown curve.

Example 15-6. A 10-ft circular sewer laid on a gradient of 0.5 ft per 1,000 discharges 106 cfs into a pump well. The water level in this well rises, at times, 10 ft above the invert elevation of the incoming sewer. Trace the profile of the water surface in the sewer. Assume a coefficient of roughness of 0.012 for the full sewer.

a. A 10-ft sewer on a grade of 5×10^{-4} has a capacity of 400 cfs by Manning's formula. The value of q/Q, therefore, equals $106/400 = 0.263$, and d/D from Figure 15-1 equals 0.40 for variable N/n. Hence the initial depth of flow is $0.40 \times 10 = 4.0$ ft, and the terminal depth 10 ft.

b. The length of reach in which the depth changes by a chosen amount is given by Equation 15-25. The calculations are shown in Table 15-6. The length of run in which the transition from a depth of 4.0 to 10.0 ft takes place is 14,440 ft, or slightly under 3 miles.

TABLE 15-6. Calculation of Backwater Curve (Example 15-6)

d (1)	d/D (2)	a/A (3)	r/R (4)	N/n (5)	a (6)	r (7)	v (8)	$h_v \times 10^2$ (9)	$d + h_v$ (10)
10.0	1.00	1.000	1.000	1.00	78.5	2.50	1.35	2.83	10.028
8.0	0.80	0.858	1.217	0.89	67.5	3.04	1.57	3.83	8.038
6.0	0.60	0.626	1.110	0.82	49.1	2.78	2.16	7.23	6.072
4.0	0.40	0.373	0.857	0.79	29.3	2.14	3.62	20.3	4.203

$n \times 10^2$ (11)	$nv \times 10^2$ (12)	Average			$s \times 10^5$ (16)	$(s - i) \times 10^5$ (17)	$\Delta(d + h_v)$ (18)	Δl (19)	$\Sigma \Delta l$ (20)
		r (13)	$r^{2/3}$ (14)	$nv \times 10^2$ (15)					
1.20	1.62								0
		2.77	1.97	1.87	4.07	−45.9	−1.990	4,330	
1.35	2.12								4,330
		2.91	2.04	2.63	7.53	−42.5	−1.966	4,620	
1.46	3.15								8,950
		2.46	1.82	4.32	15.97	−34.0	−1.869	5,490	
1.52	5.50								14,440

The calculations involve no difficulties. The values shown in the successive columns of Table 15-6 are found as follows:

Column 1: Assumed depths between initial depth of 4 ft and terminal depth of 10 ft.

Column 2: Column 1 ÷ 10 (the diameter of the sewer).

Columns 3, 4, and 5: a/A, r/R, and N/n read from Figure 15-1.

Column 6: Column 3 × 78.5 (the area of the sewer).

Column 7: Column 1 × 2.50 (the hydraulic radius of the sewer).

Column 8: 106 (the rate of flow) ÷ Column 6.

Column 9: $v^2/2g$ for Column 8.

Column 10: Column 9 + Column 1.

Column 11: 0.012 (Manning's N for the sewer) ÷ (Column 5).

Column 12: Column 11 × Column 8.

Column 13: Arithmetic mean of successive pairs of values in Column 7.

Column 14: (Column 13)$^{3/5}$.

Column 15: Arithmetic mean of successive pairs of values in Column 12.

Column 16: (Column 15 ÷ 1.486 × Column 14)^2, i.e., $s = \left(\dfrac{nv}{1.486r^{2/3}} \right)^2$.

Column 17: Column 16 − 50.

Column 18: Difference between successive pairs of values in Column 10.

Column 19: Column 18 ÷ Column 17 × 10^{-5}, i.e., $\Delta l = \dfrac{\Delta(d + h_v)}{s - i}$.

Column 20: Cumulative values of Column 19.

Example 15-7. A 10-ft circular sewer laid on a gradient of 0.5 ft per 1,000 discharges freely into a water course. Trace the profile of the water surface in the sewer when it is flowing at maximum capacity without surcharge.

TABLE 15-7. Calculation of Drawdown Curve (Example 15-7)

d (1)	d/D (2)	a/A (3)	r/R (4)	N/n (5)	a (6)	r (7)	v (8)	h_v (9)	$d + h_v$ (10)
4.7	0.47	0.463	0.960	0.79	36.4	2.40	11.0	1.88	6.58
6.0	0.60	0.626	1.110	0.82	49.1	2.78	8.15	1.02	7.02
8.0	0.80	0.858	1.217	0.89	67.5	3.04	5.93	0.54	8.54
10.0	1.00	1.000	1.000	1.00	78.5	2.50	5.10	0.40	10.40

$n \times 10^2$ (11)	$nv \times 10^2$ (12)	Average			$s \times 10^4$ (16)	$(s - i) \times 10^4$ (17)	$\Delta(d + h_v)$ (18)	Δl (19)	$\Sigma\Delta l$ (20)
		r (13)	$r^{2/3}$ (14)	$nv \times 10^2$ (15)					
1.52	16.8								0
		2.59	1.88	14.3	26.2	21.2	0.44	210	
1.46	11.9								209
		2.91	2.04	9.9	10.65	5.65	1.52	2,690	
1.35	7.99								2,900
		2.77	1.97	7.1	5.90	0.90	1.86	20,700	
1.20	6.12								23,600

a. The maximum capacity of this sewer, as shown in Example 15-6, is 400 cfs for $N = 0.012$.

b. To discharge in free fall, the flow must pass through the critical depth. Since

$$\left(\frac{Q}{A\sqrt{gD}}\right)^2 = \left(\frac{400}{78.5\sqrt{10g}}\right)^2 = 0.0807$$

$d_c = 0.47 \times 10 = 4.7$ ft, from Figure 15-4 or Equation 15-20.

c. The length of reach in which the depth changes from 10 ft to 4.5 ft is calculated in Table 15-7 in accordance with Equation 15-25 and as in Example 15-6.

The drawdown, therefore, extends over a length of 23,600 ft, or over 4 miles, between the full depth of the sewer and a critical depth of 4.5 ft. There is a further short stretch of flow between the point of critical depth and the end of the sewer. This additional distance, however, is small and seldom in excess of $5d_c$, or 23.5 ft in the example chosen.

15-8. Length of Overfalls or Side Weirs. The length of weir required to carry away storm flows in excess of intercepter capacity

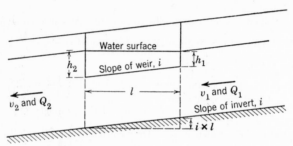

Figure 15-5. Flow over a side weir.

varies with the general dimensions and hydraulic characteristics of the sewer and with the nature and orientation of the weir employed. True side weirs parallel the direction of flow and have capacities that are but a small fraction of weirs that are placed at right angles to the direction of flow.

For the conditions of flow outlined in Figure 15-5, application of Bernoulli's theorem gives the following relationship if we include a loss of head factor based upon Manning's formula.

$$\frac{v_1^2}{2g} + il + h_1 = \frac{v_2^2}{2g} + h_2 + l\left(\frac{nv}{1.486r^{\frac{2}{3}}}\right)^2$$

Hence

$$h_2 - h_1 = \frac{Q_1^2 - Q_2^2}{2ga^2} + il - l\left[\frac{n(Q_1 + Q_2)}{2 \times 1.486ar^{\frac{2}{3}}}\right]^2 \qquad 15\text{-}26$$

Here the parameters a and r are chosen for the average dimensions of the filled channel, i.e., at the center of the weir for example. Taking the flow over the weir Q, as approximated by $clh^{3/2}$,

$$Q = cl\left(\frac{h_1 + h_2}{2}\right)^{3/2} \quad \text{and} \quad h_2 + h_1 = 2\left(\frac{Q_1 - Q_2}{cl}\right)^{2/3} \quad \text{15-27}$$

Given Q_1, Q_2, a, r, i, n, and h_2, values of l and h_1 are readily determined by trial, as shown in Example 15-8. This approach to the problem of side-weir flow was first suggested by Forchheimer.[13] Other formulations have been presented by Engels [14] for uniform and for contracted channels as follows:

For uniform channels,

$$Q = 3.32l^{0.83}h_2^{1.67} \quad \text{15-28}$$

and for contracted channels,

$$Q = 3.32l^{0.9}h_2^{1.6} \quad \text{15-29}$$

In the contracted section, the weir occupies either the contracting side of the channel or the straight side in juxtaposition to the contracting side. It will be noted that, in terms of Engels' equations, the requisite length of side weirs that will discharge at the same rate as a sharp-crested, transverse weir of unit length and head h_2 is closely equal to $(l/h_2)^{0.17}$ and $(l/h_2)^{0.1}$ unit lengths respectively. Since the order of magnitude of l/h_2 generally lies between 10^2 and 10^3, the length of side weirs must be respectively 1.7 to 2.1 (contracted section) and 2.2 to 3.2 (uniform section) times as great as the length of weirs at right angles to flow. Forchheimer's analysis yields somewhat lower ratios.

Example 15-8. Given $Q_1 = 30$ cfs; $Q_2 = 16$ cfs; $a = 32$ sq ft; $r = 1.6$ ft; $i = 10^{-4}$; $n = 1.25 \times 10^{-2}$; and $h_2 = 0.50$ ft.

Find l and h, by Forchheimer's method; assume $c = 3.33$.

By Equation 15-26: $h_1 = 0.49022 - 8.04 \times 10^{-5}l$.

By Equation 15-27: $h_1 = 5.20l^{-2/3} - 0.5$. Hence $(0.99022 - 8.04 \times 10^{-5}l)l^{2/3} = 5.20$, or $(12,320 - l)l^{2/3} = 64,700$.

By trial

$$l = 12 \text{ ft} \quad \text{and} \quad h_1 = 0.49 \text{ ft} \quad \textit{Answer,}$$

or

$$l = 12,248 \text{ ft} \quad \text{and} \quad h_1 = -0.49 \text{ ft}$$

15-9. Capacity of Street Inlets. As stated in Section 3-6, the street inlets that admit runoff from rainfall to storm-drainage systems are

[13] Philip Forchheimer, *Hydraulik*, B. Teubner, Leipzig, 406, 1930.

[14] Hubert Engels, *Handbuch des Wasserbaues*, W. Engelmann, Leipzig, Vol. 1, p. 501, 1921.

placed and designed to concentrate and remove the flow in gutters at minimum cost with minimum interference to traffic, both pedestrian and vehicular. Some features of design that improve hydraulic capacity are costly and interfere with traffic. The wide variety of designs encountered represents different compromises between these factors (see Figure 3-3). There are three general types of inlets: curb inlets, gutter inlets, and combination inlets. The last-named combine curb openings with gutter openings. Where traffic speed is low, the gutter surface and gutter inlets may be depressed in order to increase their intake capacity. Flow in gutters can be expressed by a formulation such as Manning's. The value of the coefficient of roughness is quite high (0.015 or more).

The intake capacity of inlets, particularly that of curb inlets, increases with decreasing street slope and with increasing crown slope. However, curb inlets with diagonal deflectors placed in the gutter along the opening become more efficient as the street grade increases. Gutter inlets are more efficient in capturing gutter flow than are curb inlets; but clogging by debris is a problem. Combination inlets are better still, especially if the grating is placed downstream from the curb opening. Debris accumulating on the grating will then deflect water into the curb inlet. The most efficient grating for gutter inlets is one in which the bars lie parallel to the curb. If cross bars are added for structural reasons, they should be depressed to near the bottom of the longitudinal bars. Depression of the inlet enhances its capacity. The capacity of curb inlets is increased most thereby. Long shallow depressions are as effective as short deep ones. If a small amount of flow is allowed to pass by the inlet, the relative intake of water is greatly increased. Significant economies can be effected, therefore, by permitting a small carry-over flow and arranging for its acceptance by a down-grade inlet.

On the basis of model studies and street tests Li[15] and others have developed empirical formulas for the flow into gutter inlets and curb inlets with and without depressions. The relationship for curb openings without depressions is

$$Q/l = 4.82 \times 10^{-3}d\sqrt{gd} = 2.73 \times 10^{-2}d^{3/2} \qquad 15\text{-}30$$

or

$$d = 11.05(Q/l)^{2/3} \qquad 15\text{-}31$$

Here Q is the discharge into the inlet in cubic feet per second, l is the

[15] W. H. Li, J. C. Geyer, G. S. Benton, and K. K. Sorteberg, "Hydraulic Behavior of Storm-Water Inlets—Parts I and II," *Sewage and Ind. Wastes, 23,* 34, 722 (1951).

length of the opening in feet, g is the gravitational acceleration in feet per second squared, and d is the depth of gutter flow at the curb in inches. The value of d may be calculated from Manning's formula. The equation for a gutter that is wedge shaped in cross-section is

$$d = 0.1105 \frac{(1 + \sec \theta)^{\frac{1}{4}}}{\tan^{\frac{3}{8}} \theta} \left(\frac{Q_0}{\sqrt{s}/n} \right)^{\frac{3}{8}} \qquad 15\text{-}32$$

where Q_0 is the flow in the gutter in cubic feet per second, θ is the angle between the vertical curb and the mean crosswise slope of the gutter within the width of flow, n is the coefficient of roughness of the gutter, and s is the slope of the hydraulic gradient. This slope is assumed to be parallel to the longitudinal slope of the street surface.

Combining Equation 15-32 with Equation 15-31 and solving for Q/l,

$$\frac{Q}{l} = 1.74 \frac{(1 + \sec \theta)^{\frac{3}{8}}}{\tan^{\frac{15}{16}} \theta} \left(\frac{Q_0}{\sqrt{s}/n} \right)^{\frac{9}{16}} \qquad 15\text{-}33$$

For cross-sectional street slopes of 10^{-3} to 10^{-1}, Equation 15-33 is closely approximated by

$$\frac{Q}{l} = 1.87 i^{0.579} \left(\frac{Q_0}{\sqrt{s}/n} \right)^{0.563} \qquad 15\text{-}34$$

Here i is the mean crosswise slope of the gutter within the width of flow.

Example 15-9. For a flow of 1.0 cfs, a longitudinal street grade of 2.0%, a mean crosswise street grade of 5.6%, and a Kutter coefficient of roughness of 0.015, find (a) the length of an undepressed curb inlet required to capture 90% of the flow, and (b) the maximum depth of flow in the gutter.

a. By Equation 15-34: $Q/l = 1.87 \times 0.056^{0.579}[1/(\sqrt{0.02}/0.015)]^{0.563} = 0.10$, or $l = 10Q = 10 \times 0.9 \times Q_0 = 10 \times 0.9 \times 1.0 = 9$ ft.

b. By Equation 15-31: $d = 11.05 \times 0.10^{\frac{2}{5}} = 2.4$ in.

15-10. Flow in Depressed Sewers and Appurtenant Structures. The purpose and method of performance of depressed sewers or inverted siphons have been discussed in Section 3-6. The design of the siphon pipes presents no special problems. They flow full, and the velocity of flow varies directly with the rate of discharge. In order to prevent deposition of solids in pipes in which the flow fluctuates, relatively high velocities are assigned to these pipes: namely, 3 fps when they carry sanitary sewage and 5 fps when they contain storm or combined sewage. The smallest diameter of pipe employed is 6 in., and the choice of pipe material is adjusted to the hydrostatic head under which they must operate.

Inlet chambers, as suggested in Figure 3-5, generally include lateral weirs which are submerged when they receive their full flow. Losses of head are incurred in passing over these weirs and in entering the pipes to which they lead. Outlet chambers are streamlined to reduce hydraulic losses and to keep eddy currents from sweeping sewage solids into idle pipes. A by-pass over the obstruction that is circumvented by the siphon or a relief outlet to a receiving water may be provided to avoid flooding overflows when the siphon clogs or its capacity is exceeded.

15-11. Racks and Screens. Racks and screens are both sewer appurtenances and waste-water treatment units. They are employed

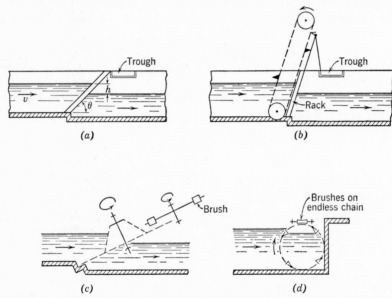

Figure 15-6. Racks and screens: (*a*) hand-cleaned inclined rack; (*b*) mechanically cleaned rack; (*c*) brush-cleaned disk screen (*Riensch-Wurl*); (*d*) brush-cleaned drum screen (*Link-Belt Co.*), sewage leaves through open end of drum.

in the first sense (1) to protect sewage pumps against trash and other clogging matter and (2) to remove from sewage outfalls coarse, floating solids that render receiving waters unsightly and reduce the efficiency of chlorination because the solids cannot be penetrated by the disinfectant.

Coarse racks of steel bars have clear openings of $1\frac{1}{2}$ to $2\frac{1}{2}$ in. or more. The openings of fine racks may be as small as $\frac{1}{2}$ in. Screens are expected to collect sewage matters down to $\frac{1}{16}$ in. in size. They may possess openings as small as $\frac{1}{32}$ in. in their smallest, or controlling, dimension, but they may be many inches long. Racks are cleared by hand, long-handled rakes being used for this purpose, or they are stripped by mechanical scrapers. See (a) and (b) in Figure 15-6. The rack area may be increased by placing the bars on a slope. Ratios of 1 vertical to 1, 2, or 3 horizontal are common. Cage racks are arranged in pairs (in series). For clearing, they are lifted from the sewage channel by elevator mechanisms. Screens are always mechanically driven. They rotate through the water as endless bands, disks, or drums and are cleaned by brushes, jets of water, or blasts of air. See (c) and (d) in Figure 15-6.

Hydraulic requirements are (1) that the approach velocity of the sewage in the raking or screening channel shall not fall below a self-cleaning value (1.25 fps) or rise to a magnitude at which the rakings or screenings will be dislodged from the bars or screens (3.0 fps); and (2) that the loss of head through the rack or screen shall not back up the flow sufficiently to place the entrant sewer under pressure. The loss of head through racks and screens can be formulated as an orifice loss. As such, it is a function of the velocity head. Kirschmer [16] has developed the following empirical relationships for racks constructed of bars of different shapes:

$$h = \beta(w/b)^{4/3}h_v \sin \theta \qquad\qquad 15\text{-}35$$

Here h is the loss of head in feet, w is the maximum width of the bars facing the flow, b is the minimum width of the clear openings between pairs of bars, h_v is the velocity head (in feet) of the water as it approaches the rack (face velocity), θ is the angle of the rack with the horizontal, and β is a bar shape factor. Kirschmer's values of β are 2.42 for sharp-edged rectangular bars, 1.83 for rectangular bars with semicircular upstream face, 1.79 for circular bars, 1.67 for rectangular bars with semicircular upstream and downstream faces, and 0.76 for bars with semicircular upstream face and tapering in a symmetrical curve to a small, semicircular, downstream face (tear-drop). The effective velocity is assumed to be the geometric mean of the horizontal, longitudinal, approach velocity v and the component of the velocity at right angles to the rack ($v \sin \theta$), i.e., $v\sqrt{\sin \theta}$.

A rack of $\frac{3}{8}$-in. rectangular bars placed at an angle of 60 deg (sin $\theta = 0.866$) to the horizontal and possessing clear openings of $\frac{3}{4}$ in., for example, produces a loss of head $h = 2.42(\frac{1}{2})^{4/3}h_v \times 0.866 = 0.83h_v$ when the rack is clean.

[16] O. Kirschmer, "Untersuchungen über den Gefällsverlust an Rechen," Trans. Hydraulic Inst., Munich, R. Oldenbourg, 21 (1926).

The maximum head loss through clogged racks and screens is generally held at about 2.5 ft. Racks with clear openings of 0.5, 1, and 2 in. collect respectively about 0.2, 0.1, and 0.02 cu ft of rakings per capita annually. Fine screens remove 0.2 to 1.0 cu ft of screenings or from 2 to 20% of the suspended solids depending upon the size of the openings. Peak collections of rakings and screenings may be as high as 5 times the average quantity.

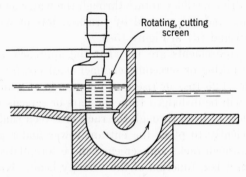

Rotating, cutting screen

Figure 15-7. Cutting screen or comminuter. *Chicago Pump Co.*

Rakings and screenings are unsightly. Their water content is high but can be reduced to about 65% in presses or centrifuges. Disposal may be by digestion with other solids (Section 26-11), by burial, or by incineration. Removal of rakings or screenings and their separate disposal are avoided if they are comminuted in the flowing sewage. A cutting screen or comminuter is used for this purpose (see Figure 15-7). The revolving, slotted drum of this device is equipped with cutters that shear the coarse materials collected on the drum against a comb. The solids are chopped down until they can pass through the $\frac{3}{15}$-in. to $\frac{3}{8}$-in. slots of the drum. Materials of this size do not tend to float at the water surface or to clog pumps.

16 ——————— COLLECTION OF SEWAGE AND STORM DRAINAGE

16-1. Needed Topographic Information. The elements of capacity, hydraulic, and hydrological design of sewers and drains have been discussed in Chapters 3, 5, 7, and 15. It remains for this chapter to show how individual sewers are integrated into a comprehensive drainage scheme. Surveys will provide the needed topographic information—both surface and underground—in the form of: (1) plans and profiles of the streets to be sewered; (2) plans and contour lines of the properties to be drained; (3) sill or cellar elevations of buildings to be connected; (4) location and elevation of existing or projected building drains; (5) location of existing or planned surface and subsurface utilities; (6) character and location of soils and rock through which sewers must be laid; (7) depth of ground-water table; (8) location of divides of drainage areas; (9) nature of street paving; (10) projected changes in street grades; (11) location and availability of sites for pumping stations and treatment works; and (12) character of receiving bodies of water or other disposal facilities.

Much of the topographic information needed is assembled for illustrative purposes in Figure 16-1 for a single sanitary sewer in a street that also contains a storm drain.

16-2. Expected Variations in Flow. The variations in flow that must be handled by sanitary sewers are determined (1) by the anticipated growth in population and water use during the design period and (2) by the fluctuations in flow that spring from normal water use. The design period itself remains a function of population increase and interest rates (Section 5-2). By contrast the design period for storm drains and combined sewers is of importance only in estimating the effect of future development of drainage areas on the runoff coefficient and on the magnitude of damage caused by flooding. The required capacity of storm drains is determined primarily by the variations in time, or recurrence interval, of flooding rainstorms of different intensities. Since storms of high intensity occur at random, the design

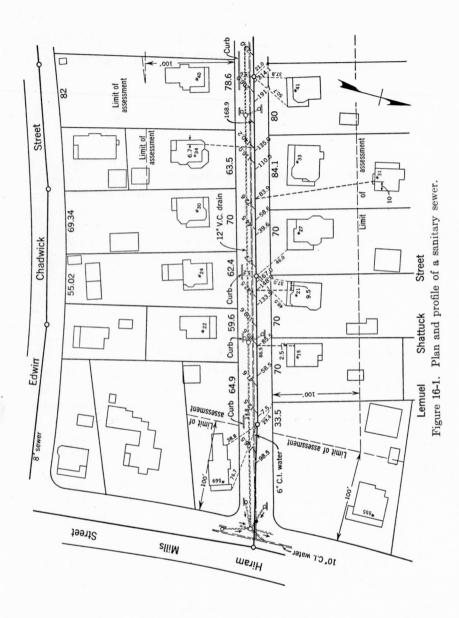

Figure 16-1. Plan and profile of a sanitary sewer.

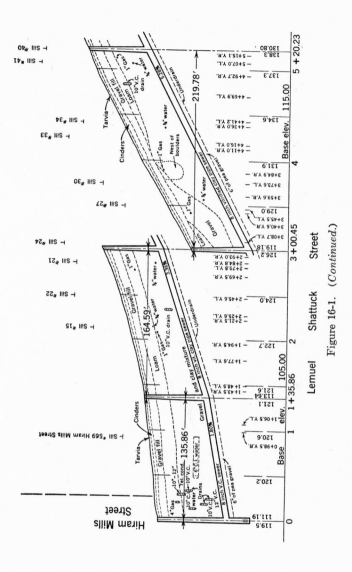

Figure 16-1. (*Continued.*)

values adopted for these systems may be reached and even exceeded as soon as the sewers and drains are laid.

a. Sanitary Sewers. Critical rates of flow in sanitary sewers are encountered at the beginning as well as at the end of the design period. They must be taken into consideration if the system is to function properly. Critical rates are outlined in the following schedule.

Beginning of design period: (a) Extreme minimum flows = ½ of minimum daily flows. Critical for velocities of flow and cleanliness of sewers. (b) Minimum daily flows = ⅔ of average daily flows. Critical for subdivision of units in treatment works.

Beginning and end of design period: (c) Average daily flows at beginning of design period = ½ average daily flows at end of period. Critical for velocities of flow in force mains.

End of design period: (d) Maximum daily flows = 2 × average daily flows. Critical for capacity of treatment works. (e) Extreme maximum flows = 1½ × maximum daily flows. Critical for capacity of sewers and pumps.

The flow ratios included in this outline are suggestive of small sewers and relatively rapidly growing areas, the over-all ratio of the extremes being $(2 \times 1.5 \times 2 \times 2 \times 1.5 = 18):1$. For large sewers and stationary populations the over-all ratio is more nearly 4:1. The influence of this variation on depth and velocity of flow on the self-cleaning force of the system is shown in Example 16-1.

Example 16-1. What are the depth ratios and the velocities of flow in sewers that carry (a) ¼ their full flow and (b) ⅟₁₈ their full flow, the velocity of the full section being 2 fps?

The pertinent ratios read from Figure 15-1 are:

a. For $q/Q = 0.25$: $d/D = 0.34$, $r/R = 0.76$, $v/V = 0.83$, and $N/n = 0.78$; and for $N/n \times q/Q = 0.25$: $d/D = 0.39$, $r/R = 0.84$, and $N/n \times v/V = 0.70$. For $N = n$, therefore, $v = 0.83 \times 2 = 1.66$ fps, and for $N = 0.78n$, $v = 0.70 \times 2 = 1.40$ fps.

In accordance with Equation 15-1, the intensity of tractive force of the filled section for constant s is $r/R \times$ the intensity of tractive force of the full section. Hence the relative intensities of tractive force of the filled section are 76% for $N = n$ and 84% for $N = 0.78n$.

b. For $q/Q = 0.056$: $d/D = 0.16$, $v/V = 0.53$, and $N/n = 0.80$; and for $N/n \times q/Q = 0.056$: $d/D = 0.18$, and $N/n \times v/V = 0.46$. For $N = n$, therefore, $v = 0.53 \times 2 = 1.06$ fps; and for $N = 0.80n$, $v = 0.46 \times 2 = 0.92$ fps.

The relative intensities of tractive force are 39% for $N = n$ and 44% for $N = 0.80n$. The apparent paradox of higher cleaning action at lower velocity is explained by the increase in the friction factor n.

b. Storm Drains and Combined Sewers. Storm drains are dry much of the time. When the rainfall is gentle, the runoff is relatively clear, and low flows present no serious problem. Flooding runoffs, however, wash a heavy load of solids into the systems. But the drains then flow full or nearly full and thereby tend to keep themselves clean. In terms of Fuller's flood frequency factor (Section 7-10), for example, a drainage system that is designed to handle the 10-year storm may be expected to carry $(1 + 0.8 \log T_1)/(1 + 0.8 \log T_{10}) = 1/1.8 = 55\%$ of the 10-year storm at least once a year. Similarly, in accordance with Equations 7-1 and 7-8, the proportion of the 10-year storm flow that would be produced once a year on an average would by $(T_1/T_{10})^m = 0.1^{0.372} = 42\%$.

The situation is not as favorable when storm and sanitary flows are combined. If a combined sewer is designed for a runoff of 1 in. per hr, for example, the storm flow from a single acre will be at the rate of 1 cfs or 646,000 gpd as against an average daily dry-weather contribution of about 10,000 gpd from an area that is very densely populated. The resulting ratio of $q/Q = 0.016$ is associated with a depth ratio of but 0.07 and a velocity ratio of 0.3. The need for a high design velocity, such as 3.5 fps at full depth, for combined sewers is apparent if putrescible solids are not to accumulate during dry weather. These solids give rise not only to septic conditions and offensive odors; they also increase the amounts of sewage solids that escape through storm overflows when the accumulated deposits are dislodged by sudden high flows.

16-3. Common Elements of Sewer Design. For specified conditions of minimum velocity, minimum depth of sewer, and maximum distance between manholes, a number of situations repeat themselves in general schemes of sewerage wherein street gradient, sewer gradient, size of sewer, and depth of sewer become interrelated elements of design. Some of these recurrent situations are illustrated in Figure 16-2 and involve, beside a flow formulation such as Manning's, the following simple equational relationship:

$$h_1 - h_2 = l(g - s) \qquad\qquad 16\text{-}1$$

where h_1 and h_2 are sewer depths *in excess of minimum requirements*, l is the distance between manholes, and g and s are respectively the street and sewer grades. Conditions of flow are stated below Figure 16-2.

Case a is encountered whenever the required sewer grade is greater than the grade of the street. Arriving at a depth equal to or greater than the minimum requirement, 7.0 ft, the depth of the sewer becomes greater and greater until it is more economical to lift the sewage by

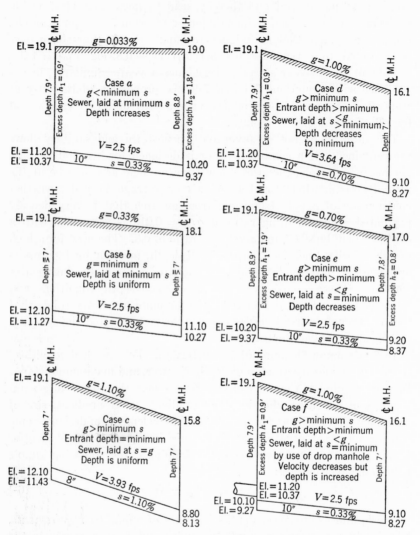

Figure 16-2. Common elements of sewer design. Required $q = 1.2$ cfs ($Q = 1.2$ cfs); $V = 2.5$ fps; $N = 0.012$; $l = 300$ ft. Minimum depth to crown = 7.0 ft; 8-in. sewer $Q = 1.2$ cfs; $S = 0.84\%$; $V = 3.4$ fps; 10-in. sewer $V = 2.5$ fps; $S = 0.33\%$; $Q = 1.36$ cfs.

placing a pumping station in the line. Specifically for Case a in Figure 16-2, the sewer grade is held at minimum (0.33%), and

$$h_2 = h_1 - l(g - s) = 0.9 - 3(0.033 - 0.33) = 1.8 \text{ ft}$$

i.e., the depth increases by $(1.8 - 0.9) = 0.9$ ft.

Case b is unusual in that the required sewer grade is the same as the street grade. The depth of the sewer, therefore, remains unchanged.

Case c introduces a street grade that is steep enough to provide, in a sewer paralleling it, the required capacity in an 8-in. rather than a 10-in. conduit. Arriving at minimum depth, there is no possibility of utilizing the available fall in part or as a whole to recover minimum depth as will be indicated in Cases d and e. The reduced size of pipe becomes the sole means of profiting from the steep street grade, provided, of course, that the upstream sewer is also no greater than 8 in.

Case d aims at maximum reduction of excess depth by placing a 10-in. sewer on minimum grade, or, in accordance with Equation 16-1, $s = g - (h_1 - h_2)/l$. For $h_2 = 0$, $s = 1.00 - (0.9 - 0.0)/3 = 0.70\%$ which is more than the required minimum of 0.33%. Hence the sewer can be brought back to minimum depth, or $h_2 = 0$.

Case e is like Case d, but full reduction to minimum depth is not attainable, because $s = 0.70 - (1.9 - 0)/3 = 0.07\%$. This is less than the required minimum of 0.33%. Hence the minimum grade must be used, and $h_2 = 1.9 - 3(0.70 - 0.33) = 0.8$ ft.

Case f illustrates how high velocities can be avoided by the use of drop manholes on steep slopes. Case f parallels Case d but introduces a drop of 1.1 ft to place the sewer on minimum grade and give it minimum velocity. This arrangement is normally considered only when grades are extraordinarily steep. Excessive drops and resulting excessive sewer depths can then be avoided by breaking the drops into two or more steps through the insertion of intermediate drop manholes.

It should be noted that no attention has been paid to actual velocities and depths of flow in these illustrative cases. The reason for this lies in the fact that the sewers flow nearly full. In these circumstances, too great refinement in calculations is not warranted by the information upon which rates of flow must be based. Consideration of actual depths and velocities of flow is generally restricted to the upper reaches of sewers that flow less than half full. The designer may have to forgo the use of grades that will insure self-cleaning velocities in such lateral sewers when the self-cleaning grades bring the laterals to the main sewer at depths below those required for the main itself and thereby require the lowering of the main arteries of the system over appreciable distances.

Generally speaking, the designer should attempt to attain the fullest possible utilization of the capacity of minimum-sized sewers before joining them to a larger sewer. The implications of this statement are demonstrated in Figure 16-3. There Scheme *a* is seen to keep lateral

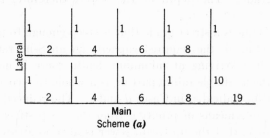

Scheme *(a)*

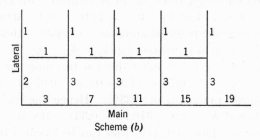

Scheme *(b)*

Figure 16-3. Relative utilization of the capacity of lateral sewers.

flow from joining the main conductor until as many as 10 units of flow have accumulated, whereas no lateral carries more than 3 units in Scheme *b*. As a result, the main in Scheme *b* exceeds 10 units in two sections in which the required capacities of the mains in Scheme *a* are still 6 and 8 units respectively.

Sanitary Sewerage

16-4. Capacity Design of Sanitary Sewerage Systems. Systems of sanitary sewers carry the water-borne wastes from households, from mercantile and industrial establishments, and from public buildings and institutions. In addition they receive more or less ground water by infiltration from the soil and sometimes, too, illicit storm drainage or surface runoff. The requisite capacity of sanitary sewers, therefore, is determined by the tributary domestic and institutional population, commercial water use, industrial activity, height of ground-water table, and enforcement of rain-water separation. To translate all these matters into working figures for individual runs and for a complex of sewers is a responsibility that cannot be taken lightly.

It is generally found convenient to arrive at unit values of domestic sewage on the basis of the population density and area served; but it would also be possible to develop figures for the number of people per front foot in districts of varying occupancy and make sewer length rather than area served the criterion of capacity design. Length (sometimes coupled with diameter) of sewer, indeed, offers the more rational basis for the estimation of ground-water infiltration. Unit values for flow from commercial districts are generally expressed in terms of the area served. The quantities of waste waters produced by industrial operations are more logically evaluated in terms of the units of daily production, e.g., gallons per: barrel of beer, 100 cases of canned goods, 1,000 bushels of grain mashed, 100 lb of live weight of animals slaughtered, or 1,000 lb of raw milk. Common values are suggested in Chapter 29.

Peak domestic and commercial flows may be assumed to originate at about the same hour of the day but must travel varying distances through the collecting systems before they can reach a given point in the sewerage system. Hence a reduction in, or damping of, the peak of the cumulative flows is generally assumed to obtain. In a fashion similar to the reduction in flood flows with time of concentration (as represented by the size of drainage area), the lowering of peak flows in sanitary sewers is conveniently related to the volume of flows or to the number of people served, and unit values of design are generally not accumulated in direct proportion to the rate of discharge (Equation 5-9) or to the tributary population (Equation 5-10).

16-5. Layout and Hydraulic Design of Sanitary Sewerage Systems. Before entering upon the design of individual sewer runs, a preliminary layout is made of the entire system. Sanitary sewers are so placed in streets, or alleys (where they exist), that a connection can be provided to each building served. Terminal manholes of lateral sewers are generally placed within the service frontage of the last lot that is to be sewered, with due regard to the location of the building sewer.

In general, sewers should slope with the ground surface and should conduct the sewage to the point of discharge by as direct a route as topography and street layout will permit. Thus the flow in a well-designed system will follow approximately the same path as the surface runoff.

Where alleys are part of the community plan, local considerations of the relative advantages of placing the sewers in the alleys rather than the streets will govern the choice of location. Alley location offers important advantages, particularly, in business districts.

After lines representing all the sewers have been drawn on the preliminary layout and arrows have been inserted to show the direction of flow, manholes are indicated at changes in direction, at sewer junctions, and at intermediate points that will hold their spacing to the allowable maximum or less. The manholes are then numbered for identification, and the hydraulic design of the system can begin. Alternate layouts will determine the final design.

The hydraulic design of a system of sanitary sewers is straightforward and is readily carried to completion by a series of systematic computations such as those outlined in Example 16-2.[1]

Example 16-2. Determine the required capacity and find the slope, size, and hydraulic characteristics of the system of sanitary sewers shown in the accompanying tabulation (Table 16-1) of their location, the areas and population served, and the expected sewage flows.

Capacity requirements are based upon the following assumptions:

a. Water consumption: Average day, 95 gpcd; maximum day, 175% of average; maximum hour, 140% of maximum day.

b. Domestic sewage: 70% of water consumption; maximum 285 gpcd for 5 acres decreasing to 245 gpcd for 100 acres or more.

c. Ground water: 30,000 to 50,000 gpd per mile of sewer for low land and 20,000 to 35,000 gpd per mile of sewer for high land; or 0.0014 to 0.0015 cfs per acre for 8-in. to 15-in. sewers in low land and 0.0009 to 0.0011 cfs per acre in high land.

d. Commercial sewage: 25,000 gpd per acre = 0.0388 cfs per acre.

e. Industrial sewage: Flow in accordance with industry.

Hydraulic requirements are as follows:

a. Minimum velocity in sewers: 2.5 fps (actual).

b. Kutter's coefficient of roughness $N = 0.015$ includes allowances for change in direction and related losses in manholes except for (*c*) below.

c. Crown of sewers is made continuous to prevent surcharge of upstream sewer.

Columns 1–4 identify the location of the sewer run. The sections are continuous.

Columns 5–8 list the acreage immediately adjacent to the sewer.

Column 9 gives the density of the population per domestic acre.

Column 10 = Column 9 × Column 8.

Columns 11–13 list the accumulated acreage drained by the sewer. For example, in Section *b*, Column 13 is the sum of Column 8 in Sections *a* and *b*, or $(40 + 27) = 67$.

----

[1] The numerical values shown in this example are taken from computations for the sewerage system of Cranston, R. I., by the firm of Fay, Spofford, and Thorndike as reported in *Eng. News-Rec.*, *123*, 419 (1939). Some of the values given do not agree in detail with values suggested in this book.

TABLE 16-1. Illustrative Computations for a System of Sanitary Sewers * (Example 16-2)

Location of sewer				Adjacent area						Total tributary area				
Section	Street	Stations or limits		Total acres	Industrial acres	Commercial acres	Domestic acres	Population		Industrial acres	Commercial acres	Domestic acres	Population	
		From	To					Per acre	Total				Per acre	Total
(1)	(2)	(3)	(4)	(5)	(6)	(7)	(8)	(9)	(10)	(11)	(12)	(13)	(14)	(15)
a	A Ave.	B Ave.	C St.	49	5	4	40	27	1,080	5	4	40	27.0	1,080
b	D Ave.	C St.	E St.	37	3	7	27	19	513	8	11	67	23.8	1,593
c	F St.	G St.	H St.	29	8	1	20	25	500	16	12	87	24.1	2,093
d	I St.	J St.	K St.	63	..	10	53	21	1,113	16	22	140	22.9	3,206

	Maximum volume of sewage, cfs					Design profile										
Section	Indus-trial	Com-mercial	Domestic	Infiltra-tion	Total	Size, in.	Slope	Capac-ity, cfs	Velocity, fps		Depth of flow, in.	Length, ft	Invert elevation		Cut	
									Full	Actual			Upper end	Lower end	Upper end	Lower end	Average
(1)	(16)	(17)	(18)	(19)	(20)	(21)	(22)	(23)	(24)	(25)	(26)	(27)	(28)	(29)	(30)	(31)	(32)
a	.156	.155	.440	.044	.795	8	.008	0.82	2.35	2.72	6.37	850	120.00	113.20	7.50	11.50	9.50
b	.248	.429	.650	.086	1.413	10	.007	1.42	2.22	3.02	8.1	1,260	113.03	104.21	11.67	8.50	10.08
c	.496	.468	.852	.115	1.931	12	.0045	2.23	2.45	2.84	9.7	1,880	104.04	95.58	8.67	12.00	10.33
d	.496	.858	1.300	.178	2.832	15	.003	3.35	2.35	2.72	12.0	1,760	95.33	90.05	12.25	11.00	11.63

* Note: Sections of sewers rather than runs between manholes are shown in this example in order to include major changes in required capacity and consequent size.

Column 14 gives the average density of the population for the total tributary area. For example, in Section b,

$$\text{Column (14)} = \frac{40 \times 27 + 27 \times 19}{40 + 27} = 23.8$$

Column 15 = Column 14 × Column 13.

Column 16 lists values obtained in a survey of industries in the areas served.

Column 17 = Column 12 × 0.0388.

Column 18 = Column 15 × (245 to 285) × (1.547×10^{-6}). For example, in Section a, $1,080 \times 264 \times (1.547 \times 10^{-6}) = 0.440$ cfs.

Column 19 = Sum of Columns 11–13 × rate of infiltration. For example, in Section a, $(5 + 4 + 40) \times 0.0009 = 0.044$ cfs.

Column 20 = Sum of Columns 16–19.

Columns 21–29 record the size of sewer for required capacity and available, or required, grade together with depth and velocity of flow. For example in Section a, an 8-in. sewer laid on a grade of $6.8/850 = 0.008$ will discharge $Q = 0.82$ cfs at a velocity of 2.35 cfs when it flows full. Hence for $q/Q = 0.795/0.82 = 0.971$: $d/D = 0.796$, $v/V = 1.16$, or $d = 8 \times 0.796 = 6.37$ in.; $v = 2.35 \times 1.16 = 2.72$ fps.

Columns 28–31 are taken from profile of street and sewer.

Column 28, Section b shows a drop in the manhole of $(113.20 - 113.03) = 0.17$ ft compared with Column 28, Section a. This allows for a full drop of $0.17 \times 12 = 2$ in. to offset the increase in the diameter of the sewer from 8 in. to 10 in.

Column 32 = arithmetic mean of Columns 30 and 31.

Storm Drainage

16-6. Capacity Design of Storm-Drainage Systems. The concepts of the rational method of estimating runoff from rainfall which generally provide the hydrological basis for the capacity design of storm-drainage systems have been discussed in Section 7-9. If in accordance with this method Equation 7-7, $Q = cia$, is made the axiom of design, it becomes the responsibility of the designer to arrive at the best possible estimates of c, the runoff-rainfall ratio, and i, the rainfall intensity, the determination of the value of a being a simple matter of measurement. Both c and i are variable in time. Hence the storm flows reaching a given point in a drainage system are compounded of the waters that have fallen within the stretch of time, or time of concentration, during which the runoff from the farthest portions of the tributary area travels to the point in question.

a. Time of Concentration. The time of concentration is composed of two parts: (1) the inlet time, or time required for runoff to gain entrance into a sewer, and (2) the time of flow in the sewerage system.

There is no ready rule for the determination of the inlet time, which is a function of (1) the roughness of the surfaces offering resistance to flow and storage of water in depressions, (2) the steepness of the slope, (3) the size of block or distance from the periphery of the area to the sewer inlet, and (4) the method of roof and surface drainage including the spacing of street inlets. In large communities in which roofs shed their water directly to the sewers and the runoff from paved yards and streets enters the sewer through closely spaced street inlets, the inlet time will be less than 5 min. In commercial districts with relatively flat slopes and greater inlet spacing, the inlet time lengthens to 10 to 15 min. In relatively flat residential areas in which street inlets are minimal, inlet times of 20 to 30 min are observed. For steeper slopes, these values must be reduced in magnitude.

The time of flow in the system is accumulated in passage to the point of concentration from the most distant sewer. Elapsed time is calculated as the sum of the quotients of the length of the individual sewers and their velocity when flowing full. Neither the increase in time which results from the filling of the sewers nor the decrease in time which is produced by the flood waves created by the rapid discharge of lateral sewers is ordinarily taken into account in calculating the time of flow in the system.

b. *Runoff Coefficients.* Runoff from storm rainfall is reduced by evaporation, storage in depressions, required wetting of surfaces before they will shed water, and percolation of rain into the ground. All these losses decrease in magnitude with the duration of storms. As a result, the value of the runoff-rainfall ratio, or shedding characteristic of the area c, increases proportionately. The value of c may exceed unity. It may do so, for example, when melting ice and snow contribute to runoff. Ordinarily c approaches unity, in the absence of melting ice and snow, only when the area drained is essentially impervious and storms are of long duration. Generalized values for the runoff coefficient in its relation to duration of rainfall and type of area drained are plotted in Figure 16-4. Choice of a suitable runoff coefficient is seen to present some difficulty. The matter is further complicated by the possibility that a flooding rainstorm may set in after the area to be drained has been wetted by light showers.

The basic coefficients plotted in Figure 16-4 apply to areas that shed their waters in a relatively short time. As shown in Figure 16-5, the runoff coefficient that applies for a particular time of concentration should logically be averaged in accordance with the geometric configuration of the area draining to the point of concentration. A weighted average can then be calculated as $c = \Sigma ca / \Sigma a$; but the fundamental evaluation of c as well as i is generally not sufficiently exact to warrant this refinement. Up to 60 min, the weighted average coefficient of runoff is approximately 80% of the basic coefficient for

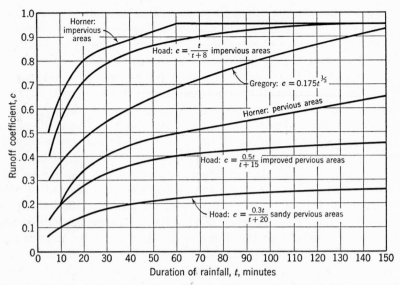

Figure 16-4. Variation in runoff coefficients with duration of rainfall and nature of area drained.

the pertinent time of concentration in a sector-shaped area; for a rectangular area 4 times as long as wide, the corresponding value is about 85%. For pervious areas these percentages decrease to 60% for sector-shaped areas and 75% for rectangular areas.

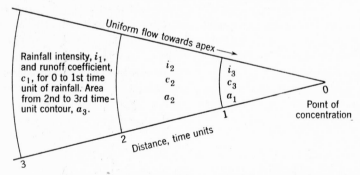

Figure 16-5. Composition of runoff reaching a point of concentration at the apex of a sector-shaped area. $Q = c_3 i_3 a_1 + c_2 i_2 a_2 + c_1 i_1 a_3 = \Sigma cia$. For i averaged in the rainfall analysis, $Q = i\Sigma ca$ and weighted average $c = \Sigma ca / \Sigma a$.

The probable future proportion of impervious and pervious areas in the district to be drained can be gaged from surveys of typical zones of the community. The percentage range of impervious surfaces in North American cities is about as shown in Table 16-2.

TABLE 16-2.   Range of Impervious Surfaces in North American Cities

	Per Cent
Mercantile districts	70–90
Commercial districts	40–50
Industrial districts	35–60
Residential districts	
Apartment houses	40–80
Single- and two-family houses	20–50

The impervious surfaces in a city block [2] 172.5 ft by 860 ft, or 3.38 acres in extent, are listed in Table 16-3 for illustrative purposes.

TABLE 16-3.   Impervious Surfaces in a City Block

	Sq ft	Per cent of total area
Streets	20,000	13.7
Alleys	6,500	4.5
Sidewalks	6,500	4.5
Yard walks	2,000	1.4
Subtotal	35,000	24.1
House roofs	27,500	18.9
Shed roofs	4,000	2.7
Subtotal	31,500	21.6
Total	66,500	45.7

House and shed roofs are seen to constitute about half of the impervious portion of this city block.

Because of the uncertainties involved in the estimates of rainfall intensities and inlet times, a constant value of the runoff coefficient, or shedding coefficient, is assumed by some engineers. The reported range in magnitude of the coefficient is shown in Table 16-4.

TABLE 16-4.   Range of Runoff Coefficients in North American Cities

	Runoff coefficient
Mercantile districts	0.70–0.95
Commercial districts	0.60–0.85
Industrial districts	0.55–0.80
Residential districts	
Apartment houses	0.5 –0.7
Single- and two-family dwellings	0.25–0.6
Parks	0.25
Undeveloped areas	0.05–0.25

---

[2] St. Louis, Mo.

c. Intensity of Rainfall and Runoff. The analysis of storm rainfalls has been discussed in Sections 7-3 to 7-6. After the rainfall-intensity curve has been selected in accordance with the principles there outlined, it is often convenient to combine corresponding values of c and i, as shown in Figure 16-6. The curves drawn trace the rate

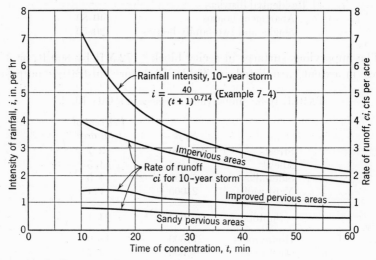

Figure 16-6. Time intensities of rainfall and related runoff for areas of varying imperviousness.

of runoff, or product of c and i, for a 10-year storm by applying Hoad's runoff coefficients to the storm-rainfall experience analyzed in Example 7-4.[3] Runoff values for areas that differ in characteristics from the three types shown in Figure 16-6 can be had by interpolation between the two curves most nearly approximating the characteristics of the district to be drained.

16-7. Capacity Design by Other Methods. As discussed in Section 7-10, the variations of c and i with time, when time is expressed in terms of the size of the water shed, produce over-all runoff formulations for a given locality. An example is the relationship devised by McMath for the design of sewers in St. Louis, Mo. Such formulations antedate the rational method. However, they were not derived from a study of the individual elements entering into the problem but from correlations of the magnitude of runoff from rainfall of flooding proportions to areas of given magnitude. Hence their use in sewer design has been called the empirical, in contrast to the rational, method. The

---

[3] The product ci records runoff in cubic feet per second per acre because of the close numerical equivalence of inches per hour per acre and cubic feet per second per acre.

McMath formula $Q = cia^{4/5}s^{1/5}$ introduces a slope factor s as a modifier of the time of concentration and the runoff coefficient. The values of c and i themselves are constants for a given locality and drainage area. With more complete knowledge of the variations of rainfall and runoff, it is possible to devise over-all formulas that will yield results for the capacity design of storm sewers comparable to those obtained by the rational method.

Where storm drains are in existence in a community, the capacity design of a drainage system for adjacent unsewered areas, or the capacity design of relief sewers, can receive aid from gagings of sewers in time of heavy rainfall or from surcharge experience in its relation to storms of varying magnitude. Surcharge must be linked to sewer capacity on the basis of size and slope, care being taken to identify possible downstream influences upon the section of sewer in which surcharge occurs. Gagings and observations of surcharge provide values for the runoff for areas of given magnitudes, and these values, together with a consideration of the type of district drained, can then be used in the capacity design of the drains that are to be added to the community.

New approaches to the capacity design of storm drains, somewhat akin to those underlying the unit hydrograph method, are being investigated but as yet lack adequate numerical information to be applied in general practice.[4]

16-8. Layout and Hydraulic Design of Storm-Drainage Systems. The layout of a storm-drainage system has much in common with that of a system of sanitary sewers. Ordinarily the layout is related, however, to the location of street inlets instead of the buildings to be served. When roof and areaway drains are to be connected directly to the storm sewer rather than discharging into the street gutters, however, the location of the buildings must also receive consideration. Street inlets are placed at the intersections of streets to keep the crossings for pedestrians passable. They are also inserted at intermediate points as need be to prevent the flooding of gutters and to hold the flow in the gutters within the capacity of the inlets. The area that can be drained through a street inlet is determined by the capacity of the inlet (Section 15-9) in relation to the product of the runoff coefficient and the rainfall intensity for a given inlet time.

Example 16-3. A street inlet has a capacity of 3 cfs. What is the maximum area that can be drained to the inlet if runoff conditions are reflected by the curve for improved pervious areas in Figure 16-6 and the inlet time is 20 min? From Figure 16-6, $ci = 1.3$ cfs per acre. Hence $a = Q/(ci) = 3.0/1.3 = 2.3$ acres.

---

[4] W. W. Horner and F. L. Flynt, *Trans. Am. Soc. Civil Engrs.*, *101*, 140 (1936); W. W. Horner and S. W. Jens, *Trans. Am. Soc. Civil Engrs.*, *107*, 1039 (1942).

After the probable location of the street inlets has been identified, the sewer lines are laid out to collect the water (1) from the inlets and (2) from the buildings or areaways draining directly to the sewers. The lines should proceed by the most direct route to outlets that empty into natural drainage channels. Easements or rights of way across private property may shorten the path of the drains. Manholes are placed as for sanitary sewers but with due reference to the need for emptying street inlets directly into them.

Surface topography determines the area tributary to each inlet. For the sake of simplicity, however, it is often assumed that lots drain to adjacent street gutters. Direct drainage of roofs and areaways to storm drains reduces the inlet time and thereby places a greater intensity of load upon the drainage system. Necessary computations are illustrated in Table 16-5 which accompanies Example 16-4.

Example 16-4. Determine the required capacity and find the slope, size, and hydraulic characteristics of the system of storm drains shown in the accompanying tabulation of location, tributary area, and expected storm runoff.

Capacity requirements are based upon the rainfall and runoff curves included in Figure 16-6. The area is assumed to be an improved pervious one, and the

TABLE 16-5. Illustrative Computations for a System of Storm Drains
(Example 16-4)

Line number	Location of drain			Tributary area, acres, a		Time of flow, min		Runoff, cfs, Q	
	Street	Manhole from	Number to	Increment	Total	To upper end	In drain	Per acre ci	Total
(1)	(2)	(3)	(4)	(5)	(6)	(7)	(8)	(9)	(10)
1	A	1	2	2.19	2.19	20.0	1.5	1.30	2.85
2	A	2	3	1.97	4.16	21.5	1.9	1.27	5.28
3	B	3	4	3.05	7.21	23.4	1.3	1.25	9.02

Line number	Design				Profile			Invert elevation	
	Diameter, in.	Slope, ft/1,000	Capacity, cfs	Velocity, fps	Length, ft	Fall, ft	Drop in M.H., ft	Upper end	Lower end
(1)	(11)	(12)	(13)	(14)	(15)	(16)	(17)	(18)	(19)
1	12	6.42	3.09	3.94	340	2.18	0.00	86.46	84.28
2	18	2.71	5.93	3.35	340	0.92	0.42	83.86	82.94
3	24	1.50	9.48	3.02	440	0.66	0.46	82.48	81.82

inlet time is assumed to be 20 min. Hydraulic requirements include a value of $N = 0.012$ in Manning's formula and drops in manholes equal to $\Delta(d + h_v) +$ $0.2 \Delta h_v$ (Equation 15-16) for the sewers flowing full.

Columns 1–4 identify the location of the drains. The runs are continuous.

Column 5 records the area tributary to the street inlets that discharge into the manhole at the upper end of the line.

Column 6 gives the cumulative area tributary to a line. For example, in Line 2, Column 6 is the sum of Column 6, Line 1 and Column 5, Line 2, or $(2.19 + 1.97) = 4.16$.

Columns 7 and 8 record the times of flow to the upper end of the drain and in the drain. For example, the inlet time to Manhole 1 is estimated to be 20 min, and the time of flow in Line 1 is calculated to be $340/(60 \times 3.94) = 1.5$ min from Column $15/(60 \times \text{Column } 14)$. Hence the time of flow to the upper end of Line 2 is $(20 + 1.5) = 21.5$ min.

Column 9 is the ci value read from Figure 16-6 for the time of flow to the upper end of the line.

Column $10 = $ Column $9 \times$ Column 6. For example, the runoff entering Line 1 is $1.30 \times 2.19 = 2.85$ cfs.

Columns 11–14 record the chosen size and resulting capacity and velocity of flow of the drains for the tributary runoff and available or required grade. For example, in Line 1, a grade of 6.42 ft per 1,000 and a flow of 2.85 cfs call for a 12-in. drain. This drain will have a capacity of 3.09 cfs and flow at a velocity of 3.94 fps.

Columns 15–19 identify the profile of the drain. Column 15 is taken from the plan or profile of the street; Column $16 = $ Column $15 \times$ Column 12; Column 17 is obtained from Equation 15-16, the required drop in Manhole 2 being $\Delta(d + h_v)$ $+ 0.2 \Delta h_v = \{[(1.5 + 0.14) - (1.0 + 0.23)] + 0.2(0.14 - 0.23)\} = 0.39$ ft; and Column $19 = $ Column $18 -$ Column 16, Column 18 furthermore being Column 19 for the entrant line $-$ Column 17. For example, for Line 2, $(84.28 - 0.42) = 83.86$ and subsequently $(83.86 - 0.92) = 82.94$.

16-9. Design of Combined Sewerage Systems.

The capacity design of combined sewers makes allowance for the maximum rate of sewage flow in addition to the storm-water runoff. If the rain water entering the system is confined to the discharge of roof water, the flow of sanitary sewage is a considerable item in required sewer capacity, and the system is sometimes called a roof-water system rather than a combined system. If the runoff from storms of unusual intensity is carried away by the system, the flow of sanitary sewage, on the other hand, becomes relatively insignificant as an item of required sewer capacity.

The hydraulic design of combined sewerage systems is essentially the same as that for storm sewerage systems. Combined sewerage systems, however, often include structures not ordinarily associated with separate systems. Among these, intercepters, overflows, regulators, and storm-water stand-by tanks are discussed in Sections 3-6, 8-8, and 15-8.

17

PHYSICAL PROPERTIES
OF WATER

17-1. Properties to Be Considered. Among the physical properties of water that are of importance in its hydraulic and sanitary management are its density, viscosity, vapor pressure, surface tension, resistance to diffusion, power of solution and suspension, absorption of light, heat capacity, and absorption and transfer of heat. Many of these properties have already received some consideration in the preceding chapters of this book. Most of them will be summarized in the present chapter or in immediately following chapters, as an aid to the understanding of their impact on water quality and the treatment of water and waste waters.

Most of the physical properties of water, as well as most of its chemical and biological properties, are functions of temperature. Dependence of the physical properties of water upon temperature is so great, in fact, that we have become accustomed to speak of temperature as the factor controlling the behavior of water instead of thinking in terms of the specific properties themselves.

17-2. Density and Viscosity. The density and viscosity of water are among its most important hydraulic properties whenever resistance to motion, especially laminar motion, is involved. They are integral parts of the Reynolds number, for example, and as such enter into the formulation of the settling of particles and the filtration of water through sand. Vertical variation in density of deep bodies of water is responsible for the seasonal stratification and overturning of lakes and reservoirs and through them for wide variations in water quality (Section 17-8). Density currents create short-circuiting in settling tanks as well as larger bodies of water, and viscosity is an important element in flocculation (Section 23-4).

a. Density. The density of water is expressed in one of three ways: (1) as the mass density ρ or mass per unit volume (dimensions: ml^{-3}); (2) as the specific weight γ or weight per unit volume (dimensions: $ml^{-2}t^{-2}$); and (3) as the specific gravity $s = \rho/\rho_0 = \gamma/\gamma_0$ (dimensionless). The subscript zero denotes the density at a standard temperature such as the temperature of maximum density, 4 C (39.2 F) at which water weighs 1 gram per ml. The variation in the density of water [centimeter-gram-second (cgs) system] with temperature is shown in Table 17-1 (also see Table A-3 in the Appendix).

TABLE 17-1. Variation of the Density of Water with Temperature

Temperature, C	0	5	10	15	20	25	30
Density (ρ, γ, s)	0.9999	1.0000	0.9997	0.9991	0.9982	0.9971	0.9957

In the cgs system, ρ and γ are grams/cm^3, mass and force respectively. To convert to pounds per cubic foot, multiply by 62.427. When water freezes it expands by about $\frac{1}{8}$ its volume. The resulting density of ice is 88 to 92% that of water of maximum density.

By contrast, pressure affects the density of water but slightly. The coefficient of compressibility is only about 5×10^{-5} for each added atmosphere of pressure or increase in depth of 33.9 ft. Dissolved impurities change the density of water in direct proportion to their concentration and the magnitude of their own density. The density of sea water is also a function of its "salinity." This varies considerably in different oceans, seas, and salt lakes. The specific gravity of normal sea water is 1.025. Brackish waters near the rim of oceans and in tidal estuaries share the densities of their constituent parts of fresh and salt water.

b. Viscosity. The viscosity of water is expressed in one of two ways: (1) as the absolute or dynamic viscosity μ, or mass per unit length and time (dimensions: $ml^{-1}t^{-1}$), and (2) as the kinematic viscosity $\nu = \mu/\rho$, or length squared per unit time (dimensions: l^2t^{-1}). In the cgs system, the usual measure of absolute viscosity is the centipoise (named after Poiseuille: 1 centipoise $= 10^{-2}$ poise) or 10^{-2} (dyne) (sec)/cm$^2 = 10^{-2}$ (gram mass)/(cm)(sec). To convert to (lb force) (sec)/sq ft, multiply by 2.088×10^{-5}. The standard measure of kinematic viscosity, in the cgs system, is the centistoke (named after Stokes: 1 centistoke $= 10^{-2}$ stoke) or 10^{-2} cm^2/sec. To convert to units of sq ft per sec, multiply by 1.075×10^{-3}. The variation of viscosity with temperature is shown in Table 17-2 (also see Table A-3 in the Appendix).

TABLE 17-2. Variation of the Viscosity of Water with Temperature

Temperature, C	0	5	10	15	20	25	30
Dynamic viscosity (μ), centipoise	1.792	1.519	1.310	1.145	1.009	0.8949	0.8004
Kinematic viscosity (ν), centistoke	1.792	1.519	1.310	1.146	1.011	0.8975	0.8039

The variation in viscosity with temperature is seen to be substantially greater than that in density. Effects of other common factors of water quality are generally not significant. Sewage sludges are plastic rather than viscous (Section 26-9).

Viscosity effects are so common and so great that one should have at least a rough concept of the variation of viscosity with temperature. The following approximation suggested by Hazen [1] will serve this purpose for the normal range of water temperatures (32 to 80 F):

$$\mu_T/\mu_{50} = \nu_T/\nu_{50} = 60/(T + 10) \qquad 17\text{-}1$$

Here T is the temperature in degrees Fahrenheit, and the subscripts denote the viscosities at a temperature of T F and 50 F respectively.

17-3. Vapor Pressure and Surface Tension. Both of these properties are manifested principally at the interface between water and air. The vapor pressure of water is one of the controlling factors in its evaporation whether from a free water surface (Section 6-7) or from the surface of sewage sludge that is to be air-dried (Section 26-18). Air or gas in contact with water is soon saturated with water vapor. This reduces the exchange of gases between water and the atmosphere and creates a partial pressure of water vapor in the overlying atmosphere (Section 17-5). The vapor pressure of water also reduces the suction lift of pumps in proportion to this partial pressure.

Surface tension governs the capillary rise of water (Section 9-12) and is an important link in the exchange of substances from and to water (Section 25-3). The greater the surface tension of a liquid, the poorer is its wetting ability. Surface-tension depressants, such as soap, are employed, therefore, to improve the wetting and deterging effect of water. Dust, pollen, and other foreign particles are held at the air-water interface by surface tension.

a. Vapor Pressure. Air and other gases in contact with water are said to be saturated with water vapor when the vapor is in equilibrium with the water. Until then, there may be undersaturation or supersaturation. The vapor pressure of water p_w is generally expressed in the same terms as barometric pressure (mm Hg at 0 C for example). Its equilibrium values at different temperatures are given briefly in Table 17-3. At the freezing point, the vapor pressure of ice is the

TABLE 17-3. Variation of the Vapor Pressure of Water with Temperature

Temperature, C	0	5	10	15	20	25	30
Vapor pressure (p_w), mm Hg	4.58	6.54	9.21	12.8	17.5	23.8	31.8

[1] Allen Hazen, *Annual Report of the Massachusetts State Board of Health,* 1892.

same as that of water. It drops to 3.01 and 1.95 mm Hg at -5 C and -10 C, respectively.

b. *Surface Tension.* Surface tension has been discussed in Section 9-12 in connection with the capillary rise of ground water. The interfacial tension between a liquid and a gas is essentially a property of the liquid alone. Its dimensions are those of energy per unit area or force per unit length (dimensions: mt^{-2}). The surface tension of water in contact with air is relatively great. Its variation with temperature is shown in the following brief table.

TABLE 17-4. Variation of the Surface Tension of Water in Contact with Air with Temperature

Temperature, C	0	5	10	15	20	25	30
Surface tension (σ), dyne/cm	75.6	74.9	74.2	73.5	72.8	72.0	71.2

17-4. Molecular Diffusion of Dissolved Substances. Even in the absence of mechanical mixing, the concentration of substances that are dissolved in water will eventually become uniform throughout a given volume of water. The process of equalization of concentration is called molecular diffusion. It is extremely slow. Fick's law of diffusion is analogous to the law of heat conduction (Section 17-7). It states that the rate of diffusion $\partial W/\partial t$ across an area A is proportional to the concentration gradient $\partial c/\partial l$ of the substance from a point of higher concentration to one of lower concentration, or

$$\partial W/\partial t = k_d A \; \partial c/\partial l \qquad 17\text{-}2$$

Here W is the weight of dissolved substance, t is the time, A is the cross-sectional area, c is the concentration, l is the distance, and k_d is a proportionality factor called *the coefficient of diffusion.* The magnitude of k_d decreases as the molecular weight increases and varies with temperature in accordance with the van't Hoff-Arrhenius relationship (Section 18-17). For gases, it varies furthermore as the square root of their density. Since the concentration gradient decreases as diffusion takes place, Fick's law is written as a partial differential equation. Solution of this equation may be had by the use of a Fourier series. A solution proposed by Black and Phelps [2] establishes the following series:

$$c_t = c_s - 0.811(c_s - c_0)(e^{-K_d} + \tfrac{1}{9}e^{-9K_d} + \tfrac{1}{25}e^{-25K_d} + \cdots) \qquad 17\text{-}3$$

Here c_s is the saturation concentration of the dissolved substance, c_0

[2] W. M. Black and E. B. Phelps, *Report to the Board of Estimate and Apportionment*, New York, N. Y., 1911.

and c_t are its concentrations at time zero and time t respectively, and

$$K_d = \pi^2 k_d t / (4l^2) \qquad 17\text{-}4$$

The coefficient of diffusion is usually expressed as the grams of solute diffusing through 1 sq cm in 1 hr when the concentration gradient is 1 gram per cc per linear cm. The dimensions of k_d are then $[l^2 t^{-1}]$, and K_d is dimensionless. A few coefficients of molecular diffusion are listed in Table 17-5.

TABLE 17-5. Coefficients of Molecular Diffusion of Gases in Water

Substance	Molecular weight	Temperature, C	k_d, cm^2/hr
NH$_3$	17	15.2	6.4×10^{-2}
O$_2$	32	20.0	6.7×10^{-2}
Cl$_2$	71	12.0	5.1×10^{-2}
CuSO$_4$	98	17.0	4.8×10^{-2}

Within the normal range of water temperatures, the change in the coefficient of diffusion of oxygen in water is closely represented by the equation

$$k_d = (6.7 \times 10^{-2}) \times 1.016^{T-20} = 6.7 \times 10^{-2} e^{0.159(T-20)} \text{ cm}^2/\text{hr} \quad 17\text{-}5$$

where T is the temperature in degrees Centigrade. The coefficient of diffusion of carbon dioxide in water is of the same order of magnitude.

Example 17-1. The initial dissolved oxygen concentration of a quiescent body of water 1 ft (30.48 cm) deep is 3.0 mg/l. Find the concentration after 12 days if the temperature of the water is 18 C on the assumption that the rate of absorption of oxygen from the atmosphere is sufficiently fast to saturate the surface layer of the water in a relatively short time.

For a coefficient of diffusion $k_d = 6.7 \times 10^{-2} \times 1.016^{18-20} = (6.5 \times 10^{-2})$cm^2/hr, Equation 17-4 states that

$$K_d = \frac{\pi^2 \times (6.5 \times 10^{-2}) \times 12 \times 24}{4 \times (30.48)^2} = 0.05$$

Since, at 20 C, the dissolved oxygen saturation value of the water exposed to the atmosphere is 9.2 mg/l (Table A-6 in Appendix), Equation 17-3 gives:

$$c_t = 9.2 - 0.811(9.2 - 3.0)(e^{-0.05} + \tfrac{1}{9}e^{-0.45} + \tfrac{1}{25}e^{-1.25} + \cdots)$$

and

$$c_t = 9.2 - 5.0 \times 1.036 = 4.0 \text{ mg/l}$$

i.e., it takes 12 days to increase the oxygen concentration at the 1-ft level by 1 mg/l when the increase is due to molecular diffusion alone.

The assumption that oxygen is absorbed at the air-water interface faster than it can diffuse downward into the body of water is supported in the next section of this chapter.

17-5. Absorption and Precipitation of Gases. The absorption and precipitation of gases by water is a function of the following:

a. The solubility of the gas, which depends, for a given gas, on (1) the partial pressure of the gas in the atmosphere with which the water is in contact; (2) the temperature of the water; and (3) the concentration of impurities in the water.

b. The rate of solution and precipitation of the gas, which is controlled by (1) the degree of undersaturation or supersaturation of the water; (2) the temperature of the water; and (3) the exposure of the water to contact with the gas, including the prevention, by movement of the atmosphere and the water, of the formation of stationary films at the gas-water interface.

c. The rate of dispersion of the gas in the water by (1) molecular diffusion; (2) convection currents (eddy diffusion); and (3) agitation (eddy diffusion).

a. Solubility of Gases. If a gas does not react chemically with water, when it is taken into solution, its solubility is defined in terms of Henry's law. Of the gases in the earth's atmosphere, oxygen, nitrogen, and the rare gases come strictly within this classification, whereas carbon dioxide reacts with water to the extent of about 1% to form carbonic acid. Among other gases of significance in natural and treated water and in waste waters and products of waste waters such as digesting sludge, methane and hydrogen are inert, and hydrogen sulfide less so. Chlorine is strongly reactive.

In accordance with Dalton's law for gaseous mixtures, each component gas exerts a pressure approximately proportional to the product of the volume percentage of the gas and the total pressure of the mixture. This pressure is known as the *partial pressure* of the gas. Henry's law states that the concentration of a gas in a liquid, such as water, is directly proportional to the concentration, or partial pressure, of the gas in the atmosphere in contact with the liquid or solution, i.e.,

$$c_s = k_s p \qquad\qquad 17\text{-}6$$

Here c_s is the saturation concentration of the gas in the water, p is the partial pressure of the gas in the gas phase, and k_s is the proportionality constant, called *the coefficient of absorption*. The units of c_s are conveniently ml/l, for p as a proportionality volume and for k_s in ml/l. These volumes are converted to weights on the basis of Avogadro's hypothesis that equal volumes of ideal gases contain, at the same temperature and pressure, equal numbers of molecules. At standard temperature and pressure (0 C and 760 mm Hg, or 32 F and 29.92 in. Hg), the molal volume of any gas is 22,412 ml per gram-mol or 359 cu ft per lb-mol. Reduction of the volume of gas at a given temperature and pressure to standard conditions is made by means of the perfect gas equation $pV = NRT$, as

$$V_0 = V \frac{p - p_w}{p_0} \frac{T_0}{T} \qquad 17\text{-}7$$

Here N is the number of mols of gas in the volume V; R is the universal gas constant (8.3156×10^7 dyne-cm per gram-mol and deg C absolute, or 1,546 lb-ft per lb-mol and deg F absolute); T is the absolute temperature ($273.1 + $ deg C, or $459.7 + $ deg F); p is the absolute pressure; p_w is the vapor pressure of water; and the subscript zero denotes standard conditions. A pressure of 1 atm or 760 mm Hg is commonly specified for k_s. For other pressures, suitable adjustments must be made in applying Equation 17-6. The solubilities of a number of gases that are important in water supply and waste disposal are shown in Table 17-6.

TABLE 17-6.   Absorption Coefficients of Common Gases in Water

(Milliliter of gas, reduced to 0 C and 760 mm Hg, per liter of water when partial pressure of gas is 760 mm Hg)

Gas	Molecular weight	Weight at 0 C and 760 mm, gram per l	Temperature				Boiling point, C
			0	10	20	30	
Hydrogen, H₂	2.016	0.09004	21.5	19.6	18.2	17.0	−253
Methane, CH₄	16.03	0.7160	55.6	41.8	33.1	27.6	−165
Nitrogen, N₂	28.02	1.251	23.0	18.5	15.5	13.6	−195
Oxygen, O₂	32.00	1.429	49.3	38.4	31.4	26.7	−183
Ammonia, NH₃	17.03	0.7706	1,300	910	711	....	−38.5
Hydrogen sulfide, H₂S	34.08	1.523	4,690	3,520	2,670	....	−60
Carbon dioxide, CO₂	44.00	1.977	1,710	1,190	878	665	−80
Ozone, O₃	48.00	2.144	641	520	368	233	−119
Sulfur dioxide, SO₂	64.06	2.927	79,800	56,600	39,700	27,200	−10
Chlorine, Cl₂	70.91	3.167	4,610	3,100	2,260	1,770	−33.6
Air *	......	1.2928	28.8	22.6	18.7	16.1	....

* At sea level dry air contains 78.03% N₂, 20.99% O₂, 0.94% A, 0.03% CO₂, and 0.01% other gases by volume. For ordinary purposes it is assumed to be composed of 79% N₂ and 21% O₂.

Example 17-2. What is the concentration of oxygen in pure water at 0 C exposed to air under a barometric pressure of 760 mm?

From Table 17-6, $k_s = 49.3$ ml per l. Since dry air normally includes 20.99% of oxygen by volume and it must be assumed that the air in contact with the water is saturated with water vapor, the partial pressure of the oxygen is 0.2099 $(760 - 4.58) = 158$ mm Hg, the value of 4.58 being the vapor pressure of water at 0 C. The volume concentration of oxygen, therefore, is $49.3 \times 158/760 = 10.2$ ml/l, and since 1 ml of oxygen weighs $2 \times 16 \times 10^{-3}/22,412 = 1.43$ mg, the weight concentration of oxygen is $1.43 \times 10.2 = 14.6$ mg/l.

Water is saturated with a gas when the proportionality implied in Henry's law is fully established. Rising temperatures decrease the saturation value as do the salts of hard and brackish waters. Increasing altitude or a falling barometer reduces the solubility in the ratio of the observed pressure to the standard pressure. The approximate change in pressure with altitude is 1% for every 270 ft of elevation. The saturation values for oxygen in fresh and brackish waters at different temperatures are given in Table A-6 in the Appendix. If the salinity of sea water is expressed in milligrams per liter of chlorides n, the dissolved oxygen saturation value of salt water is approximated by multiplying the value for fresh water by $(1 - n \times 10^{-5})$. See Section 20-12. Sea water of substantially full strength from the North Atlantic has a chloride content of about 18,000 mg/l. Its dissolved-oxygen saturation value is, therefore, about 82% that of fresh water. The corresponding value for domestic sewage [3] is reported to be 95%.

b. *Rate of Absorption of Gases.* If, as suggested at the outset of this section, it is postulated that the rate of absorption of a gas is proportional to its degree of undersaturation (or saturation deficit) in the absorbing liquid, we may express the rate of absorption of a gas as

$$dc/dt = K_g(c_s - c) \qquad 17\text{-}8$$

Here dc/dt is the change in concentration or the rate of absorption of the gas at time t; c_s is the saturation concentration of the gas at a given temperature; c_t is its concentration at time t; and K_g is the rate constant of solution or gas transfer for the conditions of exposure. Integration between the limits c_0 at $t = 0$ and c_t at $t = t$ yields the equation:

$$c_t - c_0 = (c_s - c_0)(1 - e^{-K_g t}) \qquad 17\text{-}9$$

The magnitude of K_g increases with the temperature. It increases also with the degree of mixing to which the gas and liquid are subjected, i.e., with the rate of renewal of the gas-liquid interface and the degree of eddy diffusion. The temperature effect can be expressed in terms of the van't Hoff-Arrhenius equation (Section 18-17), but the degree of mixing or rate of renewal of the interface and of eddy diffusion is difficult of definition, unless the physical power involved can be identified. Since entrance of a gas into a liquid must take place at the gas-liquid interface, K_g becomes more specific if the area of the interface in its relation to the volume of the liquid can be identified. This can be done, for example, where water is sprayed into the air in droplets, or when air is bubbled through water. The over-all value of K_g is then $k_g A/V$, where k_g is *the gas-transfer coefficient* and A/V is the inter-

[3] W. A. Moore, *Sewage Works J.*, *10*, 241 (1938).

facial area between the gas and liquid per unit volume of the liquid.

An assumption implicit in the determination of the magnitude of k_g is that the rate of gas transfer across the gas-liquid interface is the controlling factor rather than the rate of diffusion of the dissolved gas within the liquid. Values of k_g in centimeters per hour observed by Becker [4] for the rate of absorption by water of oxygen, nitrogen, and air from bubbles may be expressed as follows for a temperature range of 3.5 to 35 C: O_2, $32.3 \times 1.018^{T-20}$; N_2, $34.0 \times 1.019^{T-20}$; air, $32.1 \times 1.019^{T-20}$. Here T is the temperature in degrees Centigrade and k_g, which has the dimension of velocity $[lt^{-1}]$, is the coefficient of gas transfer. It should be noted that these values of k_g apply only to the conditions of exposure that obtained in Becker's experiments. Both higher and lower values can be observed in different circumstances.

Ordinarily, boundary films form at the interface both in the liquid and in the gas. Passage through these stationary layers is then a matter of diffusion. Hence it is determined by the thickness of the films. Film thickness, although fundamentally a function of kinematic viscosity, is decreased by stirring or agitating the main body of gas or liquid. In the passage of oxygen from air into water, for example, the oxygen must diffuse through the stationary air and water films at the interface. In accordance with Section 17-4, the rate of diffusion depends upon the area of the interface and the concentration gradient, or

$$dW/(A\ dt) = k_{d(g)}(p_g - p_i) = k_{d(l)}(c_i - c_l) \qquad 17\text{-}10$$

where $dW/(A\ dt)$ is the quantity of gas passing through a unit area in a unit time; p_g and p_i are respectively the partial pressures of the gas in the main body of the gas and at the interface; c_i and c_l are respectively the concentration of the gas at the interface and in the main body of the liquid; and $k_{d(g)}$ and $k_{d(l)}$ are respectively diffusion coefficients of the gas in the gaseous and liquid phases. These coefficients equal the true diffusion coefficient per unit film thickness. They possess the dimension of velocity $[lt^{-1}]$. Equilibrium obtains at the interface. Hence p_i is a function of c_i and equals c_i/k_s when Henry's law applies. Three general situations occur:

1. When a gas is highly soluble in a liquid (e.g., NH_3 in water), c_i will be large even when p_i is small. Passage of the gas across the gas film is then the controlling factor, and Equation 17-10 approaches a value of $dW/A\ dt = k_{d(g)}p_g$ because p_i is negligible. Therefore, we may write $dc/dt = k_{d(g)}p_g A/V$, and it

[4] H. G. Becker, "Mechanism of Absorption of Moderately Soluble Gases in Water," *Ind. Eng. Chem.*, *16*, 1220 (1924).

follows that gas transfer is promoted by reducing the thickness of the gas film by moving or stirring the gas.

2. When the solubility of a gas in a liquid is low (e.g., O_2, N_2, and CO_2 in water) c_i is practically equal to c_s, the concentration at which the dissolved gas is in equilibrium with the gas in the atmosphere (saturation concentration). Passage of the gas through the liquid film is then the controlling factor, and Equation 17-10 approaches a value of $dW/A \, dt = k_{d(l)}(c_s - c)$, where $c = c_l$ is the concentration in the liquid. Hence $dc/dt = k_{d(l)}(c_s - c)A/V$ which is identical with Equation 17-8. Gas transfer is then promoted by reducing the thickness of the liquid film by stirring or agitating the liquid.

3. For gases of intermediate solubility (e.g., H_2S in water) the effect of both films remains important. Both gas and liquid must, therefore, be stirred or agitated to hold down film thicknesses if gas transfer is to be promoted. If Henry's law can be applied with reasonable satisfaction, an over-all coefficient k, which depends upon both film coefficients, can be used, and we may write:

$$dc/dt = k(c_s - c)A/V \qquad\qquad 17\text{-}11$$

Observed magnitudes of $k_{d(l)}$ for gases of low solubility are summarized in Table 17-7.

TABLE 17-7. Coefficients of Diffusion of Gases of Low Solubility in Water

A. Diffusion through plane surfaces

Gas	Stirring rate, rpm	$k_{d(l)}$, cm/hr	Liquid film * thickness, cm	Observer
Air	0	0.4	1.7×10^{-1}	Adeney and Becker
O_2	60	3.3	20×10^{-2}	Davis
Air	150	5.0	1.3×10^{-2}	Becker
CO_2	250	7.5	....	Bohr
Air	1,000	15.0	4.5×10^{-3}	Becker

B. Diffusion through spherical bubbles

Gas	Size of sphere, cm^3	$k_{d(l)}$, cm/hr	Liquid film * thickness, cm	Observer
Air	15	60	1.1×10^{-3}	Adeney and Becker
Air	9	30	2.2×10^{-3}	Adeney and Becker
Air	3.4×10^{-3}	10	3.4×10^{-2}	Alty
CO_2	3.3×10^{-2}	40	....	Ledig and Weaver
CO_2	2.7×10^{-3}	20	....	Ledig and Weaver

* The liquid film thickness equals the coefficient of molecular diffusion (Table 17-5) divided into $k_{d(l)}$.

If the concentration gradient across the interface of a bubble is constant, the diameter of the bubble will decrease linearly with time. The rate of decrease is proportional to the gas transfer coefficient and concentration gradient and inversely proportional to the molecular weight of the gas. Turbulence, temperature, and concentration of dissolved substances all play a part. The higher the concentration of dissolved substances, the lower is the transfer coefficient.

The rate at which a gas is absorbed by a falling drop of water or a rising bubble of gas is greatest at the moment of formation. It decreases rapidly thereafter, because the surface film of water increases in thickness in the absence of internal liquid motion.

c. Rate of Precipitation of Gases. In contrast to absorption, the rate of precipitation or dissolution of a gas from a liquid becomes proportional to its degree of oversaturation in the precipitating liquid or the saturation surplus. It follows that the equations for rates of absorption should apply also to rates of dissolution. The fact that the saturation concentration c_s will be less than the observed concentration c_0 makes for negative differences that indicate precipitation.

Example 17-3. In an experiment on the removal of carbon dioxide from water sprayed into the air in droplets 0.55 cm in diameter, the initial supersaturation of the water with carbon dioxide was 27.5 mg/l. After 1 sec exposure this was reduced to 11.5 mg/l. Find the coefficient of gas transfer.

Since $c_s - c_0 = -27.5$ mg/l and $c_t - c_s = 11.5$ mg/l, $c_t - c_0 = -16$ mg/l. In accordance with Equation 17-9, therefore, $(-16) = -27.5(1 - e^{-K_g \times 1})$, and $K_g = 0.872$ per sec. The volume of droplet per unit surface area being $0.55/6 = 0.0917$ cm, $k_g = 0.872 \times 0.0917 = 0.0800$ cm/sec. The transfer coefficient then equals $0.0800 \times 3,600 = 288$ cm/hr.

17-6. Solution and Suspension of Solids. The solution of a solid in water cannot be estimated in terms comparable to the solution of ideal gases. The solubility is a function of temperature, the nature of the solid, and the nature and concentration of the impurities in the water. As a general rule, the solubility of solids, in contrast with the solubility of gases, increases with temperature; but it may vary considerably within different temperature ranges. Heat causes some substances to break down into component constituents the solubility of which then controls their maintainable concentration. The precipitation, by heat, of calcium carbonate, $CaCO_3$, from calcium bicarbonate, $Ca(HCO_3)_2$, is an example of this effect. Carbon dioxide and water, or carbonic acid, are released at the same time. Pressure, on the other hand, has little measurable effect on the solution of solids. The state and behavior of substances dissolved in water is discussed in Chapter 18.

The rate of solution of solids in water, like that of gases, is proportional to the degree of undersaturation of the solid in solution. It varies, furthermore, directly with the surface area of the solid and is inversely proportional to the volume of the liquid. The larger the surface area of the solid per unit volume of water, the more rapid is its solution. A theoretical relationship for the rate of solution of solids is, therefore, much like that for gases. Since the surface area of a given weight of material that is subdivided into n nearly spherical particles varies as $n^{1/3}$, particle size is seen to exert considerable influence on the rate of solution of a given weight of solid.

Suspended solids are so coarsely divided that they are visible to the naked eye, either directly or by their capacity to absorb or scatter light. They are the cause of turbidity and include substances emptied into water, lifted into it by scour, or developing in the water by chemical precipitation or by the growth of living organisms.

17-7. Absorption of Light and Heat. The absorption of solar energy by water is important in three respects: (1) utilization of radiant energy through photosynthesis, by chlorophyllaceous organisms, and stimulation of plankton growth (Section 19-1); (2) destruction of living organisms and bleaching of color, especially natural color, by actinic, or chemically active, wave lengths, more particularly, by ultraviolet light (Section 27-3); and (3) conversion of absorbed energy into heat.

a. Absorption of Sunlight. Not all of the solar energy that falls upon a body of water penetrates into it. Part is reflected at the surface, the amount of reflection increasing as the angle at which the sun's rays strike the surface becomes more acute. As a result, the period of daylight under water is much shorter than that in the atmosphere. Reflection is further increased through the ruffling of the water surface by wind.

Absorption of solar radiation is selective. It is described, for a given wave length, by the equation

$$di/dl = -k_e i \qquad\qquad 17\text{-}12$$

whence

$$i/i_0 = e^{-k_e l} \qquad \text{or} \qquad \log i = \log i_0 - (k_e \log e)l \qquad 17\text{-}13$$

and

$$p_e = (i_0 - i)/i_0 = 1 - e^{-k_e l} \qquad\qquad 17\text{-}14$$

Here i is the intensity of the radiation at a depth [5] l below the surface; i_0 is the initial or surface intensity; k_e is *the coefficient of extinction* or rate of absorption (dimensions l^{-1}) of a given wave length; and p_e is the proportion of energy absorbed.

Values of k_e and p_e per foot of depth of distilled water for wave lengths close to the mean of each color range within the visible spectrum are shown in Table 17-8. They are based on measurements by

[5] More exactly, the length of path of the light beam.

TABLE 17-8.   Absorption of Light by Distilled Water within the Visible Spectrum

Color	Wave length, Angstrom units *	Coefficient of extinction, k_e per ft	Proportionate absorption, $100p_e$ per ft
(Upper limit)	8,000	5.7×10^{-1}	43
Red	7,200	3.2×10^{-1}	27
Orange	6,125	7.7×10^{-2}	7.4
Yellow	5,650	1.3×10^{-2}	1.3
Green	5,040	3.1×10^{-3}	0.30
Blue	4,730	1.6×10^{-3}	0.16
Violet	4,078	3.1×10^{-3}	0.30
(Lower limit)	3,650	1.1×10^{-2}	1.1

* 1 Angstrom unit $= 10^{-4}$ microns $= 10^{-8}$ cm.

James and Birge.[6] The intensity of the radiations is seen to drop faster from the blue outward to both ends of the spectrum. There results a shift in the spectral distribution of solar energy with increasing depths. In natural waters, the coefficient of extinction is increased by the presence of dissolved and suspended substances. These substances, too, have a selective absorption. Changes in water quality with depth complicate the picture further. The absorption of disinfecting ultraviolet light, 2,537 Angstrom units (A), by natural waters is appreciable: $k_e = 0.2$ per cm approximately and $100p_e = 18\%$ per cm (Section 27-3). In northern latitudes the bleaching of natural color in bodies of water of moderate depth proceeds at a rate of about 20% per month.

b. *Heat Capacity.* The heat capacity of water is great. Much heat is required to warm it, and much cold to cool it. Heat capacity is the amount of heat required to raise a unit mass of water 1 deg in temperature. Specific heat is the ratio of the heat capacity at a given temperature to that of water at a standard temperature. For most engineering calculations, specific heat and heat capacity may be considered numerically equal. The units of measurement of heat capacity are calories per gram per degree Centigrade or British thermal units per pound per degree Fahrenheit. They are numerically the same. The variation in the heat capacity of water with temperature is small. At atmospheric pressure it is 1.00 Btu/(lb)(deg F) at 39.2 F, and 1.02 at 212 F. An average value is normally used for a given temperature range. The specific heat of ice is but half that of the water from which

6 H. R. James and E. A. Birge, "A Laboratory Study of the Absorption of Light by Lake Waters," *Trans., Wisconsin Acad. Sci., 31,* 1 (1938).

it is formed. By comparison, the specific heat of dry air is 0.24 Btu/(lb) (deg F) and varies but slightly with temperature. The value for moist air is closely 0.25.

The heats of fusion and vaporization of water are also great. The heat of fusion of ice is 144 Btu/lb. The heat of vaporization of water at normal water temperatures is $(1,094 - 0.56T)$ Btu/lb where T is the temperature of the water. At 212 F, it is 970 Btu/lb. To convert from Btu/lb to cal/gram, multiply by 0.554.

c. Absorption and Transfer of Heat. Most of the energy absorbed from the sun by a natural body of water is converted into heat. If the sun's rays were monochromatic and the warming of the water took place only by radiation, while the absorptive capacity of the water itself remained uniform, the temperature of the water would decrease logarithmically from the surface to the bottom (Equation 17-14). Selective absorption, however, steepens the gradient within the upper layers of water. Even more radical shifts are induced by conduction and convection. Radiant energy absorbed by the bottom of bodies of water is released in the form of longer wave lengths that are then trapped by the overlying water. The temperature of bottom sediments is less than that of the water in summer and more in winter. The deeper the deposit, the greater is the difference.

Both air and water are poor conductors of heat. In the absence of mass motion, transfer of heat by conduction, after a steady state has been reached, is defined by the equation

$$dQ/dt = -k_T A \, dT/dl \qquad 17\text{-}15$$

Here Q is the quantity of heat transferred in time t, A is the area through which flow takes place, T is the temperature change in the distance l, and k_T (the proportionality factor) is *the thermal conductivity*. The results of measurements of thermal conductivity are cal/(sec) (cm^2) (deg C per cm) or Btu/(hr) (sq ft) (deg F per ft). The thermal conductivity of water is 0.34 Btu/(hr) (sq ft) (deg F per ft) at 32 F and increases to 0.42 at 212 F. The corresponding values for air are 0.014 and 0.018 respectively. To convert to cal/(sec) (cm^2) (deg C per cm) multiply by 4.13×10^{-3}. The thermal conductivity of ice is about twice as great as that of the water from which it is formed.

There is a close analogy between heat conduction and molecular diffusion (Section 17-4). The method of attack that can be employed in solving problems relating to one of them applies equally well to the other.

Example 17-4. For conditions of steady state, find the rate of transfer of heat through one sq ft of water 8.8 ft in depth when the difference in temperature is 20 F, the average water temperature being 60 F.

Assuming linear variation in k_T, its value at 60 F is 0.35, and by Equation 17-15:

$$Q/t = 0.35 \times 1 \times (20/8.8) = 0.80 \text{ Btu/hr}$$

As shown in this example, changes in water temperature due to conduction would be extremely small and slow, were it not for modifying influences at the air-water interface. Since the specific heat of water is about four times that of dry air (0.24), and since the mass of water is relatively much greater than that of air, the temperature at the interface tends to approach that of the water quite closely. Equilibrium conditions are upset by wind and water movements. Air motion is normally the more vigorous of the two, and heat is distributed through a body of water, both horizontally and vertically, by wind action. Lack of wind-induced currents explains why the loss of heat from an ice-covered body of water is small in spite of the smaller specific heat and higher conductivity of the ice.

Equilibrium conditions are destroyed also by temperature changes due to heat transfer from one fluid to the other, including changes in temperature produced by evaporation. If the surface water is cooled, either by contact with cold air or by evaporation, it becomes denser and must sink. Vertical (convective) currents are thereby set in motion, and heat is transferred within the mass of water itself.

If the water temperature lies below the wet-bulb temperature of the overlying air, the water will be warmed by the air; there will be no thermal convection in either fluid, and little exchange of heat will occur. If, on the other hand, the water temperature is higher than the wet-bulb temperature of the air, the water will be cooled by evaporation; thermal convection currents will be set in motion in both fluids; and the interchange of heat will be considerable.

Example 17-5. Find the depth to which surface evaporation of 0.1 in. of water will cool a body of water by 1.0 F when the temperature of the water is 60 F.

Since the latent heat of vaporization of water at 60 F is $(1,094 - 0.56 \times 60) = 1,060$ Btu/lb, the surface evaporation of 0.1 in. of water will cool 1,060 in. or 8.8 ft of underlying water by 1.0 F.

d. Thermal Resistance to Mixing. The water that is driven to the windward shore builds up a head which generates return currents. Depending upon the topography of the shore, these currents travel at or below the water surface. The returning water is displaced downward in coves and laterally where points of land jut out from shore. The vertical distribution of wind-induced currents in an idealized cross-section of lake or reservoir is illustrated in Figure 17-1. The depth of the return currents depends upon the temperature of the water. The greater the change in temperature with depth, the greater is the thermal resistance to mixture and the more will the return currents be confined to the upper layer of water. By thermal resistance is meant the resistance of colder and therefore denser and lower-lying water to be displaced by warmer and therefore lighter and higher-lying water. The shearing plane divides the surface currents that follow the wind from the return currents that run counter to the wind.

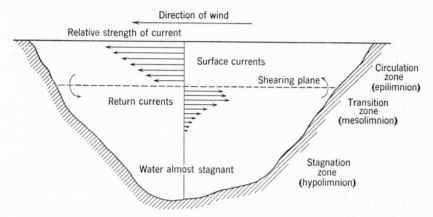

Figure 17-1. Direction and relative horizontal velocity of wind-induced currents in a lake or reservoir (idealized). *After Whipple, Fair, and Whipple.*

Birge[7] has suggested the following relationship for the work done by the wind against gravity in mixing a column of water in which the temperature gradient is uniform in order to bring the column of water to uniform density:[8]

$$W = \frac{AL^2}{12}(\gamma_2 - \gamma_1) \qquad\qquad 17\text{-}16$$

Here W is the work done by the wind, A is the cross-sectional area of

[7] E. A. Birge, "The Work of the Wind in Warming a Lake," *Trans. Wisconsin Acad. Sci.*, *24*, 341 (1914).

[8] This equation is derived from the general premise that

$$W = A \int_0^L \phi(l) \left[l - \frac{L}{2} \right] dl$$

in which l is the distance from the top of the column and $\phi(l)$ is a function expressing density in terms of l. When the temperature gradient is uniform, $\phi(l)$ is a rational integral function of the second degree, because the weight density $\gamma = c_1 T^2 + c_2 T + c_3$, where T is the temperature and c_1, c_2, and c_3 are numerical constants.

a column of height L, and γ_2 and γ_1 are the specific weights of the upper and lower strata of the column respectively. This relationship is not presented for purposes of making calculations but in order to explain the differences in the seasonal overturnings that are discussed in the next section of this chapter.

17-8. Thermal Stratification and Seasonal Change in a Body of Water. The interplay of temperature, density, and wind during the different seasons of the year produces a characteristic pattern for the

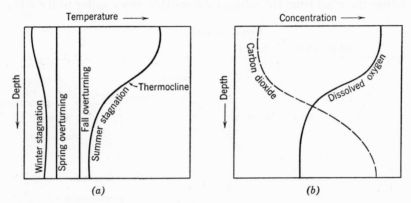

Figure 17-2. Vertical gradients of temperature and water quality in lakes, reservoirs, and other deep bodies of water (idealized). (*a*) Characteristic thermal gradients. (*b*) Oxygen and carbon dioxide gradients during summer stagnation.

thermal stratification of lakes and reservoirs. Figure 17-2*a* shows a series of characteristic temperature gradients for waters in the middle latitudes of the temperate zone.

During the winter, the water immediately below the ice stands substantially at 32 F, although the ice itself is often much colder at and near its surface. At the same time, the temperature at the bottom of the lake or reservoir is not far from that of maximum density (39.2 F). The water is in comparatively stable equilibrium and inversely stratified insofar as temperature is concerned. This is the condition of *winter stagnation.* Ice cover blankets off the lake from wind disturbances, and there is no significant vertical or horizontal movement of the water.

As soon as the ice breaks up in the spring, the water near the surface begins to warm up. Until it reaches the temperature of maximum density, it also becomes denser and tends to sink. Unstable equilibrium, caused by diurnal fluctuations in temperature and aided by wind, results in vertical circulation. It becomes particularly pronounced when the temperature of the water throughout the vertical is practically uniform and close to the temperature of maximum density. This is the condition of *spring circulation* or *spring overturning*. It lasts several weeks but varies in length during different years.

As spring turns into summer, the surface water becomes progressively warmer. Lighter water overlies denser water, and, as the temperature differences increase, circulation is confined more and more to the upper layers of water. A second period of stable equilibrium is established, and the water becomes directly stratified. This is the condition of *summer stagnation*. In northern latitudes, this period extends from April to November. The water below 25 ft is nearly stagnant, and the bottom temperature remains almost constant and near the temperature of maximum density.

As the autumn advances, the surface water cools and sinks. Equilibrium once again becomes unstable. The water is stirred to greater and greater depths. When the temperature gradient has become substantially vertical the *great overturning* or *fall overturning* takes place, because all of the water is easily put in circulation by autumn winds. Subsequent freezing of the surface water once again creates the condition of winter stagnation.

Zonal differentiation of water strata is most pronounced during the period of summer stagnation. As shown in Figure 17-1, we can identify three zones: the circulation, the stagnation, and the transition zones. The *circulation zone* is so named because the water within it is of substantially the same temperature and density and hence easily mixed horizontally by wind-induced currents and vertically by convective currents. This uppermost zone is separated from the lowermost *stagnation zone* by a relatively thin stratum in which the temperature changes rapidly. This intermediate stratum is called the *transition zone*. It is generally defined arbitrarily as comprising that layer of water in which water temperatures change by 0.5 F per ft or more (Figure 17-2a). In the stagnation zone, horizontal movements are very slight, and vertical ones almost absent. The circulation, transition, and stagnation zones are also called the epilimnion, thermocline or mesolimnion, and hypolimnion respectively.[9]

That the distribution of heat can be much more rapid in the spring than it is later in the season is shown by the following sample calculation of the relative amount of work that must be done by the wind in mixing water near the temperature of maximum density on the one hand and at a summer temperature on the other.

---

[9] The prefixes of these words have their origin in the Greek words for upon (above), middle, and under (below). The word limnion comes from the Greek *limne*, a lake.

Example 17-6. Find the relative thermal resistance to mixing water at 39.2 F (4.0 C) and at 78.0 F (25.6 C) if the difference in temperature within the water stratum is 1.8 F.

In accordance with Equation 17-16, $W_2/W_1 = \Delta\gamma_2/\Delta\gamma_1$, where the subscripts 1 and 2 denote the higher and lower temperatures respectively and $\Delta\gamma$ represents the difference in the specific weights within the water stratum

Since $\Delta\gamma$ is 0.8×10^{-5} at 39.2 F and 26×10^{-5} at 78.0 F, $W_2/W_1 = 32$. This signifies that the wind must do 32 times as much work at the higher temperature as it does at the lower one.

The variation in the density of water with temperature, therefore, explains why the period of the spring overturn is relatively short, whereas that of the fall overturn, when the water is much warmer, may be quite protracted. During the summer, the rapid drop in temperature within the thermocline produces a barrier that, because of the elevated temperatures and associated great differences in density, is not easily disturbed by the wind. As a result, a lake, as suggested by Birge, really consists of two lakes, one superimposed upon the other.

17-9. Distribution of Dissolved Gases and Other Substances in a Body of Water. Because of the slowness of molecular diffusion, the thermal gradients of lakes and other bodies of water are likewise gradients in the concentration of gases dissolved in the water. The surface of a body of water is not only a window through which it receives radiant energy. It is also a lung through which it takes in oxygen from the atmosphere and releases to it carbon dioxide and other dissolved gases that are generated within the water. Oxygen is taken in at the surface and distributed by circulating water within the epilimnion. Conversely gases of decomposition are released by being brought into contact with the air that overlies the surface of the water. As shown in Figure 17-2b, there is within the thermocline a sharp drop in dissolved oxygen and a rise in the concentration of gases of decomposition. Below the thermocline the concentration of dissolved oxygen reaches a minimal value (often zero), that of the gases of decomposition a maximum one. The degree of undersaturation of dissolved oxygen and the degree of supersaturation of the gases of decomposition in the bottom water depend upon the intensity of the processes of decomposition that are taking place in the water. Decomposition is obviously a function of water quality and of the cleanliness of the bottom itself (see Section 10-4).

Thermal stratification reflects the mass movement that takes place in an otherwise substantially quiescent body of water. As a result, thermal stratification produces gradients in water quality that are images (e.g., dissolved oxygen) or mirrored images (e.g., carbon dioxide) of the thermal gradient. There is, therefore, a vertical, seasonal variation in water quality within a reservoir or similar body of water as well as a seasonal variation in water temperature. This fact underlies the practice of shifting the depth of draft to select water of the best quality available for the purposes that it is to serve (Section 10-9).

The quality gradient, which like the thermal gradient is pronounced during the period of summer stagnation and less so during that of winter stagnation, is suppressed during the overturns. The quality of the water at all depths then becomes substantially the average of the entire body of water, and the selection of water of better than average quality becomes impossible. For this reason, the periods of overturning, in particular that of the fall or long overturning, are often periods of noticeably deteriorated water quality in communities that are not provided with purification works. During the overturns, the vertical mixing of the water may carry resting cells of light-loving organisms from the dark depths, into which they have settled, upward to the surface where they can flourish. Food substances, too, are made available within the upper strata. The overturns may then be accompanied or followed by sudden, heavy growths of algae (particularly diatoms) and other microorganisms.

18-1. General Considerations. Natural waters are never completely pure. During their precipitation and their passage over or through the ground they acquire a wide variety of dissolved or suspended impurities. The concentrations of these substances are seldom large in the ordinary chemical sense. Nonetheless, they may profoundly modify the chemical behavior of the water or its usefulness for the purposes that it is to serve. As a result the term "water chemistry" refers principally, not to water itself, but to the chemical properties in aqueous solution of the wide variety of substances (1) found as impurities in natural waters, (2) added to water during treatment, (3) picked up in the flow of water through pipes or other conduits, and (4) imposed upon water by the manifold uses that convert it to household, municipal, or industrial waste water.

The chemical substances of interest to the engineer range from dissolved gases through numerous inorganic materials to the complex organic compounds that impart color to natural waters or are characteristic of sewage and other water-borne wastes. It is the purpose of this chapter to present the principles that form a common basis for considerations of the specific chemistry of any of these materials. Only a few typical applications of the general relations to the field of sanitation are presented in this chapter; more detailed treatment of the applied chemistry is found in later chapters of this book.

18-2. Solution and Suspension of Impurities. In reference to the degree of dispersion or size of the ultimate particles, the impurities in water are classified broadly as (1) suspended, (2) colloidal, and (3) dissolved. This classification is used especially for solid materials.

Substances so coarse that they can be removed (1) by settling or (2) by ordinary filtration through filter paper or the asbestos mat of a Gooch crucible are said to be in suspension. Technically they are referred to as *settleable solids* when they conform to the first criterion, and as *suspended solids* when they meet the latter one. The lower limit of the size range for this class of materials lies between

462

0.1 and 1 micron (1 micron or $\mu = 10^{-4}$ cm) varying somewhat with the shape and density of the particles. This is about the common size of bacteria and the wave length of visible light (0.4–0.8 μ) and so represents also about the lower limit of microscopic visibility.

In the *dissolved* state the divided material or *solute* is homogeneously and molecularly (or ionically) dispersed in the *solvent* to form a *true solution*. Particle diameters range from those of single atoms, 2×10^{-8} to 3×10^{-8} cm, up to about 1 mμ (10^{-7} cm), approximately the resolution limit of the electron microscope. Materials in true solution cannot be separated from the solvent by any form of filtration.

Between the upper limit of true solutions and the lower limit of suspensions lies the *colloidal* range. In colloidal dispersions, the particles: (1) cannot be removed from the water by means of ordinary filtration but can be separated by processes of *ultrafiltration* or of *dialysis* through the pores of animal or artificial membranes; (2) are not microscopically visible, but can be visualized as specks of light in the *ultramicroscope* and can be photographed by the electron microscope; and (3) will not settle under the action of gravity because of their "Brownian motion," but can be caused to settle in a centrifuge or, better, in an ultracentrifuge. Colloidal particles may either be aggregates or single large molecules, such as those of proteins or starches.

Many substances of interest to the field of sanitary engineering occur as colloidal dispersions; the stain or color of natural waters, the proteins of sewage, and highly dispersed forms of the hydrated oxides of iron, aluminum, and silicon are examples of such materials. Their chemical behavior is discussed in Section 19 of this chapter.

18-3. Solutions and Solubility. Gases, liquids, and solids may all dissolve in water to form true solutions. The amount of solute present may vary continuously below a certain limit, the *solubility*. The solubility is the concentration of solute present when the solution is in a state of equilibrium with an excess of the pure solute.

The principles, especially Henry's law, applicable to the solubility in water of gases that do not react with it have already been discussed in Section 17-5. Comparable, simple, quantitative principles cannot be given for the solubilities of solids and liquids or of the more reactive gases. In general, the solubility of solids and liquids is but slightly dependent on pressure, so that for practical purposes the solubility of a given liquid or solid may be considered a function of temperature alone, unless extreme pressure conditions are involved, and hence is a constant at a given temperature. The solubilities of most inorganic salts increase with rise in temperature, but a number of the calcium compounds of sanitary interest, including $CaCO_3$, $CaSO_4$, and $Ca(OH)_2$, decrease in solubility with increase in temperature.

Two types of solution in water may be distinguished. Solutes like oxygen, alcohol, or sugar are dispersed as single molecules by the solvent water. Other substances, principally those classed as salts, acids, or bases, dissolve in or react with the water to give solutions containing charged particles called *ions*. The solubilities of substances yielding ionic solutions are greatly affected by the presence of additional amounts of any one of the constituent ions. This effect is treated quantitatively in Section 18-9.

Apparent solubilities of all types of materials may be affected by chemical reaction with the water or with other solutes. Thus calcium carbonate, which has a true solubility of 13 mg/l in pure water, shows a much higher apparent solubility in water containing carbon dioxide because of chemical reaction with it. However, the true solubility of calcium carbonate is actually less under these conditions than in pure water.

18-4. Chemical Units and Conversions. In chemical work, the concentrations of dissolved materials in water are usually expressed as *molarity*, defined as the number of gram molecular weights or *mols* of substance present in a liter of the solution. Solutions of equal *molarity* then have equal numbers of molecules of dissolved substance per unit volume. Thus a 1-*molar* solution of urea, $CO(NH_2)_2$, with a molecular weight of 60, contains 60 grams per liter of solution, and a 1-*molar* solution of cane sugar, $C_{12}H_{22}O_{11}$, contains 342 grams per liter, but the two have equal numbers of solute molecules.

Molarity is related to weight (wt) of dissolved material, in grams, by the equation:

Wt in grams = Molarity $\times$ Vol. solution in liters

$\times$ Gram-molecular wt   18-1

It may be converted to concentration in parts per million (ppm), the unit that has been commonly recorded in sanitary engineering, through the relation [1]

$$\text{Parts per million} = \frac{\text{Molarity} \times \text{Gram-molecular wt} \times 10^3}{\text{Density of solution}} \quad \text{18-2}$$

In practice, sanitary chemical analyses have been performed with measured volumes of water rather than weighed amounts. The results, therefore, should be recorded in milligrams per liter (mg/l). This

---

[1] The units of the gram-molecular wt are grams per mol.

unit is used in this book in the interest of precision. Numerically, the results obtained in almost all circumstances are identical whether they are expressed as ppm or mg/l. The relation between mg/l and molarity is

$$\text{Milligrams per liter} = \text{Molarity} \times \text{Gram-molecular wt} \times 10^3 \qquad \text{18-3}$$

If it is desired to express the mg/l in some conventional term, such as mg/l of Mg as $CaCO_3$, the gram-molecular weight of the substance in terms of which the result is to be expressed (or an appropriate multiple) should be used in place of the gram-molecular weight of the substance actually present.

A second concentration unit, the *normality*, is also used, especially in analytical chemistry. A *normal* solution contains 1 *gram-equivalent wt* of solute per liter of solution, the *gram-equivalent weight* being defined as a gram-molecular weight divided by the number of units of reaction capacity [2] per molecule.

A related quantity is the *milliequivalent* (me) equal to $\frac{1}{1,000}$ the gram-equivalent weight. The normality of a solution multiplied by its volume in milliliters gives the number of milliequivalents of solute. Concentrations in milliequivalents per liter (me/l) are obtained simply by multiplying the normality by 10^3.

Normality is particularly useful in analytical work because equal volumes of solutions with equal normality contain exact reacting proportions or *stoichiometric* amounts of the reactants. More generally, if V_A and N_A represent volume and normality of solution A, and V_B and N_B those of solution B, then at the point of complete chemical interaction or *equivalence point*

$$V_A N_A = V_B N_B \qquad \text{18-4}$$

This relation is often used for the determination of an unknown concentration N_A through reaction with a solution of known normality N_B, the relative reacting volumes V_A and V_B being measured precisely.

One deficiency of the normal system is that the normality of a given solution may depend upon the chemical reaction in which it participates. For example, a solution of ferrous sulfate containing 15.2 grams of $FeSO_4$ per l is 0.1 normal for a reaction in which the ferrous iron

---

[2] A complete treatment of the reaction capacity would be rather lengthy. Briefly, the number of reaction capacity units is equal (1) to the number of hydrogen ions per molecule reacting, or reacted with, for an acid-base reaction; (2) to the number of electrons gained or lost per molecule for an oxidation-reduction reaction; and (3) to the total valence per molecule of the reacting group for a precipitation reaction.

is oxidized, but it is 0.2 normal for a precipitation reaction. It is important, then, in stating normality to specify the type of reaction to which it refers. In practice little confusion occurs, for most analytical solutions are used for only a single type of reaction.

Example 18-1. Find the weight of the salt $BaCl_2 \cdot 2H_2O$ that should be taken to prepare 500 ml of (a) an 0.150-molar solution; (b) an 0.150-normal solution.

a. To prepare 1 l of a 1-molar solution, a gram-molecular weight, 244.4 grams (the water of crystallization must be included) is required. Five hundred milliliters of an 0.150-molar solution, therefore, requires $(244.4 \times 10^{-3}) \times 500 \times 0.150$ = 18.33 grams.

b. The gram-equivalent weight of barium chloride is ½ its gram-molecular weight. Therefore $244.4/2 = 122.2$ grams are required for 1 l of a 1-normal solution, or $18.33/2 = 9.165$ grams for 500 ml of an 0.150-N solution.

Example 18-2. It takes 32.50 ml of 0.0200-N HCl to neutralize 50.0 ml of a solution of limewater, $Ca(OH)_2$. Find the hardness of this solution as $CaCO_3$ (a) in me/l, and (b) in mg/l.

a. Substitution in Equation 18-4 gives

$$32.5 \times 0.0200 = 50.0 N_{Ca(OH)_2} \quad \text{or} \quad N_{Ca(OH)_2} = 0.0130$$

or

$$me/l = 0.0130 \times 10^3 = 13.0$$

b. Multiplication by the gram-equivalent weight of $CaCO_3$, 100/2, gives grams per liter as $CaCO_3$; grams per liter times 1,000 gives milligrams per liter. Hence

$$\text{Mg/l hardness} = 0.0130 \times \tfrac{100}{2} \times 1,000 = 650 \text{ mg/l}$$

18-5. Solutions of Ionized Solutes. Most of the common inorganic salts exist as ions not only in water solution but also in the solid state. Thus the crystals of common salt, NaCl, are made up of sodium ions Na^+ and chloride ions Cl^- arranged alternately in a three-dimensional space lattice and bound together by electrostatic forces. For such substances, the process of solution is the separation of the individual ions from the lattice by the solvent water. Other substances, principally acids and weak bases, that occur as neutral molecules in the pure state react with water to produce solutions made up wholly or partially of ions. For example, hydrogen chloride, when pure, occurs as molecular HCl, but reacts with water to give a solution containing H^+ (or H_3O^+) and Cl^- ions. Solutes of either class that exist substantially completely as ions in solution are termed *strong* electrolytes. Those that react incompletely with the water so that both neutral molecules and ions formed from them are present are called *weak* electrolytes.

a. *Independence of Ions.* The properties of solutions of strong electrolytes are essentially those of the ions present in the solution and not those of any assumed combination of the ions. Thus, solutions of sodium chloride, magnesium chloride, or hydrochloric acid all exhibit reactions and properties characteristic of chloride ions, *regardless* of the particular positive ions with which the chloride may be conventionally associated. A solution made from calcium chloride and magnesium sulfate shows properties and reactions identical with those of an equivalent solution made from calcium sulfate and magnesium chloride. It is thus more desirable and accurate to speak of a hard water as containing calcium ions or magnesium ions rather than as containing calcium bicarbonate or some other assumed combination of the calcium or magnesium ions. It is understood, when reference is made to a solution of calcium ions, that a sufficient number of negative ions is present to make the solution electrically neutral. Since the properties of the calcium ions are essentially independent of the nature of the negative ions, the negative ions need not be mentioned.

b. Conductance. Solutions containing ions exhibit the ability to conduct an electric current, the magnitude of the conductance being dependent on the nature and concentrations of the ions present. For dilute solutions, the *specific conductance* or *conductivity,* defined as the reciprocal [3] of the specific resistance of the solution in ohms, is approximately proportional to the concentration of ions present. Moreover, the total conductivity of a solution containing several kinds of ions is found to be equal to the sum of the conductivities of the individual ions present. Since equal weights of most ions commonly found in water (except for H^+, OH^-, and, to a lesser extent, Mg^{++}) impart approximately equal conductivities to water, measurements of conductivity frequently may be used to obtain a rapid measure of the total dissolved salts in water to a precision of about 10% (see Chapter 29).

c. Ionic Strength. The quantitative properties of ions in solution are not entirely independent of the presence of other ions. Because of electrical attractions and repulsions between the various ions, the *activity* or effective concentration of each ion, which determines its quantitative chemical behavior, is generally less than its molar concentration. The magnitude of the effect is a function of the total *ionic strength,* defined by the equation

$$\mu = \tfrac{1}{2} \sum_{1}^{i} c_i z_i^2 \qquad \text{18-5}$$

Here μ is the ionic strength, c_i is the molarity of the ith type of ion, and z_i is the magnitude of its charge. The summation is carried out for all types of ions, both positive and negative, in the solution.

[3] This reciprocal is referred to as mhos.

Example 18-3. Compute the ionic strength of a water 2×10^{-3} molar in Ca^{++}, 3×10^{-3} molar in HCO_3^-, 0.5×10^{-3} molar in Na^+, and 1.5×10^{-3} molar in Cl^-. *Answer:* $\mu = \frac{1}{2}(2 \times 10^{-3} \times 2^2 + 3 \times 10^{-3} \times 1^2 + 0.5 \times 10^{-3} \times 1^2 + 1.5 \times 10^{-3} \times 1^2) = 6.5 \times 10^{-3}$.

In very dilute solutions, activities and molar concentrations are substantially equal. In somewhat more concentrated solutions, such as those generally encountered in sanitary engineering, the ratio of the activity to the molar concentration, called the *activity coefficient* f_i, may be obtained with sufficient accuracy for most purposes by means of the approximate equation

$$- \log f_i = 0.5 z_i^2 \frac{\sqrt{\mu}}{1 + \sqrt{\mu}} \qquad 18\text{-}6$$

This equation is useful for all types of ions up to about 0.1 ionic strength, corresponding to 6,000 mg/l of NaCl or 3,400 mg/l of $CaSO_4$

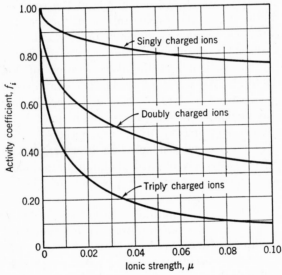

Figure 18-1. Activity coefficients as a function of ionic strength (Equation 18-6).

in the temperature range 0 to 40 C. Values of f_i, calculated from Equation 18-6 for ions with various charges, are shown in Figure 18-1 as a function of ionic strength.

Although it is often possible to neglect differences between activity and concentration in an approximate treatment of ionic solutions, there are many phenomena that cannot be interpreted adequately unless activity effects are considered. Important uses of the activity concept will be considered in later sections of this chapter.

18-6. Chemical Reactions of Ions. Except for oxidation-reduction processes, chemical reactions involving ions in water solution will proceed to substantial completion only when one of the following criteria is satisfied:

1. An insoluble or very slightly soluble product is formed. Reactions of this type are termed precipitation reactions. A typical example is the formation of slightly soluble silver chloride when a solution of a silver salt is mixed with a chloride solution to give the reaction [4]

$$Ag^+ + Cl^- \rightarrow AgCl \downarrow \qquad \text{18-7}$$

2. One of the reaction products is a gas which escapes from the reaction mixture. Thus, the acidification of a bicarbonate solution causes gaseous CO_2 to be evolved in accordance with the equation

$$H^+ + HCO_3^- \rightarrow CO_2 \uparrow + H_2O \qquad \text{18-8}$$

3. A non-ionizing or weakly ionizing substance is one of the reaction products. Neutralization of an acid by a base proceeds to completion, because of the formation of very weakly ionizing water as a product. A typical equation for this type of reaction is

$$H^+ + OH^- \rightarrow H_2O \qquad \text{18-9}$$

4. A stable, complex molecule or ion is formed. Color formation in the thiocyanate test for iron results principally from the reaction

$$Fe^{+++} + CNS^- \rightarrow Fe(CNS)^{++} \qquad \text{18-10}$$

In all these instances, the original ion is either removed from solution or tied up through the formation of a non-ionic bond. Conversely, addition of a solution of $CuSO_4$ to one of $Mg(NO_3)_2$ results in no reaction, for none of these conditions is fulfilled. The same ions are present in solution before and after mixing.

Chemical Equilibria in Solution

18-7. Equilibrium Theory. Many chemical reactions are obviously incomplete; others sufficiently complete for many practical purposes are not absolutely so. For example, the precipitation of AgCl, shown in Equation 18-7, although satisfactory for the determination of chloride, is not absolutely complete because AgCl has a finite solubility in water. Solid silver chloride shaken with water dissolves very slightly according to the reaction

$$AgCl \text{ (solid)} \rightarrow Ag^+ + Cl^- \qquad \text{18-11}$$

---

[4] The vertical arrow indicates the separation of silver chloride as a suspension or precipitate. An upward-directed arrow would indicate separation as a gas (Equation 18-8). Horizontal arrows indicate the direction in which reactions proceed.

When solutions of Ag^+ and of Cl^- are mixed, precipitation proceeds only until a state of balance is reached between reactions 18-7 and 18-11. At this point a condition of *chemical equilibrium* exists.

Consider any such reversible system, represented by the balanced general equation

$$mA + nB + \cdots \rightleftarrows pC + qD + \cdots \qquad \text{18-12}$$

The capital letters refer to the types of molecules or ions taking part in the reaction, the lower case letters to the number of them. Then it can be shown on the basis of thermodynamic principles that the relation

$$\frac{(C)^p(D)^q \cdots}{(A)^m(B)^n \cdots} = K \qquad \text{18-13}$$

is universally true, the parentheses indicating *activities* of the enclosed substances. The *equilibrium constant* K has a characteristic value for each reaction that is dependent only on the temperature. Provided that appropriate numerical values of K are known, specific expressions of this type can be used for the solution of numerous problems concerned with the relative quantities of substances present at equilibrium and with the effects produced by changes of condition.

Replacement of the activities in Equation 18-13 by the product of the molar concentrations and the appropriate activity coefficients leads to the equation

$$\frac{c_C{}^p c_D{}^q \cdots}{c_A{}^m c_B{}^n \cdots} = K \frac{f_A{}^m f_B{}^n \cdots}{f_C{}^p f_D{}^q \cdots} = K' \qquad \text{18-14}$$

For work with solutions, this form of the equilibrium equation is often more convenient than Equation 18-13, but K', the *concentration equilibrium constant*, is dependent on factors (such as ionic strength) that affect the relative values of the activity coefficients as well as on the temperature. However, in very dilute solutions like many waters, the f values are close to unity, and K and K' are nearly the same. For precise work at higher concentrations, activity coefficients,[5] calculated by means of Equation 18-6, can be used to compute K' from K.

The temperature dependence of the equilibrium constant is given by the equation

$$\frac{d(\log_e K)}{dT} = \frac{\Delta H}{RT^2} \qquad \text{18-15}$$

[5] In this chapter, specific equilibrium equations are presented in exact algebraic form, whether they are given in terms of K and activities or in terms of K' and molar concentrations. For approximate numerical calculations, it is often possible to neglect activity coefficients. Then K equals K', and activities equal molar concentrations.

in which ΔH is the enthalpy change per gram-molecular weight for the reaction from left to right, R is the gas constant, and T is the absolute temperature.

Example 18-4. (a) write the equilibrium expression for the hydrolysis of chlorine in water according to the equation $Cl_2 + H_2O \rightleftharpoons HOCl + H^+ + Cl^-$; and (b) find the value of the ratio $(HOCl)/(Cl_2)$ in a water with $(H^+) = 10^{-5}$ (pH 5) and $(Cl^-) = 3 \times 10^{-3}$ (approximately 100 mg/l), if the equilibrium constant has the value 4.5×10^{-4} (mols/l)^2 at 25 C.

a. By Equation 18-13: $\dfrac{(H^+)(Cl^-)(HOCl)}{(Cl_2)} = K$; the water is omitted because its activity is taken as unity when it is present as the solvent.

b. By substitution $\dfrac{(10^{-5})(3 \times 10^{-3})(HOCl)}{(Cl_2)} = 4.5 \times 10^{-4}$ and $(HOCl)/(Cl_2) = \dfrac{4.5 \times 10^{-4}}{(3 \times 10^{-3})(10^{-5})} = 1.5 \times 10^4$.

It is obvious that Cl_2 is virtually completely hydrolyzed to HOCl under these conditions.

18-8. Acid-Base Equilibria.

One important application of equilibrium theory is in the study of weak acids and bases.

Acids may be defined as substances that react with water to yield hydronium (or hydrogen) ions, H_3O^+ (or for simplicity H^+). For a weak acid, such as nitrous acid or hydrocyanic acid, the reaction is incomplete and may be represented by the generalized reversible equation

$$HA \rightleftharpoons H^+ + A^- \qquad \text{18-16}$$

to which equilibrium considerations are applicable.

The equilibrium expression has the form

$$\frac{(H^+)(A^-)}{(HA)} = K \qquad \text{18-17}$$

the equilibrium constant K in mol/l being designated specifically an *acid dissociation* or *ionization constant*. Relative strengths of weak acids are proportional to the magnitude of their dissociation constants.

Some acids, like carbonic acid, H_2CO_3, have more than one dissociation step. For such materials, there is a dissociation constant that is applicable to each incomplete dissociation reaction. The successive constants are usually distinguished by subscript numerals. For carbonic acid, these steps are:

$$H_2CO_3 \rightleftharpoons H^+ + HCO_3^- \qquad \text{18-18}$$

with the equilibrium expression

$$\frac{(H^+)(HCO_3^-)}{(H_2CO_3)} = K_1 \qquad 18\text{-}19$$

and

$$HCO_3^- \rightleftarrows H^+ + CO_3^= \qquad 18\text{-}20$$

and the corresponding equation

$$\frac{(H^+)(CO_3^=)}{(HCO_3^-)} = K_2 \qquad 18\text{-}21$$

In the use of equations like these, the numerical values to be substituted for the activity terms are not just the quantities derived from the operation of the reaction under consideration, but rather the total activity of the substance in the solution whatever its source. Moreover, when more than one chemical equilibrium exists, all of the pertinent equilibrium equations must be satisfied simultaneously. Thus, for solutions of carbonic acid, the value of (H^+) to be used in Equations 18-19 and 18-21 includes contributions from both reactions 18-18 and 18-20 plus any other sources of hydrogen ion. Also, the values of the other quantities must be such that Equations 18-19 and 18-21 are simultaneously satisfied. This condition, especially, is effective in determining the relative concentrations of carbonic acid (carbon dioxide, CO_2), bicarbonate (HCO_3^-), and carbonate ($CO_3^=$) that can coexist in solution.

Bases, complementary to acids, are substances that take or *accept* hydrogen ions from water or acids, or that yield hydroxyl ions in water.[6] Weak bases are those that react incompletely. A typical one is ammonia, NH_3, which reacts in accordance with the equation

$$NH_3 + H_2O \rightleftarrows NH_4^+ + OH^- \qquad 18\text{-}22$$

The equilibrium expression for this reaction is written

$$\frac{(NH_4^+)(OH^-)}{(NH_3)} = K \qquad 18\text{-}23$$

the activity term for H_2O being customarily omitted, because in all dilute aqueous solutions it is substantially constant at the value of unity defined for pure water as solvent. The constant for this type of reaction is specifically termed the *basic dissociation* or *ionization constant*. Weak bases that are able to take on more than 1 hydrogen

[6] Complete treatment of the acid-base concept is beyond the scope of this chapter. The definitions given are adequate for water solutions.

ion exhibit successive reaction steps and equilibrium expressions, just as acids like H_2CO_3 do.

Table 18-1 lists values of the dissociation constants at 25 C for a number of acids and bases of interest to sanitary engineers.

TABLE 18-1. Dissociation Constants for Acids and Bases in Water Solution at 25 C

Substance and significance	Equilibrium reaction	K (mol/l)	pK ($-\log K$)
Hypochlorous acid, disinfection	$HOCl \rightleftharpoons H^+ + OCl^-$	2.85×10^{-8}	7.55
Phenol, taste control	$C_6H_5OH \rightleftharpoons H^+ + C_6H_5O^-$	1.2×10^{-10}	9.92
Carbonic acid, corrosion, coagulation, pH, buffering control	H_2CO_3 or $(CO_2 + H_2O) \rightleftharpoons H^+ + HCO_3^-$	$4.45 \times 10^{-7}(K_1)$	6.35
	$HCO_3^- \rightleftharpoons H^+ + CO_3^-$	$4.69 \times 10^{-11}(K_2)$	10.33
Hydrogen sulfide, aeration, odor	$H_2S \rightleftharpoons H^+ + HS^-$	$6.3 \times 10^{-8}(K_1)$	7.20
	$HS^- \rightleftharpoons H^+ + S^-$	$1.3 \times 10^{-12}(K_2)$	11.89
Phosphoric acid, buffer for BOD dilution-water, softening	$H_3PO_4 \rightleftharpoons H^+ + H_2PO_4^-$	$7.52 \times 10^{-3}(K_1)$	2.12
	$H_2PO_4^- \rightleftharpoons H^+ + HPO_4^-$	$6.32 \times 10^{-8}(K_2)$	7.20
	$HPO_4^- \rightleftharpoons H^+ + PO_4^-$	$4.8 \times 10^{-13}(K_3)$	12.32
Sulfuric acid, pH control, coagulation	$H_2SO_4 \rightleftharpoons H^+ + HSO_4^-$	strong	.....
	$HSO_4^- \rightleftharpoons H^+ + SO_4^-$	$1.20 \times 10^{-2}(K_2)$	1.92
Sulfurous acid, dechlorination	H_2SO_3 or $(SO_2 + H_2O) \rightleftharpoons H^+ + HSO_3^-$	$1.72 \times 10^{-2}(K_1)$	1.76
	$HSO_3^- \rightleftharpoons H^+ + SO_3^-$	$6.3 \times 10^{-8}(K_2)$	7.20
Ammonia, disinfection	$NH_3 + H_2O \rightleftharpoons NH_4^+ + OH^-$	1.65×10^{-5}	4.78
Magnesium hydroxide, softening	$Mg(OH)^+ \rightleftharpoons Mg^{++} + OH^-$	$2.6 \times 10^{-3}(K_2)$	2.58

Equilibrium expressions may be treated mathematically as if they were simple algebraic equations. For example, multiplication of Equations 18-19 and 18-21 yields the equally valid equation

$$\frac{(H^+)^2(CO_3^=)}{(H_2CO_3)} = K_1 K_2 = K_{1\,2} \qquad 18\text{-}24$$

The corresponding chemical equation

$$H_2CO_3 \rightleftharpoons 2H^+ + CO_3^= \qquad 18\text{-}25$$

is the sum of Equations 18-18 and 18-20. In general, the equilibrium equation or constant corresponding to the sum of two or more chemical equations is given by the product of the equilibrium equations or constants for the individual chemical reactions. Similarly, the equation or constant for a process corresponding to the difference between two reversible reactions is the quotient of those for the initial reactions. If a reversible reaction is written in the opposite direction, the equilibrium expression is inverted and the constant is the reciprocal of the initial value.

a. Ionization of Water. Water itself is weakly ionized. The equation for the process

$$H_2O \rightleftarrows H^+ + OH^- \qquad 18\text{-}26$$

shows that water may function either as a weak acid or as a weak base. In pure water at room temperature, the extent of this ionization is very small. Only about 10^{-7} molar concentrations of (H^+) and (OH^-) are present at equilibrium. Nonetheless, many significant features of water chemistry result from this dissociation.

The equilibrium equation is usually written

$$(H^+)(OH^-) = K_w \qquad 18\text{-}27$$

the essentially constant activity of the water being included in the constant. The constant K_w, termed the ion product of water, has a value of 1.01×10^{-14} (mols per liter)^2 at 25 C. Values at other temperatures are shown in Figure 18-2.

b. The pH Scale. Equation 18-27 must always be satisfied in dilute aqueous solutions, regardless of what other materials or chemical equilibria are involved. Hence the acid or basic character of any aqueous solution can be defined by means of a single variable: the hydrogen-ion activity. For many purposes this variable is conveniently expressed in terms of the function *p*H, which is defined by the relation [7]

$$pH = -\log_{10}(H^+) = \log_{10}\frac{1}{(H^+)} \qquad 18\text{-}28$$

In pure water, at 25 C, $(H^+) = (OH^-) = 1.00 \times 10^{-7}$ and so $pH = 7.00$. This is the *p*H corresponding to exact neutrality at 25 C. At this temperature, acidic solutions have *p*H values less than 7 (hydrogen-ion activities $> 10^{-7}$); basic solutions have *p*H values greater than 7 (hydrogen-ion activities $< 10^{-7}$). Because K_w changes with temperature the *p*H value corresponding to neutrality is not exactly 7 except at 25 C; the change with temperature is shown as a part of Figure 18-2.

The *p*H function has been so convenient that similar functions and symbols are now widely used for other terms. Thus *p*OH, *p*K, *p*K_w stand respectively for the negative logarithms of hydroxyl-ion activity,

[7] For precise electrochemical work, a more operational definition is required, but the difference is not important for most applications.

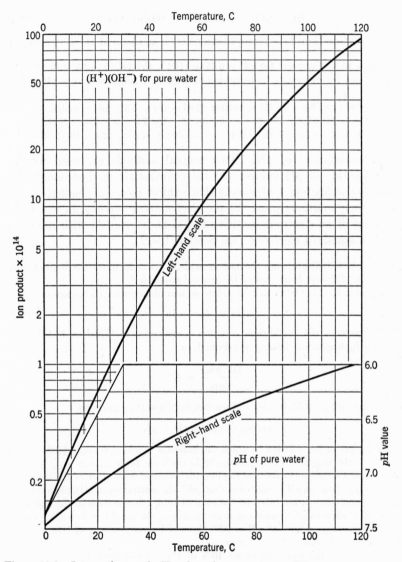

Figure 18-2. Ion product and pH value of pure water at different temperatures.

equilibrium constant, and ion product of water. Equation 18-27 in these terms has the form

$$pH + pOH = pK_w = 14.00 \text{ (at 25 C)} \qquad 18\text{-}29$$

This equation facilitates computations such as those of (OH^-) and pH.

Example 18-5. Convert: (a) $pH = 6.35$ to $(H+)$, (b) $(H+) = 7.3 \times 10^{-9}$ mol/l to pH; and (c) determine hydroxyl-ion activity in a solution having pH 6.35 at 25 C.

a. $(H+) = $ antilog $(-6.35) = $ antilog $(3.65 - 10) = 4.5 \times 10^{-7}$ mol/l.
b. $pH = -\log (7.3 \times 10^{-9}) = -\log 10^{-9} - \log 7.3 = 9 - 0.86 = 8.14$.
c. $pOH = 14 - 6.35 = 7.65$. $(OH^-) = $ antilog $(-7.65) = 2.2 \times 10^{-8}$ mol/l.

c. Measurement of pH. Two general methods are used for the determination of pH values: (1) the *colorimetric* method, employing *acid-base indicators* (substances that exhibit colors dependent on the pH of their solutions), and (2) the *electrometric method,* in which the potential of an electrode sensitive to pH is determined with reference to some standard electrode (see Section 18-12).

1. Acid-base indicators are themselves acids or bases in which the ionized form has a color different from that of the neutral molecule.[8]

An acid indicator (HIn) will dissociate in accordance with the equation

$$HIn \rightleftharpoons H^+ + In^- \qquad 18\text{-}30$$

For this process, the equilibrium equation is analogous to Equation 18-14 except that the hydrogen-ion activity is retained, or

$$\frac{(H^+)c_{In^-}}{c_{HIn}} = K' \qquad 18\text{-}31$$

Taking logarithms of both sides and rearranging gives the expression

$$\log (c_{In^-}/c_{HIn}) = pH - pK' \qquad 18\text{-}32$$

When the pH of the solution to which the indicator is added is appreciably greater than pK', the indicator exists principally in the ionic form $(c_{In^-} > c_{HIn})$ and the solution then assumes the color of the ion, the so-called *basic* color of the indicator. Conversely, when the pH is much less than pK', the neutral form, HIn predominates over In^- and the solution takes on the color of HIn, the *acid* color of the indicator. When pH is close to pK', mixed colors are produced, the exact hue depending on the resulting c_{In^-}/c_{HIn} ratio. At $pH = pK'$, the equal concentrations of HIn and In^- yield the *neutral* color of the indicator.

In general, a minimum of about 10% of the colored form present in lesser amount is necessary for the eye to distinguish a difference in hue. Therefore, the visible range of most acid-base indicators is 1.6 to 1.8 pH units, with a mid-point near $pH = pK'$. Table 18-2 lists a number of acid-base indicators with their pertinent characteristics.

---

[8] This is somewhat of a simplification but serves to account for the behavior as an indicator.

The usual technique for colorimetric determination of pH is to add to the solution being tested a small, specified quantity of indicator solution and then to compare the color produced with that of standards of known pH value containing the same concentration of the same indicator. Artificial standards duplicating the colors of the solution standards may be substituted for them. The determination is meaningful only when the pH falls within the useful range of the indicator; therefore tests must be conducted with indicators of different useful ranges until one is found that meets this criterion. Ordinarily, a precision of 0.1 pH can be attained.

TABLE 18-2. Characteristics of Acid-Base Indicators

Substance	Acid color	Base color	pK′ *	Useful pH range
Thymol blue (first ionization)	red	yellow	1.7	1.2–2.8
Bromphenol blue	yellow	blue	4.0	3.0–4.6
Methyl orange	red	yellow	3.7	3.0–4.4
Bromcresol green	yellow	blue	4.7	3.8–5.4
Methyl red	red	yellow	5.1	4.4–6.2
Chlorphenol red	yellow	red	6.0	4.8–6.4
Bromcresol purple	yellow	purple	6.3	5.2–6.8
Bromthymol blue	yellow	blue	7.0	6.0–7.6
Phenol red	yellow	red	7.9	6.8–8.4
Cresol red	yellow	red	8.3	7.2–8.8
Thymol blue (second ionization)	yellow	blue	9.0	8.0–9.6
Phenolphthalein	colorless	red	9.4	8.2–10.0 †
Alizarine yellow	yellow	lilac	....	10.1–12.0
Trinitrobenzene	colorless	orange	13.0	12.0–14.0 †

* For $\mu = 0.05$.

† Depends on indicator concentration.

As shown in Section 18-7, values of K' will vary with the ionic strength of the water. Hence the useful range and indicator color characteristic of a given pH value shift somewhat with salt concentrations. For colorimetric pH measurements accurate to better than 0.2 pH units, color standards adjusted to the salt concentration of the solutions being tested are required.

2. Of the numerous electrodes that develop potentials dependent on the pH of aqueous solutions two, the *quinhydrone* electrode and the *glass* electrode, have been extensively used for the routine measurement of pH values. Either of these is usually combined with a *calomel* electrode as reference to complete an electrical cell. The potential developed when either electrode combination is immersed in the solution being tested (usually measured by means of a potentiometer arrangement) serves to determine the pH of the solution. Diagrams of these electrodes and a typical measuring arrangement are shown in Figure 18-3.

Quinhydrone is an organic compound comprised of equimolecular proportions of hydroquinone, $C_6H_4(OH)_2$, and quinone, $C_6H_4O_2$. When dissolved in water, quinhydrone dissociates into these components, which then form a reversible oxidation-reduction system having a potential directly proportional to the pH of the solution. A platinum wire immersed in the solution acquires the potential of the quinhydrone system, so that the potential difference between the wire and the calomel reference electrode is a direct measure of pH.

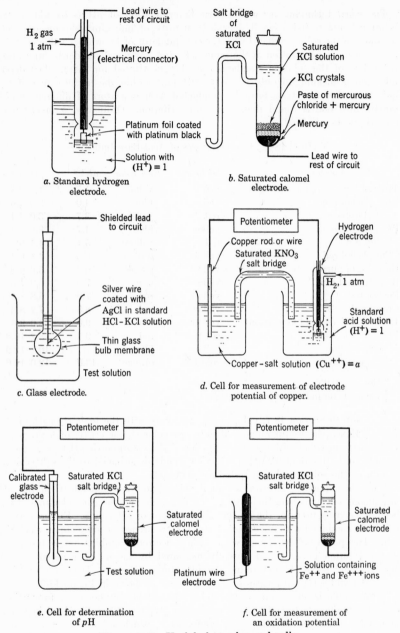

Figure 18-3.   Useful electrodes and cells.

The applicable equation [9] is

$$pH = \frac{E_c - E_Q{}^\circ - E}{1.983 \times 10^{-4}T}$$

18-33

in which E is the measured electromotive force (emf) of the system in volts, $E_Q{}^\circ$ is the standard potential of the quinhydrone system, E_c is the potential of the calomel electrode, and T is the Kelvin temperature. The last two quantities are constants at a fixed temperature. At 25 C and with a "saturated" calomel electrode, the equation [9] reduces to

$$pH = \frac{0.455 - E}{0.0591}$$

18-34

Because of the direct proportionality between pH and measured emf, the potential reading scales of commercial instruments are often inscribed directly in pH units rather than in volts. However, since the conversion factor varies with temperature, such scales are only accurate at one temperature (usually 25 C) unless a corrective device is incorporated in the circuit of the instrument.

The quinhydrone-electrode system is simple and rugged and produces an easily measured potential. Precision of $0.05pH$ unit is readily obtained. However, it is not suitable for accurate work above pH 8 or in the presence of oxidizing agents.

The glass electrode (see Figure 18-3) also exhibits a potential directly proportional to the pH of the solution in which it is immersed. When it is combined with a calomel electrode, the equation for the cell is

$$pH = \frac{E + E_G{}^\circ - E_c}{1.983 \times 10^{-4}T}$$

18-35

Unfortunately, $E_G{}^\circ$, the "standard potential" of the glass electrode, varies from electrode to electrode and also changes slowly with time for a given electrode. It is therefore necessary to calibrate the glass-electrode system with a solution of known pH before it can be used successfully.

Once calibrated, the glass electrode has a broad range of application for measurement of pH. It can be used in the presence of oxidizing or reducing agents, with solutions containing dissolved gases, and in highly turbid or colored solutions. Since no foreign material is added to the sample, the glass electrode gives reliable results with distilled or very pure waters and can be used for continuous measurements on flowing systems. A limitation of earlier glass electrodes, the so-called "alkaline error" that led to low readings in solutions with $pH > 9$, has been largely eliminated through the development of new types of glasses.

The major disadvantage of the glass electrode, apart from the need for calibration, is its high resistance, which necessitates the use of electronic amplification in the equipment used to measure the E of the system. Appropriate electronic amplification is an integral part of the numerous commercial instruments designed for use with the glass electrode. With many such instruments a precision of 0.03 pH unit is attained readily.

d. *Buffer Action.* Addition of a single drop (0.05 ml) of 1-N HCl to a liter of pure water causes the pH to change from 7.0 to about 4.3.

[9] Equations 18-33 and 18-34 assume that the platinum wire is the positive pole of the cell. Above pH 7.8 the polarity is reversed and the E values are considered to be negative.

On the other hand, a similar addition to a solution at pH 7 containing appreciable quantities of monosodium phosphate (NaH_2PO_4) and disodium phosphate (Na_2HPO_4) results in a barely perceptible change in pH. Solutions like this that undergo only a slight change in pH when acid or base is added (within limits) are called *buffer solutions*.

Buffer solutions commonly contain a weak acid plus a sodium or potassium salt of the acid, or a weak base plus a suitable salt of the base. For example, carbonic acid (carbon dioxide) and bicarbonate ions comprise a buffer mixture of almost universal occurrence in natural waters.

The action of buffer solutions is readily accounted for by chemical equilibrium theory. In a solution containing an acid (HA) at molar concentration (c_{HA}) and a salt of the acid providing a molar concentration (c_A) of the anion (A^-), the hydrogen-ion activity will be determined by the equation

$$\frac{(H^+)c_A}{c_{HA}} = K' \qquad \qquad 18\text{-}36$$

Transformation to logarithmic form and rearrangement gives

$$pH = pK' + \log \frac{c_A}{c_{HA}} \qquad \qquad 18\text{-}37$$

The pH of a buffer solution is thus a function of the pK' of the weak acid and the ratio of salt concentration to acid concentration, c_A/c_{HA}.

When strong acid is added to such a buffer solution, the equilibrium is disturbed. Removal of hydrogen ions by the reaction $H^+ + A^- \rightarrow HA$ then takes place until equilibrium conditions are restored. Provided that the amount of strong acid added is small compared with the amounts of weak acid and its salt present, the ratio c_A/c_{HA} does not change greatly as a result of this action, and the final pH is only slightly lower than the initial one. In like manner, added hydroxyl ions are removed by the reaction $HA + OH^- \rightarrow A^- + H_2O$, so that the pH will again not alter greatly provided that the amount of added strong base is not too large.

For a given total concentration of $c_{HA} + c_{A^-}$, the greatest buffer capacity is obtained when $c_{HA} = c_{A^-}$, or when $pH = pK'$. The useful range of a particular buffer system covers about 2 pH units, corresponding to $pK' \pm 1$. The total concentration of the buffer substances does not affect the operating pH range except for activity effects on pK'. But total concentration obviously does determine the amount of acid or base that can be effectively neutralized.

Buffer solutions prepared from mixtures of the salts monopotassium phosphate (KH_2PO_4) and disodium phosphate (Na_2HPO_4) are of widespread use in biology and sanitary engineering. Here, the weak acid is the ion $H_2PO_4^-$, derived from the KH_2PO_4, and the salt ion is $HPO_4^=$, derived from the Na_2HPO_4. The pertinent buffer equation is

$$pH = pK_2' + \log \frac{c_{Na_2HPO_4}}{c_{KH_2PO_4}} \qquad 18\text{-}38$$

At the total buffer concentrations most frequently used (0.01 to 0.1 M), $pK_2' = 6.8$ to 6.9. Therefore, this system provides good buffer action at pH values close to the neutral point, a factor of great importance in BOD tests or other biological studies.

In the calibration of glass electrodes, standard buffer solutions are generally used, for their known pH values are but slightly affected by accidental dilution or contamination with other acidic or basic materials.

Example 18-6. Five hundred milliliters of a buffer solution with a pH of 7.2 are to be prepared using the salts KH_2PO_4 and Na_2HPO_4. The total phosphate concentration is to be 0.05 molar. Find the quantities of each phosphate that should be used.

By Equation 18-38: $pH - pK_2' = \log \frac{c_{Na_2HPO_4}}{c_{KH_2PO_4}}$. For 0.05-molar solution, pK_2
$= 6.85$. Hence $\log \frac{c_{Na_2HPO_4}}{c_{KH_2PO_4}} = 7.2 - 6.85 = 0.35$ and $\frac{c_{Na_2HPO_4}}{c_{KH_2PO_4}} = 2.24$. This, together with the condition $c_{Na_2HPO_4} + c_{KH_2PO_4} = 0.05$ gives $c_{Na_2HPO_4} = 0.0346$ molar, $c_{KH_2PO_4} = 0.0154$ molar. Hence

$$\text{Wt } Na_2HPO_4 = 0.0346 \times \frac{500}{1,000} \times 142 = 2.46 \text{ grams}$$

$$\text{Wt } KH_2PO_4 = 0.0154 \times \frac{500}{1,000} \times 136.1 = 1.05 \text{ grams}$$

e. Hydrolysis. When a salt derived from a weak acid is dissolved in water, the anion combines with hydrogen ions from the water until the dissociation equilibrium of the corresponding acid is satisfied. For example, in water solutions of sodium carbonate, Na_2CO_3, the carbonate ion derived from the salt reacts according to the equation

$$CO_3^= + H^+ \rightleftharpoons HCO_3^- \qquad 18\text{-}39$$

until a condition satisfying the expression

$$\frac{(H^+)c_{CO_3^=}}{c_{HCO_3^-}} = K_2' \quad \text{(for } H_2CO_3\text{)} \qquad 18\text{-}40$$

is reached. Removal of hydrogen ions by reaction 18-39 leads to an increase in pH and in hydroxyl-ion activity, because the equation

$(H^+)(OH^-) = K_w$ must also be satisfied. Consequently, solutions of salts derived from weak acids and strong bases show basic reactions as a result of this *hydrolysis*.

The pH of such a *hydrolyzed* solution is given approximately by the equation

$$pH = \tfrac{1}{2}(pK_w + pK' + \log c) \qquad 18\text{-}41$$

in which K' is the ionization constant for the weak acid and c is the molar concentration of the salt.

Similarly, solutions of a salt, such as $MgCl_2$, derived from a weak base and a strong acid will show acid reactions because of hydrolysis. Magnesium ions, for example, will react with hydroxyl ions from water according to the equation

$$Mg^{++} + OH^- \rightleftharpoons Mg(OH)^+ \qquad 18\text{-}42$$

until the expression

$$\frac{c_{Mg^{++}}(OH^-)}{c_{Mg(OH)^+}} = K_2' \quad \text{[for } Mg(OH)_2] \qquad 18\text{-}43$$

is satisfied.

The pH in such solutions is given approximately by the equation

$$pH = \tfrac{1}{2}(pK_w - pK' - \log c) \qquad 18\text{-}44$$

in which K' is the basic dissociation constant of the weak base and c is the molar concentration of the salt. The acid reactions of solutions of iron and aluminum salts, among others, are accounted for in this way.

18-9. Solubility Constants. The solubility relations of ionized solutes are also derived from chemical equilibrium theory. The equilibrium between a slightly soluble salt, such as $CaCO_3$, and its ions in a saturated solution is given by an equation such as

$$CaCO_3 \text{ (solid)} \rightleftharpoons Ca^{++} + CO_3^= \qquad 18\text{-}45$$

for which the equilibrium expression is

$$\frac{(Ca^{++})(CO_3^=)}{(CaCO_3)_{solid}} = K \qquad 18\text{-}46$$

The activity of the solid is constant at a given temperature and is ordinarily assigned unit activity. Hence Equation 18-46 simplifies to

$$(Ca^{++})(CO_3^=) = K(CaCO_3)_{solid} = K_s \qquad 18\text{-}47$$

the constant K_s being called the *solubility constant*. In general, the solubility constant for a salt A_mB_n that gives m ions of A and n ions of B is given by the expression

$$(A)^m(B)^n = K_s \qquad \text{18-48}$$

This solubility equation defines the conditions of saturation for any ionized solute, though it is most useful for those of low solubility. If the ion product for a given substance (the left-hand side of Equation 18-48) is less than K_s, the solution is unsaturated with respect to that substance, and further solution will occur in the presence of additional solid until the solubility equation is satisfied. If the ion product is greater than K_s, the solution is supersaturated and tends to precipitate the excess either as a sludge or as a scale deposit.

Table 18-3 lists solubility constants for a number of slightly soluble substances. Some of the constants, particularly those for $Fe(OH)_3$ and $Al(OH)_3$, are more or less empirical, because pure crystalline solid phases with the given formulas are not obtained. However, use of the

TABLE 18-3. Solubility Constants of Electrolytes at 25 C

Substance	Ion product	K_s	Principal significance
$Al(OH)_3$ $AlO(OH)$	$(Al^{+++})(OH^-)^3$	1.9×10^{-33}	Coagulation
$HAlO_2$ or	$(AlO_2^-)(H^+)$	4×10^{-13}	Coagulation
$Fe(OH)_2$	$(Fe^{++})(OH^-)^2$	1.65×10^{-15}	Deferrization and coagulation
$Fe(OH)_3$	$(Fe^{+++})(OH^-)^3$	4×10^{-38}	Coagulation and corrosion
$FeCO_3$	$(Fe^{++})(CO_3^=)$	2.11×10^{-11}	Deferrization
FeS	$(Fe^{++})(S^=)$	1.0×10^{-19}	Precipitation of sulfide by iron, corrosion
$Cu(OH)_2$	$(Cu^{++})(OH^-)^2$	5.6×10^{-20}	Corrosion
$Pb(OH)_2$	$(Pb^{++})(OH^-)^2$	2.8×10^{-16}	Corrosion
$PbCO_3$	$(Pb^{++})(CO_3^=)$	1.5×10^{-13}	Corrosion
PbS	$(Pb^{++})(S^=)$	1.0×10^{-29}	Analytical method
$Mn(OH)_2$	$(Mn^{++})(OH^-)^2$	7.1×10^{-15}	Demanganization
$MnCO_3$	$(Mn^{++})(CO_3^=)$	8.8×10^{-11}	Demanganization
$Zn(OH)_2$	$(Zn^{++})(OH^-)^2$	4.5×10^{-17}	Corrosion
$Ca(OH)_2$	$(Ca^{++})(OH^-)^2$	7.9×10^{-6}	Softening
$CaCO_3$	$(Ca^{++})(CO_3^=)^2$	4.82×10^{-9}	Softening and corrosion control
$CaSO_4 \cdot 2H_2O$	$(Ca^{++})(SO_4^=)$	2.4×10^{-5}	Softening and scale formation
$Mg(OH)_2$	$(Mg^{++})(OH^-)^2$	5.5×10^{-12}	Softening
$MgCO_3 \cdot 3H_2O$	$(Mg^{++})(CO_3^=)$	1×10^{-5}	Softening
CaF_2	$(Ca^{++})(F^-)^2$	3.9×10^{-11}	Fluoridation and defluoridation
MgF_2	$(Mg^{++})(F^-)^2$	6.4×10^{-9}	Fluoridation and defluoridation
$AgCl$	$(Ag^+)(Cl^-)$	1.7×10^{-10}	Analytical method

listed equations and constants leads to predictions in accordance with observed behavior.

Example 18-7. How much fluoride will be dissolved by a water at 25 C passed through a bed of CaF_2 at such a rate that saturation is reached (a) if the hardness of the water is zero; (b) if the water contains 200 mg/l of Ca hardness?

a. The applicable equation is $(Ca^{++})(F^-)^2 = 3.9 \times 10^{-11}$ or, if activity coefficients are neglected, $c_{Ca^{++}} \times c_{F^-}^2 = 3.9 \times 10^{-11}$. In the zero-hardness water $C_{F^-} = 2Ca^{++}$, because each time a molecule of CaF_2 dissolves, one calcium ion and two fluoride ions are produced. Letting $c_{F^-} = x$ and substituting, we obtain $x^3/2 = 3.9 \times 10^{-11}$, or $x = 4.3 \times 10^{-4}$ mols per l. In mg/l this is $4.3 \times 10^{-4} \times 19 \times 10^3 = 8.2$ mg/l.

b. In addition to the Ca^{++} from the CaF_2, the 200 mg/l or 2×10^{-3} molar Ca^{++} hardness in the water must be taken into account, so that for this case $\left(2 \times 10^{-3} + \dfrac{x}{2}\right) x^2 = 3.9 \times 10^{-11}$. Since $x/2$ is small compared to 2×10^{-3} it may be neglected, giving $x^2 = 1.95 \times 10^{-8}$ or $x = 1.4 \times 10^{-4}$ mols per l $= 1.4 \times 10^{-4} \times 19 \times 10^3 = 2.7$ mg/l.

a. *Common-Ion Effect.* In a solution containing 100 ppm of carbonate alkalinity, $CaCO_3$ has a solubility of only 0.5 ppm, although its solubility in pure water is about 13 ppm. In the presence of excess carbonate, the calcium-ion activity, which is a measure of the calcium carbonate solubility, must be correspondingly reduced in order to maintain the ion product equal to K_s. This repression of solubility in the presence of an excess of one of the ions concerned in the solubility expression is called the *common-ion effect.* One application of the principle of the common-ion effect in water treatment is the addition of excess chemical to obtain more complete removal of some constituent. An example is the use of excess $Ca(OH)_2$ to obtain more complete removal of Mg as $Mg(OH)_2$ in water softening.

b. *Secondary Salt Effect.* The solubility of slightly soluble salts is increased when other salts that do not have an ion in common with the slightly soluble substance are present. The increased ionic strength of the solution resulting from the foreign salt causes a decrease in the activity coefficients of the slightly soluble substance as shown in Section 18-5c. Therefore, in order for the *activity product* of the ions of the slightly soluble salt to remain at the constant level specified by the solubility expression, their concentrations must increase.[10] Calcium carbonate is observed to be several times as soluble in sea water as in fresh water as a result of this secondary salt effect.

18-10. Oxidation-Reduction Processes. A chemical substance is *oxidized* when it loses electrons to a second substance that is *reduced* as it acquires the transferred electrons. The material oxidized acts as

[10] $a = f_i c$; to maintain a constant, c must increase as f_i decreases.

TABLE 18-4. Oxidation Reactions and Potentials at 25 C

Half-reaction	E^0, volts	Significance and direction

A. Corrosion of metals and cathodic protection

$Mg = Mg^{++} + 2e$	2.34	First step $(\rightarrow)$
$Al = Al^{+++} + 3e$	1.67	First step $(\rightarrow)$
$Zn = Zn^{++} + 2e$	0.762	First step $(\rightarrow)$
$Fe = Fe^{++} + 2e$	0.409	First step $(\rightarrow)$
$Pb = Pb^{++} + 2e$	0.126	First step $(\rightarrow)$
$Cu = Cu^{++} + 2e^-$	-0.3448	First step $(\rightarrow)$
$Fe^{++} = Fe^{+++} + e$	-0.771	Second step $(\rightarrow)$
$Fe = Fe^{+++} + 3e$	0.036	Over-all reaction $(\rightarrow)$
$Fe(OH)_2$ solid $+ OH^- =$ $Fe(OH)_3$ solid $+ e$	0.56	Mechanics of second step $(\rightarrow)$

B. Discharge of hydrogen and oxygen allied to corrosion

$H_2 = 2H^+(10^{-7} M) + 2e$	0.414	Polarization of metal in pure water $(\leftarrow)$
$H_2 = 2H^+ + 2e$	0.000	Discharge of H_2 gas in acid solution $(\leftarrow)$
$4OH^- = 2H_2O + O_2 + 4e$	-0.401	Discharge of O_2 in strongly basic solution $(\leftarrow)$
$2H_2O = O_2 + 4H^+(10^{-7} M)$ $+ 4e$	-0.815	Discharge of O_2 in pure water $(\leftarrow)$
$2H_2O = O_2 + 4H^+ + 4e$	-1.229	Discharge of O_2 in strongly acid solution $(\leftarrow)$

C. Oxidation processes of concern in disinfection and odor destruction

$2I^- = I_2 + 2e$	-0.5345	$I_2 < Br_2 < Cl_2 (\leftarrow)$
$2Br^- = Br_2 + 2e$	-1.087	$Br_2 < Cl_2$ but $> I_2 (\leftarrow)$
$2Cl^- = Cl_2 + 2e$	-1.3583	$Cl_2 > Br_2 > I_2 (\leftarrow)$
$ClO_2^- = ClO_2 + e$	-1.15	$ClO_2 < Cl_2 (\leftarrow)$
$O_2 + 2OH^- = O_3 + H_2O + 2e$	-1.24	In basic solution $O_3 < Cl_2 (\leftarrow)$
$O_2 + H_2O = O_3 + 2H^+ + 2e$	-2.07	In acid solution $O_3 > Cl_2 (\leftarrow)$
$Cl^- + H_2O = HOCl + H^+$ $+ 2e$	-1.49	Dependence on $H^+ (\leftarrow)$
$2H_2O = H_2O_2 + 2H^+ + 2e$	-1.77	$(\leftarrow)$

D. Reduction related to dechlorination and anaerobic digestion

$H_2SO_3 + H_2O = SO_4^= + 4H^+$ $+ 2e$	-0.20	Reduction of chlorine by sulfite $(\rightarrow)$
$S^= = S + 2e$	0.508	Reduction of sulfur to sulfide $(\leftarrow)$
$H_2S = S + 2H^+ + 2e$	-0.141	Reduction of sulfur to H_2S in acid solution $(\leftarrow)$
$2OH^- + NO_2^- = NO_3^- + H_2O$ $+ 2e$	-0.01	Reduction of nitrate to nitrite $(\leftarrow)$

E. Electrode reactions

H_2 gas $= 2H^+ + 2e$	0.0000	Zero electrode potential
$Cl^- + Ag = AgCl$ solid $+ e$	-0.2222	Standard electrode reference $(\rightleftharpoons)$
$Cl^- + Hg = HgCl + e$	-0.2676	Calomel electrode $(\rightleftharpoons)$

a *reducing agent,* because it causes the reduction of the second substance; similarly, the material reduced acts as an *oxidizing agent* in bringing about the oxidation of the first substance.

Although oxidation and reduction always occur together, the processes may be written separately as half-reaction equations. Thus the oxidation of iodide to iodine by hypochlorous acid according to the equation

$$HOCl + H^+ + 2I^- = I_2 + Cl^- + H_2O \qquad 18\text{-}49$$

may be separated into two half-equations,[11] one

$$2I^- = I_2 + 2e \qquad 18\text{-}50$$

representing the oxidation of the iodide, and the other

$$HOCl + H^+ + 2e = H_2O + Cl^- \qquad 18\text{-}51$$

representing the reduction of the HOCl. Addition of these half-equations, neither of which occurs by itself, gives the complete oxidation-reduction equation 18-49. Similarly, any two oxidation-reduction half-reactions, when combined algebraically so as to eliminate the free electrons, give a complete oxidation-reduction equation. However, additional information is necessary to determine the direction and completeness of the reaction.

A number of important half-reactions are given in Table 18-4. All of them have been written in the direction of oxidation, i.e., with free electrons as a product. But, since they are all theoretically reversible, they may be written equally well in the opposite direction.

18-11. Electrode Potentials. A potential difference between a metal and a solution of its ions is called an *electrode potential.* When, for example, a copper wire is dipped into a solution of a copper salt, such as copper sulfate, an equilibrium is established at the surface of the wire in accordance with the half-equation $Cu = Cu^{++} + 2e$. The potential difference is created as a part of the establishment of this equilibrium, its sign and magnitude being dependent on the position of equilibrium, the activity of the copper ions, and other factors. Similar characteristic relations obtain for other metals and solutions of their ions.

The absolute magnitude of any of these electrode potentials cannot be measured; but, if two such electrodes and their solutions are connected so as to make a complete circuit or *electrochemical cell,* the potential difference between the electrodes can be determined. More-

---

[11] The symbol e stands for a molar number of electrons, equal to one Faraday or 96,500 coulombs of electricity.

over, if one particular electrode is chosen as standard and assigned an arbitrary potential, then those of other electrodes can be expressed with respect to the standard.

The potential of the standard hydrogen electrode, corresponding to the equilibrium of the half-reaction H_2 (gas) $= 2H^+ + 2e$ with the hydrogen ions at unit activity and the hydrogen gas at 1 atm pressure, is universally taken as such a standard and is assigned an electrode potential of zero at each temperature.

The variation of electrode potentials with the activities of the reacting substances is given by the Nernst equation,

$$E = E° - \frac{RT}{zF} \log_e q \qquad 18\text{-}52$$

in which R is the gas constant, T is the Kelvin temperature, F is the value of the Faraday, and z is the number of electrons in the half-reaction corresponding to the electrode process. The term q is the equilibrium expression for the half-reaction (omitting the electron activity), and $E°$, the *standard electrode potential*, is the value of the potential when all the reacting substances are at unit activity. For the copper electrode the equation reduces to $E_{Cu} = E_{Cu}° - \frac{RT}{2F} \log_e (Cu^{++})$, the activity of the pure copper wire being taken as unity.

The electrode material need not participate in the reaction; it may be an inert metal that serves as a source or sink for electrons and as a conductor. It is necessary, however, that equilibrium conditions for the half-reaction of interest be established at the electrode surface. Potentials can thus be determined, at least in theory, for any reaction yielding or utilizing electrons, i.e., for any oxidation-reduction half-reaction. For example, an inert platinum wire dipping into a solution of ferrous and ferric ions (half-reaction $Fe^{++} = Fe^{+++} + e$) will exhibit a potential in accord with the equation

$$E_{Fe^{++},\,Fe^{+++}} = E_{Fe^{++},\,Fe^{+++}}° - \frac{RT}{F} \log_e \frac{(Fe^{+++})}{(Fe^{++})} \qquad 18\text{-}53$$

Potentials of this type are often called *oxidation potentials*.

In Table 18-4 are given the standard electrode or oxidation potentials for the listed oxidation-reduction half-reactions. Positive values indicate a tendency for the half-reaction to proceed as written from left to right at unit activity of the reacting substances, whereas negative values indicate a tendency for the reactions to proceed in reverse, from right to left. The magnitude of each $E°$ value is a measure of the driving force behind the reaction or its tendency to completion in the appropriate direction. Reversal of the direction in which the half-reactions are written involves changing the sign of the $E°$ values.

18-12. Electrochemical Cells. Any two electrode systems may be combined to make an electrochemical cell, just as any two oxidation-reduction half-equations may be combined to give an equation for a complete process. Sometimes both electrodes may dip into the same solution, but more frequently a "salt-bridge" is required to complete the circuit through the electrode solutions while keeping them separate so that extraneous reactions will not occur (see Figure 18-3).

The emf exhibited by an electrochemical cell and the chemical reaction corresponding to its operation are obtained conventionally by subtracting the potential and half-equation for the electrode system on the right from those for the electrode on the left, both being written with electrons on the right as in Table 18-4. Mathematically,

$$\Delta E_{cell} = E_l - E_r = E_l° - E_r° - \frac{RT}{zF} \log_e \left(\frac{q_l}{q_r} \right)$$

$$= \Delta E° - \frac{RT}{zF} \log_e Q \qquad\qquad 18\text{-}54$$

The difference $\Delta E°$ is the *standard* emf for the cell, and Q, the activity ratio, has the same algebraic form as the equilibrium expression for the chemical reaction of the cell.

If ΔE, the resulting cell emf, is positive, chemical reaction proceeds spontaneously in the written direction. Moreover, the electrode on the left is then the cathode $(-)$, that on the right is the anode $(+)$, and positive current flows through the external circuit from right to left. If the cell emf is negative, chemical reaction tends to occur in the reverse direction (right to left in the chemical equation) and the polarities and current direction in the cell are also reversed.

When electrochemical emf measurements are used for determining the properties of solutions (as in the measurement of pH), it is customary to employ an *indicator electrode*, sensitive to some constituent or constituents in the solution, and a *reference electrode*, one with a fixed, known potential relative to the standard hydrogen electrode. A common reference electrode is the saturated *calomel electrode* (see Figure 18-3), which is used because of its reproducibility and ease of preparation. This electrode has an E value at 25 C equal to -0.246 volt compared with the standard hydrogen electrode. Therefore, emf measurements at 25 C, using the saturated calomel electrode as reference, can be corrected to the hydrogen scale by subtracting 0.246 volt from the appropriate measured values.

It should be noted that the desired equilibrium emf values can be obtained only when the current through the cell is infinitesimal. Cell emf values are therefore invariably determined with the aid of some sort of potentiometric arrangement that permits a balancing of the cell emf against a known emf so that no current passes at the balance point.

18-13. Electrode Potentials and Chemical Equilibrium. When the left and right electrode potentials of a cell are equal, so that $\Delta E = 0$, the substances involved in the complete chemical reaction for the cell are at equilibrium. The value of the activity ratio Q is then equal to the equilibrium constant K and Equation 18-54 reduces to the general and important relation

$$\Delta E^\circ = \frac{RT}{zF} \log_e K \qquad\qquad 18\text{-}55$$

Equilibrium constants can therefore be evaluated from standard electrode potentials and *vice versa*.

Example 18-8. Determine the equilibrium constant at 25 C for the reaction

$$Fe + NO_3^- + H_2O = Fe^{++} + NO_2^- + 2OH^-$$

Since $\Delta E^\circ = E_{Fe,\,Fe^{++}}^\circ - E_{NO_2^-,\,NO_3^-}^\circ = 0.409 + 0.01 = 0.419$ volt, $\dfrac{RT}{2F} \log_e K$ $= 0.419$. At 25 C, the fraction $\dfrac{RT}{2.303F} = 0.0591$ volt, so that $0.0296 \log K = 0.419$, $\log K = 15.2$ and $K = 1.6 \times 10^{14}$. This large value of K indicates that the reaction, as given, will go substantially to completion, in agreement with the observation that reduction of nitrates to nitrites takes place in waters in contact with iron surfaces.

Rates of Chemical Reactions

18-14. Chemical Kinetics. Frequently, reactions of chemical interest are so slow that the rates at which they proceed rather than the final equilibrium conditions are of primary concern. This is true, for example, for the processes of aeration, BOD removal, disinfection, break-point chlorination, and sludge digestion. The study of the time dependence of such operations and its variation with conditions is the field of *chemical-reaction kinetics*.

The type equation for studies in chemical kinetics is

$$\pm dc/dt = k \cdot \phi(R) \qquad\qquad 18\text{-}56$$

Here c represents the concentration of the material of interest, the positive sign being associated with formation of the material, and the negative sign with its destruction or removal; $\phi(R)$ is some function of the concentrations of the substances concerned in the reaction; and

k, the *specific reaction-rate constant,* is independent of the substances covered by $\phi(R)$, but may depend on temperature, solution conditions, or other unexplored factors.

18-15. Reaction Orders. Simple rate processes are classified according to the mathematical order of the differential rate Equation 18-56. Thus a *first-order reaction* is one that exhibits a rate directly proportional to the concentration of a single reacting substance. A typical equation is

$$-dc_A/dt = kc_A \qquad\qquad 18\text{-}57$$

for a reaction in which substance A is reacting.

There are two types of *second-order reactions* corresponding to reactions of the types $(A + A) \rightarrow$ *products* and $(A + B) \rightarrow$ *products.* The type equations are

$$-dc_A/dt = kc_A{}^2 \qquad\qquad 18\text{-}58$$

and

$$-dc_A/dt = kc_Ac_B \qquad\qquad 18\text{-}59$$

Equation 18-59 is also said to be first order with respect to the individual reactants A or B.

Reactions of higher order are defined similarly, but occur only rarely. Reactions of zero order (certain catalytic reactions) and of fractional order are also found, and there are complex reactions that cannot be classified into any one order.

It is generally *not* possible to determine the order of a chemical reaction from the usual chemical equations, because the kinetic equation depends on the path of the reaction and not simply on the initial and final materials. The decomposition of hydrogen peroxide is usually written $2H_2O_2 \rightarrow 2H_2O + O_2$, implying a second-order reaction conforming to Equation 18-59. Experimentally, however, the reaction is observed to be first order.[12] See c in this section.

a. First-Order Reactions. The type Equation 18-57 for a first-order reaction is integrated as follows: [13]

$$-\int_{c_1}^{c_2} dc_A/c_A = k\int_{t_1}^{t_2} dt \qquad\qquad 18\text{-}60$$

---

[12] The terms unimolecular, bimolecular, etc., have often been used as synonymous with first order, second order, and so on. The former terms refer to the mechanism of the reaction, not to its experimental rate, and so should be avoided except in discussions of mechanism.

[13] By substitution of $k' = 0.4343k$, Equations 18-61, 18-62, and 18-64 may be written

$$\log_{10}(c_1/c_2) = k'(t_2 - t_1) \qquad \text{or} \qquad c_2 = c_1 10^{-k'(t_2-t_1)}$$

$$\log_{10}(c_0/c) = k't \qquad \text{or} \qquad c = c_0 10^{-k't}$$

Whence

$$\log_e (c_1/c_2) = k(t_2 - t_1) \quad \text{and} \quad c_2 = c_1 e^{-k(t_2-t_1)} \qquad \text{18-61}$$

For a concentration c_0 at zero time,

$$\log_e (c_0/c) = kt \quad \text{and} \quad c = c_0 e^{-kt} \qquad \text{18-62}$$

If the differential equation is written in terms of the amount of reaction y which has occurred in time t, it has the form

$$dy/dt = k(c_0 - y) \qquad \text{18-63}$$

and the integrated equation becomes

$$\log_e \frac{c_0}{c_0 - y} = kt \quad \text{or} \quad y = c_0(1 - e^{-kt}) \qquad \text{18-64}$$

For a first-order reaction a constant fraction of the available material reacts in each unit of time. This leads to still another formulation

$$c = c_0(1 - r)^t \qquad \text{18-65}$$

in which r is the fraction reacting per unit of time. By comparison with Equation 18-62, $(1 - r)^t = e^{-kt}$, and therefore $k = -\log_e (1 - r)$.[14]

The value of k for a first-order reaction is independent of the concentration units used, the dimensions being simply $(\text{time})^{-1}$. In general k is most easily evaluated by means of the logarithmic forms of the equation, since $\log c$ or $\log (c_0 - y)$ is a linear function of time. Values of $\log c$ or $\log (c_0 - y)$, calculated from measurements of c or y at various times, may be plotted as a function of time, and k (k' if base-10 logarithms are used) may be determined graphically as the slope of the straight line of best fit. Alternately, the logarithmic values at various times may be subjected to least-squares analysis for determination of k. In the graphical method, use of semilogarithmic or ratio paper will avoid the transformation of c or $(c_0 - y)$ values into logarithmic form.

Values of k may also be obtained by determining the time required for half of the initial material to react. This is called the half-life period

and

$$\log_{10} \frac{c_0}{c_0 - y} = k't \quad \text{or} \quad y = c_0(1 - 10^{-k't})$$

This substitution is generally made in published works on sanitary engineering. In the opinion of the authors, this is to be regretted because further mathematical treatment of the resulting equations is obscured.

[14] $k' = -\log_{10} (1 - r)$.

or half-time $t_{1/2}$ for the reaction. Substitution of $c = c_0/2$ in Equation 18-62 yields

$$k = \log_e 2/t_{1/2} = 0.693/t_{1/2} \qquad \text{18-66}$$

Similar equations result for other fractions of the total reaction.[15]

Application of these equations to problems of BOD and disinfection is found in Chapters 19, 27, and 28.

b. Second-Order Reactions. The second-order rate Equation 18-58, applicable when only one reactant is involved or when both reactants are present in equal concentration, integrates to

$$\frac{1}{c} - \frac{1}{c_0} = kt \qquad \text{or} \qquad \frac{y}{c_0(c_0 - y)} = kt \qquad \text{18-67}$$

Straight-line variation of $1/c$ with t is, therefore, characteristic of second-order behavior, and the slope of the line is equal to k. The half-time for this type of reaction, obtained by substituting $c_0/2$ for c, is expressed by the equation

$$t_{1/2} = 1/(c_0 k) \qquad \text{or} \qquad k = 1/(c_0 t_{1/2}) \qquad \text{18-68}$$

Hence the half-time is inversely proportional to the initial concentration for a second-order reaction. Also, in contrast to first-order reactions, the numerical value of k is dependent upon the concentration units employed. When the preferred molar concentrations are used, the dimensions of k are $(\text{mols/liter})^{-1}(\text{time})^{-1}$.

Equation 18-59, used when the initial reactant concentrations are not equal, integrates to

$$\frac{1}{c_{0(A)} - c_{0(B)}} \log_e \frac{c_{0(B)} c_A}{c_{0(A)} c_B} = kt \qquad \text{18-69}$$

The concept of a half-time is not a very useful one for this sort of reaction.

c. Pseudo First-Order Reactions. If one of the participants in a second-order reaction is present in such large excess that its concentration does not change greatly during the course of the reaction, the rate will follow a first-order pattern. For example, in the hydrolysis of ordinary sugar in water solution according to the equation $C_{12}H_{22}O_{11} + H_2O \rightarrow 2C_6H_{12}O_6$, the complete kinetic equation is

$$-\frac{dc_{C_{12}H_{22}O_{11}}}{dt} = kc_{C_{12}H_{22}O_{11}} \cdot c_{H_2O} \qquad \text{18-70}$$

[15] An equation often found convenient is $k = 2.303/t_{90}$, $k' = 1/t_{90}$, for reaction of 90% of the initial material.

but the dependence on water concentration is not observed, because it is present in such large excess.

Reactions like this can be handled in the same way as true first-order reactions. However, the reaction-rate constant obtained by normal methods will include the concentration of the substance in excess, and this must be eliminated to obtain a true theoretical constant.

18-16. Complex Reactions. Most chemical reactions, as ordinarily observed, are not simple processes. Rather, they are composed of a number of steps. The various types of complications may be classified as:

1. *Competing reactions*, such as the simultaneous occurrence of $(A + B) \rightarrow AB$ and $(A + C) \rightarrow AC$.

2. *Back reactions*, for example, $(A + B) \rightarrow (C + D)$ combined with $(C + D) \rightarrow (A + B)$.

3. *Consecutive reactions*, such as $(A + B) \rightarrow C$ followed by $(C + D) \rightarrow E$ and then by $E \rightarrow (F + G)$.

Complete determination of the rate pattern for complex reactions of these types involves simultaneous solution and integration of the differential kinetic equations for each of the individual steps. This process is often extremely difficult or impossible. Discussion of the special techniques used in certain instances can be found in textbooks on physical chemistry or reaction kinetics.

Treatment of the third type of complication—that of consecutive reaction steps—is simplified if one of the reaction steps proceeds much more slowly than any of the others. The single slow step then becomes the *rate-determining* step of the over-all reaction and identifies the kinetic order as well as the absolute rate of the reaction. If, for example, the reaction $(A + B) \rightarrow C$ in the series listed under the third type is much slower than the following ones, then the reaction would be observed to be second order conforming to the equation

$$dy/dt = k_1 c_A c_B \qquad \text{18-71}$$

and the over-all rate, say the rate of formation of G, would be that of this first step. Note that even though the complete chemical reaction $(A + B + D) \rightarrow (F + G)$, obtained by combining the three steps algebraically, indicates the participation of substance D as a reactant, nevertheless the rate of the reaction is independent of the concentration of D present.

Conversely, if it is shown that the rate of a complex reaction is independent of the concentration of one of the reacting substances, it may be concluded that the substance does not participate in the rate-determining step. Thus, the observation that the rate of exertion of BOD is independent of the concentration of dissolved oxygen (above a minimum limit) indicates that molecular oxygen is not a reactant in the rate-determining step of this complex biochemical process.

18-17. Temperature Dependence of Reaction Rates. The rates of most chemical reactions increase greatly as the temperature is raised. A frequently used very approximate rule, enunciated by van't Hoff, is that the rate doubles for each rise in temperature of 10 C.

Mathematically, the change in specific rate constant with temperature for any simple chemical reaction is given by the Arrhenius equation,

$$d(\log_e k)/dT = E/(RT^2) \qquad 18\text{-}72$$

Here k is the specific reaction rate constant, T is the Kelvin temperature, R is the gas constant (1.99 cal per deg C), and E, a constant characteristic of the reaction, is termed the *activation energy*. Integration of Equation 18-72 between the limits T_1 and T_2 gives

$$\log_e \frac{k_2}{k_1} = \frac{E}{RT_1} - \frac{E}{RT_2} = \frac{E(T_2 - T_1)}{RT_1T_2} \qquad 18\text{-}73$$

The specific rate constant at any desired temperature can thus be calculated from a knowledge of E and of the rate constant at some one temperature.

For evaluation of E, one of the indefinite forms of the integral is generally used, namely,

$$\log_e k = A - E/(RT)$$

$$\log_{10} k = A' - E/(2.303RT) \qquad \text{or} \qquad k = Ze^{-E/(RT)} \qquad 18\text{-}74$$

Here $A = \log_e Z$, or $A' = \log_{10} Z$, and Z is the *reaction opportunity*. Values of $\log k$ for a number of temperatures can then be plotted against or analyzed for their variation with the reciprocal of the absolute temperature. The slope of the straight line of best fit is E/R for base-e logarithms, $E/(2.303R)$ for base-10 logarithms. In place of the values of $\log k$ the logarithms of any other measured quantities proportional to k may be used. Frequently, logarithms of the half-times or the times for any fixed fraction of complete reaction at a standard concentration are employed; then the slope of the straight line of best fit is $-E/R$ or $-E(2.303R)$, since fractional times are inversely proportional to rate constants.[16]

Values of E for reactions occurring with a conveniently measurable rate at room temperature usually lie in the range 10,000 to 20,000 cal

---

[16] Variations in the percentage of reaction as a function of temperature for a fixed time of reaction give the correct value of E only if the reaction is first order.

per deg C. The corresponding values of the factor $e^{-E/RT}$ of Equation 18-74 are 10^{-8} to 10^{-16}. This factor represents the fraction of reaction opportunities (i.e., when the reactant molecules are in contact or have a proper spatial configuration) in which the minimum energy E necessary for reaction is available. Hence the fraction of opportunities that results in successful reaction is very small for processes with readily measurable rates; also the higher the value of E, the smaller is the reaction opportunity.

Two other methods for expressing the temperature dependence of a reaction rate are often encountered. They are: $k_2/k_1 = \Theta^{T_2 - T_1}$, whence $\Theta = k_2/k_1$ for $T_2 - T_1 = 1$, and $Q_{10} = k_2/k_1$ for $T_2 - T_1 = 10$. Here T_2 and T_1 are measured in degrees Centigrade. From Equation 18-73,

$$\log_{10} \Theta = \frac{E}{2.303 R T_1 (T_1 + 1)} = \frac{E}{385{,}000} \quad \text{(near 17C)} \quad 18\text{-}75$$

and

$$\log_{10} Q_{10} = \frac{10E}{2.303 R T_1 (T_1 + 10)} = \frac{E}{38{,}500} \quad \text{(near 17C)} \quad 18\text{-}76$$

Obviously $Q_{10} = \Theta^{10}$.

The usefulness of Q_{10} or of Θ as an alternative means for indicating the temperature dependence of reaction rates is limited because of their variations with temperature.

18-18. Catalysis. Rates of chemical reactions are often affected by the presence of catalysts, i.e., substances that increase the rate of reaction without being used up in it. The role of the catalyst is usually to decrease the energy required for the reaction to occur (the activation energy E) by producing an alternate reaction path and thus to increase the effective fraction of reaction opportunities.

Two main classes of catalysts, *homogeneous* and *heterogeneous*, may be distinguished. Homogeneous catalysts function in the same phase as the chemical reactants, i.e., they are gases for gas-phase reactions or dissolved substances for reactions in solution. They operate, in general, by interacting with one or more of the reactants to form an intermediate compound or complex which is then acted upon by other reactants to produce the products and regenerate the catalyst. Ferric and cobalt ions act in this way as catalysts for the decomposition of H_2O_2 and of hypochlorite. Many reactions in water solution are catalyzed in this way by acids or bases. The observed rates are then pH dependent.

Heterogeneous catalysis occurs at the surfaces of solids or liquids in contact with the reaction medium. Such catalysts usually function by *adsorption* (see Section 18-19) of one or more reactants in an "activated" state, thereby decreasing the energy required for reaction. Heterogeneous catalysts are widely employed in industrial chemical processes to facilitate desired syntheses.

Both types of catalysis play extremely vital roles in reactions involving living organisms. The processes of biochemical synthesis and decomposition are almost universally accomplished through the agency of proteinlike catalytic materials, called *enzymes*, formed in living cells. These enzymes are ultimately responsible for the oxidation of organic matter in sewage treatment and in the exertion of BOD for the decomposition of organic matter in sludge digestion, for the photosynthetic processes of algae, and most other processes involving living matter. Chlorine in water kills bacteria and other microorganisms by destroying certain enzymes necessary for cellular metabolism.

Enzymic reactions are believed to proceed through reversible formation of complexes between the enzyme and the reactants (called the substrate), followed by decomposition of the complex to give the products of the reaction. Schematic equations illustrating this concept, developed by Michaelis, are

$$[\text{E (enzyme)} + \text{S (substrate)}] \underset{k_1'}{\overset{k_1}{\rightleftarrows}} \text{ES (complex)} \qquad \text{18-77}$$

$$\text{ES} \xrightarrow{k_2} [\text{E} + \text{P (products)}] \qquad \text{18-78}$$

Appropriate combination of the differential rate equations for these reactions gives the expression

$$-\frac{dc_S}{dt} = \frac{k_2 c_E \cdot c_S}{\dfrac{k_1' + k_2'}{k_1} + c_S} \qquad \text{18-79}$$

for the rate of disappearance of substrate. When c_S is small compared with $(k_1' + k_2')/k_1$, the rate is dependent on both enzyme and substrate concentrations. When c_S is much larger than the rate-constant ratio, the reaction rate is virtually independent of c_S and a zeroth-order reaction with respect to the substrate is observed. It is obvious that such a scheme may be pertinent with reference to the utilization of the substrate (oxygen) in BOD tests.

Colloids

18-19. The Colloidal State. The feature that distinguishes materials of colloidal size and is responsible for many of the characteristic properties of colloidal substances is their large specific surface area.

For example, 1 cc of a colloid composed of cubical particles 10^{-6} cm on a side has a surface area of 6,500 sq ft. The distinctive behavior observed for colloids as compared with coarse suspensions is due to the predominance of surface properties to such an extent that colloid chemistry and surface chemistry are nearly synonymous terms.

Two general characteristics of colloids are of particular interest: (1) the tendency of colloid-sized materials to concentrate other substances at their surfaces, which leads to the phenomenon of *adsorption;* and (2) the tendency for surfaces to acquire charges, which gives rise to the *electrokinetic properties* of colloids.[17]

a. Adsorption. The quantity of substance adsorbed by a given *adsorbent* depends on the nature of the substance, its concentration, and the temperature. Ordinary or physical adsorption is generally a rapid process, so that a condition of equilibrium between adsorbed and dissolved *adsorbate* is quickly reached after contact of the adsorbent with a solution or gas.

Adsorption isotherms express the variation in quantity of material adsorbed with concentration. Two mathematical formulations for these isotherms are in common use. The first, the Freundlich equation, is strictly empirical but has been found adapted to a wide variety of data, particularly for adsorption from liquid solutions. It has the form

$$y/m = Kc^{1/n} \qquad \text{18-80}$$

in which y/m is the amount of material adsorbed per unit weight of adsorbent, c is the concentration of material in solution at equilibrium, and K and n are empirical constants. Values of n are normally greater than unity; consequently adsorption is relatively more efficient at low concentrations.

The logarithmic form of the Freundlich isotherm

$$\log (y/m) = \log K + (1/n) \log c \qquad \text{18-81}$$

is frequently used for testing the fit of data and for evaluating the constants K and n, on the basis of the indicated linear variation of $\log y/m$ with $\log c$.

A second equation, the Langmuir isotherm, has some theoretical basis. It has the form

$$y/m = Kc/(1 + K_1 c) \qquad \text{18-82}$$

Although the constants K and K_1 have theoretical significance, their values are usually obtained empirically from observed data. Equation

---

[17] These properties are exhibited by all surfaces but obviously become most pronounced with large specific surface areas.

18-82 is somewhat limited in its application, because the derivation assumes only a monomolecular layer of adsorbed material. However, some data, especially those obtained over wide concentration ranges, are fitted better with this equation than with the Freundlich isotherm. The Langmuir equation is conveniently used in the form

$$\frac{c}{y/m} = \frac{1}{K} + \frac{K_1}{K} c \qquad\qquad 18\text{-}83$$

which predicts a linear variation of $\dfrac{c}{y/m}$ with c.

The elimination of excessive tastes and odors from water by activated carbon is probably the most important, direct use of adsorption in sanitary engineering (see Section 27-21). A part of the action of coagulants in removing color from water may be due to adsorption, and certain processes for the removal of silica or fluorides also utilize this phenomenon. Adsorption plays a part, too, in filtration and biological flocculation and precipitation.

b. *Electrokinetic Properties.* Colloidal particles are normally charged with respect to the surrounding medium. If electrodes from a DC source are placed in a colloidal dispersion, the particles migrate toward one or the other of the poles. This phenomenon is called *electrophoresis.* Conversely, if the colloidal material is held fixed, the application of a DC potential causes the liquid to flow in a direction opposite to that in which the particles would normally move. This phenomenon, *electroosmosis,* has been used for the dewatering of sludge.

Colloidal silica and silicate minerals like the clays, the tealike organic color of natural waters, and most proteins have been found by measurement of electrokinetic properties normally to be negatively charged in waters with pH values near 7, whereas the hydrated oxides of iron and aluminum are usually positively charged.

c. *Stability of Colloids.* The presence of electric charges on the surfaces of colloidal particles is largely responsible for their stability. The like charges cause the particles to repel one another and thus prevent their coalescence.[18] In many cases, the stability is found to be dependent on the magnitude of the *zeta-potential,* ζ, defined by the equation

$$\zeta = 4\pi\delta q/D \qquad\qquad 18\text{-}84$$

in which q is the charge on the particle (or the charge difference be-

[18] This statement is only partly true for *hydrophilic* colloids, such as starches and proteins, that are also stabilized by bound water layers around the particles.

tween the particle and the body of the solution), δ is the thickness of the layer around the particle through which the charge difference is effective, and D is the dielectric constant of the medium. The zeta-potential is thus a measure both of the charge on a colloidal particle and of the distance into the solution to which the effect of the charge extends. (See Figure 18-4.) Colloids like hydrated ferric or alu-

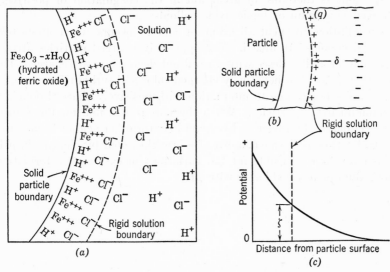

Figure 18-4. Electrical relations at surfaces of colloids: (a) Diagrammatic representation of charge distribution in neighborhood of surface of particle of ferric oxide solution formed by dispersing $FeCl_3$ in water. (b) Simple Helmholtz picture of particle surface showing net charge q and double-layer distance δ. (c) Potential relations corresponding to charge distribution shown in (a). Note that the zeta-potential is the potential at the "rigid-solution boundary" with respect to the bulk solution. The ordinary range of ζ is 10 to 200 millivolts.

minum oxides are stable so long as the zeta-potential exceeds a critical value. If it drops below this, coagulation tends to occur, slowly in the immediate neighborhood of the critical zeta-potential, much more rapidly the nearer it gets to zero.

  d. *Coagulation of Colloids.* Colloids are generally a nuisance in water sanitation. Colloidal organic color and turbidity are objectionable in water supplies, conditions leading to colloid formation must be avoided in alum treatment, and colloids must be coagulated for effective handling of sewage or sludge.

  To coagulate colloids, the zeta-potential can be lowered either by neutralizing the charge q on the colloids or by decreasing the distance δ of charge effectiveness. The latter is accomplished by increasing the ion concentration of the solution. It accounts for the relative ease with which coagulation of hydrated aluminum or ferric oxides is obtained in a saline water as compared with distilled water. The particular ions causing this effect are those of opposite sign from that of the electrical charge on the colloid; ions with double or triple charges are much more effective than those of single charge. The presence of $SO_4^=$ ions is therefore of great aid in the coagulation of positively charged aluminum or ferric oxide colloids.

Coagulation by neutralization of charge occurs when oppositely charged colloids are mixed. The oppositely charged particles attract one another and coalesce with a resultant decrease in net charge. The effective removal of negatively charged color and turbidity from water by alum is partly due to interaction with positively charged colloidal aluminum oxide particles. When the ions responsible for the charge on a colloid are hydrogen or hydroxyl ions (or other acid or basic ions) neutralization of charge can often be brought about by changes in pH. This effect is responsible for the variations in ease of floc formation from alum or ferric chloride with pH.

19 ———————————— BIOLOGY OF WATER AND WASTE WATER

19-1. General Considerations. The living organisms that have their natural habitat in water or that are introduced into water in the course of its use by man are of deep concern to the engineer who is charged with the supply of water to communities and with the removal of their waste water.

As explained in Chapter 1 some of the living organisms that may find their way into water—bacteria, viruses, and protozoa—are infectious to man and responsible for the outbreak of serious, sometimes fatal, water-borne diseases. Other organisms—the algae and related plankton—are responsible for the occurrence of tastes and odors in water supplies and may, at times and if left uncontrolled, infest water supplies in such numbers as to (1) render the water unfit for human consumption, (2) be responsible for the sudden death of cattle, and (3) produce the mass destruction of fish when the plankton growth dies and decays. Yet others—both microscopic plants and animals as well as larger organisms such as mussels—may flourish in water conduits, both open and closed, and reduce their capacity. Others again —the water weeds—may invade lakes and reservoirs and grow so luxuriantly as to interfere with their normal use, or the plants may thrive in stream beds in such profusion as to impede flow and cause the inundation of lowlands. The uncontrolled occurrence in water of these categories of organisms is objectionable, and their destruction, or the prevention of their growth, is an important responsibility.

By contrast, water may be expected to contain living organisms in wide variety and great number that are engaged in the cleansing of polluted waters and the stabilization of organic waste materials in nature. These biological workmen may be called upon by the engineer for the purification of waste waters in biological treatment works and, often too, for the stabilization of putrefactive by-products of such treatment—more particularly of sewage sludge. The beneficent organisms range over the whole spectrum of life. The funda-

501

mental work in the biological chain reaction that returns water to normal purity, however, is accomplished very largely by the humblest forms of living things: bacteria, protozoa, fungi, and worms.

19-2. Biological Classification of Significant Organisms. The following selective, simplified, and specialized scheme of classification is intended to identify the groups of organisms that are of importance in the sanitary economy of water and to show their position in the scale of life.

PLANT KINGDOM

HIGHER PLANTS (Spermatophyta[1]). The higher aquatic plants are generally attached but occasionally free floating (duckweed or *Lemna*). They do not commonly depend upon seed reproduction, but are mostly perennial and propagate by means of runners, tubers, buds, or stem fragments. Under conditions favorable to their growth, these water weeds may infest lakes, ponds, reservoirs, and the backwaters of streams. Their autumnal decay releases large amounts of organic matter to the water. The deep color of swamp water is derived from this source as well as from the decay of flooded terrestrial plants.

LOWER PLANTS (Thallophyta[2]). This group is composed of plants of simplest structure. At this level of life, the division into plant and animal groups is not rigid, and some organisms possess characteristics of both plants and animals. The following groups are of interest.

ALGAE. The fresh-water forms are generally microscopic in size, but the salt-water forms include giant kelps several hundred feet in length. The algae contain chlorophyll and often additional pigments that categorize the different families. The pigments enable them to utilize radiant energy. The physiological process involved is called photosynthesis and is associated, among other things, with the release of oxygen and the consumption of carbon dioxide.

BLUE-GREEN ALGAE (Cyanophyceae or Myxophyceae). These occur as single cells, as filaments, or in colonies. They may grow in numbers so large as to cover much of the surface of a body of water. Runaway growths of this kind are known as water blooms. The odors imparted to water by the blue-green algae are generally grassy, but they may turn to the odor of a pig-pen when large growths begin to disintegrate seasonally. The blue-green algae abound particularly in the late summer when surface waters are warm. Examples are shown in Figure 19-1.

GREEN ALGAE (Chlorophyceae). Some of these are single celled, others many celled. Some are non-motile, others are equipped with swimming flagella (whip-like organs of locomotion). The odors associated with them are often fishy, sometimes grassy. The sea lettuce *Ulva* is a many-celled genus. Like the blue-green algae, the green algae are most abundant during the summer. Examples are shown in Figure 19-2.

DIATOMS (Bacillariophyceae). These yellow-green organisms are generally single celled, less frequently colonial. They have silica-impregnated cell walls and are often motile. The accumulated skeletons of diatoms that flourished in

---

[1] From the Greek words *spermatos,* meaning a sperm, seed, or germ, and *phyton,* a plant.

[2] A thallus is a vegetative body without differentiation into stem, leaf, and root.

lakes in early geological times often form large deposits of "diatomaceous earth." The essential oils released by diatoms frequently impart an aromatic, sometimes a fishy, odor to water. The diatoms have a spring and fall pulse that appears to be associated with the overturns (see Section 17-8). A few of the many varieties of diatoms are shown in Figure 19-3.

OTHER ALGAE. Classes of algae that are less frequently encountered include yellow or yellow-green varieties (Heterokontae) and yellow-brown varieties

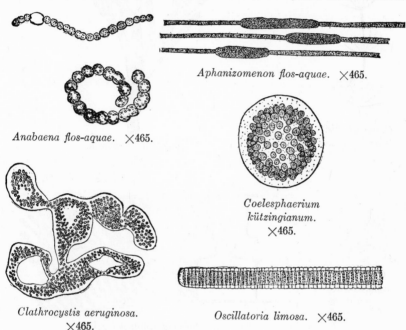

Aphanizomenon flos-aquae. ×465.

Anabaena flos-aquae. ×465.

Coelesphaerium kützingianum. ×465.

Clathrocystis aeruginosa. ×465.

Oscillatoria limosa. ×465.

Figure 19-1. Common blue-green algae. From H. B. Ward and G. C. Whipple, *Freshwater Biology,* John Wiley & Sons, New York, 1918.

(Chrysophyceae). The chlorophyllaceous flagellates may be classified as plants or as animals. They are listed among the Protozoa in the present scheme.

FUNGI. The molds, yeasts, and bacteria are members of this group. The cells do not contain chlorophyll and are usually colorless. The molds are filamentous and branching. The yeasts are non-filamentous and usually budding. The bacteria are listed separately. The mold flora of sewage may be large. The mold *Leptomitus* is an example. See Figure 19-6.

The molds are strictly *heterotrophic* in their nutrition, i.e., they are dependent upon organic matter for their energy. They can decompose carbohydrates such as sugars, starches, cellulose, higher alcohols, and fat as well as proteins and other nitrogenous substances. Most of the molds are true *aerobes*, i.e., they grow only in the presence of free or dissolved oxygen. Their optimum temperature lies between 20 and 30 C. They flourish over a wide range of pH (4.0 to 10.0) and modify the pH by the production of organic acids on the one hand and ammonia on the other. When they occur in large numbers, the individual mold

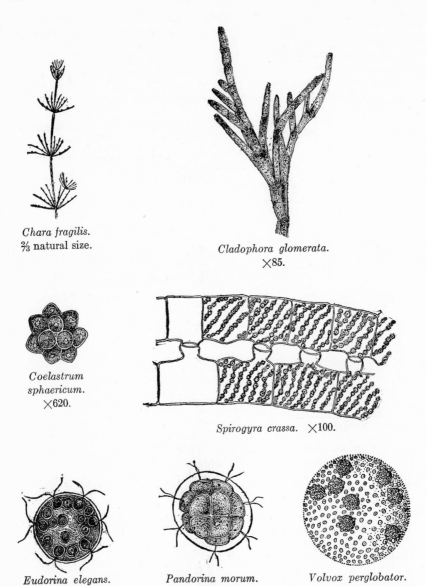

Chara fragilis.
⅔ natural size.

Cladophora glomerata.
×85.

*Coelastrum
sphaericum.*
×620.

Spirogyra crassa. ×100.

Eudorina elegans.
×250.

Pandorina morum.
×385.

Volvox perglobator.
×50.

Figure 19-2. Common green algae. *Eudorina, Pandorina,* and *Volvox* are also classified as flagellate protozoa. From H. B. Ward and G. C. Whipple, *Fresh-water Biology,* John Wiley & Sons, New York, 1918.

hyphae or threads form a network or web, called a *mycelium,* that resembles a wad of cotton or sometimes a cat's tail. Such growths are visible to the naked eyê and are generally characteristic of heavy pollution. Filaments of higher bacteria are often included.

BACTERIA. There are two groups: the higher bacteria and the lower bacteria.

Among the higher bacteria, the iron and filamentous sulfur bacteria are important, also the so-called sewage fungus *Sphaerotilus* (see Figures 19-6 and 25-4).

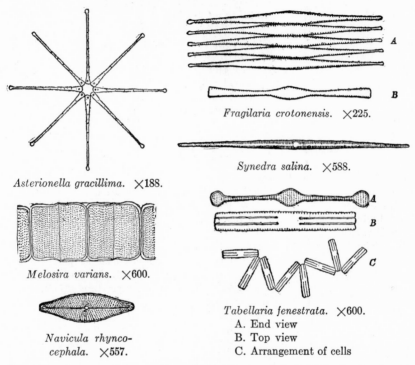

Fragilaria crotonensis. ×225.

Synedra salina. ×588.

Asterionella gracillima. ×188.

Melosira varians. ×600.

Navicula rhynco-cephala. ×557.

Tabellaria fenestrata. ×600.
A. End view
B. Top view
C. Arrangement of cells

Fig. 19-3. Common diatoms. From H. B. Ward and G. C. Whipple, *Freshwater Biology,* John Wiley & Sons, New York, 1918.

All higher bacteria are filamentous, and some are characterized by false branching. The iron bacteria are generally surrounded by a gelatinous sheath that is covered with iron or manganese hydrates. They may infest water—such as ground water—that is rich in iron or manganese and in organic matter and that is more or less devoid of oxygen. Tufts of filaments are sometimes matted together in a feltlike layer of substantial thickness. *Crenothrix* is a common representative. The filamentous sulfur bacteria contain granules of free sulfur. Unlike the pigmented members of the lower bacteria, they do not contain bacteriopurpurin or bacteriochlorophyll. They develop best in the presence of hydrogen sulfide. *Beggiatoa* is a common representative. See Figures 19-6 and 25-4.

The higher bacteria are generally considered to be *autotrophic* in their nutrition, i.e., they obtain their energy from the oxidation of simple inorganic substances. Carbon needed for structural purposes, for example, is obtained either from carbon dioxide or carbonates. The sulfur bacteria obtain their energy from the oxidation of inorganic sulfur compounds such as hydrogen sulfide, sulfur, and thiosulfate. The iron bacteria make similar use of inorganic, reduced forms of iron such as ferrous iron; but they can have a heterotrophic nutrition in the presence of organic matter.

The lower bacteria that are pathogenic to man have been described in Chapter 1. The *saprophytic* bacteria—or bacteria that live on decaying organic matter—are similar to the pathogenic bacteria in size and shape; but their food habits are such that they, more than any other group of organisms, are responsible for the processes of decomposition by which waste organic matter is simplified and eventually mineralized or stabilized. The bacteria occur (1) as spherical cells singly (cocci), in pairs (diplococci), in chains (streptococci), or in clusters (staphylococci); (2) as rod-shaped cells singly (bacilli), or in chains (streptobacilli); and (3) as corkscrew-shaped cells (spirilla or *spirochetes*). The saprophytic bacteria multiply most rapidly in warm water.

The heterotrophic bacteria decompose carbonaceous materials and nitrogenous materials. Some also reduce nitrates and sulfates in the absence of free oxygen, provided that other sources of energy are available. Among autotrophic bacteria, the nitrifying organisms are of importance in the sanitary economy of water and sewage. They require the presence of free oxygen, an alkaline pH, and the presence of carbon dioxide or carbonate. Other autotrophic bacteria derive their energy from the oxidation of methane or hydrogen. They are not to be confused with the heterotrophic bacteria that produce methane under anaerobic conditions.

All bacteria are sensitive to reaction (pH) and temperature. Some can tolerate low pH values, but the optimum is generally in the vicinity of 6.5 to 7.5; maximal and minimal values are normally 4.0 and 9.5 respectively. According to the temperatures at which they flourish, bacteria are classified as *psychrophilic* (10–20 C), *mesophilic* (20–40 C), and *thermophilic* (40–65 C). Most of the organisms that are pathogenic to man flourish at body temperature (37 C). The spores of spore-forming bacteria are more resistant to heat than are the vegetative forms. The bacteria are less sensitive to cold than to heat. At low temperatures, they are essentially dormant and can persist for long times. Waste products of bacterial growth may be inhibiting or even toxic to the organisms producing them.

ANIMAL KINGDOM

VERTEBRATES (Vertebrata). The higher aquatic animals include the fish and amphibians. The welfare of game fish is of particular importance in connection with the control of algal growths by copper sulfate and with the pollution of natural waters.

MOLLUSKS (Mollusca). These occur in wide variety in water as snails, mussels, and shellfish in general. The sanitary protection of edible varieties is of importance. The encroachment by mussels of water intakes has already been mentioned.

ARTHROPODS (Arthropoda). This group possesses jointed legs or leglike appendages. The three classes to be considered here are the crustaceans (Crustacea), the *insects* (Insecta), and the spiders, mites, and water bears (Arachnida). The crustaceans and arachnids include both large and small genera. Microscopic representatives are shown in Figure 19-4. The larval stages of some insects abound in water. Some of the semiaquatic forms infest trickling filters (see Section 25-4).

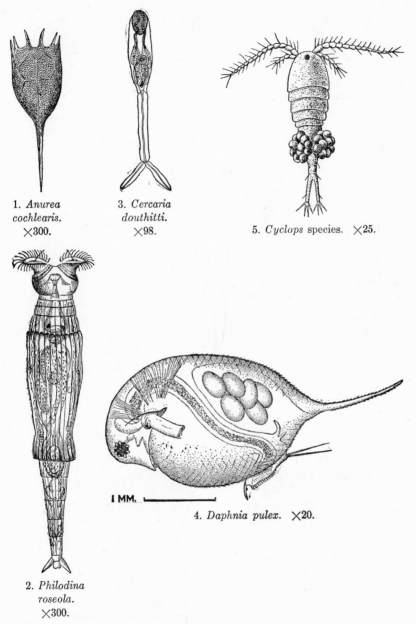

1. *Anurea cochlearis.* ×300.

3. *Cercaria douthitti.* ×98.

5. *Cyclops* species. ×25.

I MM.

4. *Daphnia pulex.* ×20.

2. *Philodina roseola.* ×300.

Figure 19-4. Common rotifers (1 & 2), crustaceans (4 & 5), and the larva (Cercaria) of a flat worm (3). 1-4 from H. B. Ward and G. C. Whipple, *Freshwater Biology,* John Wiley & Sons, New York, 1918. 5 from G. C. Whipple, G. M. Fair, and M. C. Whipple, *Microscopy of Drinking Water,* John Wiley & Sons, New York, 1927.

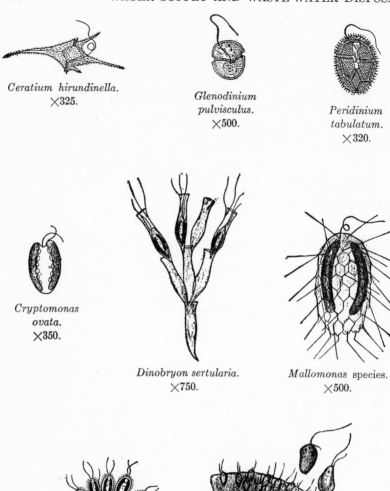

Ceratium hirundinella.
×325.

*Glenodinium
pulvisculus.*
×500.

*Peridinium
tabulatum.*
×320.

*Cryptomonas
ovata.*
×350.

Dinobryon sertularia.
×750.

Mallomonas species.
×500.

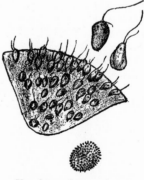

Synura uvella ×600.

*Uroglenopsis americana.
Individual cells.* ×1,500.

Figure 19-5.   Common protozoa.   From H. B. Ward and G. C. Whipple, *Fresh-water Biology,* John Wiley & Sons, New York, 1918.   For other protozoa see Figure 25-4.

WORMS (Helminthes). There are three aquatic groups: the annelids (Annelida) or aquatic earthworms, the trochal worm (Trochelminthes) which include the rotifers (Rotatoria), or wheel animalcules, and the nematodes (Nemathelminthes) or roundworms. With the exception of the rotifers, these organisms occur in particular in bottom deposits (see Figure 19-6). Some of the rotifers are illustrated in Figure 19-4. They are important scavengers. The pathogenic worms have been referred to in Chapter 1.

METAZOA other than worms. Included in this group are the sponges (Porifera), moss animals (Bryozoa or Polyzoa), and Hydrozoa. The sponges are agglomerations of animal cells in gelatinous masses. The Bryozoa form moss-like or coral-like calcareous or chitinous aggregations that may reach relatively enormous size. The Hydrozoa generally occur singly but grow occasionally in huge numbers in water reservoirs and on slow sand filters.

PROTOZOA. This phylum includes all the unicellular animals. Reference has been made in Chapter 1 to the pathogenicity of certain protozoa. The normal aquatic representatives are important scavengers and fall into three classes, examples of which are shown in Figures 19-5 and 25-4.

AMOEBOID PROTOZOA (Sarcodina). These organisms are irregular in shape, naked or shelled, single or colonial. They move by means of pseudopodia (false feet). Some genera form cysts.

FLAGELLATE PROTOZOA (Mastigophora). The flagellates are characterized by whiplike or lashlike appendages. They occur singly or in colonies, naked or with a cellulosic shell. The chlorophyllaceous protozoa are often classified as algae. Many of them produce fishy odors of great potency. *Uroglenopsis* is an example. Others impart a bitter cucumber taste; *Synura* is a common offender. The invasion of mussel beds by salt-water dinoflagellates that contain a highly toxic principle has been mentioned in Chapter 1.

CILIATE PROTOZOA (Infusoria). The ciliates are characterized by hairlike appendages. They occur singly or in colonies. Most of them are bacteria-eaters and appear to be important in the destruction of pathogenic as well as normal water varieties. They occur in large numbers in polluted water. The protozoa may be *holozoic, saprozoic,* or *holophytic* (facultatively autotrophic). The holozoic protozoa ingest other living organisms, principally bacteria. The saprozoic protozoa utilize carbohydrates and proteins that have been made soluble by bacteria and other organisms. The holophytic protozoa contain chlorophyll or other pigments and absorb radiant energy. Some protozoa thrive under aerobic conditions, others under anaerobic conditions. Still others are facultatively aerobic or anaerobic.

Assemblages of aquatic organisms that drift about in a body of water, more or less passively, in response to waves and currents are called *plankton* from the Greek word for "wandering." The individual organisms composing the assemblage are referred to as *planktonts* but more commonly by the name of their most common representatives the *algae*. Assemblages of organisms that freely change their location by the efforts of their members are designated *nekton* from the Greek word for "swimming." Growths attached to the shore or bottom, particularly the latter, or seeking a livelihood on or in the mud and ooze are called *benthos* from the Greek word for "the bottom of the sea."

For a systematic classification and description of individual organisms, the student is referred to standard works on these subjects. The discussion of water biology which follows is confined to those aspects of the subject that are of more immediate interest to engineers, namely: (1) the selection of organisms as indicators of contamination and pollution; and (2) the relation of biological associations to the decomposition of organic waste materials. The control of algae and related organisms is considered in Chapter 27, the natural die-away of bacteria in Chapter 28. The destruction of pathogens by disinfection is treated in Chapter 27. The process of biological flocculation is made part of Chapter 25.

19-3. Biological Indicators of Contamination and Pollution. As suggested in a footnote to Section 1-1, the biological *contamination* of water is defined as the introduction into, or the release or development in, water of potentially pathogenic organisms that render the use of the water hazardous and, therefore, unfit for human consumption or domestic purposes. A similar definition applies to biological contaminants that are potentially pathogenic to animals. Strictly speaking, *pollution* of a body of water is defined as the introduction into it of substances of such characteristics and in such quantity as to render it offensive to the senses of sight, smell, or taste. The term pollution is more generally used, however, to include also the concept of potential contamination.

The otherwise fortunate circumstance that the number of pathogens in natural waters is small, together with the fact that they occur in wide variety, imposes a severe restriction on their direct, and more particularly their quantitatively direct, determination in routine water analysis. As a result we are forced to resort to indirect quantitative evidence of the presence of biological contaminants. *Indicator* organisms provide the substitute. As their name implies, their determination points to pollution and to the possible presence of contaminating organisms. Therefore they are, in essence, measures of guilt by association. The coliform group of bacteria, for example, has as one of its primary habitats the intestinal tract of human beings. Hence the presence in water of members of the coliform group is an indication of the potential presence of other organisms that originate in the human intestinal tract and, in particular, in the tract of individuals who are ill with an enteric disease such as typhoid fever or who are carriers of a pathogen such as the typhoid bacillus.

To be of value to the engineer, a biological indicator of contamination or pollution must satisfy the following criteria:

1. It must be a reliable measure of the potential presence of specific contaminating organisms both in natural waters and in waters that have been subjected to treatment. To meet this requirement, the indicator organism or organisms must react to the natural aquatic environment and to treatment processes, including disinfection, in the same way relatively as do the contaminating organisms. When such an indicator organism is used experimentally, it becomes a useful simulant.

2. It must be present in numbers that are relatively much larger than those of the contaminating organism whose potential presence it is to indicate. Otherwise the presence of the contaminating organism itself would serve a more directly useful purpose.

3. It must be readily identified by relatively simple analytical procedures. Few sanitary works can afford the services of biological specialists.

4. It must lend itself to numerical evaluation as well as qualitative identification since a knowledge of the degree of contamination is an essential interest and responsibility of the engineer.

a. The Coliform Group of Organisms. The coliform group of bacteria possesses the faculty of fermenting lactose or milk sugar with the production of gas and can thereby be made to offer simple, visible evidence of the presence of one of its members in water that is added to and incubated in broth containing lactose. However, other bacteria, too, possess the power to ferment lactose, and additional growth reactions must be used to confirm the presence of a member of the coliform group. The so-called fecal coli (*Escherichia coli*) constitute about 90% of the coliforms discharged in fecal matter whereas the so-called non-fecal coli (*Aerobacter aerogenes*) usually originate in soil, grain, and decaying vegetation. Although it is possible to differentiate between the two species as well as intermediate organisms by certain test procedures, the grouping together of the different lactose-fermenting species is generally considered adequate for the purposes of the water engineer in view of the fact that this grouping is in the nature of a factor of safety.

The coliform group of organisms meets the criteria for a satisfactory biological indicator of contamination or pollution that have been discussed at the beginning of this section.

1. As a statistical average, about half the tests for the presence of coliform organisms in sewage are found to represent lactose-fermenting organisms that originate in fecal matter. Since human feces are the primary source of pathogenic enteric organisms, the presence in water of coliforms offers significant evidence of the potential presence of such pathogens. The rate of destruction or death of the coliforms and the rate of their removal from water and sewage, furthermore, is substantially parallel to that of the pathogenic enteric bacteria, and the coliform

group is, if anything, more resistant to disinfection than are the pathogenic enteric bacteria.

2. The number of coliform organisms in human feces and in sewage is very great. The daily per capita excretion of this group varies from 125 to 150 billion in winter and is close to 400 billion in summer. Parenthetically, the *total* number of bacteria in fecal matter than can be counted by simple bacteriological techniques is approximately a thousand times greater still. Without going into the exact details of current American standards for drinking water, the U. S. Public Health Service requirements for water supplied to interstate carriers, over which the Service has jurisdiction, are, generally speaking, that these waters shall contain fewer than one coliform organism in 100 ml, or 40 coliforms per gal. The dilution factor by which the normal domestic sewage production of American communities (about 100 gpcd) will be reduced to acceptable drinking water would, therefore, be about $(400 \times 10^9)/(40 \times 10^2) = 10^8$ or 100 million. In other words, each gallon of sewage would have to be dispersed in about 100 million gallons of clean water. Actually the number of coliforms that may enter bodies of water used as a source of drinking water is decreased: (1) by death, in time, of these organisms because they do not generally maintain themselves in sewage or in cleaner water; (2) by the removal and destruction of these organisms in sewage treatment works before discharge into receiving waters; and (3) by their removal and destruction in water-supply and water-purification works before the water is used for domestic purposes. The expected effects of time and treatment in reducing the coliform load are discussed in other chapters of this book. The important conclusion to be drawn at this juncture is that the large numerical presence of coliform organisms in human excreta makes them excellent biological indicators of potential contamination by pathogenic enteric bacteria specifically, by other intestinal pathogens less specifically, and by the pollutional matters contained in human sewage, in broad measure.

Nevertheless, the generalized standard of approximately 1 coliform organism in 100 ml of water is, in a sense, a standard of expediency: it does not exclude entirely the possibility of acquiring an intestinal infection. The standard is one that can be attained (1) by the economic development of available water supplies, their disinfection and, if need be, treatment in purification works by economically feasible methods and (2) by the economic development of waste-water disposal systems including the necessary degree of treatment of the waste waters in suitable works by economically feasible processes. The exposure to typhoid fever by the consumption of water that meets the current bacteriological standard of the U. S. Public Health Service can be gaged from statistical studies by Kehr and Butterfield [3] of the ratio of *Salmonella typhosa* to coliforms in sewage and polluted streams. In accordance with the results of these workers the number y of *Salmonella typhosa* per million coliforms varies, as is to be expected, with the incidence of typhoid in the community, as expressed, for example, by the annual death rate r from typhoid fever per 100,000 population. A plot of available data suggests the following relationship:

$$y = ar^n = 9r^{0.461} \qquad \text{19-1}$$

For a death rate of 1.3 per 100,000 per annum, for example, $y = 10$ typhoid organisms per million coliforms.

[3] R. H. Kehr and C. T. Butterfield, "Some Notes on the Relation between Coliforms and Enteric Pathogens," *U. S. Public Health Rept.* 58, 589 (1943).

Since the number of coliforms in a gallon of water that meets the bacteriological standard of the U. S. Public Health Service may average as high as 40 coliforms, it would be possible to find a single *S. typhosa* in $1/(40 \times 10 \times 10^{-6}) =$ 2,500 gal water that is polluted by the sewage of a community with an annual typhoid death rate of 1.3 per 100,000. Three lessons may be drawn from a calculation such as this: (1) that the current coliform standard of water quality is by no means a standard of perfection but, as previously suggested, a standard of expediency which offers, as it has in the past, a challenge for improvement; (2) that it is hardly practicable to develop a direct test for a specific pathogen such as *S. typhosa;* and (3) that an acceptable standard should be related to the prevalence of water-borne disease in the region in which the standard is to apply.

3. The test for organisms of the coliform group, as previously indicated, is sufficiently simple of performance to place it in the hands of the kind of personnel that is currently recruited for the supervision of the quality of public water supplies.

4. As discussed in Section 20-13, numerical evaluation of the density of coliform organisms in samples of water and sewage is readily accomplished by dilution methods.

A matter of concern in evaluating the relative danger of spread of enteric infections is the large number of potentially pathogenic organisms included in the excreta of carriers and patients. A carrier of typhoid fever, for example, may excrete up to 200 billion *S. typhosa* per day; a carrier of amebic dysentery up to 10 million cysts of *E. histolytica* per day. The smaller the quantities of water exposed to the excreta of a patient or carrier, therefore, the greater becomes their concentration of viable organisms and the greater, too, becomes the chance of infecting a person who consumes the water. Although the minimum infective dose of water-borne infections has not been established, there is statistical evidence that typhoid fever will be produced in 1 to 2% of the persons who ingest a single viable cell of *S. typhosa*. Massive doses are known to break down the immunity acquired by inoculation.

Because a large proportion of the coliform group of bacteria originates in the intestinal tract of warm-blooded animals, including man, the identification of this group has long been the preferred indicator of the potential presence of intestinal pathogens not only in water, but also in ice—both natural and artificial—and in shellfish. The waters to which the coliform test is applied include those that are employed in domestic and industrial supplies, natural bathing waters, and the waters overlying shellfish areas. When applied to the waters of indoor or artificial pools, the test gives evidence only of contamination that should be avoided by requiring all bathers to take a cleansing shower before entering the pool or returning to it after using the toilet. Standards for bathing waters and waters that wash shellfish areas are discussed in Chapter 21.

b. Other Bacterial Indicators. Much thought has been given to the use of bacterial indicator organisms of sewage pollution other than the coliform group; among them, in particular, of the so-called sewage streptococci. Houston,[4] for example, interested himself in their identification as indicating dangerous pollution since they were "readily demonstrable in waters recently polluted and seemingly altogether absent from waters above suspicion of contamination." Many of the organisms classified as sewage streptococci originate in the mouth and throat of warm-blooded animals, including man. The enterococci found in feces are the true intestinal inhabitants and have a greater heat and acid tolerance than the other streptococci. Since enterococci are discharged in much smaller numbers than coliforms and since the test for enterococci is qualitative rather than quantitative, there is no present ground for a change from, or supplementation of, the use of the coliform group as bacterial indicators of contamination or pollution of the water supplies of communities. The same statement holds true, in principle, for another common intestinal organism, *Clostridium perfringens.*

In the sanitary control of indoor swimming pools, however, there is need for an indicator organism or group of organisms that will reflect the contamination of the pool water by potentially pathogenic organisms that have their habitat in the eyes, nose, mouth, and throat as well as on other mucous surfaces of the body and on the skin. Numerous streptococci and staphylococci are implicated in infections of these organs and body areas. In the absence of a simple test for significant organisms of this kind, the 37-C plate count is generally employed in gaging the bacterial contamination of indoor pools. Permissible numbers are discussed in Chapter 21.

c. Other Biological Indicators. The discharge into natural bodies of water of sewage and related wastes provides a wide variety of food materials that can be used by water-dwelling organisms, large and small. As a result there is established in the polluted waters a flora and fauna commensurate with and characteristic of the amount and quality of food material as well as the conditions of existence that are created by changes in the physical, chemical, and biological environment resulting from pollution. The ecological systems that are developed can tell the experienced biologist much about the pollutional status of the water. The many types of living things encountered can be broadly classified as *pollutional* and *cleaner-water* organisms.

[4] Houston, A. C., Supplements to the 28th and 29th Annual Reports of the Local Government Board Containing the Report of the Medical Officer of Health for 1889–99 (p. 439) and 1899–1900 (p. 467) respectively, London, England.

The relative preponderance of the one or the other group will then be a measure of pollution. Organisms that are *tolerant* to both polluted and clean water are of little value as biological indicators of water quality.

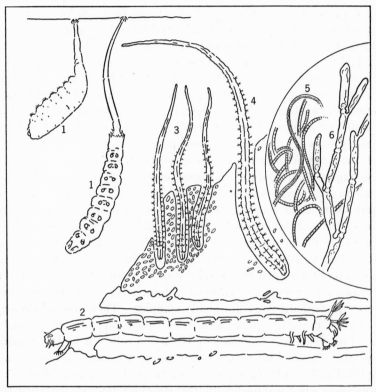

Figure 19-6. "Indicator organisms" of polluted waters. 1. Rat-tail maggot, *Eristalis*, the larva of the drone fly, ×5. 2. Blood worm, *Chironomus*, the larva of the midge fly, ×5. 3. Sludge worm, *Tubifex*, a bristle worm, ×5. 4. Sludge worm, *Limnodrilus*, a bristle worm, ×5. 5. Sewage fungus, *Sphaerotilus*, a higher bacterium, ×500. 6. Sewage fungus, *Leptomitus*, a mold, ×500.

Although a study of the environmental adaptation of the wide variety of organisms involved in the pollution and natural purification of water is always fascinating and often fruitful, the requisite competence is possessed by few, and the work involved is generally so time-consuming and costly that it is commonly performed only in connection with research projects or special investigations. There are, however, a few "type organisms of heavy pollution" that are (1) sufficiently large to be seen as individuals or in colonial growths by the naked eye and (2) sufficiently common in pollutional environments to serve as useful inspectional indicators of pollution. Some of these "type" organisms are shown in Figure 19-6. They include the rat-tail maggot, *Eristalis*, or larva of the drone fly; the blood worm, *Chironomus*, or larva of the midge fly; the sludge worms, *Tubifex* and *Limnodrilus*; and the so-called sewage fungi, *Sphaerotilus* and *Leptomitus*. *Sphaerotilus* is actually a higher bacterium.

19-4. Decomposition or Decay. Waste organic substances find their way into water in many ways: trees along the banks of a stream shed their leaves into it; the runoff from agricultural lands carries manures and decaying vegetation into drainage ditches that empty into water courses; the washings from streets and roads that traverse the drainage area unload suspended matter into sewers and streams; the water-carried wastes of human habitations and industries that are discharged into the natural drainage channels of the region impose a varied burden upon them; and the substances contributed by the life or death of the varied organisms that make the water itself their habitat constitute an inherent source of waste matter. The organic matter and some of the complex mineral portions of these substances are utilized as a source of energy by a succession of living things. A series of biochemical reactions is thereby set in motion, and polluted waters are eventually returned to a normal state of purity. The mechanisms by which substances are synthesized into living cells and analyzed to provide needed energy are highly complex. They proceed through the agency of large protein molecules called enzymes, or ferments, which are themselves produced by the living cells. A host of specific enzymatic reactions intervenes before complex organic substances are simplified and eventually returned to a more stable mineral level.

Engineers are concerned with the reactions that characterize the decomposition or decay of waste organic substances and, in particular, with the rates at which these reactions proceed in nature and can be made to proceed in treatment works by providing environments in which the processes of decomposition can operate at maximal rates. For the purposes of the engineer, identification of the cyclical changes that take place is generally restricted (1) to measurement of characteristic compounds of the elements that constitute organic and other nutritional matters, notably nitrogen, carbon, and sulfur, and (2) to measurement of the oxygen used up in accomplishing the changes or of the gases released in the course of decomposition.

The basis for these measurements is shown in Figure 19-7 for aerobic decomposition and in Figure 19-8 for anaerobic decomposition.

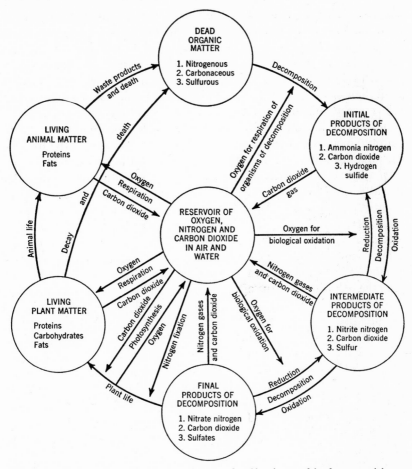

Figure 19-7. Cycle of nitrogen, carbon, and sulfur in aerobic decomposition.

a. Aerobic Decomposition. Figure 19-7 idealizes the cycles of nitrogen, carbon, and sulfur in aerobic decomposition. Organic nitrogen, for example, is seen to be converted successively by living things to ammonia nitrogen, nitrite nitrogen, and nitrate nitrogen. Nitrate nitrogen is then assimilated by plants, with the aid of sunlight (photosynthesis), to build living plant matter which is used in turn by animals to construct animal tissue. The progress of decomposition can be determined chemically in terms of the interrelated amounts of organic nitrogen, ammonia nitrogen, nitrite nitrogen, and nitrate nitrogen that are present in water into which waste organic nitrogenous substances have been discharged. The cyclical changes in nitrogen, therefore, underlie the nitrogen determinations of a sanitary water analysis. Changes similar to those of nitrogen obtain and can be determined for carbon and sulfur.

Figure 19-7 shows, furthermore, that oxygen is needed for the respiration of the organisms that are responsible for the decomposition represented in the descending arc of the circle as well as for the respiration of the plants and animals that resynthesize organic matter in the ascending arc of the circle. Gaseous oxygen furnishes the normal needs in aerobic decomposition. Terrestrial organisms draw upon the oxygen of the atmosphere, aquatic organisms on the oxygen dissolved in water. Since the atmosphere contains about 21% of oxygen by volume, whereas water holds but 0.8% by volume in solution at normal temperatures (50 F), the aquatic environment is inherently and critically sensitive to the oxygen demands of the organisms that populate it. Determinations of the amount of oxygen dissolved in water (DO) relative to its saturation value and of the amount and rate of oxygen utilization called the biochemical oxygen demand (BOD), therefore, furnish some of the best means for identifying the pollutional status of water and by indirection also the amount of decomposable, or organic, matter contained in it.

Plants, as seen in Figure 19-7, have the physiological property of releasing oxygen during photosynthesis and of using carbon dioxide. This activity must be taken into account in striking oxygen balances where plants flourish in water. Although carbon dioxide and nitrogen gases are exchanged between the living organisms and their environment, these gases do not lend themselves as readily to the determinations that have been described for oxygen. They are followed only in specialized researches.

b. Anaerobic Decomposition. When the oxygen dissolved in water becomes exhausted by the heavy demand made upon it by living organisms that are busily engaged in the destruction of nutrient matter, the *aerobic* organisms, which are not able to utilize oxygen from sources other than dissolved, or free, oxygen, succumb. Their place is taken by *anaerobic* or *facultatively anaerobic* organisms, which can draw upon the oxygen of the organic matter itself. Anaerobic decomposition then supplants aerobic decomposition, and the cycles of nitrogen, carbon, and sulfur, which are idealized in Figure 19-8 for purposes of illustration, are set in motion. The initial products of anaerobic decomposition are seen to be organic acids, acid carbonates, carbon dioxide, and hydrogen sulfide; the intermediate products are ammonia nitrogen, acid carbonates, carbon dioxide, and sulfides; the final products are ammonia nitrogen, humus, carbon dioxide, methane, and sulfides. The gases of decomposition that are released to the water

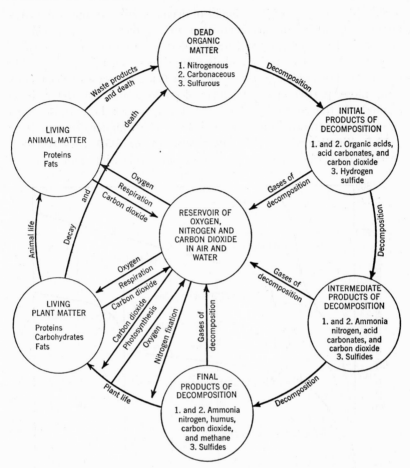

Figure 19-8. Cycle of nitrogen, carbon, and sulfur in anaerobic decomposition.

escape from it to the atmosphere in contact with the water as soon as the water has become saturated with these gases. The characteristic and identifiable gases are carbon dioxide and methane. The latter is the "will o' the wisp" of the marsh (or marsh gas). It is combustible and of high calorific power. In the anaerobic decomposition of sewage sludge, called sludge digestion, the methane produced is generally captured and utilized as an important source of energy. Together with the sludge humus, indeed, methane constitutes an important by-product of sewage treatment.

The end products of anaerobic decomposition are plant foods. They are utilized by plants and through them by animals in the reconstruction of the substances from which these products were derived.

Suitable measures of the amount of decomposable, or organic, matter undergoing anaerobic decomposition in a given time are (1) the volume and rate of gas production and (2) the reduction in weight of volatile (organic) material and its rate of loss. Of these, gas production offers the readier measure for identifying the rate of decomposition, more particularly of sludge digestion, and for determining, through it, the controlling environmental factors: both those which are conducive to rapid digestion and those which hinder decomposition.

19-5. Kinetics of Aerobic Decomposition, or BOD. As stated in Section 19-4, the progress of aerobic decomposition and hence of

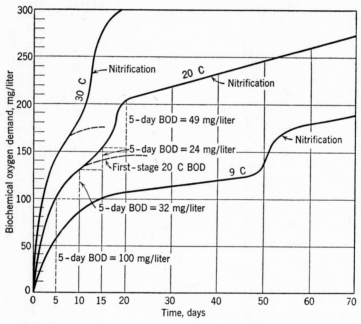

Figure 19-9. Progress of biochemical oxygen demand (BOD) at 9, 20, and 30 C.
After Theriault.

stabilization of putrescible (organic) matter in water and sewage is reflected in the gradual withdrawal of oxygen from solution or the gradual satisfaction of the BOD. As shown in Figure 19-9, the progressive exertion of the BOD of freshly polluted water generally breaks down into two stages: a first stage in which it is largely the carbonaceous matter that is oxidized and a second stage in which nitrogenous substances are attacked in significant amounts and nitrification takes place. If the temperature of freshly polluted water is 20 C, for example, the first stage extends about to the tenth day and is characterized by a progressive falling off of the actual BOD exerted in each interval of time. Analysis of the first-stage experience demonstrates that the amount of BOD exerted in a unit of time relative to the BOD remaining to be exerted during the first stage is substantially constant. In the succeeding second stage, the BOD rises sharply as nitrification becomes dominant. Oxygen utilization then reaches a fairly uniform rate that is maintained for a protracted period of time.

A knowledge of the progressive utilization of oxygen by polluting substances that are undergoing decomposition is of importance for at least three reasons: (1) as a generalized measure of the amount of oxidizable matter contained in water, or the pollutional load placed upon it; (2) as a means for predicting the progress of aerobic decomposition in polluted waters and the degree of self-purification accomplished in given intervals of time; and (3) as a yardstick of the removal of putrescible matter which accompanies different treatment processes. However, only the first stage of decomposition appears to be sufficiently constant to be generalized in mathematical terms.

a. Formulation of the First-Stage BOD Curve. The first-stage BOD has generally been interpreted as a first-order reaction, dependent on the concentration of oxidizable organic material present, but independent of the oxygen concentration, provided that it is greater than a critical value of about 4 mg/l at 20 C for example. This means that the rate-determining steps in the reaction are not ones that involve oxygen. Alternatively, since the reactions are enzymatic ones, the lack of oxygen dependence is consistent with the case outlined in the last paragraph of Section 18-16.

The resulting first-order equation may be written in the form

$$y = L(1 - e^{-kt}) = L(1 - 10^{-k't}) \qquad 19\text{-}2$$

in which L is the initial first-stage BOD of the water, y is the oxygen demand exerted in time t, and k or k' are the rate constants related respectively to a base e and a base 10. The BOD remaining at time t is equal to $(L - y)$, and the proportion of BOD exerted in time t is $y/L = (1 - e^{-kt}) = (1 - 10^{-k't})$, k' being equal to 0.4343k.

Practical evaluation of this equation is complicated by the fact that L, as well as k or k', is usually unknown. A number of methods for finding the magnitudes of L and k or k' from a series of observations of y and t have been proposed. Of these the "method of moments" developed by Moore, Thomas, and Snow [5] appears to be the most

[5] E. W. Moore, H. A. Thomas, Jr., and W. B. Snow, "Simplified Method for Analysis of BOD Data," *Sewage and Ind. Wastes 22,* 1343 (1950).

convenient. In this method, the data are fitted with a first-order curve that has its first two moments [Σy and $\Sigma(ty)$] equal to those of the experimental points. The equations that express this condition for a series of n values of y in any specified time sequence in which i denotes the numerical order of the sequences are:

(1) for the zero moment

$$\sum_{i=0}^{n} y_i = \sum_{i=0}^{n} L(1 - e^{-kt_i}) = (n+1)L - L\sum_{i=0}^{n} e^{-kt_i} \qquad \text{19-3}$$

And (2) similarly for the first moment

$$\sum_{i=0}^{n} (t_i y_i) = \sum_{i=0}^{n} Lt_i(1 - e^{-kt_i}) = L\sum_{i=0}^{n} t_i - L\sum_{i=0}^{n} (t_i e^{-kt_i}) \qquad \text{19-4}$$

Division of the first moment into the zero moment eliminates L to give the equation

$$\frac{\displaystyle\sum_{i=0}^{n} y_i}{\displaystyle\sum_{i=0}^{n} (t_i y_i)} = \frac{\displaystyle n - \sum_{i=1}^{n} e^{-kt_i}}{\displaystyle\sum_{i=0}^{n} t_i - \sum_{i=0}^{n} (t_i e^{-kt_i})} \qquad \text{19-5}$$

in which the magnitude of the right-hand member can be computed once and for all for different values of k and varying time sequences. For the time series $t = 1, 2, 3$ days, and for $k = 1$ or $k' = 0.434$, for example, $n = 3$, $\displaystyle\sum_{i=0}^{n} t_i = 6$, $\displaystyle\sum_{i=1}^{n} e^{-kt_i} = e^{-1} + e^{-2} + e^{-3} = 0.5530$, and $\displaystyle\sum_{i=0}^{n} (t_i e^{-kt_i}) = e^{-1} + 2e^{-2} + 3e^{-3} = 0.7879$. Hence $\Sigma y_i / \Sigma(t_i y_i) = (3 - 0.5530)/(6 - 0.7879) = 0.4694$. This value of $\Sigma y/\Sigma(ty)$ for $k = 1.0$ or $k' = 0.4343$ is plotted in Figure 19-10 together with correspondingly derived values of the ordinate $\Sigma y/\Sigma(ty)$ for other values of the ordinate k or k'. It should be noted that the time sequence may be expressed in any convenient unit: hours, days, weeks, months, or years, and multiples of each.

The value of L is obtained by eliminating the term $t = 0$, $y = 0$ from Equation 19-3, and expressing $\displaystyle\sum_{i=1}^{n} y_i$ in terms of L, or

$$\sum_{i=1}^{n} y_i/L = n - \sum_{i=1}^{n} e^{-kt_i} \qquad \text{19-6}$$

The right-hand term of this equation is seen to equal the numerator of

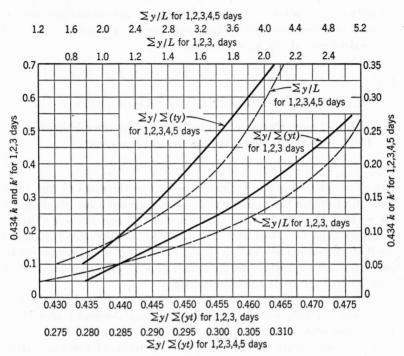

Figure 19-10. Values of $k' = 0.434\,k$ for calculated magnitudes of $\Sigma y/\Sigma(yt)$ and values of $\Sigma y/L$ for these values of k' for 3-day and 5-day sequences. *After Moore, Thomas, and Snow.*

the right-hand term of Equation 19-5. For the time series previously considered, therefore, the value

$$\sum_{i=1}^{n} y_i/L = 3 - 0.5530 = 2.4470$$

is incorporated in Figure 19-10. A plot of the elements necessary to find the values of $0.434k$ or k' and of L for a 5-day sequence is also shown. Use of this diagram is illustrated in the following example.

Example 19-1. Given the following BOD determinations at 20 C.

Time, days	1	2	3	4	5
BOD exerted, mg/l	82	112	153	163	176

Find the magnitudes of the rate of reaction k or k' and the first-stage BOD L. The necessary calculations are $\sum_{i=0}^{n} y_i = 686$; $\sum_{i=0}^{n} (t_iy_i) = 2{,}297$; and $\sum_{i=0}^{n} y_i/\sum_{i=0}^{n} (t_iy_i) = 686/2{,}297 = 0.2987$. From Figure 19-14, read $0.434k$ or $k' = 0.227$ per day, or $k = 0.523$ per day; and $\sum_{i=1}^{n} y_i/L = 3.64$, whence $L = 686/3.64 = 188$ mg/l.

Thomas [6] has proposed a simple graphical approximation for the evaluation of the constants of the BOD curve. His method is based on the similarity of the two functions

$$(1 - e^{-kt}) = kt[1 - kt/2 + (kt)^2/6 - (kt)^3/24 + \cdots]$$

and

$$kt(1 + kt/6)^{-3} = kt[1 - kt/2 + (kt)^2/6 - (kt)^3/21.6 + \cdots]$$

Equation 19-2 may, therefore, be approximated by the relationship $y = Lkt(1 + kt/6)^{-3}$ which takes the straight-line form:

$$(t/y)^{1/3} = (kL)^{-1/3} + [k^{2/3}/(6L^{1/3})]t \qquad 19\text{-}7$$

If $(t/y)^{1/3}$ is plotted as the ordinate against t as the abscissa, the value of the intercept on the ordinate at $t = 0$ of a straight line fitted by eye is $a = (kL)^{-1/3}$ and the value of the slope of this line is $b = k^{2/3}/(6L^{1/3})$. It follows that $k = 6b/a$ and $L = 1/(ka^3)$. Experimental values of $y > 0.9L$ should not be used in fitting the straight line because deviations from the approximating linearized plot become significant when about 90% of the BOD has been exerted.

b. *Temperature Effects.* For a given sample of water, both the rate of reaction k and the magnitude of the first-stage demand L or oxidizability of the organic matter increase with temperature. The observed effects of temperature can be formulated in terms of the van't Hoff-Arrhenius relationship described in Section 18-17 and expressed as the energy of activation E, the temperature characteristic C (and its power function, the temperature coefficient $\Theta = e^C$), or the temperature quotient $Q_{10} = e^{10C} = \Theta^{10}$. Hence

$$k/k_0 = e^{C_k(T - T_0)} = \Theta_k{}^{(T - T_0)} \qquad 19\text{-}8$$

$$L/L_0 = e^{C_L(T - T_0)} = \Theta_L{}^{(T - T_0)} \qquad 19\text{-}9$$

$$kL/k_0L_0 = e^{(C_k + C_L)(T - T_0)} = (\Theta_k\Theta_L)^{(T - T_0)} \qquad 19\text{-}10$$

where T is the temperature and the subscript zero denotes the reference values of k, L, and T.

Expansion of $e^{C(T - T_0)}$ yields the series:

$$[1 + C(T - T_0) + \tfrac{1}{2}C^2(T - T_0)^2 + \tfrac{1}{6}C^3(T - T_0)^3 + \cdots]$$

Retention of but the first two terms of the expansion then results in the following approximate relationships:

$$k/k_0 = 1 + C_k(T - T_0) \qquad 19\text{-}11$$

$$L/L_0 = 1 + C_L(T - T_0) \qquad 19\text{-}12$$

---

[6] H. A. Thomas, Jr., "Graphical Determination of BOD Curve Constants," *Water and Sewage Works, 97,* 123 (1950).

From about 15 to 30 C, the activation energy E of the BOD reaction is 7,900 cal, corresponding to values of $C_k = 0.046$ per deg C, $\Theta_k = 1.047$, and $Q_{10} = 1.58$. At lower temperatures, E increases to as much as 20,000 cal near 0 C. Above 30 C, a decrease in rate with increasing temperature is observed, probably resulting from a thermal inactivation of the enzymes responsible for oxidation. It is well to remember that low values of E are associated with fast reactions that are little affected by changes in temperature.

As shown by Theriault[7] the biological oxidizability of polluted water increases, in the vicinity of 20 C, by about 2% for each degree Centigrade. In terms of Equation 19-9, therefore, the temperature characteristic C_L has a magnitude of 0.02 per deg C, the corresponding values for E, Θ_L, and Q_{10} being 3,400, 1.020, and 1.22 respectively. There is evidence, however, that these values, too, may vary in different temperature ranges.

Example 19-2. If the BOD of a waste water has a first-stage value of $L = 188$ mg/l and a reaction velocity constant $k_0 = 0.523$ per day at 20 C (Example 19-1), what is its expected 5-day BOD at 30 C, assuming that $C_k = 0.046$ and $C_L = 0.020$?

By Equation 19-8, $k = 0.523e^{0.46} = 0.828$ per day.
By Equation 19-9, $L = 188e^{0.20} = 229$ mg/l.
By Equation 19-2, $y = 229(1 - e^{-0.828 \times 5}) = 225$ mg/l.

c. Limitations of the Formulation. Theriault[7] found that the value of k was fairly constant for a variety of sewage-polluted waters and possessed a mean magnitude of 0.23 days^{-1} at 20 C ($k' = 0.1$). Later investigations of the behavior of sewage samples have shown, however, that k may vary considerably, ranging from 0.16 to 0.70 days^{-1} at 20 C, and that the mean value is more nearly 0.39. The possible variation in k implies that the 5-day 20-C, BOD is not by itself a complete measure of the strength of sewage or degree of pollution of water because it is not a constant proportion of the L value. The proportion of first-stage demand reached in a 5-day period at the stated variations in k values lies between 55.1 and 97.0%. It follows that comparisons can be drawn between the 5-day, 20-C BOD values of different waters only if their reaction velocity constants are identical.

Other complications occur, too. In unseeded samples (i.e., samples that harbor initially an inadequate flora and fauna to activate the BOD reactions), "lag" periods are experienced before the reactions proceed normally. By contrast, sewages that have undergone partial

[7] E. J. Theriault, "The Oxygen Demand of Polluted Waters," *U. S. Public Health Service Bull.* 173 (1927).

anaerobic decomposition or that contain reducing chemical substances, such as originate in certain industries, may exert an "immediate" demand (sometimes called a chemical demand) at the beginning of the BOD run. This is not part of the normal BOD.[8] In some instances, furthermore, the values of k diminish as the percentage of reaction increases. This probably results from differences in ease of oxidation of the materials present, the rate decreasing as the more easily oxidized substances are used up. The onset of nitrification, finally, may produce increases in rate in the later stages of the reaction, particularly in highly diluted samples.

Estimation of k and L is more difficult when these complications occur, but suitable methods have been published to cope with this situation.[9]

The BOD of sludge and mud deposits is discussed and formulated in Section 28-8.

19-6. Kinetics of Anaerobic Decomposition, or Gasification. As stated in Section 19-4, the progress of anaerobic decomposition or stabilization of putrescible matter that is separated from water and sewage as sludge can be measured by capturing the gases of decomposition that are released from known amounts of the decaying substance. For purposes of comparison, the amounts of gas collected are generally related to the amounts of organic (volatile) solids present at the beginning of the tests. Determination of the constituent gases is likewise of importance.

As shown in Figure 19-11, gas production from a single batch of organic material traces an S-shaped curve not unlike that described in Section 5-4 for the growth of living things, including human populations, within a limited space. This means that from the beginning of the process to a point in time near the halfway mark of total gas evolution, the yield of gas in a unit of time becomes progressively greater. After this point has been reached, the yield becomes constantly less and a limiting value is gradually approached. This behavior of organic materials that are undergoing anaerobic digestion is characteristic of processes in which the accumulation of enzymes plays a part. The first-order reaction that appears to characterize the destruction of organic matter and that has been usefully applied to aerobic decomposition, as measured by BOD, is presumably catalyzed in anaerobic decomposition of a batch of material by the products of

[8] High initial demands establish a negative lag phase.

[9] H. A. Thomas, Jr., "Analysis of the Biochemical Oxygen Demand Curve," *Sewage Works J., 12,* 504 (1940). See also the immediately preceding references.

the reaction. The principal active products are probably the enzymes that are associated with the process. The factor exerting a controlling influence may, therefore, be interpreted as one of autocatalysis.

When successive increments of putrescible material are added to organic substances that are submitted to normal anaerobic digestion, the catalyzing substances are presumably present in sufficient quantity to cause digestion to progress in ways more nearly approaching aerobic decomposition. For this reason, there has been sketched into Figure

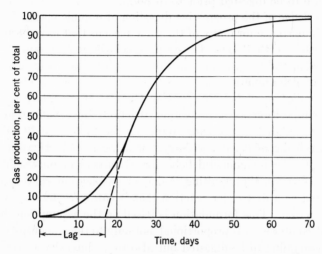

Figure 19-11. Progress of gas production by organic matter undergoing anaerobic decomposition at 20 C.

19-11 a broken line which converts the S-shaped curve to one approximating the BOD curve. A "lag" period, which is observed also for unseeded BOD samples, is thereby established. In continuous digestion, this lag period may well be suppressed. In anaerobic digestion, as discussed in Chapter 26, seeding does not only add the flora and fauna and their enzymatic systems that are responsible for decomposition. It creates also other environmental conditions, such as suitable pH values or elimination of organic acids, that favor biochemical activity and with it decomposition.

It is evident from the time scale of Figure 19-11, which records the progress of gasification at 20 C, that the rate of anaerobic decomposition of organic matter is substantially lower than the rate of aerobic decomposition. At this temperature, for example, the rate of gasification of seeded sludge solids is 8.4% per day as against a rate of BOD of 32.3% per day at a k value of 0.39. As shown for BOD, both the rate of anaerobic decomposition and its limiting value vary with temperature.

In the sanitary economy of water and waste waters, anaerobic decomposition plays a part (1) when streams or other bodies of water are overloaded with waste materials; (2) when solids settle from the water and accumulate in sludge banks of sufficient thickness to become anaerobic, although the supernatant water may still contain dissolved oxygen; and (3) when sludges derived from water, sewage, or industrial wastes are to be digested prior to disposal.

A knowledge of the progressive digestion of organic matter is, therefore, of importance for many of the same reasons that have been stated in connection with BOD. The rate of volatile-matter destruction is closely comparable with the rate of gas production, but it is more difficult of determination.

a. Formulation of the Gasification Curve. If we interpret anaerobic decomposition as a first-order reaction, the gasification curve can be formulated in the same terms as the first-stage BOD curve, allowance being made, if necessary, for a lag phase. If we are concerned with the fundamental behavior of batches of putrescible substances, however, the resulting S-shaped gasification curve must be formulated as a first-order reaction that is catalyzed by the products of the reaction. This formulation is based on the assumption that the rate of decomposition is proportional, not only to the amount of organic matter remaining to be digested but also to an intensity factor which is, itself, a function of the amount of organic matter that has already undergone decomposition. The resulting autocatalytic equation is written in differential form as

$$dy/dt = k_1(L - y) + k_2y(L - y) \qquad \text{19-13}$$

where y is the amount of gas produced in time t, L is the total amount of gas that can be potentially released, and k_1 and k_2 are the rates of reaction or intensity factors.

Integration of Equation 19-13 gives

$$t = \frac{1}{k_1 + k_2L} \log_e \frac{L(k_1 + k_2y)}{k_1(L - y)} = \frac{2.303k_1^{-1}}{1 + (k_2/k_1)L} \log_{10} \frac{1 + (k_2/k_1)y}{1 - y/L} \qquad \text{19-14}$$

The S-shaped curve described by this equation possesses a point of inflection at

$$t = \frac{2.303}{k_1 + k_2L} \log \frac{k_2}{k_1} L \qquad \text{and} \qquad y = \frac{1}{2}\left(L - \frac{k_1}{k_2}\right) \qquad \text{19-15}$$

Evaluation of the magnitudes of k_1, k_2, and L from observed results of gasification offers some difficulty,[10] and the range of values of k_1 and k_2 has as yet not been sufficiently well established to be of practical service to the engineer. As indicated in Figure 19-11, a "lag" phase may be substituted for autocatalysis. The formulation is thereby reduced to that of a simple first-order reaction.

b. Temperature Effects. There is evidence that the reaction velocity constants of anaerobic digestion as well as the limiting value of gas

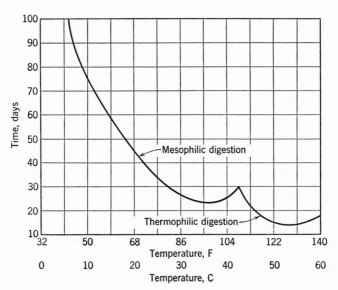

Figure 19-12. Time required for 90% digestion of plain-sedimentation primary sewage sludge at different temperatures.

production increase with temperature and that the temperature effect can be expressed in terms of the van't Hoff-Arrhenius relationship described in Section 18-17. When the constants of the autocatalytic first-order reaction have not been determined, it is still possible to establish an over-all evaluation of the temperature effect by finding, through inspection of the digestion results, the times required for gasification to reach a certain degree of completion such as 90%. We may then write

$$t/t_0 = e^{C_t(T - T_0)} = \Theta_t^{(T - T_0)} \qquad 19\text{-}16$$

in much the same fashion as before.

[10] For methods of evaluation see G. M. Fair and E. W. Moore, *Sewage Works J.*, *4*, 433 (1932); and G. M. Fair, E. W. Moore, and H. A. Thomas, Jr., *Sewage Works J.*, *13*, 1227 (1941).

The best estimate of the effect of temperature on the digestion of sludges may be had from observations such as those plotted in Figure 19-12 for plain sedimentation, primary sewage sludge. Two significant temperature zones are recognized: (1) a zone of moderate temperatures, in which the common moderate-temperature-loving (mesophilic) saprophytes and methane formers are active, and (2) a zone of high temperatures in which heat-loving (thermophilic) organisms are responsible for digestion. The upswing of the mesophilic curve appears to identify the approach to the thermal death point of normal saprophytes.

The effect of temperature on the decomposition of river muds or benthal sludges is discussed in Section 28-8.

20-1. General Considerations. The examination of water and waste water involves (1) surveys of the conditions under which the water or waste water exists or is produced; (2) observations and examinations of certain attributes or properties of the water or waste water in the field; and (3) laboratory determinations of specific qualities or properties of the water or waste water.

Field surveys are called sanitary surveys when they are concerned with the identification of the conditions that affect or may affect the sanitary quality of water for water-supply purposes; they are called pollutional surveys when they are to determine the effect of waste water upon receiving bodies of water, and industrial-waste surveys when they deal with the amounts and characteristics of the waste waters discharged by industrial establishments.

Observations and examinations of water and waste water *in the field* fall into two groups: (1) observation of gross qualities such as growths of water weeds and algae, unsightly floating matter, sludge banks, growths of sewage fungi and other microscopic indicators of pollution, and conditions that are offensive to the sense of smell, and (2) examination of physical properties such as temperature and the determination or fixing of chemical constituents such as carbon dioxide and dissolved oxygen that change rapidly during transportation and storage of samples in advance of their analysis in the laboratory.

The examination of water and waste water *in the laboratory* is concerned with the analysis of samples collected in the field, in treatment plants, or from sampling points in the distribution system of water supplies or the collecting system of waste waters. A knowledge of the conditions under which the water or waste water is found and of the conditions of sampling is essential to the interpretation of laboratory analyses. The analysis of a single sample of water or waste water establishes but a single cross-sectional pattern of the quality of the water or waste water at the time of collection, although certain groups of tests performed on a single sample, such as those for nitrogen in

531

its various forms, may give some information, too, on the pollutional history of the water. Multiple samplings and analyses are needed to delineate the profile of the water either in terms of the variation of its essential qualities or properties in time, or in terms of the progressive changes that take place as water moves about in nature and is collected, stored, purified, used, and becomes waste water which, in turn, is collected, treated, and discharged into natural bodies of water or onto land.

The methods of collection and analysis must be standardized in procedure if the results obtained by different laboratories are to be comparable and if they are to have legal validity. In the United States, "Standard Methods for the Examination of Water and Sewage" have been prepared, approved, and published jointly by the American Public Health Association and the American Water Works Association. These methods have been accepted also by the American Chemical Society and the Federation of Sewage and Industrial Wastes Associations.

Based upon standardized methods of analysis are (1) standards of water quality for the various purposes that the water is to serve, and (2) standards of the quality of sewage effluents and industrial waste-waters. Standards of water quality delimit the concentration of the various component properties or attributes of water which experience or scientific judgment have shown to be safe, acceptable, and attainable from available sources, if need be, after subjecting the collected water to economically justifiable and available methods of purification. Standards of quality for sewage effluents have been developed as criteria for the maintenance of acceptable conditions in water courses or on land areas that are to receive the effluents. Such standards are based upon a general consideration of the water and land economy of the region and the economy of available treatment methods. See Chapter 21.

It is not possible within the covers of this book to describe or explain the methods of analysis themselves. Instead, it must be assumed that the reader is acquainted with the techniques involved. It will suit our purposes better to explain the reasons for the different examinations and the significance of the needed tests and to follow this with a presentation of accepted standards and the interpretation of analytical results. Consideration will be confined in the present chapter and in Chapter 21 to domestic water and to sewage. Industrial waters and waste waters are taken up in Chapter 29.

20-2. Standard Tests. Although many of the tests employed in the examination of samples of water and sewage are identical, the information sought has very different purposes. The essential purpose of a water analysis is to determine the fitness, or potential fitness, of the water for the uses that it is to serve in household and industry. The essential purpose of a sewage analysis, by contrast, is to find the composition, concentration, and condition (or state) of the sewage, or effluent from a sewage treatment plant, and the effect, or potential effect, of its discharge into receiving bodies of water or onto land areas.

We speak of domestic waters as safe or unsafe, pure or impure, palatable or unpalatable, hard or soft, corrosive or uncorrosive, sweet or saline, as the case may be. Of sewages or sewage effluents, on the other hand, we say that they are putrescible or non-putrescible, strong or weak, fresh or septic, to mention but one characteristic under each of the three categories: composition, concentration, and condition. As outlined in the following schedules, the tests to which we submit water and sewage in order to gather the information that is pertinent to the purposes of the analysis are many and diverse.

a. Examination of Water. "Standard Methods" includes the following tests. Tests that are not routinely part of a sanitary analysis are printed in italics.

PHYSICAL AND CHEMICAL EXAMINATION.
Temperature, turbidity, color, and odor (cold and hot).
Residue: solids after evaporation (total, *dissolved, suspended;* for each the fixed portion and the loss on ignition).
Solids: by *electrolytic conductivity.*
Hardness: by Schwarzenbach (Versenate) method and by calculation from a mineral analysis.
Acidity: including mineral acids, alkalinity (phenolphthalein and total), pH value, carbon dioxide (free and *total*), *bicarbonate ion, carbonate ion,* and *hydroxide.*
Oil.
Silica.
Copper, lead, aluminum, iron, *chromium, manganese,* and *zinc.*
Magnesium, calcium, sodium, and *potassium.*
Nitrogen: ammonia, albuminoid, *organic,* nitrite, and nitrate.
Chloride, *iodide,* and *fluoride.*
Phosphate: orthophosphate, pyrophosphate, and *metaphosphate.*
Sulfate, sulfite, and *sulfide.*
Arsenic, boron, cyanide, and *selenium.*
Tannin and *lignin.*
Active chlorine (free available and combined available chlorine) and chlorine demand.
Dissolved oxygen, hydrogen sulfide, and *methane.*
Phenols.
BIOLOGICAL EXAMINATION.
Examination and enumeration of microscopic organisms and amorphous matter.

Tests for the presence of members of the coliform group.
Plate counts (normally only for swimming pools and bathing places).

b. Examination of Sewage. "Standard Methods" includes the following tests. Tests that are not routinely performed are again printed in italics.

PHYSICAL AND CHEMICAL EXAMINATION.
Temperature, *turbidity, color,* and *odor,* the color determination not being on a quantitative basis.
Residue, or solids: by evaporation (total, dissolved, suspended, settleable; for each the volatile and fixed portions).
Acidity, alkalinity, and pH value.
Nitrogen: ammonia, organic (Kjeldahl), *nitrite,* and *nitrate.*
Oxygen consumed from dichromate.
Dissolved oxygen, biochemical oxygen demand (5-day, 20 C, BOD) and relative stability.
Chloride and *sulfide.*
Active chlorine and chlorine demand.
Grease.
BIOLOGICAL EXAMINATION.
Bacteriological examination is not specified but can be conducted as for water.
Microscopic examination of sewage sludges and river muds, but not of sewage, is specified.

The need for many of these tests has been discussed in broad terms in the first three chapters of this book, and the underlying physical, chemical, and biological considerations have been presented in Chapters 17 to 19. Reference is made to special tests in connection with treatment methods and with the limnology and natural purification of water. The significance of common tests is considered in Section 4 of the present chapter.

20-3. Classification of Tests. Some of the tests that are employed in the analysis of water or sewage are more useful and more generally applicable than others. Some are of long standing, others more recent in concept. Some give direct information on certain constituents of water and sewage, others are inferential in character. The engineer should know which test or group of tests will serve best to answer the question asked. He is not confined in his choice to the tests listed. In certain circumstances, other tests may prove more satisfactory.

a. Examination of Water. Generally speaking, the tests that may be included in the analysis of water may be divided into four more or less overlapping categories as follows:

1. Tests that measure or reflect the safety and wholesomeness of water: (a) tests for contamination as measured by the presence of members of the coliform group of organisms, sometimes supplemented by plate counts, especially in the

waters of swimming pools; (b) tests for toxic quantities of arsenic, lead, chromium, boron, selenium, barium, cyanide, nitrate (methemoglobinemia), and fluoride (mottled enamel of the teeth); (c) tests for physiologically beneficial quantities of iodide (endemic goiter) and fluoride (dental caries); (d) tests for pollution as indicated by the relative amounts of organic, albuminoid, nitrite, and nitrate nitrogen present; and (e) tests for laxative properties in the form of magnesium and sulfate.

2. Tests that measure or reflect the palatability or esthetic acceptability of water: (a) temperature, turbidity, color, and odor—sometimes supplemented (b) by the microscopical examination and by tests for residues and metals, chloride, active chlorine, hydroxide, tannin, and lignin, and hydrogen sulfide, one or the other of which may explain the origin of the observed turbidity, color, odor, and taste.

3. Tests that measure the economic usefulness of water: substantially all the tests listed in "Standard Methods" but depending for their selection upon the use to which the water is to be put (see Chapter 29). For ordinary municipal purposes the following tests are important: (a) hardness in relation to soap consumption and use of water for heating purposes or steam making; (b) dissolved oxygen as well as pH and carbon dioxide together with its related substances in connection with the corrosion of metals; (c) iron and manganese; and (d) hydrogen sulfide as well as carbon dioxide and related substances in connection with the destruction of cement and concrete.

4. Tests that are related in particular to water treatment processes: Examples, in addition to the pertinent tests for the substances removed or destroyed, or to be removed or destroyed, are (a) tests for alkalinity, pH, carbon dioxide, and aluminum or iron in connection with the use of coagulants; (b) tests for odor and copper after the destruction of algae by copper compounds; (c) tests for chlorine demand, pH, and active chlorine in connection with chlorination; (d) tests for stability, phosphate, silicate, pH, and hydroxide following treatment for corrosiveness; (e) tests for hydroxide, sodium, potassium, and silica, in connection with water softening; and (f) tests for pH, carbon dioxide, and dissolved oxygen in connection with deferrization and demanganization.

b. Examination of Sewage. The tests that are included in the analysis of sewage may also be divided into four more or less overlapping categories, as follows:

1. Tests that measure or reflect the concentration or strength of sewage: (a) tests for solid matter in its various states and hence for the potential offensiveness of sewage to the sense of sight—total, suspended, dissolved, and settleable solids, grease, and, in the case of treatment-plant effluents, turbidity; and (b) tests for organic matter and, in view of the putrescibility of organic matter, for the potential offensiveness of sewage to the sense of smell—volatile components of the total, suspended, dissolved, and settleable solids, biochemical oxygen demand (including relative stability), organic nitrogen, oxygen consumed from dichromate, odor, and grease. Together, these tests measure or reflect the composition of sewage in terms of solids and organic constituents.

2. Tests that measure the composition of sewage in terms of specific substances or types of substances in addition to those included in the preceding paragraph: (a) tests for the various forms of nitrogen—ammonia, organic (Kjeldahl), nitrite,

and nitrate nitrogen; and (b) tests for dissolved oxygen, chloride, sulfide, acidity, and alkalinity.

3. Tests that measure the condition of sewage and assist in explaining the progress of decomposition of organic substances in sewage, effluents, and receiving waters: (a) physical and chemical tests—dissolved oxygen, biochemical oxygen demand (including relative stability), sulfide, odor, nitrogen, in its various forms, pH value, and temperature; and (b) biological tests—growths of microscopic and macroscopic indicators of pollution; and bacteria (including coliform organisms).

4. Tests that are related in particular to sewage treatment processes: (a) the most common comparative tests are those for the removal of suspended and settleable solids, and for biochemical oxygen demand—others include, in particular, the tests for nitrogen in its various forms, and oxygen consumed from dichromate; (b) in connection with disinfection, the important tests are chlorine demand, pH value, and active chlorine as well as bacteriological tests; and (c) for effluents, the most significant information relates to the suspended solids, the dissolved oxygen and biochemical oxygen demand, and often, instead of the BOD the relative stability.

It should be obvious that other groupings of tests can be selected to give information of a special nature about both water and sewage.

20-4. Expression of Test Results. As indicated in Chapter 18, the results of chemical analyses have commonly been expressed in parts per million by weight (ppm) but are recorded more precisely in milligrams per liter (mg/l). The results of tests for color and turbidity were formerly forced into line by placing the comparative color and turbidity simulants (platinum in potassium chloroplatinate for color and silica in diatomaceous or fuller's earth for turbidity) on a ppm basis. Results of these tests are now recorded as units of color and turbidity. Mineral analyses are preferably reported in terms of the concentration of the ions. Expressing the results in milliequivalents per liter (me/l) simplifies computations (Sections 20-9 and 23-3). Odor intensity is given by the reciprocal of the dilution ratio with odor-free water that will reduce the odor to a point at which it is just noticeable. If, for example, 5 ml of sample are diluted to 200 ml to reduce the odor to its just noticeable, or threshold, intensity, the threshold odor number is 200/5 = 40. Hydrogen-ion concentration is expressed in terms of the pH value. Bacteriological results are stated in terms of the plate count per milliliter or the most probable number of coliform bacteria per 100 ml. Algae and related plankton are counted, or their bulk is measured and expressed in terms of standard units per milliliter. A volumetric standard unit contains $20 \times 20 \times 20 = 8,000$ cubic microns.[1] Settleable solids are sometimes determined volumetrically (ml/l) instead of gravimetrically.

[1] The rationalizing of this unit is long overdue. It has its origin in the observation that the cells of many algae are about 20 microns in length. The areal standard unit of $20 \times 20 = 400$ square microns was used for many years.

Nature and Significance of Common Tests

20-5. Physical Tests. The physical tests included in "Standard Methods" need little explanation. They each evaluate a readily understood property or quality of water and sewage.

Temperature measurements are important not only for their own sake but also because they identify the magnitude of the density, viscosity, vapor pressure, and surface tension of the fluid, the saturation values of solids and gases that are or can be dissolved in it, and the rates of chemical, biochemical, and biological activity such as corrosion, BOD, and growth and death of microorganisms.

The *turbidity* of a sample is a measure of the interference presented by suspended matter to the passage of light. It is not a direct equivalent of the amount of suspended matter, since the interference is a function of the size and, with it, the number of suspended particles that compose a given weight. Turbidity measurements are generally restricted to water. They are made occasionally on sewage effluents. The turbidity of water is due to the suspension in it of clay, silt, finely divided organic matter, microscopic organisms, and similar substances.

The *color* of natural waters is due to dissolved or colloidal substances of vegetable origin extracted from leaves, peaty matter, and the like. It is quite as harmless as tea and consists of tannins, glucosides, and their derivatives as well as iron and other substances. The intensity of color in a given supply bears a close relation both to the amount of albuminoid nitrogen and oxygen consumed. The color is most intense in water draining from swamps. It is reduced by storage or ageing of the water and by the bleaching action of sunlight. Industrial wastes may contain dyes and other coloring substances of varying hues that are not measured by the standard test for color. The color of sewage reflects its strength and condition. Fresh sewage is gray; septic sewage is black.

Odors in water are caused by volatile substances associated with organic matter, living organisms, principally algae and related organisms, and gases such as hydrogen sulfide. The odors produced by plankton growths have been mentioned in Section 19-2 and are listed for specific genera in Section 27-14. The chlorination of water may produce odors of its own or intensify those of odor-producing agencies. As previously stated, measurements of odor intensity are made by diluting the sample with odor-free water to the threshold value. Since the keenness of odor perception varies with individual observers, and with fatigue of the olfactory nerves in the same observer, odor measurements are by no means absolute. Heating of the water generally intensifies the odor. The nature of the odor is commonly noted. Often this gives a clue to the nature of the substances or living organisms responsible for the odor. The threshold concentration of the odor-producing substance (i.e., the concentration in mg/l that can just be sensed) is rarely known. When this value has been established, the concentration of the odor in mg/l equals the product of the threshold odor number and the threshold odor concentration.

Observation of the odor of sewage provides a superficial but valuable indication of its condition. It tells, in particular, whether the sewage is fresh, stale, or septic; it may also indicate the presence of certain trade wastes.

Tastes in water are generally due to the presence of chloride or sulfate ions associated with sodium, calcium, or magnesium ions. True tastes may be produced, however, also by plankton organisms that contain a taste principle and by industrial wastes. The intensity of such tastes is often magnified by chlorine either through the destruction of the responsible organism and liberation of its taste principle or through the formation of reaction products with this principle or with substances that are contained in industrial wastes. Examples are the bitter, cucumberlike taste produced by the chlorophyllaceous protozoon *Synura* and the iodoform or medicinal taste that has its source in phenoloid or comparable substances. The phenolic tastes are very disagreeable and cause widespread consumer complaints. Extremely small concentrations of the offending substance $(1\mu g/l = 10^{-3}$ mg/l, or 1 ppb $= 10^{-3}$ ppm) may be responsible. Phenols, cresols, and allied substances find their way into water from industrial works, such as coke by-products plants and gas works.

Measurement of taste intensity can be performed in the same manner as that of odor intensity. The threshold concentration of the offending substances varies in individuals. Sodium chloride is detected in concentrations from 300 to 900 mg/l of NaCl and becomes objectionable enough to curtail water consumption when its concentration reaches 1,000 to 1,500 mg/l. There is reason to assume that the sulfates of sodium as well as the chlorides and sulfates of potassium, calcium, and magnesium possess thresholds of detection and refusal of like order of magnitude. On the other hand, the hydroxides and carbonates of sodium, potassium, calcium, and magnesium can be detected in much smaller concentrations. Perception of the presence in water of free available chlorine as well as other chemicals may well be a manifestation of "the common chemical sense" rather than the senses of taste or odor.

20-6. Residue or Solid Matter (Water and Sewage). The tests for residue or solid matter are measures of the concentration and physical state of the principal constituents of water and, more especially, of sewage. Evaporation of water or sewage to dryness and weighing of the residue gives the *total residue* (water) or *total solids* (sewage) content of the sample. Ignition of the residue and reweighing establishes the *fixed residue* or *solids* and by difference the *volatile residue* or *solids*. Since organic matter burns, the *loss on ignition* is a measure of the amount of organic matter present, but it must be realized that ignition volatilizes also some mineral matter.

Filtration of the sample measures the *suspended residue* or *solids*, the volatile component again being found by ignition. The ratio of the weight of suspended solids to the turbidity is called the *coefficient of fineness*. The smaller this coefficient, the smaller is the size of the particles causing turbidity. The difference between the total and the suspended residue or solids measures the *dissolved residue* or *solids* and its volatile and fixed components. These can also be obtained by evaporation and ignition of the filtrate. Settling of the sample for a given period before making the solids determinations evaluates the *settleable solids*. The results of this separation as well as of suspended matter are generally more important in sewage analyses than water analyses. The suspended load renders sewage unsightly, and the settleable load indicates the portion of suspended matter that is removable by plain sedimentation. When water carries a heavy load of coarse silt, corresponding information is also of value.

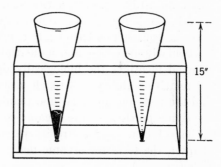

In the control of sewage treatment works, the volumetric determination of *settleable solids* in an Imhoff cone (Figure 20-1) is often convenient.

Figure 20-1. Imhoff settling cones for the volumetric determination of settleable sewage solids. *After Imhoff.*

The difference between the suspended-solids content and the settleable content is a measure of the finely divided, non-settleable solids.

The amount and nature of colloidal matter is not readily ascertainable. Determination of the concentration of color colloids by matching the tealike natural color against platinum-cobalt standards establishes but an indirect equivalence of certain colloidal matters. Special methods of separation, including electrophoresis and dialysis, must be employed if significant results are to be obtained. Required techniques are difficult and time consuming. They have application only in special investigations.

Aside from the classification of residue or solids according to their state, and through subdivision into volatile (largely organic) matter and fixed (largely mineral) matter or ash, the chemical constitution of significant portions of the solids can be determined by suitable analytical techniques. Solids determinations are a forecast of the magnitudes to be expected. The determination of total dissolved solids by electrolytic-conductivity measurements is common in industrial operations, especially those connected with steam generation.

20-7. Organic Matter. Organic matter in water and sewage has its origin in plant and animal matter. It includes so great a variety of compounds in such varied and individually minute amounts that they cannot be isolated directly. Tests are generally confined to the determination of gross organic matter and its subdivisions into nitrogenous and carbonaceous matter; suspended, filtrable, and settleable organic matter; putrescible organic matter and relative stability; and living organic matter.

In addition to "loss on ignition" which records the amount of volatile and combustible organic constituents, the nitrogen determinations are useful in both water and sewage analysis; the test for oxygen consumed gives information on chemically oxidizable carbonaceous matter (more particularly of sewage and industrial wastes) ; the biochemical oxygen demand identifies the biologically decomposable substances; the test for relative stability is a rough measure of the stability of a sample; and the tests for bacterial and plankton populations identify some of the living portions of the organic content. With the exception of the biological tests, which are discussed in Sections 13 and 14 of this chapter, the tests for organic matter are described more fully in the following.

a. Nitrogen. The cycle of nitrogen in water and sewage has been discussed in Section 19-4. Determination of the various forms of nitrogen looks to this cycle to throw light on the pollutional history of the carrying water. Results for all forms of nitrogen are expressed in mg/l of nitrogen (N).

Plant and animal proteins are contained in living cells, in the waste products of these cells, and in cell extracts or residues. This *organic nitrogen* is determined by effecting the complete destruction of organic matter by concentrated sulfuric acid (the Kjeldahl method) and the conversion of all organic nitrogen in the sample to ammonia. Filtration of the sample before analysis will separate the organic nitrogen into the suspended and the colloidal and dissolved fractions. The suspended fraction includes the nitrogen of the plankton and organic debris; the colloidal and dissolved fractions contain the nitrogen from extracted or secreted materials. Since animal tissue is richer in nitrogen than plant tissue, high concentrations point to pollution of animal origin. In accordance with the nitrogen cycle, high values are also characteristic of fresh or recent pollution.

Albuminoid nitrogen is that portion of the organic nitrogen that can be liberated by the action of alkaline permanganate upon the nitrogenous matter. Since albumins release their nitrogen under the action of alkaline permanganate, the portion of nitrogenous matter decomposed is called albuminoid nitrogen. It bears a variable ratio to the organic nitrogen. In relatively clean waters, it is often about a half of the total organic nitrogen and is related to color and colloidal matter. Large numbers of algae produce high albuminoid values as does sewage pollution.

Ammonia nitrogen is also called free ammonia because it can be expelled or freed by boiling or distilling the sample after alkalinizing. Ammonia nitrogen is the initial product in the decomposition of nitrogenous organic matter. It is also formed when nitrates and nitrites are reduced to ammonia either biologically or chemically; the latter, possibly, by the reducing action of ferrous salts sometimes encountered in deep well waters and bottom waters of deep lakes or reservoirs. Some ammonia, too, may be swept out of the atmosphere by rain water.

Nitrite nitrogen is usually an oxidation product of ammonia, more rarely a reduction product of nitrates. The significance of nitrites, therefore, varies with their amount, source, and relation to other constituents of the sample, notably the relative magnitude of ammonia and nitrate present. Nitrite nitrogen can be determined in minute quantities (0.001 mg/l). Since nitrite is rather rapidly and easily converted to nitrates, its presence in concentrations greater than a few thousandths of a milligram per liter is generally indicative of active biological processes in the water. The sensitivity of the test makes nitrites useful chemical tracers in model experiments of flow such as the passage of water through settling tanks and filters, provided that biological activity does not change the nitrite concentration.

Nitrate nitrogen is the end product of decomposition of nitrogenous matter, and its presence carries this significance. Its concentration is of particular interest in relation to the other forms of nitrogen that may be present in the sample. Nitrates occur in the crust of the earth in many places and are a source of its fertility. The relation of nitrates to the occurrence of methemoglobinemia in infants has been discussed in Section 1-5.

b. Oxygen Consumed. Oxidizing agents, such as potassium permanganate and potassium dichromate in acid solution, will oxidize the carbon in many types of organic matter. The amount of oxidizing chemical consumed is expressed as equivalent oxygen. Only a part of the organic matter reacts with the permanganate or dichromate, and the test does not offer a predictable differentiation between biologically stable and unstable organic matter. In order to obtain reproducible and comparable results, the test procedure must be rigidly regulated. "Standard Methods" suggests use of the permanganate test for the analysis of potable water and of the dichromate test for the analysis of sewage, sewage effluents, polluted waters, and suitable trade-waste waters. The dichromate test is considered of value as an estimate of the strength of waste waters when their BOD cannot be determined because of the presence of toxic substances or when information supplementary to the BOD test is to be obtained. Correlation of oxygen consumed with BOD exerted and of similar chemical oxidations (chlorine demand for example) with BOD has not been fruitful. As normally performed, the chlorine-demand test has a fundamentally different purpose (see Section 27-6).

c. Biochemical Oxygen Demand. The significance of the BOD test has been explained in Chapter 19. Its use is commonly restricted to sewage, sewage effluents, industrial wastes, and polluted waters. The "standard" test for BOD is confined to the determination of the oxygen used up during incubation of samples for 5 days at 20 C, the normal summer temperature of natural waters. For purposes of comparison, the sample is provided with suitable salts and buffered to normalize the pH effect upon the life activities of the organisms responsible for decomposition. Bactericidal and other growth-inhibiting substances must be removed or neutralized, and the sample must be seeded, when necessary, with normal sewage organisms. To satisfy the oxygen requirements of the active organisms, most samples must be diluted with BOD-free water that will not itself inhibit growth. The samples are placed in incubation bottles that are filled completely and tightly stoppered in order to avoid aeration of the samples. The rate of decomposition is influenced among other things by the amount of glass surface to which the sample is exposed. Hence bottles of standard size and shape must be used.

The BOD test is a highly informative one. It is also very delicate. Its correct performance requires both skill and experience, its correct interpretation a thorough acquaintance with its nature and limitations. The BOD is given by the difference between the dissolved-oxygen content of the sample at the beginning and end of the incubation period. Several dilutions are ordinarily made. Dilutions that record 40 to 70% depletion of the initial oxygen content are considered most reliable. Allowance may have to be made for an immediate oxygen demand by subtracting the oxygen used up in the first 15 min after dilution.

In the operation and control of sewage disposal works, the BOD test has largely superseded the tests for "nitrogen" and "oxygen consumed from permanganate." The BOD test possesses an important advantage over these tests, as well as the test for "loss on ignition," in that it records the decomposability or putrescibility of the organic matter. It is, therefore, a measure of the potential "nuisance level" of the sewage or industrial waste, effluent, or polluted water. In 5 days at 20 C, however, it is practically only the carbon of the organic matter that has been oxidized. A full picture of probable decomposition can be had only by long-term BOD tests.

d. *Relative Stability.* Relative stability may be defined as the percentage ratio of the oxygen available as dissolved oxygen, nitrite oxygen, and nitrate oxygen to the oxygen required to satisfy the first-stage BOD. However, this percentage ratio is obtainable only if the rate constants and limiting values of the first-stage BOD of the sample are known. Calculations are then based on the number of days required to exhaust the available oxygen in the sample. The discoloration of methylene blue is used as the point of timing because this occurs when the last trace of oxygen has been removed.

Because the basic rates of deoxygenation are not constant, this determination has lost and should lose favor. When the laboratory facilities of small treatment plants are poor, the relative stability may still perform a "stop-gap" function. However, the severe limitations of the test must be fully recognized.

20-8. Hardness (Water). Hardness is of special concern in water supply. Hard water requires much soap before a lather is formed, and hard water deposits sludges or incrustations on surfaces with which it comes into contact and in vessels and boilers in which it is heated. The responsible substances are calcium and magnesium ions and to a lesser extent (because of their normally smaller concentration) those of iron, manganese, strontium, and aluminum. The pseudohardness of brines is related to the prevention of solution of sodium salts by sodium ion.

"Standard Methods" requires that hardness be expressed in mg/l of equivalent calcium carbonate. It may also be expressed in me/l. *Total hardness* was formerly measured by adding a standardized soap solution to a sample of the water until a persistent lather was formed on the surface of the sample. Precautions were needed to identify the true end point and to differentiate between calcium and magnesium hardness. For this reason and reasons of convenience and precision, a "complexometric" titration of hardness using disodium dihydrogen ethylenediaminetetraacetate (Versenate) and a dye indicator has been substituted.

When the total hardness has a value greater than the sum of the carbonate and bicarbonate alkalinity (see Section 20-9), the amount of hardness equivalent to the alkalinity is called carbonate, or alkaline, hardness and the amount in excess of this is called non-carbonate, or non-alkaline, hardness. When the total hardness has a value equal to or smaller than the sum of the carbonate and bicarbonate alkalinity, there is no non-carbonate hardness.

The differentiation between carbonate and non-carbonate hardness is important. Carbonate hardness is thrown down when water is boiled. A soft deposit is formed which is readily removed from boilers by blowing them down. Non-carbonate hardness includes in particular chlorides and sulfates, but possibly also nitrates, of calcium and magnesium. Evaporation of waters containing these ions renders the water highly corrosive ($CaCl_2$, $MgCl_2$, and $MgSO_4$) and creates a hard and brittle scale ($CaSO_4$) that opposes heat transfer in boilers in the approximate ratios of 17:1 for $CaCO_3$ and 48:1 for $CaSO_4$, both relative to wrought iron. The sudden production of large volumes of steam when thick scales crack and water comes into contact with overheated metal surfaces may cause explosions. Local overheating causes the "bagging" of boiler tubes and shells.

Determinations of calcium, magnesium, sodium, and potassium, as well as of bicarbonate ion, carbonate ion, hydroxide, chloride, sulfate, nitrate, and silica, are part of a more complete analysis of water. They are of significance in connection with the softening of water, the coagulation of water, the interpretation and control of corrosion, and the preparation of boiler feed-waters. See Chapters 23 and 29.

20-9. Alkalinity and Related Quantities. The *alkalinity* of water, which may be defined as its capacity for neutralizing acid, is usually due to the presence of bicarbonate and carbonate ions. In treated waters, and occasionally in natural waters, hydroxide, borate, silicate, or phosphate ions may also contribute to it. Determinations of alkalinity and its forms, along with the interrelated determinations of pH, acidity, carbon dioxide, and hardness are of interest in water softening, coagulation, and corrosion control.

The *total alkalinity* of water is determined by titration with sulfuric acid or other strong acid of known strength to the end point of the combined indicators bromcresol green and methyl red (pH 4.8), or of methyl orange indicator (pH 4.3) for alkalinities above 400 mg/l. Results are expressed as me/l, or as mg/l of calcium carbonate equivalent to the determined alkalinity.

The relative bicarbonate and carbonate alkalinities and the amount of hydroxyl alkalinity are fixed by the pH of the water in accordance with the equilibrium equations in Section 18-8. When they are the only forms of alkalinity present, the distribution of the alkalinity among them is determined [2] from the measured total alkalinity and pH by means of Equations 20-1 to 20-4.

If the concentrations of $[HCO_3^-]$, $[CO_3^=]$, and $[OH^-]$ are expressed in milliequivalents per liter, whereas $[H^+]$ is given in mols per liter as a matter of convenience, and if the total alkalinity $[A]$ is expressed as milliequivalents of titratable alkalinity the equation for alkalinity is:

$$[A] + 10^3[H^+] = [HCO_3^-] + [CO_3^=] + [OH^-] \qquad \text{20-1}$$

Using the same method of expressing concentrations, Equations 18-21 and 18-27 then establish the following relationships:

$$[HCO_3^-] = \frac{[A] + 10^3[H^+] - 10^3 K_w'/[H^+]}{1 + 2K_2'/[H^+]} \qquad \text{20-2}$$

$$[CO_3^=] = \frac{2K_2'}{[H^+]} \left(\frac{[A] + 10^3[H^+] - 10^3 K_w'/[H^+]}{1 + 2K_2'/[H^+]} \right)$$

$$= \frac{2K_2'}{[H^+]} [HCO_3^-] \qquad \text{20-3}$$

$$[OH^-] = 10^3 K_w'/[H^+] \qquad \text{20-4}$$

The value of K_2, the second ionization constant of carbonic acid (Equation 18-21), is 4.69×10^{-11} at 25 C, and the value of the ion product of water K_w is taken as 10^{-14} at 25 C. These values must be corrected

[2] Another, less accurate, method for determining the distribution of these three forms of alkalinity requires two titrations with acid—one with phenolphthalein as indicator (end point at pH 8.3) to neutralize hydroxide alkalinity and half the carbonate alkalinity, the other with the combined indicator or with methyl orange to measure the total alkalinity. On the assumption that bicarbonate and hydroxyl alkalinities do not exist together (a poor assumption) the following relations hold, P being the phenolphthalein alkalinity, T the total alkalinity: (1) when $P = T$, only hydroxyl alkalinity present; (2) when $2P = T$, only carbonate alkalinity present; (3) when $P = 0$, only bicarbonate alkalinity present; (4) when $0 < 2P < T$, both carbonate and bicarbonate alkalinities present and equal to $2P$ and $T - 2P$ respectively; (5) when $2T > 2P > T$, both carbonate and hydroxide alkalinities present and equal to $2(T - P)$ and $2P - T$ respectively.

for differences in temperature and for ionic strength, activity, or salinity (Section 18-5). The correction for activities is derived as follows: When the concentration of ions is measured in terms of their activity,

$$K_2 = \frac{(H^+)(CO_3^=)}{(HCO_3^-)}$$

For molar concentrations, therefore,

$$K_2 = \frac{f_{H^+}[H^+] \times f_{(CO_3^-)}[CO_3^=]}{f_{HCO_3^-}[HCO_3^=]}$$

Since

$$K_2' = \frac{[H^+][CO_3^=]}{[HCO_3^-]}$$

$$K_2' = K_2 \left(\frac{f_{(H^+)} \times f_{(CO_3^-)}}{f_{HCO_3^-}} \right)^{-1}$$

Writing this relationship in logarithmic form,

$$\log K_2' = \log K_2 - \log f_{H^+} - \log f_{(CO_3^-)} + \log f_{HCO_3^-}$$

Using the approximate relationship between the activity coefficient f_i and the ionic strength μ,

$$\log f_i = -0.5 z_i^2 \frac{\sqrt{\mu}}{1 + \sqrt{\mu}}$$

by Equation 18-6. For f_{H^+} equal to $f_{HCO_3^-}$ and $z_i = 2$ for $CO_3^=$, therefore,

$$\log K_2' = \log K_2 + \frac{2\sqrt{\mu}}{1 + \sqrt{\mu}} \qquad 20\text{-}5$$

Here $\mu = \frac{1}{2} \sum_{1}^{i} c_i z_i^2$ for molar concentrations (Equation 18-5), or $\mu = 5 \times 10^{-2} \sum_{1}^{i} c_i z_i$ for me/l (Equation 23-47). As shown later, too, $\mu = 2.5 \times 10^{-5} S_d$ approximately, where S_d is the dissolved solids content of the water (Equation 23-48). Similarly,

$$\log K_w' = \log K_w + \frac{\sqrt{\mu}}{1 + \sqrt{\mu}} \qquad 20\text{-}6$$

where K_w is the ionization constant of water. Also

$$\log K_1' = \log K_1 + \frac{\sqrt{\mu}}{1 + \sqrt{\mu}} \qquad 20\text{-}7$$

where K_1 is the first ionization constant of carbonic acid (Equation 18-19).

Example 20-1. The total alkalinity of a sample of water with a pH of 10.0 is 50 mg/l, or $50/(\frac{1}{2} \times 100) = 1.0$ me/l. Find the distribution of the alkalinity as (a) bicarbonate, (b) carbonate, and (c) hydroxide alkalinity in me/l and in mg/l as $CaCO_3$. Assume that $K_2' = K_2$ and $K_w' = K_w$.

a. By Equation 20-2:

$$[HCO^{3-}] = \frac{1.0 + 10^{-7} - 10^{-11}/10^{-10}}{1 + 2(4.69 \times 10^{-11})/10^{-10}} = (4.64 \times 10^{-1}) = 0.464 \text{ me/l},$$

or

$$50 \times 0.464 = 23.2 \text{ mg/l as } CaCO_3$$

b. By Equation 20-3:

$$[CO_3^=] = 2 \times 4.69 \times 10^{-1} \times 4.64 \times 10^{-1} = 0.436 \text{ me/l}$$

or

$$50 \times 0.436 = 21.8 \text{ mg/l as } CaCO_3$$

c. By Equation 20-4:

$$[OH^-] = 10^3 \times 10^{-14}/10^{-10} = 0.1 \text{ me/l} \qquad \text{or} \qquad 50 \times 0.1 = 5.0 \text{ mg/l}$$

The solution of the three equations that define the distribution of the three forms of alkalinity may be generalized by plots of families of straight lines for specified pH values.[3]

Alkalinity in some form is essential for the formation of floc in coagulation with aluminum and iron salts, carbonate alkalinity is necessary for the removal of calcium hardness in softening, and hydroxide alkalinity is required for the removal of magnesium hardness. See Chapters 23 and 29.

Acidity, like alkalinity, is a capacity factor and may be defined as the capacity for neutralizing base. In contrast, pH (see Section 18-8b) is an intensity factor, expressing the existing concentration of hydrogen ions. Acidity is normally associated with the presence of carbon dioxide, mineral and organic acids, and salts of strong acids and weak bases, like $Al_2(SO_4)_3$, that are acid by hydrolysis.

Acidity is determined by titration with sodium or potassium hydroxide of known strength using methyl orange and phenolphthalein indicators. The mineral acidity is said to be neutralized when the methyl-orange end point is reached, the total acidity at the phenolphthalein end point. The former titration is not valid in the presence of organic acids or of ferric or aluminum salts. To facilitate comparison with alkalinity and hardness results, acidity determinations are expressed as me/l or as mg/l of equivalent calcium carbonate.

Frequently, dissolved carbon dioxide is the sole source of acidity in water. Then the titration for acidity is also a determination of the

---

[3] E. W. Moore, "Graphic Determination of Carbon Dioxide and the Three Forms of Alkalinity," *J. Am. Water Works Assoc., 31,* 51 (1939).

carbon dioxide present and may be conventionally expressed as mg/l or me/l of carbon dioxide. Alternatively, the amount of carbon dioxide can be calculated from the pH value and total alkalinity by means of Equation 20-8, derived from equilibrium considerations. The latter technique is usually the more accurate and is the only valid one when other acid substances are present. Carbon dioxide and the forms of alkalinity can also be calculated from measurements of pH and "total carbon dioxide," the sum of carbon dioxide, bicarbonate ion and carbonate ions, evaluated by determining the carbon dioxide evolved when an excess of acid is added.

If K_1 is the first ionization constant of carbonic acid (Equation 18-19),

$$[CO_2] = \frac{2[H^+]}{K_1'} \left(\frac{[A] + 10^3[H^+] - 10^3 K_w'/[H^+]}{1 + 2K_2'/[H^+]} \right)$$

$$= \frac{2[H^+]}{K_1'} [HCO_3^-] \qquad\qquad 20\text{-}8$$

where $[A]$ and $[H^+]$ are expressed as in Equations 20-2 to 20-4, and $K_w = 10^{-14}$, $K_2 = 4.69 \times 10^{-11}$, and $K_1 = 4.45 \times 10^{-7}$ at 25 C (Table 18-1). The solution of this equation may be generalized in the same way as for Equations 20-2 to 20-4.

Example 20-2. The total alkalinity of a sample of water with a pH value of 7.0 is 15.0 mg/l or $15.0/(\frac{1}{2} \times 50) = 0.3$ me/l. Find the concentration of CO_2 in me/l and mg/l as CO_2, assuming that $K_1' = K_1$ and $K_w' = K_w$. By Equation 20-8:

$$[CO_2] = \frac{2 \times 10^{-7}}{4.45 \times 10^{-7}} \frac{0.3 + 10^{-4} - 10^{-11}/10^{-7}}{1 + 2(4.69 \times 10^{-11})/10^{-7}} = 0.136 \text{ me/l}$$

or

$$22 \times 0.136 = 3.0 \text{ mg/l}$$

The concentration of carbon dioxide in water in equilibrium with a normal atmosphere is approximately 1 mg/l. Larger amounts may be absorbed from ground air that is enriched in CO_2 by the decomposition of organic matter. They may also be formed by oxidation of organic matter in water or sewage, or they may result from a lowering of pH for some reason in water containing reserve alkalinity.

Since the amount of dissolved carbon dioxide in equilibrium with the atmosphere is small, great care must be exercised in the collection and titration of samples containing much CO_2 in order to avoid loss to the air. Loss of CO_2 also leads to erroneous pH determinations. Alkalinity values are not affected, however.

20-10. Chloride, Sulfate, and Sulfide. *Chlorides* are widely distributed in nature. They are present in mineral deposits, in sea and brackish water, in ocean vapors and spray carried inland by the wind, in human excreta (more particularly urine), in other water-carried wastes from households, and in industrial wastes. As stated in Section 17-5, sea water contains about 18,000 mg/l of chloride, brackish water in tidal estuaries proportionately less. Some inland "salt lakes" such as the Dead Sea and Great Salt Lake contain about 150,000 mg/l of chloride. The human body wastes from 8 to 15 grams of sodium chloride (5 to 9 grams of chloride) a day. In the absence of pollution and mineral deposits, the "normal chloride" of most surface and ground waters is small, varying with the distance from the ocean or other bodies of salt water and the prevailing winds. The chloride content of water is not affected by normal passage over the ground or through it. Hence an increase in chloride above the "normal" is a pollution index that does not change with time. Hence, also, chlorides can be added to water to trace flow, especially underground flow. However, there are more sensitive tracers such as fluorescine (Section 9-14). In general, there are more direct and informative tests of pollution than chloride determinations. Examples are those for coliform bacteria, BOD, and the nitrogens.

In water supply, the chloride determination is of importance principally in connection with salty tastes produced by high chloride content and in identifying the nature of non-carbonate hardness. When sewage is disposed of in tidal estuaries or salt water, the chloride content must be known since it affects the solubility of dissolved oxygen (see Sections 17-5 and 20-12).

As shown in the cycle of sulfur in nature (Figures 19-7 and 19-8), *sulfate* and *sulfide* are common decomposition products of organic matter. Sulfide also results from the reduction of sulfur. In both water and sewage, the reduction of compounds of sulfur to sulfide and the anaerobic destruction of other sulfur-containing matters produce objectionable odors. As previously stated, calcium sulfate forms hard and brittle scales, and hydrogen sulfide is responsible for the destruction of cement and concrete as well as the corrosion of metals. Sulfate ions, furthermore, produce certain undesirable physiological effects in man (Section 1-5c).

More than half of the people who are dependent on supplies of saline water report laxative effects [4] when the sulfate content of the water, or its magnesium and sulfate content taken together, exceeds 1,000 mg/l and when the total dissolved solids exceed 2,000 mg/l.

[4] Communication from the North Dakota State Department of Health analyzed by E. W. Moore.

In water, sulfate, like chloride, is of significance in identifying the nature of non-carbonate hardness. "Standard Methods," therefore, includes tests for sulfate in the analysis of water and for sulfide in the analysis of both water and sewage. Sulfide may be determined as (1) total sulfide which includes all dissolved sulfide and also soluble metallic sulfide present as suspended matter, (2) dissolved sulfide, and (3) un-ionized hydrogen sulfide. In acid solution, sulfide (both suspended and dissolved) liberates hydrogen sulfide. The concentration of free, uncombined, or un-ionized hydrogen sulfide can be calculated from the dissolved sulfide concentration if the pH value of the sample is known (Table 18-1).

20-11. Iron and Other Metals. The presence in water of the ions of iron, manganese, lead, copper, zinc, and other metals is of special concern in water supply. *Iron* compounds are generously distributed in nature. They occur in soil and rocks and are common constituents of plant matter. Iron is normally the favored metal for water pipes, and iron compounds are also widely used as coagulants. Growths of filamentous iron bacteria are dependent on the presence of iron in water. Ferrous iron is quite soluble in water. Dissolved-oxygen oxidizes dissolved ferrous iron and precipitates it as flocculent ferric hydroxide. This imparts a rusty color or turbidity to the water. Heavy corrosion of iron in distribution systems, including the piping of buildings, is spoken of as "red water trouble." In nature, the release of iron from organic matter and the reduction of iron in the soil in the presence of organic matter are responsible for the solution of iron in water. This statement applies particularly to ground water and water from the stagnant portions of deep lakes and reservoirs. Iron may also occur in water as the result of the solution of ferrous carbonate. Much the same can be said of *manganese,* except that this metal is less common in occurrence. It forms black precipitates that may accumulate in distribution systems to be released in occasional large shocks. These cause "black water trouble."

The *lead, copper, zinc,* and other ions found in water are normally taken into solution from pipes that contain the metals, but they may have their origin in industrial wastes along with many other substances such as arsenic, chromium, and cyanide. Copper may also be present as a result of its use for the control of algae. The danger of poisoning by lead, arsenic, hexavalent chromium, and cyanides has been discussed in Chapter 1, as have been the taste-producing properties of most metals and their staining qualities.

Where much copper is used in industry, the industrial wastes and sewage with which they are mixed may contain sufficient amounts to interfere with biological treatment processes and even to render them ineffective. Arsenic and cyanides may be similarly implicated.

The laboratory tests for the various metals are specific analytical procedures chosen for their sensitiveness to what are often microquantities.

20-12. Dissolved Oxygen. The role of oxygen in the biological economy of water, its relation to processes of aerobic decomposition, and its part in the solution of metals and precipitation of iron and manganese make its determination in water and sewage extremely important. Because of the rapid absorption of oxygen from the atmosphere, suitable precautions must be taken in the collection of samples for analysis. Special sampling equipment may have to be employed. The Winkler method for the determination of dissolved oxygen (DO) depends on the fact that, in alkaline solution, the dissolved oxygen oxidizes manganous ion to manganic ion which, in turn, oxidizes iodide ion to free iodine in quantities equivalent to the amount of oxygen present. After iodometric titration, the results are reported as mg/l of dissolved oxygen and frequently also as the percentage saturation with dissolved oxygen. Calculation of the latter requires a knowledge of the dissolved-oxygen saturation value c_s. This can be calculated if the temperature of the water T, the saturated vapor pressure of water p_w at that temperature, the barometric pressure p, or altitude of the collecting point, and the salinity or chloride content n of the water are known (see Section 17-5).

When c_s and n are recorded in mg/l, T in degrees C, and p and p_w in mm of Hg, the saturation value of dissolved oxygen in water is approximated by the following empirical equations:

Between 0 C and 30 C,

$$c_s = 0.678(p - p_w)(1 - n \times 10^{-5})/(T + 35) \qquad \text{20-9}$$

Between 30 C and 50 C,

$$c_s = 0.827(p - p_w)(1 - n \times 10^{-5})/(T + 49) \qquad \text{20-10}$$

Example 20-3. Find the DO saturation value at 10 C and 760 mm of (a) distilled water and (b) salt water containing 18,000 mg/l of chlorides. Find (c) the percentage saturation of these waters when their DO content is 5 mg/l. The vapor pressure of water at 10 C is 9.2 mm.

a. By Equation 20-9:

$$c_s = 0.678(760 - 9.2)/(10 + 35) = 11.3 \text{ mg/l}$$

b. By Equation 20-9:

$$c_s = 11.3(1 - 18,000 \times 10^{-5}) = 11.3 \times 0.82 = 9.3 \text{ mg/l}$$

c. For $c_s = 11.3$ mg/l, the percentage saturation is $100 \times 5/11.3 = 44.2\%$. For $c_s = 9.3$ mg/l, the percentage saturation is $100 \times 5/9.2 = 54.8\%$.

A table of dissolved-oxygen saturation values for fresh and saline water is included in the Appendix of this book (Table A-6).

20-13. Bacteriological Tests. To be of value in the sanitary analysis of water and sewage, bacteriological tests must be quantitative. "Standard Methods" suggests three such tests:

1. The tests for the coliform group of bacteria. Many members of this group originate in the intestinal tract of man and other warm-blooded animals. They share the fate of the most significant pathogenic enteric bacteria outside of the human and animal body both in rate of die-away under natural conditions and in rate of removal or destruction when water is purified or sewage is treated by available processes, and they can be enumerated by relatively simple and reproducible analytical techniques. These techniques involve the inoculation of multiple, geometrically (normally decimal) serial quantities of the sample into a liquid nutrient medium suitable for the identification of the presence of the group and confirmatory testing of the results obtained.

2. The 24-hr agar plate count at 37 C. This test is a measure of a heterogeneous group of bacteria, developing under conditions of cultivation that are, presumably, favorable to the growth of colonies multiplying from individual bacteria having their natural habitat and optimum environment in the bodies of man and other warm-blooded animals and adapted to their body temperatures. Except when fewer than 30 bacteria will develop from 1 ml of sample, serial dilution in the culture medium is employed in order to hold the number of developing colonies between 30 and 300. These are numbers that do not cause interference between colonies.

3. The 48-hr agar or gelatin plate count at 20 C. This test is a measure of another heterogeneous group of bacteria, developing under conditions of cultivation selected with a view to favoring the growth of colonies developing from individual bacteria having their natural habitat and optimum environment in nature outside the bodies of man and other warm-blooded animals within the usual range of temperature. To a certain extent, this test overlaps with the 24-hr agar plate count at 37 C, because many bacteria are able to develop at both temperatures and substantially as well on nutrient gelatin as on nutrient agar. For purposes of precision, the density of developing colonies is held within the limits stated for the 24-hr agar plate count at 37 C.

The reasons for selecting the coliform group of bacteria as indicators of pollution have been given in Chapter 19. Quantitative interpretation of the results obtained requires the application of statistical methods. A rough estimate of the density of coliform organisms is obtained by calculation of the "indicated number" (IN). A statistically more informative estimate is derived from the calculation of the "most probable number" (MPN).

a. The Indicated Number of Coliform Organisms. In calculating the indicated number, it is assumed that a positive result for the smallest portion of multiple, geometrically serial quantities is produced by the presence of a single organism. Hence the indicated number is obtained by taking the reciprocal, or in multiple tests the averaged reciprocal, of the smallest positive portion or dilution in a decimal series. If a negative result is reached for a portion larger than the smallest portion giving a positive result, it is converted by convention to a positive result in exchange for a negative result in the smallest positive portion.

Calculation of the indicated number for single series is illustrated in Table 20-1, using a plus sign (+) to record the presence and a negative sign (−) the absence of coliform bacteria in the various

TABLE 20-1. Calculation of Indicated Number of Coliform Organisms

	Portion of sample tested and result				Indicated number per 100 ml
Series	10 ml	1.0 ml	0.1 ml	0.01 ml	
1	+	−	−		$100/10 = 10$
2	+	+	−	−	$100/1 = 100$
3	+	+	−	+	$100/0.1 = 1,000$
4	+	+	+	−	$100/0.1 = 1,000$
5	+	+	+	+	$100/0.01 = 10,000$

portions tested. All these series with the exception of the second are lacking in full support. The second, it will be noted, has two positive as well as two negative decimal portions. The result for the fifth series should preferably be reported as ≧10,000, i.e., as inconclusive. The indicated number is often made the basis of reporting results for sewage and polluted waters and, sometimes also, for raw and partially finished water.

b. The Most Probable Number of Coliform Organisms. The most probable number in a sample of water is the density most likely to produce a particular analytical result.

If, as shown by Greenwood and Yule,[5] the distribution of n organisms in V ml of water from which 1-ml portions of water are drawn for analysis is assumed to be random, the probable numbers of 1-ml portions containing 0, 1, 2, 3, etc., organisms in each 1-ml portion are given by the expansion of the fundamental binomial relationship,

$$\left(\frac{V-1}{V} + \frac{1}{V}\right)^n \qquad \qquad 20\text{-}11$$

Since both n and V are numerically large, it is possible, according to Poisson, to transform expression 20-11 into

$$e^{-\lambda} + \lambda e^{-\lambda} + \frac{\lambda^2}{2!}e^{-\lambda} + \frac{\lambda^3}{3!}e^{-\lambda} + \cdots \qquad \qquad 20\text{-}12$$

[5] J. Greenwood and G. Udny Yule, "On the Statistical Interpretation of Some Bacteriological Methods Employed in Water Analysis," *J. Hygiene, 16* (1917).

where $\lambda = n/V$ (or the average density of coliform bacteria), e is the base of the Napierian system of logarithms, and the successive terms in the series represent respectively the probability of the 1-ml portion containing exactly 0, 1, 2, 3, etc., coliform bacteria. Hence the probability of a 1-ml portion of sample being found negative is $e^{-\lambda}$ and that of its being positive $(1 - e^{-\lambda})$. For portions containing N ml of the sample, similarly, the probability of a negative result is $e^{-N\lambda}$ and of a positive result $(1 - e^{-N\lambda})$.

Further development of the most probable number may be had by examples such as the following:

Assume a decimal series in which the 100-ml and 10-ml portions of the sample are positive for coliform bacteria, and the 1-ml, 0.1-ml, and 0.01-ml portions negative. The probability P that these results will occur at the same time and that the density of coliform bacteria falls between $\lambda = 0$ and $\lambda = \lambda$, is then

$$P = \frac{\int_0^\lambda (1 - e^{-100\lambda})(1 - e^{-10\lambda})e^{-\lambda}e^{-0.1\lambda}e^{-0.01\lambda}\,d\lambda}{\int_0^\infty (1 - e^{-100\lambda})(1 - e^{-10\lambda})e^{-\lambda}e^{-0.1\lambda}e^{-0.01\lambda}\,d\lambda} \qquad 20\text{-}13$$

Since the denominator is a definite integral with a numerical value of $a = 0.8100018$, the equation of the probability curve of densities is

$$y = 1.234565(e^{-1.11\lambda} - e^{-11.11\lambda} - e^{-101.11\lambda} + e^{-111.11\lambda}) \qquad 20\text{-}14$$

and y, as shown in Figure 20-2, has a maximum or modal value when $\lambda = n/V = 0.230$, or 23 coliform organisms per 100 ml. Similar equations, curves, and maximal values can be derived for other combinations of results. If multiple plantings are made of decimal portions, the results from only three are significant. How these are chosen and what adjustment must be made in apparently anomalous cases is explained in "Standard Methods." Reference should be made to this source for useful tables of the most probable numbers associated with different test results. A single numerical value is obtained for a series of analytical results by finding the MPN for each result and calculating the median MPN.

The general form of the probability curve of coliform densities for the three significant results is

$$y = \frac{1}{a}[(1 - e^{-N_1\lambda})^p(e^{-N_1\lambda})^q][(1 - e^{-N_2\lambda})^r(e^{-N_2\lambda})^s][(1 - e^{-N_3\lambda})^t(e^{-N_3\lambda})^u]$$

$$20\text{-}15$$

where y, a, and e have the significance previously indicated; p, r, and t are the numbers of positive portions of size N_1, N_2, and N_3 ml respectively in the decimal series; and q, s, and u are the numbers of negative portions of size N_1, N_2, and N_3 ml respectively in the decimal series.

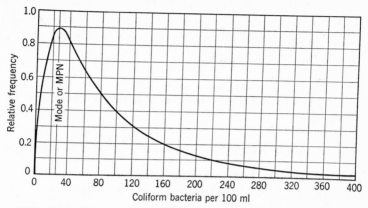

Figure 20-2. Probability curve of coliform organisms in a sample for which the 100-ml and 10-ml portions are positive, and the 1-ml, 0.1-ml, and 0.01-ml portions, negative.

As previously suggested, the most probable numbers are normally calculated more particularly for finished waters for which four or less of five 10-ml plantings are positive. The possible results and the equations of the corresponding frequency curves are shown together with the mode, most probable number, and indicated number in Table 20-2.

TABLE 20-2. Equations of Probability Curves and Magnitudes of Modes and Most Probable Numbers and Indicated Numbers of Coliform Bacteria for Different Results Obtained in the Planting of Five 10-ml Portions of a Sample of Water

Test series	Number of 10-ml portions		Equation of probability curve	Mode	MPN per 100 ml	IN per 100 ml
	Positive	Negative				
1	0	5	$y = 50e^{-50\lambda}$	0.000	<2.2	<2
2	1	4	$y = 200e^{-40\lambda}(1 - e^{10\lambda})$	0.022	2.2	2
3	2	3	$y = 300e^{-30\lambda}(1 - e^{10\lambda})^2$	0.051	5.1	4
4	3	2	$y = 200e^{-20\lambda}(1 - e^{10\lambda})^3$	0.092	9.2	6
5	4	1	$Y = 50e^{-10\lambda}(1 - e^{10\lambda})^4$	0.160	16.0	8

When five 100-ml portions are examined, the MPN values are <0.22, 0.22, 0.51, 0.92, and 1.60 respectively.

Thomas [6] has suggested the following approximate equation for the most probable number:

$$MPN = \frac{100 \times \text{Number of positive portions}}{\sqrt{(\text{Ml in all negative portions})(\text{Ml in all portions})}} \quad 20\text{-}16$$

This approximate formula gives close values for series of multiple portions when the multiple portions of largest size that are all positive are omitted from the calculation.

The following test series will serve as an example: 10-ml ⅗, 1-ml ⅕, 0.1-ml ⅗ positive, i.e., 3 in 5 10-ml portions, 1 in 5 1-ml portions, and 0 in 5 0.1-ml portions are positive.

By Equation 20-16:

$$MPN = 100 \times 4/\sqrt{24.5 \times 55.5} = 11 \text{ coliform bacteria per 100 ml}$$

20-14. Microscopic Tests. The identification and enumeration of algae and other, principally microscopic, organisms other than bacteria serves a useful function both in water supply and sewage disposal. The nature of the evidence presented by the microscopical examination is both direct and indirect. In water supply, direct information is obtained on the number, mass, or bulk of the different genera present and on the known effects of these organisms upon the quality of the water in which they have their habitat. As stated in Chapter 19, immediate effects include (a) the production of odors and tastes, and of color and turbidity; (b) the release of oxygen and utilization of carbon dioxide by photosynthetic activities of chlorophyllaceous organisms during hours of daylight; (c) the reverse by their respiration during the night; (d) the possible clogging of conduits and filters; and (e) the production of water blooms. The examination may also throw light upon the origin and history of the water. Conversely, a knowledge of the nutritional requirements of the different organisms present gives information on the presence of elements that are essential to their growth. Surveys of the distribution of algae and related organisms are needed if their growth is to be controlled or prevented. These surveys must encompass both their horizontal and vertical distribution in lakes and reservoirs and in tributary waters.

In sewage disposal, the microscopical examination provides a measure of the pollutional status of receiving waters and their natural purification. It is of assistance, too, in explaining the mechanism of biological treatment processes.

[6] H. A. Thomas, Jr., "Bacterial Densities from Fermentation Tube Tests," *J. Am. Water Works Assoc., 34*, 572 (1942).

Microscopic organisms, finally, are an integral part of the food economy of fish, shellfish, and other aquatic organisms. The microscopic organisms may, however, be a hindrance as well as an aid to the growth of higher aquatic life.

The collection of plankton and other organisms may involve the use of specialized equipment, as may their concentration for the determination of their quantitative presence. Results are reported either in numbers per liter or 100 liters or in cubic standard units per milliliter, liter, or 100 liters.

Interrelation of Common Tests

20-15. General Considerations. The scope of tests employed in the examination of water and sewage is purposely broad. The uses of water are many, and the nature of the waste matters that constitute sewage and that pollute water is varied. Many of the tests that can be performed are interrelated. Certain of them throw light on others. When considered in various combinations, they supply the body of knowledge that is needed to answer the questions that have been proposed in the first two sections of this chapter. No fixed rules can be given for the interpretation of an analysis. The essential quality that distinguishes the sanitary or public-health engineer from the civil or hydraulic engineer is the possession of a broad acquaintance (1) with the composition of water in nature and the significance and behavior of its components under natural conditions and (2) with the conditions imposed upon water and its many constituents (a) by normal, natural conditions of precipitation, runoff, and percolation, (b) by pollution, natural purification, purposeful treatment, and use, and (c) by its collection or distribution as water, or by its collection and dispersal as sewage.

20-16. Illustrative Example. For purposes of illustrating the interrelation of common tests, a series of hypothetical analyses [7] of samples collected from different places on two catchment areas shown in Figure 20-3 is presented in Table 20-3.

It should be noted that the stream from the northwest has two branches. The one in the west drains wooded upland country devoid of habitations and flows thence through an agricultural region. The one to the east rises in a swamp contiguous to sparse population. The

---

[7] The underlying information is a modification of a discussion of the relations of microscopic organisms to the sanitary analysis of water included in *The Microscopy of Drinking Water,* by Whipple, Fair, and Whipple, 4th ed., John Wiley & Sons, 1948.

TABLE 20-3. Typical Analyses of Surface Waters. *After Whipple, Fair, and Whipple.*

Results of chemical analyses are expressed in milligrams per liter.

Field record

Sample number	Time of collection Date	Time of collection Hour	Description of sample	Temperature, °F	Gases — Dissolved oxygen mg/l	Gases — Dissolved oxygen Per cent saturation	Gases — Carbon dioxide
A	1 Sep.	1 PM	Upland stream near headwaters	65	9.48	100	1.5
B	1 Sep.	2 PM	Stream below cultivated land and farm houses	68	8.80	96	2.1
C	1 Sep.	3 PM	Stream below a swamp	66	7.96	85	4.4
D	1 Sep.	4 PM	Lower end of reservoir, surface sample	72	10.12	115	0.8
E	1 Sep.	4 PM	Lower end of reservoir, bottom sample, 60 ft deep	50	0.00	0	21.4
F	1 Sep.	5 PM	Upland stream above city	65	9.48	100	2.4
G	1 Sep.	5.30 PM	Sewage at outfall of main sewer, in fresh condition	75	0.85	10	23.0
H	1 Sep.	6 PM	Stream below outfall	71	3.55	40	8.7

Organic matter

Sample number	Odor number * Cold	Odor number * Hot	Color	Loss on ignition Total	Loss on ignition Suspended	Loss on ignition Dissolved	Nitrogen Total organic	Nitrogen Albuminoid	Oxygen consumed	Biochemical oxygen demand
A	1V	2V	12	10	: : :	: : :	: : :	0.035	2.1	: : : :
B	4V	7V	18	15	: : :	: : :	: : :	0.085	3.0	: : : :
C	7V + 4M	14M	125	30	: : :	: : :	: : :	0.210	16.5	: : : :
D	5M + 18G	20G	55	21	: : :	: : :	: : :	0.320	11.0	: : : :
E	14Cₛ	5D + 7Cₛ	200	46	: : :	: : :	: : :	0.155	18.0	: : : :
F	1V	2V	5	7	: : :	: : :	: : :	0.020	1.8	: : : :
G	18D	30D	22	480	215	265	15	5.00	15.0	180
H	4M + 10D	10M + 10D	13	25	: : :	: : :	2.1	0.750	8.0	: : :

	Living organisms														Mineral and organic matter			
	Bacteria						MPN per 100 ml	Plankton, Standard units per ml							Turbidity	Residue or solids		
	Plate count per ml		Coliform					Total organisms	Principal genera							Total	Suspended	Dissolved
	20 C	37 C	.01 ml	0.1 ml	1.0 ml	10 ml			Diatoms	Blue-greens	Protozoa	Fung.						
A	50	10	..	0	0	3/5	9	50	40	.....	...	...			2	30	...	...
B	350	150	..	0	+	+	230	300	175	60	30	...			4	42	...	...
C	390	50	..	0	0	2/5	5	550	200	.....	175	100			3	55	...	...
D	150	20	..	0	0	1/5	2	3,200	300	2,600	...	...			8	46	...	...
E	650	70	..	0	0	4/5	16	400	100	.....	...	225			15	79	...	...
F	35	4	..	0	0	2/5	5	25	20	.....	...	...			1	49	...	...
G	2×10^6	1.8×10^6	+	+	+	+	$\geqq 2.3 \times 10^4$	150	25	.....	70	50			220	825	295	530
H	9×10^3	7.5×10^3	0	+	+	+	2.3×10^3	1,000†	...	200	500	150			25	65	...	...

	Mineral matter												
	Fixed residue or solids			Chlorides	Hardness	Alkalinity	Non-carbonate hardness	Iron	Magnesium	pH value	Nitrogen		
	Total	Suspended	Dissolved								Ammonia	Nitrite	Nitrate
A	20	..	...	2.3	12.0	10.0	2.0	0.1	....	7.1	0.0006	0.001	0.20
B	27	..	...	2.6	16.0	11.0	5.0	0.2	....	7.0	0.025	0.002	0.75
C	25	..	...	2.4	10.0	9.0	1.0	0.4	....	6.6	0.040	0.001	0.35
D	25	..	...	2.5	13.0	10.0	3.0	0.2	....	7.4	0.020	0.002	0.10
E	33	..	...	2.6	15.0	11.0	4.0	2.5	....	6.0	0.180	0.000	0.00
F	42	..	...	2.3	27.0	20.0	7.0	0.1	4.0	7.2	0.004	0.000	0.15
G	350	85	265	55.0	80.0	95.0	0.0	1.5	12.0	6.9	14.0	0.250	0.20
H	70	..	...	4.0	30.0	23.0	7.0	0.2	6.5	6.7	2.20	0.100	0.20

* Odor characteristics: C_s = sulfuretted; D = disagreeable; G = grassy; M = musty; M_m = moldy; V = vegetable.
† Includes 150 standard units of rotifers and crustaceans.

two branches unite before they enter an impounding reservoir. The catchment area of the waters from the northwest includes drainage only from rural communities. The stream from the northeast also rises in upland country, but later cuts through the center of a city. The principal sewer outfall of the community lies just below the city limits and discharges into the stream. The analytical results of

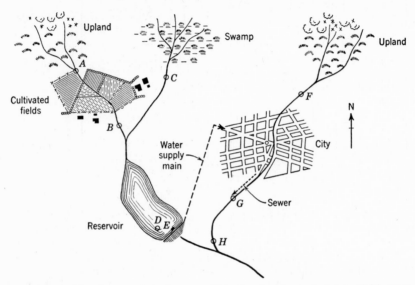

Figure 20-3. Sketch map of stations at which the samples included in Table 20-2 were collected. *After Whipple, Fair, and Whipple.*

samples from typical collecting stations on the two streams are considered individually and in their relation to samples from upstream points.

a. *Upland Stream* (Station A). This sample is characteristic of water originating in wooded uplands. The very faint vegetable odor is due to a small amount of organic matter of plant origin. There is a faint but noticeable color. The water contains little organic nitrogen, and its decomposition and oxidation products are small in concentration. The oxygen consumed value is correspondingly small. The water is saturated with oxygen, and contains a minimum of carbon dioxide. The turbidity and residue (mostly fixed) and the hardness and alkalinity are common to a clear soft water. The water is about neutral and contains little iron. Nutrients such as nitrates and phosphates are not present in large enough amounts to stimulate the growth of microscopic organisms, and the water movement is sufficiently swift to obstruct the growth of all but the less fragile diatoms. The plate counts are low, and the coliform bacteria present are either of the *Aerobacter* variety or traceable to the normal animal life of the upland.

b. *Stream below Farm Lands* (Station B). The drainage from the farm lands and dwellings between Stations B and A has contributed mineral and organic matter. All forms of nitrogen have increased along with color, turbidity, residues, and oxygen consumed. There is slightly more chloride, hardness, alkalinity, and iron. Carbon dioxide has increased slightly, and the water is no longer fully saturated with oxygen. Some decomposition is in progress. River plankton have established themselves and have contributed to the increase in albuminoid nitrogen and vegetable odor. The plate counts are considerably higher, and the density of coliform organisms marks the contamination derived from animal and human sources.

c. *Stream below Swamp* (Station C). The swamp shows its presence in the large content of organic matter extracted from vegetation. The high color and oxygen consumed, low turbidity, high ratio of oxygen consumed to albuminoid nitrogen, and distinct vegetable and musty odor all point to the plant origin of most of the organic constituents. Except for iron associated with the color, the mineral constituents in this eastern branch of the stream are much like those of the western branch. Dissolved oxygen is below the saturation value. Organic acids and high carbon dioxide content, commonly found in swamp water, produce a low pH value. The carbon dioxide along with the nitrogen has permitted the development of plankton life. The infusion of vegetable matter has given rise to protozoa in fair numbers. Normal water bacteria, as indicated by the 20 C count, prevail over pollutional organisms. The 37-C count is low, and the test for coliforms particularly so.

d. *Lower End of Reservoir, Surface Sample* (Station D). The quality of the reservoir water is the resultant of the mixing of the waters from the two branches with allowance for the effects peculiar to storage: opportunity for sedimentation and for bleaching of color by the sun as well as destruction of bacteria, on the one hand, and growth of plankton on the other. Effects of photosynthesis accompany the growth of plankton. Hence the dissolved-oxygen content is above the saturation value. Plankton requirements have reduced the carbon dioxide to less than 1 mg/l. As a result, the pH value has been raised. Nitrates have been reduced considerably. Low ammonia nitrogen and bacterial densities show that the microscopic organisms are in a thriving state and that they are not undergoing decomposition. Organic nitrogen and oxygen consumed are correspondingly high. Part of the color and turbidity, as well, are due to the plankton. Some of the color originally present has disappeared by bleaching, and some of the entering turbidity and iron have been removed by sedimentation.

e. *Lower End of Reservoir, Bottom Sample* (Station E). As noted in the table, the depth of sampling is 60 ft. The difference between top and bottom water during the period of summer stagnation is strikingly illustrated. Mixing of the upper waters is occurring only to depths of 30 or 40 ft. The fall overturn is still a few weeks away. There is an accumulation of organic matter in the bottom waters, and anaerobic conditions prevail there. Iron is present in large amounts. Color, difference between total and fixed residue (loss on ignition), albuminoid nitrogen, and oxygen consumed indicate the amount of organic matter present. The plate counts are high, the MPN of coliform bacteria low. The life activities of the bacteria are manifest from the large amounts of ammonia nitrogen and carbon dioxide present and the absence of oxygen. The microscopic examination yields small numbers of organisms, most of which are expected to be in an attenuated state except for iron and sulfur bacteria. Iron-encrusted sheaths of the iron bacteria (*Crenothrix*) have doubtless added to the turbidity and color. The acid reaction of the water is worthy of note. It goes with the high carbon dioxide content.

f. Upland Stream above City (Station F). This sample resembles that at Station A, but is harder and more alkaline. Certainly it is physically quite clean and contains few living organisms, either bacteria or microscopic organisms.

g. Sewage (Station G). The city is supplied with water from the impounding reservoir. Its sewerage system is built on the separate plan, and there are but small manufacturing interests. At the point at which the sample of sewage was drawn, the sewage had begun to undergo decomposition. As a result, the dissolved oxygen is low, but the nitrate nitrogen has not been increased. There is an abundance of organic matter and of solids, both suspended and dissolved. Bacteria, including coliform organisms, are numerous. Protozoa and fungal debris are present in small amounts; other microscopic organisms are almost absent.

h. Stream below Sewer Outfall (Station H). The load of sewage matters imposed upon the stream has changed its waters markedly in character, but some natural purification has taken place by the time the stream reaches Station H. This is indicated by the dissolved oxygen and nitrate content of the water. Bacteria have died off to some extent, whereas protozoa have increased in number. Scavenging rotifers and crustaceans have made their appearance. The water possesses a musty and disagreeable odor. It is still decidedly polluted.

20-17. Composition of Municipal Sewage. The factors that determine the composition, concentration, and condition of municipal sewage have been discussed in Chapters 1, 3, and 5 of this book. In a given community the wastes discharged from households and related establishments, including hotels, hospitals, restaurants, offices, and commercial buildings, are composited within the sewerage system to produce relatively constant per capita amounts of suspended solids, of organic matter as measured in terms of biochemical oxygen demand, and of other substances that are of special concern in the disposal of sewage. If the nature and capacity of the industries of the community are known, an estimate can be made also of the per capita contribution, or better the population equivalent, of waste matters from industrial sources. The population equivalent is defined as the ratio of the amount of suspended solids, putrescible matter in terms of BOD, or other significant substances issuing from an industry to the per capita amount of these respective substances normally found in domestic sewage. If significant amounts of the substances under consideration are present in the water supply of the community, in ground water that enters the collecting system, or in storm runoff that is collected incidentally or purposefully (by combined systems, for example), additional per capita allowances or population equivalents come into play. Information pertaining to industrial wastes is found in Chapter 29. Average values for domestic sewage are presented in Table 20-4.

TABLE 20-4. Average Per Capita Solids and BOD in Domestic Sewage, grams per capita per day (1 gram per capita = 2.2 lb per 1,000 population)

State of solids (1)	Mineral (2)	Organic (3)	Total (4)	5-day, 20 C BOD (5)
1. Suspended	25	65	90	42
a. Settleable	15	39	54	19
b. Non-settleable	10	26	36	23
2. Dissolved	80	80	160	12
3. Total	105	145	250	54

Some variation from these figures must be expected. All the values given are affected by the wealth and habits of the population. The magnitude of the dissolved and total solids are a function, too, of the hardness and other mineral substances in the water supply and the infiltering ground water. The BOD population equivalent of storm water carried into combined systems varies widely. A background figure lies in the vicinity of 1.4 times the tributary population.

Of the organic matter in average domestic sewage about 40% is composed of nitrogenous substances, 50% of carbohydrates, and 10% of fats. The daily per capita contribution of nitrogen (as N) and fats (as ether-soluble matter) is estimated at 10 and 15 grams respectively. These general figures are of interest in connection with the utilization of the fertilizing value of nitrogen or the recovery of fats from sewage. The bacterial content of sewage, its seasonal variation, and its significance as an indicator of pollution have been discussed in Chapter 19.

The strength of sewage or concentration of sewage matters in it depends upon water use, general nature and tightness of the system, and the degree of admission of storm waters. In the United States, the volume of domestic sewage averages 80 gpcd. Since 1 gram of waste substance per capita daily equals $264/Q$ mg/l, where Q is the sewage flow in gpcd, and since the common sewage flow of communities in the United States is 80 gpcd, 1 gram per capita daily = 3.31 mg/l, and the average strength of domestic sewage becomes of the order shown in Table 20-5. For sewage flows larger or smaller than 80 gpcd, the concentrations of the various substances are changed more or less proportionately, unless the municipal water or infiltering ground water contains unusually large amounts of solid matter. While the change in the pollutional load remains substantially unchanged, dilution does reduce the settleability of the suspended solids to some extent.

TABLE 20-5.   Average Composition of Domestic Sewage, mg/l

State of solids (1)	Mineral (2)	Organic (3)	Total (4)	5-day, 20 C BOD (5)
1. Suspended	85	215	295	140
a. Settleable	50	130	180	65
b. Non-settleable	35	85	115	75
2. Dissolved	265	265	530	40
3. Total	350	480	825	180

The condition of sewage at the outfall of the sewerage system, or at the treatment works, is a function of the length and grade of the collecting system and the temperature of the sewage. Long lines, low grades (sluggish flow), and high temperatures decrease the freshness of the sewage. Fresh domestic sewage has little odor; it is gray in color; the sewage solids are only slightly comminuted; and dissolved oxygen is present. As decomposition becomes active, the sewage becomes stale, and it may become septic if the dissolved oxygen is exhausted. Septic sewage has a foul odor (hydrogen sulfide); its color is black; and the floating and suspended solids are disintegrated.

In the course of the day, sewage varies in strength as well as in flow. The interrelationship is idealized in Figure 20-4. It is seen that the volume of flow generally reaches a maximum in the early forenoon and that the strength of the sewage is also greatest at this time. The collection of representative samples is not a simple matter. Daily samples must be composited in proportion to flow if they are to reflect average conditions. Attention must be paid also to the vertical distribution of suspended solids in conduits. They are generally most concentrated near the bottom.

The nature and composition of industrial waste waters are discussed in Chapter 29.

Synthetic detergents are finding their way into sewers in increasing quantities from both household and industry. When the detergents are present in sufficient concentration, some of the properties that make them good cleansing agents will also cause them to interfere with the normal operation of certain waste-water treatment processes. For this reason they are of special interest. Even in great dilution, the synthetic detergents lower the surface, or interfacial, tension of water and increase its ability to wet substances with which it comes into contact. They are little affected in their cleansing action by acid or alkali, or by the alkaline earth metals. Other properties are: (1) the emulsifying of grease and oil; (2) the peptizing or deflocculating of colloids; (3) flotation and foaming; and (4) destruction of bacteria and other living organisms. There are three general types of synthetic detergents: anionic (commonly containing as their soluble groups sodium sulfates and sulfonates), cationic (mainly quaternary ammonium compounds), and non-ionic (condensation products of ethylene

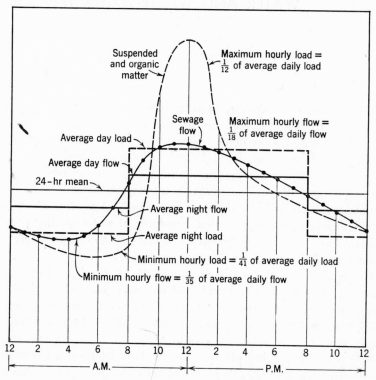

Figure 20-4. Hourly variation in flow and strength of municipal sewage. *After Imhoff and Fair.*

oxide with phenolic materials or fatty acids). The anionic detergents are in widest general use. Their cost is small, and they are stable in hard waters. The cationic detergents are quite expensive, but they possess the best bactericidal and bacteriostatic properties. Their use is normally confined to the disinfection of eating utensils. The BOD of the synthetic detergents is much smaller than that of soap, but their emulsification of grease and oil may carry a larger than normal BOD load through settling basins onto biological treatment units.

21 — STANDARDS OF WATER QUALITY AND UNIT OPERATIONS OF WATER AND WASTE-WATER TREATMENT

21-1. Reasons for Quality Standards. In earlier chapters of this book reference has been made to the need for standards of quality for waters that are to serve domestic, municipal, and industrial purposes and for standards of quality that are to be maintained in bodies of water into which sewage and industrial waste waters are discharged. The importance of quality standards for sewage effluents that are to be disposed of on land has also been mentioned. A reading of Chapter 20 will suggest, furthermore, that standards of water quality provide a useful basis for the interpretation of some of the immediately significant results of water and sewage analysis.

The equitable and intelligent use of the natural resources of a country, including its water and land resources, is a responsibility of every progressive government. Implied are (1) the promulgation of legislation governing the proper utilization of the fundamental resources and (2) the adoption of administrative practices and standards that are in keeping with the times. If legislation and standards are drawn with foresight, they will advance the general economy and stimulate scientific and technological progress in the collection, distribution, and purification of water and in the collection, treatment, and disposal of sewage and other waste waters. Water supply and waste-water disposal, as stated repeatedly before, are interrelated responsibilities and functions. One contributes to the other. A summary of the current status of the unit operations of water and sewage treatment will show what is already available to meet current standards. Hence it is made part of the present chapter. At the same time, it should serve as an introduction to the remaining chapters of this book.

The sanitary engineer can best meet his responsibility for the planning, design, and operation of useful public works if he looks at the water needs of the whole region in which individual works are to be situated. In a sanitary sense, no community is sufficient unto itself. It is an integral part of the drainage basin in which it is placed. At the community level, therefore, plans must be directed towards regional problems; at the state level towards interregional problems; and at the national level towards interstate and international problems.

Standards of Water Quality [1]

21-2. Drinking Water. In the United States, the standards promulgated from time to time by the United States Public Health Service are widely accepted by governmental agencies and by public utilities. Conformance to them is obligatory for water-supply systems that are used by common carriers (railways, ships, buses, and aircraft engaged in interstate commerce) and by other enterprises that are subject to Federal Quarantine Regulations.

The Public Health Service Drinking Water Standards include (1) general rules relating to the source of the water and its protection and (2) specific rules defining acceptable limits for bacteriological quality and for some of the physical and chemical characteristics of the water delivered to the consumer. These rules are outlined in the following paragraphs of this section.

a. Source and Protection. The Public Health Service Standards require: (1) that, unless the collected water is adequately purified by suitable treatment methods, the supply must be obtained either from a source free from pollution or from one in which the water, though at one time polluted, has been adequately purified by natural agencies; and (2) that all parts of the water-supply system must be free from sanitary defects and health hazards. In reference to health hazards, there must be no connections or arrangements by which unsafe liquids or chemicals can be drawn into the water supply. In support of the control of possible hazards, suitable regulations must be promulgated and enforced, and programs of detection of possible hazards must be vigorously prosecuted.

b. Bacteriological Quality. Samples for bacteriological examination must be collected from representative points in the distribution system with sufficient frequency to establish the safety of the water in all parts of the system. The larger the system, the greater must

[1] For industrial water quality requirements, see Chapter 29.

be the number of collections. The minimum number of samples prescribed is shown in Table 21-1 on a population basis.[2]

TABLE 21-1. Frequency of Collection of Samples, Public Health Service Standards

Population served	Minimum number of samples per month
2,500 or less	1
10,000	7
20,000	25
100,000	100
1,000,000	300
2,000,000	390
5,000,000	500

Certain rules are laid down as to the collection and consideration of special samples after discovery that any part of the system is dispensing water of unsatisfactory quality.

The bacteriological standards delimit the density of coliform bacteria present in the water as determined by the examination of five 10-ml (or 100-ml) portions of each sample. The results must satisfy the following statistical criteria:

1. Not more than 10% of all the 10-ml portions (or 60% of all the 100-ml portions) examined per month may be positive for organisms of the coliform group.

2. Occasionally three or more of the five 10-ml portions (or all of the 100-ml portions) of a single sample may be positive, provided that this does not occur (a) in consecutive samples, (b) in more than 5% of 20 or more samples per month when 10-ml portions are examined (or 20% of 5 or more samples per month when 100-ml portions are examined), or (c) in one sample among 20 or less samples per month when 10-ml portions are examined (or among 5 or less samples per month when 100-ml portions are examined).

3. When three or more of the five 10-ml portions (or all of the 100-ml portions) of a single sample are positive, daily samples must be collected from the offending point or points and tested in multiple portions of a decimal series ranging to 0.1 ml or less, until two consecutive samples show that the water is again of satisfactory quality. Multiple portions of a decimal series yielding significant results must be used also when the quality of the water examined is unknown.

As stated before, these bacteriological standards imply in general that the water must not contain more than a single coliform organism

[2] A plot of these values, conveniently made on double-log paper, permits interpolations for communities of other size.

in 100 ml. The fundamental bacteriological quality of raw water that can be purified sufficiently by conventional methods to meet the Public Health Service Standards is discussed in Section 24-14. It is well to remember that the bacteriological standards of the U. S. Public Health Service reflect the relative safety of drinking-water supplies only in relation to the prevailing endemicity of water-borne infections. Their direct application to areas of high endemicity may well be challenged. See Section 19-3a.

c. *Physical and Chemical Characteristics.* The Public Health Service Standards impose the upper limits shown in Table 21-2 on certain

TABLE 21-2. Upper Limits of Impurities, Public Health Service Standards

Characteristic or substance	ppm
Turbidity (silica scale)	10
Color (platinum-cobalt scale)	20
Lead (Pb)	0.1
Fluoride (F)	1.5
Arsenic (As)	0.05
Selenium (Se)	0.05
Hexavalent chromium (Cr)	0.05

physical characteristics and chemical substances [parts per million rather than milligrams per liter are indicated in current (1946) standards]. The water must not possess an objectionable taste or odor, and it must not contain excessive amounts of soluble mineral substances or of chemicals employed in its treatment. Analyses for lead, fluoride, arsenic, selenium, and hexavalent chromium are not prescribed when experience, examination, and other available evidence indicate that these substances are neither present nor likely to be present in a supply. If, however, there is reason to suspect their possible presence, semiannual examinations must be made. More frequent examinations are required, if there is cause to believe that the prescribed limits may be exceeded. Salts of barium, hexavalent chromium, heavy metal glucosides, or other substances with deleterious physiological effects must not be added to the water system for treatment purposes. No upper limits have yet been imposed for nitrates. A value of 10 mg/l is indicated by available information.

Natural and treated waters should preferably not contain the chemical substances listed in Table 21-3 in excess of the amounts stated in connection with them.

Chemically treated waters must meet the requirements given in Table 21-4 pertaining to their treatment.

TABLE 21-3.   Limits of Additional Impurities, Public Health Service
Standards

Substance	ppm
Copper (Cu)	3.0
Iron (Fe) and manganese (Mn) together	0.3
Magnesium (Mg)	125
Zinc (Zn)	15
Chloride (Cl)	250
Sulfate (SO₄)	250
Phenolic compounds (as phenol)	0.001
Total solids	500 *

* 1,000 ppm when water of better quality is not obtainable; see Section 20-6.

TABLE 21-4.   Alkalinity Requirements for Chemically Treated Waters,
Public Health Service Standards

Characteristics or substance	Concentration
Phenolphthalein alkalinity ($CaCO_3$)	15 ppm + 0.4 × total alkalinity *
Normal carbonate alkalinity ($CaCO_3$)	120 ppm
Total alkalinity ($CaCO_3$)	35 ppm + hardness

* This limits the permissible pH value to about 10.6; see Section 20-9.

A closer identification of the quality of natural waters that are to
serve (a) as sources of supply for drinking, culinary, or food-processing purposes; (b) for bathing; (c) for fishing; or (d) for agriculture
or industrial cooling or processing is given by water-pollution control
agencies that are normally operative either at the state or drainage-
basin level. The classifications and standards of such boards are useful supplements to the Public Health Service Standards.

21-3. Bathing Waters.   As pointed out before, the sanitary examination of swimming-pool and other bathing waters must have aims
that are somewhat different from those for drinking water. A distinction must also be drawn (a) between water in swimming pools, both
indoor and outdoor, in which the water is readily amenable to purification, including the maintenance of a disinfecting concentration of
chlorine at all times and (b) between water at bathing beaches and
similar places. In reference to the latter it must be remembered that
their use is often seasonal and that bright sunlight and the low incidence of respiratory infections commonly associated with the bathing
season, as well as less crowding of bathers, decrease the hazards to
the health of the bather.

a. Swimming-Pool Water. In the absence of a satisfactory test for mouth and related organisms, the 24-hr, 37 C plate count serves a useful purpose in the examination of swimming-pool waters. It is generally supplemented by tests for coliform bacteria as a measure of the effectiveness of bather supervision. All bathers should be required to take a cleansing shower before entering the pool or returning to it after using the toilet.

The standards recommended by the American Public Health Association [3] are examples of responsible thinking. The bacteriological standard requires that not more than 15% of the samples covering any considerable period of time shall record (1) plate counts of more than 200 colonies per ml or (2) positive results for coliform bacteria in any of five 10-ml portions of the samples. Since swimming pools are normally disinfected with chlorine, all samples must be dechlorinated at the time of collection. This is done by adding suitable amounts of sodium thiosulfate to the sample bottles. Marginal concentrations of active chlorine are respectively 0.4 to 0.6 mg/l of free available chlorine and 0.7 to 1.0 mg/l of combined available chlorine. High-rate chlorination (several milligrams per liter) has come into use and offers increased protection. There is evidence that this can be done without causing irritation of the eyes and other mucous membranes. Maintenance of an alkaline reaction ($pH \gtrless 7.0$) in the water is desirable to prevent such irritation.

Pool waters should be highly transparent. Otherwise bathers swimming under water are endangered. Clearness is adequate only when a black and white disk 6 in. in diameter placed at the bottom of the pool at its deepest point is clearly visible from the sidewalks of the pool up to a distance of 30 ft measured horizontally. A water temperature no higher than 78 F is desirable for heated pools. At higher temperatures, saprophytic bacteria multiply rapidly.

b. Water at Other Bathing Places. In the United States, state and municipal regulations have set widely varying bacteriological standards for waters at beaches and in streams and lakes that are used for recreational bathing. Prescribed limits for waters that are not chlorinated lie between indicated numbers of 50 and 1,000 coliform bacteria per 100 ml. This is 100 to 2,000 times the generally allowable indicated number for drinking water. The relative exposure to enteric infections during recreational bathing, however, is of such an order that the risk of contracting an enteric infection through a drinking-

[3] *Recommended Practice for Design, Equipment, and Operation of Swimming Pools and Other Public Bathing Places,* 1949.

water supply conforming to the Public Health Service Standards appears to be about as great as through a bathing-water supply with the stated indicated numbers of coliform organisms. The amount of drinking water consumed in a year is relatively great, whereas the amount of water that is swallowed by a bather during the bathing season is relatively small. Reasoning statistically, therefore, the bacteriological standards for bathing water should be the more stringent, the longer the bathing season. Judgment of needed water quality should be based also on the relative prevalence of enteric diseases in the drainage area of the bathing waters, upon information obtained through a survey of pollutional hazards, and upon bacteriological examinations. A relative classification of bathing waters suggested by the American Public Health Association is shown in Table 21-5.

TABLE 21-5. Relative Classification of Natural Bathing Waters, American Public Health Association

Relative classification	A	B	C	D
Indicated number of coliforms per 100 ml	50	51–500	501–1,000	>1,000
Quality designation *	Good	Doubtful	Poor	Very poor

* Depending upon the judgment of the health authority.

Natural bathing waters should be free from schistosome cercariae that can infect man or cause skin irritation (swimmer's itch).

21-4. Fishing Waters. Ellis [4] has suggested that five categories or groups of impurities are hazardous to fish life.

1. Settleable matters (such as sawdust). They may deposit a pollutional carpet on the bottom of bodies of water and on submerged objects in the water. They may thereby smother the plant and animal life that constitutes fish food.

2. Substances that exert an oxygen demand of sufficient intensity to depress the DO content of the water below the level needed to support fish life. Water temperature is of great moment in this connection. To flourish at normal water temperatures, most food fish require a DO concentration of at least 4 ppm, trout one of at least 5 ppm. As the temperature of water rises, the BOD increases and the DO saturation value declines. At the same time, the rate of respiration of the fish and their threshold of asphyxiation go up. For a rise in temperature of 10 C, for example, the oxygen intake of goldfish has been shown to increase more than threefold and the point of asphyxiation of trout almost twofold.[5] In

---

[4] M. M. Ellis, "Detection and Measurement of Stream Pollution," *U. S. Bur. Fisheries Bull.* **22**, 365 (1937).

[5] B. A. Southgate, *Treatment and Disposal of Industrial Wastes, H. M. Stationery Office,* 1948.

the absence of an adequate supply of DO, furthermore, fish become more susceptible to metallic poisons and other hazards. The time required for potassium cyanide to exert its toxic effects on trout, for example, is substantially cut in two for a rise in temperature of 10 C.

3. Compounds that raise the pH above a value of about 8.4 or lower it below a value of about 6.8. Acid and alkaline wastes may be directly lethal in their effects, and changes in pH may throw out of balance the tolerances of fish to high temperatures and to low DO concentrations. Acid wastes are especially detrimental.

4. Wastes, such as oil-well brine, that change the salinity of the water and with it the osmotic pressure of the water.

5. Wastes that contain specifically toxic substances.

The New York State Water Pollution Control Board lists the limiting values shown in Table 21-6 for certain toxic substances. The

TABLE 21-6.   Limits of Toxic Waste Substances, New York State Water Pollution Control Board

Substance	Limiting concentration, ppm
Ammonia or its compounds (NH_3)	2.0 at $pH \gtrless 8.0$
Cyanide (CN)	0.1
Ferro- or ferricyanide [$Fe(CN_6)$]	0.4
Copper (Cu)	0.2
Zinc (Zn)	0.3
Cadmium (Cd)	0.3

destructive concentration of these and other substances, as previously indicated, depends also upon other factors of water quality including its temperature and buffering power as well as the multiple presence of toxic substances.

The immobilization of the water flea (*Daphnia*) has been proposed as a means of determining the toxicity thresholds of toxic substances, but the death of minnows offers a more direct screening test for tolerable limits.

A factor sometimes overlooked in the management of public waters is that some wastes, including sewage, contribute to the fertility of the aquatic meadows in which fish browse for food. The purposeful fertilizing of fish ponds with suitable manures has indeed found wide favor.

21-5. Shellfish Waters.   The fact that shellfish grown in polluted waters have been responsible for numerous outbreaks of typhoid fever makes it necessary to place the saline waters in which they are cultivated in a special category. The bacteriological standard of the U. S. Public Health Service for *satisfactory* shellfish waters is 70 or less coliform bacteria per 100 ml based on a median MPN of a series of samples that are representative of area, tide, and season. Waters that record a median MPN of 700/ml or more are classified as *grossly polluted*. The areas covered by them may not be used to grow shellfish. Waters of intermediate bacteriological quality are designated *moderately polluted, restricted*. Oysters may be taken from such waters during the period of hibernation, provided that the temperature of the waters remains consistently below 41 F (5 C) and the oysters do not show a coliform content of more than 20 per ml. A sanitary survey is required in support of the various findings. The relaying in clean waters of shellfish taken from polluted areas is subject to special restrictions.

21-6. Irrigation Waters. The standards of quality of waters that are to be used for the irrigation of crops fall into a number of categories that are established by the uses to which the crops are to be put and the conditions under which they are grown. The practice of applying human excreta as well as animal manures to the land is ingrained in many peoples, and it is often essential to their economy.

Since the introduction of sewerage systems accompanies an advancing economy, the utilization of the fertilizing constituents of sewage can generally be dispensed with or closely circumscribed without detriment to the standard of living in favor of protecting the public health. Most health authorities, therefore, do not permit the irrigation of crops with partially treated or undisinfected sewage when the crops are vegetables, garden truck, berries, or low-growing fruits. Similar restrictions are applied to the waters of vineyards or orchards where windfalls or fruit lie on the ground. Irrigation waters of this nature are allowed to be used for watering nursery stock, vegetables used exclusively for seed purposes, cotton, and field crops such as hay, grain, rice, alfalfa, fodder corn, cow beets, and fodder carrots. However, milk cows and goats are not permitted to be pastured on the irrigated land when it is moist with sewage and these animals are not given access to irrigation ditches that carry sewage. If the produce of sewage-irrigated areas is such that it will be cooked before consumption, irrigation with sewage is required to be stopped at least a month prior to the harvest. Commercial canning of such crops is sometimes permitted under proper controls of the health authorities. The use of sewage sludge as a fertilizer or soil builder is discussed in Section 26-8.

21-7. Receiving Waters. Standards of quality for waters that are to serve primarily as recipients of sewage and other waste waters normally look to the preservation of the general attractiveness of natural bodies of water and to the prevention of nuisance. To this end it is usually prescribed by water pollution control agencies that receiving waters must meet the following requirements: (1) they must not contain floating or settleable solids, oil, or sludge deposits attributable to waste waters in amounts that are offensive to the sense of sight; and (2) they must not produce odors that are offensive to the sense of smell. Since the production of objectionable odors is associated most commonly with anaerobic decomposition, the amount of decomposable waste matter added to the water must not be great enough to exhaust the DO content of the water.

It is obvious that the maintenance of desirable standards of water quality implies a proper balance between (a) the volume (and where necessary the quality) of the receiving water and (b) the volume and strength of the waste water discharged into it. Attaining a proper balance may require a prescription of the degree of treatment to which sewage and other waste waters must be submitted before discharge.

For fresh waters, the standards of the British Royal Commission on Sewage Disposal for sewage and sewage effluents are significant (see Table 21-7). These standards were promulgated in 1912 and must be viewed with this date in mind. Cognizance must be taken, too, of the relatively small size and length of British streams, the great population density, the highly industrialized nature of the areas drained, the strength of British sewage (2 to 4 times as strong as American sewage), and the prevailing climatic conditions. The basis of the British standards is that the 5-day, 65 F BOD of the receiving waters, immediately below the point of sewage discharge, should not exceed 4 ppm in order to maintain satisfactory conditions during periods of low flow and at summer temperatures of 65 F.

TABLE 21-7.   Standards for Sewage and Sewage Effluents, British Royal Commission on Sewage Disposal

Classification of standard	5-day, 65 F BOD, ppm	Suspended solids, ppm	Type of sewage treatment presumably satisfying the standards
	Required condition of sewage or effluent		
1. General standard	$\lesssim 20$	$\lesssim 30$	Complete treatment
2. Special standards, flow ratio of receiving water to sewage			
150 to 300	....	$\lesssim 60$	Chemical precipitation
300 to 500	....	$\lesssim 150$	Plain sedimentation
Over 500	....	.....	No treatment required

For tidal waters, the specifications of the interstate compact of the states of Connecticut, New York, and New Jersey for the control of pollution may serve as an illustration of reasonable prescription (see Table 21-8).

TABLE 21-8.　Interstate Compact Requirements of Connecticut, New York, and New Jersey for Treatment of Sewage Discharged into Their Tidal Waters

	Requirements for	
Characteristics of sewage (1–3) or receiving water (4)	Waters expected to be used primarily for recreational purposes, shellfish culture, and development of fish life	All other waters
1. Floating solids	Full removal	Full removal
2. Suspended solids	60% removal	10% removal or enough to avoid sludge deposits
3. Coliform bacteria during bathing season	MPN of not more than 1/ml in 50% of 1-ml samples	
4. DO saturation in vicinity of outfall	Not less than 50%	Not less than 30%

A further classification of receiving waters according to use and requisite quality which includes a statement of needed sewage treatment is presented in Table 21-9. This table is based on a similar compilation by Imhoff and Fair.[6] The suggestions contained in Columns 3, 4, and 5 of this table must be interpreted broadly. They should not be regarded as rigid rules. A sufficiently long stretch of receiving water must be considered as a whole to permit evaluation of treatment requirements in terms of the indicated standards of water quality and classes of water use.

Unit Operations of Water and Sewage Treatment

21-8. Outline of Unit Operations. Fundamentally, water purification and waste-water treatment do not differ in principle; only in the degree of pollution of the influent water with which they have to contend and the quality of the effluent that they must turn out. For this reason, they share in most essentials the same unit operations of treatment: operations that are employed for the removal of unwanted

[6] Karl Imhoff and Gordon M. Fair, *Sewage Treatment*, John Wiley & Sons, New York, 1940.

TABLE 21-9.   Classification of Receiving Waters According to Use and Requisite Quality

| Use (1) | Standards of quality at low-water stage (2) | Required treatment of sewage before discharge | | Required treatment of water before use shown in Column (1) (5) |
		Normal (3)	Emergency (4)	
Industrial uses not needing a high-quality water; irrigation of crops not subject to contamination when intended for human consumption; and receipt of wastes without the creation of nuisance.	Absence of nuisance— odors, slick, and unsightly suspended or floating matters; dissolved oxygen present at outfall.	Sedimentation except when receiving waters are large in volume.	Chlorination for removal of hydrogen sulfide; addition of nitrate to supply oxygen.	Sometimes none; chlorination where needed.
Fishing; recreational boating; raising of seed oysters; and industrial use after treatment.	Absence of slick, odors, and visible floating and suspended solids. DO $\leqq$ 3 mg/l and preferably $\geqq$ 5 mg/l; CO_2 < 40 mg/l and preferably < 20 mg/l.	Sedimentation, chemical precipitation, or biological treatment depending upon degree of dilution.	Aeration; addition of diluting waters.	Withdrawal of water not implied.
Bathing, recreation, and shellfish culture.	Clear; no visible sewage matter; a coliform IN less than 100 to 1,000 per 100 ml depending on length of bathing season; DO near saturation.	Sedimentation, chemical precipitation, or biological treatment, depending upon degree of dilution; chlorination of effluent.	Heavy chlorination.	Withdrawal of water not implied.
Drinking water and related uses.	Chemical standards for substances not removable by common water-treatment methods; clear; DO near saturation; coliform MPN of 50/100 ml when chlorination is the only treatment; up to 20,000/100 ml when treatment is complete.	Sedimentation, chemical precipitation or biological treatment depending upon degree of dilution; chlorination of effluent.	Heavy chlorination.	Chlorination when coliform MPN is less than 50/100 ml; pre- and post-chlorination, coagulation, sedimentation, and filtration when coliform MPN is up to 20,000/100 ml.

or objectionable substances, or for the transformation of these substances into acceptable form. But they do not share them in the same intensity. An outline of the most important unit operations follows.

1. *Gas Exchange.* An operation by which gases are precipitated from water or taken into solution by water through exposure of the water to air or to special atmospheres under normal, increased, or reduced pressures. Examples of gas exchange are: (1) the addition of oxygen to water or waste water by spray or bubble aeration for deferrization and demanganization (water) and for the creation or maintenance of aerobic conditions (waste water); (2) the removal of carbon dioxide, hydrogen sulfide, and volatile, odorous substances from water by

spray or bubble aeration for odor and corrosion control; (3) the addition of ozone or chlorine to water or waste water in ozone towers and gas chlorinators respectively for disinfection; and (4) the removal of oxygen from water by evacuation in degasifiers for corrosion control. The release of methane and carbon dioxide from sewage sludge that is undergoing decomposition is, in principle, also a form of gas exchange. On the other hand, the oxygenation of water for deferrization and demanganization is, in principle, also a form of chemical precipitation.

2. *Screening.* An operation whereby floating and suspended matter that is larger in size than the openings of the screening device is "strained" out and removed for disposal. Shredding devices combined with screens convert coarse matter into fine matter. This is normally returned to the water to be removed by sedimentation. Examples are: (1) the removal from water of leaves, sticks, and other debris by racks and screens, and the straining out of algae by what are called microscreens; and (2) the removal from sewage of coarse suspended and floating matter by racks and of finer suspended matter by screens. The comminution of substances intercepted by screens within the sewage is a special use of screens. Rakings and screenings must be removed from racks and screens for disposal by burial, incineration, or digestion (including composting). Comminution of screenings and their return to the flowing sewage is an indirect method of screenings disposal. They are added to the sewage sludge and disposed of with the sludge (see Section 26-2). Filtration is, in part, screening.

3. *Sedimentation.* An operation by which the carrying and scouring powers of flowing water are reduced in magnitude until suspended particles settle out by gravitational pull and are not resuspended by scour. Examples are: (1) the removal of sand and heavy silt from water in settling basins; (2) the collection of heavy mineral solids from waste waters by differential sedimentation and scour (grit chambers); (3) the removal of settleable, suspended sewage solids in settling tanks; and (4) the removal from water and sewage of non-settleable substances that have been rendered settleable by chemical or biological coagulation or precipitation. The settled substances are known as sludge. This must be removed from the sedimentation devices for disposal with or without treatment (see Section 26-2). Filtration is, in part, sedimentation.

4. *Flotation.* An operation by which (*a*) the transporting power of flowing water is reduced by quiescence or (*b*) the suspending power of water is overcome by quiescence and by the addition of "flotation agents." Substances naturally lighter than water or substances that are rendered lighter than water rise to the water surface and are skimmed off. Flotation agents include fine air bubbles and chemical compounds that, singly or in combination, are wetting and foaming agents. If these agents are also hydrophobic, their power of flotation is increased. Examples are: (1) the removal of grease and oil from waste waters with or without the benefit of aeration in skimming tanks or tanks that serve the primary purpose of sedimentation; (2) the release of air into waste waters by the diffusion of compressed air or by precipitation of dissolved air through reduction of the pressure of the overlying atmosphere, the fine air bubbles attaching themselves to suspended particles, imparting buoyancy to them, and lifting them to the surface; and (3) the addition to water and waste water of flotation agents that attach themselves to suspended matter or attach suspended matter to bubbles of air and lift the particles to the surface. The skimmings or foam must be

removed from the flotation device and disposed of. Examples of flotation agents are the anionic, neutral, or cationic detergents, and also oil, grease, resin, and glue.

5. *Chemical Coagulation.* An operation of chemical treatment in which floc-forming chemicals are added to water and waste water for the purpose of en-meshing, or combining with, settleable, but more particularly with non-settleable, suspended and colloidal matter. Rapidly settling aggregates, or flocs, are created. The added chemicals, called coagulants, are soluble, but they are precipitated by reacting with substances in or added to the water or waste water. In water purification, the floc that has not been removed by sedimentation (see 3) is generally removed by filtration; in waste-water treatment, the floc is removed by filtration or by biological treatment. The most common coagulants are aluminum and iron salts while the precipitating substances are, usually, naturally present alkalinity or, more rarely, added alkalinity released by substances such as soda ash. Examples are: (1) the addition of aluminum sulfate to water and (2) of ferric chloride to water or waste water.[7] Dosing, mixing, and flocculating (or stirring) devices are needed adjuncts to the required settling basins.

6. *Chemical Precipitation.* An operation whereby dissolved substances are thrown out of solution. The added chemicals are soluble and react with chemicals in the water or waste water to precipitate them. Examples are: (1) flocculation of iron by the addition of lime to iron-containing water or waste water, the reaction being carried to completion by dissolved oxygen, and sedimentation of suspended solids being enhanced by the resulting coagulation; (2) precipitation of iron and manganese from water by aeration, the reaction being one of oxidation by dissolved oxygen; (3) softening of water by the addition of lime (carbonate hardness) and soda ash (non-carbonate hardness); and (4) precipitation of fluorides from water by the addition of tricalcium phosphate, or by their precipi-tation along with magnesium in connection with water softening. Dosing, mixing, and flocculating devices are needed adjuncts to required settling basins (see 5 and 3).

7. *Ion Exchange.* An operation by which certain ions in water are exchanged for complementary ions that are part of the complex of a solid exchange medium. Examples are: (1) the exchange of calcium and magnesium for sodium by passage of water through a bed of sodium zeolite which is regenerated by brine (base or cation exchange); (2) the exchange of sodium and potassium as well as calcium and magnesium by synthetic organic cation exchangers and absorption of the acids produced on other synthetic organic anion exchangers, the cation exchanger being regenerated with acid, the anion exchanger with sodium carbonate; and (3) the precipitation of iron and manganese on manganese zeolite and the regeneration of the zeolite with potassium permanganate. In a sense the last example is one of surface or contact precipitation rather than ion exchange. The by-products of ion exchange are the spent, regenerating washes.

8. *Physical Adsorption and Contact.* An operation in which adsorptive and other physical interfacial forces combine to remove substances from solution and to concentrate them at the interface, sometimes as precipitates. Examples

---

[7] The addition of coagulating chemicals to waste water is erroneously, but generally, referred to as chemical precipitation. The explanation of this usage of the term precipitation is traceable to the fact that flocculation of sewage was first employed with sewages rich in iron wastes to which only lime had to be added to produce settling flocs.

are: (1) the adsorption on beds of coke, crushed stone, or other granular materials, of iron and manganese that are precipitating from water; and (2) the adsorption of odor- and taste-producing molecules on beds of granular carbon or on powdered activated carbon that is suspended in water and removed by sedimentation or filtration. Biological contact processes are outlined in the next paragraph of this section. Contact beds are regenerated by washing. Spent powdered activated carbon is wasted. Filtration is, in part, a contact process.

9. *Biological Flocculation and Precipitation.* A contact operation in which the formation of biologically active flocs or slimes of living organisms is promoted under aerobic conditions for the purpose of transferring to the floc or slime interface putrescible, principally finely divided and dissolved, substances. These substances are partially stabilized by biological activity, some of the soluble and stable end products of biological activity being returned to the water. Examples are: (1) the biological treatment of sewage on trickling filters and (2) the aeration of sewage in activated-sludge units. The filtration of water through slow sand filters is, in part, biological contact. The treatment of sewage on intermittent sand filters and the disposal of sewage by irrigation are likewise, in part, biological contact. The biological slimes are unloaded intermittently from trickling filters as settleable solids or trickling-filter humus, and more or less continuously as excess activated sludge from the settling tanks that follow activated sludge units.

10. *Filtration.* An operation in which straining, sedimentation, and interfacial contact combine to transfer suspended matter onto grains of sand, coal, or other granular materials from which it must later be removed. Examples are: (1) the slow filtration of water through beds of sand, the clogged surface layers of which are scraped off successively but relatively infrequently and washed before being returned to the bed; (2) the even slower filtration of sewage through beds of sand (usually natural deposits) that are allowed to rest and reaerate between dosings; and (3) the rapid filtration of water through beds of sand, the accumulated impurities being scoured from the filter medium in place through the action on it, singly or in combination, of water, air, or mechanical rakes. The wash water is a by-product of water filtration.

11. *Disinfection.* An operation by which living, potentially infectious organisms are killed. Examples are: (1) the chlorination of water and sewage (chemical disinfection) and (2) the boiling of water (heat disinfection).

12. *Chemical Stabilization.* A variety of operations in which chemicals are added for the purpose of converting objectionable substances into unobjectionable forms without their removal. Examples are: (1) the chlorination of water for the oxidation of hydrogen sulfide into sulfate; (2) the liming of water or passage of water through chips of marble or limestone for the conversion of carbon dioxide into soluble bicarbonate; (3) the recarbonation of water (that has been softened by excess-lime treatment) to convert excess lime into soluble bicarbonate; (4) the superchlorination of water or addition of chlorine dioxide for the oxidation of odor-producing substances; (5) the removal of excess chlorine by reducing agents such as sulfur dioxide; (6) the addition to water of complex phosphates to keep iron in solution; and (7) the addition to water of lime, complex phosphates, or sodium silicate to protect metallic surfaces by forming deposit coatings on them or otherwise reducing the corrosive action of water.

This list, although fairly complete, by no means includes all of the unit operations of water purification and waste-water treatment. For example, the addition to water of fluoride for the control of dental caries in children and the use of copper salts to prevent the growth of algae and related organisms, or to destroy them, do not find a ready place in the schedule of unit operations. There are specialized operations, furthermore, in connection with the preparation of boiler feed-water, other industrial process waters, and industrial waste-waters. Many of these are identified in Chapter 29. The unit operations of sludge treatment and methods of sludge disposal are considered in Section 26-2.

21-9. Synthesis of Unit Operations into Treatment Processes. The unit operations of water purification and waste-water treatment are applied in treatment works in many different combinations to meet (1), in water-purification works, existing conditions of raw-water quality and requirements of pure-water quality, and (2), in sewage-treatment works, prevailing situations of sewage concentration, composition, and condition and specifications of effluent quality. The selection and elaboration of the unit operations to be employed constitutes "the process design" of the treatment works.

a. Water Purification. In order to direct attention to feasible combinations of water-treatment operations, the attributes of water affected by the more conventional unit operations and processes of treatment are identified in Table 21-10. In this table, the relative

TABLE 21-10. Common Attributes of Water Affected by Conventional Unit Operations and Water-Treatment Processes

Attribute (a)	Aeration (b)	Coagulation and sedimentation (c)	Lime-soda softening and sedimentation (d)	Slow sand filtration without (c) (e)	Rapid sand filtration preceded by (c) (f)	Disinfection (chlorination) (g)
Bacteria	0	++	(+++) (1, 2)	++++	++++	++++
Color	0	+++	0	++	++++	0
Turbidity	0	+++	(++) (2)	++++ (3)	++++	0
Odor and taste	++ (4)	(+)	(++) (2)	++	(++)	++++ (5)
						-- (6)
Hardness	+	(--) (7)	++++	0	(--) (7)	0
Corrosiveness	+++ (8)	(--) (10)	(11)	0	(--) (10)	0
	--- (9)					
Iron and manganese	+++	+ (12)	(++)	++++ (12)	++++ (12)	0

(1) When very high pH values are produced by excess lime treatment; (2) by inclusion in precipitates; (3) but filters clog too rapidly at high turbidities; (4) not including chlorophenol tastes; (5) when break-point chlorination is employed or superchlorination is followed by dechlorination; (6) when (5) is not employed in the presence of intense odors and tastes; (7) some coagulants convert carbonates into sulfates; (8) by removal of carbon dioxide; (9) by addition of oxygen when it is low; (10) some coagulants release carbon dioxide; (11) variable, some metals are attacked at high pH values; (12) after aeration.

degree of effectiveness of each unit operation or process is indicated by the number of plus signs (+) up to a limit of four; adverse effects are shown by minus signs (−) also to degree; and indirect effects are recorded by parentheses placed around the signs. Limitations and other factors are explained in footnotes.

Combinations of unit operations often used in water-treatment practice are illustrated in Figure 2-5.

b. *Waste-Water Treatment.* Why the unit operations of sewage treatment must be applied in different combinations to meet particular conditions of sewage disposal is evident from Tables 21-7 to 21-9. The degree of treatment that can be accomplished by different unit operations and treatment processes may be gaged from Table 21-11.

TABLE 21-11. Relative Efficiencies of Sewage-Treatment Operations and Processes

Percentage Removal

Treatment operation or process (a)	5-*day*, 20 C BOD (b)	Suspended solids (c)	Bacteria (d)
1. Fine screening	5–10	2–20	10–20
2. Chlorination of raw or settled sewage	15–30	. . . . .	90–95
3. Plain sedimentation	25–40	40–70	25–75
4. Chemical precipitation	50–85	70–90	40–80
5. Trickling filtration preceded and followed by plain sedimentation	80–95	70–92	90–95
6. Activated-sludge treatment preceded and followed by plain sedimentation	85–95	85–95	90–98
7. Intermittent sand filtration	90–95	85–95	95–98
8. Chlorination of biologically treated sewage	. . . . .	. . . . .	98–99

Discrepancies between theoretical values and recorded results must be expected. High efficiencies cannot be obtained, for example, when treatment plants are overloaded and part of the sewage is by-passed, or when sludge cannot be fully treated and some of it must be wasted into the effluent channel. Attention must be paid to "sludge liquor" discharged from separate sludge-digestion tanks, mechanical sludge-dewatering equipment, or inefficient drying beds. This liquor often has a high BOD and spoils the performance of the plant if it is discharged into the effluent without treatment.

Although any desired degree of purification can be obtained by suitable combinations of unit operations, economic considerations ultimately govern the selection of the operations used. As a general rule, treatment works that include complete treatment by intermittent sand filters, trickling filters, or activated-sludge units may be expected to turn out an effluent having a BOD of 10 to 20 mg/l and a suspended-solids content of less than 30 mg/l. Such effluents ordinarily are stable for 10 days or more, in part, because of their incipient nitrification. Partial treatment can be secured by modification as well as by selection of different treatment processes.

Combinations of unit operations often used in sewage-treatment practice are illustrated in Figure 3-7.

21-10. Treatment Works and Water-Quality Standards. In the evolution of standards of water quality and the creation of works for the attainment of existing standards, engineers have progressed from a prescription of removal efficiencies to one of defined quality. At one time, for example, 99.99% removal of bacteria by water-purification plants was an accepted standard without adequate regard to the bacterial load imposed upon the plants by the raw water that they received. Such a standard is no longer honored. Instead, progress in water-treatment methods has permitted the establishment of defined standards of drinking-water quality. Although these standards are, in a sense, still standards of expediency (the equivalence of sterile, distilled water not yet being prescribed for drinking water), they are standards which, experience has shown, provide the greatest possible protection to health, enjoyment, and usefulness justified by the existing economy.

In North America, the step from prescription of removal efficiency to that of defined quality has not yet been taken as fully in the treatment and disposal of sewage and other waste waters. That this is so is shown, for example, by the requirements included in the Tri-State Compact summarized in Table 21-8. It stands to reason, however, that completion of the step is but a matter of time and that standards for sewage-treatment plant performance like those of the British Royal Commission (Table 21-7) will eventually be evolved also in North America. The advances that have already been made in waste-water treatment methods support this judgment. The fields of research and development, however, must not be allowed to lie fallow so long as expediency still remains a controlling consideration.

22-1. Definitions and Uses. *Sedimentation* or the removal, by gravitational settling, of suspended particles that are heavier than water is an important factor in the natural purification of streams, lakes, and tidal waters. It is also the most widely useful operation in the treatment of water and sewage. When the impurities are separated from the suspending fluid by the action of natural forces alone, i.e., by gravitation and natural aggregation of the settling particles, the operation is called plain sedimentation. When chemicals or other substances are added to induce or hasten the aggregation of finely divided suspended matter, the operation is called flocculation or coagulation. Finally, when chemicals are added to throw dissolved impurities out of solution, the operation is called chemical precipitation.

In modern water-purification works, settling tanks are included for the removal of (1) flocculated impurities, such as color and turbidity, and (2) precipitated impurities, such as hardness and iron. The settling tanks may be preceded by flocculation or reaction chambers, but rigid separation of the functions of coagulation or precipitation and of sedimentation is sometimes dispensed with, and the same tank may then serve both purposes. River waters that carry a heavy load of silt are often subjected to sedimentation both in advance of flocculation and afterwards.

In the treatment of sewage and industrial wastes, sedimentation is a function of: (1) grit chambers that separate heavy mineral or otherwise inert solids from the flowing liquid (usually combined sewage) by differential sedimentation and scour; (2) primary, or preliminary, settling tanks that collect much of the suspended load of impurities prior to the discharge of the clarified effluent into receiving waters or prior to its further treatment; and (3) secondary, or final, settling tanks that collect those matters which have been converted into settleable solids, or otherwise rendered settleable, by biological or related treatment processes. The addition of flocculating or precipitating

584

agents to sewage or industrial wastes may precede sedimentation and improve its efficiency.

Fill-and-draw operation of settling tanks is confined, nowadays, very largely to the preparation of boiler feed waters and the treatment of industrial wastes that are discharged in batches. Continuous-flow basins are used, almost exclusively, in modern municipal water-purification and sewage-treatment works.

Flotation or the removal, by gravitational rising, of suspended particles that are lighter than water is the converse of sedimentation. It is more or less confined to the treatment of sewage and industrial wastes in current practice. Grease, oil, and other matters ascend naturally to the surface of skimming tanks during substantial quiescence. Flotation can be hastened and extended to particles that are heavier than water by introducing or otherwise releasing finely divided air or gas bubbles that attach themselves to the particles. These bubbles not only impart buoyancy to the particles but also entangle them in the surface foam that the bubbles create. The addition of wetting and foaming agents in connection with flotation corresponds to the addition of coagulating or precipitating agents in connection with sedimentation. Generally speaking, however, flotation is a process of relatively minor significance in the operation of municipal treatment works.

Principles of Sedimentation and Flotation

22-2. Settling and Rising Velocities of Discrete Particles. A discrete particle is one that, in rising or settling, does not alter its size, shape, and weight. When such a particle is falling or rising through a quiescent fluid, it will accelerate until the frictional resistance, or drag, of the fluid equals the impelling force acting upon the particle. Subsequently the particle will settle or rise at a uniform velocity which, as we shall see, is an important hydraulic attribute of the particle. • The impelling force equals the effective weight of the particle or its weight in the suspending fluid, i.e.,

$$F_I = (\rho_s - \rho)gV \qquad 22\text{-}1$$

where F_I is the impelling force, g is the gravity constant, V is the volume of the particle, and ρ_s and ρ are respectively the mass density of the particle and of the fluid.

The drag force F_D of the fluid, on the other hand, is a function of the dynamic viscosity μ and mass density ρ of the fluid and of the velocity v_s and a characteristic diameter d of the particle. To be fully representative, the diameter must reflect (1) the orientation of the particle relative to its direction of motion, as represented for example by its cross-sectional area, or projected area at right angles to motion, and (2) the relative frictional surface of the particle in contact with the fluid, as represented for example by its surface area in relation to its volume. Dimensionally, therefore,

$$F_D = \phi(v_s, d, \rho, \mu)$$

or, designating dimensional relations by square brackets,

$$[F_D] = [v_s{}^x d^y \rho^p \mu^q]$$

Introducing the fundamental units of mass m, length l, and time t of the various parameters into this equation,

$$[mlt^{-2}] = [m^{p+q} l^{x+y-3p-q} t^{-x-q}]$$

and solving for x, y, and p in terms of q,

$$F_D = v_s{}^2 d^2 \rho \phi(v_s \, d\rho/\mu) = v_s{}^2 \, d^2 \rho \phi(\mathbf{R}) \qquad 22\text{-}2$$

where $\mathbf{R}$ is the Reynolds number.

This dimensionally derived relationship for the frictional drag has been verified experimentally.

If we substitute the cross-sectional, or projected, area A_c at right angles to the direction of settling for d^2, the dynamic pressure $\rho v_s{}^2/2$ for $\rho v_s{}^2$, and Newton's *drag coefficient* C_D for $\phi(\mathbf{R})$,

$$F_D = C_D A_c \rho v_s{}^2/2 \qquad 22\text{-}3$$

The value of C_D is not constant, as Newton [1] assumed, but varies [2] with $\mathbf{R}$ as shown in Figure 22-1. For spheres, the observational relationships between C_D and $\mathbf{R}$ shown in this figure are approximated by the following equation (upper limit $\mathbf{R} = 10^4$):

$$C_D = \frac{24}{\mathbf{R}} + \frac{3}{\sqrt{\mathbf{R}}} + 0.34 \qquad 22\text{-}4$$

A brief list of related values is shown in Table 22-1.

TABLE 22-1.   Values of Reynolds Number and Newton's Coefficient of Drag

$\mathbf{R}$	10^{-3}	10^{-2}	10^{-1}	1	10	10^2	10^3	10^4
C_D	24.1×10^3	24.3×10^2	25.0×10	27.3	36.9×10^{-1}	88.0×10^{-2}	45.9×10^{-2}	37.2×10^{-2}

[1] *Mathematical Principles of Natural Philosophy.*

[2] This variation is similar to that for pipes (Section 12-2).

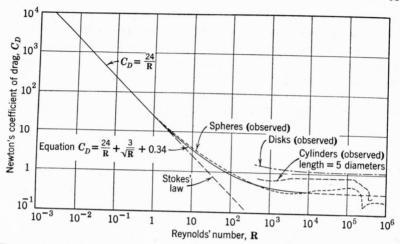

Figure 22-1. Newton's coefficient of drag for varying magnitudes of Reynolds number. "Observed Curves after Camp," *Trans. Am. Soc. Civil Engrs., 103*, 897 (1946).

We can now equate F_I and F_D (Equations 22-1 and 22-3) and establish a general equation for the settling or rising of free and discrete particles, as follows:

$$v_s = \sqrt{\frac{2g}{C_D} \frac{\rho_s - \rho}{\rho} \frac{V}{A_c}} \qquad 22\text{-}5$$

or, for spherical particles, $V = (\pi/6)d^3$ and $A_c = (\pi/4)d^2$,

$$v_s = \sqrt{\frac{4}{3} \frac{g}{C_D} \frac{\rho_s - \rho}{\rho} d} \qquad \text{or closely} \qquad \sqrt{\frac{4}{3} \frac{g}{C_D} (s_s - 1)d} \qquad 22\text{-}6$$

Here s_s is the specific gravity of the particle and $d = \tfrac{3}{2} V/A_c = 6V/A$ where A is the surface area of the particle.

For eddying resistance at high Reynolds numbers ($\mathbf{R} = 10^3$ to 10^4), C_D has a value of about 0.4, and

$$v_s = \sqrt{3.3g(s_s - 1)d} \qquad 22\text{-}7$$

For viscous resistance at low Reynolds numbers ($\mathbf{R} < 0.5$), $C_D = 24/\mathbf{R}$, and Equation 22-6 reads as follows:

$$v_s = \frac{g}{18} \frac{\rho_s - \rho}{\mu} d^2 \qquad \text{or closely} \qquad \frac{g}{18} (s_s - 1) \frac{d^2}{\nu} \qquad 22\text{-}8$$

This is Stokes's law,[3] and ν is the kinematic viscosity.

To span the region between the Stokes range and the turbulent range a curve such as that shown in Figure 22-2 is useful. The parameters of diameter and velocity in this figure were obtained (1) by equating d and v_s in the velocity-diameter Reynolds-number relationship $\mathbf{R} = v_s d/\nu$ and in the velocity-diameter coefficient of resistance relationship (Equation 22-6), and solving for v_s and d in terms of $[g(s_s - 1)\nu]^{-\frac{1}{3}}v_s = (\frac{4}{3}\mathbf{R}/C_D)^{\frac{1}{3}}$ and $[g(s_s - 1)/\nu^2]^{\frac{1}{3}}d = (\frac{3}{4}\mathbf{R}^2 C_D)^{\frac{1}{3}}$.

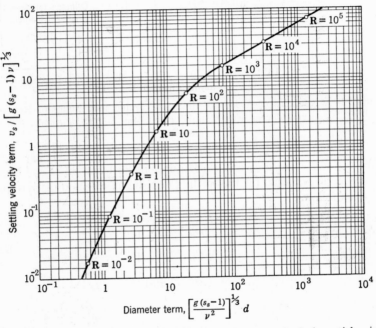

Figure 22-2. Settling and rising velocities of discrete spherical particles in a quiescent fluid in terms of the specific gravity of the particle (as related to the fluid), the kinematic viscosity of the fluid, and the gravity constant.

Example 22-1. Find: (a) the settling velocity in water at 20 C of spherical particles 5×10^{-3} cm in diameter and specific gravity 2.65; (b) the rising velocity of particles of the same diameter but a specific gravity of 0.80; and (c) the settling velocity in water at 20 C of spherical particles 10^{-1} cm in diameter and specific gravity 2.65.

a. Settling velocity of particle 5×10^{-3} cm in diameter and specific gravity 2.65.
1. From Table 17-2, $\nu = 1.010 \times 10^{-2}$ cm^2/sec.

---

[3] Stokes derived his law from theoretical considerations of the motion of a spherical pendulum in a fluid. [*Trans., Cambridge Philosophical Soc., 8,* 287 (1845).]

2. From Equation 22-8, $v_s = \dfrac{981}{18} \dfrac{(2.65 - 1.00)}{1.01 \times 10^{-2}} (5 \times 10^{-3})^2 = 0.222$ cm/sec.

3. $R = (2.22 \times 10^{-1})(5 \times 10^{-3})/(1.01 \times 10^{-2}) = 1.1 \times 10^{-1}$, and Stokes's law applies.

b. Rising velocity of particle 5×10^{-3} cm in diameter and specific gravity of 0.80.

1. From Equation 22-8, $v_s = 0.222(0.80 - 1)/(2.65 - 1) = -2.69 \times 10^{-2}$ cm/sec.

2. $R = (1.1 \times 10^{-1})(2.69 \times 10^{-2})/(2.22 \times 10^{-1}) = 1.3 \times 10^{-2}$, and Stokes's law applies.

c. Settling velocity of particle 10^{-1} cm in diameter and specific gravity of 2.65.

1. Diameter term $10^{-1}[981 \times 1.65/(1.01 \times 10^{-2})^2]^{1/3} = 2.52 \times 10$.

2. From Figure 22-2, the velocity term is $7.0 = v_s/(981 \times 1.65 \times 1.01 \times 10^{-2})^{1/3}$ or $v_s = 7.0(981 \times 1.65 \times 1.01 \times 10^{-2})^{1/3} = 1.77 \times 10$ cm/sec, and Stokes's law does not apply. From Figure 22-2, $R = 1.8 \times 10^2$, whence $C_D = 7 \times 10^{-1}$.

The suspended matter in water and sewage is seldom truly spherical. The irregular particles of which the suspensions are generally composed possess greater surface area relative to their volume than do spheres, and they settle more slowly than do spheres of equivalent volume. The frictional drag changes, furthermore, with the orientation of the particle relative to the direction of motion. As shown in Figure 22-1, irregularities in shape exert their greatest influence on drag at high velocities. For the evaluation of particle shape, see Section 24-4.

22-3. Hindered Settling of Discrete Particles. In a suspension of discrete particles, the settling velocity of each particle remains unchanged throughout the settling period except when the particles are so closely spaced in the suspending medium that their velocity fields interfere. Under these conditions, there is an appreciable upward displacement of the fluid, and settling is hindered. In laboratory observations of settling velocities, the walls of a narrow cylindrical container in which a single particle is settling exert a similar hindering influence. Measurements show, however, that this wall effect becomes negligible at high Reynolds numbers or when the diameter of the particle is less than about 1% of the diameter of the cylinder.

It appears from Equation 24-22 that the settling velocity is reduced to 99% of its unhindered value when the volume concentration of suspended solids, $c\rho/\rho_s$, where c is their concentration by weight, is about 0.22%. In the absence of flocculation, or entrainment of water by the clustering of particles, this corresponds to a weight concentration of about 6,000 mg/l of river silt, sewage grit, or precipitated calcium carbonate and 2,500 mg/l of suspended sewage solids. Natural and induced aggregation of particles increase the volume concentration of suspended matter, but most suspensions that are subjected to sedimentation in water and sewage treatment, with the exception of activated sludge, may be considered to settle freely. If the solids suspended in water or sewage are well graded, the settling velocities may be such as to crowd the particles together when they catch up with one another as they approach the bottom of the settling tank. Settling may then be hindered locally. Crowding is produced also in vertical-flow tanks in which those particles that possess a settling velocity closely approximating that of the rising fluid accumulate in a blanket or suspended filter layer through which the rising fluid must pass. There is hindered flotation as well as hindered sedimentation.

Hydraulically, the process of hindered settling is analogous to the expansion of filtering materials in backwashing and can be formulated in those terms (see Section 24-7).

22-4. Settling of Flocculent Suspensions. Most granular solids settle as discrete particles. Organic matter and the flocs formed by coagulants or zoogleal growths tend to agglomerate when they collide and to form clusters of different size, shape, and weight. The settling velocity of the clusters is ordinarily increased, and they are more readily removed. Particles collide when fast-settling particles overtake slower ones or when turbulence bumps particles together within the liquid. In vertical-flow tanks, rising particles collide with settling particles.

In accordance with Smoluchowski's theory,[4] the aggregation of uniform particles is given by the following relationship:

$$\frac{1}{n_2} - \frac{1}{n_1} = k(t_2 - t_1) \qquad 22\text{-}9$$

where n_1 and n_2 are the numbers of particles at times t_1 and t_2 respectively, and k is a rate constant that reflects the number of contacts between the particles per unit of time.

The number of contacts N per unit volume and time may be estimated from the size and number of particles on the assumption that, in settling, a particle of diameter d' and settling velocity v_s' will come into contact in a unit of time with a smaller particle of diameter d'' and settling velocity v_s'' if the particles are present in a cylinder of diameter $d' + d''$ and height $(v_s' - v_s'')$. The latter equals the vertical distance that can separate the particles and still permit the upper, larger particle to catch up with the lower, smaller particle in a unit of time. If a unit volume of the fluid contains n' particles of diameter

---

[4] M. von Smoluchowski, "Versuch einer mathematischen Theorie der Koagulationskinetik kolloider Lösungen," *Zeitschrift für physikalische Chemie, 92,* 155 (1917).

d' and n'' particles of diameter d'', the number of contacts per unit volume and unit time is

$$N = n'n''(\pi/4)(d' + d'')^2(v_s' - v_s'') \qquad \text{22-10}$$

because each particle of diameter d' can catch up with each particle of diameter d''. If the particles are of equal density and of such size that they settle in accordance with Stokes' law,

$$v_s' - v_s'' = \frac{g}{18}\frac{(s_s - 1)}{\nu}(d'^2 - d''^2) \qquad \text{22-11}$$

Combining Equations 22-10 and 22-11, the following important relationship is obtained:

$$N = n'n''\frac{\pi}{72}g\frac{s_s - 1}{\nu}(d' + d'')^3(d' - d'') \qquad \text{22-12}$$

It follows that contact, and with it possible aggregation, is greatest for a large concentration of particles of large size, large relative weight, and large size-difference in a liquid of small viscosity (e.g. water of high temperature).

Most flocs formed in water and waste water are quite fragile. As they grow in size, the velocity gradient across them increases, and they tend to be broken up. This creates a limiting size. As a rule, flocculent suspensions entering settling tanks in water and waste-water treatment works have not yet reached this limit, and sedimentation is improved materially by further floc growth. Floc formation, depending upon the nature of the settling process, may either be self-induced or promoted by the addition of coagulating substances.

The composition of flocculating suspended solids and the opportunities for contact are so complex that there is no satisfactory method for evaluating the acceleration of settling by the aggregation of flocculent particles.

Flocculated aggregates entrain more or less water and thereby enlarge their over-all size while decreasing their gross density. The clustering of any number of identical particles of specific gravity s_s, for example, will on entraining $p\%$ water (by weight) of specific gravity s decrease the specific gravity s_m of the mass to

$$s_m = \frac{100}{(100 - p)/s_s + p/s} \qquad \text{22-13}$$

and replace the combined volume ΣV of the particles by

$$V_m = \frac{s_s}{s_m}\left(\frac{100}{100 - p}\right)\Sigma V \qquad\qquad 22\text{-}14$$

Here V_m is the volume of the mass that includes $p\%$ of entrained water by weight. If $s_s = 2.65$, for example, and $p = 90\%$, s being closely equal to unity, $s_m = 1.065$ and $V_m = 25 \Sigma V$.

The expansion and coalescence of gas bubbles rising through a liquid are somewhat analogous to the settling of flocculating particles.

22-5. Efficiency of an Ideal Settling Basin. For purposes of discussion, we may divide a continuous-flow basin into four zones: (1) an inlet zone in which influent flow and suspended matter disperse over the cross-section at right angles to flow; (2) a settling zone in which the suspended particles settle within the flowing water; (3) a sludge zone adjacent to the bottom, in which the removed solids accumulate and from which they are withdrawn for disposal; and (4) an outlet zone in which the flow and remaining suspended particles assemble and are carried to the effluent conduit. These zones are shown in Figure 22-3 for horizontal-flow tanks. Similar zones exist in vertical-flow tanks.

In order to devise a framework for the formulation of sedimentation in continuous-flow basins, certain simplifying assumptions must be introduced. For horizontal-flow tanks, these include the following:

1. Within the settling zone of the tank, sedimentation takes place exactly as in a quiescent container of equal depth.

2. The flow is steady, and, upon entering the settling zone, the concentration of suspended particles of each size is uniform throughout the cross-section at right angles to flow.

3. A particle that enters the sludge zone is and stays removed.

The paths traced by discrete particles that are settling in a rectangular or circular basin are shown in Figure 22-3. They are determined by the vector sums of the settling velocity v_s of the particle and the displacement velocity V of the basin. All particles with a settling velocity $v_s \gtreqless v_0$ are removed, v_0 being the velocity of that particle that falls through the full depth h_0 of the settling zone in the detention time t_0. Since $v_0 = h_0/t_0$ and $t_0 = C/Q$, where Q is the rate of flow and C is the volumetric capacity of the settling zone, and since $C/h_0 = A$, the surface area of this zone, it is true, furthermore, that $v_0 = Q/A$, the surface loading or overflow velocity of the basin. In vertical-flow basins particles with velocity $v_s < v_0$ are not removed. In horizontal-flow basins such particles can be removed, but only if they are within a vertical striking distance $h = vt_0$ from the sludge zone. If y_0 particles

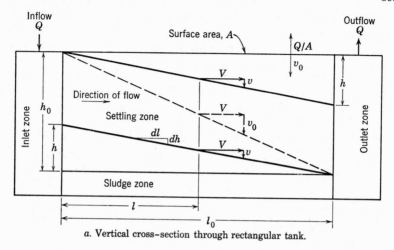

a. Vertical cross-section through rectangular tank.

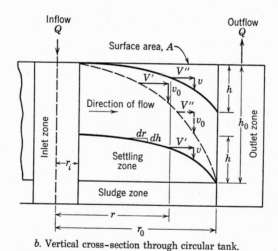

b. Vertical cross-section through circular tank.

Figure 22-3. Settling paths of discrete particles in horizontal flow tanks (idealized). The capacity of the settling zone is C, and its surface area is A.

possessing a settling velocity $v_s \gtrless v_0$ compose each size represented in the suspension, the proportion y/y_0 of particles that are removed in a horizontal-flow tank is

$$\frac{y}{y_0} = \frac{h}{h_0} = \frac{v_s\, t_0}{v_0\, t_0} = \frac{v_s}{v_0} = \frac{v_s}{Q/A} \qquad \text{22-15}$$

This equation can be derived also from the geometric relations shown in Figure 22-3.

For a rectangular basin of width W, $dh/dl = (v_s \, dt)/(V \, dt) =$ constant because both v_s and V are constant. Hence, $h = (v_s/V)l$, and

$$\frac{h}{h_0} = \frac{v_s}{V} \frac{l}{h_0} = \frac{v_s}{V} \frac{lW}{h_0 W} = \frac{v_s}{Q/A}$$

For a circular basin of radius r, $V = Q/(2\pi r h_0)$ is variable, and

$$\frac{dh}{dr} = \frac{v_s}{V} = \frac{2\pi r h_0 v_s}{Q} \quad \text{or} \quad h = \frac{\pi h_0 v_s}{Q} (r_0{}^2 - r_i{}^2) = \frac{h_0 v_s A}{Q}$$

and $h/h_0 = v_s/(Q/A)$ as for a rectangular basin.

Derived by Hazen [5] in somewhat different fashion, the relationship represented by Equation 22-15 states that, for discrete particles and unhindered settling, the efficiency of a basin is solely a function of the settling velocity of the particles and of the surface area and rate of flow of the basin which, in combination, constitute the surface loading or overflow velocity. The efficiency is independent of the depth of the basin and of the displacement time or detention period. It follows from this equation, furthermore, that all particles with velocity $v_s \gtreqless v_0$ are removed and that particles with velocity $v_s < v_0$ can be fully captured in horizontal-flow basins if false bottoms or trays are inserted in the tank at intervals $h = v_s t_0$ ideally. The greater the number of these trays, the smaller may be the settling velocity of the particles all of which are to be removed. As we shall see later, water or sewage filters approximate, in a sense, settling basins equipped with a very large number of trays. The number of trays that can actually be included in a sedimentation basin is limited, however, by required clearances and needed cleaning facilities.

22-6. Size-Weight Composition and Removal. As a factor in sedimentation, the size-weight composition of a suspension can be expressed in terms of the frequency distribution of the settling velocities of the particles (Figure 22-4). This frequency distribution is obtained by measuring the concentration of particles before and during quiescent settling in a tall, ordinarily cylindrical, tube from which samples can be withdrawn at different intervals of time and preferably from more than one depth. Concentration is measured in terms of a critical property of the suspension such as its color, turbidity, weight, and volume, or its content of alumina or iron. Settling velocity is

[5] Allen Hazen, "On Sedimentation," *Trans., Am. Soc. Civil Engrs., 53*, 63 (1904).

given by the quotient of the depth of the sampling point to the time elapsing from the beginning of the test.

A cumulative frequency distribution of settling velocities is sketched in Figure 22-4 (after Camp [6]). In horizontal-flow tanks, that propor-

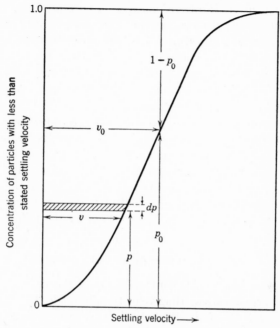

Figure 22-4. Cumulative frequency distribution of the settling velocities of particles in a suspension of discrete particles. *After Camp.*

tion $(1 - p_0)$ of particles with settling velocities $v_s \gtreqqless v_0$ is removed in its entirety. Of the remainder $\int_0^{p_0} (v_s/v_0) \, dp$ reaches the bottom, and the over-all removal p becomes

$$p = (1 - p_0) + (1/v_0) \int_0^{p_0} v_s \, dp \qquad 22\text{-}16$$

In vertical-flow tanks, the over-all removal is $p = 1 - p_0$, unless there is clumping of particles.

Since the make-up of suspensions varies widely, Equation 22-16 is best evaluated for each suspension by measuring the area to the left

[6] T. R. Camp, "Sedimentation and the Design of Settling Tanks," *Trans., Am. Soc. Civil Engrs., 111,* 895 (1946).

of the summation curve below p_0. For an analysis of the frequency distribution, the methods outlined in Chapter 4 apply.

22-7. Reduction in Basin Efficiency by Currents. The efficiency of settling basins is reduced (1) by eddy currents which are set up by the inertia of the incoming fluid; (2) by wind-induced currents when basins are not covered; (3) by convection currents that are thermal in origin; and (4) by density currents that cause cold or heavy water to underrun a basin and warm or light water to flow across its surface. All of these currents may contribute to short-circuiting of the flow.

In accordance with Hazen's theory of sedimentation,[5] allowance can be made for the departure of a basin from the ideal by assuming that the suspended matter is redistributed uniformly, both horizontally and vertically, within successive hypothetical subdivisions, or cells, of the basin that are placed across the tank at right angles to the direction of flow. The greater the number of these cells, the better is the suppression or damping of turbulence and related factors that retard settling. Redistribution is confined to one cell at a time, and the horizontal dispersion of suspended matter is correspondingly reduced.

This concept of damping can be expressed by the following general relationship:

$$dy/dt = F(y_0 - y) \qquad 22\text{-}17$$

where $F = 1/[t_0 + (1/n)t]$ is a function (1) of the time $t_0 = h_0/v_0$ required for a particle with settling velocity v_0 to settle through the depth of the basin and (2) of the theoretical displacement time $t = C/Q = Ah_0/Q$, and $(y_0 - y)$ is the amount of suspended matter of settling velocity v_0 remaining at time t. The coefficient n measures the number of hypothetical damping cells or the degree to which interfering currents are suppressed. It ranges in magnitude from unity for a poor basin to infinity as a theoretical maximum. The reciprocal of n conversely is a measure of the turbulence and resulting short-circuits. It has a lower limit of zero, and there is no upper limit. In a sense, therefore, $1/n$ provides a wider concept of basin performance than does n. Integrating Equation 22-17 and solving for y/y_0,

$$\int_0^y \frac{dy}{y_0 - y} = \int_0^t \frac{dt}{t_0 + (1/n)t}$$

and

$$\frac{y}{y_0} = 1 - \left(1 + \frac{1}{n}\frac{t}{t_0}\right)^{-n} \qquad 22\text{-}18$$

or, since

$$t/t_0 = v_0/(Q/A)$$

$$\frac{y}{y_0} = 1 - \left(1 + \frac{1}{n}\frac{v_0}{Q/A}\right)^{-n}$$

22-19

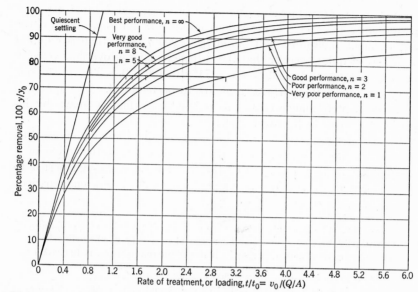

Figure 22-5. Performance curves for settling basins of varying effectiveness. *After Hazen.*

Settling curves tracing these equations for values of $n = 1, 2, 3, 5$, and 8, and [7] for $n = \infty$ are shown in Figure 22-5. The maximum removal associated with a value of $v_0/(Q/A)$ or t/t_0 equal to unity is seen to be but 63%, instead of the 100% expected for perfect quiescence.

[7] For $n = \infty$, $y/y_0 = 1 - e^{-t/t_0} = 1 - e^{-v_0/(Q/A)}$.

A physical concept of the differential form of Equation 22-18 may be gained by equating the amount of settleable matter dy removed at time t to the product of (1) the volume of water cleared of settleable matter in time dt, namely $v_0\,dt$, per unit area of basin, and (2) the concentration of the settleable matter in the water at time t. This concentration equals the amount of residual settleable matter $(y_0 - y)$ divided by the volume C' of water still containing settleable matter. Based on a unit area of basin, this volume may possess one of four generalized magnitudes:

1. When the basin is operated on a fill-and-draw basis and is absolutely quiescent, $C' = h_0 - v_0 t$, where h_0 is the volume of the basin and $v_0 t$ is the volume of water that has been clarified up to time t. Hence $dy = v_0\,dt\,(y_0 - y)/(h_0 - v_0 t)$ or $dy = dt\,(y_0 - y)/(t_0 - t)$, because $h_0/v_0 = t_0$.

2. When, in the same circumstances, mixing currents carry the residual, settleable matter into some of the clarified water and leave but $1/n'$ of this water clear, $dy = dt\,(y_0 - y)/[t_0 - (1/n')t]$.

3. When the basin is operated on a continuous basis and currents distribute the

For 75% removal of particles with given settling velocity, the values of t/t_0 and $v_0/(Q/A)$ are seen to equal 1.4 for best possible performance ($n = \infty$), 1.5 for very good performance ($n = 8$), 1.7 for good performance ($n = 4$), 2.0 for poor performance ($n = 2$), and 3.0 for very poor performance ($n = 1$). These values imply that for 75% removal the displacement time must be from 40% to 200% more than is required with perfect quiescence, or that the surface loading or overflow velocity must be reduced to from $100/1.4 = 71\%$ to $100/3.0 = 33\%$ of the settling velocity of the particles that are to be removed. The approach of Hazen's performance curves to quiescent settling is shown by inclusion of a straight line for the latter.

From a mathematical analysis of longitudinal mixing in settling tanks, Thomas and Archibald [8] have suggested that the value of n is approximated by the ratio of the mean flowing-through period to the difference between the mean and modal flowing-through periods (see Section 22-8).

Example 22-2. Find the settling velocity and size of particles of specific gravity 1.001 of which 80% are expected to be removed in a very good settling basin at an overflow rate of 1,000 gpd per sq ft, if the water temperature is 10 C (50 F).

1. $Q/A = 1,000 \times 1.547 \times 10^{-6} \times 30.48 = 4.72 \times 10^{-2}$ cm/sec.
2. From Figure 22-5, $v_0/(Q/A) = 1.8$ for $n = 8$ and $y/y_0 = 80\%$. Hence $v_0 = 1.8 \times 4.72 \times 10^{-2} = 8.5 \times 10^{-2}$ cm/sec.
3. For use of Figure 22-2, the velocity term is computed as

$$v/ [g(s_s - 1)\nu]^{1/3} = (8.5 \times 10^{-2})/(981 \times 10^{-3} \times 1.31 \times 10^{-2})^{1/3} = 3.6 \times 10^{-1}$$

for a kinematic viscosity of 1.308×10^{-2} stokes. The diameter term is then found to be $d \left[g \dfrac{(s_s - 1)}{\nu^2} \right]^{1/3} = 2.7$, whence $d = 2.7[(1.31 \times 10^{-2})/(981 \times 10^{-3})]^{1/3} = 0.15$ cm.

22-8. Short-Circuiting and Basin Stability.

In an ideal basin, displacement is steady and uniform, and each unit volume of fluid is detained for a time $t = C/Q$. In actual operation, on the other hand, straying currents cause some of the inflow to reach the outlet in less

residual settleable solids to the water in the basin and therefore also to the water that has moved through it in time t, $C' = h_0 + v_0 t$ and $dy = dt (y_0 - y)/(t_0 - t)$.

4. When, in the same circumstances, mixing currents carry the residual settleable solids into but $1/n$ of the water that has moved through the basin in time t, $C' = h_0 + (1/n)v_0 t$ and $dy = dt (y_0 - y)/[t_0 + (1/n)t]$. By letting n' represent negative values of n, the single continuous equation $dy/dt = (y_0 - y)/[t_0 + (1/n)t]$ is obtained (Equation 22-17). Integrated, it takes the form of Equation 22-18.

[8] H. A. Thomas and R. S. Archibald, "Longitudinal Mixing Measured by Radioactive Tracers," *Trans., Am. Soc. Civil Engrs.*, *117*, 839 (1952).

than the theoretical detention period and some to take much longer. The degree of short-circuiting and extent of retardation can be measured by adding a dye, electrolyte, or other tracer substance to the basin influent and observing the time required for the substance to reach the outlet. After the first measurable amount of tracer substance has arrived, its concentration in the effluent rises, as shown in Figure 22-6, until a maximum is reached. Then the concentration

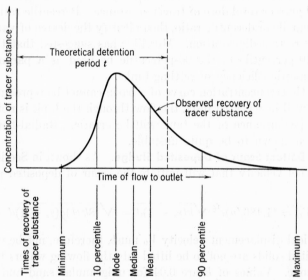

Figure 22-6. Dead spaces and short-circuiting in a settling basin as reflected by the concentration and time of recovery of tracer substances.

drops off, usually more slowly than it has risen. In accordance with the principles of Chapter 4, modal, median, and mean flowing-through periods characterize the central tendency of the time-concentration distribution. Relating the observed times to the theoretical detention period t permits making comparisons between different basins.

If a tank contains spaces in which the flow rotates upon itself, these spaces receive no suspended solids and can do no work. Hence, they reduce the effective capacity of the basin and the flowing-through times relative to the theoretical detention period. In the absence of such currents, the ratio of the mean time to t must equal unity. In the absence of short-circuiting, the mean, median, and mode must coincide. Short-circuiting is characterized, therefore, by the ratio of the mode or median to the mean being less than unity or by the ratio of the difference between the mode and mean, or the median and mean, to the mean being large.[9]

If there is some interchange of flow between the ineffective spaces and the active portions of the tank, the time-concentration curve becomes unduly elongated as small amounts of tracer material are released to the moving water for capture in the effluent. The proportion of tracer substance that arrives at the outlet in a given time is measured by the ratio of the area under the curve up to the given time to the total area or total dose of tracer substance. Percentile ratios, such as the quartile or decentile ratio, then identify the degree of variability of exposure to sedimentation. Morrill[10] has suggested that the ratio of the 10-percentile to the 90-percentile be used as a parameter of the volumetric efficiency of settling tanks.

If the time-concentration curve of a basin cannot be reproduced reasonably well in repeated tests, the flow through the tank is not stable, and the performance of the tank will be erratic. Radial-flow tanks have been shown to be quite unstable.

22-9. Bottom Scour of Deposited Sludge. As shown in Section 15-2, the channel velocity that will initiate the scour of deposited particles is

$$V_0 = (1.486/n)r^{1/6} \sqrt{k(s_s - 1)d} = \sqrt{(8k/f)g(s_s - 1)d} \qquad 15\text{-}5, 6$$

The critical displacement velocity V_0 must, therefore, not be exceeded if deposited solids are not to be lifted into the flowing waters from the sludge zone. Values of k are 0.04 for unigranular sand and 0.06 or more for non-uniform (interlocking) sticky materials. If scouring velocities are to be avoided, the ratio of length to depth of basin, or of surface area A, to cross-sectional area a, must be kept below a value of

$$l_0/h_0 = A/a = (V_0/v_0)(t/t_0) = (t/t_0)\sqrt{(6k/f)C_D} \qquad 22\text{-}20$$

where t/t_0 equals unity for an ideal basin.

Example 22-3. Find (a) the velocity at which coal dust ($s_s = 1.5$) 10^{-2} cm in diameter can be removed from the wash water of a colliery without danger of resuspension by scour, and (b) the limiting length/depth ratio of the basin in which this removal can be effected.

a. Assuming $k = 0.04$ and $f = 0.03$ in Equation 15-6,

---

[9] Parenthetically, the ratio of the difference between the mode and mean to the mean is the product of the coefficient of variation and the coefficient of skewness of the time-frequency distribution.

[10] Arthur B. Morrill, "Sedimentation Basin Research and Design," *J., Am. Water Works Assoc., 24,* 1442 (1932).

$$V_0 = \sqrt{\frac{8 \times 4 \times 10^{-2}}{3 \times 10^{-2}}} \, 981 \times 0.5 \times 10^{-2} = 7.2 \text{ cm/sec} = 0.24 \text{ fps}$$

b. By Stokes's law, Equation 22-8, $v_0 = 2.1 \times 10^{-1}$ cm/sec for $s_s = 1.5$ and 10 C (50 F). Hence $l_0/h_0 = (7.2/0.21)(t/t_0) = 34.2 t/t_0 = 34.2$ for an ideal basin ($t/t_0 = 1$). For a poor basin, ($t/t_0 = 2.0$ for 75% removal), l_0/h_0 or $A/a = 68$.

Settling and Skimming Tanks

22-10. Elements of Tank Design. Each of the four functional zones of sedimentation basins or flotation tanks—(1) the inlet zone, (2) the settling or rising zone, (3) the sludge or scum zone, and (4) the outlet zone—presents special problems of hydraulic and process design that depend upon those properties of the suspended matter which govern its behavior, within the tank, during removal, and after deposition as sludge or scum.

The size, density, and flocculating properties of the suspended solids, together with their tendency to entrain water, as we have seen, determine the geometry of the settling or rising zone. Their concentration by volume and length of storage establish the dimensions of the sludge or scum zone. However, the design of both the settling and sludge or scum zone must also take account of the possible putrescence of liquid and sludge. Otherwise, the liquid may become septic during treatment, and gas-lifted sludge may damage the quality of the effluent or form unsightly scum that is removed with difficulty from the tank surface.

Where sludge volumes are large or where putrefaction of sludge in contact with the flowing water is to be avoided, sludge removal must become a more or less continuous operation. On a volume basis, use of mechanical sludge-removal devices is estimated to become economical when the volume of settleable matter (including entrained water) is more than 0.1% of the volume of the flowing liquid.[11] The devices used for this purpose influence tank design as well as operation. Thermal convection currents and wind-induced motion are prevented by housing or covering the tanks. Choice of tank number is governed by desired flexibility of operation and economy of design.

Use of flocculating or flotation agents may add as many as three ancillary functions to settling or flotation: (1) rapid distribution of the agent throughout the water to be treated; (2) provision of reaction time or time for floc growth to take place; and (3) return of floc to the influent for the purpose of promoting flocculation. These func-

[11] J. R. Baylis, "Recent Developments in Water Treatment and Filtration," *Water Works, 67*, 38 (1928).

tions are best accomplished in separate units designed for each particular purpose (Section 23-4). They are sometimes made part of the joint performance of the settling basin, especially in water-treatment works. Large, open basins, constructed by diking off a low-lying area or by cut-and-fill methods, for example, make refinement in design unnecessary and permit throwing the responsibility for ancillary as well as key functions on the basin itself. Such basins are cleaned but rarely.

22-11. General Dimensions. Horizontal-flow tanks and vertical-flow tanks have been constructed in great variety. Thumbnail sketches

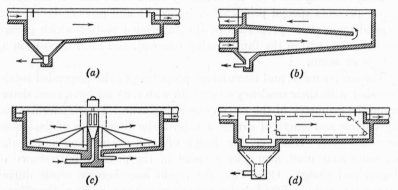

(a)   (b)

(c)   (d)

Figure 22-7. Representative designs of horizontal-flow settling tanks. (a) Rectangular tank with longitudinal flow. Tank is thrown out of operation for cleaning. Sludge is flushed to sump for removal from the dewatered tank. (b) Rectangular tank with longitudinal flow and single tray. (c) Circular tank with radial flow. Sludge is scraped to central sump and withdrawn during operation. The rotary mechanism carries plows. (d) Rectangular tank with longitudinal flow. Sludge is scraped to influent end and thence to sump to be withdrawn during operation. In some designs the sludge is collected at the effluent end.

of representative designs are shown in Figures 22-7 and 22-8. Circular, square, or rectangular in plan, they vary in depth from 7 to 15 ft, 10 ft being an average value. Circular tanks are as large as 200 ft in diameter with a 100-ft maximum commonly preferred. Square tanks are generally smaller, a side length of 70 ft being common. Rectangular tanks have reached lengths of almost 300 ft, but 100 ft is common. The width of mechanically cleaned, rectangular tanks is dictated by the available length of wooden scrapers. This is 16 ft, but scrapers can be arranged in parallel. A width of 30 ft is common. The diameter of circular tanks is governed by the structural requirements of the trusses that carry the scraping mechanisms. Unless it is broken up into steep hoppers, the bottom of most settling

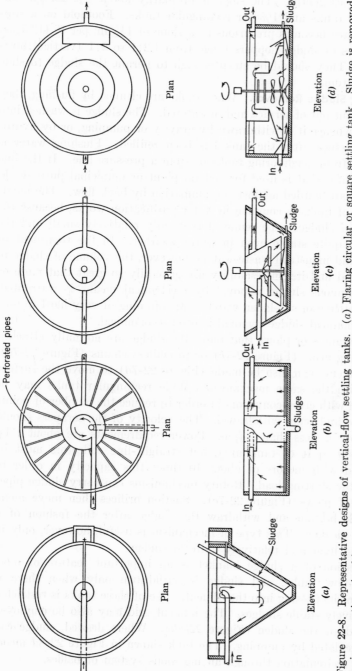

Figure 22-8. Representative designs of vertical-flow settling tanks. (a) Flaring circular or square settling tank. Sludge is removed during operation; in this case hydrostatically. (b) Circular settling tank with central mixing and flocculating chamber. Pipe grid distributes flow and collects sludge. (c) Circular, flaring, settling tank with central mixing and flocculating chamber. *Spaulding Precipitator.* (d) Circular settling tank with central mixing and flocculating chamber, and means for sludge recirculation. *Accelator.*

tanks slopes gently. The slope is ordinarily about 8% for circular or square tanks and 1% for rectangular tanks. Foothold on a slippery surface becomes precarious at a slope of 1½ in. per ft (12.5%). The slopes of sludge hoppers range from 1.2:1 to 2:1 (vertical:horizontal). They should be steep enough to permit the sludge to slide to the bottom.

22-12. Sludge Removal. When tanks are cleaned by flushing, they must be cut out of service and unwatered. The sludge is washed into a sump, whence it is withdrawn by gravity or pumping, or by hydrostatic pressure after the tank has been refilled. Flushing water is obtained from neighboring tanks or from a pressure line. If the line carries water that is used for general plant or municipal purposes, it must be safeguarded against contamination by back-flow. The hand-cleaning of tanks is common in water purification works, because the amount of sludge to be removed is usually relatively small and the sludge is quite stable even in warm weather. In the treatment of sewage and industrial waste-waters, however, the volume of sludge to be handled and its putrescibility are generally so great that more or less continuous sludge removal by mechanical means is warranted. In the settling of silt-laden waters and softening of very hard waters, too, mechanical sludge removal is often economical.

The scrapers or plows that move the sludge are normally attached to rotating arms (Figure 22-7c) or to endless chains (Figure 22-7d). Arrangements can also be made (Figure 22-7d) to move the surface scum with the same mechanism. Wide rectangular tanks may be provided with cross-conveyors in order to reduce the number of points of sludge and scum withdrawal. The velocity of the scrapers should preferably be less than 1 fpm. Power requirements are about 1 hp for 10,000 sq ft of tank area, but straight-line collectors must be furnished with motors of about 10 times this capacity in order to master the starting load. Rotary mechanisms can carry sludge pipes instead of plows (Figure 22-7c). Suction orifices then move along the tank bottom and withdraw the sludge after the fashion of a vacuum cleaner. This type of mechanism is useful, however, only in removing light and relatively uniform sludge.

Formation of a sludge blanket is an important feature of most vertical-flow tanks, and sludge is withdrawn only when there is danger of its passing into the effluent. Use of these tanks is restricted to relatively stable sludges. The influent grid may also be employed to withdraw the sludge (Figure 22-8b). Where desired, sludge can be recirculated by pumping. The tank shown in Figure 22-8d incorporates recirculation through an ingenious system of baffles.

By contrast, full separation of accumulating sludge from flowing sewage is aimed for in two-story tanks (Figure 22-9). The sewage is then kept fresh, and storage space can be provided for the digestion of the accumulating solids. The two chambers are so constructed that rising gas bubbles and sludge particles cannot escape from the sludge hopper into the settling compartment.

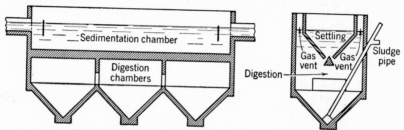

Figure 22-9. Two-storied Imhoff or Emscher tank.

22-13. Inlets. For high efficiency, inlets must distribute flow and suspended matter as uniformly as possible between tanks and within tanks. Hydraulic equality is obtained either by subjecting the dividing flow to equal frictional resistances or by inserting at each point of discharge a controlling loss of head that is large in comparison with the frictional resistances between inlets. The water levels in the different tanks are held the same by outflow regulation. If suspended matter moves along the bottom of the influent conduit, equality of loading is not necessarily insured by these arrangements, and adjustments must then be made by trial. The principles involved in flow regulation, when referred to Figure 22-10, are as follows:

a. The flow originating at I in (a) traverses identical paths before its discharge at A, B, C, and D. Hence inflow at these four points must be equal except when the elevation of the water surface in the two tanks is not the same. Equality will then be restricted to pairs of points in each tank.

b. The flow originating at I in (b) is to be subdivided in such manner that the discharge q_n at any inlet will be held to mq_1, where $m < 1$ and q_1 is the discharge at the first inlet. Considering the inlet an orifice, the discharge head, or head lost, must be

$$h_n = kq_n{}^2 = k(mq_1)^2 = m^2h_1 \qquad 22\text{-}21$$

or, if h_λ is the lost head between points of discharge (1 and n),

$$h_n = h_1 - h_\lambda = m^2h_1$$

and

$$h_1 = h_\lambda/(1 - m^2) \qquad 22\text{-}22$$

The magnitude of h_λ can be estimated from friction losses and changes in velocity. Distribution of flow by the piping shown in Figure 22-8b and in filter underdrains (Section 24-9) can also be secured in this manner.

Example 22-4. In a settling tank, the inlet farthest from the point of supply is to discharge 99% of the flow delivered by the nearest inlet. Find, in terms of the friction head h_λ, the required head loss through the nearest inlet and the associated head loss through the farthest inlet.

1. From Equation 22-22, $h_1 = h_\lambda/[1 - (0.99)^2] = 50.3h_\lambda$.
2. From Equation 22-21, $h_n = (0.99)^2 h_1 = 0.980h_1 = 49.3h_\lambda$.

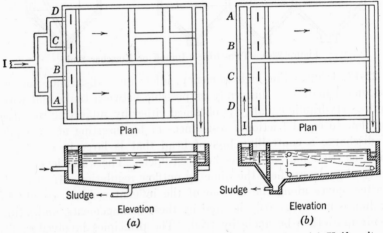

Figure 22-10. Inflow and outflow structures of settling tanks. (a) Uniformity of inflow is secured by equality of resistance. (b) Uniformity of inflow is secured by control of resistance.

Baffle boards in front of inlet openings will destroy the kinetic energy of the incoming water and assist in distributing the flow laterally and vertically over the basin.

Training or dispersion walls perforated by holes or slots (Figure 22-10) operate on the principle demonstrated in Equation 22-22 by introducing a controlling head loss. Frictional resistance in advance of the openings is a function of the velocity head of the eddy currents. Baffles of this kind contribute also to stability of flow. By creating and destroying velocity, however, baffles can quickly build up losses of head for which there is little return in the form of increased basin efficiency.

Velocities in inlet conduits and orifices should be high enough to prevent deposition of solids but sufficiently low to keep fragile floc from being broken up.

Model analysis of inlet structures is often rewarding.

22-14. Outlets. Control of outflow is generally secured by a weir attached to one or both sides of single or multiple outlet troughs. If the weirs in different tanks are placed at the same elevation and discharge freely, the loading of equal basins will be kept within the limits of inflow variation. If the effluent weir is submerged, the degree of submergence will vary along the trough. Draw-off then becomes

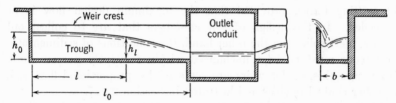

Figure 22-11. Drawdown of water surface in an outlet trough.

unequal and induces short-circuiting, unless a training wall similar to the inlet training wall again introduces a controlling loss of head.

Outlet troughs are lateral spillways. Required dimensions are given by the drawdown curve of the water surface in the trough (Figure 22-11). As shown for wash-water troughs of rapid filters (Section 24-10), the depth of water h_0 at the upstream end of a trough with level invert can be estimated from Equation 24-42. If friction is neglected,

$$h_0 = \sqrt{h_l^2 + \frac{nq^2 l^2}{gb^2 h_l}}$$ 24-42

Here h_l is the depth of water at a distance l from the upstream end, $n = 1$ when one side weir receives the flow and $n = 2$ when there are two weirs, q is the discharge per unit length of weir, g is the gravity constant, and b is the width of the trough. For long troughs an allowance for friction must be made.

Weir length relative to surface area determines the strength of outlet current. A unit length of weir at the end of a rectangular tank serves an area equal to the length of the tank—100 sq ft in a 100-ft tank, for example. In a circular tank, the area served by a unit length of peripheral weir equals $\frac{1}{4}$ the tank diameter—25 sq ft in a tank 100 ft in diameter, for example. Multiplying these values by the surface loading of the tank gives the rate of weir discharge. Experience shows that this should be held below 50,000 gpd per ft if surges are to be avoided. When weirs are very long in relation to flow, it may be difficult to secure uniform discharge over their entire length unless a saw-toothed edge breaks up the weir into triangular notches with jets of adequate thickness.

In sewage treatment, a scum board, or shallow baffle plate, placed in front of the outlet weir, will hold back floating solids, grease, and oil.

Variations in flow are ordinarily of little concern in the operation of settling tanks, provided that the maximum design flow is not exceeded. In the design of grit chambers that are to collect only heavy, inert solids, on the other hand, the conditions of sedimentation and scour must be kept unchanged within relatively narrow limits. To assure this, outlet weirs are replaced by proportional-flow weirs or other control devices as illustrated in Section 22-17.

22-15. Common Tank Loadings and Detention Periods.   Except when tanks receive suspensions that are composed of discretely settling particles of known size and density, an experimental settling-velocity analysis will furnish the only reliable information on which to base tank design. Certain general values, supported by operating experience, will indicate the order of magnitude of permissible tank loadings.

Sand, silt, and clay have a specific gravity of about 2.65. The grain-size range of particles of this kind ordinarily subjected to plain sedimentation extends upward from 10^{-3} cm and creates settling velocities at 10 C as low as 6.9×10^{-3} cm/sec [12] corresponding to a maximum surface loading as low as $21,200 \times 6.9 \times 10^{-3} = 146$ gpd per sq ft of tank surface [13] and a minimum detention period as high as $8.47 \times 10^{-2}/6.9 \times 10^{-3} = 12.3$ hr in a 10-ft basin.

Alum and iron flocs possess specific gravities as low as 1.002 due to adsorbed and entrained water, but they may be as large as 0.1 cm in diameter. Their settling velocities at 10 C are then about 8.3×10^{-2} cm/sec, corresponding to a maximum surface loading of 1,760 gpd per sq ft and a minimum detention period of 1.02 hr in a tank 10 ft deep. Similar values are associated with the precipitation of calcium, the crystals of calcite and adsorbed water being about 10^{-2} cm in

---

[12] 1 cm/sec = 21,200 gpd per sq ft, and surface loading varies directly with velocity.

[13] 1 cm/sec = 8.47×10^{-3} hr of detention per ft of basin depth, and the detention period varies directly with depth and inversely with velocity.

diameter and possessing a specific gravity close to 1.2. In practice, smaller surface loadings ($<$ 900 gpd per sq ft) and longer detention periods ($>$ 2 hr) are employed.

Sewage solids, excepting grit, vary in specific gravity from less than 1.0 to about 1.2 on a dry basis. They may be several centimeters in diameter, and their wet specific gravity is about 1.001. If their size is 10^{-1} cm, they will have a settling velocity of about 4.2×10^{-2} cm/sec and will be removed, at 100% efficiency, in a tank loaded to a maximum of 890 gpd per sq ft and affording a minimum detention period of 2.0 hr in a 10-ft tank.

In general, therefore, coagulated and lime-softened water, as well as sewage that is to be subjected to plain sedimentation or coagulation in primary tanks, should be given a detention period of about 2 hr, corresponding in a 10-ft tank to a surface loading of 900 gpd per sq ft. Tank space assigned to the sludge zone is additional.

Activated sludge is so bulky that settling is generally hindered, the free settling velocity of particles 10^{-1} cm in diameter with a specific gravity of 1.005 being reduced from 2×10^{-1} cm/sec to about 10^{-1} cm/sec. Under ideal conditions, the surface loading of secondary settling tanks treating activated sludge may, therefore, be as high as 2,000 gpd per sq ft, and the detention period as low as 8.47×10^{-1} hr or 50 min in a tank 10 ft deep. In practice, a loading value of 1,200 gpd per sq ft makes allowance for poorly settling sludge.

Departure from the ideal either decreases the permissible loadings and increases the requisite detention periods, or it decreases tank efficiencies. Hazen's theory of sedimentation will give some clue to attainable or required values. Basin capacities must be increased if the reaction times for coagulation and precipitation are to be included with the detention period needed for settling, but the use of vertical-flow tanks that promote floc growth by sludge-blanket formation may more than offset the time required for the precipitating or flocculating reaction. Loadings of about 1,500 gpd per sq ft may be attained in the coagulation or softening of water.

In sewage treatment, smaller capacities than normal are employed when removal of coarse solids alone meets the needs of the situation; e.g., when effluent is discharged into a receiving water of large capacity, or when sewage is settled in advance of chemical precipitation or activated-sludge treatment. Capacities larger than normal are provided when stress is laid on removal of BOD as well as suspended solids (Figure 22-12), when the settling tanks serve as buffers against surges of sewage and industrial wastes (especially toxic wastes), and when abnormally large amounts of combined sewage are to receive some treatment in the settling units.

22-16. Tank Performance. Most settling basins that are incorporated in water-purification works are preceded by or include coagulation or chemical precipitation processes. Interest then centers on the removal of substances, such as color, turbidity, hardness, and iron. The performance of settling tanks is allied, therefore, to the performance of the preparatory processes. It is not generally a unique measure of settling efficiency. Only when turbid river waters are subjected to

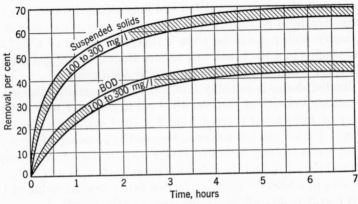

Figure 22-12. Removal of suspended solids and biochemical oxygen demand from sewage by plain sedimentation in primary tanks.

plain sedimentation is it common practice to report the percentage removal of the suspended solids. The weight of suspended matter in turbid river waters is often measured in thousands of milligrams per liter. Recorded efficiencies vary widely for different rivers and different stretches of the same river. As little as 30% and as much as 75% of the suspended matter may settle out in 1 hr, and as little as 50% and as much as 90% in 2 hr. That long periods of settling may be required when the silt is fine has already been indicated in Section 22-15.

By contrast, the settling tanks of sewage-treatment works are generally devoted to plain sedimentation by itself. Performance is usually related to the removal of suspended solids and biochemical oxygen demand. Typical settling curves for primary tanks are shown in Figure 22-12.

22-17. Grit Chambers. Grit chambers are included in sewerage systems when combined sewage, industrial wastes, or illicit storm drainage transport significant quantities of sand or other heavy or otherwise inert matter in suspension. Removal of these substances in advance of pumps and treatment units prevents wear of machinery and unwanted accumulation of grit in settling tanks. It also facilitates the handling of the sludge produced by the various treatment processes. Grit chambers may be installed, too, in advance of inverted siphons.

Removal of suspended matter in grit chambers is desirably confined to the inert components, because the exclusion of decomposable solids simplifies the problem of grit disposal. Purposeful inclusion of organic matter with the grit converts grit chambers into *detritus tanks*. As shown in Section 22-18, the organic matter may subsequently be separated from the grit and returned to the flowing sewage.

Grit chambers are generally constructed as fairly shallow and elongated channels that capture particles of specific gravity 2.65 and 2×10^{-2} cm in diameter. Depth of flow is normally governed by the size of the outfall sewer. Except for the space assigned to grit storage, the invert of the chamber is made continuous with that of the outfall sewer.

The problem of selective deposition of heavy inert particles is complicated by fluctuations in rate of flow, especially those that accompany storm rainfalls. Aside from subdividing the grit chamber into several compartments that can be shunted in and out in succession, a solution is sought by combining (1) opportunity for sedimentation of wanted particles with (2) scour or resuspension of unwanted particles. In accordance with the principles discussed in the first part of this chapter, this implies (1) provision of adequate surface area and (2) maintenance of adequate displacement velocity. Fluctuations in flow require, ideally, that both (1) a constant value of Q/A and (2) a constant displacement velocity V be maintained in the chamber. Ordinarily a compromise solution is offered in order to keep the required structure simple. The cross-section of the chamber at right angles to the direction of flow is made uniform throughout its length, and its shape is so chosen that the displacement velocity is held substantially constant at all depths of flow. To this purpose, a flow control device, such as a proportional-flow weir, a vertical throat, or a standing-wave flume, may be placed at the end of the chamber. The area of the water surface at maximum flow is then made large enough to insure deposition of wanted large and heavy particles, the selective movement and resuspension of smaller and lighter particles which will settle as flow is reduced being cared for by the constant scouring action of the flowing water.

Two outlet control devices are shown in Figure 22-13: (1) a proportional-flow weir and (2) an adjustable throat. A standing-wave flume attached to the grit chamber can serve both as a control and measuring device. The discharge Q through devices such as these is a simple

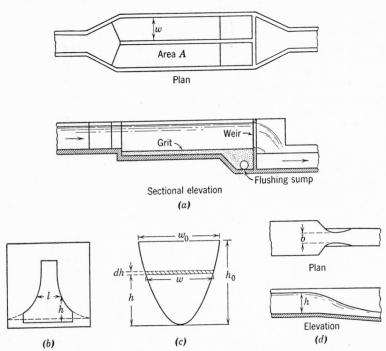

Figure 22-13. Grit chamber and outlet control devices. (a) Twin-compartment grit chamber with weir control. (b) Proportional-flow weir plate. Narrowing opening at base is replaced by rectangular notch. $Q = kh$ because sides of opening are curved to make $lh^{1/2}$ constant. (c) Hypothetical cross-section of channel controlled by throat. Cross-sectional area $a = \int_0^h w\, dh$. (d) Outlet throat. $Q = kbh^{3/2}$.

function of channel depth or head, $Q = kh^n$, where k and n are constants. To have these control devices produce a constant displacement velocity in the chamber, therefore, the width w of the chamber, as shown in Figure 22-13, must be so chosen that $Q = kh^n = V\int_0^h w\, dh$. As shown by Camp,[14] this condition is satisfied when

$$w = nkh^{n-1}/V \qquad\qquad 22\text{-}23$$

[14] T. R. Camp, "Grit Chamber Design," *Sewage Works J., 14,* 368 (1942).

If flow is controlled by a proportional-flow weir, for example, $Q = kh$ or $n = 1$. Then $w = k/V$ = constant, and the channel must be rectangular. If flow is controlled by a throat, $Q = kbh^{3/2}$, or $n = 3/2$, and $w = 3/2(kbh^{1/2}/V) = 3/2(Q/hV)$. This is the equation of a parabola, and the channel must be parabolic in cross-section or approach a parabola sufficiently closely.

Example 22-5. Two grit chambers, controlled by outlet throats 3 in. wide, are to remove particles of specific gravity $s_s = 2.65$ and diameter $d = 2 \times 10^{-2}$ cm from combined sewage. The maximum rate of flow Q_{max} is 15 cfs; the minimum rate of flow Q_{min} is 3 cfs. Find the settling velocity v at 10 C, the displacement velocity V, maximum and minimum depths of flow, h_{max} and h_{min} respectively, the maximum and minimum width of channel, w_{max} and w_{min} respectively, and the maximum and minimum required length of channel l_{max} and l_{min} respectively.

1. From Figure 22-2 for $d = 2 \times 10^{-2}$ cm, $v_s = 2.1$ cm/sec = 0.0689 fps.
2. From Equation 15-6, assuming $k = 0.06$ and $f = 0.03$,

$$V = \sqrt{(8 \times 0.06/0.03) \times 32.2 \times 1.65 \times (2 \times 10^{-2}/30.48)} = 0.75 \text{ fps}$$

3. For a discharge of $Q = kbh^{3/2}$, where $b = 0.25$ ft and k approximates 3.5,

$$h = \left(\frac{Q}{3.5 \times 0.25}\right)^{3/5}$$

and

$$h_{max} = \left(\frac{7.5}{3.5 \times 0.25}\right)^{3/5} = 4.18 \text{ ft} \quad \text{or} \quad h_{min} = \left(\frac{1.5}{3.5 \times 0.25}\right)^{3/5} = 1.43 \text{ ft}$$

4. From Equation 22-23, $w = 3/2\, kbh^{1/2}/V = 3/2\,(Q/hV)$,

$w_{max} = \frac{3}{2}\, 7.5/(4.18 \times 0.75) = 3.59$ ft $\quad$ and $\quad w_{min} = \frac{3}{2}\, 1.5/(1.43 \times 0.75) = 2.10$ ft

5. From Equation 22-15, $y/y_0 = v_s/(Q/A)$, and for 100% removal $Q/A = v_s$, or

$$hwV/(lw) = v_s \quad \text{and} \quad l = h(V/v_s)$$

Hence $l_{max} = 4.18(0.75/0.069) = 45.5$ ft, and $l_{min} = 1.43(0.75/0.069) = 15.5$ ft. The settling zone must, therefore, be given a length of 45.5 ft. If in accordance with Figure 22-5, the chamber can be classified only as a good basin, its over-all length, to insure 75% removal of the wanted particles, should be made 1.7 times as long, or 77.4 ft.

The amount of grit that is collected in grit chambers varies from 1 to 12 (average 4) cu ft per million gallons treated and depends upon the topography, surface cover, type of roadway and sidewalk, size of intercepter, and intensity of storm rainfall on the area sewered. Daily maxima of 10 to 30 cu ft per mg and as high as 80 cu ft per mg have been reported. Grit storage is generally provided by lowering the invert of the chamber 6 to 18 in. below that of the inlet and outlet channels. In small plants, the accumulated solids are removed from the unwatered channels by hand or by flushing the grit onto a disposal area. In large plants, some type of mechanical grit conveyor is generally employed to remove grit without draining the compartment to be cleaned.

22-18. Detritus Tanks. Short-period sedimentation in a tank that operates at substantially constant level produces a mixture of grit and organic solids, called detritus. The light organic solids can be washed out of the mixture before, during, or after removal from the tank in one of the following ways:

1. Compressed air is blown through the deposited detritus from time to time and resuspends the light solids.
2. The removed detritus is washed in a grit washer, the wash water being returned to the effluent from the detritus tank. A sand washer such as that shown in Figure 24-5 can be used for this purpose.
3. A scraper delivers the detritus to a conveyor that moves the solids through and out of the water in such a way that the organic solids are flushed back into the flowing sewage. The scrapers are like those illustrated in Figure 22-7. Some conveyors are patterned after classifying machinery used in the mining industry for the separation of ores.

22-19. Skimming Tanks. These tanks are commonly designed as long, trough-shaped structures. Surface area, in accordance with the principles of sedimentation and flotation, is a governing factor. Detention periods are short and seldom exceed 3 min. In the tank shown in Figure 22-14, provision is made to blow air into the sewage from

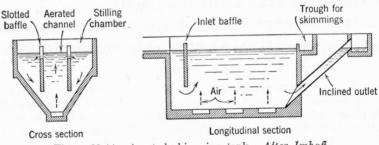

Figure 22-14. Aerated skimming tank. *After Imhoff.*

diffusers situated in the bottom. This keeps heavy solids from settling and captures light solids in the surface froth. Vertical baffle walls separate the tanks into a central aerated channel and two lateral stilling chambers in which oil and grease gather at the surface. The baffles are slotted near the flowline to provide entrance into the stilling compartments. Settleable matter slides back into the central channel which moves it forward and eventually delivers it to the inclined outlet from the tank. The outlet velocity is sufficient to resuspend the solids. Oil and grease are drawn off from time to time into a channel that leads to a separator. Air requirements are small, about 0.03 cu ft per gallon of sewage. Induced flotation is discussed in Section 22-1. The mechanisms that remove sludge from settling tanks can be arranged to serve also as scum collectors (Figure 22-7d). Unless some advantage is to be secured from the aeration of the sewage that takes place in an aerated skimming tank, or unless the unsightliness of the scum is objectionable, separate skimming tanks may be omitted where the settling tanks can be provided with scum-removal mechanisms.

The grease removed from tanks that include domestic or municipal sewage is generally too polluted to be of commercial value. If it includes much mineral oil, it is best buried or burned together with rakings and screenings. If grease predominates, the skimmings can be added to sludge that is to be digested anaerobically to produce gas of high fuel value (Section 26-6). The volume of skimmings from municipal sewage is estimated at 0.1 to 6.0 cu ft per mg, or 0.003 to 0.2 cu ft per capita per year. Some industrial wastes, wool-scouring wastes for example, contain much grease which can be recovered for sale.

Grease traps, intercepters, or separators are employed in some industries and in connection with many large kitchens. They are designed as small skimming tanks with submerged inlet and bottom outlet. Gasoline and other light oils originating in garages, dry-cleaning establishments, and related industries should not be admitted to sewerage systems because they create fire and explosion hazards. Oil separators can be provided to capture them (see Figure 14-10).

23 ——— CHEMICAL COAGULATION, PRECIPITATION, ION EXCHANGE, AND STABILIZATION

23-1. General Considerations. The unit operations of chemical coagulation, precipitation, ion exchange, and stabilization have been outlined in Section 21-19. All of them produce changes in the chemical quality of the water or waste water treated. Some of them are aimed at the removal of suspended and colloidal substances; others at the removal of dissolved substances; yet others at the conversion of dissolved substances from an objectionable to an unobjectionable form. Some chemicals, finally, may be added for their own sake.

Not all the chemical processes that are useful in the treatment of water and waste water will be discussed in this chapter. Some find a better place in other chapters of this book. To these suitable reference will be made. Conversely, there are certain non-chemical phenomena and processes, a consideration of which fits conveniently into this chapter. These will, therefore, be discussed here.

Some of the processes to be considered are not ends in themselves, but ancillary to other treatment methods. For this reason, they are often called preparatory processes. Coagulation, for example, prepares water or waste water for sedimentation. Precipitation, too, must be followed by sedimentation and sometimes also by coagulation and filtration. Ion exchange, on the other hand, usually is a complete process. That it requires regeneration of the exchange medium brings it into somewhat the same category as those treatment methods in which the substance removed must be subjected to further handling and often also to further treatment. These statements merely confirm the fact that the treatment of water and waste water is, more often than not, a synthesis of a number of different operations. Individual operations are selected because they affect particular attributes of the water or waste water. The process design of water and waste-water treatment works must weld the individual operations into an harmonious whole.

Most of the many chemicals that may find application in the treatment of water and waste water are listed in Table A-5 in the Appendix of this book together with their trade names, availability, methods of shipping and handling, storage requirements, solubility, commercial strength, and purpose of use.

23-2. Chemical Coagulation. The principal function of *chemical coagulation* is the destabilization, aggregation, and binding together of colloids. In water- and waste-water-works practice, chemical coagulation involves the formation of chemical flocs that adsorb, entrap, or otherwise bring together suspended matter; more particularly, suspended matter that is so finely divided as to be colloidal. The unique properties of colloids have been discussed in Sections 18-2 and 18-19. Use of the term *destabilization* applies accordingly. Chemical coagulation is commonly accomplished by the addition of one of the following floc-forming substances: filter alum, or aluminum sulfate, $Al_2(SO_4)_3 \cdot 18H_2O$; copperas, or ferrous sulfate, $FeSO_4 \cdot 7H_2O$; ferric sulfate, $Fe_2(SO_4)_3$; ferric chloride, $FeCl_3$; and chlorinated copperas, a mixture of ferric sulfate and ferric chloride.

a. Theories of Coagulation. The process of chemical coagulation involves complex equilibria among a number of variables including the colloids or dispersed matter, the water or dispersion medium, and the coagulating chemical, or collecting medium. The driving forces include (1) a lowering of the zeta-potential of the colloid and (2) a neutralization of charge by oppositely charged hydrous oxide colloids formed by reactions of the coagulant with ions in the water. Destabilization of the coagulant colloids, themselves, produces hydrous oxide binder materials or floc matrix.

In the coagulation of water and waste water, attention centers on two principal types of colloids: (1) those present in the water or waste water to be treated and (2) those formed by the added coagulants. The colloids of natural waters are clays and tealike organic color, whereas waste waters include a variety of colloidal proteins and other substances. All of them are primarily negatively charged. By contrast, the colloids produced by coagulants, the hydrous oxides of iron or aluminum, for example, are generally positively charged.

Although the charge on a colloidal particle may be produced by direct ionization of one of its constituents, the charge is believed to be due, in most instances, to the preferential adsorption of ions, usually H^+ or OH^- ions, from the suspending water. Colloids that acquire their charge by ionization of some constituent usually behave like weak acids or bases. Their ionization and, with it, their charge are elevated or depressed by the addition of H^+ or OH^- ions, and "double-layer" ions are formed. Hydrous aluminum and ferric oxide, and indeed many other *sols*, can acquire both positive or negative charges. If the concentration of aluminum or ferric ions is large, the charge becomes positive; but if hydroxyl ion is present in excess, the charge becomes negative. This may be represented as follows for hydrous ferric oxide:

$$(Fe_2O_3 \cdot xH_2O)Fe^{+++} \mid 3OH^- \qquad \text{positive charge}$$

$$(Fe_2O_3 \cdot xH_2O)OH^- \mid H^+ \qquad \text{negative charge}$$

The dotted vertical line indicates the approximate limit of the fixed portion of the double layer. The factor x shows that the oxide is hydrated, but that the extent and nature of hydration are unknown. The fact that one kind of ion is shown on each side of the dotted line implies only that the respective ions predominate. It is the alteration of the type and number of the double-layer ions that reduces the zeta potential below its critical value for colloid stability and brings about coagulation.

The negative charge on a clay particle is probably due to the firm attachment of hydroxyl or other anions from the water and the creation of the solid-phase side of the fixed portion of the double layer. The negative charge attracts positive ions, some of which are held in the liquid-phase side as shown in Figure 18-4. The balance form the diffuse or mobile part of the double layer. If the concentration of electrolyte is increased, cations accumulate on the solution side of the fixed part of the double layer. The charge q and the distance to which it is effective δ are then both reduced. This decreases the zeta potential in accordance with Equation 18-84 and thereby promotes coagulation. As shown in Table 23-1, the coagulating power of ions rises rapidly with their valence. This is known as the Schulze-Hardy rule. For the coagulation of negative and positive sols, Al^{+++} and $SO_4^=$ ions are respectively several hundred times as effective as Na^+ and Cl^- ions, for example.

Freundlich has explained the change in zeta potential and the influence of valence by assuming that the decrease in zeta potential results from adsorption of ions of opposite sign from that of the particle charge. If the reactions are due to adsorption, the ratio of uni-, bi-, and tri-valent ions adsorbed should be 3:1.5:1 for equal

TABLE 23-1.   Coagulating Effect of Various Ions.   *After Glasstone.*

	Ferric oxide (positive) sol			Arsenious sulfide (negative) sol	
Electro-lyte	Anion valence	Minimum Concentra-tion *	Electro-lyte	Cation valence	Minimum concentra-tion *
KCl	1	103	NaCl	1	51
KBr	1	138	KNO$_3$	1	50
KNO$_3$	1	131	K$_2$SO$_4$	1	63
K$_2$CrO$_3$	2	0.325	MgSO$_4$	2	0.81
K$_2$SO$_4$	2	0.219	BaCl$_2$	2	0.69
K$_2$C$_2$O$_4$	2	0.238	ZnCl$_2$	2	0.68
K$_3$Fe(CN)$_6$	3	0.096	AlCl$_3$	3	0.09

* Millimols per liter.

effect.   The amounts adsorbed may be related to concentration by the Freundlich isotherm,

$$y/m = Kc^{1/n} \qquad\qquad 18\text{-}80$$

If all ions are adsorbed to the same extent, the values of K and n must be the same and $Kc_1^{1/n} = 3$, $Kc_2^{1/n} = 1.5$, and $Kc_3^{1/n} = 1$.   Here c_1, c_2, and c_3 are the concentrations necessary to cause a $3:1.5:1$ ratio of adsorption of uni-, bi-, and tri-valent ions.   Assuming a value of $n = 6$, the ratios $c_1:c_2:c_3$ are $729:11.4:1$.   These values are in fair agreement with the ratios of the minimum concentration values recorded in Table 23-1.

According to Langelier [1] and his associates, the rate of coagulation depends on the exchange capacity of the colloids to be removed.   The exchange capacity is a measure of the tendency for replacement of low-valence cations with ones of high valence.   On entering the liquid side of the fixed portion of the double layer, these high-valence ions depress the charge and its effective distance and thus lower the stability of the colloid.   When the exchange capacity is low, the process is slow unless a binding agent is present.   A metal oxide precipitate can serve as such a binding material.   However, since the hydrous oxides form positively charged colloids, which are attracted by and interact with the negative colloids, mutual coagulation is also an important part of the process.   If exchange capacity is high, the need for binder material is less important and coagulation results chiefly from de-

[1] W. F. Langelier, H. F. Ludwig, and R. G. Ludwig, "Flocculation Phenomena in Turbid Water Clarification," *Proc., Am. Soc. of Civil Engrs.,* **78,** Separate No. 118 (1952).

stabilization of colloids originally present in the water. Exchange capacity is due primarily to the presence of particles smaller than 1μ in diameter. The presence of such particles is, therefore, important to destabilization and mutual coagulation. If such particles are not present in the water or waste water to be treated, it may be advisable to add them. Clay, activated silica, and other so-called

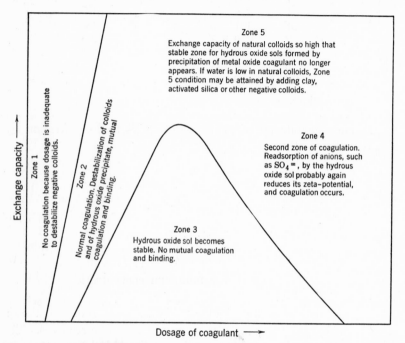

Figure 23-1. Relationships between exchange capacity, coagulant dose, and other coagulation phenomena. *After Langelier, Ludwig, and Ludwig.*

coagulant aids serve this purpose. Particles larger than 1μ in diameter also assist coagulation. They provide nuclei on which floc can grow and they add weight. The probable relationships between exchange capacity and other coagulation reactions are outlined in Figure 23-1.

b. Properties of Common Chemical Coagulants. The compounds of iron and aluminum generally used for removing turbidity, bacteria, color, and other finely divided matter from water and waste water are electrolytes, i.e., substances that ionize in water to produce a solution that will conduct an electric current. They produce cations and anions of high valence and react with alkalinity to form insoluble hydrous oxide precipitates. The cations destabilize the negatively charged colloids, the anions the positively charged hydrous ferric or aluminum oxides. The reactions are sensitive to the pH of the water and to the ion balance. Negatively charged particles, particularly color colloids, coagulate best at low pH values, whereas hydrous oxides are generally least soluble and flocculate best at higher values. Overdosing with electrolytes may reverse the zeta potential and interfere with the coagulation of colloids. However, when very large amounts are applied, the zeta potential may again be driven towards zero. Sulfates of aluminum and sulfates and chlorides of iron are normally employed because they are the cheapest available chemical coagulants.

Aluminum and iron coagulants react in much the same manner. Stated in the simplest terms, the first reaction is one of solution; the second, one of combination with OH^- ions made available by the alkalinity of the water (Equation 20-1). The reactions of alum, for example, are: [2]

$$Al_2(SO_4)_3 \cdot 18H_2O \rightleftarrows 2Al^{+++} + 3SO_4^= + 18H_2O \qquad 23\text{-}1$$

and

$$2Al^{+++} + 6OH^- \rightleftarrows Al_2O_3 \cdot xH_2O \downarrow \qquad 23\text{-}2$$

If the natural alkalinity of the water is inadequate, it must be brought to needed concentration by the addition of substances such as hydrated (slaked) lime, $Ca(OH)_2$, soda ash, Na_2CO_3, or lye, $NaOH$. In practice, more than the amount required for reaction is added in order to leave a residual of unreacted alkalinity in the water. Needed amounts are generally less than those that can be calculated stoichiometrically from reactions such as the following:

$$Al_2(SO_4)_3 \cdot xH_2O + 3Ca(HCO_3)_2 \rightarrow$$

$$3CaSO_4 + 2Al(OH)_3 \downarrow + 6CO_2 + xH_2O \qquad 23\text{-}3$$

Taking the molecular weight of alum as 600 [it is 666.4 for $Al_2(SO_4)_3 \cdot 18H_2O$] and the molecular weight of the natural bicarbonate alkalinity as 3×100 (as $CaCO_3$), the indicated relative amount of reacting alkalinity is 300:600, or 1:2. Similarly, the relative amount of free CO_2 (molecular weight 44) released from bicarbonate alkalinity is 284:600, or about 1:2. As a rule, the actual amount of CO_2 liberated is also less than its possible value. Although the reaction presented

---

[2] Filter alum contains a slight excess of alumina and less water of crystallization. An empirical formulation is $Al_2(SO_4)_{2.87} \cdot 15H_2O$ for the slightly basic commercial product that contains 17% water-soluble Al_2O_3.

is an oversimplification of what actually takes place, it does indicate orders of magnitude and the fact that both non-carbonate hardness (as indicated also by Equation 23-1) and CO_2 may be formed in the reaction of both aluminum and iron coagulants, unless lime or lye is added to the water.

The solubility constants of the hydrated oxides of aluminum and iron are given in Table 18-3. As indicated in Section 18-9, their value is affected by both temperature and dissolved solids. The hydrous oxide of aluminum is an *amphoteric* [3] substance, i.e., it dissolves both in the presence of H^+ and OH^- ions. In the presence of caustic alkalinity (in connection with the softening of water by lime, for example) aluminum oxide dissolves as an aluminate, or

$$Al_2O_3 + 2OH^- \rightleftarrows 2AlO_2^- + H_2O \qquad 23\text{-}4$$

Iron does not behave in this way.

Neglecting activities, the calculated solubilities of the hydrous oxides of aluminum and iron in mg/l are shown in Table 23-2. The solubility

TABLE 23-2. Calculated Solubilities of the Hydrous Oxides of Aluminum and Iron in Pure Water at 25 C

Ion product	K_s	Solubility, mg/l	pH	Decrease in solubility with pH
$(Al^{+++})(OH^-)^3$	1.9×10^{-33}	51.3 as Al	4.0	1,000-fold for each unit rise
$(AlO_2^-)(H^+)$	4×10^{-13}	10.8 as Al	9.0	10-fold for each unit fall
$(Fe^{+++})(OH^-)^3$	4×10^{-38}	2.23 as Fe	3.0	1,000-fold for each unit rise
$(Fe^{++})(OH^-)^2$	1.65×10^{-15}	92.1 as Fe	8.0	100-fold for each unit rise

of the hydrated aluminum oxide (molecular wt of Al $= 27.0$) at pH 4, for example, is $1.9 \times 10^{-33} \times 27 \times 10^3/10^{-3(14-4)} = 51.3$ mg/l. The amounts of coagulant ordinarily used vary upward from 0.3 grain per gal for clear waters to 10 or 20 times this dosage for highly turbid waters or for waste waters. Since 1 grain per gal is equivalent to 17.1 mg/l, the mg/l of Al or Fe released by the common coagulants for each grain per gal of coagulant are: 1.54 mg/l Al for filter alum (mol wt 600); 2.38 mg/l Fe for ferric sulfate [$Fe_2(SO_4)_3$]; 5.89 mg/l Fe for ferric chloride ($FeCl_3$); and 3.43 mg/l Fe for copperas ($FeSO_4 \cdot 7H_2O$). Ordinarily, the best precipitates are obtained at points of low solubility.

The time required for floc to form is likewise least at points of low solubility. The rate of floc formation and the effect of various ions on the time of floc formation may be gaged from fundamental studies

[3] From the Greek *amphoteros*, both.

such as those of Bartow [4] and his associates. Figure 23-2 presents but a partial series of such results.

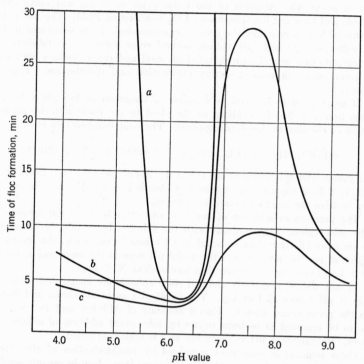

Figure 23-2. Zone and time of floc formation by ferric sulfate at various pH values and effect of added sodium sulfate. (a) Ferric sulfate only; 1.6 grams per gal of $Fe_2(SO_4)_3 \cdot 9H_2O$. (b) Ferric sulfate and 50 ppm of $Na_2SO_4 \cdot 10H_2O$. (c) Ferric sulfate and 250 ppm of $Na_2SO_4 \cdot 10H_2O$. *After Bartow, Black, and Sansbury.*

The following statements summarize the practical aspects of the indicated properties of colloids and the indicated dosage and behavior of common coagulants:

1. The pH range of relative insolubility is 5 to 7 for alum, above 4 for ferric iron, and above 9.5 for ferrous iron.

2. Because of the high solubility of copperas below pH 9.5, it is a useful coagulant only in highly alkaline waters. Otherwise lime must be added to raise the pH. The combined use of copperas and lime is known as the *iron and lime*

[4] Edward Bartow, A. P. Black, and W. E. Sansbury, "Formation of Floc by Ferric Coagulants," *Trans., Am. Soc. Civil Engrs.,* 100, 263 (1935).

process. The hydrous ferrous oxide is oxidized to the ferric state in the presence of dissolved oxygen ($4FeO + O_2 \rightleftarrows 2Fe_2O_3$). This renders the oxide less soluble at lower pH values and extends the range of usefulness of copperas down to a pH value of about 8.5. Aeration of the water prior to liming will make oxygen available and blow out lime-consuming CO_2 (see Section 23-3). The use of large amounts of lime may render the process uneconomical, unless treatment includes lime softening. At high pH values, natural color colloids are stabilized, and calcium carbonate may be precipitated on sand and other surfaces with which the water comes in contact during purification and distribution. This is a nuisance.

3. If copperas is to be used as a source of coagulant at low pH values, the ferrous iron may first be oxidized at the plant to the ferric state by adding a solution of chlorine to dissolved copperas. The oxidation reaction is

$$6(FeSO_4 \cdot 7H_2O) + 3Cl_2 \rightleftarrows 6Fe^{+++} + 6SO_4^{=} + 6Cl^{-} + 42H_2O \qquad 23\text{-}5$$

Both sulfate and chloride ions are released. About $(3 \times 71):(6 \times 278)$, or 1 lb of Cl_2 to 8 lb of copperas are required. Chlorine is generally added in excess in order to drive the reaction toward completion.

4. The presence or addition of negative ions extends the useful range of pH in the acid region. In accordance with the Schulze-Hardy rule, bivalent $SO_4^{=}$ ions are more effective than monovalent Cl^{-} ions. Conversely, the presence or addition of positive ions extends the useful pH zone in the basic region, bivalent Ca^{++} ions being more effective than monovalent Na^{+} ions.

5. In soft waters, negatively charged color colloids are coagulated most effectively at pH values of 4 or less. The trivalent ions of aluminum and iron are then the precipitating agents. Excess amounts of Al^{+++} and Fe^{+++} may have to be removed as hydrous oxides by subsequent addition of alkaline substances. In practice, a pH value as low as 4 is seldom attained.

6. Color removal is sometimes improved by prechlorination of alum-treated waters. This may be due to oxidation of ferrous iron. Iron in organic combination in highly colored waters has also been effectively oxidized and precipitated by potassium permanganate at a pH of 8.8 to 9.8 (Section 23-3).

7. The coagulation of very clear waters may be improved by the addition of finely divided clay (15 to 100 mg/l), activated silica, or other coagulant aids. As previously stated, these provide nuclei about which the precipitate can collect. They also weight the floc and hasten its settling.

8. Iron and manganese naturally present in water can be called into use as coagulants and to speed their own removal (Section 23-3).

9. Coagulation is a time-concentration phenomenon. Concentration increases the opportunity for contact and decreases the time required for floc formation.

10. Stirring increases the opportunity for contact and decreases the time for floc formation. It also promotes floc growth (Section 23-4).

c. Determination of Coagulant Dose. Because waters and waste waters vary widely in quality and change in characteristics from time to time, and because coagulation is so complex a reaction, the optimum dosage of coagulants must be determined in practice by trial. Ordinarily, a single chemical coagulant is applied, its dosage being regulated to the minimum amount necessary for rapid and adequate coagulation. Only if such treatment is uneconomical or gives poor results, are alkalinity or colloidal particles added or chemicals used to regulate the pH or to introduce reactions other than those inherent in the use of the coagulant by itself.

Trial determinations of coagulant dosage, commonly called *jar tests*, are made in a laboratory stirring device of the type shown in Figure 23-3. The amount of coagulant is increased stepwise, and all jars are mixed simultaneously for 10 to 30 min. The jar in which floc first makes its appearance is generally assumed to have received the most

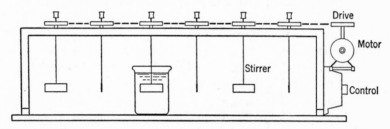

Figure 23-3. Laboratory apparatus for determination of the optimum dosage of coagulating chemicals and needed stirring. A variable-speed motor is provided. Tyndall beams directed through the beakers are of assistance.

economical dose. However, the size of floc and its settling characteristics and filterability must also be taken into consideration in terms of available flocculation chambers, settling basins, and filter capacities. The usefulness of alkalies, pH regulation, and the introduction of coagulant aids such as clay, activated silica, or hydroxyethyl cellulose may have to be investigated. In treatment plants, jar tests are made with sufficient frequency to assure optimum results and economical use of chemicals. When the characteristics of the water or waste water to be coagulated change rapidly, testing may have to proceed almost continuously. In water purification, this may happen when floods, or the onsets of the fall and spring overturns, bring about rapid shifts in water quality. In waste-water works, rapid changes are produced by rainfall (combined sewerage) and the sudden discharge of batches of industrial wastes. Jar tests also offer essential means for controlling the dosage of sewage sludge with chemicals in order to speed and improve its filtration or drying. This is called sludge conditioning (Section 26-15).

23-3. Chemical Precipitation. The two most important classes of substances dissolved in water and waste water that are amenable to precipitation by added chemicals are: (1) hardness and (2) iron and manganese. In water supply, removal of hardness is called water softening, removal of iron and manganese respectively deferrization and demanganization. Precipitation of hardness from industrial waste waters is not unusual. As explained in Section 21-9, the early improvement in the removal of suspended and colloidal matter from sewage accompanying the precipitation of iron from iron-rich sewage by lime is responsible for the continuing use of the term chemical precipitation in sewage treatment even when coagulants are added. The precipitation of iron and manganese by dissolved oxygen is generally accomplished by aeration. But the reaction involved is one of chemical precipitation. By contrast, the escape of CO_2, H_2S, CH_4, and odor-producing substances from water and waste water by aeration is physical, rather than chemical, precipitation. Removal of fluorides along with magnesium is a process of adsorption. However, adsorption is generally involved also in coagulation. A number of industrial waste substances are precipitated from solution by suitable chemical treatment methods (see Chapter 29).

It will be convenient to discuss in the present section (a) the removal of hardness by conventional methods of chemical precipitation together with the incidental removal of fluorides and (b) the removal of iron and manganese by precipitation.

Natural waters, more particularly well waters, may contain hundreds and even thousands of milligrams per liter of hardness as $CaCO_3$. Waters containing less than 50 mg/l of hardness are considered soft; those containing more than 100 to 150 mg/l, the magnitude depending upon the regional composition of available water supplies, are considered hard. The iron content of natural waters rarely exceeds 10 mg/l, but it may go above 50 mg/l. The manganese content is generally lower. It rarely exceeds 3 mg/l. Ground water is again the most common offender.

a. Precipitation of Hardness. The hardness-forming constituents, as stated in Section 20-8, are principally the ions of calcium and magnesium. Their relationship to other mineral ions in water is shown schematically in Figure 23-4. Chemical precipitation of hardness is generally accomplished by lime or by lime and soda ash (the *lime-soda* process of water softening developed by Clark in 1841). In the removal of Ca^{++}, lime converts free CO_2 and bicarbonate ion to normal carbonate ion. Relatively insoluble precipitates of calcium carbonate ($K_s = 4.82 \times 10^{-9}$, Table 18-3) are formed and removed by settling. For the precipitation of Mg^{++}, hydroxyl ion must be provided in order to form an insoluble precipitate of magnesium hydroxide

$(K_s = 5.5 \times 10^{-12})$. The solubility of magnesium carbonate $MgCO_3 \cdot 3H_2O$ is relatively high $(K_s = 1 \times 10^{-5})$. An excess of 2 or 3 grains per gal of hydrated lime is needed to promote the formation of $Mg(OH)_2$. This is called *excess-lime* treatment. As stated in Section 18-9a, this is a useful application of the principle of the common-ion effect.

If the amount of $SO_4^=$, Cl^-, and NO_3^- exceeds the amount of Na^+ and K^+ naturally present in the water, i.e., if the water contains non-carbonate hardness, there is insufficient carbonate ion to remove the

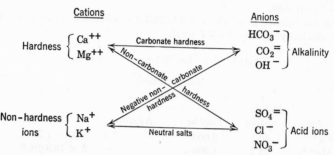

Figure 23-4. Relationship of Ca^{++} and Mg^{++} to other mineral ions in water.

Ca^{++}. Soda ash is added to provide carbonate ion for this Ca^{++} and for the Ca^{++} associated with the excess lime. Cold-process softening falls short of Ca^{++} and Mg^{++} removals that are theoretically possible. Slowness of the final precipitations combines with economic limits on the size of reaction and settling tanks to account for this. In order to prevent cementing of filters and incrustation of pipes and to rid the water of unwanted causticity, excess-lime treatment must be followed by carbonation with CO_2 gas. This cuts off the precipitation of Ca^{++} and Mg^{++} and stabilizes the water (see Section 23-6). The softening and recarbonation reactions are:

$$Ca(OH)_2 \leftrightharpoons Ca^{++} + 2OH^- \qquad 23\text{-}6$$

$$CO_2 + OH^- \leftrightharpoons HCO_3^- \qquad 23\text{-}7$$

$$HCO_3^- + OH^- \leftrightharpoons CO_3^= + H_2O \qquad 23\text{-}8$$

$$Ca^{++} + CO_3^= \leftrightharpoons CaCO_3 \downarrow \qquad 23\text{-}9$$

$$Mg^{++} + 2OH^- \leftrightharpoons Mg(OH)_2 \downarrow \qquad 23\text{-}10$$

In calculating the requisite amounts of chemical to be added, the assumption is made that the reactions go to completion. A balance sheet is struck for the significant positive and negative ions, and the free CO_2 is included in it (see Example 23-1). In the presence of Mg^{++}, the amount of lime must be sufficient not only to convert all the free CO_2 and HCO_3^- to $CO_3^=$ but also to produce $Mg(OH)_2$ with the required excess of OH^-.

Example 23-1. Calculate the necessary amounts of lime (mol wt of $CaO = 56.1$) and soda ash (mol wt of $Na_2CO_3 = 106$) to soften a raw water of the following composition: total hardness as $CaCO_3$ 215 mg/l; alkalinity as $CaCO_3$ 185 mg/l; magnesium as Mg 15.8 mg/l; sodium as Na 8.0 mg/l; sulfate as SO_4 28.6 mg/l; chloride as Cl 10.0 mg/l; nitrate nitrogen as N 1.0 mg/l; carbon dioxide as CO_2 25.8 mg/l; pH 6.69.

1. The ion balance is struck in Table 23-3 for a hardness of $215/50 = 4.3$ me/l and an alkalinity of $185/50 = 3.7$ me/l.

TABLE 23-3. Ion Balance (Example 23-1)

Ion	Molecular weight	Milliequivalents per liter		Calculations
		Positive	Negative	
Ca^{++}	40.1	3.000	.....	$4.30 - 1.30$
Mg^{++}	24.3	1.300	.....	$2 \times 15.8/24.3$
Na^+	23.0	0.348	.....	$8.0/23.0$
HCO_3^-	61.0	.....	3.686	By Equation 20-2 *
$CO_3^=$	60.0	.....	0.014	By Equation 20-3 *
$SO_4^=$	96.1	.....	0.594	$2 \times 28.6/96.1$
Cl^-	35.5	.....	0.282	$10.0/35.5$
NO_3^-	62.0	.....	0.072	$1.0/14$
Total	....	4.648	4.648	....
CO_2	44.0	1.175		$2 \times 25.8/44.0$

* The concentrations of the monovalent and bivalent ions are 4.388 me/l and 4.911 me/l respectively. By Equation 23-48, therefore, $\mu = 0.711$, and by Equations 20-5 to 20-7, $K_1' = 1.28 \times 10^{-6}$, $K_2' = 3.85 \times 10^{-10}$, and $K_w' = 2.86 \times 10^{-14}$.

2. The required dosages of lime and soda ash in me/l are shown in Table 23-4.

TABLE 23-4. Calculated Dosages of Lime and Soda Ash (Example 23-1)

Lime for		Soda ash for	
CO_2	1.175	$SO_4^=$	0.594
HCO_3^-	3.686	Cl^-	0.282
Mg^{++}	1.300	NO_3^-	0.072
Excess	0.923 $(2 \times 2 \times 17.1/74.1)$	Excess	0.923
[2 grains/gal as $Ca(OH)_2$]		Subtotal	1.871
		Less Na^+	0.348
Total	7.084	Total	1.523

The calculated 7.084 me/l of lime are provided by $7.1 \times 56.1/2 = 199$ mg/l of pure CaO. This equals $199/17.1 = 11.6$ grains per gal, or $199 \times 8.32 = 1{,}650$ lb per mg. The calculated 1.523 me/l of soda ash are provided by $1.523 \times 106/2 = 79.3$ mg/l of pure Na_2CO_3, by 4.63 grains per gal, or by 660 lb per mg. The commercial strength of these chemicals is given in Table A-5 in the Appendix.

The composition of water that has been softened by chemical precipitation is a function of the concentration of the component substances and their dissociation. Assuming that equilibrium is established, Ca, Mg, CO_3, and OH are present both as precipitates and as ions. The following equations, in which the subscripts s and t designate precipitates and totals respectively, must then apply when the concentrations of the constituent radicals (with the exception of H^+ which is kept in mols per liter for convenience) are expressed in milliequivalents per liter:

$$[Ca^{++}] + [Ca]_s = [Ca]_t = a \qquad \text{23-11}$$

$$[Ca]_s = [CO_3]_s = x \qquad \text{23-12}$$

$$[CO_3^=] + [CO_3]_s + 2[HCO_3^-] = [CO_3]_t + 2[HCO_3^-] = b \quad \text{23-13}$$

$$[Ca^{++}][CO_3^=] = 4.82 \times 10^{-9} \times 4 \times 10^6$$

$$= 1.928 \times 10^{-2} \quad \text{(uncorrected) Table 18-3} \quad \text{23-14}$$

$$[Mg^{++}] + [Mg]_s = [Mg]_t = c \qquad \text{23-15}$$

$$[Mg]_s = [OH]_s = y \qquad \text{23-16}$$

$$[OH^-] + [OH]_s - [HCO_3^-] = [OH]_t - [HCO_3^-] = d \quad \text{23-17}$$

$$[Mg^{++}][OH^-]^2 = 5.5 \times 10^{-12} \times 2 \times 10^9$$

$$= 1.1 \times 10^{-2} \quad \text{(uncorrected) Table 18-3} \quad \text{23-18}$$

$$[H^+][OH^-] = 10^{-14} \times 10^3 = 10^{-11} \qquad \text{18-27}$$

$$[H^+][CO_3^=]/[HCO_3^-] = 4.69 \times 10^{-11} \times 2 = 9.38 \times 10^{-11}$$

$$\text{(uncorrected) Table 18-1} \quad \text{23-19}$$

If we assume that OH^- reacts with HCO_3^- to form $CO_3^=$ and to remove it, HCO_3^- must be closely equal to zero, and the following equations apply approximately:

$$[Ca^{++}] = a - x \qquad \text{23-20}$$

$$[CO_3^=] = b - x \qquad \text{23-21}$$

$$(a - x)(b - x) = 1.928 \times 10^{-2} \qquad \text{or}$$

$$x = \tfrac{1}{2}(a + b) \pm \sqrt{\tfrac{1}{4}(a - b)^2 + 1.928 \times 10^{-2}} \qquad 23\text{-}22$$

$$[Mg^{++}] = c - y \qquad 23\text{-}23$$

$$[OH^-] = d - y \qquad 23\text{-}24$$

$$(c - y)(d - y)^2 = 1.1 \times 10^{-2} \qquad \text{or}$$

$$y = d \pm \sqrt{1.1 \times 10^{-2}/(c - y)} \qquad 23\text{-}25$$

where $0 \lesseqgtr y \lesseqgtr c$.

$$[H^+] = 10^{-11}/(d - y) \qquad 23\text{-}26$$

The results of calculations, even if all ten equations are solved, are only approximate. Temperature and secondary salt effect (Section 18-5b), for example, change the solubility of the precipitates; and temperature as well as ionic strength changes the magnitude of the dissociation and solubility constants.

When the amount of lime added is equivalent to the CO_2 and the calcium alkalinity only (ordinary lime softening), the HCO_3^- remaining in solution will approximately equal the sum of the Mg^{++} and Na^+ less the sum of the $SO_4^=$, Cl^-, and NO_3^-, provided that this difference is positive and the assumption that HCO_3^- must be closely equal to zero does not apply.

Example 23-2. Find the approximate composition of the water of Example 23-1 after treatment with the calculated doses of lime and soda ash.

1. Expressed in me/l, the balances of radicals after addition of the chemicals are shown in Table 23-5.

TABLE 23-5. Balance of Radicals after Lime-Soda Softening (Example 23-2)

Radical	Original	Added	From $CO_2 + 2OH^-$	From $HCO_3^- + OH^-$	Total
Ca	3.000	7.084	....	....	10.084
Mg	1.300	.....	....	....	1.300
Na	0.348	1.523	....	....	1.871
				Total	13.255
HCO_3	3.686	.....	....	−3.686	0.000
CO_3	0.014	1.523	+1.175	+7.372	10.084
SO_4	0.594	.....	....	....	0.594
Cl	0.282	.....	....	....	0.282
NO_3	0.072	.....	....	....	0.072
OH	.....	7.084	−1.175	−3.686	2.223
				Total	13.255

2. The values of a, b, c, and d in me/l are $a = 10.084$; $b = 10.084$; $c = 1.300$; and $d = 2.223$. Hence $(a + b)/2 = 10.084$ and $(a - b)/2 = 0$; all in me/l.

By Equation 23-22: $x = 10.084 \pm \sqrt{(0.0)^2 + 1.928 \times 10^{-2}} = 10.223$, or 9.945 me/l.

By Equation 23-20: $[Ca^{++}] = (10.084 - 9.945) = 0.139$ me/l, or $50 \times 0.139 = 7$ mg/l as $CaCO_3$.

By Equation 23-25: $y = 2.223 \pm \sqrt{1.1 \times 10^{-2}/(1.300 - y)}$. In this case $y <$ but nearly $= c$. By trial $y = 1.287$ me/l.

By Equation 23-23: $[Mg^{++}] = (1.300 - 1.287) = 0.013$ me/l, or $50 \times 0.013 = 0.7$ mg/l as $CaCO_3$.

By Equation 23-21: $[CO_3^=] = (10.084 - 9.945) = 0.139$ me/l, or $50 \times 0.139 = 7$ mg/l as $CaCO_3$.

By Equation 23-24: $[OH^-] = (2.223 - 1.287) = 0.936$ me/l, or $50 \times 0.936 = 46.8$ mg/l as $CaCO_3$.

By Equation 23-26: $[H^+] = 10^{-11}/0.936 = 1.07 \times 10^{-11}$, and $pH = 10.97$.

3. With excess-lime treatment, the residual Mg^{++} is so low that it may be assumed to have been completely removed; and Equations 23-23 and 23-25 need not be used.

4. As a check, the ion balance is $Ca^{++} + Mg^{++} + Na^+ = 2.023$ me/l, and $HCO_3^- + CO_3^= + SO_4^= + Cl^- + NO_3^- + OH^- = 2.023$ me/l.

5. The carbonation necessary to remove the caustic alkalinity, and the resulting ion content of the recarbonated water can be calculated.

Precipitation processes are elaborated in various ways to effect the required degree of softening:

1. Subjecting part of the water to excess-lime or lime-soda treatment and mixing the settled effluent with unsoftened water, called *split treatment*, generally makes carbonation unnecessary.

2. In lime softening combined with ion-exchange softening (Section 23-5), the lime throws down most of the carbonate hardness, while the ion exchanger eliminates the remaining amount as well as the non-carbonate hardness.

3. Coagulants are added to increase removals of precipitates or to shorten the requisite time of settling. For this purpose, filter alum, sodium aluminate, and activated silica have been found useful either singly or in combination.

4. Recirculation of a portion of the settled sludge or slurry accelerates precipitation and may reduce the consumption of chemicals.

5. Free CO_2 may be reduced by aeration prior to softening. Removal of CO_2 breaks down some of the HCO_3^- in accordance with Equation 23-7. The OH^- produced then raises the pH value, but the alkalinity of the water is only slightly reduced because some of the OH^- combines with $H+$ to form water.

6. Recarbonation after excess-lime treatment may be made to serve more than the single purpose of removing causticity. If the amount of CO_2 added is such that caustic alkalinity is converted to carbonate alkalinity (Equations 23-7 and 23-8), a fine precipitate of $CaCO_3$ is formed and further softening results. The precipitate may be removed by filtration or by coagulation and secondary settling. A pH in the vicinity of 9.5 is required to effect these changes.

7. Secondary carbonation just before the water is applied to filters will reduce precipitation of $CaCO_3$ on sand grains and supporting gravel.

8. Incrustation of sand may also be prevented by the addition of small amounts of hexametaphosphate as a sequestering agent.

9. The advantages of softening by recarbonation must be balanced against those of producing a stable water (see Section 23-5). It may be better to add sufficient CO_2 to reach the equilibrium point between carbonate and bicarbonate ions and to forgo some reduction in hardness.

10. The solubilities of Ca^{++} and Mg^{++} decrease with rising temperatures. Therefore, hot-process softening is common in boiler-water treatment (Section 29-5) in order to economize on the use of precipitants and to obtain water of lowest possible hardness.

11. In practice, the softening of water by chemical precipitation generally aims at the following targets: (1) reduction of calcium alkalinity by lime softening to values of 75 to 100 mg/l in the absence of significant amounts of Mg^{++}; (2) reduction of calcium and magnesium alkalinities by excess-lime treatment to values of 30 to 50 mg/l in the absence of significant amounts of non-carbonate hardness; (3) reduction of calcium and magnesium hardness by the lime-soda process to 30 to 40 mg/l; and (4) reduction of calcium and magnesium hardness by the hot, lime-soda process to less than 10 mg/l.

An important side reaction of the excess-lime treatment of high-magnesium waters is the observed reduction in fluorides when they, too, are present. Removal appears to be due to adsorption of F^- on the $Mg(OH)_2$ floc. Scott [5] and his associates have suggested the following empirical relationship for the removal of F^- by precipitation of Mg^{++}:

$$P = 100 - 7\sqrt{Mg} \qquad\qquad 23\text{-}27$$

Here P is the percentage removal of fluoride as F, and Mg is the mg/l of magnesium precipitated. Reduction of 3.3 mg/l of F^- to 1.0 mg/l, for example, requires the precipitation of 100 mg/l of Mg^{++}. In the absence of adequate amounts of magnesium, a salt of this metal can be added to bring about the desired fluoride removal.

b. Precipitation of Iron and Manganese. As shown in Table 18-3, the solubility of inorganic ferrous (Fe^{++}) and manganous (Mn^{++}) compounds is high, that of ferric (Fe^{+++}) compounds low. The solubility of manganic compounds is also low. For these reasons, inorganic iron and manganese normally occur in solution in highest concentration when water is devoid of dissolved oxygen. However, very acid wastes, such as those draining from mines, may hold large amounts of iron in solution even in the presence of oxygen. The anions present in iron- and manganese-bearing waters are much the same as those found in hard waters (Figure 23-4). In combination with organic matter, iron and manganese are extremely stable.

[5] R. D. Scott, A. E. Kimberley, H. L. van Horn, L. F. Ey, and F. H. Waring, Jr., "Fluoride in Ohio Water Supplies," *J. Am. Water Works Assoc., 29,* 9 (1937).

A number of different processes can be employed for the precipitation of iron and manganese from water. Choice and economy of the treatment method depend upon the characteristics of the water and the nature of the iron and manganese.

Aeration of water low in dissolved oxygen and high in CO_2 will add oxidizing oxygen and raise the pH value by flushing out CO_2. Both effects decrease the solubility of inorganic iron and manganese. However, the amounts present are relatively so small and the amounts that may be left in solution are relatively so minute (Fe and Mn together <0.3 mg/l), that self-precipitation is protracted (see Equation 22-9). Rates of flocculation are, therefore, accelerated in practice by contact and by catalysis. For these purposes, the water is generally caused to trickle over coke, or crushed stone, or to flow upward through the contact material. Deposits of iron and manganese accumulate on the contact surfaces and catalyze the precipitation of ferrous and manganous oxides. Limestone is an effective contact medium because of its basic reaction. Pyrolusite (MnO_2 ore) possesses high catalytic power. Iron and manganese bacteria (Section 19-2) may grow luxuriantly on the contact media. Filters are generally made part of the treatment works because they, too, provide contact and because they remove finely divided precipitates.

But 0.14 mg/l O_2 is needed to convert 1 mg/l Fe^{++} to ferric hydroxide. Therefore little aeration is required for the purpose. Vigorous aeration may not only add excess oxygen, it may also remove more than the excess CO_2 (Section 23-6) and shift the calcium carbonate equilibrium of hard water to precipitate finely divided $CaCO_3$. At pH values greater than 7.1, positively charged ferric hydroxide particles may be adsorbed on the negatively charged calcium carbonate particles and remain in colloidal suspension. Waters high in organic matter, too, may have to be aerated sparingly, because overaeration may produce relatively stable colloids. Oxidation of the organic matter by potassium permanganate or chlorine may be more helpful. The oxidants destroy the complex compounds of iron and manganese and oxidize the iron and manganese released. Oxide precipitates are formed. The settling of precipitates can be hastened by coagulation. Alum, but preferably iron, coagulants will, indeed, remove small amounts of iron and manganese from some waters without preparatory treatment. Chlorination may then be of assistance. The calculated solubilities of the hydrated oxides of iron have been given in Section 23-1. These values are such that iron is rendered substantially insoluble after oxidation by chlorine, ozone, potassium permanganate, or other means at any pH value above about 4. The precipitation of manganese is more complex. Catalysis performs an important function, and a simple generalization of oxidation effects is not possible.

Precipitation of iron and manganese from hard waters by lime is quite similar to, and fully as effective as, the precipitation of calcium and magnesium. If oxygen is kept out of the system, iron precipitates as ferrous oxide (FeO) or ferrous carbonate ($FeCO_3$); manganese as hydrous manganous oxide ($MnO \cdot H_2O$). The solubility of $(Mn^{++})(OH^-)^2$ calculated from the solubility product of 7.1×10^{-15} shown in Table 18-3 is 3.90 mg/l as Mn at a pH of 9.0. It decreases 100-fold for each unit rise in pH. The solubility of $(Fe^{++})(OH^-)^2$ is somewhat smaller (Section 23-2b). Precipitation of Fe^{++} and Mn^{++} can, therefore, proceed only above pH values of about 9.5 and 10 respectively. For economic reasons, the use of lime for deferrization and demanganization is commonly restricted to hard waters that are to be softened at the same time or to waters that need to be stabilized.

The contact beds of deferrization and demanganization plants are normally 6 to 10 ft deep with surface loadings of 40 to 80 mgad. They are operated either as down-flow tricklers or as up-flow submerged beds. Upward flow makes for a longer period of contact. The contact medium is ordinarily 1½ to 2 in. in size, but coarse and fine gravels have also been employed successfully. The aerators of trickling contact beds are ordinarily proportioned to the size of the beds above which they operate. Heads on aerators are commonly kept to a few feet. Accumulations of iron and manganese are flushed out of coarse beds by rapid drainage, if necessary after filling the beds to near overflow level. Gravel beds are washed in much the same way as rapid sand filters. A flocculating and settling basin is generally interposed between the contact unit and slow or rapid filters where these are used. An hour or two of detention is normally provided. The rates of filtration are in the vicinity of 10 mgad for slow filters and 125 mgad for rapid filters (Chapter 24). Precipitation of manganese is normally much slower than that of iron. Most of the manganese load may, therefore, fall on the filters.

The hydrous oxides of iron and manganese precipitated from water by lime in the absence of oxygen are removed effectively by filtration. Enclosed (pressure) units are used for this purpose.

23-4. Flocculation. In their initial phases, coagulation and precipitation produce finely divided, or colloidal, suspensions. These suspensions are converted into settleable solids by agglomeration. In a quiescent fluid, colloids collide because of their Brownian movement, and finely divided solids come into contact with one another when more rapidly settling solids overtake more slowly settling ones (Section 22-4). As a result, flocs of ever-increasing size are formed. Floc growth by these means, however, is exceedingly slow. It can be hastened by stirring the water. This increases the number of collisions or contacts. The increased opportunity for contact is called *flocculation*. It may be provided by hydraulic or mechanical means, including the injection of air.

a. Theoretical Considerations. The stirring of water or waste water imparts velocity to it and to the colloids or suspended matter contained in it. Differences in velocity across the path of flow create velocity gradients. These gradients are the controlling factors in flocculation. If the temporal mean velocity gradient in a shearing fluid is designated by the letter G where G is the difference in velocity dv in a given distance dy at right angles to the direction of flow, Equation 22-10 takes the following form: [6]

$$N = n'n''(\tfrac{1}{6}G)(d' + d'')^3 \qquad 23\text{-}28$$

As before, N is the number of contacts per unit time per unit volume, and n' and n'' are the numbers of particles per unit volume of water with diameters of d' and d'' respectively. It follows that N varies directly with G. The magnitude of G is a function of power input P per unit volume and of the absolute viscosity of the fluid μ. Specifically,

$$G = \sqrt{P/\mu} \qquad 23\text{-}29$$

for shear along parallel planes of an elemental volume of water. This relationship can be derived from a consideration of the forces acting upon the cube of water shown in Figure 23-5.

Equating the forces acting on the fluid element in shear in one direction to those acting in the opposite direction:

$$p \cdot \Delta y \cdot \Delta z + \left(\tau + \frac{d\tau}{dy} \Delta y \right) \Delta x \cdot \Delta z$$

$$= \tau \cdot \Delta x \cdot \Delta z + \left(p + \frac{dp}{dx} \Delta x \right) \Delta y \cdot \Delta z \qquad 23\text{-}30$$

Here p is the intensity of pressure, τ is the intensity of shear, and x, y, and z are the dimensions of the cube. It follows that

$$d\tau/dy = dp/dx \qquad 23\text{-}31$$

[6] T. R. Camp and P. C. Stein, "Velocity Gradients and Internal Work in Fluid Motion," *J. Boston Soc. Civil Engrs.*, *30*, 219 (1943).

Since the power P' expended, or the rate at which work is done by the couple, equals the torque times the angular velocity dv/dy,

$$P' = (\tau \, \Delta x \, \Delta z) \, \Delta y \, dv/dy \qquad \qquad 23\text{-}32$$

Accordingly the power consumption per unit volume P is

$$P = P'/(\Delta x \, \Delta y \, \Delta z) = \tau \, dv/dy = \mu(dv/dy)^2 = \mu G^2 \qquad 23\text{-}33$$

because $\tau = \mu \, dv/dy$ and $G = dv/dy$ by definition. Consequently,

$$G = \sqrt{P/\mu} \qquad \qquad 23\text{-}29$$

Expressed in these terms, Smoluchowski's equation then becomes

$$N = n'n''(\tfrac{1}{6}\sqrt{P/\mu})(d' + d'')^3 \qquad \qquad 23\text{-}34$$

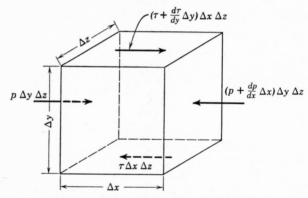

Figure 23-5. Shear forces along parallel planes of an elemental volume of a fluid.

This equation shows that the number of contacts per unit time, and thus the rate of flocculation, increases with the number and size of particles and with the power input, whereas it decreases with the viscosity of the fluid. In a given suspension, the number of flocculating particles decreases rapidly as their size increases. The total available binding energy also declines with neutralization of charge and increase in size of particle, until the floc attains a size at which the shearing action of the fluid overbalances any further tendency for aggregation. Under favorable conditions, the flocs may attain a size about equal to the dimensions of snowflakes.

For baffled channels of length l and cross-sectional area a in which a loss of head h is incurred by a flow Q,

$$P = Qwh/(al) = vwh/l = v\rho gs = wh/t = \rho gh/t \qquad 23\text{-}35$$

or

$$G = \sqrt{v\rho g s/\mu} = \sqrt{vgs/\nu} = \sqrt{gh/\nu t} \qquad 23\text{-}36$$

Here ρ is the mass density of the fluid, g is the gravity constant, ν is the kinematic viscosity of the fluid, s is the slope of the water surface and t is the period of detention. Each foot of lost head equals $62.4 \times 1.547/550 = 0.175$ hp per mgd or $62.4 \times 1.547/737.6 = 0.131$ kw per mgd. In practice, velocities vary between 0.3 and 3 fps, detention times between 10 and 90 min, and head losses between 1 and 3 ft.

For mechanical mixers, operated by paddles, the useful power input is a function of the drag of the paddles. If D is the drag in lb, C_D is the coefficient of drag for plates moved face-on to the fluid, A is the area of the paddles in sq ft, v is the velocity of the paddles relative to that of the liquid in fps, and V is the volume of the flocculator in cu ft, the drag is

$$D = C_D A w v^2/2g = C_D A \rho v^2/2 \qquad 23\text{-}37$$

and the power per unit volume of water, which equals force times velocity divided by volume, becomes

$$P = C_D A \rho v^3/(2V) = \mu G^2 \qquad 23\text{-}38$$

or

$$G = \sqrt{C_D A v^3/(2\nu V)} \qquad 23\text{-}39$$

In practice peripheral speeds of paddles range from 3 fps to 0.3 fps.

Example 23-3. A flocculator designed to treat 20 mgd is 100 ft long by 40 ft wide by 15 ft deep. It is equipped with 12-in. paddles supported parallel to and moved by four horizontal shafts which rotate at a speed of 2.5 rpm. The center line of the paddles is 6.0 ft from the shaft which is at middepth of the tank. Two paddles are mounted on each shaft, one opposite the other. If the mean velocity of the water is approximately ¼ the velocity of the paddles (as is generally true in this type of stirring device), find: (a) the velocity differential between the paddles and the water, (b) the hydraulic power and energy consumption if the velocity differential between the water and the paddle is 75% of the linear velocity of the paddle blades and the coefficient of drag for flat plates is 1.8, (c) the time of flocculation, and (d) the value of G.

a. Speed of rotation. If n is the number of revolutions per minute and r is the distance of the center of the paddle blade from the center of the shaft, $2\pi rn = 60\, v_p$, or $v_p = 2\pi \times 6 \times 2.5/60 = 1.57$ fps, where v_p is the linear velocity of the paddle blades.

b. Power consumption. Since the area of the paddles is $A = 40 \times 2 \times 4 \times 1 = 320$ sq ft, and the coefficient of drag $C_D = 1.8$, the total power input, P_t, by Equation 23-38 is: $P_t = 1.8 \times 320 \times 62.4 \times (0.75 \times 1.57)^3/(2 \times 32.2) = 918$ ft-lb per sec, and $918/550 = 1.67$ hp, or 1.24 kw.

The energy consumption per mg, therefore, is $1.67 \times 24/20 = 2.0$ hp-hr per mg, or 1.5 kwh per mg treated. For electrical drive, there must be added the energy required to overcome mechanical friction and to provide for electrical losses in the lines and motor. (In practice, flocculators consume 2 to 6 kwh per mg treated.)

c. Time of flocculation. Since the volume of the tank is $4 \times 100 \times 15 = 6 \times 10^4$ cu ft, the detention period $t = 6 \times 10^4 \times 7.48 \times 24 \times 60/(20 \times 10^6) = 32.5$ min.

d. Value of G. By Equation 23-39:

$$G = \sqrt{1.8 \times 320 \times (1.18)^3/(2 \times 1.41 \times 10^{-5} \times 6 \times 10^4)} = 24 \text{ fps per ft}$$

and

$$Gt = 24 \times 32.5 \times 60 = 4.7 \times 10^4$$

Experience has shown that the value of G should be greater than 10 fps per ft in order to promote flocculation but less than 75 fps per ft if disintegration of the floc by shear is to be avoided. Optimum values appear to lie between 30 and 60 fps per ft. The detention period should be at least 10 min. Longer times (30 min or more) are indicated for low values of G, and there is reason to believe that for satisfactory performance the dimensionless product of G and t may range within the limits of 10^4 and 10^5. If the value of G is adjusted to floc size and growth requirements by being given a high initial value and being decreased progressively, the initial values of G may be made as high as 100 fps per ft. The final values may then be dropped to as low as 10 fps per ft in order to preserve floc structure.

b. *Mixing and Flocculating Devices.* The suspended or dissolved chemicals that are to be added to water or waste water must be dispersed uniformly through the water or waste water that is to be treated. The more rapidly this can be done, the less time is wasted in setting the chemicals to work. To this purpose, the chemicals may be introduced (1) in advance of hydraulic structures in which the water is agitated violently but which have some other function to perform as well or (2) into special mixing units. Examples of the first are turbines, pumps, and spray or injection aerators; examples of the second are heavily baffled basins, or tanks equipped with mechanical stirrers or air diffusers. Exposures of 30 to 60 sec are commonly enough.

By contrast, floc growth is encouraged by gentle stirring. This, too, may be accomplished by hydraulic means such as baffling, by mechanical means such as revolving paddles, or by air diffusion. Detention periods must be adjusted to chemical dosage. They may be as low as 10 min, but 30 to 60 min are more common. The velocity in conduits connecting flocculation chambers with settling tanks should lie between 0.5 fps and 1.0 fps. They should be large enough to prevent deposition of floc but small enough to prevent its disintegration. A combined mixing and flocculation basin is illustrated in Figure 23-6, and a number of units incorporating mixing, flocculation, and settling are shown in Figure 22-8. Means may be provided for the return of slurry or sludge in order to promote floc formation and growth. Activated-sludge units are biologically activated flocculating units.

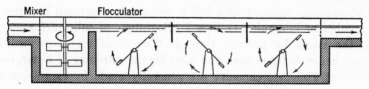

Figure 23-6. Mixing and flocculation basin.

23-5. Ion Exchange. Ion exchange is the displacement of one ion by another. Deionization, demineralization, or de-ashing embraces the removal of substantially all ionizable materials that will leave a residue on evaporation. Both cations and anions may be exchanged between a liquid and a solid exchange medium. Cation or base exchange is employed to soften water, to remove iron and manganese, and to reduce the concentration of fluorides to tolerable or desirable values. It has been used experimentally to remove and recover ammonia (NH_4^+) from sewage, and it may be employed in the laboratory to prepare ammonia-free water. In industry, both cation and anion exchangers find use in the preparation of boiler feed-water and in numerous industrial processes. The exchange media are placed in beds through which the fluid to be treated passes as in sand filters (Chapter 24).

In order to be effective in the treatment of water, ion-exchange media must possess the following properties: (1) they must be of large surface, since ion exchange is a surface reaction, but their resistance to flow must be compatible with hydraulic requirements; (2) they must possess a high exchange capacity and be readily cleaned by back-washing and regenerated by suitable chemicals; (3) they must be physically durable (not subject to attrition) and resistant to chemical attack (chemically stable); (4) they must be relatively inexpensive and capable of being regenerated by relatively inexpensive chemicals; and (5) they must be non-toxic and must not discolor the water (free from color throw).

Surface area is a function of particle size and shape, size-and-shape variation, packing volume or bed porosity, and particle porosity. Particle size is generally expressed in terms of the *effective size*, and size variation in terms of the *uniformity coefficient* (Section 24-4). Effective sizes of 0.25 to 0.6 mm and uniformity coefficients of 1.7 to 2 are common and in line with sand-filter practice. The porosity of exchange beds, too, accords with that of sand filters. The porosity of the grains of exchange media, themselves, varies with the nature of the medium and the method of its preparation. It may be zero or extremely high.

The exchange capacity of a bed is commonly expressed in terms of the number of kilograins (1 lb = 7 kilograins) of substance removed from the liquid by passage through 1 cu ft of exchange medium. Because ion exchangers were first used for the softening of water, comparisons of exchange capacity are generally made by expressing the substance removed in terms of hardness as $CaCO_3$. A more useful unit of exchange capacity is the number of gram equivalents of the ions removed by a unit volume of exchanger. Gram equivalents per kilogram or milliequivalents per gram may be used instead. The ideal unit would be gram equivalents per square meter of surface. Unfortunately, the effective surface area cannot be measured satisfactorily. When a bed is no longer capable of useful ion exchange, it is said to be exhausted and in need of regeneration.

The water that is to be treated in ion exchangers must be relatively free from suspended matter, oil, H_2S, and Fe^{+++}, or Fe^{++} that is oxidized to Fe^{+++} during treatment. Otherwise, the active surfaces become coated and lose their exchange capacity, and the beds clog and must be washed too frequently. The applied water must also be free from chemicals that will attack the exchange medium. The regenerating wash must likewise be free from interfering substances.

The regenerating requirements of a bed are expressed in pounds of chemical per cubic foot of exchanger or per kilograin of substance removed from the liquid. Here again the substitution of gram equivalents for kilograins, and also for pounds of chemical is a useful procedure.

The nature and performance of ion exchangers commonly used in the treatment of water are discussed below. The minimum depth of bed is generally 24 in., the loading 2 gpm per cu ft, and the rate of flow of the regenerant 1 gpm per cu ft. Rinse-water requirements after regeneration vary from 30 to 100 gal per cu ft. Wash-water needs and rates depend respectively upon the quality of the water treated and the degree of bed expansion to be employed (Section 24-7). Ion exchangers that are synthesized from organic radicals swell, or expand, when the reactive groups on the exchanger are converted from one form to another. The swelling of most organic exchangers is less than 5%, but it is as high as 55% for some of them.

a. Zeolite Exchangers.[7] Zeolites are insoluble sodium-aluminosilicates that are capable of exchanging monovalent sodium ions (1) for multivalent ions of the alkaline earth group, (2) for ammonia, and (3) for the divalent ions of some of the metals in water. They are employed in particular for the removal of Ca^{++} and Mg^{++} in water softening, and for the removal of relatively small amounts of Fe^{++} in deferrization. The chemical structure of the sodium zeolites is portrayed by the formula $Na_2O \cdot Al_2O_3 \cdot xSiO_2 \cdot yH_2O$. For convenience, this formula may be written Na_2Z, the letter Z symbolizing that part of the zeolite which is not exchanged. The common exchange reactions may be written as follows:

$$Na_2Z + \begin{bmatrix} Ca^{++} & Ca \\ Mg^{++} & \rightleftarrows & Mg \\ Fe^{++} & Fe \end{bmatrix} Z + 2Na^+ \qquad 23\text{-}40$$

The ion concentrations of natural, fresh waters are normally such that the reaction is driven to the right. The reaction is reversed, and the zeolite is regenerated by a solution of common salt, or brine, of high Na^+ concentration. The reciprocal exchange of Na^+ creates the sodium cycle. Since no anions are involved in the reaction, either directly or indirectly, alkalinity, acidity, and molar concentrations of reacting as well as non-reacting substances in the water remain unchanged. However, the weight concentration of dissolved solids left in the treated water may be moved either upward or downward. Exchange of $2Na^+$ (atomic wt 23.0) for Mg^{++} (atomic wt 23.4), for example, increases the dissolved solids, whereas exchange of $2Na^+$ for Fe^{++} (atomic wt 55.8) decreases the dissolved solids.

Two types of zeolites are in common use: (*a*) natural non-porous, greensand (glauconite [8]) zeolites and (*b*) synthetic, porous, gel zeolites. The natural zeolites are derived from greensand by washing, heating to slight surface fusion, and treatment with NaOH. The synthetic zeolites are prepared from solutions of Na_2SiO_3 and alum or sodium aluminate ($NaAlO_2$) which set to a gel of $Al(OH)_3$ and H_2SiO_3. The specific gravity of all zeolites, when dry, is 2.1 to 2.4, i.e., not much

[7] Zeolites (from the Greek words *zein* to boil and *lithos* stone) are a family of hydrous silicates originally occurring as secondary minerals in the cavities of lavas. The term *zeolite* has been applied loosely to all cation exchangers. This should not be done.

[8] From the Greek word *glaucos,* blue-green.

smaller than that of quartz sand (2.65). Natural zeolites, however, retain about 10% water, synthetic zeolites as much as 50%. This reduces their apparent specific gravity, and their weights become 100 lb per cu ft (natural) and 55 to 70 lb per cu ft (synthetic). The exchange capacity of the zeolites and their regeneration requirements are summarized in Table 23-6.

TABLE 23-6. Approximate Exchange Capacities and Regeneration Requirements of Ion Exchangers

	Exchange capacity			Regeneration requirements		
Exchanger and cycle (1)	Observed kilograins per cu ft as CaCO₃ (2)	Observed gram equivalents per cu ft (3)	Regenerator (4)	Observed pounds per kilograin exchanged (5)	Observed equivalents per equivalent exchanged (6)	Theoretical pounds per kilograin exchanged (7)
Cation Exchangers						
Natural zeolite, Na	3–6	4–8	NaCl	0.5–1	3–6	0.167
Synthetic zeolite, Na	6–16	8–20	NaCl	0.4–0.5	2–3	0.167
Carbonaceous and resin, Na	5–40	7–50	NaCl	0.3–0.6	1.8–3.6	0.167
Carbonaceous and resin, H	5–40	7–50	H₂SO₄	0.3–0.6	2–4	0.137
Anion Exchangers						
Resin	12–25	16–33	NaOH	0.6–1.0	5–8	0.120
Tricalcium phosphate	0.4–0.9 as F	1.3–3.0	{ NaOH	1.4–3.3	4.7–10	0.300
			{ HCl	0.7–1.7	2.6–6.2	0.275

Columns 2 and 5: Reported values. (1 lb = 7,000 grains = 454 grams.)

Column 3: $(10^3 \times 454)/(7 \times 10^3 \times \text{equivalent wt}) = 64.9/(\text{equivalent wt})$, e.g., $64.9/50 = 1.30$ for $CaCO_3$ and $64.9/19 = 3.41$ for F.

Column 5: To obtain lb per cu ft multiply Column 5 by Column 2. The efficiency of regeneration is $100 \times$ Column 7/ Column 5.

Column 6: $(1/\text{equivalent wt of regenerator})/[10^3/(7 \times 10^3 \times \text{equivalent wt of substance removed})] = (7 \times \text{equivalent wt of substance removed})/(\text{equivalent wt of regenerator})$, e.g., $7 \times 50/58.5 = 5.98$ for NaCl and $CaCO_3$. To obtain 1,000 me per cu ft multiply Column 6 by Column 3. The efficiency of regeneration is 100/Column 6.

Column 7: $(\text{Equivalent wt of regenerator})/(7 \times 10^3 \times \text{equivalent wt of substance removed}/10^3)$, e.g., $58.5/(7 \times 50) = 0.167$ for NaCl and $CaCO_3$.

Natural zeolites are durable and chemically stable. Their use is preferred for water relatively low in hardness (never > 850 to 1,000 mg/l as $CaCO_3$), relatively high in Fe^{++} (but < 1.5 to 2 mg/l), relatively low in silica (which is picked up by the zeolite), and either high or low in pH value. Synthetic zeolites are less durable and less stable chemically. They disintegrate in the presence of 15 mg/l or more of CO_2. Their use is preferred for waters relatively low in Fe^{++} and possessing normal pH values. If the formation of surface coatings of iron is to be prevented, dissolved oxygen must be kept out of the water; otherwise Fe^{++} will precipitate as Fe^{+++}.

Example 23-4. Find (1) the length of time during which a bed of natural zeolite 42 in. deep and operated at a rate of 6 gpm per sq ft will continue to remove

2.01 me/l of Ca^{++}, 0.95 me/l of Mg^{++}, and 0.04 me/l of Fe^{++}, and (2) the amount of salt required for regeneration of the bed at the end of this period. Use the average values given in Columns 3 and 6 of Table 23-6 for the necessary computations.

a. The volume of the bed is $42/12 = 3.5$ cu ft per sq ft. Assuming that the bed will remove 6 gram equivalents per cu ft (Table 23-6), the exchange capacity of the bed is $6 \times 3.5 = 21$ gram equivalents. Since the sum of the substances removed is 3.0 me/l, 21 gram equivalents are removed from $21/(3.0 \times 10^{-3}) = 7.0 \times 10^3$ liters, or $7.0 \times 10^3/3.78 = 1.85 \times 10^3$ gal. The length of the softening cycle, therefore, is $1.85 \times 10^3/6 = 310$ min, or 5 hr and 10 min. The Ca^{++} and Mg^{++} hardness of the water, incidentally, is $2.96 \times 50 = 143$ mg/l as $CaCO_3$.

b. Assuming a salt requirement of 4.5 equivalents per equivalent exchanged, the salt requirement is $4.5 \times 21 = 95$ equivalents, or $95 \times 58.5 = 5,560$ grams per sq ft. This equals $5,560/454 = 12.2$ lb per sq ft of bed. The salt requirement per mg of water treated then becomes $12.2 \times 10^6/1.85 \times 10^3 = 6.6 \times 10^3$ lb or 3.3 tons.

If the desired Ca^{++}, Mg^{++}, and Fe^{++} content of the treated water is to be 0.5 me/l, $(3 - 0.5)/3 = \frac{5}{6}$ of the water should be passed through the exchanger, and $\frac{1}{6}$ by-passed to be mixed with the softened water.

For the removal of iron and manganese by contact oxidation, zeolites may be treated with manganous sulfate and potassium permanganate. Higher oxides of manganese are deposited on the zeolite granules, and both iron and manganese are oxidized to insoluble hydrous oxides. They are washed from the bed when the head loss becomes excessive. Potassium permanganate serves as the regenerant.

b. Carbonaceous and Resinous Exchangers. Carbonaceous cation exchangers are prepared from substances containing humates (coal), lignins (wood), or tannins (tan bark) by treating them with agents such as fuming sulfuric acid, sulfur trioxide, or chlor-sulfonic acid. Resinous cation exchangers are synthesized from substances such as phenol sulfonic acid, formaldehyde, and sulfonated polystyrene. Resinous anion exchangers contain carboxyl groups, amines, and quaternary ammonium compounds.

The cation exchangers are operated either on the sodium or the hydrogen cycle. For the removal of hardness from water, the sodium cycle is common. Regeneration is then by salt. The hydrogen cycle is employed when sodium and potassium as well as hardness must be removed. Regeneration is then by an acid such as sulfuric acid. Letting the letter R stand for that part of the exchanger which is not exchanged, the reactions for operation on the sodium and hydrogen cycles, respectively, are:

$$Na_2R + \begin{bmatrix} Ca^{++} \\ Mg^{++} \end{bmatrix} \rightleftarrows \begin{Bmatrix} Ca \\ Mg \end{Bmatrix} R + 2Na^+ \qquad 23\text{-}41$$

$$H_2R + \begin{bmatrix} Ca^{++} & Ca \\ Mg^{++} & Mg \\ 2Na^+ & Na_2 \\ 2K^+ & K_2 \end{bmatrix} \rightleftarrows R + 2H^+ \qquad 23\text{-}42$$

The ions removed by hydrogen cation exchanges are, therefore, replaced by hydrogen ions, and the pH of the water is lowered. The carbonate equilibrium is upset, and CO_2 is freed (Sections 20-9 and 23-6). Its removal by aeration or by degasification, through heat and vacuum, will reduce the solids concentration of waters in which bicarbonate ion predominates. Anions such as $SO_4^=$ and Cl^- are neutralized economically by split treatment. They can also be removed in an anion exchanger, sometimes called an acid absorber. This will further deionize the water. In the presence of much Na^+ and $SO_4^=$ or Cl^-, acid regeneration of hydrogen cation exchangers may permit the passage, *elution,* or *slippage* of Na^+. This can be reduced by recirculating water treated in an anion exchanger to the influent to the cation exchanger. (See Figure 23-7.)

Synthetic resins derived from the condensation of aromatic amines with aldehydes, e.g., aniline and formaldehyde, or from quaternary ammonium compounds, are good adsorbers of anions such as Cl^- and $SO_4^=$. Letting R_3N represent the complex radical of the resin, the reactions involved in adsorption and in regeneration with soda ash may be written as follows:

$$(R_3N)_2 + \begin{cases} 2Cl^- \\ SO_4^= \end{cases} \rightleftarrows (R_3N)_2 \begin{cases} Cl_2 \\ SO_4 \end{cases} \qquad 23\text{-}43$$

$$(R_3N)_2 \begin{cases} Cl_2 \\ SO_4 \end{cases} + Na_2CO_3 \rightleftarrows 2(R_3N) + Na_2 \begin{cases} Cl_2 \\ SO_4^= \end{cases} + CO_3^= \quad 23\text{-}44$$

Sodium hydroxide is preferred for the regeneration of certain resins. Some of the resins are weakly basic and adsorb little, if any, carbonic acid. For this reason, they may be inserted in the treatment system ahead of aerators or degasifiers. Silicic acid, too, is not removed by such resins. Other resins are strongly basic and will adsorb both carbon dioxide and silicic acid. Silica and the silicates of calcium and magnesium form hard scales in boilers. Sodium chloride and carbonate may cause foaming and priming, and the decomposition of sodium bicarbonate promotes corrosion (by CO_2) and caustic embrittlement (by $NaOH$). See Section 29-2.

The approximate exchange capacities and regeneration requirements of carbonaceous and resinous ion exchangers are included in Table 23-6. These exchangers are resistant to attack by chemicals, and they do not pick up silicon. They are relatively light, weighing but 30 to 50 lb per cu ft when dry. The operation of cation and anion

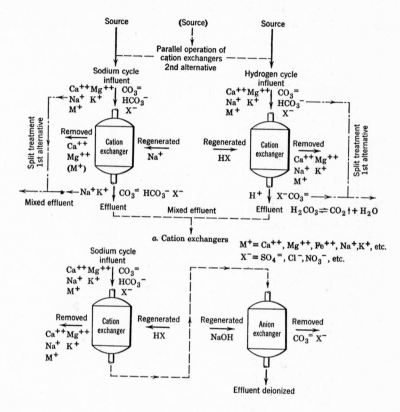

Figure 23-7. Operation of cation and anion exchangers.

exchangers is outlined in Figure 23-7. The ion exchangers presently available are not suitable for the demineralizing of waters containing more than 3,000 to 5,000 mg/l of dissolved solids.

c. Fluoride Exchangers. A processed tricalcium phosphate composed of granules of $Ca_3P_2O_8 \cdot H_2O$ and $3Ca_3P_2O_8 \cdot Ca(OH)_2$ has been found to remove fluorine by ion exchange. Degreased, protein-free bone functions in much the same way. Removals attained and regeneration requirements are included in Table 23-6.

d. Desalting Processes Other than Ion Exchange. They are two in number: (1) electrochemical desalting and (2) distillation. *Electrochemical desalting* is accomplished by membranes that are selectively permeable to cations or anions. These membranes are, in a sense, ion exchangers, but the driving force is electrochemical. The electrochemical desalting device shown in Figure 23-8 consists of a series of alternating anion-permeable and cation-permeable membranes that are mounted in an insulating frame. A cathode is at one end of the

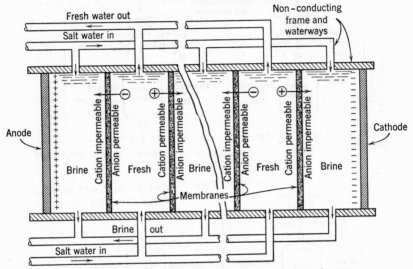

Figure 23-8. Device for electrochemical desalting of water.

series of cells; an anode at the other end. Water held in alternate cells is demineralized by passage of direct-current electricity through the battery of compartments. Anions are driven toward the anode and pass out of those cells that have an anion-permeable membrane on the anode side. These anions are then trapped in the next space which has a cation-permeable (anion-impermeable) membrane on the side toward the anode. The cells losing anions toward the anode also lose cations toward the cathode, while the alternate cells retain both anions and cations. If water that is to be desalted is fed through the ion-losing cells and concentrated brine is bled from the ion-gaining cells, it becomes possible to demineralize water electrochemically in continuous flow. Development of the necessary equipment and economic evaluation of the process are in progress.

Distillation is the oldest method of demineralization. It is currently also the only method by which water containing more than

5,000 mg/l of dissolved solids can be demineralized economically and effectively. Of importance in this connection is the fact that the cost of distillation rises only slightly with increasing salinity. Single-effect, multiple-effect, and vapor-compression stills are employed. A single-effect still is inefficient because it permits the use of only about $\frac{1}{6}$ the latent heat of vaporization to bring the incoming water to the boiling point. The balance must be wasted. Multiple-effect stills are so arranged that each evaporator derives its heat from and serves as the condenser for the vapor from the preceding one. In order to reduce the boiling temperature in each effect and thus to obtain the necessary temperature gradient for multiple-effect operation, each successive effect must be operated at a somewhat lower pressure than the last one. Double- and triple-effect evaporators are generally used for demineralizing water. Theoretically, each pound of steam should evaporate 1 lb of water in a single-effect evaporator, 2 lb in a double-effect evaporator, and 3 lb in a triple-effect evaporator. Because of heat losses, however, the respective performances are only about 0.9, 1.7, and 2.5 lb of evaporated water.

The re-use of latent heat in an evaporator can be increased and the complexity of the device decreased by compressing the vapor produced. The temperature of the vapor can thereby be raised sufficiently to cause the evaporating water to boil. The heating coils in a vapor-compression still serve as the condenser. The still is heated by electricity, or by fuel, until the initial vapor for compression is produced. Thereafter, the heat derived from the mechanical energy developed by the motor that drives the compressor may supply all needs. Compressors driven by electric motors will do this. Compressors driven by internal combustion engines provide additional heat in their cooling jackets and exhaust gases.

Single-effect, double-effect, and triple-effect evaporators produce respectively about 12, 23, and 33 lb of demineralized water for each pound of fuel oil consumed. The yield of diesel-engine-operated, vapor-compression stills is about 200 lb of water per lb of fuel oil.

23-6. Chemical Stabilization. Stabilization is the adjustment of the pH and alkalinity of a water to its calcium carbonate saturation-equilibrium value. At this point the water will neither dissolve nor deposit calcium carbonate, and protective coatings of this substance on the interior walls of pipes are thereby stabilized. If the pH lies below the equilibrium values, no protective coatings are formed, and the water has free access to the metal. Natural waters of low alkalinity and hardness, or of high CO_2 content, and coagulated, ion-exchange-softened, or demineralized waters fall into this category. If the pH lies above the equilibrium value, deposits of calcium carbonate accumulate in distribution mains, meters, hot-water heaters, and other equipment. This reduces their carrying capacity, or it causes poor heat transfer or the overheating of metals in boilers. Other problems, such as the incrustation of sand or gravel in filters, are also created. Since the equilibrium point shifts with temperature, it is not possible to attain a perfect balance for both cold-water and hot-water systems at the same time.

The pH associated with calcium carbonate equilibrium can be calculated or it can be determined by test. The equations developed by Langelier[9] form the basis for the necessary calculations. In laboratory tests, the equilibrium point is assumed to have been reached after water has stood overnight in contact with pure, washed calcium carbonate powder. The pH value measured at that time is given the subscript s, i.e., pH$_s$. The equilibrium equation is constructed from Equations 20-3 and 18-47:

$$[CO_3^=] = \frac{2K_2'}{[H^+]}\left(\frac{[A] + 10^3[H^+] - 10^3K_w'/[H^+]}{1 + 2K_2'/[H^+]}\right) \qquad 20\text{-}3$$

$$[Ca^{++}][CO_3^=] = 4 \times 10^6 K_s' \quad \text{or} \quad [CO_3^=] = 4 \times 10^6 K_s'/[Ca^{++}] \qquad 18\text{-}47$$

where $[Ca^{++}]$, $[CO_3^=]$, and $[A]$ are expressed in me/l while $[H^+]$ is given in mol/l. Equating the two expressions for $[CO_3^=]$,

$$4 \times 10^6 K_s' = \frac{2K_2'[Ca^{++}]}{[H^+]}\left(\frac{[A] + 10^3[H^+] - 10^3K_w'/[H^+]}{1 + 2K_2'/[H^+]}\right) \qquad 23\text{-}45$$

The molar concentrations of H^+ and $OH^- = K_w'/[H^+]$ are sufficiently small to be neglected unless the saturation pH value is greater than about 10.3. The following logarithmic approximation of the equilibrium equation is thereby obtained:

$$p\text{H}_s = \log\frac{K_s'}{K_2'} - \log[Ca^{++}] - \log[A] + 6.301$$

$$+ \log(1 + 2K_2'/[H^+]) \qquad 23\text{-}46$$

The last term in this equation may be omitted when the saturation pH value is less than about 9 because the magnitude of this term is then but 0.05. At pH 10.3, however, it is 0.45. If the water contains significant amounts of dissolved solids, the values of K_s' and K_2' must allow for the activity or effective concentration of the ions (Sections

[9] W. F. Langelier, "The Analytical Control of Anticorrosion Water Treatment," J., Am. Water Works Assoc., 28, 1500 (1936).

18-5 and 20-9). This is a function of the total ionic strength. If concentrations are expressed in me/l, the relationship of ionic strength μ to concentration c_i and charge z_i is

$$\mu = 5 \times 10^{-2} \sum_{1}^{i} c_i z_i \qquad \text{23-47}$$

This is a modification of Equation 18-5. In the absence of a complete mineral analysis, μ can be evaluated approximately from a knowledge of the total dissolved-solids content of the water. For ionic strengths between 2.5×10^{-3} and 10^{-2}, or for a total dissolved-solids content S_d of less than 500 mg/l, the following observational equation may be written:

$$\mu = 2.5 \times 10^{-5} S_d \qquad \text{23-48}$$

The activity coefficient f_i is approximated by Equation 18-6:

$$- \log f_i = 0.5 z_i^2 \frac{\sqrt{\mu}}{1 + \sqrt{\mu}} \qquad \text{18-6}$$

In accordance with the activity concept both K_s' and K_2' must be activity constants and the resulting salinity-correction term $S = \dfrac{2\sqrt{\mu}}{1 + \sqrt{\mu}}$ must be added to Equation 23-46. Larson and Buswell [10] have proposed a salinity term of $S = \dfrac{2.5\sqrt{\mu}}{1 + 5.3\sqrt{\mu} + 5.5\mu}$. Substituting the salinity-correction term S in Equation 23-46,

$$p\mathrm{H}_s = \log \frac{K_s}{K_2} - \log [\mathrm{Ca}^{++}] - \log [\mathrm{A}] + 6.301 + S \qquad \text{23-49}$$

For $K_s = 4.82 \times 10^{-9}$ and $K_2 = 4.69 \times 10^{-11}$,

$$p\mathrm{H}_s = 8.313 - \log [\mathrm{Ca}^{++}] - \log [\mathrm{A}] + S \qquad \text{23-50}$$

In order to provide a measure of the stability of a given water, Langelier has proposed naming the difference between the measured pH of the water and its calculated or observed $p\mathrm{H}_s$ the saturation index I. A value of $I = p\mathrm{H} - p\mathrm{H}_s = 0$ indicates that the water is in equilibrium; a positive value that the water is oversaturated with $CaCO_3$ (or lacking in excess CO_2) and will tend to deposit $CaCO_3$; a

[10] T. E. Larson and A. M. Buswell, "Calcium Carbonate Saturation Index and Alkalinity Interpretations," *J. Am. Water Works Assoc.*, *34*, 1667 (1942).

negative value, conversely, that the water is undersaturated (or possessed of excess CO_2) and will tend to dissolve existing deposits of $CaCO_3$. Excess, or *aggressive*, CO_2 is the amount of free CO_2 in excess of that required to maintain $CaCO_3$ in solution. Substitution of the measured H^+ concentration and the calculated H_s^+ concentration (Equation 23-45) in Equation 20-8 establishes the following relationship when the terms recording molar concentrations of H^+ and OH^- are neglected as before:

$$[CO_2]_{excess} = 2\frac{[A]}{K_1'}\left([H^+] - \frac{2K_2'[A][Ca^{++}]}{4 \times 10^6 K_s'}\right) \qquad \text{23-51}$$

Here $[CO_2]_{excess}$, $[Ca^{++}]$, and $[A]$ are expressed in me/l, and $[H^+]$ in mol/l.

Temperature corrections as well as salinity corrections must be applied to the constants K_1, K_2, and K_s. Since (H^+) varies directly as K_1, Larson and Buswell have suggested that the saturation index I at a given temperature should vary from that at the reference temperature (25 C) by the difference between the logarithm of K_1K_s/K_2 at the reference temperature and that at the given temperature. This difference is approximately 1.5×10^{-2} units per deg C.

Example 23-5. A sample of water has a pH of 7.00 at 25 C and contains 7.5 mg/l of Ca^{++}, 30 mg/l of alkalinity as $CaCO_3$, and 50 mg/l of dissolved solids. Find (*a*) the saturation index at 25 C, (*b*) the amount of excess CO_2 in the water, and (*c*) the saturation index at 60 C. Assume the following base values for the ionization and solubility constants at 25 C: $K_1 = 4.45 \times 10^{-7}$, $K_2 = 4.69 \times 10^{-11}$, and $K_s = 4.82 \times 10^{-9}$.

a. By Equation 23-48: $\mu = 2.5 \times 10^{-5} \times 50 = 12.5 \times 10^{-4}$. The correction for salinity is, therefore: $S = \dfrac{2 \times \sqrt{12.5 \times 10^{-4}}}{1 + \sqrt{12.5 \times 10^{-4}}} = 6.8 \times 10^{-2}$. For $7.5/(40.1/2) = 0.374$ me/l of Ca^{++} and $30/50 = 0.60$ me/l of alkalinity, Equation 23-50 states that pH$_s = 8.313 - \log 0.374 - \log 0.60 + 0.068 = 9.03$.

Hence $I = 7.00 - 9.03 = -2.03$.

b. By Equation 23-51:

$$[CO_2]_{excess} = \frac{2 \times 0.60}{4.45 \times 10^{-7}}\left(10^{-7} - \frac{2 \times 4.69 \times 10^{-11} \times 0.60 \times 0.374}{4 \times 10^6 \times 4.82 \times 10^{-9}}\right) = 0.27 \text{ me/l},$$

or $0.27 \times 22 = 5.9$ mg/l uncorrected for salinity.

c. For a temperature of 60 C or a difference of $(60 - 25) = 35$ C, $I = -2.03 + 1.5 \times 10^{-2} \times 35 = -1.5$.

23-7. Corrosion and Electrolysis. The corrosion of metals is a complex and, as yet, poorly understood electrochemical process by which metals deteriorate and are eventually destroyed. Electrolysis is the deterioration or destruction of metals by straying electrical currents. Both corrosion and electrolysis are of great importance in water supply and waste-water disposal.

a. Processes of Corrosion. The processes involved in corrosion are best exemplified by the corrosion of a metal such as iron in contact with water. Three principal steps may be distinguished: (1) an anodic reaction by which the metal goes into solution and electrons are freed to flow through the metal to a cathode, (2) a cathodic reaction that makes use of the liberated electrons, and (3) a series of reactions of the metal ions with the water. The last step, ordinarily, results in the formation of insoluble products of corrosion which are precipitated from the water. This completes the cycle of corrosion and clears the way for renewed solution of the metal. Interruption of, or interference in, any one of these steps will alter the course or the rate of corrosion. The chemistry of the corrosion reactions has been outlined in Section 18-10. It is summarized below in order to identify the cycle of corrosion.

1. The anodic reaction is a function of the oxidation potential of the metal, or that of its alloy or oxide, whichever happens to be present at the metal-water interface. As shown in Table 18-4, the anodic reaction (or first step) of pure iron is: $Fe = Fe^{++} + 2e$ with a standard half-cell potential of $+0.409$ volts.

2. The cathodic reaction (or second step) that follows is more complex and less well understood. At pH values below 4.5, gaseous hydrogen is evolved according to the reaction $2H^+ + 2e = H_2$ which has the reference potential of zero. The evolution of hydrogen frees the metal surface for further corrosion. In these circumstances pH is an important factor in determining the rate of corrosion. In pure water ($H^+ = 10^{-7}$), hydrogen is plated out on the metal which is then said to be *polarized* or protected. The reaction is again $2H^+ + 2e = H_2$, but the standard electrode potential, or driving force, is -0.414 volts.

In the presence of oxygen other half-reactions may go into operation. They are taken from Table 18-4 as

$$O_2 + 4H^+ + 4e = 2H_2O, (H^+ = 10^0), +1.229 \text{ volts in strongly acid solutions}$$
$$O_2 + 4H^+(10^{-7} M) + 4e = 2H_2O, (H^+ = 10^{-7}), +0.815 \text{ volts in pure water}$$
$$2H_2O + O_2 + 4e = 4OH^-, (H^+ = 10^{-14}), +0.401 \text{ volts in strongly basic solutions}$$

It is seen that the driving force is greatly increased in the presence of oxygen and that it is greatest in strongly acid solutions.

Wagner [11] has shown that hydrogen peroxide or peroxyl ion is formed as an intermediate substance in the reduction of oxygen, not only in acid but also in alkaline solution. The following half-actions may be written:

---

[11] H. B. Wagner, *Relationship of Peroxide Formation to Ferrous Corrosion,* Dissertation, The Johns Hopkins University, May, 1948.

$$O_2 + 2H^+ + 2e = H_2O_2, (H^+ = 10^0), +0.682 \text{ volts}$$

$$O_2 + 2H^+ + 2e = H_2O_2, (H^+ = 10^{-7}), +0.269 \text{ volts}$$

$$O_2 + H_2O + 2e = OH^- + HO_2^-, (H^+ = 10^{-14}), +0.076 \text{ volts}$$

Wagner believes it quite probable that on the acid side of the pH scale the cathode potential corresponds to that for complete reduction of oxygen, $+1.229$ volts, whereas on the alkaline side the cathode potential corresponds more nearly to that of the equation for incomplete reduction of peroxyl ion, $+0.076$ volts. The lower cell potential would help to explain the lower corrosion rates observed in alkaline solutions.

3. The reactions of the metal ions (or third step) constitute the most complex phase of the corrosion cycle. In the presence of carbon dioxide and alkaline ions, the formation of ferrous bicarbonate, followed ultimately by its oxidation to ferric hydroxide, may play an important role. For this reason a carbon dioxide theory of corrosion of iron was once accepted. Whatever the processes, the end result is the deposition of an insoluble hydrous oxide of iron, or *rust*.

The composition of natural waters is so varied that present knowledge of what takes place in the three steps that have been outlined does not, as yet, offer a satisfactory explanation, and especially not a quantitative evaluation, of corrosion effects. However, the following qualitative observations are of interest:

1. Oxygen and water are essential to corrosion. In the absence of either one, there is essentially no corrosion.

2. Contact between dissimilar metals or the existence of areas of dissimilar oxidation potentials in the same metal promotes corrosion. A galvanic cell is formed, and the rate of corrosion is stepped up.

3. The anodic metal or area, which possesses the highest oxidation potential, corrodes; the cathodic metal or area does not. Zinc, for example, is anodic to copper or iron. This accounts for the dezincification of yellow brass and for the reduced corrosion of iron in galvanized-iron pipes until the zinc coating has been destroyed. Iron, in turn, is anodic to copper. Red or rusty water may therefore issue from a bronze faucet attached to an iron pipe.

4. Accumulation of the products of corrosion in the vicinity of the anode decreases the rate of corrosion, while replenishment of oxygen and of hydrogen ion at the cathode increases the rate of corrosion. For this reason, the rate of corrosion is decreased with time owing to the accumulation of rust or similar oxidation products, and it is increased by high velocities of flow owing to the more rapid removal of corrosion-retarding substances and the replenishment of corrosion-promoting substances.

5. The presence of electrolytes promotes corrosion by facilitating the flow of electricity.

6. Corrosion is more rapid in acid than in alkaline solutions.

7. Direct-current electricity corrodes the metal of the pole that serves as the anode. Underground pipes are corroded by stray electrical currents at points where positive electricity leaves the pipe.

b. Control of Corrosion. The selection of materials and of methods of corrosion control are directed toward interrupting or controlling one or more of the three steps in the cycle of corrosion. The materials and methods commonly employed include the following:

1. Corrosion-resistant metals or alloys. They are materials that either possess low solution potentials or that lay down protective coatings of dense oxides when they are corroded. Stainless steel, Monel metal, tin, and copper are examples.

2. Non-metallic materials. Poor conductors of electricity and non-electrolytes resist attack by most waters. Such materials include reinforced-concrete, asbestos-cement, fiber, and plastic pipes.

3. Coatings. Coatings interrupt both anodic and cathodic reactions by preventing escape of cations and denying access of water and oxygen. Either metallic (for example, zinc, tin, and chromium) or non-metallic coatings (for example, paints, cement, bituminous materials, and plastics) are suitable.

4. Deactivation. Deactivation is the removal of oxygen. It may be accomplished by heating and degasification, by the direct application of a vacuum, or by passage of water over iron filings or turnings.

5. Cathodic protection. Cathodic protection is provided (1) by using direct-current electricity to feed electrons into a metal and render it cathodic or (2) by attaching a metal of higher oxidation potential which, being anodic, will corrode and be sacrificed to provide the desired protection. Electrical bleeding of distribution mains and other underground utilities and cathodic protection of steel water-storage tanks are examples of the first method. Attaching plates of zinc to the hulls or other underwater metal parts of ships and the insertion of magnesium plugs in hot-water heater tanks are examples of the second.

6. Insulation. Insulation is the creation of resistance to the flow of electrical currents. Examples are (1) the insertion of insulating couplings or connectors between dissimilar metals to prevent the production of galvanic currents and (2) the use of insulating joints in water mains to oppose the flow of stray electrical currents.

7. Deposition of protective coatings. The deposition of coatings of calcium carbonate on pipes has been discussed in Section 23-6. Silicate films have also been employed. Small amounts of sodium silicate ($Na_2O \cdot 3.25SiO_2$ or $Na_2O \cdot 2SiO_2$) will deposit dense, adherent but slightly permeable films. An initial dosage of 12 to 16 mg/l as SiO_2 is introduced into the water for about a month. After that, dosage is reduced to the amount necessary to maintain a residual of 1 mg/l in remote parts of the distribution system.

8. Inhibitors. Inhibitors are substances that are believed to form adsorbed films on the metals they are to protect. Polyphosphates are reported to reduce corrosion by interrupting catalytic reactions in the corrosion cycle. Sodium hexametaphosphate, $(NaPO_3)_6$, sodium heptaphosphate, $Na_2O \cdot (NaPO_3)_7$, or tetra-sodium pyrophosphate, $Na_4P_2O_7$, are examples of these chemical agents. Initial dosages of 6 to 12 mg/l are later reduced to 2 to 6 mg/l to maintain a minimum residual of about 0.5 mg/l. The polyphosphates also function as sequestering agents that prevent the precipitation of calcium, magnesium, and iron.

23-8. Handling, Storing, and Feeding Chemicals. The properties of chemicals that are commonly used in the treatment of water and

waste water are listed in Table A-5 in the Appendix to this book. This information permits a determination of the handling facilities, storage requirements, and feeding arrangements that must be provided for the safe, economical, and satisfactory operation of a given treatment works. Size and location of plant as well as available sources of supply and shipping facilities for chemicals are also important elements in the engineering design. In small plants, chemicals may be handled satisfactorily by simple hoisting equipment and two-wheeled trucks (1) to be stored on open floors in their shipping containers and (2) to be moved to the feeding devices. Receiving and feeding weights may be determined by simple beam scales with platforms placed at floor level for convenience. Large plants generally require the installation of mechanical or pneumatic material-handling equipment to unload dry bulk chemicals from freight cars or automotive trucks and to transport them to storage bins, similar to grain storage bins, whence they can flow by gravity to weighing and feeding machines. In such plants, liquids are pumped to storage and to feeding devices. Liquefied gases such as chlorine and ammonia will generally flow under their container pressure. (See Figure 2-5.)

With rare exceptions, the chemicals are dissolved or suspended in water before they are introduced into feed lines. Feeding devices regulate the amounts of chemicals to be added to the water or wastewater. Dry-feed machines control the dosage by the rate of volumetric or gravimetric displacement of dry chemicals. Volumetric machines generally plow, push, or shake the chemical off a receiving table onto which the chemical drops from a hopper-shaped supply bin, as in a "chicken-feed" device. Solution feed depends upon the regulated displacement of liquid chemicals or of dry chemicals that have been dissolved or suspended in water to produce solutions of known strength or suspension of known concentration. Measurement is by constant-head orifices or by pumps. Pumped flow may be proportioned automatically to the rate of flow of the water or waste water to be treated.

The dissolved or suspended chemical is conveyed to the point of application through pressure or gravity pipelines. These pipelines must be resistant to attack by the chemical transported. Suitable materials are indicated in Table A-5 of the Appendix. To avoid clogging and permit cleaning, lines are liberally dimensioned and laid out in straight runs. Clean-outs are provided.

For the carbonation of water, CO_2 is commonly generated at the plant in a coke, oil, or gas burner. The gas may be cooled, scrubbed, and dried by passage through limestone chips and steel turnings before it is compressed and delivered to diffusers or bubblers in the carbonation chamber. A gas-flow meter measures the amount added. For the feeding of gaseous chemicals other than CO_2, see Section 27-12. Carbon dioxide, ozone, and chlorinated copperas are the only chemicals that must be produced at the site or that can ordinarily be produced there more economically than in commercial chemical plants.

Flow sheets for chemicals can be elaborated in wide variety depending upon the treatment processes involved. The points of application should be kept as flexible as possible. Treatment methods and with them the points best suited to the introduction of chemicals are subject to change with the development of new chemicals and treatment processes, with varying quality of the water or waste water, with seasonal requirements, and with demands for higher standards of performance.

23-9. Disposal of Waste Products of Chemical Treatment. The waste products of chemical coagulation, precipitation, and ion exchange include both sludges and liquids. Liquids are normally discharged into waste-water systems or directly into receiving waters. The treatment and disposal of sludges are considered in Chapter 26. The possible recovery of the chemicals from sludges and liquids continues to present a challenge. Recovery of the large amounts of calcium needed for the softening of hard waters and of the calcium thrown down in the process is particularly attractive. To be used again, the dewatered, dried, and calcined sludge must not contain much magnesium. Calcining is the heating of the dried solids to drive off carbon dioxide. Both CaO and MgO are produced. Incidentally, carbon dioxide may be provided in this way for needed carbonation of the softened water.

One of two processes is normally employed to remove magnesium from the sludge to be recovered. In the Lykken-Estabrook process the entire amount of recovered chemical is added to about 12% of the water to be softened. Sludge thrown down contains the MgO in the added chemical as well as some of the magnesium in the water treated. It is, therefore, wasted. The overtreated water is then mixed with the balance of the water and softens it. Lime is recovered from the resulting sludge. The Hoover process also uses two-stage treatment but in different fashion. The lime added in the first stage is so proportioned that only the calcium will be removed from the water. Magnesium is precipitated by the lime introduced in the second stage. The sludge from the first stage is recovered; that from the second is wasted. Where a third or final clarification of the water follows recarbonation, the precipitated lime of this stage is also recovered.

24-1. General Considerations. When water flows through a porous, or open-textured, medium such as sand, some of the suspended and colloidal impurities in the water are left behind in the pores or openings or upon the medium itself. This process of separating impurities from the carrying liquid is called filtration. The water may (1) fill the pores of the medium, as it does in the sand filters commonly used in water purification, (2) trickle over the medium, as it does over the crushed rock of a sewage filter, or (3) be held in the medium from which it must be pressed or sucked out, as from the pores of sewage sludge.

Discussion of filters and the processes of filtration is confined in this chapter to the passage of water through fine-grained materials, the voids of which are filled with the flowing water. Sewage treatment on trickling filters is considered in Chapter 25, and the dewatering of sludge on cloth filters in Chapter 26.

Filtration is an important and active process in the natural purification of ground water. Observation of the relative freedom of such waters from objectionable impurities offers the probable background for the first large-scale use, in 1829, of beds of sand by James Simpson for the clarification of river water pumped from the Thames by the Chelsea (London) Water Company.

24-2. Theory of Filtration. A number of different processes combine to produce the over-all removal of impurities associated with the filtration of water through granular substances. The most important of these processes are straining, sedimentation, flocculation, and, for heavily polluted waters and sewage, biological activity.

a. Straining. This is the simplest of the filtration phenomena. It takes place, almost entirely, at the surface of the filter where the water enters the pores of the filter bed. Initially, straining removes only those substances that are larger than the pore openings. As filtration is continued, the substances strained out accumulate on the surface of the filter in a mat [1] through which the water must pass before it can reach the filter medium itself. Removal of impurities is thereby further restricted to the surface of the filter.

Where the water to be filtered contains much organic matter, adventitious organisms, principally saprophytic bacteria, will utilize these substances for energy and growth within the surface mat provided that the mat is left in place over a considerable period of time: for days rather than hours. Multiplication of zoogleal organisms will then render the mat sticky or slimy, and the effectiveness of the straining process will be further enhanced. The resulting progressive increase in efficiency is referred to as the ripening or breaking-in of the filter. The time consumed in ripening the filter varies principally with the concentration and availability of the impurities as food for microorganisms and with the temperature of the water. High concentrations and food values and high temperatures encourage cell growth and produce a heavy surface mat. Waters that are rich in algae and related organisms may build up surface mats of considerable thickness. Removal of the mat and of the supporting surface layer of the filter medium becomes necessary when the resistance to filtration has mounted to excessive values or when the surface mat is in danger of being ruptured.

Water that has been coagulated or from which iron has been precipitated generally contains enough residual floc to build up a mat of the floc upon the filter surface. Addition of filter aids, such as diatomaceous earth, creates a cake upon the supporting medium. Such mats also act as straining media.

b. Sedimentation. Hazen [2] has proposed that the removal by filters of particles that are smaller than the pore space is analogous to sedimentation in a basin filled with a very large number of trays. In this connection it is well to realize that a cubic meter of spherical sand grains 5×10^{-2} cm in diameter, for example, contains, together with 40% void space, $0.6 \times 10^6/[(\pi/6) \times 125 \times 10^{-6}] = 9.15 \times 10^9$ particles with a gross surface area of $9.15 \times 10^9 \times \pi \times 25 \times 10^{-4} \times 10^{-2} = 7.2 \times 10^3$ sq m. If we assume with Hazen that but $\frac{1}{6}$ of the area is horizontal and facing upwards, $\frac{1}{2}$ being in contact with other sand grains, and $\frac{1}{3}$ of the remainder being exposed to scour, the effective

---

[1] This mat was called a *Schmutzdecke* or cover of filth by early German investigators. The German expression, perhaps because it was less objectionable in its connotation than its literal meaning, has been adopted into the English language as a technical term.

[2] See Section 22-5.

surface area of an equivalent settling basin would be ($\frac{1}{6} \times \frac{1}{2} \times \frac{2}{3} = \frac{1}{18}$) $\times 7.2 \times 10^3 = 400$ sq m, or 400 trays, per meter of depth. In accordance with Equations 22-15 and 22-8, the settling velocity of removable particles is thereby $\frac{1}{400}$ and their diameter $\frac{1}{20}$ that of a particle that can be deposited in a settling basin of equal loading. Since slow sand filters are made about 1 m deep and ordinarily receive but $\frac{1}{10}$ the amount of water per unit surface that settling basins do, it follows that a slow sand filter, in comparison with settling basins, can be expected to remove particles with $\frac{1}{4,000}$ the settling velocity and of less than $\frac{1}{60}$ the diameter.

The efficiency of filtration, like that of sedimentation, is observed to decrease with temperature, although the resistance to filtration increases.

c. Flocculation. Floc formation in a filter may be explained in terms of Smoluchowski's equation and the principles laid down in Section 23-4. In addition, a filter offers opportunity for contact between the impurities contained in water and waste water and the large surface of the grains composing the filter. As the floc builds up in size, it becomes large enough to be retained in the constrictions between the individual pores in spite of increasing pore velocities. Encroachment of the waterway, however, carries non-flocculated solids deeper and deeper into the filter. At low temperatures, the viscosity of water is high and flocculation is decreased. Also the shearing force of the water is increased. When this force exceeds the shearing strength of the floc, the floc particles are torn apart. Again they penetrate farther into the bed. For these reasons, too, the efficiency of filtration decreases with temperature.

d. Biological Activity. How microorganisms may take part in the straining process has already been described. They may also contribute to sedimentation and flocculation by forming sticky, gelatinous coatings on the surface of the filter grains. To these coatings finely divided solids adhere, while colloidal and even dissolved solids are utilized for energy and growth. The mechanism of biological activity is that described in connection with biological flocculation and precipitation (Chapter 25). It produces chemical as well as physical changes in water quality. These can be of considerable magnitude in highly polluted waters and waste waters. In such waters the oxygen requirements of the saprophytes are relatively so great that filter beds treating them would quickly become septic if the beds were not operated intermittently and in such manner as to permit the drawing of air into the filter for the maintenance of aerobic conditions. In the treatment of relatively clean waters, on the other hand, or waters that have been suitably prepared by coagulation and sedimentation, biological activity is unimportant.

24-3. Types of Filters. A number of different kinds of granular filters have been used for the purification of water and the treatment of waste water. But few of the different devices, however, have stood the test of experience.

a. Granular Water Filters. There are two common types of granular water filters. These differ hydraulically and structurally (1) because the filter beds are intended to be operated either at relatively low rates (1 to 10 mgad) or at relatively high rates (100 to 200 mgad), and (2) because penetration of suspended matter and its subsequent removal during cleaning operations are purposely confined to the surface layer of "slow" filters, whereas substantially the full depth of "rapid" filters is intended to contribute to purification and hence also to require cleaning. Natural silica sand is a common filtering medium, but there are other fine-grained filtering materials, such as crushed anthracite. The two kinds of filters are generally referred to as "slow sand filters" and "rapid sand filters."

Figure 24-1 shows typical sections through, and plans of, a slow sand filter and a rapid sand filter. See also Figures 24-12 and 2-5. A rough comparison of the general features of the two filters is presented in Table 24-1.

It is seen that rapid filters operate at approximately thirty times the rate of slow sand filters, and it is understandable that they should need to be cleaned about thirty times as often. Back-washing the filter, with or without the assistance of added mechanical scour (1) by stirring the suspended sand with rakes,[3] (2) blowing air into the bed before or during back-washing (generally the former), or (3) directing jets of water into the expanded sand, is a distinguishing feature of the rapid sand filter. High rates of flow and the need to carry wash water under pressure through the underdrainage system and remove it from the top of the filter further complicate the network of conduits and appurtenances required in rapid sand filters. Nevertheless, the rapid filter has essentially displaced the slow sand filter in North American practice where it has proved itself to be a flexible, adaptable, and economical water-purification device. A very high degree of purification can be reached by placing slow filters in series with rapid filters. This arrangement, however, is generally confined to plants in which the performance or capacity of existing slow filters has had to be supplemented.

[3] Use of rotating rakes led to the name "mechanical filter."

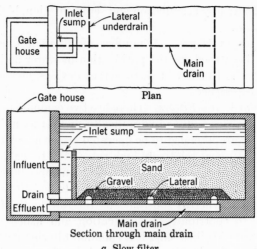

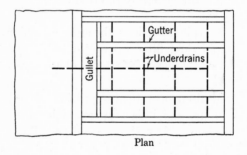

Section through main drain

a. Slow filter

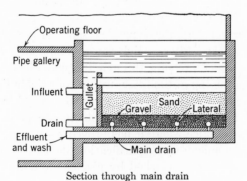

Section through main drain

b. Rapid filter

Figure 24-1. Diagrammatic sections through and simplified plans of a slow and a rapid sand filter.

TABLE 24-1. General Features of Construction and Operation of Slow and
Rapid Sand Filters *

	Slow sand filters	Rapid sand filters
Rate of filtration	1 to **4** to 10 mgad	100 to **125** † to 200 mgad
Size of bed	Large, ½ acre	Small, ¹⁄₁₀₀ to ¹⁄₁₀ acre
Depth of bed	12 in. of gravel; 42 in. of sand, usually reduced to 24 in. by scraping	18 in. of gravel; 30 in. of sand, **or less**
Size of sand ‡	Effective size 0.25 to **0.3** to 0.35 mm; uniformity coefficient 2 to **2.5** to 3	0.45 mm and higher; uniformity coefficient 1.5 and lower
Grain size distribution of sand in filter	Unstratified	Stratified with smallest grains at top and coarsest at bottom
Underdrainage system	Split tile laterals laid in coarse stone and discharging into a tile or concrete main drain	(1) Perforated pipe laterals discharging into main pipe, or (2) diffuser-plate bottom
Loss of head	0.2 ft initial to 4 ft final	1 ft initial to 9 ft final
Length of run between cleanings	20 to **30** to 60 days	12 to **24** to 40 hr
Penetration of suspended matter	Superficial	Deep
Method of cleaning	(1) Scraping off surface layer of sand and washing removed sand, (2) washing surface sand in place by traveling washer	Scour by mechanical rakes, air, or water; and removal of dislodged suspended matter by upward flow or backwashing which stratifies the bed
Amount of wash water used in cleaning sand	0.2 to 0.6% of water filtered	1 to **4** to 6% of water filtered
Preparatory treatment of water	Generally confined to aeration, but could also include flocculation and sedimentation	Flocculation and sedimentation are common
Supplementary treatment of water	In absence of flocculation, confined to chlorination	Chlorination and other supplementary treatment are common
Cost of construction	Higher	Lower
Cost of operation	**Lower**	Higher
Depreciation of plant	Lower	Higher

* The most common values are shown in boldface type.
† 125 mgad = 2 gpm per sq ft.
‡ For a definition of sand-size terms, see Section 24-4.

When rapid filters must be placed under pressure, they are housed in a pressure-resisting shell and called pressure filters. Use of these units is normally confined to industrial and swimming-pool installations. In case of trouble, many of their parts are not as accessible, and their space requirements are not as favorable as those of gravity filters.

b. Granular Waste-Water Filters. Because of its putrescibility and its high content of clogging substances, sewage cannot be applied to rapid filters unless it has undergone treatment that would ordinarily permit its being discharged into a receiving water without added filtration. Where rapid sand filters have been employed for the treatment of waste water, they are patterned after water filters, but grain size is increased substantially (1×10^{-1} to 3×10^{-1} cm) whereas rates of filtration are generally lower than 2 gpm per sq ft and filter runs are shortened.

Rapid filters using a thin layer (about 3 in.) of granular magnetite ore as the filtering medium have in some instances been attached to the effluent weirs of settling tanks or built as separate structures. The magnetite is relatively coarse (6×10^{-2} to 1.5×10^{-1} cm) and weighs about twice as much as sand. It is lifted by a traveling solenoid

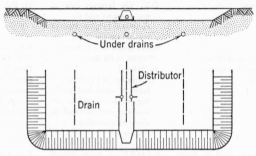

Figure 24-2. Intermittent sand filter with central distribution. *After Imhoff and Fair.*

and washed by influent sewage that is pumped through the expanded magnetite.

Where natural sand deposits are available, they have been successfully converted into sand filters that treat sewage and industrial wastewaters intermittently at rates varying from between 20,000 and 80,000 gpd per acre to between 400,000 and 800,000 gpd per acre, depending upon the degree of pretreatment to which the sewage has been subjected. The lower range of values is a minimum for raw sewage, the higher one a maximum for biologically treated sewage. An intermediate range of 40,000 to 120,000 gpd per acre holds for settled sewage. At these rates, intermittent sand filters produce an excellent effluent.

Construction of an intermittent sand filter is illustrated in Figure 24-2. Drainage pipes, laid with open joints, are ordinarily placed at depths of 3 to 4 ft and surrounded with graded layers of gravel and coarse stone that keep the sand out of the drains. In deep sand deposits, the effluent may seep into the ground-water stream, and drains may not be needed. Waste water is piped to the beds and discharged onto a protective stone or concrete apron or into a concrete flume or carrier which distributes the waste water over the bed. The depth of flooding is 1 to 4 in. in 7 to 20 min. Each dose carries from 25,000 to 100,000 gal onto an acre of bed. One or more doses are applied each day. Surface accumulations of solids and, where necessary, surface sand are scraped off from time to time. They are ordinarily disposed of by burying or filling. Beds are resanded when they become too shallow. In cold climates, the beds are furrowed and then dosed deeply on a cold night to create a surface sheet of ice that will span the furrows and keep the bed itself from freezing and cracking.

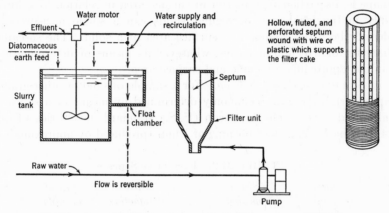

Figure 24-3. Operation of a small diatomaceous earth filter.

Water containing a great deal of organic matter has, in at least one instance,[4] been treated intermittently on sand filters.

c. Diatomaceous-Earth Filters. In this water filter, a layer of diatomaceous earth is built up on a supporting medium or septum that simultaneously acts as the drainage device. Water is then filtered through this layer (precoat). If the water is very turbid, additional diatomaceous earth (body feed) must be carried onto the precoat. Diatomaceous earth consists of the skeletons of diatoms 0.5 to 12 μ in size. Precoating requires the addition to recirculating water of 0.1 to 0.5 lb of earth per sq ft of septum. If the water to be filtered contains inorganic silts, body feed must be added in the ratio of about 1.25 to 1 on a dry-weight basis. For organic slimes this ratio must be increased to about 3 to 1. Filtration is at a rate of 2.5 to 6 gpm per sq ft. Back-washing at rates of 7 to 10 gpm per sq ft removes the filter cake. Figure 24-3 shows a diagram of the operation of a diatomaceous-earth filter. Filters such as this are intended principally for portable and emergency use.

[4] Ludlow Supply of Springfield, Mass.

Granular Filtering Materials

24-4. Grain Size and Shape. The granular materials employed in filtration differ in size and size distribution, in shape and shape variation, and in density and chemical composition. These variations must be known if the use of the materials is to be based on rational considerations. Both size and shape may be expressed in a number of different ways. Size is three-dimensional and generally implies volume. Shape is, in particular, a matter of surface area in relation to volume. Only in the ideal case of regular solids can a single measurement identify both the volume and surface area of a solid. The so-called diameter of irregular particles, whatever its means of determination, can but approximate volume and surface area.

a. Size and Size Distribution. For a sample of sand or other granular material, these are commonly determined by means of a series of calibrated sieves. The American (U. S.) standard sieve series (Table 24-2) is based on a sieve opening of 1 mm (produced by approximately

TABLE 24-2. U. S. Sieve Series

Sieve designation * number	Size of opening, mm	Sieve designation number	Size of opening, mm
200	0.074	20	0.84
140	0.105	(18)	(1.00)
100	0.149	16	1.19
70	0.210	12	1.68
50	0.297	8	2.38
40	0.42	6	3.36
30	0.59	4	4.76

* Approximately the number of meshes per inch.

18 meshes to the inch). Sieves in the "fine series" stand successively in the ratio of $\sqrt[4]{2}$ to one another, the largest opening in this series being 5.66 mm (produced by approximately 3½ meshes to the inch), and the smallest 0.037 mm (produced by approximately 400 meshes to the inch). The sieves may be calibrated directly in one of three ways: (1) by measurement of a representative number of screen openings in a given sieve, if necessary with the aid of a microscope; (2) by counting and weighing a representative number of particles that just pass a given sieve; and (3) by counting and measuring an easily identifiable diameter of a representative number of particles that just pass a given sieve. An indirect calibration involves sieving a sand the

size distribution of which has been determined by means of calibrated sieves. The first method of direct rating is generally employed and is known as the manufacturer's rating. The second method was suggested by Allen Hazen [5] at a time when the weaving of screen cloth was poorly standardized. The sieve opening is here expressed in terms of the diameter of the equivalent volume sphere which is calculated from the known weight W and number N of the particles collected and from a determination of their specific weight γ_s. This diameter d_0 is

$$d_0 = \sqrt[3]{\frac{6}{\pi\gamma_s}\frac{W}{N}} \qquad\qquad 24\text{-}1$$

Within limits, this method of rating compensates for differences in grain shape, and sieves so calibrated give about the same value of diameter for different types of grains used in their rating. The third method of counting and measuring particles is principally a research tool. Though tedious, it is rewarding, because it identifies more closely the factors that control the resistance offered to filtration by granular materials.

The size distribution or variation of a sample of granular material is determined by sieving the sample through a series of standard sieves that, depending upon the precision of detail wanted, stand in the ratio of $\sqrt[4]{2}$, $\sqrt[2]{2}$, or $2:1$ to one another. Starting with the weighing of the portion of the sample caught on the pan, successive portions of the sample held between adjacent sieves are added, and the cumulative weights are recorded. Converted into percentages by weight equal to or less than the size of separation of the overlying sieve, the cumulative frequency distribution can then be plotted for purposes of generalization. For many natural granular materials this curve approaches geometric normality. Logarithmic-probability paper (Section 4-14), therefore, assures an almost straight-line plot in which interpolation is facilitated (Figure 24-4). The geometric mean M_g and geometric standard deviation σ_g are then useful parameters of central tendency and variation. Their magnitudes may be determined from the plot by reading the 50% and 15.84% values. The parameters most commonly used, however, are the effective size E, or 10-percentile P_{10}, and the uniformity coefficient U, or ratio of the 60-percentile to the 10-percentile P_{60}/P_{10}. Use of the 10-percentile was suggested by Allen Hazen [5] because he had observed that the resistance to the passage of water offered by a bed of sand within which the grains

[5] Allen Hazen, *Annual Report of the Massachusetts State Board of Health,* 1892.

are distributed homogeneously remains almost the same, irrespective of size variation (up to a uniformity coefficient of about 5.0), provided that the 10-percentile remains unchanged. Hydraulic effectiveness is, therefore, implied. It is of interest, in this connection, that a size frequency distribution of the *number of particles* rather than their

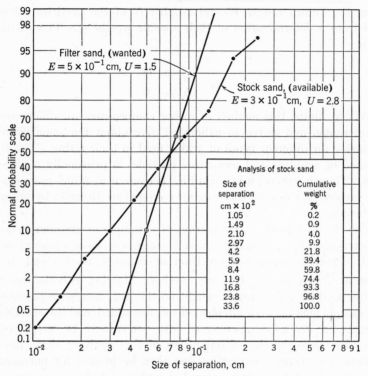

Figure 24-4. Grain size distribution of a stock sand and required sizing of a filter sand.

weight will show that the 10-percentile by weight corresponds in size closely to the median by count. This is to be expected since it is the number of particles rather than their weight that determines the frictional surface of the filter. Use of the ratio of the 60-percentile to the 10-percentile as a measure of uniformity [6] was suggested by Hazen because this ratio covered the range in size of half the sand. On the basis of logarithmic normality, the probability integral (Table 4-11)

[6] It would be more logical to speak of this ratio as a coefficient of non-uniformity because the coefficient increases in magnitude as the non-uniformity increases.

establishes the following relations between the effective size and uniformity coefficient and the geometric mean size and geometric standard deviation:

$$E = P_{10} = M_g \cdot \sigma_g^{-1.282} \qquad\qquad 24\text{-}2$$

$$U = P_{60}/P_{10} = \sigma_g^{1.535} \qquad\qquad 24\text{-}3$$

b. *Shape and Shape Variation.* If we let α equal the surface-area shape factor such that αd^2 is the surface area A of a particle of measured diameter d, and if we let β equal the volume shape factor such that βd^3 is the volume V of this particle, then the ratio of surface area to volume becomes

$$A/V = (\alpha/\beta)(1/d) \qquad\qquad 24\text{-}4$$

In place of α and β the sphericity factor ψ is often referred to in the literature. This factor is defined as the ratio of the surface area A_0 of the equivalent volume sphere (of diameter d_0) to the actual surface area of the particle, or

$$\psi = \frac{A_0}{A} = \frac{\pi d_0^2}{\alpha d^2} = 4.84 \frac{\beta^{2/3}}{\alpha} \qquad\qquad 24\text{-}5$$

Of these parameters, V and hence β and A_0 can be determined as statistical averages for particles of irregular shape by finding the weight W, specific weight γ_s, and measured diameter d of a representative number of N particles:

$$V = W/(\gamma_s N) = \beta d^3 = \tfrac{1}{6}\pi d_0^3 = \tfrac{1}{6} A_0 d_0 \qquad\qquad 24\text{-}6$$

No satisfactory means are as yet available to find the actual surface area A and the dependent parameters α and ψ of particles of irregular shape. The surfaces dealt with are not sufficiently extensive to obtain measurable values for the adsorption of unimolecular layers of a gas. Comparison of the rate of solution of a given particle with that of a particle of the same composition but of regular geometric shape is a difficult undertaking and gives only approximate results, because the rates of solution from points and surfaces are not the same. Establishment of the area-volume relationship from the observed settling velocity of particles or from the observed resistance to flow offered by a bed of these particles is the most useful means so far available, but it defeats the purpose of the measurement, which is to find these very sedimentation and filtration characteristics. Approximate values of β, α/β, and ψ for sharp and rounded sand the size of which has been determined in sieves rated by the manufacturer's method are listed in Table 24-3.

TABLE 24-3. Approximate Values of Sand Shape Factors *

Type of sand	β	α/β	ψ
Angular	0.64	6.9	0.81
Sharp	0.77	6.2	0.85
Worn	0.86	5.7	0.89
Rounded	0.91	5.5	0.91
Spherical	0.52	6.0	1.00

* The fact that grain diameter is measured indirectly and imperfectly when sand is sieved and sieves are rated by the manufacturer's method accounts for the otherwise unexpected variation in the magnitudes of β and α/β.

Particles of the same origin may be expected to be substantially alike in shape, if they are of approximately the same size. Present methods for determining shape are such, however, as to force us to deal with measures of shape only as approximate averages for the sample as a whole.

Example 24-1. For the size frequencies by weight and by count of the sample of sand listed in Figure 24-4, find (a) the effective size E and uniformity coefficient U; (b) the geometric mean size M_g and geometric standard deviation σ_g; and (c) the effective size calculated from M_g and σ_g and the uniformity coefficient calculated from σ_g.

a. From Figure 24-4, $E = P_{10} = 3.0 \times 10^{-2}$ cm. $U = P_{60}/P_{10} = 8.5 \times 10^{-2}/3.0 \times 10^{-2} = 2.8$.

b. From Figure 24-4, $M_g = P_{50} = 7.1 \times 10^{-2}$. $\sigma_g = P_{50}/P_{16} = 7.1 \times 10^{-2}/3.7 \times 10^{-2} = 1.9$.

c. By Equation 24-2, $E = 7.1 \times 10^{-2} \times 1.9^{-1.282} = 3.1 \times 10^{-2}$ against an observed value of 3.0×10^{-2}. By Equation 24-3, $U = 1.9^{1.535} = 2.7$ against an observed value of 2.8.

24-5. Preparation of Filter Sand. "Run-of-bank" sand may be too coarse, too fine, or too non-uniform for use in filters. Within economical limits, proper sizing and uniformity are obtained by screening out coarse components and washing out fine components. In rapid filters, the removal of "fines" may be accomplished by stratifying the bed through back-washing and then scraping off the layer that includes the unwanted sand.

If the sand to be used in a filter is specified in terms of effective size and uniformity coefficient, and a sieve analysis of the stock sand has been made (Figure 24-4), the coarse and fine portions of stock sand that must be removed in order to meet the size specification are ascertained in terms of p_1, the percentage of stock sand that is smaller than the desired effective size, and p_2 the percentage of stock sand that is smaller than the desired 60-percentile size. The percentage of usable stock sand p_3 is then

$$p_3 = 2(p_2 - p_1) \qquad 24\text{-}7$$

because the sand lying between the P_{60} and P_{10} sizes will constitute half the specified sand. To meet the specified composition, this sand can contain but $0.1p_3$ of sand below the P_{10} size. Hence the percentage p_4 below which the stock sand is too fine for use, becomes

$$p_4 = p_1 - 0.1p_3 = p_1 - 0.2(p_2 - p_1) \qquad 24\text{-}8$$

The grain size associated with p_4 must, in addition, be equal to or greater than the smallest size of sand to be included in the filter. We have now accounted for a percentage of stock sand equal to $p_3 + p_4$ of which p_3 is usable and p_4 too fine. Therefore, the percentage p_5 above which the stock sand is too coarse is

$$p_5 = p_3 + p_4 = p_1 + 1.8(p_2 - p_1) \qquad 24\text{-}9$$

A sand or grit washer can be used to separate fines from stock sand before it is placed in a filter. The same device can be employed also to wash sand removed from a filter—a slow sand filter, for example—and to wash grit that contains too much organic matter. As shown in Figure 24-5, such a washer is essentially an upward-flow, settling tank. Ideally, therefore, the rate of overflow of the washer must not exceed the settling velocity of the smallest particle to be retained while at least equaling, insofar as the first restriction permits, the settling velocity of the largest particle to be removed. Turbulence (Section 22-7) and sand concentration (Sections 22-3 and 24-5) reduce the needed rate of overflow appreciably. The sand or grit that settles to the bottom is ejected hydraulically, or it is withdrawn by gravity through a shear gate. About 1 cu yd of sand per hour can be washed per sq ft of washer surface.

Example 24-2. What must be done to the stock sand of Figure 24-4 to convert it into a filter sand of effective size 5×10^{-2} cm and uniformity coefficient 1.5?

a. From Figure 24-4, the proportion of sand p_1 less than the desired effective size of 5×10^{-2} cm is 30.0%, and the proportion of sand p_2 less than the desired sixty percentile of $5 \times 10^{-2} \times 1.5 = 7.5 \times 10^{-2}$ cm is 53.5%. Hence by Equation 24-7, the proportion p_3 of usable sand is $p_3 = 2(53.5 - 30.0) = 47.0\%$.

b. The percentage p_4 below which the stock sand is too fine is given by Equation 24-8 as $p_4 = 30.0 - 4.7 = 25.3\%$, and the diameter of this sand from Figure 24-4 is 4.4×10^{-2} cm. The settling velocity of this sand, and hence the overflow rate of an ideal washer, from Figure 22-2, is 6.4 cm/sec or 94 gpm per sq ft at 10 C (50 F).

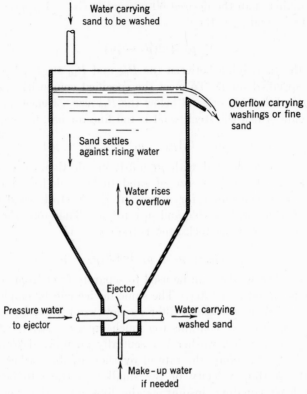

Figure 24-5. Sand washer.

c. The percentage p_5 above which the stock sand is too coarse is given by Equation 24-9 as $p_5 = 47.0 + 25.3 = 72.3\%$, and the diameter of this sand from Figure 24-4 is 1.10×10^{-1} cm.

d. It follows that all stock sand finer than 4.4×10^{-2} cm and all stock sand coarser than 1.10×10^{-1} cm must be wasted in order to create the desired filter sand.

24-6. Hydraulics of Filtration. The resistance offered by granular materials to the passage of fluids is analogous both to the resistance offered by small pipes to fluids carried by them and to the resistance offered by a fluid to the settling of particles.

For purposes of dimensional analysis, Rose [7] has set up equations that include the following essential parameters:

[7] H. E. Rose, "On the Resistance Coefficient-Reynolds Number Relationship for Fluid Flow through a Bed of Granular Material," *Proc., Inst. Mech. Engrs.*, *153*, 154 (1945); also "Further Researches in Fluid Flow through Beds of Granular Material," *160*, 493 (1949).

Equation 22-2 states that the drag force exerted on a particle settling in a

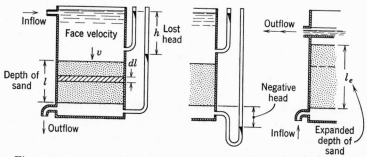

Figure 24-6. Head loss in filtration, and expansion in back-washing.

$$\left(\frac{h}{l}\right) = \phi \left\{\left(\frac{vd}{\nu}\right)\left(\frac{v^2}{gd}\right)(f)\right\} \qquad 24\text{-}10$$

Here h is the loss of head in a depth l (Figure 24-6), v is the face velocity, or velocity of the water moving down upon the sand bed, d is a characteristic diameter of the sand grains defined as $6V/A$ where V and A are respectively the volume and surface area of the sand particles, g is the acceleration due to gravity, ν is the kinematic viscosity of the water, and f is the porosity ratio of the filter bed. It can be deduced from experimental investigations of beds composed of closely graded, smooth, spherical particles that $\left(\dfrac{h}{l}\right) \propto \left(\dfrac{v^2}{gd}\right)$; that $\left(\dfrac{h}{l}\right) \propto \left(\dfrac{1}{f}\right)^4$; and that the equation can be balanced by a resistance coefficient which is a function of the Reynolds number and equal to $1.067C_D$ where C_D is the coefficient of drag as recorded in Equation 22-3.

a. General Equation. Substitution of these relationships in Equation 24-10 establishes the following general equation for the resistance to flow offered by beds of granular material.

$$\frac{h}{l} = 1.067 \frac{C_D}{g} \frac{1}{f^4} \frac{v^2}{d} = 0.178 \frac{C_D}{g} \frac{v^2}{f^4} \frac{A}{V} \qquad 24\text{-}11$$

where

---

fluid is $v_s{}^2 d^2 \rho \phi(v_s d/\nu)$. Translated to the conditions of flow in filtration, the drag force also equals the difference in pressure (loss of head) between two horizontal planes through a sand bed 1 grain diameter apart and 1 grain diameter square in area. Hence $h\rho g d^2 \times d/l$ varies as $v_s{}^2 d^2 \rho \phi(v_s d/\nu)$. If a function of the porosity f is included to allow for the packing of sand grains in filters, the relationship shown in Equation 24-10 is obtained.

$$C_D = \frac{24}{R} + \frac{3}{\sqrt{R}} + 0.34 \qquad\qquad 22\text{-}4$$

and

$$\frac{A}{V} = \frac{\alpha}{\beta}\frac{1}{d} \qquad\qquad 24\text{-}4$$

For the rate of flow (2 gpm per sq ft $= 1.35 \times 10^{-1}$ cm/sec) and grain size (6×10^{-2} cm) commonly employed in rapid sand filters in North American practice, the value of R at 20 C is about 0.8 and the magnitude of $1.067C_D$ becomes about 36. If the porosity ratio is 0.42, the loss of head created by a bed of sand 3 ft deep is then of the order of 1 ft. For the rates of flow (3 mgad $= 3.24 \times 10^{-3}$ cm/sec) and grain size (3.5×10^{-2} cm) commonly employed in slow sand filters, the values of R and $1.067C_D$ at 20 C are 1.1×10^{-2} and 2.2×10^3 respectively, and the loss of head in a bed of sand with a porosity ratio of 0.40 and a depth of 3 ft is about 0.1 ft.

When the flow is laminar, C_D approaches a value of $24/R$ and Equation 24-11 becomes [8]

$$\frac{h}{l} = 25.6\,\frac{\nu}{g}\frac{1}{f^4}\frac{v}{d^2} = 0.711\,\frac{\nu}{g}\frac{v}{f^4}\left(\frac{A}{V}\right)^2 \qquad\qquad 24\text{-}12$$

whence, for v in m/day, d in mm, and $f = 0.4$,

$$v = 850d^2\,\frac{h}{l}\frac{\nu_{10}}{\nu_t} = cd^2\,\frac{h}{l}\frac{T+10}{60} \qquad\qquad 24\text{-}13$$

This is Hazen's [5] classical formula for the flow of water through homogeneously packed sand, d being the effective size of the sand, and T the temperature of the water in degrees F. The value of the coefficient of compactness c was reported by Hazen to vary from 600 to 1,200. Hazen's equation was derived empirically for sharp sands with a uniformity coefficient of less than 5 and offers the basis for his suggesting the effective size as a measure of hydraulic central tendency. The voids and porosity ratio do not appear in Hazen's equation because, within the indicated variation in porosity, the otherwise important influence of these ratios is offset by wider variability in grain size. As stated again later on, this makes (1) for the inclusion of more large-sized grains and a resulting decrease in resistance due to a reduction in surface area per unit volume and (2) for a counter-

[8] This equation yields substantially the same values as the Kozeny equation in which the term $(1-f)^2/f^3$ replaces the term $1/f^4$ and the numerical constants are about 7 times as great [*Wasserkraft und Wasserwirtschaft*, *22*, 67 (1927)].

balancing increase in resistance due to a reduction in pore space by small grains occupying much of the space between large grains.

As previously stated, the earliest formulation of laminar flow through granular materials is that of Darcy (1856):

$$v = Ks = Kh/l \qquad\qquad 9\text{-}4$$

where K is the coefficient of permeability, or velocity at unit slope.

b. Area-Volume Ratio. Except for the diameter term $d = 6V/A$, evaluation of the various factors that enter into Equation 24-11 is straightforward. Determination of the magnitude of A/V, as discussed in Section 24-4, presents some difficulty even for a single particle. Since aggregations of particles can be arranged in different ways, a further complication is added when the total loss of head through a filter is to be found.

If all the grains in a filter are uniform in size and shape, the value of A/V for a single grain is the same as that for the bed as a whole or, in accordance with Equation 24-4, $A/V = (\alpha/\beta)(1/d)$.

If the grains vary in size, they may either be packed homogeneously within the bed, or they may be arranged, or stratified, in order of magnitude from the coarsest to the finest. Homogeneous packing obtains in slow sand filters that are cleaned by scraping off the surface layer; stratification is induced by the back-washing of rapid filters.

For *homogeneous packing* of equally shaped particles, the area-volume relationship for any portion of the bed or for the bed as a whole is

$$A/V = (\alpha/\beta)\int_{P=0}^{P=1} dP/d \qquad\qquad 24\text{-}14$$

where dP is the proportion of particles of size d. Assuming that the particles lying between adjacent sieves are substantially uniform in size, the area-volume relationship in terms of the component sieve separations p becomes [9]

$$A/V = \alpha/\beta\Sigma(p/d) \qquad\qquad 24\text{-}15$$

---

[9] If the results of the sieving are generalized in terms of the geometric mean and geometric standard deviation, introduction of the logarithmic transform of the normal equation into Equation 24-14 and integration gives

$$A/V = (\alpha/\beta)(\sigma_g{}^{0.5\,\log_e\,\sigma_g}/M_g)$$

In accordance with Equations 24-2 and 24-3, furthermore,

$$A/V = (\alpha/\beta)(EU^{0.835-0.487\log U})-1$$

Stratification separates the grains into individual filtering layers that are piled up one upon another like the sieve separations in a grain size analysis but in inverse order. If the porosity is uniform, the thickness of each layer $dl = l\ dP$, and the loss of head through it is

$$\frac{dh}{dl} = 0.178 \frac{C_D}{g} \frac{v^2}{f^4} \frac{A}{V} = \text{constant } C_D \frac{\alpha}{\beta} \frac{1}{d} \qquad 24\text{-}16$$

It follows that the total loss of head

$$h = \int_0^h dh = \text{constant } (\alpha/\beta) \int_0^l C_D\ dl/d$$

$$= \text{constant } (\alpha/\beta) l \int_{P=0}^{P=1} C_D\ dP/d \qquad 24\text{-}17$$

Again assuming that the particles between adjacent sieves are substantially uniform in size,

$$h/l = \text{constant } (\alpha/\beta)\Sigma C_D p/d \qquad 24\text{-}18$$

It follows that the product of the area-volume relationship and the coefficient of resistance, $C_D' A'/V'$, for an equivalent bed of uniform particles would be [10]

$$C_D' A'/V' = (\alpha/\beta)\Sigma C_D p/d \qquad 24\text{-}19$$

The area-volume ratio of gravel is small and makes for a low loss of head. During filtration, the lines of flow curve towards the underdrains, but flow is viscous over most of the path. Rates of wash may be sufficiently high, however, to create transitional flow and a significant loss of head. Approximate values for h/l are 0.001, 0.025, and 0.075 for gravel 1 in., $\frac{1}{2}$ in., and $\frac{1}{4}$ in. in size when the rate of wash-water rise is 24 in. per min. For other rates, h/l varies about as the $\frac{3}{2}$ power of the velocity.

Example 24-3. Find the loss of head for the sharp filter sand shown in the first three columns of the accompanying schedule of computations (Table 24-4).

---

[10] For a logarithmically normal size-frequency distribution,

$$C_D' \frac{A'}{V'} = \frac{\alpha}{\beta} \left[24 \frac{\nu}{v} \Sigma \frac{p}{d^2} + 3 \left(\frac{\nu}{v}\right)^{\frac{1}{2}} \Sigma \frac{p}{d^{\frac{3}{2}}} + 0.34\Sigma \frac{p}{d} \right]$$

where

$$\Sigma p/d^2 = \sigma_g^{2\log_e \sigma_g}/M_g^2 = (E^2 U^{1.67-1.95\log U})^{-1}$$

$$\Sigma p/d^{\frac{3}{2}} = \sigma_g^{1.388\log_e \sigma_g}/M_g^{\frac{3}{2}} = (E^{\frac{3}{2}} U^{1.25-1.11\log U})^{-1}$$

and

$$\Sigma p/d = \sigma_g^{0.5\log_e \sigma_g}/M_g = (E U^{0.835-0.487\log U})^{-1}$$

This sand is being used (a) in a slow filter 30 in. in depth and operated at a rate of 10 mgad (1.08×10^{-2} cm/sec) and (b) in a rapid filter 30 in. in depth and operated at a rate of 125 mgad (1.35×10^{-1} cm/sec). The sand has a specific gravity of 2.65, an effective size of 2.55×10^{-2} cm, a uniformity coefficient of 1.63, and a surface area-volume shape factor of 6.0. The porosity ratio of the unstratified sand bed is 0.394, that of the stratified sand bed 0.414. The lowest temperature of the water to be filtered is 4 C (39.2 F) and the kinematic viscosity, accordingly, 1.568×10^{-2} stoke. Necessary calculations are included in Table 24-4.

TABLE 24-4. Calculation of Loss of Head in Sand Filters (Example 24-3)

Sieve number (1)	Geometric mean size 100d, cm (2)	Percentage of sand 100p (3)	$\dfrac{p}{d}$ (4)	C_D (5)	$C_D \dfrac{p}{d}$ (6)
14–20	10.0	0.92	0.09	31.3	3
20–28	7.0	4.71	0.67	43.8	30
28–32	5.4	14.67	2.72	56.3	153
32–35	4.6	17.9	3.89	65.5	255
35–42	3.8	17.5	4.61	78.8	363
42–48	3.2	19.8	6.19	94.0	582
48–60	2.7	15.4	5.71	109.5	626
60–65	2.3	7.1	3.09	128.2	396
65–100	1.8	2.0	1.11	162.7	181
Sums		100.0	28.08		2,589

Columns 1 to 3 record the results of the sieve analysis of the sand. Column 4 = Column 3 ÷ Column 2, the sum being 28.1. Column 5 gives the value of C_D for the rapid filter in accordance with Equation 22-4. Column 6 = Column 5 × Column 4, the sum being 2,589.

a. Loss of head in slow filter. By Equation 24-15: $A/V = 6.0 \times 28.1 = 169$. Since $R = \dfrac{1.08 \times 10^{-2}}{1.568 \times 10^{-2}} \dfrac{6}{169} = 2.45 \times 10^{-2}$, the value of the coefficient of drag becomes, by Equation 22-4, $C_D = 1,000$. Making the necessary substitutions in Equation 24-11, therefore:

$$\frac{h}{l} = 0.178 \frac{1,000}{981} \times \frac{(1.08)^2 \times 10^{-4}}{(0.394)^4} \times 169 = 0.15$$

and $h = 0.15 \times 2.5 = 0.38$ ft.

By Equation 24-13, assuming that $c = 1,200$ for clean, compacted sand:

$$h/l = 10 \times 0.935 \times 60/[1,200 \times (2.55)^2 \times 10^{-4} \times 49.2] = 0.15$$

and $h = 0.15 \times 2.5 = 0.38$ ft.

b. Loss of head in rapid filter. By Equation 24-19: $C_D'A'/V' = 6.0 \times 2,589 = 15,534$. Making the necessary substitutions in Equation 24-11, therefore:

$$\frac{h}{l} = \frac{0.178}{981} \frac{(1.35)^2 \times 10^{-2}}{(0.414)^4} \times 15{,}534 = 1.76$$

and $h = 1.76 \times 2.5 = 4.4$ ft.

It is obvious that use of so fine a sand results in excessive head loss in a rapid filter. Removal of the five smallest sieve separations of sand (61.8%) will leave 38.2% of the sand and reduce $\Sigma C_D p/d$ to $\frac{441}{0.382} = 1{,}155$ and h/l to $1.76 \times 1{,}155/2{,}589$ $= 0.786$. If the depth is held at 30 in., $h = 0.786 \times 2.5 = 1.96$ ft.

24-7. Hydraulics of Filter Washing. The burden of suspended matter collected in filters and on their grains is removed and the bed restored to capacity either by washing the filter material in place or by removing the clogged portions of the bed. Development of means for washing sand in place created the rapid sand filter towards the end of the nineteenth century and made it possible to distribute the load, to a far greater degree than before, through the depth of the filter. In the absence of these means, filters had to be operated at low rates, and clogging had purposely to be confined to the surface layers of sand that could be scraped off and either wasted or reclaimed for use by washing.

The scouring of granular materials in place is accomplished with the aid of water that rises through the bed and lifts the filter grains into suspension. This is called *sand expansion* (Figure 24-6). Substances that have been transferred into the bed during filtration from the water are then flushed upward through the suspended or expanded bed and wasted with the wash water. At the same time, the substances adhering to the filter grains are dislodged either by the shearing action of the rising water or by the rubbing together of the suspended grains. Scour is important and can be promoted by stirring the expanded filter mechanically with rakes, pneumatically with air (either during or, more commonly, before expansion), or hydraulically with jets of water that are directed into the suspended sand.

As against this, the washing of granular materials after removal from the filter—or for that matter before placement as a means of cleaning or sizing—is also in the nature of differential sedimentation. The relatively coarse and heavy filter grains are allowed to settle against rising water which carries away the dislodged fine and light suspended matter. The washing of detritus for the removal of putrescible organic matter also follows this pattern.

Traveling washers that move over the surface of drained slow sand filters jet water into the sand and pump the rising water out of the filter.

a. General Equations. The maximum frictional resistance that individual filter grains or collections of grains that are free to move can offer to a fluid is their weight in water. The cleansing action of water upon filter grains is not increased, therefore, by rates of wash that are higher than necessary to suspend the active portion of a filter. Increased flow merely separates the grains more widely. But this may be necessary in order to permit the enmeshed suspended matter to escape from the pores. If we call l_e the depth of bed that is expanded and f_e its porosity ratio, the mass density of the grains and fluid being ρ_s and ρ respectively, and the specific gravity of the grains being s_s,

$$h\rho g = l_e(\rho_s - \rho)g(1 - f_e)$$

and

$$h/l_e = [(\rho_s - \rho)/\rho](1 - f_e) = (s_s - 1)(1 - f_e) \quad \text{closely} \quad 24\text{-}20$$

This is the loss of head h incurred in expanding the filter.

The grains are kept from settling, because the drag exerted on them by the rising water equals the settling force. The settling force is given by Equation 22-1 as $(\rho_s - \rho)gV$, the drag force by a modification of Equation 22-3 as $C_D A_{cp}(v^2/2)\phi(f_e)$. The function of f_e is introduced because v is the face, or approach, velocity of the wash water, whereas the drag is due to the settling velocity, v_s of the particles. To bring the settling force into equilibrium with the drag force, therefore,

$$\phi(f_e) = (v_s/v)^2 \qquad 24\text{-}21$$

By experiment, $(v_s/v)^2 = (1/f_e)^9$, whence

$$v_s = v/f_e^{4.5}; \quad v = v_s f_e^{4.5}; \quad f_e = (v/v_s)^{0.22}; \quad \text{and} \quad f_e^{4.5} = v/v_s \quad 24\text{-}22$$

Since the volume of sand per unit area of bed is constant and equal to $(1 - f)l$ or $(1 - f_e)l_e$, where l is the unexpanded depth of the bed and l_e is the expanded depth, the relative expansion of a layer of thickness dl is

$$dl_e/dl = (1 - f)/(1 - f_e) \qquad 24\text{-}23$$

For a bed of uniform sand grains, therefore,

$$l_e/l = (1 - f)/(1 - f_e) = (1 - f)/[1 - (v/v_s)^{0.22}] \qquad 24\text{-}24$$

and the rate of rise of wash water required to maintain the same degree of expansion at different water temperatures varies directly as the settling velocity of the grains at these temperatures.

b. Expansion of Non-Uniform Beds. Each grain size in a stratified bed is carried into suspension in succession as the drag of wash water equals the weight of the particles. Only those sizes are lifted, therefore, for which $v > f^{4.5}v_s$.

If dP is the proportion of sand of a given size, the ratio of the fully expanded depth L_e to the unexpanded depth of sand L becomes

$$L_e/L = (1 - f)\int_{P=0}^{P=1} dP/(1 - f_e) \qquad\qquad 24\text{-}25$$

Assuming that the particles lying between adjacent sieves are substantially uniform in size,

$$L_e/L = (1 - f)\Sigma p/(1 - f_e) \qquad\qquad 24\text{-}26$$

Here f_e must be calculated by means of Equation 24-22. Substitution of a sand bed composed of uniform grains of equivalent size as a means of finding a single expression for the expansion ratio can be made only when the substitution is limited to the portion of sand that is actually suspended.

Example 24-4. A somewhat worn, sharp sand with the grain size distribution shown in Table 24-5 is placed in a bed 30 in. deep which is washed at a rate of 24 in. per min (1.016 cm per second) when the water temperature is 10 C (50 F), or $\nu = 1.31 \times 10^{-2}$ stoke. The porosity ratio of the stratified bed is 0.414 and the shape factor $\alpha/\beta = 6.0$. Find (*a*) the degree of expansion of the bed, and (*b*) the loss of head through the expanded portion. Fundamental calculations are included in Table 24-5.

TABLE 24-5. Calculation of Sand Expansion (Example 24-4)

Sieve No. (1)	100d cm (2)	100p (3)	v_s cm/sec (4)	$100\dfrac{v}{v_s}$ (5)	f_e (6)	$\dfrac{100p}{1 - f_e}$ (7)
8–10	21.8	0.5	30.7	3.31	0.473	0.9
10–14	15.4	2.3	23.7	4.29	0.500	4.6
14–20	10.0	9.3	15.9	6.39	0.543	20.3
20–28	7.0	24.8	11.1	9.15	0.591	60.2
28–32	5.4	20.6	8.36	12.2	0.630	55.3
32–35	4.6	16.4	6.69	15.2	0.661	47.9
35–42	3.8	12.1	5.58	18.2	0.687	38.4
42–48	3.2	14.0	4.18	24.3	0.733	53.2
Sum						280.8

Columns 1 to 3 record the results of the sieve analysis of the sand. Column 4 is calculated from values of $[g\nu(s_s - 1)]^{-\frac{1}{3}}v_s = [981(1.31 \times 10^{-2}) \times 1.65]^{-\frac{1}{3}}v_s = v_s/2.77$ for values of $[g(s_s - 1)/\nu^2]^{\frac{1}{3}}d = [981(1.65 \times 10^4)/(1.31)^2]^{\frac{1}{3}}d = 21.2d$ in Figure 22-2. Column 5 is $100 \times 1.016 \div$ Column 4. Column 6 is $(v/v_s)^{0.222}$. Column 7 is Column 3 ÷ (1 − Column 6).

a. Since f for the unexpanded bed is 0.414, all the sand is expanded. By Equation 24-26, therefore, $L_e/L = (1 - 0.414) \times 2.81 = 1.65$, i.e., the bed is expanded 65%, and

$$L_e = 30 \times 1.65 = 49.5 \text{ in.}$$

b. Since all the sand is expanded, the loss of head through the lifted sand is $^{30}\!/_{12} \times 1.65 \times (1 - 0.414) = 2.42$ ft, in accordance with Equation 24-20.

c. *Back-Wash Scour.* The scouring action associated with the washing of filters may be calculated in accordance with the principles laid down in Section 23-4. The power input equals the drag force times the settling velocity. Hence

$$F_D v_s = C_D A_c \rho v_s^3 / 2 \qquad\qquad 24\text{-}27$$

and the power input P per unit volume of expanded sand $V/(1 - f_e)$ is

$$P = \frac{C_D A_c \rho v_s^3 (1 - f_e)}{2V} = \frac{3}{4} C_D \rho \frac{v_s^3}{d} (1 - f_e) = \mu G^2 \qquad 24\text{-}28$$

It follows that G, the velocity gradient, must be

$$G = \sqrt{\frac{3}{4} \frac{C_D}{\nu} \frac{v_s^3}{d} (1 - f_e)} = \sqrt{\frac{g}{\nu} (s_s - 1)(1 - f_e) v_s} \qquad 24\text{-}29$$

and that the number of contacts between soiled particles is greatest when that portion of the bed which has been penetrated by floc or other impurities is only just fully lifted. Expansion greater than this makes for fewer contacts. However, the bed must be opened up enough to permit included floc to escape.

d. *Auxiliary Scour.* Means for stirring the sand in order to improve scour are illustrated in Figure 24-7. Of these means, only surface wash is currently included in new designs in North America.

The rakes used for mechanical agitation of the sand should penetrate the active or expanded sand. They generally reach within 2 or 3 in. of the gravel. The raking arms revolve at a rate of 8 to 9 rpm. The teeth are often wedge shaped and are spaced 6 in. on centers. Upward flow is held to between 12 and 18 in. per min.

Air scour generally proceeds at a rate of 3 to 5 cfm per sq ft of filter for several minutes before back-washing the filter at a rate of 12 to 18 in. per min. The air is normally introduced above the gravel line from a pipe grid similar in its principles of design to the perforated pipe systems that underdrain the filters.

Surface wash by jets of water adds from 3 to 11 in. per min of water to the back-wash (about 16 in.). A basic expansion of about 10% is induced before the jets are directed into the sand. The jets issue under a pressure of 10 psig or more. They may be supplied from a stationary grid or a rotating arm.

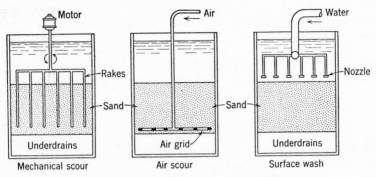

Figure 24-7. Auxiliary scour of rapid filters.

e. Hindered Settling and Time of Settling of Expanded Beds. As suggested in Section 22-3, expansion and hindered settling are complementary phenomena. Hence the velocity of fall in hindered settling is identified by Equation 24-22 rather than Equation 22-5 or 22-6, and the time t_s required for the smallest and hence most highly expanded grain size in an expanded bed to settle back into place becomes

$$t_s = (L_e - L)/(v_s f_e^{4.5}) \hspace{3cm} \text{24-30}$$

where v_s is the settling velocity of the smallest sand grains. The finest grains obviously take the longest time and fix the length of time required for the sand bed to consolidate after washing is discontinued. Since $v_s f_e^{4.5} = v$, the rate of rise of the wash water that suspended the bed, $t_s = (L_c - L)/v$ also.

f. Hindered Rising and Time of Rising of Expanding Beds. Whereas an expanded bed settles back into place at a uniform rate, its rate of rise is non-uniform because the porosity increases in the course of expansion from a value of f to one of f_e. In practice, furthermore, the rate of back-washing is increased gradually to its maximum value in order to drive off first the *schmutzdecke* and then the larger concentrations of floc and other impurities from the upper layers of the expanding bed. For the simple case of a constant rate of up-flow and a layer of uniform sand of depth l, the porosity f_x at a distance x above the level of the unexpanded bed is given by Equation 24-22 as

$f_x^{4.5} = v/v_s$ where f_x is a function of x. This function, according to Equation 24-24, is $(lf + x)/(l + x)$. For a rise $dx = f_x^{4.5}v_s\,dt$, the time of rise t_r becomes

$$t_r = \int_0^{t_r} dt = \frac{1}{v_s} \int_0^{l_e - l} \left(\frac{l + x}{lf + x}\right)^{4.5} dx \qquad 24\text{-}31$$

This integral can be evaluated but involves a geometric series of eight terms. An approximation may be had in the form

$$t_r = \left[\left(\frac{1}{f}\right)^{4.5} + 2\left(\frac{1}{f_e}\right)^{4.5}\right] \frac{l(f_e - f)}{3v_s(1 - f_e)} \qquad 24\text{-}32$$

Example 24-5. Find: (a) the velocity gradient G; (b) the time of rise t_r; and (c) the time of settling t_s of a bed of sand 30 in. (76.2 cm) deep consisting of sharp grains $(a/\beta = 6.0)$ 4.6×10^{-2} cm in diameter when the rate of washing is 24 in./min (1.016 cm/sec) and the water temperature is 10 C (50 F), or $\nu = 1.31 \times 10^{-2}$ stoke. In accordance with Example 24-4, the settling velocity of the grains is $v_s = 6.7$ cm/sec, and the bed is expanded from a porosity ratio $f = 0.414$ to one of $f_e = 0.658$. The specific gravity of the grains is 2.65.

a. By Equation 24-29:

$$G = \sqrt{\frac{981(2.65 - 1)(1 - 0.658)6.7}{1.31 \times 10^{-2}}} = 530 \text{ cm/(sec)(cm) or } 530 \text{ ft/(sec) (ft)}$$

b. By Equation 24-32:

$$t_r = \left[\left(\frac{1}{0.414}\right)^{4.5} + 2\left(\frac{1}{0.658}\right)^{4.5}\right] \frac{76.2(0.658 - 0.414)}{3 \times 6.7(1 - 0.658)} = 180 \text{ sec}$$

c. By Equation 24-24: $L_e = 76.2(1 - 0.414)/(1 - 0.658) = 130.6$ cm, and the rise of the bed is $(130.6 - 76.2) = 54.4$ cm. By Equation 24-30: $t_s = \dfrac{54.4}{6.7(0.658)^{4.5}}$ $= 53$ sec, or $t_s = 54.4/1.016 = 53$ sec.

Design of Filters

24-8. Required Depth of Filters. The existing body of knowledge on the behavior of filters under load is inadequate. As a result, the depths of different types of filters have been kept substantially constant since their first use, and rates of filtration have been allowed to vary only within a narrow range. In the hydraulically most heavily loaded filter (the rapid sand filter), the one significant change in the course of a half century has been a shift towards the use of coarser sands.

The depth to which impurities will penetrate into a filter is a function of many factors. They fall into two broad categories: (1) the composition, concentration, and condition of the substances to be removed from the applied water and (2) the reaction of these substances to removal by filtration. Their reaction is a function of readily measurable factors such as (1) the rate of filtration; (2) the size of the filter grains and their variation with depth; (3) the packing of the sand grains or the porosity of the bed; (4) the temperature of the water; and (5) the terminal loss of head or the increase in loss of head beyond that of the clean bed.

When water is coagulated and settled prior to filtration, the load imposed on the filter consists largely of a carry-over of coagulant flocs. At a given time and place, the flocs are relatively uniform in nature and amount. In these circumstances, the load can be expressed, with fair satisfaction, in terms of the amount of aluminum or iron contained in the flocculated water. In the absence of preparatory treatment, on the other hand, the applied load may vary widely and defy significant numerical identification. Depth of penetration of impurities into a uniform bed of sand would be reflected by a logarithmic law, were it not for the fact that some impurities are intercepted by the accumulating surface film while other impurities are carried deeper and deeper into the bed as pore space is reduced by the accumulating solids and velocities of flow are raised sufficiently to prevent further deposition or to induce scour of accumulating substances. In the absence of a more significant parameter, therefore, the applied load is normally related to the surface area of the bed and not to its volume.

The reaction of impurities to removal by filtration varies not only with differences in the nature of the impurities but also with the conditions under which specific impurities are subjected to filtration. Working with a uniform floc of ferric oxide and adsorbed radioactive iodine, Stanley [11] established the following relationships for the reaction of the floc to unigranular beds of sand: (1) depth of penetration varies directly with the concentration of iron per unit surface area of bed and establishes as a suitable "index of penetration" the ratio of depth of penetration to intensity of surface loading; (2) this ratio becomes larger as (a) floc concentration, (b) rate of flow, and (c) sand size are increased; (3) this ratio becomes larger, too, when electrolytes, such as NaCl, Na_2SO_4, and $MgSO_4$, are added to the applied water; (4) this ratio becomes smaller (a) as the floc is increased in size and (b) as the floc is subjected to aging; and (5) this ratio shifts with the pH of the applied water and reaches a minimum as the neutral point

[11] D. R. Stanley, *Penetration of Floc into Sand Filters*, Thesis, Harvard University, 1952.

(pH 7.0) is approached. From the results obtained by other investigators,[12] it appears that penetration increases, furthermore, with the viscosity of the applied water and with the porosity of the bed. The terminal loss of head, or better, the terminal increase in loss of head, is a measure of bed clogging or of the total amount of material removed from the water. Use of this parameter in formulations of penetration obviates a specification of loading intensity. Two such formulations are discussed below, not because they offer a reliable basis for filter design, but because they are signposts of the direction in which future investigations must move.

a. *Uniform Sand.* For an increase of 8 ft in head loss at 25 C (77 F), Stanley has tied depth of penetration of iron floc, l in in., to diameter of sand grains, d in cm, and rate of filtration, Q in gpm per sq ft, in the following observational equation:

$$l = kd^{2.46}Q^{1.56} \qquad\qquad 24\text{-}33$$

where the coefficient k has a value of 1,850. For a terminal loss of head of 8 ft and an effluent containing 0.2 mg/l of turbidity or less, the results reported by the American Society of Civil Engineers for a constant rate of filtration of 2 gpm per sq ft are approximated by the following relationship:

$$l = kd^{5/3}\frac{60}{T + 10} = kd^{5/3}\frac{\nu_t}{\nu_{10}} \qquad\qquad 24\text{-}34$$

Here T is the temperature of the water in degrees Fahrenheit, or ν_t and ν_{10} are respectively the kinematic viscosity of the water at t C and 10 C. The observed magnitudes of k for alum-coagulated and settled waters are 582 for a turbid river water [13] which is coagulated with ease and 796 for a relatively clear lake water [14] which is flocculated with difficulty.

b. *Non-Uniform Sand, Unstratified.* On a weight basis, non-uniformity of the sand in an unstratified bed makes (1) for a small surface area per unit volume by the inclusion of large particles and (2) for small void space by fine particles filling the voids between large particles. On the assumption that these two factors offset each other to a considerable extent, the required depth of an unstratified

[12] See Am. Soc. Civil Engrs., "Water Treatment Plant Design," *Manuals of Engineering Practice*, No. 18, 63 (1939).

[13] Gunpowder Falls, Baltimore, Md.

[14] Lake Ontario, Toronto, Ontario.

bed of non-uniform sand is, therefore, a function of the effective size of the sand.

c. *Non-Uniform Sand, Stratified.* The requisite depth of a stratified bed of non-uniform sand can be based on relationships such as those suggested in Equations 24-33 and 24-34 by making the following assumptions:

1. The depth of a layer of sand composed of a given sieve separation is assumed to bear the same relation to the total depth that the sieve separation does to the total amount of active sand. This presupposes that the porosity of the bed is constant throughout its depth. By the term "active sand" is meant that fraction of the sand which is held responsible for the removal of impurities. Neither the supporting layer of coarse sand nor the surface layer of fine sand that is scraped off before the bed is first put into normal use can be considered to be active.

2. The effectiveness of each constituent layer of sand is assumed to equal the ratio of the actual depth of the layer to the depth that would be required if the filter had to be built up in its entirety of sand of a size equal to that composing the layer.

If we let l_0 equal the total active depth, l the requisite depth of a given constituent layer of substantially uniform sand, and dP the proportion of this sand in an elemental layer of active sand, 100% efficiency is implied when

$$\int_{P=0}^{P=1} \frac{l_0 \, dP}{l} = 1 \quad \text{or} \quad \int_{P=0}^{P=1} \frac{dP}{l} = \frac{1}{l_0} \qquad \text{24-35}$$

Substituting the value of l from Equation 24-34,

$$\frac{1}{l_0} = \frac{T+10}{60k} \int_{P=0}^{P=1} \frac{dP}{d^{5/3}} = \frac{v_{10}}{kv_t} \int_{P=0}^{P=1} \frac{dP}{d^{5/3}} \qquad \text{24-36 [15]}$$

In terms of a sieve analysis, therefore,

$$\frac{1}{l_0} = \frac{T+10}{60k} \Sigma \frac{p}{d^{5/3}} = \frac{v_{10}}{kv_t} \Sigma \frac{p}{d^{5/3}} \qquad \text{24-37}$$

---

[15] For geometric normality

$$\int_{P=0}^{P=1} \frac{dP}{d^{5/3}} = \frac{\sigma_g^{3.20 \log \sigma_g}}{M_g^{1.67}} = \frac{U^{1.36 \log U - 1.39}}{E^{1.67}}$$

The general equation for

$$\int_{P=0}^{P=1} d^n \, dP = M_g^n \sigma_g^{\frac{1}{2}n^2 \log_e \sigma_g} = M_g^n \sigma_g^{1.151 n^2 \log \sigma_g}$$

$$= E^n U^{0.488 n^2 \log U + 0.835 n}$$

d. Gravel. It is the function of gravel to support the overlying sand and to conduct the filtered water to the underdrains of slow and rapid filters, while acting as a dispersing medium for the wash water of rapid filters. To these ends, the gravel must be carefully graded from coarse to fine vertically. The over-all depth of gravel is usually 12 in. in slow filters and 18 in. in rapid filters. If the particles are sized by screening, the depth l in inches of a layer of size d in inches, where $d > \frac{3}{64}$ in., may be estimated from the following observational equation: [16]

$$l = k(\log d + 1.40) \qquad 24\text{-}38$$

Here k varies in magnitude from 10 to 14 and averages 12. Within reason, the percentage distribution of gravel indicated by Equation 24-38 is geometrically normal, the geometric mean size ordinarily being about $\frac{1}{4}$ in. ($E = 6.4 \times 10^{-1}$ cm), and the geometric standard deviation 3.5 ($U = 7.0$). Stones as large as 3 in. may be placed near the filter underdrains, but a maximum size of 1 to 2 in. is more common. To preserve its stability under back-washing, the screened gravel should be carefully packed, the larger sizes being placed by hand.

Example 24-6. A rapid sand filter is to purify a relatively clear lake water that becomes as cold as 40 F in winter.

a. How deep must the bed be made (assuming that Equation 24-34 applies), if the sand to be used is constituted as shown in the first three columns of Table 24-6 and, for purposes of illustration, no sand equal to or larger than number 12 sieve is to be considered active in purification? Needed calculations are included in Table 24-6.

For $k = 796$ and $T = 40$ F, $\dfrac{1}{l_0} = \dfrac{50 \times 82.3}{60 \times 796} = 0.086$ by Equation 24-37, and l_0

$= 11.6$ in. To include the coarse sand, the depth must be $\dfrac{11.6 \times 100}{100 - 11.85} = 13.2$ in.

Adding 25% for safety, the depth becomes 16.5 in.

b. The sand is to be supported on gravel $\frac{3}{32}$ to $1\frac{1}{2}$ in. in size. What are the requisite depths?

Based upon Equation 24-38 and a value of $k = 12$, the calculations are as follows for sieve ratios of 2:1:

Size, in.	$\frac{3}{32}$	$\frac{3}{16}$	$\frac{3}{8}$	$\frac{3}{4}$	$1\frac{1}{2}$
Depth, in.	4.4	8.2	11.8	15.3	19.0
Increment, in.	4.4	3.8	3.6	3.5	3.7

The total required depth of gravel is 19 in. composed of five layers that are about 4 in. in thickness.

[16] J. R. Baylis, "Filter-Bed Troubles and Their Elimination," *J., New Eng. Water Works Assoc., 51,* 17 (1937).

TABLE 24-6.   Calculation of Filter Depth (Example 24-6)

Sieve No. (1)	Size of separation, cm $\times 10^2$ (2)	Proportionate weight of sand on sieve, $p \times 10^2$, % (3)	Geometric mean size of sand held between sieves, d, cm $\times 10^2$ (4)	Corrected proportionate weight $p \times 10^2$ (5)	$\dfrac{p}{d^{5/3}}$ (6)
35	5.0	6.20	5.4	7.03	9.14
30	5.9	47.0	6.5	53.3	50.3
25	7.1	20.2	7.7	22.9	16.8
20	8.4	6.83	10.0	7.75	3.67
16	11.9	7.92	14.1	8.98	2.36
12	16.8	6.26	20.0	......	.....
8	23.8	5.59	28.3	......	.....
6	33.6	......	....	......	.....
Sums	....	100.0	....	100.0	82.3

Columns 1 to 3 record the results of the sieve analysis of the stock sand. It is seen that $(5.59 + 6.26) = 11.85\%$ of the sand is greater than number 12 sieve.

Column 4 gives the geometric mean size of sand held between adjacent sieves; for example, $\sqrt{5.0 \times 5.9} = 5.4$.

Column 5 gives the corrected proportionate weight of the sand smaller than number 12 sieve; for example, $(6.20 \times 100)/(100 - 11.85) = 7.03$.

Column 6 = Column 5 ÷ (Column 4)$^{5/3}$.

24-9. Filter Underdrains.   The underdrainage system of a filter is intended to collect the filtered water and, where necessary, to distribute the wash water in such fashion that all portions of the bed perform nearly the same amount of work and, if washed, receive nearly the same amount of cleansing. Since the rate of wash is many times the rate of filtration, the former is the governing factor in the hydraulic design of filters that are cleaned by back-washing.

Equality of filtration and washing is created most conveniently by introducing a controlling loss of head at the contact between the filtering medium and the underdrainage system. The magnitude of this loss can be fixed in accordance with Equation 22-22.

a. Perforated Pipes.   The underdrainage system of rapid filters commonly consists of a main, or manifold, and perforated pipe laterals. The velocity of the jets issuing from the perforations or orifices is destroyed by directing the openings downward against the filter bottom and into the coarse gravel surrounding the pipes. The lost head, therefore, equals the driving head. In practice, this controlling head loss is set between 3 ft and 15 ft. At a wash-water rate of 36 in. a minute, this corresponds to a ratio of orifice area to bed area of

$(\frac{3}{60})/(0.75\sqrt{2gh}) = 0.5\%$ to 0.2%, on the assumption that the coefficient of discharge of the orifices is 0.75. If the orifice farthest away from the first orifice in the lateral adjacent to the manifold or main is to be held to a value mq_1 and $m = 0.9$, for example, the permissible friction loss in the lateral, according to Equation 22-22, becomes $h_f = (1 - m^2)h_1 = 0.19h_1 = 0.57$ to 2.85 ft.

As shown in Figure 24-8, flow through perforated laterals decreases substantially uniformly, but actually stepwise at each orifice. If the

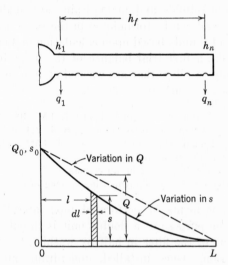

Figure 24-8. Frictional resistance to uniformly decreasing flow (idealized).

diameter is kept constant, the friction loss from the entrance of the lateral to the farthest opening is approximately equal to the loss of head due to the entrant flow passing through $\frac{1}{3}$ the length of lateral. In terms of the Chezy formula, for example, $s = v^2/c^2r = Q^2/c^2a^2r = kQ^2$, the value of c^2a^2r being almost constant. The loss of head h_f in a length l then becomes

$$h_f = \int_0^l s \, dl = k \int_0^l Q^2 \, dl = \frac{kQ_0^2}{L^2} \int_0^l (L - l)^2 \, dl \qquad 24\text{-}39$$

because in a portion l of a total length L, flow decreases from the entrant flow Q_0 to a flow $Q = Q_0(L - l)/L$. Integration of Equation 24-39 gives

$$h_f = \frac{kQ_0^2}{L^2}\left(L^2 l - Ll^2 + \frac{1}{3}l^3\right) = s_0\left(l - \frac{l^2}{L} + \frac{1}{3}\frac{l^3}{L^2}\right) \qquad 24\text{-}40$$

and for $l = L$, $h = \frac{1}{3}s_0L$ as stated at the outset. Collection of water during filtration, like distribution of water during washing, induces losses that can be formulated in exactly the same way. The flow pattern is simply reversed.

Additional losses include entrance losses, losses in fittings, and losses at each orifice corresponding to sudden enlargement of section but produced by the withdrawal of water and consequent slowing up of velocity. These losses are offset in part, and are sometimes even exceeded, by recovery of velocity head at each point of withdrawal. Losses through manifolds and main drains are analogous to losses through laterals and can be formulated in the same manner.

Certain rules of thumb, based upon calculation and experimentation, are used to strike a first trial balance of the underdrainage system. These rules apply to filters that are washed at rates of 6 to 36 in. per min and may be summarized as follows:

1. Ratio of area of orifice to area of bed served: $1.5 \times 10^{-3}{:}1$ to $5 \times 10^{-3}{:}1$.
2. Ratio of area of lateral to area of orifices served: 2:1 to 4:1.
3. Ratio of area of main to area of laterals served: 1.5:1 to 3:1.
4. Diameter of orifices: $\frac{1}{4}$ in. to $\frac{3}{4}$ in.
5. Spacing of orifices: 3 in. to 12 in. on centers.
6. Spacing of laterals: closely approximating spacing of orifices.

Common arrangements of perforated pipe laterals are shown in Figure 24-9. The purpose of a double unit is to cut the wash-water rate requirements of the filter in half by washing the two component units in succession. Once installed, underdrains are relatively inaccessible. They should, therefore, be corrosion resistant or protected against corrosion.

b. *Other Systems of Underdrainage.* There are a number of other arrangements of underdrains that are similar to perforated pipe systems and that employ a layer of gravel to support the sand, disperse the wash water, and conduct the filtrate to the collecting system. Notably different from them is the porous-plate bottom. Here the sand rests directly on a diaphragm, septum, or false bottom of porous plates like the diffuser plates of the activated-sludge process (Section 25-14). A sufficient waterway must be provided between the bottom and the plates to reduce head differentials to workable magnitudes. Whereas gravel-bottomed filters require the use of sand that grades into the supporting gravel (if the sand is not to slip through the gravel into the underdrains), sand of any wanted uniformity can be placed on porous-plate septums. Clogged plates are cleaned from time to time with acid or alkali.

Vitrified-tile pipe laid with open joints (about ⅜ in. apart) generally furnishes the underdrainage of filters that are not back-washed. The laterals of slow sand filters, for example, are usually constructed of split-tile (half-round) pipe, whereas agricultural-tile pipe or sewer

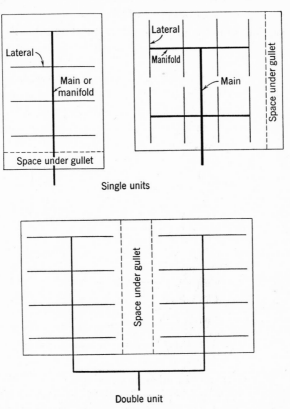

Single units

Double unit

Figure 24-9. Typical arrangements of perforated pipe underdrains in rapid filters. (Compare with Figures 24-11 and 24-12.)

pipe makes up the laterals of intermittent sand filters and of sludge-drying beds (Section 26-18). The pipe is surrounded by layers of graded gravel that gradually taper off in size to that of the filter layer of sand.

24-10. Wash-Water Gutters. If the static head on the underdrainage system is to be nearly equal over all parts of a filter bed, the wash water must be carried away without being forced to travel far over the surface. A system of weirs and troughs is ordinarily used for this purpose. Corresponding in their action to the effluent weirs and troughs of settling tanks (Section 22-14), these collecting devices are called wash-water troughs.

If certain simplifying assumptions are made, the momentum theorem can be employed to develop a general relationship for the water-surface curve of wash-water troughs and related hydraulic structures.[17] The simplifying assumptions are (1) the kinetic energy of the water falling into the trough does not contribute to longitudinal velocity; (2) friction

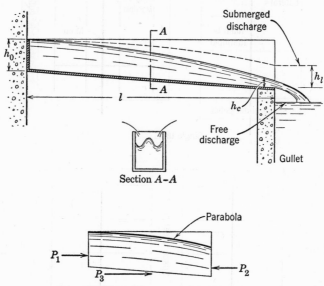

Figure 24-10. Water-surface curves in a wash-water gutter.

can be neglected; (3) flow is substantially horizontal in direction; and (4) the water-surface curve is approximated by a parabola. The forces acting to change the momentum are then solely the unbalanced static pressure forces P_1, P_2, and P_3 shown in Figure 24-10. They have the following magnitudes: $P_1 = \frac{1}{2}wbh_0^2$; $P_2 = -\frac{1}{2}wbh_l^2$; and [18] $P_3 = wbli(\frac{2}{3}h_0 + \frac{1}{6}il + \frac{1}{3}h_l)$. Here w is the unit weight of water; b, l, and i are respectively the width, length, and slope of the trough; and h_0 and h_l are respectively the initial and terminal depths of the collected water. The change in momentum, Qv_lw/g, equals wbh_c^3/h_l, because

---

[17] For a general discussion of this problem, see T. R. Camp, *Trans., Am. Soc., Civil Engrs.*, *105*, 606 (1940).

[18] Because the volume of water in the trough is

$$bl[h_0 + il - \frac{1}{2}il - \frac{1}{3}(h_0 + il - h_l)].$$

$Q = bh_cv_c$; $v_l = h_cv_c/h_l$; and $v_c = \sqrt{gh_c}$. Here Q is the rate of discharge, and v_l and v_c are the velocities of flow at the submerged depth h_l and at the critical depth h_c respectively. Equating the sum of the forces to the change in momentum and solving for h_0:

$$h_0 = \sqrt{(2h_c{}^3/h_l) + (h_l - \tfrac{1}{3}il)^2} - \tfrac{2}{3}il \qquad \text{24-41}$$

For level inverts $(i = 0)$ and for the critical depth $h_c{}^3 = Q^2/gb^2$, where Q is the total rate of discharge, and b is the width of a rectangular trough,

$$h_0 = \sqrt{h_l{}^2 + \frac{2Q^2}{gb^2h_l}} = \sqrt{h_l{}^2 + 2\frac{h_c{}^3}{h_l}} \qquad \text{24-42}$$

When discharge is free, h_l closely equals h_c, and

$$h_0 = h_c\sqrt{3} = 1.73h_c \qquad \text{24-43}$$

or

$$Q = 2.49bh_0{}^{3/2} \qquad \text{24-44}$$

Equations 24-43 and 24-44 hold also for troughs of other than rectangular cross-section. Additional drawdown of the water surface by friction can be estimated on the basis of turbulence increasing the roughness factor up to about twofold.

Lateral travel of the water overflowing into the gutters is commonly limited to between 2.5 and 3.5 ft, i.e., the clear distance between gutters is held to between 5 and 7 ft in order to keep the head of water on the underdrains, and with it the rate of wash, as uniform as possible. The vertical distance of troughs above the sand bed is determined by the degree of sand expansion. The bottom of the trough must be kept above the surface of the expanded sand if reduction in the waterway by the troughs and consequent increase in upward velocity between them is not to result in loss of sand.

As shown in Figure 24-11, troughs are arranged to run the length or the width of the filter. They discharge into a gullet, the hydraulics of which are like that of the tributary gutters except that flow increases stepwise instead of uniformly. Choice of trough cross-section depends somewhat on the material of construction. Rectangular, semicircular, semihexagonal, and semioctagonal shapes are common. Of them, the semicircle interferes least with the upward streaming of wash water and possesses the best hydraulic properties as well.

Example 24-7. Troughs 24 ft long, 18 in. wide, and 7 ft on centers are to serve a filter that is washed at a rate of 30 in. per min.

a. How deep must the troughs be made if their invert is to be kept level and they are to discharge freely into the gullet?

b. How high must the top of the trough be placed above the sand if a 30-in. bed is to be expanded 50%?

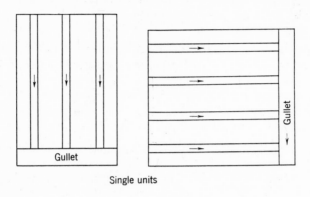

Single units

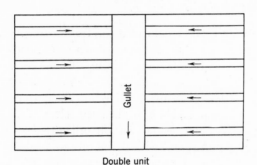

Double unit

Figure 24-11. Typical arrangements of wash-water troughs in rapid filters. (Compare with Figures 24-9 and 24-12.)

Since $Q = 24 \times 7 \times 30/(12 \times 60) = 7$ cfs, find the following:

a. By Equation 24-44: $h_0 = \left(\dfrac{7}{2.49 \times 1.5}\right)^{2/3} = 1.52$ ft, or, say, $18\frac{1}{2}$ in.

b. The troughs should be placed $(0.5 \times 2.5 + 1.52) = 2.77$ ft, or, say, 2 ft, $9\frac{1}{2}$ in. above the sand surface plus the depth of freeboard in, and thickness of, the trough.

24-11. Sizing of Filters and Conduits. The size and number of filter beds to be included in a plant become a matter of economics, once provision has been made for a sufficient number of units to permit routine cleaning or washing of beds and occasional repairs. Essential factors are the cost of the filter area, the walls, and the appurtenances. Cost analyses in accordance with the Lagrange method (Section 12-3) or with the principles of maximum-minimum analysis will identify the number of beds to be used. Final sizing must be based upon comparative designs, however. A rough estimate of the number of rapid sand units N is given by Morrill and Wallace [19] as $N = 2.7 \sqrt{Q}$ where Q is the plant capacity in mgd ($Q \lessgtr 100$). As stated before, double filter units are resorted to when it is necessary to keep the size of the wash-water system within reasonable working limits.

Allowance must be made in the sizing of filters for their time out of service. The time required to clean slow filters may be as much as three days in every thirty-day period. Rapid filters are normally expected to be thrown out of operation for about 10 min. during each cycle, normally a day. For these filters, the time out of service is composed of the following: (1) the time necessary to draw down the water to trough level or lower, either by filtration under a falling head, or by direct wasting of the water above the level of the wash-water troughs; (2) the time required to expand the sand which is purposely extended in order to permit surface deposits and the suspended matter in the top layers of sand to escape before the whole bed is suspended (Equation 24-32); (3) the time of wash which by experience is about 2 minutes per ft of sand; (4) the time required for the smaller sand grains to settle back into place after the wash water has been shut off (Equation 24-30); and (5) the time required to refill the filter box to the flowline. Allowance must be made, furthermore, for the amount of filtered water consumed in washing the beds. Including a freeboard of 1 ft, the depth of both slow and rapid filter tanks is commonly 10 ft.

Pipes and other conduits, including valves and gates, are ordinarily designed to carry water at the following velocities approximately:

	fps
Influent conduits carrying raw water	3–6
Influent conduits carrying flocculated water	1–2
Effluent conduits carrying filtered water	3–6
Drainage conduits carrying used wash water	4–8
Wash-water conduits carrying clean wash water	8–12
Filter-to-waste connections	12–15

Wash-water tanks must refill between washes and must hold for safety about 1.5 times the amount of water needed for a single bed. In large plants, wash-water is often pumped directly to the filters up to maximum rate.

24-12. Filter Appurtenances. Filter appurtenances include manually, hydraulically, or electrically operated gates on the influent,

[19] A. B. Morrill and W. M. Wallace, "The Design and Care of Rapid Sand Filters," *J., Am. Water Works Assoc., 26,* 446 (1934).

effluent, drain, and wash-water lines; measuring devices such as Venturi meters; rate controllers activated by the measuring device; loss-of-head and rate-of-flow gages; sand-expansion indicators; wash-water controllers and indicators; operating tables and water-sampling devices; sand ejectors and sand washers; and wash-water pumps and tanks. The larger the plant and the higher the rate of filtration, the greater is the justification for the inclusion of mechanical and automatic aids to operation.

  a. Rapid Filters. Much of the equipment and piping of modern rapid sand filters is shown in Figure 24-12. Attention is called to the "filter-to-waste" connection which serves the purpose of wasting the water held in the filter after washing. This connection, also called the "rewash connection," was in regular use when filters were washed with raw water. This is no longer done in modern plants, and the filter-to-waste connection is needed only when beds must, upon occasion, be cleaned with deterging chemicals such as sodium hydroxide. The chemical is then drawn into the bed from the surface and, after a sufficient contact time, washed from the bed by opening the filter-to-waste connection. This connection should lead from the filter effluent in advance of the rate controller. It consists generally of a valved stub of pipe, proportioned to discharge at about the maximum rate of filtration when the bed is clean. The waste connection should not endanger the normal filtrate by providing an opportunity for back-flow of polluted water.

  b. Slow Filters. Special appurtenances of the slow sand filter shown in Figure 24-1 are sand ejectors (Figure 24-13), sand washers (Figure 24-5), and sand-storage bins. These appurtenances are useful also in the general handling, washing, transportation, and placement of sand and other granular materials, such as grit.

  The sand removed from a filter surface by scraping is wet, i.e., its voids ($100f$ = about 40%) are filled with water. Hence its specific gravity s_w is

$$s_w = (1 - f)s_s + fs = s_s - f(s_s - s) \qquad 24\text{-}45$$

Ordinarily, $s_w = (2.65 - 0.4 \times 1.65) = 1.99$. If the proportion of wet sand in the mixture of sand and water which is transported to a washer is p, the specific gravity of the mixture s_m must be

$$s_m = (1 - p)s + ps_w = s + p(1 - f)(s_s - s) \qquad 24\text{-}46$$

Ordinarily, $s_m = 1 + 0.99p$. As shown in Figure 24-13, part of the transporting water is supplied to the ejector box for the purpose of "liquefying" the sand by creating "slush" that contains a proportion

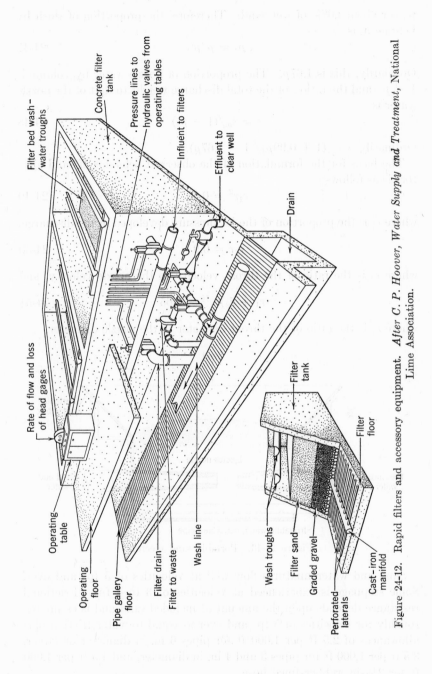

Figure 24-12. Rapid filters and accessory equipment. *After C. P. Hoover, Water Supply and Treatment*, National Lime Association.

p_w, or about 60%, of wet sand. Therefore, the proportion of slush by volume p_s is

$$p_s = p/p_w \qquad\qquad 24\text{-}47$$

Ordinarily, this is $1.67p$. The proportion of nozzle water by volume is $1 - p_s$, and the ratio r of the total discharge weight to that of the nozzle water is

$$r = s_m/(1 - p_s) \qquad\qquad 24\text{-}48$$

Ordinarily, $r = (1 + 0.99p)/(1 - 1.67p)$.

The basis for the formulation of the observed behavior of sand ejectors is as follows:

$$r_1 r^2 = 0.65 \qquad\qquad 24\text{-}49$$

where r_1 is the proportion of the jet pressure developed in the discharge,

$$r_2 r = 0.9 \qquad\qquad 24\text{-}50$$

where r_2 is the ratio of the throat velocity to the nozzle velocity, and

$$(r_1 + r_2)r_3^{3/2} = 1.65 \qquad\qquad 24\text{-}51$$

where r_3 is the ratio of the throat diameter to the nozzle diameter.

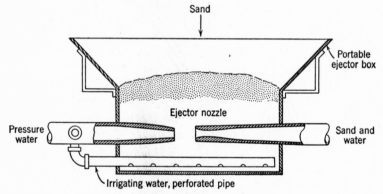

Figure 24-13. Portable sand ejector.

Sand and water mixtures flow well at velocities of 5 fps and over. Some stoppage is experienced at velocities of 3 to 4 fps. Frictional resistance depends upon the amount of included sand and is estimated roughly for velocities of 5 fps and over as equal to water friction plus allowances of 2.5 ft per 1,000 ft for pipes 6 in. in diameter or larger, 3.5 ft per 1,000 ft for pipes 3 and 4 in. in diameter, and 4.5 ft per 1,000 ft for $2\frac{1}{2}$-in. rubber-lined hose.

To store all the sand removed from a slow sand filter between re-sandings, the storage bins must hold 18 in. of sand when the filter depth is reduced from 42 in. to 24 in. in the course of time. The clean sand is carried back to the filters and separated from the flowing water by a "sand separator" such as that shown in Figure 24-14.

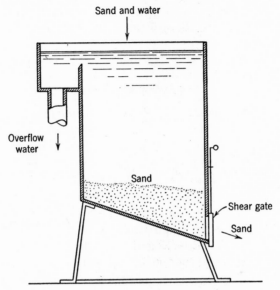

Figure 24-14. Portable sand separator.

Example 24-8. A sand ejector with 0.7-in. nozzle is to move 12.6 cu yd of sand per hour from a filter through 3-in. hose and 4-in. pipe to a sand washer situated 20 ft above the sand surface. The available water pressure at bed level is 100 psig. If the proportion of wet sand in the ejector discharge is 20%, find for the conditions ordinarily prevailing (a) the water requirements of the ejector, its best throat diameter, and the outlet pressure and velocity; and (b) the velocities in the hose and pipe and the static lift to the sand washer.

In accordance with Section 24-12, we find the following:

a. 1. For 20% of wet sand by volume, $p = 0.20$, and the rate of discharge is $(12.6 \times 27)/(0.2 \times 3,600) = 0.4725$ cfs.

2. The specific gravity of the sand-water mixture (Equation 24-46) is $s_m = (1 + 0.99 \times 0.20) = 1.20$, and the proportion of slush by volume (Equation 24-47) is $p_s = 1.67 \times 0.20 = 0.33$.

3. The proportion of nozzle water by volume then becomes $(1 - 0.33) = 0.67$, and the nozzle water itself equals $0.67 \times 0.4725 = 0.316$ cfs, the irrigation water being $(0.33 - 0.20) \times 0.4725 = 0.063$ cfs.

4. The ratio of the total discharge weight to that of the nozzle water (Equation 24-48) is $r = (1 + 0.99 \times 0.20)/(1 - 1.67 \times 0.20) = 1.80$.

5. The proportion of the jet pressure developed in the discharge (Equation 24-49) is $r_1 = 0.65/(1.80)^2 = 0.20$, and the pressure itself is 20 psig or 46 ft.

6. The ratio of the throat velocity to the nozzle velocity (Equation 24-50) is $r_2 = 0.9/1.80 = 0.50$, and the throat velocity itself is $(0.5 \times 0.316 \times 4 \times 144)/[\pi \times (0.7^2)] = 59$ fps.

7. The ratio of the throat diameter to the nozzle diameter (Equation 24-51) is $r_3{}^{3/2} = 1.65/(0.20 + 0.50) = 2.36$, or $r_3 = 1.78$, making the throat diameter $1.78 \times 0.7 = 1.25$ in.

b. 1. For a throat velocity of 59 fps, the velocities in the 3-in. hose and 4-in. piping are $59(1.25/3)^2 = 10.3$ fps and $59(1.25/4)^2 = 5.8$ fps. These values will insure free flow.

2. For a specific gravity of 1.20 the static lift to the washer is $1.20 \times 20 = 24$ ft.

Operation of Filters

24-13. Length of Filter Runs. The impurities that are transferred from the water to the filter, together with their coagulating or precipitating agents, clog the pores of the filter and increase the loss of head through it. The time rate at which head loss is increased, dh/dt, determines the "length of run" or "period of service" of the filter. Because clogging of the pores progresses downward during operation, dh/dt increases slightly with time. The magnitude of dh/dt is directly proportional to the amount of suspended matter carried onto the filter when the factors included in Equation 24-11 are held constant. For a given water, the length of run is expected to vary directly as the square of the grain size and the fourth power of the porosity, and inversely as the 3/2 power of the rate of filtration.[20] When flow is substantially laminar (Equation 24-12), the head loss varies approximately as the first power of the rate of filtration, the reciprocal of the square of the sand size, and the reciprocal of the fourth power of the porosity. It follows that the length of filter run may be expected to vary approximately inversely as the product of the initial loss of head of the clean sand bed and the square root of the rate of filtration.

Filters are normally cleaned when a loss of head has been established at which the bed and its underdrainage system are under partial vacuum or negative head (Figure 24-6). The head at a given elevation in a filter becomes negative when the loss of head through the overlying portion exceeds the static head at the point. If the rate of removal of suspended matter as well as the grain size distribution of the filter medium could be the same at all depths, negative head would mount progressively from bottom to top. Variations in these factors

[20] H. E. Hudson, "Filter Materials, Filter Runs, and Water Quality," *J. Am. Water Works Assoc.*, *30*, 1993 (1938).

may cause a negative head to appear first at an intermediate depth. Most filters operate under a partial vacuum at their lower levels towards the end of their run. Dissolved gases begin to be released when this happens. At atmospheric pressure and normal water temperatures, water can hold about 3% of air (i.e., oxygen and nitrogen) by volume in solution. Since the amount of air precipitated from solution is about $100/34 = 3\%$ per foot of negative head, it does not take long to fill much of the pore space or underdrainage system. The filter then becomes "air bound" and loses capacity.

Resistance to flow being least along the walls of a filter, the head loss adjacent to the walls is less, and the pressure at any depth is greater, than in the body of the filter. This pressure differential produces inward as well as downward flow within the filter and causes the filter grains to pull away from the walls. Water short-circuits through the resulting shrinkage cracks and fills them with caking suspended matter. Pressure differentials associated with inequalities of flow may open shrinkage cracks also in the body of the bed. Shrinkage is least for coarse sand that is well compacted and kept clean. Such sand will consolidate by less than 1% as the loss of head rises to its maximum value.

Poor distribution of wash water and inadequate scour and cleaning of the sand grains permit the accumulation of suspended matter on the grains and in the voids of the bed. Depending upon the nature of the suspended matter removed, the dirtiness of the sand can be measured in terms of the concentration of alumina, iron, color, or turbidity that is freed from a known weight or volume of sand by shaking it vigorously with a known volume of water to which a detergent or dissolving agent has been added. When the washing of a filter is inadequate, turbidity and floc, together with some sand, are cemented together to form "mud balls." The intensity of mud-ball formation can be determined by washing a known volume of sand through a 10-mesh sieve and measuring the volume of the retained mud balls by displacement in a graduated cylinder of water.[15] In a filter that is well designed and well operated, mud balls should not occupy more than about 0.1% of the volume of the top 6 in. of sand. Badly clogged filters can be improved by ejecting the sand and cleaning it in a sand washer, by agitating the expanded bed by hand with long-tined rakes, by directing hose streams into the expanded bed, or by the addition of a detergent such as a 2 to 5% solution of caustic soda (¼ to 2 lb per sq ft of filter covered with 2 to 3 in. of water).

24-14. Performance and Permissible Loading of Filters. Some of the matters relating to filter performance have been discussed in

Sections 2 and 3 of this chapter. It is the purpose of this section to carry this discussion further and to report, in particular, on the allowable coliform loading of rapid filtration plants. This is important not only in water purification but also, as we shall see later, in stream sanitation.

a. Bacterial Efficiency. Studies by engineers of the U. S. Public Health Service [21] have established the following empirical relationship between the effluent concentration E and the influent, or raw-water, concentration, R of coliform organisms in water that has been subjected to certain water-purification processes:

$$E = cR^n \qquad \text{or} \qquad \log E = \log c + n \log R \qquad 24\text{-}52$$

Here c and n are coefficients that reflect respectively the magnitude of the effluent count for a given raw-water count and the relative shift in effluent count with changing raw-water count. A low value for c represents high fundamental efficiency, and a low value for n great constancy of performance with varying raw-water quality. Observed values of c and n and of the probable number of coliform organisms per 100 ml in the raw water (R_0) that can be reduced, by different treatment processes, to the current Public Health Service standard for drinking water of about 1 per 100 ml in the effluent are shown in Table 24-7. Since filter performance alone does not govern the quality of the effluent, the efficiency of related treatment processes is included in this table.

A comparable value of R_0 for slow sand filters treating relatively clean waters that are not pretreated by flocculation or chlorination is 50 or about the same as for chlorination alone and is not far below the value of R_0 for rapid sand filtration preceded by flocculation and sedimentation. It should be noted that the values of c and n for a combination of treatment processes cannot be synthesized from the values of these coefficients for the component processes, because each component changes the quality of the water to be treated. It should be noted, too, that relatively clear lake waters are paradoxically not as amenable to treatment as is turbid river water. For the common combination (line 4 in Table 24-7) of coagulation, sedimentation, rapid sand filtration, and chlorination, the ratio of permissible coliform loadings of river water to lake water is $6{,}000/4{,}500 = \frac{4}{3}$. Turning to Section 24-8, it is seen that this is also closely the reciprocal of the ratio of the suspended-matter penetration-coefficients k (582/796) for

[21] *U. S. Pub. Health Service Bull.* 172 (1927) and 193 (1929); also *U. S. Pub. Health Rept.,* 48, 396 (1933).

TABLE 24-7. Permissible Coliform Loading of Rapid Sand Water Filters Including Related Treatment Processes

$$E = cR^n; R = R_0 \text{ when } E = 1 \text{ per 100 ml.}$$

	Turbid river water *			Clear lake water †		
Treatment process	$c \times 10^3$	n	R_0	$c \times 10^3$	n	R_0
1. Chlorination	15	0.96	80	50	0.76	50
2. Flocculation, settling, and rapid sand filtration	70	0.60	80	87	0.60	60
3. (2) and prechlorination	..	....	3,500	..	....	.....
4. (2) and postchlorination	11	0.52	6,000	40	0.38	4,500
5. (2) and double chlorination	..	....	20,000	..	....	.....
6. (4) and double settling	64	0.25	60,000	..	....	.....

* Ohio River plants.
† Great Lakes plants.

similar waters (Equation 24-34). The "reaction to filtration" of clear waters is, therefore, generally poorer than that of turbid waters.

b. Removal of Color, Turbidity, and Iron. On an average, but 30% of the natural color in water is removed by slow sand filters without the aid of coagulants. By suitable flocculation and settling prior to filtration, however, a colorless water can be produced by both slow and rapid filters. Turbidity responds well to slow sand filtration without the aid of coagulation; but it clogs these filters so quickly that raw water containing turbidities in excess of about 40 mg/l should not be applied to slow filters, unless it has previously been subjected to coagulation and sedimentation. Rapid filtration, as has been stated before, generally presupposes that the applied water has been suitably flocculated and settled. Diatomaceous-earth filters also perform most satisfactorily when the applied water has been flocculated and settled.

Both slow and rapid sand filters will remove oxidized iron and manganese. However, oxidized manganese precipitates so slowly that it responds better to slow filtration than to rapid filtration, unless it has been suitably flocculated (see Section 23-3). The presence on the sand of a coating of manganese hastens precipitation of this substance by catalysis.

c. Removal of Larger Organisms. The larger microorganisms, including the algae and diatoms, are readily removed by filtration; but the odors and tastes associated with the algae and diatoms, as well as with certain chlorophyllaceous protozoa, may remain unchanged in intensity unless treatment processes especially adapted to the removal of odor- and taste-producing substances are included in the treatment works. In the absence of turbidity, natural or due to the use of coagulants, chlorophyllaceous organisms flourish on the surface of open filters. Mats of appreciable thickness sometimes build up on open slow filters. On sunny days, photosynthesis is active, and oxygen may be released in sufficient volume to lift a section of the mat and cause the denuded spot to filter an undue share of the water. This makes for poor performance. The cells of diatoms are bad clogging agents because they interlock to form a tenacious mat.

The eggs and adults of the common, intestinal, parasitic worms, as well as the cysts of the pathogenic amoebae, are relatively so large that they cannot normally pass through a bed of sand. However, the cercariae of the blood flukes, although larger than amoebic cysts, are reported to be sufficiently motile to wriggle through beds of sand of normal depth. These worms, as well as amoebic cysts, are held back by diatomaceous-earth filters.

d. Oxidation of Organic Matter. As shown in Table 21-11, the efficiency of intermittent sand filters for the removal of bacteria and for the removal or oxidation of organic matter from sewage is very good. It is accomplished, however, only by reducing the rates of filtration to relatively small figures. Except in extraordinary circumstances, the biological oxidizing power of filters is not utilized in connection with the purification of municipal water supplies. Apart from their improving the hygienic and esthetic qualities of water, therefore, rapid and slow filters leave the remaining, largely chemical, qualities of the applied water substantially unaltered.

25 ――――――― BIOLOGICAL FLOCCULATION AND PRECIPITATION

25-1. General Considerations. Historically, the developmental sequence of methods of aerobic biological treatment of sewage and other waste waters proceeds from sewage farms or irrigation areas through intermittent sand filters to contact beds and thence to trickling filters and activated-sludge units. With certain modifications, all these methods are still in use for the treatment of sewage and related waste waters. On rare occasion, the intermittent sand filter has been employed also in the treatment of a municipal water supply that was exceptionally rich in organic matter. All the methods so far developed are based, at least in part, upon the capacity of adventitious microorganisms (1) to abstract needed food substances from suitable waste waters and (2) to elaborate gelatinous films that, together with the organisms themselves, constitute the essential elements of the most advanced aerobic, biological treatment systems. Because of their viscous, jellylike nature and their high microbial population, these films are called *zoogleal* [1] films. These biological creations possess the signal ability (1) to transfer to themselves, among other things, energy-yielding substances that were dissolved or suspended in the carrying water and (2) to release to the water some of the end products of their metabolism including water, carbon dioxide, nitrate, and sulfate. The mechanisms involved in the exchange of substances from and to the carrying water are complex and variable. For want of a better definition, they are classed as "surface," "contact," or "interfacial forces" and as "biological oxidation." Since, in the most advanced methods, the important contribution is the conversion of finely divided suspended and colloidal matter and, more important still, dissolved matter into film substance, the over-all accomplishment is referred to, in this book, as biological flocculation and precipitation, as contrasted to chemical flocculation and precipitation.

[1] From *zoo* and the Greek word *gloios*, a glutinous substance.

As is true for other methods of sewage treatment as well, the choice of a biological system depends upon local needs: size of community; agricultural value of waste waters; extent, nature, and location of available disposal areas; capacity and intended use of receiving waters; sludge-disposal requirements; and other factors that, in one way or another, determine the economy of the operation and its fitness under different conditions.

It is the purpose of the present chapter to identify the essential elements of biological flocculation and precipitation and to show how they can be put to use in engineering structures and devices for the purpose of removing from water relatively large concentrations of putrescible organic matter that cannot be dealt with effectively, or as effectively, by sedimentation, chemical coagulation and precipitation, or physical filtration. Since sewage contains large quantities of such substances, discussion is directed primarily toward biological flocculation and precipitation as a means of sewage treatment. However, a number of industrial waste waters fall under the same rubric.

25-2. Biological Treatment Units. The general features of significant, biological treatment units are described briefly below in order to provide the background against which the systems of biological flocculation and precipitation must be viewed if their essential elements are to be understood.

a. Irrigation Areas. The disposal of sewage on agricultural areas has two objectives: (1) the raising of crops and (2) the treatment of the applied sewage. The agricultural utilization of sewage is concerned both with its water value and its content of fertilizing elements. The degree of treatment received by the sewage is not necessarily proportionate to its agricultural utilization. Conflicts in the sanitary and agricultural management of irrigation areas are the result.

Irrigation methods are rationally made to conform to local needs. They vary with the characteristics of the soil, the magnitude and distribution of rainfall, the other climatic conditions that influence the raising of crops, the height of the ground-water table, the topography of the land, and the nature of the crops raised. In most areas of the world, the annual water requirements of irrigable lands are in the vicinity of 10 in., or from ½ to ⅓ of the annual precipitation in well-watered regions. This is equivalent to about 750 gpd per acre, or 10 persons per acre on the basis of a sewage flow of 80 gpcd. It is obvious, therefore, that very large areas of land are needed if agricultural needs are to govern the disposal of the sewage. If they are made subservient to it, however, the water load can be increased under the best conditions to about 3,000 gpd per acre for cultivated, agricultural lands and up to 25,000 gpd per acre for grasslands. Sanitary needs are met by suitable pretreatment of the sewage where this is indicated.

Sewage is carried to the irrigation areas in open channels or in closed pipes. It is applied to the land (1) by large revolving spray nozzles attached to movable pipelines (spray irrigation); (2) by surface flowage from ridge distributors in the form of ditches or pipes with side outlets (surface, ridge, or bed irrigation; also land filtration). Surface and flood irrigation are illustrated in Figure 25-1. For the disposal of sewage from isolated dwellings or small numbers of people, subsurface irrigation is often employed (see Chapter 30). Purposeful agricultural utilization of the sewage is then dispensed with.

In surface irrigation, the sewage flows over the cropped land. Some of it seeps into the soil, some of it is evaporated, much of it is collected after but moderate contact with soil and crops. Therefore, this form of irrigation is, at best, a process of partial biological treatment. Purification ceases in cold weather. In flood irrigation, the sewage percolates through the soil and is collected, if necessary, in under-drains. The mechanical and biological purifying powers of the soil are utilized, and treatment becomes more complete. Where desired for sanitary reasons, the sewage can be kept from contact with crops by being confined to furrows between cropped beds. Spray irrigation is a form of surface irrigation. See Section 29-12d.

The sanitary management of sewage farms is beset by a number of difficulties. Unless the sewage is fully treated before use for irrigation, odors cannot be avoided. Unless it meets the standards and restrictions discussed in Section 21-7, sanitary hazards are introduced. Spray irrigation is a particularly bad offender. At times of heavy rainfall, the crops do not need watering, while sewage volumes are often swollen by storm-runoff or ground-water infiltration. The simplest solution for some of these difficulties is the holding in reserve of about 25% of the area or, better, the shunting in of treatment devices that are routinely used for pretreatment or that stand by for times when the irrigation area is overwatered or must be laid dry in the interest of agriculture. Harvesting periods as well as rainy periods must be considered in this connection.

Operation of irrigation areas must be intermittent. Otherwise the land will not remain sweet. Overloaded areas or areas that contain soils that cannot absorb large quantities of water, or are easily clogged by suspended matter or growths, become "sewage sick." The biological films that are established on the soil grains are eventually converted to humus and may contribute to the fertility of the soil.

b. Intermittent Sand Filters. These relatively fine, granular sewage filters are described in Section 24-3b and illustrated in Figure 24-2. They are logical developments from sewage farming in regions where sandy soils prevail and direct agricultural utilization of sewage can be dispensed with in favor of intensive sewage treatment. Rates of application of sewage are thereby raised to as much as 80,000 gpd per acre without pretreatment and to as much as 800,000 gpd per acre with biological pretreatment. Heavy surface accumulations of

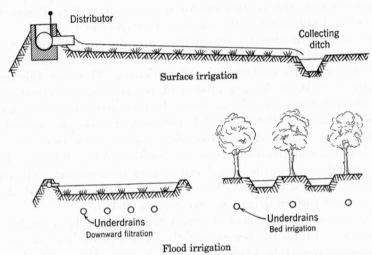

Figure 25-1. Surface and flood irrigation. *After Imhoff and Fair.*

suspended matter must be removed from time to time, but the biological films that form on the sand grains within the filter undergo continuous stabilization. Anaerobic conditions are avoided by intermittent dosing and resting of the sand beds.

c. Coarse-Grained Beds and Related Structures. Whereas biological flocculation and precipitation are more or less incidental to irrigation and intermittent sand filtration, the purposeful building up of biological slimes has become the governing principle in the development of coarse-grained beds for sewage treatment. The need for maintaining aerobic conditions has led to the evolution of two treatment devices from the prototype contact, or bacteria, bed which is now largely obsolete. The design and operating features of these devices are illustrated in Figure 25-2.

1. The fill-and-draw bed—*contact* or *bacteria bed* (see Figure 25-2a)—consists of a tank of moderate depth filled with coarse granular ballast or other materials

of large surface area. The tank is filled with sewage, allowed to stand full, and drained. It is then allowed to rest. Air is drawn into the tank or bed while it is being filled or emptied and circulates through it to some extent while it stands idle. The beds are operated as single units or in series as double or triple units. They are generally preceded by settling tanks and must be followed by such tanks, if they unload their accumulated slimes from time to time and if

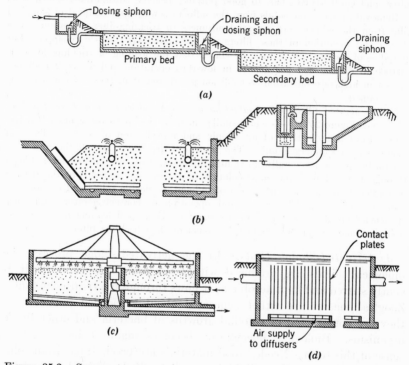

Figure 25-2. Sewage treatment in coarse-grained beds and related structures. (a) Double-contact beds with dosing and draining siphons. (b) Trickling filter with fixed nozzles and automatic dosing tank. (c) Trickling filter with rotary distributor. (d) Contact aerator. *In part after Imhoff and Fair.*

these partly stabilized slimes are to be kept out of the plant effluent. Fine-grained beds that are dosed and drained slowly may not unload. They must then fully stabilize the putrescible organic matter within their pores, if they are not to clog rapidly. The loading of contact beds is 100,000 to 300,000 gpd per acre-ft. Over-all removals of from 80 to 90% of the suspended solids, from 65 to 85% of the BOD, and from 60 to 80% of the 37 C, 24-hr. bacterial count are accomplished by proper operation.

2. The percolated bed—*trickling* or *sprinkling filter* (see Figure 25-2b and c)—is a logical development of the fill-and-draw bed.[2] The bed is similar to the

_____

[2] It should be remarked parenthetically that fill-and-draw or intermittent operation has generally preceded continuous operation in the development of most

contact bed in its basic design but differs in method of dosage and film contact. Sewage is distributed over the bed from fixed or movable nozzles, or sprays, to trickle downward over the contact surfaces, while currents of air, induced chiefly by differences in the specific weights of the atmosphere inside and outside of the bed, sweep through the interstices to carry needed oxygen to the film. Distribution of sewage, originally intermittent by projection of the experience with sand filters and contact beds, has, to good purpose, become substantially continuous.

Removal of settleable solids from the influent sewage and removal of sloughed film from the effluent are essential adjuncts to trickling-filter operation. The design and operation of these filters are elaborated later in this chapter. For purposes of comparison, it may be stated that the loading of trickling filters is 300,000 to 600,000 gpd per acre-ft in low-rate operation and above 2 mgd per acre-ft in high-rate operation, yet efficiencies greater than those of contact beds are attained.

3. The aerated filled bed—*contact aerator, aerated contact bed,* or *Emscher filter* (see Figure 25-2d)—is again similar in basic design to the contact bed but differs from it in method of air supply and introduction of sewage. The bed operates as a submerged unit. The sewage is displaced through the unit continuously and in a generally horizontal direction, while compressed air is blown through the bed to maintain circulation of the sewage and supply the oxygen requirements of the film. Removal of influent, settleable solids and of sloughed film are necessary. The design and operation of contact aerators and their efficiencies are discussed later in this chapter. For equal loading on an acre-ft basis, contact aerators are slightly less efficient than trickling filters.

d. Activated-Sludge Units. In the activated-sludge process, the biological slimes are produced within the sewage itself while it is gently stirred and kept aerobic as it flows through the treatment tanks. Zoogleal masses are either generated about suspended particles, or they are constructed of colonial growths of bacteria and other living organisms. Biological flocculation becomes manifest in the purest sense of this term. Needed food materials are precipitated from solution in addition to the colloidal as well as finely divided, suspended solids that are included in the aggregates. The flocs team with living organisms (see Figure 25-4) that, by voracious feeding, cleanse or restore the active contact surfaces; hence they are called *activated* sludge flocs. The oxygen requirements of the flocs are high and cannot be satisfied by the dissolved oxygen normally available in the sewage entering the treatment tanks. Needed dissolved oxygen is supplied by forced absorption either from the atmosphere above the flowing sewage or from air blown into it. The amount of floc that can be generated in a given volume of sewage in a given time is small and

sewage-treatment processes. The history of past experience is, more often than not, a useful signpost for possible future progress; but past experience must not be allowed to create prejudice that will shackle the mind and hand of the investigator, designer, or operator.

would not provide sufficient contact area to effect wanted purification in economically justifiable times of exposure. For this reason, a large concentration of floc is caused to accumulate in the treatment unit.

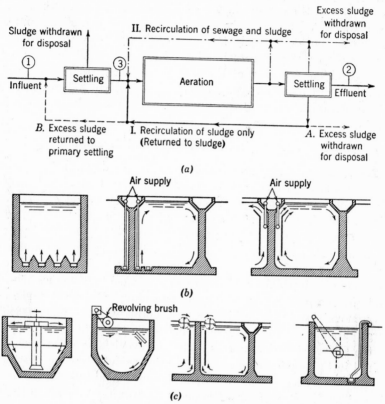

Figure 25-3. Sewage treatment in activated-sludge units. (*a*) Flow diagram. Excess sludge is either withdrawn directly for disposal or returned to primary settling. Recirculation of sewage as well as sludge is possible. (*b*) Diffused-air units: longitudinal furrows; spiral flow with bottom diffusers; and spiral flow with baffle and low-depth diffusers. (*c*) Mechanical aeration units: spray cone (*Simplex*); surface paddles or Kessener brushes; and submerged paddles with or without supplementary diffused air. *After Imhoff and Fair.*

In the normal activated-sludge process, this is done by separating formed floc from the effluent sewage by sedimentation and returning it to the influent sewage (*returned sludge*) until the desired concentration of floc is attained. After the breaking-in period, more than the required amount of floc is captured from the effluent, and some floc must be wasted (*excess or waste sludge*). Since the settled floc includes much water, the process involves a proportionate degree of recirculation of effluent. Common arrangements of activated-sludge units are shown in Figure 25-3. The loading of such units is 1 to 2 mgd per acre-ft. This is about the same as for trickling filters that are operated at high rates and for contact aerators, but the efficiency of treatment is substantially greater. The activated-sludge process, although delicate, is highly flexible. Modifications in operation, including degree of pretreatment, have been introduced to meet local needs, and the economy of the method is bound to be further improved by an imaginative approach to the design and operation of treatment units.

Operation of Biological Flocculation and Precipitation Units

25-3. Mechanism of Treatment. An analysis of the treatment devices that have just been described will show that they offer the following opportunities in common, although in different degree: (1) direct biological destruction or stabilization of putrescible matter within the sewage undergoing treatment and (2) transfer of putrescible matter onto zoogleal film surfaces followed by (a) its biological destruction or stabilization in the film and the return of certain end products of microbial metabolism to the sewage that washes the film and (b) the periodic or continuous unloading of film substance and its removal from the washing sewage, normally by sedimentation, a large part of the film substance being returned to the treatment unit in the activated-sludge process. The energy-yielding substances contained in the applied sewage are the primary substrate for the living organisms that seed themselves upon the surfaces and create the active film. The film itself forms a secondary substrate upon which the organisms feed. This they can do continuously. They need no rest. However, if the film interface becomes overloaded with food and other substances abstracted from the sewage, or if its dissolved-oxygen content approaches exhaustion (because it can be replenished only intermittently or is supplied in insufficient quantity), a so-called resting period may be required. During this period, needed oxygen is absorbed and film activity is restored.

The direct biological modification of putrescible matter within the flowing sewage in treatment units is relatively small because the mechanism of biological decomposition is extremely complex and quite time-consuming, whereas the length of time that the applied sewage remains within the unit is never long. It can be pointed out, for example, that the reduction of so simple a substance as formic acid to glucose entails at least four enzymes and seven intermediate products, some of which serve as carrier catalysts; also that actual contact periods are a matter of less than an hour in high-rate trickling filters,[3] a matter of somewhat longer periods in low-rate trickling filters and in downward percolation through soil and sand, and a matter of hours in contact aerators and activated-sludge units. The reaction velocities that would be required to effect a reasonable degree of purification by direct attack of the sewage during its stay in the treatment unit would, therefore, have to be of extraordinary magnitude. For comparison, it takes more than 3 days to satisfy 75% of the BOD of samples of sewage that are stored at 20 C in glass test bottles.

The most important element of biological flocculation and precipitation would appear to be the transfer of the pollutional load to the film. There it undergoes decomposition commensurate with the duration of its storage and releases its end products to the atmosphere or to the sewage that washes it.

Buswell[4] has given the following summary of the changes that take place at biological interfaces.

1. In the surface film of liquids the concentration of dissolved matter tends to change in such a way as to decrease surface tension. If, therefore, a substance dissolving in a liquid increases the surface tension of the solution, the film concentration of the substance tends to become less; if it decreases the surface tension its film concentration tends to become greater. (Most salts and all strong bases increase the surface tension of water; but ammonia and nitric and hydrochloric acids decrease it.) Substances in the colloidal state are believed to act in a similar way, and there are found in sewage colloidal soaps and proteins that tend to concentrate in a surface film. These changes in film concentration are not restricted to the air-liquid interface, but seem to apply also to the interface between the bacterial slime and the liquid. The extent of the interface or contact surface is, therefore, important.

2. At the jelly-sewage interface the following occurs:

a. The substances concentrating at the interface are adsorbed to the contact surfaces and thus removed from the sewage being filtered;

b. The adsorbed substances are attacked by the enzymes and living organisms present in the slime;

c. As rapidly as these substances are removed by digestion or direct adsorption into the living cells, others come to the interface and further removal is effected;

d. In the presence of air the products of decomposition of organic matter are chiefly carbon dioxide, nitrates and a humus-like residue. The gas escapes . . .

---

[3] Rudolph Pönninger has made measurements from which the following observational relationship can be derived: $t = 585e^{-2.46Q}$, where t is the time in minutes and Q is the rate of sewage application in mgd per acre-ft. ["Durchflusszeit bei Tropfkörpern," *Gesundheits-Ingenieur*, *60*, 787 (1937).]

[4] A. M. Buswell, *Chemistry of Water and Sewage Treatment*, The Chemical Catalogue Co., New York, 1928.

nitrates, being salts, increase the surface tension of water and therefore pass from the interface into the flowing sewage; the humus-like residue must either be removed . . . or sloughs off from time to time. . . . It is an important fact that the humus . . . settles readily, unlike the colloidal matter from which it largely originated.

In bed irrigation (or land filtration), subsurface irrigation, and intermittent sand filtration, stabilization of transferred substances must be carried to completion. This cannot be done without a resting period. Otherwise the pores would clog. Resting periods are required also to permit the absorption of oxygen (reaeration). Otherwise the treatment unit would become septic. Interception of substantial amounts of matter at the surface of the soil or sand reduces the subsurface load.

In trickling filters, contact aerators, and activated-sludge units, films or flocs are removed as trickling-filter humus, sloughed contact-aerator growths, and waste (or excess) activated floc. They are referred to collectively as biological or secondary sludges. Depending upon the length of their retention, temperature, and other factors (such as film thickness), these biological sludges are of lower energy value than the substances from which they were formed. They contain more or less nitrogen and other fertilizing ingredients, as well as residual energy values that keep them putrescible. The residual energy values of secondary sludges can be made to supplement those of primary sludges in terms of fuel value or of combustible, digester gas.

The amount of film substance that can be retained in trickling filters and contact aerators, and with it the length of time during which the transferred substances can undergo decomposition, is a function of (1) temperature and through it of BOD, or rate of activity, (2) areal dimensions of the supporting surfaces and their exposure to void space and moving liquid films or masses, and (3) the scour engendered by the moving fluids. The amounts are also a function of the rate of diffusion of oxygen to the inner laminae of the accumulating film or growths. Anaerobic decomposition, as pointed out in Section 19-6, proceeds at a slower rate than aerobic decomposition and is accompanied by the release of gases and the production of foul-smelling intermediate substances. The latter are unwanted. Anaerobic decomposition also destroys the gelatinous nature of the inner laminae and this, together with gas formation, causes the film or growths to slough. Since transfer of pollutional substances occurs only at the interface and since film substance and growths that are not actively engaged in this work can readily be captured as settleable secondary sludge, a certain degree of film sloughing is, ordinarily, an essential feature of trickling filters and contact aerators. In trickling filters, film sloughing, furthermore, reduces the opportunity for the development of filter flies (see Section 4 of this chapter). For contact aerators, the sloughing of stringy growths is important, because it lowers the air requirements and keeps passageways free for the circulation of sewage.

In the activated-sludge process, the amount of biologically active growth can be varied at will over a wide range of values by regulating the rate of sludge waste and return. Ordinarily, the sludge is recirculated for a few days. If large flocs are allowed to build up, they, like thick films and thick growths, will become anaerobic. They also become heavier as organic matter is mineralized and it becomes more difficult to keep the sludge in suspension. At the same time, the sludge becomes less active. In the interest of effective treatment, these conditions must be avoided.

25-4. Biological Associations. The biological associations that are responsible for the purification of sewage by flocculation and precipitation include many classes of organisms. Some of the type species are shown in Figure 25-4. The principal and most numerous biological workmen are the zoogleal bacteria. The gelatinous masses that are built by them often assume branching shapes and are then known as *Zooglea ramigera*. Closely associated with the lower bacteria are the filamentous higher bacteria and the protozoa. Among the latter, the ciliates abound. The stalked, colonial ciliates find adequate anchorage both in suspended flocs and on attached films. The free-swimming ciliates and flagellates dart in and out among the organic debris, bacterial filaments, and mold hyphae. Viewed under the microscope, the floc shows a lively and busy microbial community. The primary role of the holozoic ciliates, if we may judge from observations of their impact upon bacteria in nutrient solutions, is to keep the bacterial population from reaching a stalemate. Destruction of bacteria is then responsible for a constant renewal of bacterial growth and, with it, for a high consumption of energy-containing food materials. The prevalence of ciliates, therefore, is a valuable index of film or floc healthiness. Pathogenic bacteria are ingested along with the common saprophytic forms. This contributes to effluent safety.

In addition to the principal flora and fauna, worms and insect larvae find nutriment in the floc and film. Rotifers and crustaceans scavenge for food. Fungi utilize simple chemical substances, and surface

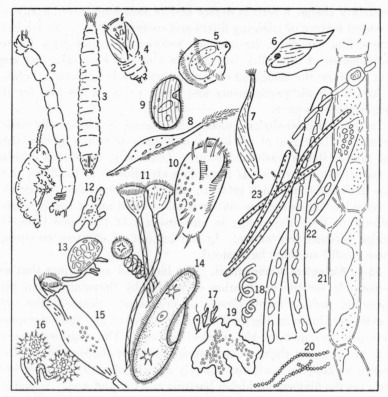

Figure 25-4.   Organisms associated with the biological treatment of sewage.   *After Imhoff and Fair.*

Numbers 1 to 4, Insects × 5

1. Water springtail, *Podura*; the genus found on trickling filters is *Achorutes*.

2. Larva of blood worm, *Chironomus*.
3. Larva of filter fly, *Psychoda*.
4. Pupa of filter fly, *Psychoda*.

Numbers 5 to 17, Protozoa × 150 *

5. *Didinium*
6. *Euglena*
7. *Choenia*
8. *Lionotus*
9. *Colpidium*

10. *Stylonichia*
11. *Vorticella*
12. *Ameba*
13. *Arcella*
14. *Paramecium*

15. *Opercularia*
16. *Anthophysa*
17. *Oikomonas* × 1,500

Numbers 18 to 23, Bacteria and fungi × 1,500

18. *Thiospirillum*
19. *Zooglea ramigera*

20. *Streptococcus*
21. *Leptomitus*

22. *Sphaerotilus*
23. *Beggiatoa*

* Excepting No. 17, *Oikomonas.*

growths of algae, along with chlorophyllaceous flagellates, join them in this activity where film is exposed to sunlight.

Trickling filters harbor large numbers of aquatic earthworms, bristle worms, and blood worms (see also Figure 19-6). In the spring of the year when large masses of film are sloughed off with the beginning of warm weather and stepped-up decay of accumulated film, masses of worms are often disgorged. During the summer, small moth-like flies of the genus *Psychoda* may infest trickling filters in such degree as to create a serious nuisance. Conditions favorable to their growth are (1) free entrance into the bed and (2) film thicknesses that will support their larvae which burrow in the film.

The so-called filter fly passes through ordinary window screens. It does not bite but gets into the eyes, ears, nostrils, and mouth of plant attendants and is extremely troublesome. Its radius of flight is short (a few hundred feet), but it may be carried quite far by the wind. The life cycle of the fly varies from 3 weeks at 60 F to a week at 85 F. The adult fly is readily destroyed by DDT residuals on walls and other surfaces on which it rests. The eggs and larvae are washed out of the filter when the film sloughs. Sloughing may be induced for this purpose (by chlorination of the applied sewage, for example), or film thickness may be held down by operating the filters at high rates of flow. A small wingless insect, the water springtail *Podura* (the genus found on trickling filters is *Achorutes*), may establish itself on the surface of ponded (surface-clogged) filters. This organism feeds upon the surface growths and may help to keep the surface clean. *Psychoda* and *Achorutes* seldom share the same filter in large numbers, because *Psychoda* needs an open bed, and *Achorutes* a clogged one.

The appearance of large numbers of filaments of the so-called sewage fungus *Sphaerotilus* is often associated with a phenomenon called the "bulking" of activated sludge (see Section 25-13). High carbohydrates appear to promote the growth of this organism. Destruction of activated sludge by the blood worm *Chironomous* has been reported.

Filamentous bacteria, such as *Sphaerotilus* and *Beggiatoa*, may be troublesome in the operation of contact aerators if they overgrow the surfaces and clog the spaces between them. Parenthetically, these organisms, together with the fungus *Leptomitus* and similar stringy growths, may attach themselves in unsightly masses to walls, gates, and baffles of sewage channels and tanks.

Active films and flocs are characterized by a preponderance of zoogleal bacteria and lively ciliates. Given a reasonable opportunity, these organisms will establish themselves spontaneously and set to work upon the sewage to bring about its purification. This is an example of *natura naturans,* or "nature mending nature," which makes nature a handmaid of the sanitary engineer. The development of pure cultures of highly active organisms remains a challenge, along with the provision of those environmental conditions that will best promote the activity of the seeded or adventitious flora and fauna that is responsible for the satisfactory performance of biological sewage-treatment works. Toxic wastes weaken biological activity. When they are discharged into sewage in high concentration, they may destroy it. Copper and arsenic have been responsible for the break-down of biological processes.

25-5. Equalization of Loading. Most water- and sewage-treatment processes operate inherently on a basis of diminishing returns. Even when the rate of purification is substantially constant (in the normal exertion of BOD, for example), the amount of work that can be done decreases in proportion to the reduction in the concentration of re-movable substances. The rate of activity of most biological treatment units (measured by the removal of BOD, suspended solids, or bacteria, for example) may reasonably be expected to be greatest at the begin-ning, because the substances that best lend themselves to removal are removed first. Stated differently, there is a purification pressure that is a function both of the concentration of removable substances and the removability of the constituent fractions.

Equalization of the load impressed upon progressive portions of treatment units can be attained in some measure by the following means: (1) serial subdivision of the treatment structure into two or more component units, or stages, and alternation of the lead unit (applicable only when the contact surfaces are fixed in place—irriga-tion, intermittent sand filtration, trickling filtration, and contact aera-tion); (2) subdivision of the applied sewage into two or more com-ponent portions and their progressive introduction along the treatment path (applied so far only when contact surfaces move with the flowing sewage—activated-sludge process); (3) recirculation of the effluent from the treatment unit to the influent to the unit and subjection of the resultant mixture to treatment (applicable in all biological treatment systems); and (4) combinations of recirculation of effluent (*a*) with serial subdivision of the treatment units (alternation of component divisions being optional) and (*b*) with progressive dosing of the treat-ment unit. The return of sludge in activated-sludge units (about 20% by volume) is a modest form of recirculation, and the short-circuiting or longitudinal mixing of sewage in such units is a modest form of sewage subdivision. A number of schemes for recirculation and stage treatment are presented in Figures 25-3 and 25-5. They all aim at a more equable distribution of load within units that are substantially

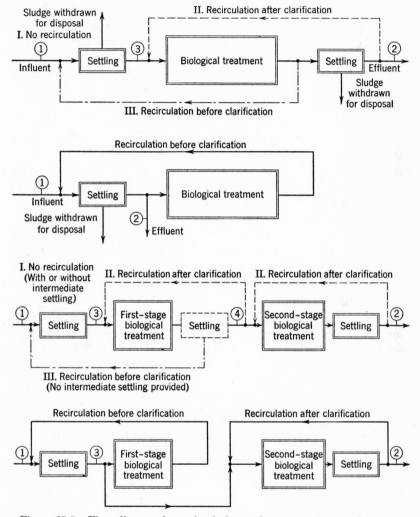

Figure 25-5. Flow diagram for recirculation and stage treatment of sewage.

constant in their purification capacity along the path of the applied sewage. Adjustment of purification capacity to variation in load within the treatment unit offers a different approach to the problem of decreasing loads. Adjustment of air supply to oxygen requirements in contact-aeration and activated-sludge units (tapered aeration) and use of coarse stone in the bottom of trickling filters are examples.

25-6. Recirculation. Recirculation adds much to uniformity and flexibility of plant operation. Besides distributing the load more effectively, an opportunity is afforded for smoothing out the rate of flow of applied sewage through adjustment of the rate of recirculation. In the best circumstances, the rate of flow of applied sewage can be held substantially constant. The quality of the effluent, on the other hand, is altered appreciably by recirculation. How this comes about is exemplified by contrasting the operation of a trickling filter that treats a unit quantity of sewage on a once-through basis with one that treats the same quantity of sewage on a recirculation basis when a unit quantity of effluent is added to the incoming sewage. In the first instance, the effluent has been produced by exposure of all of the influent sewage to the full treatment time. In the second instance, the effluent is a composite of $\frac{1}{2}$ the influent sewage that has been exposed for $\frac{1}{2}$ the treatment time, $\frac{1}{4}$ the influent sewage that has been exposed for the full treatment time, $\frac{1}{8}$ the influent sewage that has been exposed for $\frac{3}{2}$ the treatment time, $\frac{1}{16}$ the influent sewage that has been exposed for twice the treatment time, etc. It is seen that the two effluents are by no means identical, although the average exposure of the sewage to treatment is the same with and without recirculation of effluent.

If we call I the rate of incoming sewage and R the rate of recirculation, the recirculation ratio is R/I, and the average number of passages of the incoming sewage through the treatment unit is

$$F' = \frac{I + R}{I} = 1 + \frac{R}{I} \qquad 25\text{-}1$$

where F' is called "the recirculation factor." This factor can be represented, in accordance with the reasoning pursued in the preceding paragraph, also by the following series:

$$F' = \frac{I}{I + R} \times 1 + \frac{I}{I + R} \times \frac{R}{I + R} \times 2 + \frac{I}{I + R}$$
$$\times \left(\frac{R}{I + R}\right)^2 \times 3 \cdots \quad 25\text{-}2$$

If we assume that the removability of putrescible matter decreases as the number of passages is multiplied, a weighting factor f, where $f < 1$, must be introduced into Equation 25-2 to obtain a satisfactory expression for the average number of "effective" passes F of the putrescible matter through the treatment unit. Equation 25-2 then becomes

$$F = \frac{I}{R+I} \times 1f^0 + \frac{I}{R+I} \times \frac{R}{R+I} \times 2f^1$$

$$+ \frac{I}{R+I}\left(\frac{R}{R+I}\right)^2 \times 3f^2 \cdots \quad 25\text{-}3$$

or

$$F = \frac{1 + R/I}{[1 + (1-f)R/I]^2} \quad 25\text{-}4$$

If F and R/I are the dependent variables, f being constant, F reaches a maximum value at

$$R/I = (2f - 1)/(1 - f) \quad 25\text{-}5$$

The magnitude of f appears to be close to 0.9 for trickling filters,[5] but see Section 25-9.

Example 25-1. For a recirculation ratio of unity and a weighting factor of 90%, find (a) the average number of passes and (b) the average number of effective passes of the sewage through the treatment unit. Find also (c) the recirculation ratio needed to produce a maximal value of effective passes and (d) the resulting ratio of the magnitude of this value to that of the average number of passes.

a. By Equation 25-1, $F' = 1 + 1 = 2$, or, by Equation 25-2, $F' = \frac{1}{2} + \frac{1}{4} \times 2 + \frac{1}{8} \times 3 \cdots = 2$.

b. By Equation 25-4, $F = \dfrac{1+1}{(1+0.1)^2} = 1.65$.

c. By Equation 25-5, $R/I = \dfrac{2 \times 0.9 - 1}{0.1} = 8$.

d. By Equation 25-4, $F_{max} = \dfrac{1+8}{(1+0.8)^2} = 2.78$, and, by Equation 25-1, $F' = 1 + 8 = 9$. Hence $F_{max}/F' = 2.78/9 = 0.31$.

In practice, recirculation has established itself in particular in connection with the operation of trickling filters at high rates of dosage, but it should always be remembered that recirculation is a *sine qua non* of the activated-sludge process. Very high rates of recirculation become uneconomical.

25-7. Expression of Loading Intensity. Two kinds of loads are impressed on biological treatment units: (1) water loads which govern the hydraulic design of the treatment unit (hydraulic loads) and (2) loads of removable substance which govern the process design of the

[5] *Sewage Works J., 18,* 791 (1946).

treatment unit (process loads). In order to be related to performance, these loads must be expressed as load intensities.

Hydraulic loads are expressed as rates of flow, generally *mgd*. Intensities of hydraulic loads are generally measured in terms of the velocity of the sewage through the treatment unit or the time (direct or inverse) that the sewage remains within the unit. Thus, the intensity of the hydraulic load on irrigation areas, intermittent sand filters, and trickling filters is normally stated in terms of the velocity factor, *mgad;* the loading intensity of trickling filters also in terms of an inverse time factor, *mgd per acre-ft* (sometimes *gpd per cu yd*); the loading intensity of activated-sludge units and contact aerators generally in terms of a time factor, *hours of aeration*. Strictly speaking, the inverse time factor, mgd per acre-ft, is also an indirect velocity factor (hydraulic load per unit area of film surface), because the number of acre-ft contained in a bed is, by implication, a measure of the area of its contact surfaces. Therefore, the term mgd per acre-ft is, in a sense, a measure of flushing velocity. Because the water applied to the treatment unit contains the substances to be removed, the hydraulic-loading intensity of a treatment unit is also a rough measure of its process-loading intensity.

Process loads are rationally expressed in terms of the impurities that are to be removed. Since the BOD is the best over-all determinant of the putrescibility of sewage and related waste waters, the process load of biological treatment units is generally expressed in terms of the weight of BOD applied per unit of time, normally lb of 5-day, 20 C BOD per day. In special circumstances and for special purposes, other determinants are added or substituted, among them: turbidity, suspended solids, organic nitrogen, ammonia nitrogen, oxygen consumed, and bacteria. The population load can also be usefully employed with due allowance for population equivalents of storm water and industrial wastes in the influent and, where efficiency of treatment is to be established, also for the population equivalent of the effluent.

In order to be expressed as intensities, process loadings must be related to treatment opportunity. Since treatment opportunity involves a complex of design and operating factors, many different parameters of process-loading intensity have been devised. Most of them reflect treatment opportunity but partially, some of them inversely. Examples of partial and inverse loading intensities are: (1) lb of BOD per day per acre, the common process-loading parameter of irrigation areas, intermittent sand filters, and trickling filters; for trickling filters also lb of BOD per day per acre-ft, cu yd, or 1,000 cu ft; and (2) for activated-sludge units and contact aerators: (a) in reference to tank dimensions: lb of BOD per day per cu ft of tank volume, sq ft of tank surface, or ft of tank length; (b) in reference to air use: hours of aeration, or cu ft of free air per lb of BOD; (c) in reference to returned sludge (for the activated-sludge process only): percentage of sludge returned, percentage of suspended solids in mixed liquor, and sludge-volume index.[6]

If we recognize (a) area of contact surface or film and (b) opportunity for contact as the controlling factors in biological sewage treatment, we arrive at the following complex for a general parameter of loading intensity: (1) weight of removable substance applied in a unit of time to (2) a unit of contact surface for (3) a unit of contact time. The first factor in this complex is readily determined by analytical procedures and measurements of sewage flow. The second factor is readily approximated in contact aerators in which plates support the contact surface; it can be evaluated only indirectly for activated-sludge units and for so-called filtration processes. The third factor is easily ascertained as a statistical average for contact aerators and activated-sludge units but is normally unknown for other treatment devices. Suggested parameters of process-loading intensity i are:

1. *For plate-contact aerators:* lb of 5-day, 20 C BOD per day (y_0) per 1,000 sq ft of plate surface (A) per hour of aeration (t), or $i = y_0/(At)$. This parameter is readily visualized in terms of the general equation.

2. *For activated-sludge units:* lb of 5-day, 20 C BOD per day (y_0) per 1,000 lb of suspended solids (W) per hour of aeration (t), or $i = y_0/(Wt)$. Here the weight of suspended solids is an indirect and incomplete measure of the surface area of the sludge floc. It is calculated from the volume of the aeration unit and the concentration of the solids suspended in the mixed liquor. The contact time is given by the quotient of the volume of the aeration unit and the rate of flow of the *incoming* sewage.[7]

3. *For trickling filters:* lb of 5-day, 20 C BOD per day (y_0) per acre-ft, cu yd, or 1,000 cu ft (V), or $i = y_0/V$. Surface of contact, as previously stated, is included only indirectly. Time of contact is also included indirectly, since it is a function of the hydraulic load per acre-ft which is reflected by the process load. For recirculation, the volume of filter must be multiplied by the recirculation factor F to obtain the equivalent volume FV.

4. *For irrigation areas and intermittent sand filters:* lb of 5-day, 20 C BOD per day (y_0) per acre (A), or $i = y_0/A$. This parameter recognizes that the purifying activity of these treatment units is concentrated at the surface.

---

[6] Ml of sludge per gram of dry weight.

[7] The rate of flow of the incoming sewage is employed rather than the rate of flow of the mixed liquor because it represents the theoretical average time that a constituent portion of the sewage—which may also find its way from time to time into the sludge liquor—remains in the aeration unit.

That the loading intensities suggested for contact-aeration, trickling-filtration, and activated-sludge units reflect the performance of these units with a fair degree of reliability is shown in Figures 25-6, 25-7, and 25-8. The parameters selected imply that it is possible to attain a wanted degree of purification by proper proportioning of the following design and operation elements to the load: (1) in contact-aeration

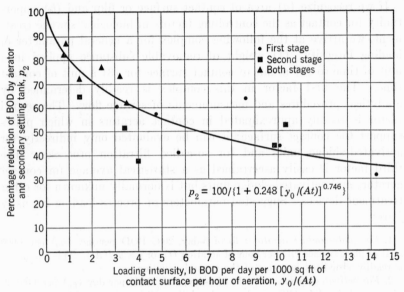

Figure 25-6. Performance-loading relationships for contact aerators. Plotted points represent the results obtained at U. S. military posts.

units—the plate area, the time of aeration, or both; (2) in trickling filters—the volume of the bed, the recirculation ratio, or both; and (3) in activated-sludge units—the weight of suspended solids in the aeration unit (per cent of returned sludge), the time of aeration, or both. Recirculation may be presumed to be effective in contact aeration and activated-sludge treatment as well as in trickling filtration. Flexibility is lent to the activated-sludge process by the ability to return more or less sludge to the treatment unit. This, as already stated, is also a form of recirculation.

25-8. Treatment Efficiency. The most advanced biological treatment systems, as has been indicated, are normally preceded by primary settling tanks. The biological, or secondary, system is composed of the biological unit and its settling tank. However, in some recirculat-

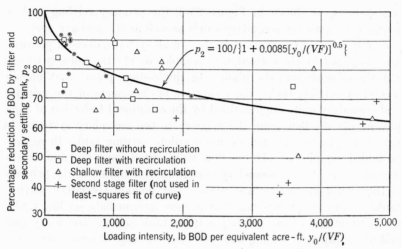

Figure 25-7. Performance-loading relationships for trickling filters. Plotted points represent the results obtained at U. S. military posts.

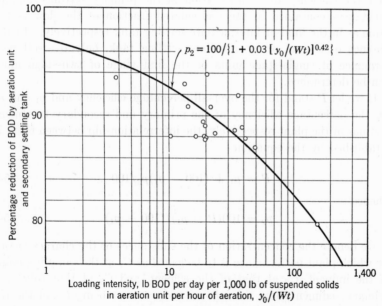

Figure 25-8. Performance-loading relationships for activated-sludge units. Plotted points represent the results obtained at diffused-air plants in North America. Logarithmic scale of abscissa makes plotting more convenient. *After Fair and Thomas.*

ing systems, as shown in Figure 25-5, the primary settling tank is required to settle the secondary solids as well as the primary ones.

a. Efficiency of Component Parts. In all systems, over-all performance is gaged by the collection of samples of (1) the influent to and (2) the effluent from the plant. In single-stage plants that include secondary settling tanks, the respective performances of the primary and secondary units are identified by the additional collection of samples of (3) the flow from the primary to the secondary system. In two-stage plants that include intermediate settling tanks there may be added samples of (4) the flow transmitted from the first to the second stage. Where secondary sewage is recirculated to the primary settling tank in single-stage plants that include secondary settling tanks, or in two-stage plants that possess intermediate settling tanks, the performance of the primary settling tank and the secondary unit and of the primary settling tank and the first stage of secondary treatment cannot be evaluated directly, because there is no direct way of identifying the amounts of primary and returned solids deposited in the primary settling tank. A close estimate is obtained if it is assumed that the efficiency of sedimentation in the primary settling tank of substances contained in the recirculated fraction of the flow is the same as in the final or intermediate settling tank respectively. In the absence of a final or intermediate settling tank, only over-all performance of single-stage units or the first stage of two-stage units can be determined.

If we let P stand for the over-all percentage efficiency and p_1 and p_2 for the percentage efficiency of the primary and secondary treatment sections of the plant respectively, the interrelationship between them is established by the equation

$$P = p_1 + (100 - p_1)p_2/100 \qquad 25\text{-}6$$

whence

$$p_2 = 100(P - p_1)/(100 - p_1) \qquad 25\text{-}7$$

If we denote the concentration of the substances or the characteristics by which plant performance is to be gaged as C_1 at the sampling point of the influent, C_2 at that of the effluent, and C_3 at that following primary sedimentation, the inflow (and outflow) being I and the recirculated flow R, the over-all efficiency of the treatment plant and its primary and secondary sections is as follows:

1. For once-through flow:

$$P = 100(C_1 - C_2)/C_1 \qquad 25\text{-}8$$

$$p_1 = 100(C_1 - C_3)/C_1 \qquad\qquad \text{25-9}$$

and

$$p_2 = 100(C_3 - C_2)/C_3 \qquad\qquad \text{25-10}$$

2. For flow recirculated to the primary settling tank, on the assumption that its removal efficiency for recirculated flows is the same as that of the secondary settling tank, the over-all removal is: $P = 100(C_1 - C_2)/C_1$ as in Equation 25-8, but the efficiency of the primary tank for the incoming sewage alone is:

$$p_1 = 100\,\frac{(C_1 - C_3)I - (C_3 - C_2)R}{C_1 I} \qquad\qquad \text{25-11}$$

whereas the efficiency of the secondary section for previously untreated sewage is:

$$p_2 = 100\,\frac{C_3(I + R) - C_2 I - C_2 R}{C_3(I + R) - C_2 R} = 100\,\frac{(C_3 - C_2)(I + R)}{C_3 I + (C_3 - C_2)R} \qquad\qquad \text{25-12}$$

Similar relationships can be elaborated for two-stage treatment with and without recirculation.

Example 25-2. A flow of 1 mgd of sewage containing 308 mg/l of BOD is passed through a settling tank and a filter.

a. In straight-through flow, the effluent from the primary tank contains 200 mg/l of BOD, and the effluent of the plant 34 mg/l.

b. When 1.5 mgd of sewage from the biological unit alone are recirculated to the primary tank, its effluent contains 108 mg/l of BOD, and the plant effluent 18 mg/l.

Find the over-all efficiencies and the efficiencies of the primary and secondary sections of the two operational arrangements.

a. By Equations 25-8, 25-9, and 25-10,

$$P = 100(308 - 34)/308 = 89.0\%$$

$$p_1 = 100(308 - 200)/308 = 35.0\%$$

$$p_2 = 100(200 - 34)/200 = 83.0\%$$

By Equation 25-7, $p_2 = 100(89 - 35)/(100 - 35) = 83.0\%$ also.

b. By Equations 25-8, 25-11, and 25-12,

$$P = 100\,(308 - 18)/308 = 94.2\%$$

$$p_1 = 100\,\frac{(308 - 108)1.0 - (108 - 18)1.5}{308 \times 1.0} = 21.1\%$$

$$p_2 = 100\,\frac{(108 - 18)(1 + 1.5)}{108 \times 1.0 + (108 - 18)1.5} = 92.6\%$$

By Equation 25-7, $p_2 = 100(94.2 - 21.1)/(100 - 21.1) = 92.6\%$ also.

b. *Performance-Loading Relationships.* An analysis of the performance of numerous sewage-treatment works by the Committee on Sanitary Engineering of the National Research Council [5] has led to the following general observational relationship between biological plant performance (expressed as percentage efficiency p_2) and plant loading (expressed in terms of the loading intensity i, discussed in Section 25-7):

$$p_2 = 100/(1 + mi^n) \qquad\qquad 25\text{-}13$$

Here m and n are coefficients of performance. Together, they determine the magnitude of the loading intensity that can be impressed on a given process to attain a desired efficiency, the coefficient n being a measure of the variability of efficiency with load intensity. The numerical value of the coefficient m depends upon the units of measurement employed. The parameters of loading intensity i and the magnitudes of m and n that enter into the observational relationships proposed by the National Research Council were derived from the summary plotting of operational results shown in Figures 25-6, 25-7, and 25-8. They may be listed as in Table 25-1.

TABLE 25-1. Values of Performance Coefficients for Biological Treatment Units

	n	m	i	Units of i for BOD * removal
Plate contact aerators	0.746	2.48×10^{-1}	$y_0/(At)$	lb/1,000 sq ft $\times$ hr of contact
Trickling filters	0.50	8.5×10^{-3}	$y_0/(VF)$	lb/acre-ft $\times$ recirculation factor
Activated-sludge units	0.42	3.0×10^{-2}	$y_0/(Wt)$	lb/1,000 lb suspended solids $\times$ hr of aeration

* 5-day, 20 C BOD.

Generally speaking, the activated-sludge process, as indicated by the magnitude of n, appears to respond better to high loading intensities than do the other processes listed. However, its response is only slightly better than that of the process of trickling filtration, and it is more sensitive to shock loads.

Example 25-3. A flow of 1 mgd of sewage containing 307 mg/l of BOD is passed through a primary settling tank, which removes 35% of the BOD, before being applied to a trickling filter and secondary settling tank. The BOD load applied to the filter from the primary tank, therefore, is $307 \times (1 - 0.35) \times 1 \times 8.34 = 1{,}665$ lb per day. If the filter has a surface area of 0.185 acre and its depth is 3.0 ft, estimate the over-all percentage reduction in BOD and the BOD remaining in the plant effluent (a) for once-through operation of the trickling filter, and (b) for recirculation of 1.5 mgd of plant effluent to the trickling filter.

  a. The rate of dosage, or intensity of the hydraulic load, is $1.0/0.185 = 5.4$ mgd per acre, or $5.4/3 = 1.8$ mgd per acre-ft. The process-loading intensity is $y_0/(VF)$ $= 1{,}665/(0.185 \times 3 \times 1) = 3{,}000$ lb per acre-ft. In accordance with Equation 25-13, the efficiency of the biological section of the plant is

$$p_2 = \frac{100}{1 + 8.5 \times 10^{-3} \times (3,000)^{0.5}} = 68.2\%$$

In accordance with Equation 25-6, the over-all plant efficiency is

$$P = 35 + (100 - 35)68.2/100 = 79.5\%$$

and the BOD remaining in the plant effluent is $(100 - 79.5)307/100 = 63$ mg/l.

b. Recirculation of 1.5 mgd of sewage increases the rate of dosage of the filter $(1 + 1.5) = 2.5$ fold to 13.5 mgd per acre, or 4.5 mgd per acre-ft. If we assume a weighting factor of 90%, the recirculation factor F becomes $\dfrac{1 + 1.5/1}{[1 + (1 - 0.9)(1.5/1)]^2}$ = 1.89 in accordance with Equation 25-4, and the process-loading intensity $y_0/(VF) = 1,665/(0.185 \times 3 \times 1.89) = 1,590$ lb per equivalent acre-ft.

In accordance with Equation 25-13, therefore, the efficiency of the secondary section of the plant is $p_2 = \dfrac{100}{1 + 8.5 \times 10^{-3} \times (1,590)^{0.5}} = 74.6\%$. The resulting over-all plant efficiency is $P = 35 + (100 - 35)74.6/100 = 83.5\%$, and the BOD remaining in the plant effluent is $(100 - 83.5)307/100 = 51$ mg/l.

25-9. Rate of Purification. It has been suggested in Section 25-5 that the purification pressure is a function both of the concentration of removable substances and the removability of the constituent fractions. Both of them decrease along the path followed by the sewage during treatment. Unlike the exertion of BOD in stored samples of sewage-polluted water (Section 19-5), therefore, the rate at which purification is accomplished in biological treatment units cannot be formulated as a simple first-order reaction unless the loading of these units is made substantially constant by high-rate treatment, recirculation, or other means. The rate of purification of trickling filters that are operated at low rates is illustrated in Figure 25-9. In general, these semilogarithmic plots of the percentages of BOD, ammonia nitrogen, and turbidity remaining at depths of 2, 4, 6, 8, and 10 ft exhibit decreasing rates of purification. Similar plots could be prepared for oxygen consumed and organic nitrogen. The rate of purification of activated-sludge units, in terms of BOD and ammonia nitrogen remaining after varying lengths of aeration, is shown in Figure 25-10 and is seen to be more nearly constant for the two sets of data employed.

The following basic relationship can be written for the rate of purification of biological sewage-treatment units no matter whether the rate is uniform throughout the process of treatment or whether it changes as purification progresses:

$$\frac{dy}{dl}\left(\text{or } \frac{dy}{dt}\right) = k\left(\frac{y_0 - y}{y_0}\right)^n (y_0 - y) = \frac{k}{y_0{}^n}(y_0 - y)^{n+1} \qquad 25\text{-}14$$

Here y_0 is the amount of removable substance present in the applied sewage; y is the amount of substance removed during the passage of

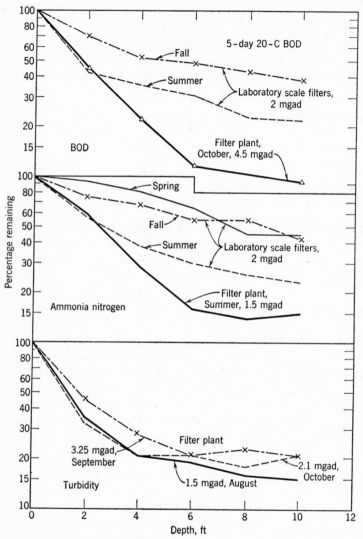

Figure 25-9. Performance-depth relationship for low-rate trickling filters. After Buswell, *Illinois State Water Survey, Bull.* 26 (1928).

the sewage through a distance l, either vertically (trickling filters) or horizontally (contact aerators or activated-sludge units), l being replaceable by time of contact t; k is a proportionality factor which by analogy to chemical reactions may be called the initial rate of reaction or reaction velocity constant of the process with the dimension of (length)$^{-1}$ or (time)$^{-1}$; and n is a coefficient which is a measure of the non-uniformity of the rate of purification. When $n = 0$, Equation 25-14 expresses the concept of a first-order reaction. The rate of removal of a given substance by the treatment unit dy/dl or dy/dt is then constantly proportional to the amount of substance $(y_0 - y)$ remaining. When $n > 0$, we can, by writing the right-hand side of

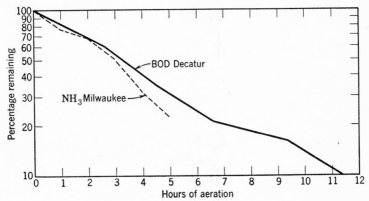

Figure 25-10. Performance-time relationship for activated-sludge units. *After Copeland (Milwaukee) and Hatfield (Decatur).*

Equation 25-14 in its uncombined form, express the thought that the rate of reaction decreases in proportion to the relative amount of purification that has been accomplished. The term dy/dl or dy/dt represents the purification power of the system or its rate of work. In biological treatment units, this power is self-generated and a function of the relative rate of work.

Integration of Equation 25-14 between the limits of y_0 and y, and 0 and t respectively results in the following relationship for values of $n > 0$:

$$y/y_0 = 1 - [1 + nkl]^{-1/n} = 1 - [1 + nkt]^{-1/n} \qquad 25\text{-}15$$

When $n = 0$, $k[(y_0 - y)/y_0]^n = k$, and

$$y/y_0 = (1 - e^{-kl}) = (1 - e^{-kt}) \qquad 25\text{-}16$$

Figure 25-11 shows the shape of the curves traced by these equations. Determination of the coefficients k and n may be made in terms of the logarithmic transform of Equation 25-14, employing the principles stated in Section 28-4. The weighting factor f of Section 25-6 is given by the ratio of the value of y determined by Equation 25-15 to that determined by Equation 25-16 for identical values of k and l or t. The two equations should be compared with Equations 28-1 and 28-2 and also with Equation 22-18.

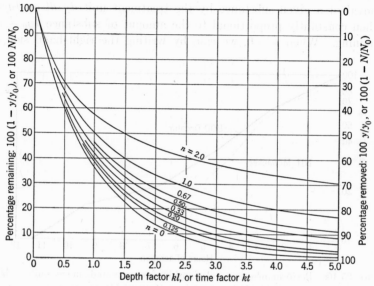

Figure 25-11. Generalized depth rates and time rates of purification.

Example 25-4. The observed BOD removal illustrated in Figure 25-9 for a trickling filter operated at a rate of 4.5 mgd was as follows:

Depth, ft	0	2	4	6	10
BOD remaining, mg/l	85	39	19	10	8

Find (a) the value of the initial rate of reaction, if the coefficient of non-uniformity is assumed to be 0.5, and (b) the resulting calculated BOD remaining.

  a. The BOD remaining being $(y_0 - y)$, y_0 being 85, and n being 0.5, Equation 25-15 states that

$$k = \frac{2}{l}\left[\left(\frac{85}{y_0 - y}\right)^{\frac{1}{2}} - 1\right] = 0.475, \ 0.555, \ 0.637, \text{ and } 0.450$$

and averages 0.53 per ft.

  b. Substitution of $k = 0.53$ in Equation 25-15 gives $y_0 - y = 85/(1 + 0.265l)^2$, and the calculated values of BOD remaining at depths of 0, 2, 4, 6, 10 ft are 85, 36, 20, 13, and 6 mg/l, against observed values of 85, 39, 19, 10, and 8 mg/l respectively.[8]

---

[8] A closer fit is obtained for $n = 0.4$.

Phelps [9] prefers to assume that the removability of the BOD in trickling filters is substantially constant but that not all of the BOD is removable. Therefore, the value of y_0 is not considered to be that of the BOD of the applied sewage but a calculated value which equals about 90% of the BOD of the applied sewage. The rate of purification can then be expressed as a first-order reaction by Equation 25-16.

The effect of temperature on rate of purification can be stated in terms of the van't Hoff-Arrhenius relationships discussed in Section 18-17. The temperature of sewage varies (1) with the nature of the source of water supply and the method of its storage and distribution, (2) with the nature of the sewerage system, separate or combined, (3) with the amount of infiltration of ground water, and (4) with the discharge of warm or cold industrial wastes into the sewerage system. In the northern United States, the mean annual temperature of sewage is about 60 F, and fluctuations of 20 F on either side of this value during winter and summer are common. The average annual air temperature, on the other hand, is more nearly 50 F with fluctuations as great as 50 F on either side not unusual during the warm and cold seasons of the year. Since sewage undergoing treatment in activated-sludge plants and contact aerators is not exposed to the atmosphere in the same degree as sewage in trickling filters, activated-sludge plants and contact aerators operate under more favorable conditions during the colder seasons of the year. The marked effect of season on the rate of purification of trickling filters is clearly shown in Figure 25-9.

Temperature affects the breaking-in or ripening period of biological treatment units as well as their normal operation. Trickling filters mature in a few weeks in summer, but several months may be required during cold weather. The operation of activated-sludge units and contact aerators is normally established in 10 days to two weeks both in summer and winter.

The information available to us on the rate of purification of different aerobic biological treatment systems, unfortunately, is very scant. Much fundamental experimentation will have to be done if we are to reduce the degree of empiricism that surrounds the subject.

25-10. Nitrification. Before the introduction of the concept of biochemical oxygen demand, great stress was placed, in the biological treatment of sewage, upon the nitrogen load and (1) the conversion of organic nitrogen to ammonia and, more particularly, (2) the subsequent conversion of ammonia to nitrite and nitrate nitrogen, called

[9] E. B. Phelps, *Public Health Engineering*, John Wiley & Sons, New York, Vol. 1, p. 562, 1948.

nitrification. The quality of the plant effluent was then generally judged by its nitrate content. A nitrate nitrogen concentration of 10 to 15 mg/l was considered desirable. Today we know (1) that the attainment of low BOD values is more desirable in the sanitary management of receiving waters than high nitrification; (2) that the attainment of low BOD values does not necessarily require high nitrification of effluents; and (3) that, although both nitrite and nitrate nitrogen

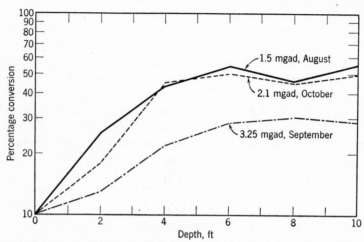

Figure 25-12. Conversion of ammonia nitrogen to nitrate nitrogen in a trickling filter. After Buswell, *Illinois State Water Survey, Bull.* 26 (1928).

constitute an oxygen reserve that will supplement the dissolved-oxygen content of the receiving water, they may, on occasion, stimulate the growth of aquatic plants, large and small, in objectionable quantities. In extreme cases, streams have been known to become choked by growths of rooted or attached plants, while sluggish water-reaches have become covered with masses of floating organisms. Death and decay of these growths has subsequently imposed new, sometimes sudden and heavy, burdens on the oxygen economy of receiving waters. It follows that nitrification should be encouraged only (1) when highly nitrified films or flocs are wanted for the conversion of the sloughed film or waste floc into a remunerative fertilizer or (2) when the sanitary condition of the receiving water is, in fact, benefited by the discharge of a highly nitrified effluent.

The conversion of ammonia nitrogen to nitrate nitrogen in a low-rate trickling filter is illustrated in Figure 25-12.

Design and Operation of Biological Treatment Units

25-11. Trickling Filters. Aside from structural matters, the problems confronting the designer of a trickling filter are essentially two in number: (a) the determination of the required area and depth of the filter and of the amount of effluent to be recirculated (the process design) and (b) the determination of the size of the influent conduits, dosing devices, distribution system, and effluent-collecting system and of the size of effluent-recirculating conduits and pumps, if any (the hydraulic design).

a. Process Design. The principles underlying the process design of trickling filters have been discussed in preceding sections of this chapter. The fundamental relationships are expressed by the equation noted on Figure 25-7. This equation can be stated in the following form for the purpose of finding the required equivalent acre-footage VF of the filter that is to receive a given daily load y_0 and effect a particular degree of purification p_2 which removes a load y.

$$VF = \frac{y_0}{13,800}\left(\frac{p_2}{100 - p_2}\right)^2 = \frac{y_0}{13,800}\left(\frac{y}{y_0 - y}\right)^2 \qquad 25\text{-}17$$

When effluent is recirculated to the filter, the value of the recirculation factor F is given by Equation 25-4. Filter depth l can be tied into performance by means of Equation 25-15 or Equation 25-16 when the values of the performance coefficients k and n are known.

A wide range of depths and loadings is employed in practice. For single-stage operation, depths are commonly held between 6 and 10 ft, while hydraulic loads lie between 2 and 6 mgad in low-rate operation and between 15 and 30 mgad in high-rate operation. These hydraulic loads imply daily BOD loads of 1,500 to 7,500 lb per acre in low-rate operation and 10,000 to 45,000 lb per acre in high-rate operation. For multistage operation (generally 2-stage without alternation of the lead filter), filter depths are generally cut in half. The effects of high-rate operation and recirculation on performance efficiency are reflected by Equation 25-17.

Example 25-5. Find (a) the acre-ft of filter required to effect 80% removal of BOD from 10 mgd of sewage containing 160 mg/l of BOD when it is applied to a trickling filter, (b) the BOD loading of the filter per acre-ft and (c) the BOD loading and hydraulic loading if the filter is made 6 ft deep. Assume that the sewage is not to be recirculated, i.e., $F = 1$.

a. By Equation 25-17, $V = \dfrac{10 \times 160 \times 8.34}{13,800}\left(\dfrac{80}{20}\right)^2 = 15.4$ acre-ft.

b. $y_0/V = 10 \times 160 \times 8.34/15.4 = 865$ lb per acre-ft.

c. $865 \times 6 = 5,190$ lb per acre, $15.4/6 = 2.57$ acres, and $10/2.57 = 3.9$ mgad.

The contact material of trickling filters must be weather resistant, strong enough to support its own weight, and not subject to decay. Crushed stone (trap rock, granite, and limestone) is commonly used, but hard coal, coke, cinders, slag, wood, and ceramic materials have been employed on occasion. The sodium sulfate soundness test [10] has been devised to simulate the effect of alternate freezing and thawing on the disintegration of mineral contact materials. The destructive force of repeated crystal formation within the pores of the rock forms the basis of the test.

The contact material must be small in order to support a large surface of active film but not so small that its pores are filled by the growths or clogged by accumulating suspended matter or sloughing film. Crushed stone $1\frac{1}{2}$ to 3 in. in size and placed in layers of uniform size with the smallest stone at the top of the bed meets these requirements satisfactorily.

b. Hydraulic Design. Sewage is generally applied to the surface of the filter in a fine spray. Uniformity of distribution and opportunity for the absorption of oxygen from the atmosphere are thereby provided. The sprays are either fixed or movable. *Fixed sprays* are formed by nozzles fed from a system of stationary pipes (Figures 25-2*b* and 25-14). *Movable sprays* are generally produced by rotating distributors (Figure 25-2*c*).[11] Movable sprays have displaced fixed sprays almost fully, but a large acreage of fixed sprays remains in operation.

In a *fixed-spray nozzle*, the sewage issues vertically from a circular orifice and impinges against a deflector mounted on a central spindle to form an umbrellalike spray (Figure 25-14). Depending upon the shape of the deflector, a circular, square, or hexagonal area of the bed is wetted. Half-sprays are sometimes placed at the edge of the bed. Since wind action modifies the spray pattern, there is little advantage in departing from the simplicity of nozzle construction afforded in the circular spray. The individual nozzles are fed by a system of pipes. The nozzles are generally placed on the apices of equilateral triangles by being staggered in position on adjacent supply pipes. Contiguous circles thereby cover 91% of the area, the corresponding value for

---

[10] Am. Soc. Civil Engrs., *Manuals of Engineering Practice, 13* (1937).

[11] Traveling distributors that move up and down the length of a bed are no longer in favor because a relatively long time intervenes between successive passages of the distributor over a given portion of the bed. Dosage is concentrated (therefore at a high local rate) and widely intermittent. Neither of these features is desirable.

nozzles at the corners of a square being but 79%. In order to make full use of the bed, the maximum spray limits are allowed to overlap, and the head on the nozzles is allowed to fall during discharge. A dosing device—generally a tank or pair of tanks and automatic flow controls—is normally employed for this purpose. The static head on the nozzles is generally 6 to 10 ft. The pipe grid of trickling filters performs substantially the same distribution function as the pipe grid of rapid sand filters (Section 24-9). The hydraulically unique features of fixed-spray systems are presented by the combination of the dosing tank and the nozzles themselves (Section 25-12). The use of fixed-spray nozzles is generally confined to low-rate filters. The hydraulics of fixed-spray nozzles enters also into the design of water aerators (Sections 23-3 and 27-19), and the hydraulics of dosing tanks is of concern also in connection with the operation of other biological treatment units, such as intermittent sand filters and trickling filters equipped with movable spray nozzles.

In the *movable spray nozzle,* the sewage issues horizontally from a circular orifice, in the side of a traveling pipe. A spreader plate is often provided below the orifice to carry the sewage as uniformly as possible onto the bed. Revolving distributors commonly consist of two or more horizontal pipes or arms attached to a central supply shaft. The center line of the pipes lies 10 to 12 in. above the surface of the bed. The arms are driven either by the reaction to the spray or by an electric motor. Self-propelled distributors require a hydrostatic head of 18 to 30 in. Unless the sewage flow is unusually even, a dosing tank must be interpolated between the primary settling tanks and the filters in self-propelled systems. When the rate of inflow to the tank is lower than that required to turn the distributor, the feed to the distributor is cut off until the tank has filled and can supply the required rate of flow. Dosing tanks add from 1 to 5 ft to the head requirements. The hydraulic features of dosing tanks are discussed in Section 25-12.

The underdrainage system of trickling filters consists of a series of laterals that carry the purified sewage and sloughed film in open-channel flow to main drains that lead to the secondary settling tanks. A suitable arrangement of laterals is illustrated in Figure 25-13. The underdrains must be self-cleansing or accessible for cleaning. Invert gradients of about 1% are common. The laterals may be carried through the walls of the filter to assist in the ventilation of the filter and to permit flushing of the underdrainage system. The main drains may be elaborated into inspection and access galleries. Hydraulically, the underdrainage system of trickling filters functions in much the same capacity as the wash-water collection system of rapid sand filters (Section 24-10) and is designed accordingly.

Differences in the specific weight of the air within and the atmosphere without the filter are primarily responsible for the vertical displacement of air through the filter. The following relationship can be derived from observations reported by Halvorson [12] for a trickling filter dosed at rates up to 20 mgad:

$$v = 0.135(T_a - T_s) - 0.46 \qquad\qquad 25\text{-}18$$

Here v is the vertical velocity of the air in feet per minute, T_a is the temperature of the atmosphere in degrees Fahrenheit, and T_s is the temperature of the sewage in degrees Fahrenheit. At a temperature

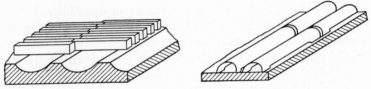

Figure 25-13.　Underdrains for trickling filters.

difference of 3.4 F, $v = 0$ and no flow obtains. Above this value, v is positive and the displacement of the air from the filter is downward; below it, v is negative and flow is upward.

During warm weather, flow of air through the filter should be encouraged because the oxygen requirements of the treatment process are high. During cold weather, however, ventilation should be restricted to a minimum to avoid unnecessary cooling of the sewage and the active film. Halvorson has suggested an air flow of 1 fpm for high-rate, single-stage, trickling filters. Since the maximum dosage of these filters is about 30 mgad, this corresponds to an air supply of 2.1 cu ft per gal of sewage, compared with an air requirement of diffused-air, activated-sludge units of 1 cu ft per gal. However allowance must be made for poorer absorption of oxygen by the stationary films of trickling filters. The cross-sectional area of each lateral and of the main drain not filled with sewage must be sufficiently large to permit the ventilating air to flow at reasonable velocities (about 200 fpm) to and from all parts of the bed. Within the underdrainage system, transportation of downward-moving air is aided by the flow of the sewage.

For protection against extreme cold, or avoidance of odor and filter-

[12] H. O. Halvorson, *Sewage Works J.*, 8, 891 (1936).

fly nuisances, trickling filters may be completely enclosed. Forced ventilation is then in order.

25-12. Hydraulics of Fixed-Spray Nozzles and Dosing Tanks. The sewage sprayed onto low-rate trickling filters through stationary nozzles commonly encounters the following hydraulic structures:

1. One or more dosing tanks supplied through an influent channel; inlet controls in the form of air-locked inlet siphons (when twin tanks are employed); an inlet weir to each storage compartment; one or two storage compartments in each tank; and a discharge siphon in each storage compartment leading to the distribution system that it feeds. See Figure 25-15.

2. One or more distribution systems consisting of a pipe grid of mains and laterals and the spray nozzles. See Figure 25-14.

The hydraulics of the dosing system are determined by the requirements of the distribution system and will be discussed first.

a. Nozzles and Piping. As shown in Figure 25-14, the hydraulics of a nozzle with deflecting cone can be expressed by the following equations, if air resistance is neglected:

Velocity of spray,

$$v = c_v\sqrt{2gh} \qquad\qquad 25\text{-}19$$

Time of rise of spray,

$$t_r = v \sin \alpha/g = c_v\sqrt{2h/g} \sin \alpha \qquad\qquad 25\text{-}20$$

Radius, or horizontal carry, of spray,

$$r = 2vt_r \cos \alpha = 2c_v^2 h \sin 2\alpha \qquad\qquad 25\text{-}21$$

Rise of spray,

$$h_r = vt_r \sin \alpha - \tfrac{1}{2}gt_r^2 = \tfrac{1}{2}c_v^2 h(1 - \cos 2\alpha)$$
$$= \tfrac{1}{2}c_v^2 h \text{ vers } 2\alpha$$

or

$$h_r = \tfrac{1}{4}r \tan \alpha \quad \text{for} \quad r > 0 \quad \text{or} \quad \alpha < 90° \qquad\qquad 25\text{-}22$$

Here, v is the velocity of spray issuing from the nozzle; h is the head on nozzle, and h_r is the height of rise; g is the gravity constant; t_r is the time of rise or $\tfrac{1}{2}$ the time of exposure; α is the angle of the deflector with the horizontal; and c_v is the coefficient of velocity of the nozzle. The magnitude of c_v varies with the head as $m'/h^{n'}$ where m' and n' are observational coefficients for a particular nozzle.[13] Neglecting the

---

[13] For a $\tfrac{7}{8}$-in. Pacific Flush Tank (PFT) circular-spray nozzle with a 45-deg cone, for example, m' and n' have values of 0.84 and 0.092, respectively, based upon the radius of carry to the point of most intense dosage, i.e., $c_v = 0.84/h^{0.092}$.

variation in the coefficient of velocity, the horizontal carry and the rise of spray are seen to vary directly with the head on the nozzle, whereas the time of rise, which is ½ the time of exposure of the droplets to

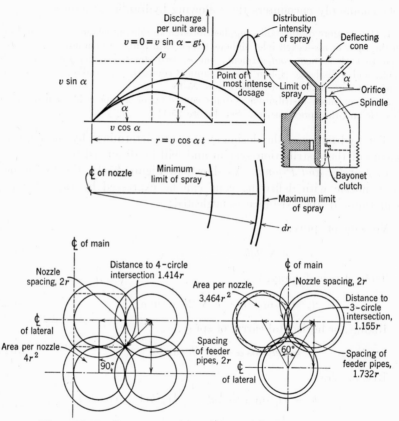

Figure 25-14. Geometry and hydraulics of fixed-spray nozzles.

aeration, varies as the square root of the head. The time of exposure, which equals twice the time of rise, governs the distance that droplets are carried by the wind since

$$l = 2C_D v_w t_r \qquad\qquad 25\text{-}23$$

where l is the distance and C_D is the coefficient of drag (about 0.6). The resistance offered to a droplet by the air is a function of $v/\sqrt{gd}$, where d is the diameter of the droplet.

If we introduce the empirical relationship between the coefficient of velocity and the head on the nozzle into Equation 25-21, we establish the observational relationship [14]

$$r = mh^n \sin 2\alpha \qquad 25\text{-}24$$

Here, $m = 2(m')^2$ and $n = 1 - 2n'$.

As previously stated, the spacing of nozzles is such that there will be some overlap of the spray under maximum head.[15] Since the head drops rapidly, the time of overlap is not great. Spacing is selected with due regard to the carry and intensity of the spray. The distance to the three-circle intersection is generally made somewhat greater than the distance to the point of most intense dosage under the maximum head. The overlap, therefore, concerns a ring of spray that is falling at decreasing intensities. Equality of distribution is aided by the lateral diversion of applied sewage within the bed itself. It is hindered by wind carriage of spray.

The discharge of the nozzle is expressed in terms of the common orifice formula $Q = ca \sqrt{2gh}$, where Q is the rate of discharge, c is the coefficient of discharge, and a is the area of the nozzle orifice. Like c_v, c varies with the head on the nozzle.[16]

Example 25-6. Assuming a velocity coefficient of 0.71 and a discharge coefficient of 0.65 for a $\frac{7}{8}$-in. nozzle with $\frac{3}{8}$-in. spindle and 45° deflector operating under an effective head of 6 ft, find (a) the rate of discharge, (b) the maximum normal horizontal carry of the spray, (c) the maximum vertical rise of the spray, (d) the time of exposure, and (e) the wind effect for a wind velocity of 10 mph.

a. $Q = 0.65 \times \dfrac{\pi}{4 \times 144} [(\frac{7}{8})^2 - (\frac{3}{8})^2] \sqrt{64.4 \times 6} = 0.0436$ cfs]$= 19.6$ gpm.

Neglecting air resistance:

b. By Equation 25-21: $r = 2 \times (0.71)^2 \times 6 = 6.04$ ft.

c. By Equation 25-22: $h_r = \frac{1}{2}(0.71)^2 \times 6 = 1.51$ ft $= \frac{1}{4}r$.

d. By Equation 25-20: $2t_r = 2 \times 0.71 \times \sqrt{\dfrac{2 \times 6}{32.2}} \times 0.707 = 0.61$ sec.

e. By Equation 25-23: $l = 0.6 \times 10 \times 0.61 \times (5{,}280/3{,}600) = 5.4$ ft.

As previously suggested, the hydraulic performance of the distribution piping conforms, in all respects, to that of pipe grids in rapid sand filters (Section 24-9).

b. *Dosing Tanks.* The hydraulic features of twin dosing tanks are illustrated in Figure 25-15. The inlet-feed and discharge siphons behave essentially as orifices. Required driving heads, therefore, are h_f

[14] For the $\frac{7}{8}$-in. (PFT) nozzle, $r = 1.42h^{0.816}$ again with reference to the point of maximum intensity.

[15] The spacing chosen for the $\frac{7}{8}$-in. Pacific Flush Tank nozzle is $3.28h^{0.737}$.

[16] For the $\frac{7}{8}$-in. Pacific Flush Tank nozzle, $c = 0.65h^{-0.005}$.

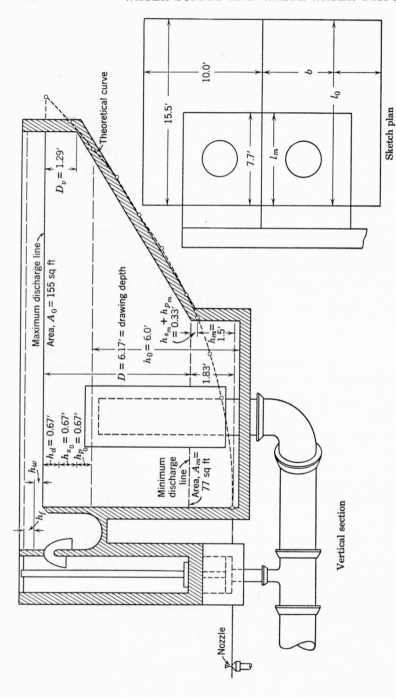

Figure 25-15. Dimensions of a twin-compartment dosing tank serving a nozzle field of one hundred ⅞-in. PFT nozzles. (See Example 25-7.)

or $h_s = \dfrac{1}{2g}\left(\dfrac{Q}{ca}\right)^2$, the value of c being close to 0.7 for the inlet-feed siphon (h_f) and about 0.6 for the discharge siphon (h_s). The weir is submerged at maximum water level. Its head requirements are expressed approximately in terms of the Francis formula with an allowance for submergence of $n = 0.95$ in the expression $Q = 3.33L(nh_w)^{3/2}$, L being the length of the weir. End contractions are normally suppressed. The head requirement h_w, therefore, is closely $h_w = 0.472(Q/L)^{2/3}$.

The unique features of dosing tanks are (1) the so-called starting or dosing-tank loss, (2) the relationship between nozzle head and required tank area, and (3) the dosing time.

1. As previously stated, twin dosing tanks are alternately filled and emptied. When the discharge siphon first goes into operation, all the water in the dosing and distributing system is at rest. Before the nozzles can discharge at maximum capacity, this mass of water must be brought to its discharge speed. The resulting gain in kinetic energy is obtained at the expense of a corresponding loss in potential energy which manifests itself as a drop in the water level of the dosing tank. This is the "starting" or "dosing-tank" loss. Equating the loss in potential energy to the gain in kinetic energy and neglecting friction,

$$wAh_d'h_t = \Sigma\tfrac{1}{2}Mv^2 = \tfrac{1}{2}\frac{w}{g}\Sigma Vv^2 \qquad\qquad \text{25-25}$$

where w is the unit weight of water; A is the surface area of the dosing tank which, in practice, is kept constant in the region in which the dosing-tank loss occurs; h_t is the total head on the nozzle field (also closely the average head at the start); h_d' or h_d is the drop in water level, or the dosing-tank loss; V is the volume of water in a given portion of the distribution system, its mass being M and its velocity v; and Σ is the sum of the values to the right of the symbol. Solving for h_d',

$$h_d' = (\Sigma Vv^2)/(2gAh_t) \quad \text{(closely)} \qquad\qquad \text{25-26}$$

To allow for the build-up in frictional resistance from zero to a maximum which accompanies the establishment of flow, we can write

$$h_d = (\Sigma Vv^2)/(2gAh_t) + \tfrac{1}{2}h_p + \tfrac{1}{2}(1 - c_s^2)h_s \qquad\qquad \text{25-27}$$

Here, h_p is the frictional resistance of the distribution, or piping, system as far as the average nozzle, and c_s and h_s are respectively the coefficient of velocity and the driving head of the siphon. The first term on the right-hand side of Equation 25-27 is small and can ordinarily be neglected in computations of h_d. The time t_d required for the system to go into full operation is a function of the volume of water displaced and the rate of discharge (the latter being a function of the maximum rate or kQ_{max}).

$$t_d = h_dA/(kQ_{max}) = h_dA/(0.8Q_{max}) \qquad\qquad \text{25-28}$$

the value of k being closely $\sqrt{2/3} = 0.8$ because of the parabolic rise in velocity that takes place.

2. A workable relationship between nozzle head and tank area can be based upon the following considerations.

To insure uniform distribution of the sewage over the bed after full operation has been established, the amount of sewage discharged in any small element of time $Q\,dt$ relative to the area of bed covered from the nozzle $2\pi r\,dr$ (see Figure 25-14) must be constant and equal to the volume V_d of water displaced from the dosing tank between the limiting operating heads of the nozzle per unit area a of bed dosed. Hence

$$Q\,dt/(2\pi r\,dr) = V_d/a = k \qquad\qquad 25\text{-}29$$

The limiting operating heads are the two effective heads on the nozzle, each augmented by the siphon and pipe losses. The volume of water displaced in bringing the system into operation should not be included. Since $Q\,dt = A\,dh$, $A\,dh = 2\pi kr\,dr$. In accordance with the empirical Equation 25-24, furthermore,

$$r\,dr = m^2 n h^{2n-1} \sin^2 2\alpha\,dh$$

Therefore,

$$A = 2\pi k m^2 n h^{2n-1} \sin^2 2\alpha$$

and

$$A/A_0 = (h/h_0)^{2n-1} \qquad\qquad 25\text{-}30$$

where $0.5 < (2n - 1) < 1.0$ ordinarily and A_0 is the area of the compartment at the maximum effective head on the nozzle.[17]

If, in accordance with Figure 25-15, the tank is given one vertical wall and the width of each compartment b is made constant, while the distance from the vertical wall up to the minimum effective head on the nozzle [18] is made l_m, $A_m/A_0 = l_m/l_0$, and any intermediate area A has a length equal to $l_0 A/A_0$. Also

$$l_m/l_0 = (h_m/h_0)^{2n-1} \qquad \text{and} \qquad l/l_0 = (h/h_0)^{2n-1} \qquad 25\text{-}31 \;^{[19]}$$

In practice, the gentle curve traced by this relationship above the minimum water level is approximated by a straight line beginning at the minimum water level and rising to a point at or somewhat below the effective water level which lies below the maximum water level by an amount equal to or greater than the dosing-tank loss.

3. For a given difference in head between the maximum water level in the dosing tank and the elevation of the nozzles, the width of the compartment b and with it the volume of the compartment determines the length of the dosing period. Within reason, short periods give the most uniform coverage of the bed. Dosing times of 2.5 to 5.5 min at maximum rate of flow are common. The inlet structures must be able to pass the maximum flows with reasonably small driving heads. These heads are not recoverable in the normal operation of dosing tanks.

In accordance with the general finding that economy of design is obtained when ¼ the available head is used up in carrying the fluid through the supply structures, the sum of the maximum, or initial, driving heads represented by (1) the dosing-

---

[17] For the ⅞-in. PFT nozzle, for example,

$$A = 2\pi k (1.42)^2 \times 0.816 \times h^{0.632} = 10.34 k h^{0.632} \quad \text{and} \quad A/A_0 = (h/h_0)^{0.632}$$

[18] In practice, this dimension is usually dictated by the space requirements of the discharge siphon.

[19] For the ⅞-in. PFT nozzle, for example, $l/l_0 = (h/h_0)^{0.632}$.

tank loss h_d, (2) the siphon loss h_s, and (3) the piping loss to the average nozzle h_p is made equal to $\frac{1}{4}$ the maximum static head on the nozzles. The component losses, furthermore, are made about equal.

Once flow comes up to full rate, the dosing-tank loss drops out, and the remaining losses decrease in proportion to the square of the rate of discharge. The minimum effective head on the nozzle is generally held between 1.0 and 2.5 ft.

The dosing time is made up of two components: (1) the starting time and (2) the time required to empty the tank after normal discharge has gone into effect. The starting time is identified by Equation 25-28, the emptying time by integration of the relationship $Q \, dt = -A \, dh$, where $Q = ca\sqrt{2gh}$ and A is constant for the upper, vertical portion of the tank and related to the head either by Equation 25-30 if the tank is given a curved side or by an expression that establishes the proper geometric relationships if a straight side, closely fitting the curve, is substituted. The Pacific Flush Tank Company (PFT) has computed tables for straight-sided dosing tanks that can be made the basis of tank design. Table 25-2 is such a table for a $\frac{7}{8}$-in. PFT nozzle.

Example 25-7. Identify the dimensions of single- and twin-compartment dosing tanks that control the flow to a nozzle field of $\frac{7}{8}$-in. PFT nozzles. Assume a maximum water level 8 ft above the elevation of the nozzle openings and a net terminal head of 1.5 ft. The following observational equations are used in the calculations.

1. $S = 3.28h_0^{0.737}$, where S is the spacing and h_0 is the effective head on the nozzle, both in ft.

2. $S_L = 3.86h_0^{0.477}$, where S_L is the spray limit in ft.

3. $Q = 0.65a_n\sqrt{2gh} \times 7.48 \times 60 = 7.98h^{0.50}$, where Q is the rate of discharge in gpm.

The calculations are shown in Table 25-3, and the dimensions of a twin-compartment tank meeting the manufacturer's recommendations are sketched in Figure 25-15, for a bed with $N = 100$ nozzles, the width of the compartments being chosen as 10 ft. The theoretical curve of tank lengths is included.

For $\frac{7}{8}$-in. PFT nozzles the diameter of the siphon d_s is given by the relationship $d_s = \sqrt{2N}$ when the driving head h_s is made $\frac{1}{3}$ the total distribution loss and this is chosen at $\frac{1}{4}$ the total available head (or $\frac{1}{3}$ the maximum nozzle head) because $NQ = 0.65Na_n\sqrt{2gh_0} = 0.60a_s\sqrt{2gh_{s0}}$ and $h_{s0} = \frac{1}{3} \times \frac{1}{3}h_0$.

Close agreement is observed between calculated and recommended values. The selected spacing is made the basis of the calculation of the tank areas. The overlapping spray of neighboring nozzles is a compensating factor in a nozzle field, except at its edges.

25-13. Activated-Sludge Units. The problems that arise in the design of activated-sludge units, aside from structural matters, are also essentially two in number: (a) the determination of the required exposure of the sewage to aeration and contact with returned activated sludge (the process design) and (b) the determination of the size of the influent conduit, the returned-sludge conduit and pumps, the dimensions of the aeration units, and the air-distribution system and

TABLE 25-2. Design Data for $\frac{7}{8}$-in. Nozzles and for Dosing Tanks for Low-Rate Trickling Filters

A distribution loss equal to 25% of the total nozzle head is assumed.

a. Single- and twin-compartment tanks

(1)		(2)	(3)	(4)	(5)	(6)	(7)	(8)	(9)
Total nozzle head, ft		5.00	6.00	7.00	8.00	9.00	10.00	11.00	12.00
Maximum net head h_0, ft		3.75	4.50	5.25	6.00	6.75	7.50	8.25	9.00
Nozzle spacing S, ft		8.66	9.90	11.10	12.25	13.40	14.50	15.50	16.50
Lateral spacing, ft		7.50	8.56	9.50	10.62	11.60	12.55	13.42	14.30
Area of bed per nozzle, sq ft		65	85	107	130	156	182	208	236
Spray limit S_L (nozzle to edge), ft		7.25	8.00	8.50	9.10	9.60	10.25	10.60	11.00
Maximum rate of discharge Q, gpm		15.50	17.00	18.35	19.60	20.80	21.90	23.00	24.00
Maximum area of compartment A_0, sq ft per nozzle		3.15	2.40	1.90	1.55	1.30	1.10	0.97	0.85
D_v in Figure 25-15, ft	1.0 *	0.78	1.01	1.26	1.53	1.79	2.07	2.35	2.64
	1.5 *	0.62	0.83	1.04	1.29	1.52	1.77	2.03	2.29
	2.0 *	0.53	0.70	0.89	1.11	1.32	1.55	1.78	2.03
Maximum drawing depth of siphon, ft	1.0 *	3.78	4.78	5.78	6.78	7.78	8.78	9.78	10.78
	1.5 *	3.17	4.17	5.17	6.17	7.17	8.17	9.17	10.17
D in Figure 25-15	2.0 *	2.56	3.56	4.56	5.56	6.56	7.56	8.56	9.56

b. Single-compartment tanks only

		(2)	(3)	(4)	(5)	(6)	(7)	(8)	(9)
Limiting rate of inflow, gpm per 100 sq ft of bed	1.0 *	9.2	7.0	5.6	4.6	3.8	3.3	2.9	2.5
	1.5 *	11.3	8.6	6.9	5.6	4.7	4.0	3.5	3.1
	2.0 *	13.0	10.0	7.9	6.5	5.4	4.7	4.1	3.6

c. Twin-compartment tanks only

		(2)	(3)	(4)	(5)	(6)	(7)	(8)	(9)
Minimum area of compartment A_m, sq ft per nozzle	1.0 *	1.63	1.13	0.83	0.63	0.50	0.40	0.34	0.28
	1.5 *	1.99	1.38	1.01	0.77	0.61	0.49	0.41	0.35
	2.0 *	2.30	1.60	1.17	0.89	0.71	0.57	0.48	0.40
Volume of compartment V_d', gal per nozzle	1.0 *	71.3	67.3	63.6	60.4	57.9	55.3	53.8	51.7
	1.5 *	63.6	61.8	59.4	57.0	54.8	52.4	51.5	50.0
	2.0 *	54.0	55.5	54.7	53.4	52.0	50.2	49.3	47.7
Time to empty compartment, min	1.0 *	5.75	5.05	4.48	4.01	3.64	3.29	3.09	2.86
	1.5 *	4.83	4.40	4.01	3.65	3.39	3.07	2.89	2.69
	2.0 *	3.90	3.76	3.53	3.29	3.07	2.84	2.70	2.53

* Minimum net head, h_m.

compressors or mechanical agitators (the hydraulic and pneumatic or mechanical design).

a. Process Design. The principles underlying the process design of activated-sludge units have been discussed in preceding sections of this chapter. The fundamental relationship for diffused-air plants is expressed by the equation noted on Figure 25-8. This can be stated in the following form for the purpose of finding the contact opportunity as the product of (1) the detention period t that must be provided in the aeration unit and (2) the weight of sludge W that must be returned

TABLE 25-3. Calculated Dimensions of Dosing Tanks (Example 25-7)

No.	Item	Recommended by manufacturer	Calculation
1.	Elevation of maximum discharge line above nozzle outlet, h_t ft	8.0	Given, varies normally between 5.0 and 12.0 ft
2.	Effective head on nozzle, ft		
	a. maximum h_0	6.0	Allows for loss of 2 ft = 25% of 8 ft distributed equally between dosing tank h_d, siphon h_s, and piping h_p (0.67 ft each)
	b. minimum h_m	1.5	Chosen normally between 1.0 and 2.5 ft
3.	Nozzle spacing, S, ft	12.25	Recommended as $3.28\,h_0^{0.737}$ by manufacturer
4.	Lateral spacing, ft	10.62	0.866×12.25 for nozzles on equilateral triangles
5.	Area a of bed per nozzle, sq ft	130	Area of hexagon inscribed in circle S ft in diam = $0.866 S^2$
6.	Spray limit of nozzle to wall, ft	9.10	Observed by manufacturer as $3.86 h_0^{0.477}$
7.	Rate of discharge of nozzle Q, gpm		a_n = area of nozzle = $\pi[(\tfrac{7}{8})^2 - (\tfrac{3}{8})^2]/(4 \times 144)$ = 3.41×10^{-3} sq ft
	a. Maximum $h_0 = 6.0$ ft	19.60	Observed by manufacturer as $Q = 7.98 h^{0.5}$ gpm $19.60/130 = 0.151$ gpm per sq ft of bed = 9.5 mgad
	b. Minimum $h_m = 1.5$ ft	9.80	$9.80/130 = 0.075$ gpm per sq ft of bed = 4.7 mgad
8.	Limiting rate of inflow Q/a, gpm per sq ft		
	a. Single compartment	0.056	75% of minimum rate of discharge to avoid continuous outflow
	b. Twin compartments	0.100	66% of maximum rate of discharge varying from 60% for high heads (12 ft) to 75% for low heads (5 ft)
9.	Volume $V_{d'}$ of tank per nozzle, gal, including volume displaced by h_d	57.0	Chosen values lie between 46 at high heads and 71 at low heads
	Twin compartments only		
	Time t to empty compartments, min	3.65	Closely $1.3\ V_{d'}/Q_{\max} = 1.3(57.0/19.6) = 3.8$ min, or $454(a_s/Q_{\max})^2$, where a_s = cross-sectional area of the siphon
10.	Area of tank, sq ft per nozzle		$A_0 = 2\pi k m^2 n h_0^{2n-1}$
	a. At maximum water level, A_0 (Recommended by manufacturer as $364\dfrac{a_s^2}{h_d Q_{\max}}$)	1.55	$k = (V_{d'} - h_d A_0)/a = [(57.0/7.48) - 0.67 A_0]/130 = 0.0586 - 0.00515 A_0$ For $S = 3.28 h_0^{0.737} = 2m h_0^n$, $A_0 = 2\pi k m^2 n h^{2n-1} = 2\pi k(1.64)^2 \times 0.737 h^{0.474}$, or $A_0 = 1.48$ at $h = 6.0$
	b. At minimum water level, A_m		
	(1) Single compartment	0.89	
	(2) Twin compartments	0.77	$A_m/A_0 = (h_m/h_0)^{2n-1} = (1.5/6)^{0.474} = 0.52$ and $A_m = 1.48 \times 0.52 = 0.77$
11.	Vertical depth below maximum discharge line D_v, ft	1.29	$> h_d = 0.67$ ft (see Figure 25-15)
12.	Vertical depth of siphon compartment, ft	>1.83	Gross heads vary as net heads $(1.5/6.0)(6.0 + 2 \times 0.67) = 1.83$
13.	Drawing depth D, ft	6.17	$8 - 1.83 = 6.17$

to it, if a particular degree of purification p_2 is to be obtained and a daily load y is to be removed from an applied daily load y_0.

$$Wt = \frac{y_0}{4,200}\left(\frac{p_2}{100 - p_2}\right)^{2.38} = \frac{y_0}{4,200}\left(\frac{y}{y_0 - y}\right)^{2.38} \qquad 25\text{-}32$$

The detention period t establishes the volume V of the aeration unit as $V = Qt$, where Q is the rate of flow of the incoming sewage. This detention period can be tied into performance by means of Equation 25-15 or Equation 25-16 (t taking the place of l) when the values of the performance coefficients k and n for different values of W are known. Detention periods are commonly 4 to 8 hr for settled sewage of average strength, but they may be as low as 1 to 2 hr for rapid or partial treatment of average sewage and as high as 16 hr for strong industrial wastes. Short periods of aeration may be insufficient to create or maintain an active sludge. The returned sludge may then have to be aerated by itself. This is called "sludge reaeration." Since the concentration of living organisms in the sludge is high, its air requirements per unit volume are great. If they are not met, the sludge will quickly become septic. It is for this reason, too, that activated sludge which has settled in secondary sedimentation tanks should be withdrawn as rapidly as possible. Short detention periods are indicated.

In practice, the relative amount of returned sludge which activates the process is identified in three ways for design and operating purposes: (1) as the volume of activated sludge returned to the influent, expressed as a percentage of the volume of the influent sewage; (2) as the relative volume of suspended matter settling from a known volume of mixed liquor; and (3) as the relative weight of solids settling from a known volume of mixed liquor.

1. The percentage volume of activated sludge P_s returned to the influent varies in practice from 10% to 30% with an average of 20%. This measure is used to determine the capacities of pumps and conduits that transport the returned sludge. It is not a reliable measure of the amount of contact material in the aeration units, because the concentration of active solids in the returned sludge (and with it their relative surface area) varies widely in different plants and periodically in the same plant. A dry-solids concentration in the sludge of 0.2% by weight is undesirably low, one of 2% desirably high.

2. The percentage volume of suspended matter P_v in the mixed liquor of the aeration unit varies normally between 10% and 25%. This ratio is generally obtained by measuring the volume of sludge settling from 1 l of mixed liquor in 30 min. The determination is not analytically exact, because the settling and compacting properties of the suspended matter vary over a wide range. But the test is easily performed and useful in the control of the process. The volume of settleable matter is inherently of the same order of magnitude as the per cent of returned sludge, because the influent sewage adds but a small amount of settleable matter (<0.05% when the sewage is settled before aeration).

3. The dry-weight concentration of suspended solids in the mixed liquor can be determined with high analytical precision. In practice, the percentage concentration of suspended solids by weight P_w varies between 0.06 and 0.4% (600 to 4,000 mg/l) and averages 0.25%. The determination is used in the performance relationship discussed in this chapter, although it is only an indirect measure of the area of contact surface provided. However, no better means is currently available, unless it is the volatile portion of the suspended solids.

The ratio of the second to the third measure is called the *sludge-volume index* I_v. Therefore, $I_v = P_v/P_w$. Specifically, I_v is the volume in ml occupied by 1 gram of sludge, dry weight, after 30 min of settling. Calculations are normally based on the ratio in the mixed liquor of the ml of settling sludge $\times$ 1,000 to the mg/l of suspended solids. The sludge-volume index of active sludge varies between 50 and 100. A "bulked" sludge possesses an index of 200 or more. Determination of the sludge-volume index is useful in the management of the treatment process. For example, the amount of return sludge necessary to maintain a desired per cent solids P_w in the mixed liquor may be expressed in terms of the recirculation ratio R/I, and the sludge volume index, as: $100R/I = 100/[100/(P_w/I_v) - 1]$. It is assumed here that the solids concentration in the sludge pumped from the secondary settlers is the same as that attained in the sludge volume index test. Since the settling conditions are different, departures from this relationship may be significant. If P_w is to be 0.25% and I_v is 80 ml/gram, the percentage return sludge should be: $100/[100/(0.25/80) - 1] = 25\%$. If I_v rises to 200, the return must be increased to $100/[100/(0.25 \times 100) - 1] = 100\%$ or be made equal to the sewage flow in order to maintain P_w at 0.25%. At the same time, operations would be hampered by the poor settling and compacting properties of the bulked sludge. For returned sludge of known percentage solids content P_s or water content $(100 - P_s)$ the following approximate relationship obtains:

$$P_w = P_s \frac{100R/I}{100 + 100R/I} = P_s(R/I)/F' \qquad 25\text{-}33$$

where F' is the recirculation factor.

Since $W = 8.34VP_w/(10^2 \times 10^3) = 8.34 \times 10^{-5}VP_w$, where W is measured in thousands of pounds and V is the tank volume in gallons, and since $t = 24V/I$, where t is the detention time in hours and I is the inflow in gallons per day,

$$V = 22.4\sqrt{I(Wt)/P_w} \qquad 25\text{-}34$$

and

$$t = 538\sqrt{(Wt)/(IP_w)} \qquad 25\text{-}35$$

Example 25-8. Find (*a*) the allowable loading intensity of a diffused-air activated-sludge plant that is to effect 80% removal of BOD from 10 mgd of sewage containing 160 mg/l of applied BOD; (*b*) the necessary time of aeration if the solids concentration is to be maintained at 0.25% in the aeration units; (*c*) the necessary solids concentration if the detention period available in the tanks is 6 hr; (*d*) the approximate percentages of sludge to be returned to the influent under (b) and (c), if the sludge-volume index is 80; and (e) the required approximate solids content of the returned, activated sludge under (b) and (c). Since the applied load is $160 \times 10 \times 8.34 = 13,300$ lb, Equation 25-32 states:

a.

$$Wt = \frac{13,300}{4,200}\left(\frac{80}{20}\right)^{2.38} = 86,300 \text{ lb-hr}$$

b. If the suspended-solids concentration in the aeration units is 0.25%, the detention time t is given by Equation 25-35 as $t = 538\sqrt{86.3}/(10^7 \times 0.25) = 3.16$ hr.

c. If the time of aeration is 6 hr, Equation 25-35 states $P_w = (538)^2 \times 86.3/[10^7 \times (6)^2] = 0.0694\%$.

d. For $I_v = 80$, the percentage of returned sludge would have to be about as follows:
For $P_w = 0.25\%$, $100R/I = 100/[100/(0.25 \times 80) - 1] = 25\%$.
For $P_w = 0.0694\%$, $100R/I = 100/[100/(0.0694 \times 80) - 1] = 5.9\%$.

e. In accordance with Equation 25-33, the approximate solids content of the returned sludge would be:
For $P_w = 0.25\%$ and $100R/I = 25\%$, $P_s = 0.25 \times (100 + 25)/25 = 1.25\%$.
For $P_w = 0.0694\%$ and $100R/I = 5.9\%$, $P_s = 0.0694 \times (100 + 5.9)/5.9 = 1.25\%$.

The process design of activated-sludge plants includes a determination of the oxygen requirements of the process. In diffused-air plants, needed oxygen is obtained from the air diffused into the sewage (bubble aeration) and from the atmosphere in contact with the sewage surface (surface aeration). In mechanical aeration plants, it comes solely from the atmosphere. Oxygen intake is aided in these plants (1) through the formation of droplets by rotating brushlike or turbine-like devices that dip into the sewage or pull sewage upward through draft tubes and shower droplets over the sewage surface (droplet aeration) or (2) through the formation of bubbles of air by rotating turbinelike devices that pull air and sewage downward through draft tubes. The transfer of oxygen to droplets of sewage is more rapid than the transfer of oxygen to sewage from bubbles of air, because the interfacial film is about ⅓ as thick. However, the attainable time of exposure of droplets is ordinarily quite short.

The principles that govern the transfer of oxygen from the air to the sewage are described in Section 17-5. The oxygen-transfer efficiency of bubble aeration is normally only 5 to 15%. Since a liter of free air contains about 273 mg of oxygen, from 14 to 41 mg of oxygen are absorbed from each liter of air during aeration.

The rate of oxygen demand of mixed liquor and the basic rate of returned sludge are idealized in Figure 25-16. A maximum demand of 50 to 80 mg/l per hr per 1,000 mg/l of volatile suspended solids (or 40 to 64 mg/l per hr per 1,000 mg/l of total suspended solids) is exerted near the beginning of the process and approaches the average base rate of the returned sludge of about 20 mg/l per hr per 1,000 mg/l of volatile suspended solids (or about 16 mg/l per hr per 1,000 mg/l of total suspended solids) in the course of 4 to 6 hr. Aeration of activated sludge by itself reduces its initial base rate of 25 to 35 mg/l per hr per 1,000 mg/l of volatile suspended solids (or 20 to 28 mg/l per hr per 1,000 mg/l of total suspended solids) by about 25 to 50% during 4 to 6 hr. Therefore, a liter of mixed liquor containing 0.25% (2,500 mg/l) of suspended solids must be provided, during 5 hr of aeration (about 6 hr of detention), with $5 \times 2.5\{16 + \frac{1}{3}[(40 -$

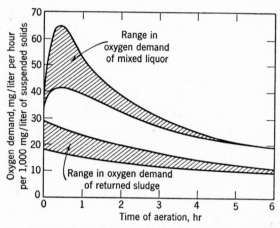

Figure 25-16.   Oxygen demands in the activated-sludge process.   Idealized.

$16)$ to $(64 - 16)]\}/[273 \times (0.05$ to $0.15)] = 7.3$ to 29.3 l of air.[20]   If it is assumed that half this amount, or 3.7 to 14.7 l, is derived from the atmosphere by surface aeration, the air requirements of diffused-air units may be estimated at 0.5 to 2.0 cu ft per gal of sewage. Actual values range from 0.5 to 1.5 cu ft per gal of sewage of average strength to much higher values for strong industrial wastes.   An observational figure, too, is 0.5 cu ft of air per 100 mg/l of influent BOD.   High air supply and long aeration periods are generally required for strong sewage.   They produce a highly nitrified effluent.   Low air supply and short periods are adequate for weak sewage and unnitrified effluents containing the minimum amount of dissolved oxygen that must ordinarily be maintained in the aeration units (about 1 mg/l). Since the oxygen requirements of the process decrease progressively in time (Figure 25-16), air supply is ordinarily proportioned to these requirements when the full amounts of sewage and sludge are brought together at the influent to the aeration units.   This proportioning is

[20] The parabolic nature of the curve introduces the factor $\frac{1}{3}$ in the numerator.

called tapered aeration. It is accomplished by providing a larger number of diffusers per unit area of tank or diffusers of greater permeability (see (b) in this section). When sewage is added stepwise along the line of flow, air requirements are more uniform. This is called step aeration or load distribution. Air requirements are also more uniform when the aeration unit is not provided with transverse baffles which reduce longitudinal mixing (or internal recirculation) in the aeration units.

Generally included in the air requirements of diffused-air plants is the air supplied to returned-sludge channels for the purpose of (1) keeping the sludge in suspension at velocities of less than 2 fps or (2) keeping the returned sludge in good condition.[21] The air introduced into influent channels to the aeration unit in which the returned sludge is mixed with the incoming sewage is also included in the over-all figure. However, when returned sludge is reaerated for a long period of time to condition it for use, separate account is normally taken of its air requirements.

b. *Hydraulic and Pneumatic, or Mechanical, Design.* Both diffused air and mechanical stirring perform two functions: (1) they supply needed oxygen, and (2) they keep the active sludge in suspension and thereby supply wanted contact between sewage and sludge. Effective velocities of at least 0.5 fps must be maintained if sludge flocs are not to settle out and become septic. Hydraulic circulation, therefore, is an important element in tank design. Circulation is commonly promoted by adding to the relatively slow, longitudinal displacement velocity of the unit (1.5 to 8 fpm) a relatively rapid upward vertical velocity that creates a complementary downward velocity, as well as transverse links. A circulating velocity well above 0.5 fps is induced. If the stirring unit (air or mechanical) is placed on one side of a long tank, the linking flows are across the tank, and the combined motions produce spiral circulation. Spiral flow is well maintained if the channel width to be spanned is not more than three times its depth. Common proportions are more nearly 1.5 (width) to 1.0 (depth).

Gyratory flow is promoted by placing deflectors at the surface of the channel and fillets at the bottom to approximate a circular cross-section in square channels and an elliptical cross-section in rectangular channels. In some designs (Figure 25-3b), in which the air is supplied from tubular diffusers that are submerged only a few feet, an air lift

---

[21] The Kutter coefficient of roughness for aerated channels is close to 0.3, because the passageway is reduced by the air.

is induced by placing longitudinal baffles close to the diffusers. The length of channels is seldom less than 100 ft or more than 400 ft. Depths are generally held at 10 to 15 ft for structural economy. Expansion and coalescence of air bubbles are also factors in circumscribing the depth of diffused-air units.

Since the physical detention period t' equals t/F, where t is the average time of treatment used in Equation 25-32 and $F = 1 + R/I$ is the recirculation factor, the hydraulic load Q on aeration units bears the following relations (1) to the width b (ft), depth d (ft), and length l (ft), of aeration channels, (2) to the physical detention period t' (hr), and (3) to the recirculation factor F of the sludge: $Q = 1 \times 7.5 \times 24/(Ft') = 180/Ft'$ gpd per cu ft, or $180bd/(Ft')$ gpd per ft length, or $7.84d/(Ft')$ mgd per acre. The length of channel, conversely, is $l = 5,560Ft'/(bd)$ ft per mgd. Good cross-sectional distribution of flow is obtained by making the channels at least five times as long as they are wide. Transverse baffles are sometimes inserted at intervals of about 50 ft in order to reduce longitudinal mixing, but their use is of doubtful value because internal recirculation is often desirable.

25-14. Air Supply for Diffused-Air Units. The air supply constitutes a unique design feature of diffused-air plants. It includes the following components: (1) diffusers, which inject fine bubbles of air into the sewage, (2) air piping, which carries the air from the compressors to the diffusers, (3) measuring devices, which record the amount of air used, (4) air compressors, which place the air under the required pressure, and (5) air filters, which clean the air drawn into the compressors in order to protect them against abrading substances and to prevent the clogging of diffusers from the air side.

Economic design of the air-distribution system commonly entails an over-all distribution loss of about 25% of the sewage depth. Therefore, the required air pressure is 1.25 × (10 to 15) ft or 5.4 to 8.1 psig. The resistance of the different portions of the system can be gaged from the following average component values:

1. Air filters, ⅛ to ⅜ in. of water for viscous filters and ½ in. for cloth filters.
2. Air meters, 1 to 2 in. of water, or 18 to 24% of the differential head.
3. Piping, $1.0v^2/2g$ ft head of air for 40 diameters of pipe [22] with $0.5v^2/2g$ ft head of air for elbows and $1.5v^2/2g$ ft head of air for globe valves, pipe velocities commonly being held between 2,000 and 3,000 fpm.
4. Diffusers, 2 to 15 in. of water.
5. Sewage, 10 to 15 ft of water.

---

[22] See Equation 12-1, $fl/d = 40f = 1.0$, or $f = 0.025$.

a. Air Diffusers. Commonly, air diffusers are flat plates or circular tubes of porous ceramic materials, but other forms and materials are also available. Plate diffusers are normally 12 in. square and 1 in. thick, tubular diffusers 24 in. long and 3 in. in internal diameter with a wall thickness of ⅝ in. The air release of circular tubes is less uniform than that of plates, because the air bubbles issuing from the bottom half of the tube tend to coalesce as they sweep around the walls of the diffuser. By convention, the *permeability* of diffusers is expressed in terms of the face velocity (fpm) of air at 70 F and 10 to 25% relative humidity that will flow through the pores of the diffuser with a loss of head of 2 in. of water, when the diffuser is tested dry in a room kept at 70 F and a relative humidity of 30 to 50%. Permeabilities of 30 to 60 fpm are commonly specified. A square foot of submerged diffuser will then deliver 1.5 to 3 cfm of air with a pressure loss of 2 to 5 in. of water when the diffuser is new. Losses rise as diffusers become clogged in service. The diffusers are generally cleaned when the loss has increased twofold.

Diffusers clog on the air side when the air carries foreign matter originating in the atmosphere or in the air piping. They are clogged on the sewage side by sewage solids and growths of microorganisms. Clogging on the air side is kept to a minimum by cleaning the air before compression (which also prevents wear on the compressors) and by constructing the air-distribution system of non-corrosive materials or of materials that are protected against erosion. Clogging on the sewage side is reduced if air pressures are maintained, without interruption, above the hydrostatic head of the sewage. The nature of the clogging substances determines the method of cleaning to be employed.

b. Air Piping. A satisfactory relation for the resistance of air piping can be based on the Darcy-Weisbach equation for the flow of incompressible fluids in pipes:

$$h_f = f \frac{l}{d} \frac{v^2}{2g} \qquad \text{12-1}$$

Conversion of Equation 12-1 to a useful equation for the flow of air as a compressible fluid in pipes is had by making the following substitutions:

1. $\Delta p = h_f \gamma / 144$, where Δp is the pressure difference in psi and γ is the weight density of the air, the value of γ being 0.076 lb per cu ft at atmospheric pressure ($p_0 = 14.7$ psia) and a temperature T_0 of 60 F (519.6 F absolute) and varying directly with the absolute pressure p and inversely with the absolute temperature T or $\gamma = 0.076(p/p_0)(T_0/T) = 2.71p/T$.

2. Since the weight of air transported is constant but varies in volume with its density, the rate of flow of the air in the pipe is $0.076Q/(2.71p/T) = 0.0282(T/p)Q$, where Q is the rate of flow of free air in cubic feet per minute. Furthermore, $Q = v \times 60 \times \pi D^2/(4 \times 144)$, where D is the diameter of the pipe in inches; and $T = 519.6(p/14.7)^{0.283}$ for adiabatic compression of the air.[23]

The resulting equation is

$$\Delta p = \frac{f}{38,000} \frac{lTQ^2}{pD^5} \qquad 25\text{-}36$$

The value of f varies for new piping from 2.5×10^{-2} for 3-in. pipe to 1.6×10^{-2} for 18-in. pipe and for old piping from 4.9×10^{-2} for 3-in. pipe to 2.8×10^{-2} for 18-in. pipe.

In accordance with observations by Fritsche,

$$f = 0.048D^{0.027}/Q^{0.148} \qquad 25\text{-}37$$

for pipes less than 10 in. in diameter.

Example 25-9. Find the pressure drop in 500 ft of 6-in. pipe transporting 500 cfm of free air under a gage pressure of 7 psig:

1. The absolute pressure of the air, $p = 7 + 14.7 = 21.7$ psia.
2. The absolute temperature of the air $T = 520(21.7/14.7)^{0.283} = 581$ F.
3. By Equation 25-37, $f = 0.048 \times 6^{0.027}/(500)^{0.148} = 0.020$.
4. By Equation 25-36, therefore,

$$\Delta p = \frac{0.020}{38,000} \frac{500 \times 581 \times (500)^2}{21.7 \times 6^5} = 0.23 \text{ psi}$$

The length of pipe that will produce the same loss of head as elbows and tees is approximated by the observational relationship:

$$l = 7.6D/(1 + 3.6/D) \qquad 25\text{-}38$$

Similarly for globe valves:

$$l = 11.4D/(1 + 3.6/D) \qquad 25\text{-}39$$

c. Air Compression. The work done by air compressors in compressing a unit volume of free air from atmospheric pressure to a pressure p and volume v, consists of (1) the work of compression, $\int p \, dv$, plus (2) the work of expulsion pv minus (3) the work done on the piston by the incoming air p_0v_0. In isothermal compression $pv = $ constant; in adiabatic compression $pv^n = pv^{1.40} = $ constant. Most air compressors

---

[23] The associated pressure (p)-volume (v) relationship being $pv = RT$, where R is the gas constant and $pv^n = $ constant, the exponent $n = 1.40$ being the ratio of the specific heats of the air at constant pressure and constant volume.

employed in sewage works operate adiabatically. The work of compression can therefore be formulated as

$$\int p\, dv = \int_{v_0}^{v} \text{constant} \times v^{-n}\, dv = -\text{Constant}\,(v_0^{1-n} - v^{1-n})/(1-n)$$

$$= (pv - p_0 v_0)/(n-1)$$

because the constant equals both pv^n and $p_0 v_0^n$. It follows that the work done by the compressor is $[(pv - p_0 v_0)/(n-1)] + pv - p_0 v_0$. Expressing v in terms of v_0 and substituting Q cfm of free air for v_0, the theoretical horsepower requirements P of the compressor are:

$$P = \frac{144}{33,000}\left(\frac{n}{n-1}\right) p_0 Q \left[\left(\frac{p}{p_0}\right)^{(n-1)/n} - 1\right] \qquad 25\text{-}40$$

or,

$$P = 0.227 Q[(p/14.7)^{0.283} - 1] \qquad 25\text{-}41$$

for an atmospheric pressure of 14.7 psia and for $n = 1.40$. Compressor efficiencies being in the vicinity of 80%, the power requirements of a compressor that is to handle 10^6 cu ft of free air per day (694 cfm) against a pressure of 7 psig are $P = 18.4$ hp theoretical and 23 hp actual. The corresponding energy requirements are 24 times as great, or 440 hp-hr theoretical and 550 hp-hr actual, or 330 kw-hr theoretical and 410 kw-hr actual. The energy requirements of mechanical stirring devices are of the same order of magnitude for identical rates of sewage flow.

Rotary and centrifugal blowers are commonly employed to deliver air at the required pressures.

d. Air Filters.[24] Two types of air filters are in general use: (1) viscous filters consisting of a mat of non-corrosive metal, glass wool, or hair covered with oil and (2) cloth filters. The viscous filters come in unit frames (20 in. square and about 4½ in. thick) and are suspended in large rectangular frames. With face velocities as high as 300 fpm, their pressure loss, as previously stated, is only ⅛ to ⅜ in. of water. Metallic filters are cleaned by immersing them in a cleansing bath. They are then recoated with oil. Glass-wool and hair filters are discarded when they become clogged. Cloth filters are given face velocities of about 200 fpm and are cleansed by back-flows of air or by vacuum-cleaning devices. The probable dust loading of filters is from 1 to 3 mg per 100 cu ft of air when the air intake is so placed as to avoid dusty areas such as driveways.

[24] See *Handbook of Air Cleaning*, U. S. Atomic Energy Commission, Government Printing Office, Washington, D. C., 1952.

26-1. General Considerations. The settleable solids that are naturally present in water and waste water, or that are derived from non-settleable matter by chemical coagulation and precipitation and by biological flocculation and precipitation, are removed from settling tanks as *sludge* (Section 22-12). When coagulating and precipitating chemicals are used, their precipitates become part of the sludge (Section 23-9). The wash water from filters also contains sludge-forming substances. Floating matters, depending upon their nature and the method of their removal, are known either as *screenings* (Section 15-11) or as *skimmings* (Section 22-19). Heavy, largely mineral, settleable solids are classed as *grit* or *detritus* (Sections 22-17 and 22-18). Screenings and skimmings, instead of being disposed of by themselves, may be converted into settleable solids by being comminuted within the suspending water or returned to it after removal and disintegration. They then become part of the sludge. When sludges contain large quantities of precipitating chemicals they are often referred to as *slurries* (Section 23-9).

Sludges are further identified in terms of the treatment processes in which they originate. Examples are the coagulation-basin, water-softening, and iron sludges of water-purification plants, and the plain-sedimentation, chemical precipitation, and activated sludges of sewage-treatment plants. Sloughed trickling-filter slimes are called *trickling-filter humus*.

On reaching the bottom of settling tanks, most sludges form loose structures of particulate or flocculent matter with included water. The pore space of these structures is large and their water content, therefore, relatively great. The resulting volume of sludge is many times that of its constituent solids. The amounts of sludge produced in water purification and waste-water treatment and the constitution and composition of the sludge are a function (1) of the nature of the waters or waste waters from which they are derived and (2) of the treatment process to which the waters are subjected. The great volumes of sludge that must be disposed of are a serious economic problem. The presence of substantial amounts of organic matter that can serve as food for saprophytic bacteria and other scavenging organisms renders many sludges, including all but exceptional sewage sludges, putrescible. Exceptional sewage sludges are those derived from waste waters containing toxic amounts of substances such as copper. Since bacteria and other organisms are concentrated in sludge and some of them may be potentially pathogenic, the hygienic significance of sludge, as well as its esthetic and economic significance, is often great. Sludge production, treatment, and disposal are particularly important in the treatment of municipal sewage because thousands of gallons of putrescible and potentially dangerous sludge are removed from each million gallons of sewage treated. For this reason the present chapter is concerned with sewage sludge more specifically than with water-treatment sludges. However, many of the matters considered apply to both types of sludges, although in different degree. The disposal of water-treatment sludges has been discussed briefly also in Section 23-9.

Many sludges contain substances of economic value. The solids in wastes from the food and beverage industry, for example, may serve as animal foods after the sludge has been adequately dewatered. Other industrial waste waters, too, contain recoverable values such as grease, fiber, or chemicals (Chapter 29). Sewage sludge includes constituents that will fertilize the land. The dry solids of sludges of large organic content are of high calorific power, and some of them, particularly sewage sludges, will yield useful amounts of combustible gases (principally methane) when the solids are submitted to anaerobic digestion.

In general, therefore, sludge constitutes the principal by-product of the treatment of water and waste waters. The sanitary disposal or utilization of this by-product is one of the most important, and often one of the most troublesome, problems associated with the design and management of treatment works.

26-2. Unit Operations of Sludge Treatment. The primary purposes of sludge treatment are (1) reduction of the volume of sludge to be disposed of and (2) control or destruction of its putrescibility. The unit operations employed for this purpose are listed in the following schedule.

1. *Thickening.* An operation in which sludge is stirred for prolonged periods for the purpose of forming larger, more rapidly settling aggregates of sludge flocs with smaller water content. An example is the thickening of activated sludge to increase its solids concentration to as much as 4% in 8 to 12 hr of stirring, chlorine being added, if necessary, to impede decomposition.

2. *Chemical conditioning.* An operation of chemical treatment, analogous to the chemical coagulation of water and sewage, which improves the dewatering characteristics of sludge. An example is the addition of ferric chloride to sewage sludge that is to be dried on open sand beds or dewatered on vacuum filters.

3. *Elutriation.* A washing operation whereby substances that interfere physically or economically with chemical conditioning and filtration are washed out of sludge. An example is the reduction in required chemical conditioning of digested sewage sludge in advance of filtration.

4. *Biological flotation.* A thickening operation whereby sludge solids are lifted by gases of decomposition. An example is the flotation of primary sludge in 5 days at 35 C and the withdrawal of the subnatant.

5. *Vacuum filtration.* An operation in which moisture is withdrawn from a layer of sludge by suction, the sludge to be dewatered being supported on a porous medium, usually cloth on screening. An example is the dewatering of chemically conditioned activated sludge on a continuous, rotary vacuum filter. A sludge paste or cake is produced.

6. *Air drying.* An operation whereby sludge run onto beds of sand or other granular materials loses moisture by evaporation to the air and by drainage to the drying bed. An example is the air-drying of well-digested sewage sludge on sand beds, a spadable, friable sludge cake being produced.

7. *Heat drying.* An operation of sludge heating or moisture evaporation by which the sludge is reduced to substantial dryness. An example is the drying of vacuum-filtered activated-sewage sludge in a continuous flash-drier. If sludge is to be marketed, its moisture content must generally be reduced to less than 10%.

8. *Digestion.* An operation of anaerobic decomposition of putrescible matter accompanied by gasification, liquefaction, stabilization, destruction of colloidal structure, and consolidation or release of moisture. The gases produced generally include, besides carbon dioxide, combustible methane and, more rarely, hydrogen. Examples are (1) the digestion of settled solids in septic tanks (single- or double-storied) and (2) the digestion in heated, separate tanks of sewage solids removed from primary or secondary settling tanks, or both, the gases of decomposition being employed for tank heating and other plant purposes.

9. *Incineration.* An operation by which heat-dried sludge is ignited and burnt, alone or with added fuel, for the purpose of heat-drying the partly dewatered sludge of which it was itself a part. Examples are (1) the incineration of heat-dried sludge for the purpose of supplying heat to a continuous flash-drier and (2) the burning of heat-dried sludge on the lower hearths of a multiple-hearth furnace on the upper hearths of which the sludge to be incinerated is being dried. The end product of incineration is ash.

There are other unit operations of sludge treatment. Among them are (*a*) conditioning by heating, freezing, or flotation and (*b*) dewatering by centrifuging and pressing. They are not described here because they are either inadequately developed or unsatisfactory or uneconomical in performance. Some of them have the further drawback of being discontinuous. None of them is, or has been, widely used.

Common combinations of unit operations are (1) air-drying of digested, plain-sedimentation sewage sludge; (2) heat-drying of thickened, chemically conditioned, vacuum-filtered activated sludge; (3) incineration of digested, elutriated, chemically conditioned, and vacuum-filtered mixtures of trickling-filter humus and plain-sedimentation sewage sludge.

Characteristics and Behavior of Sludge

26-3. Examination of Sludge. *Standard Methods for the Examination of Water and Sewage* [1] includes the schedule of procedures for the examination of sludge and mud samples that is given below. Tests that pertain to the examination of activated sludge only are printed in italics. Unless stated otherwise, they have been discussed in Section 25-13.

Physical and Chemical Examination.
Temperature, color, odor, and physical appearance—all but the temperature test are described in general terms as best suits the individual case.

Specific gravity—by comparative weights of sludge or mud (if necessary diluted with water) in relation to water.

Suspended solids of sludges and aeration-tank liquor—by suction filtration through filter paper supported on a perforated aluminum dish in a Büchner funnel.

Settleability of activated sludge—by recording the volume occupied by the sludge at various time intervals and finding the rate of settling from a volume-time plot. This test is not included in Section 25-13 in this form.

Sludge-volume index (SVI) and sludge-density index (SDI).

Reaction: acidity, alkalinity (phenolphthalein and methyl orange), and pH value.

Moisture and solids (total and volatile)—by evaporation and ignition.

Nitrogen—total, ammonia, and organic.

Grease in liquid sludge—by extraction of acidified samples with ether.

Volatile acids in liquid sludge—by steam distillation.

Biological Examination. Bacteriological examination is not specified. Ordinarily, it is conducted by methods used in the examination of water. Results may be expressed in the same terms or based on the weight of the liquid sludge.

Microscopic examination—quantitative estimate of the number, bulk, or weight of organisms or other material retained (1) on a 30-mesh sieve (590 μ openings) and (2) on a 100-mesh (149 μ openings) after passing a 30-mesh sieve.

---

[1] American Public Health Association, 10th Ed., New York, 1953.

The significance of most of the standard tests should be clear from what has been said about the examination of water and sewage (Chapter 20). In addition, reference has been made, in other chapters of this book, to tests commonly performed in the routine operation of water and waste-water works. However, there are certain properties of sludge that are deserving of special consideration or determination, among them: (a) moisture-weight-volume relationships; (b) release of moisture; (c) digestibility; (d) fuel value; and (e) fertilizer value. These properties affect individually or in combination the handling, dewatering, stabilization, utilization, and disposal of sludge and are discussed in succeeding sections of this chapter.

26-4. Moisture-Weight-Volume Relationships. If a sludge contains a weight W_s of dry solids and a weight W of water, the percentage moisture content of the sludge is $p = 100W/(W + W_s)$ and the solids concentration $(100 - p) = 100W_s/(W + W_s)$.

The specific gravity of the dry sludge (or of the sludge solids on a dry basis) is a function of the specific gravities of its component parts. If the two fractions of the solids (volatile and fixed), which are determined by evaporation of the sludge moisture and ignition of the residue, possess specific gravities of s_v and s_f respectively, the specific gravity s_s of the solids as a whole can be calculated from a knowledge of the percentage volatile matter p_v in the sludge. Writing

$$100/s_s = (p_v/s_v) + (100 - p_v)/s_f$$

it follows that

$$s_s = 100s_f s_v/[100s_v + p_v(s_f - s_v)] \qquad 26\text{-}1$$

The specific gravity of the volatile solids is normally close to 1.0 and that of the fixed solids about 2.5, or

$$s_s = 250/(100 + 1.5p_v) \qquad 26\text{-}2$$

The specific gravity of the wet sludge s is the quotient of the sums of the weights of the water and dry sludge and their respective volumes, or

$$s = \frac{p + (100 - p)}{p/s_w + (100 - p)/s_s} = \frac{100 s_s s_w}{p s_s + (100 - p)s_w} \qquad 26\text{-}3$$

For sake of completeness, the specific gravity of the water s_w is included in this formulation, although it is generally taken as 1.0. In terms of Equation 26-2, therefore,

$$s = 25,000/[250p + (100 - p)(100 + 1.5p_v)] \qquad 26\text{-}4$$

The volume V of the wet sludge equals the sum of the volumes of the water and the solids contained in the wet sludge, or

$$V = \frac{W_s}{s_s w} + \frac{W}{s_w w} = \frac{W_s}{s_s w} + \frac{pW_s}{(100-p)s_w w} = \frac{W_s}{w} \frac{100 s_w + p(s_s - s_w)}{(100-p)s_s s_w} \qquad 26\text{-}5$$

Here w is the unit weight of water. It follows that, when the volume of a given sludge is reduced by removing water from it and the attributes of the original sludge are given the subscript zero, the volume of the partially dewatered sludge will be

$$V = V_0 \frac{[100 s_w + p(s_s - s_w)]\,(100 - p_0)}{[100 s_w + p_0(s_s - s_w)]\,(100 - p)} \qquad 26\text{-}6$$

provided that the voids between the solids remain filled with water.

When s_s is close to s_w in magnitude, as is generally true,

$$V = V_0(100 - p_0)/(100 - p) \qquad 26\text{-}7$$

The loss of water from sludge, therefore, changes its volume approximately in the ratio of its solids concentration. Because of this, the solids concentration is, generally speaking, a more useful parameter than the sludge moisture. A reduction in the water content of a given sludge from 95 to 90% or increase in its solids concentration from 5 to 10%, for example, more or less halves its volume. As sludge loses water, it often acquires the plastic properties of a paste. Loss of water to the point where the voids of the sludge are no longer filled with water produces a sludge cake which is generally forkable. Except for some consolidation, the volume of sludge cake remains substantially constant at $V = W_s/(1-f)s_s w$ where f is the porosity ratio (often 40 to 50%).

Example 26-1. A primary sewage sludge, produced by plain sedimentation of domestic sewage, has a moisture content of 95%, 72.2% of the dry solids being volatile matter. Find (a) the specific gravity of the dry solids, on the assumption that the specific gravity of the volatile solids is 1.00 and that of the fixed solids 2.50; (b) the specific gravity of the wet sludge, on the assumption that the specific gravity of the included water is 1.00; and (c) the relative decrease in volume associated with a reduction of the moisture of the wet sludge to 85%.

a. By Equation 26-1 or 26-2:

$$s_s = 250/(100 + 1.5 \times 72.2) = 1.20$$

b. By Equation 26-3:

$$s = 120/(95 \times 1.2 + 5) = 1.008$$

c. By Equation 26-6:

$$\frac{V}{V_0} = \frac{(100 + 85 \times 0.20)5}{(100 + 95 \times 0.20)15} = 0.328$$

or by Equation 26-7:

$$V/V_0 = \tfrac{5}{15} = 0.333$$

26-5. Release of Moisture. The drainability of sludge, or the relative rate at which and extent to which sludge will give up its moisture (and the influence of conditioning agents upon drainability), can be determined in the laboratory by employing an apparatus such as that shown in Figure 26-1. A known weight of sludge is placed on filter

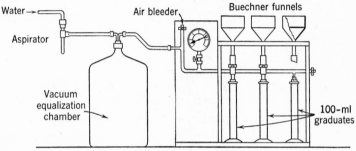

Figure 26-1. Apparatus for determining the release of moisture by sludge.

paper in a Büchner funnel, or in an aluminum dish supported on a rubber ring in the Büchner funnel, and the volume of filtrate collected in different time intervals with or without suction is noted. The moisture content of the sludge at the different time intervals is then calculated from a knowledge of the original moisture content of the sludge. If, for example, 50 ml of filtrate are collected in 10 min from 100 grams of activated sludge that contains 98% water, the moisture content of the sludge has been reduced to $(98 - 50)/(100 - 50) = 96\%$ in 10 min. A plot of observed values such as that shown in Figure 26-2 will identify the probable influence of sludge conditioning agents. If the laboratory tests are conducted under standardized conditions of sludge weight (with due allowance for added substances) or thickness, vacuum, filter-paper selection, area, and temperature, a correlation can be established with actual dewatering facilities or equipment. Laboratory-scale equipment in the form of vacuum filters, sand beds, and the like can also be usefully employed.

The thickening of sludge by stirring can be investigated in a laboratory stirring apparatus (Figure 23-3). The effects of conditioning agents on thickening and flotation can also be studied by these means to give useful information.

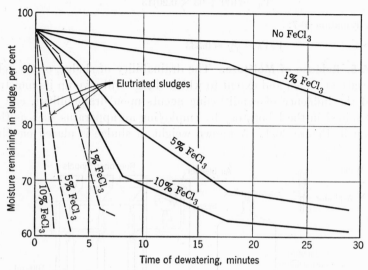

Figure 26-2. Rates of release of moisture by digested, plain-sedimentation sewage sludge.

26-6. Digestibility. The kinetics of anaerobic digestion, including the effects of temperature of digestion, have been discussed in Section 19-6. The digestion characteristics of a given sludge can be deter-

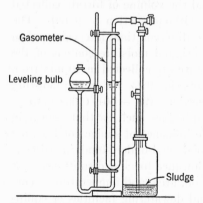

Figure 26-3. Apparatus for determining the digestibility of sludge.

mined most conveniently in the laboratory on a batch basis. The results obtained will furnish information for the design and operation of digestion units. The daily rate of digestion of continuous units may be assumed to be equal to that of a single daily charge of sludge in a period of time equal to the required period of sludge storage (see Figure 19-12). Comparative tests may include experiments on raw and seeded sludge, on sludge held at different temperatures, and on sludges subjected to liming and other treatments. A suitable testing apparatus is shown in Figure 26-3. It includes a bottle, partly filled with sludge, and a gas collector.

A constant temperature is conveniently maintained by placing the sludge bottle in a temperature-controlled water bath. The amount of gas produced in given time intervals and its composition serve as the measures of digestibility. A mixture of two parts of fresh solids to one part of digested solids, both on a basis of dry, volatile solids, is a useful first charge for sewage sludges. In continuous-digestion (steady-state) experiments, fresh sludge must be added in daily increments to the sludge bottle. The amounts added, after the normal digestion period has been reached, must be such as to maintain a steady rate of production of gas of even composition. For experimental purposes, the yield of both total gas and methane (the difference being substantially all carbon dioxide) is conveniently reported (1) in terms of volume of gas per unit weight of fresh volatile solids or volatile solids destroyed or (2) in terms of weight of gas per unit weight of volatile solids destroyed. In the laboratory, volumes of gas are generally recorded in milliliters or liters and weights of gas and solids in grams or kilograms. In plant operation, the volumes of gas are recorded in cubic feet and the weights of gas and solids in pounds. The time unit is generally a day. Gas volumes may be related also to the tributary population on a per capita basis or to the sludge volume on a cubic-foot basis. The gases released by digesting sewage sludges contain about 72% methane, the remainder being substantially all carbon dioxide. The gas is normally saturated with water vapor. Under standard conditions (0 C or 32 F, 1 atm or 29.9 in. mercury, and dryness), gas occupies a volume of 359 cu ft per lb mol (Section 17-5). Hence a cubic foot of methane (CH_4) weighs $16/359 = 0.0446$ lb and a cubic foot of carbon dioxide (CO_2) $44/359 = 0.1225$ lb. The net (or low-heat) fuel value of methane is 958 Btu per cu ft under standard conditions as against 1,080 Btu per cu ft of natural gas. The net fuel value equals the heat liberated in combustion minus the heat of condensation of water (see Section 26-14). Reduction of the volume of gas recorded at a given temperature and pressure to standard conditions is made in accordance with Equation 17-7.

$$V_0 = V \frac{p - p_w}{p_0} \frac{T_0}{T} \qquad \text{17-7}$$

Moisture in the gas is taken into account by subtracting the vapor pressure of water from the observed pressure on the assumption that the gas is saturated with moisture. For p in inches of mercury and T in degrees Fahrenheit,

$$V_0 = 16.4V \frac{p - p_w}{459.7 + T} \qquad \text{26-8}$$

Example 26-2. A sewage sludge produced by primary (plain) sedimentation of domestic sewage contains 72.2% volatile matter on a dry basis and 95% water. During experimental digestion at 30 C (86 F) of 384 grams of fresh wet sludge, the gas yield is 783 ml per gram of volatile solids, 72% by volume being methane. The wet digested sludge, exclusive of the seeding material, weighs 93 grams and contains 87% water, the volatile matter in the sludge being 38.2% on a dry basis. Find (a) the volume in cubic feet and weight in pounds of gas per pound of volatile matter destroyed; (b) the net fuel value of the gas in British thermal units per cubic foot and per pound of volatile matter destroyed; (c) the volume in cubic feet of gas per cubic foot of wet sludge daily and per capita daily on the assumption that 37.8 cu ft of wet sludge per 1,000 persons are added daily to the digestion unit, and that the daily charge of the digestion unit is proportional to the batch charge of the experimental unit; and (d) the relative volume of gas measured at a temperature of 68 F and a barometric pressure of 29.6 in.

a. The weights of volatile matter in the fresh and digested sludges are respectively: $384[(100 - 95)/100](72.2/100) = 13.9$ grams and $93[(100 - 87)/100](38.2/100) = 4.6$ grams. Hence the weight of volatile matter destroyed is $(13.9 - 4.6) = 9.3$ grams and the volume of gas per gram of volatile matter destroyed becomes $783 \times 13.9/9.3 = 1,170$ ml. Since 1 cu ft = 28.3 l and 1 lb = 454 grams, the volume of gas is $1.17 \times 454/28.3 = 18.8$ cu ft per pound of volatile matter destroyed. The weight of this gas is $(0.0446 \times 0.72 + 0.1225 \times 0.28)18.8 = 1.25$ lb per pound of volatile matter destroyed. A value of 1.25 lb of gas per pound of volatile matter destroyed is well established for the digestion of plain-sedimentation sewage solids.

b. The net fuel value of the gas is $958 \times 0.72 = 690$ Btu per cu ft, or $18.8 \times 690 = 13,000$ Btu per pound of volatile matter destroyed.

c. The gas yield of 783 ml per gram of volatile solids equals $783 \times 0.05 \times 0.722 = 28.3$ ml per gram of wet sludge. In accordance with Example 26-1, the specific gravity of the fresh wet sludge is 1.008. Therefore the gas yield is $28.3 \times 1.008 = 28.5$ ml per ml or cu ft per cu ft, and the daily per capita production of gas is $28.5 \times 37.8/1,000 = 1.08$ cu ft. A value of about 1 cu ft of gas per capita daily is a useful background figure for the gas yield of digesting, plain-sedimentation solids.

d. By Equation 17-7 or 26-8: $V/V_0 = (459.7 + 68.0)/[16.4(29.6 - 0.7)] = 1.11$. The vapor pressure of water at 68 F being 0.7 in. of mercury (Section 17-3), i.e., 1.11 cu ft of gas will be recorded for each cubic foot of gas under standard conditions.

26-7. Fuel Value.

The fuel value of sludge solids is determined in a bomb calorimeter. Since the volatile-solids content of sludge is a measure of its ignitable constituents, estimates of the fuel value may be based on a statistical correlation between pairs of observed fuel values and volatile-solids values of different sludges. For sewage sludges, the correlation may be generalized in the form

$$Q = a\left(\frac{100p_v}{100 - p_c} - b\right)\left(\frac{100 - v_c}{100}\right) \qquad 26\text{-}9$$

where Q is the fuel value in British thermal units per pound of dry solids; p_v is the proportion of volatile matter in per cent; p_c is the proportion of chemical, precipitating or conditioning, agent present in per cent; and a and b are coefficients for different classes of sludge. Characteristic magnitudes of these coefficients are:

	a	b
Plain-sedimentation sewage sludge (fresh and digested)	131	10
Activated-sludge (fresh)	107	5

A comparison of observed or calculated fuel values of sludges can be had with those of the common fuels shown in Table 26-1.

TABLE 26-1. Fuel Values of Common Fuels

Fuel	Btu per lb	lb per gal
Low-grade coal	10,000	...
High-grade coal	14,000	...
Crude petroleum	19,000	7.6
Gasoline	20,000	6.1

Example 26-3. A chemically precipitated sewage sludge contains 68.0% volatile matter on a dry basis and the precipitated chemical is 8.3% of the sludge weight. Estimate: (a) the fuel value of the sludge and (b) the percentage recovery of fuel value in sludge gas by digestion of these solids, assuming that 67% of the volatile matter is destroyed by digestion and that 72% of the gas by volume is methane, the remainder being carbon dioxide.

a. By Equation 26-9, using the values of a and b for plain-sedimentation sewage sludge,

$$Q = 131 \left(\frac{100 \times 68}{100 - 8.3} - 10 \right) \left(\frac{100 - 8.3}{100} \right) = 7,700 \text{ Btu per lb}$$

b. Since the weight of volatile matter destroyed is $0.67 \times 0.68 = 0.46$ lb per pound of dry sludge and the gas production is 1.25 lb per pound of volatile matter destroyed (Section 26-6), the weight of gas produced is $0.46 \times 1.25 = 0.57$ lb per pound of dry sludge. The volume of methane, therefore, is $(0.72 \times 0.57)/(0.72 \times 0.0446 + 0.28 \times 0.1225) = 6.2$ cu ft per pound of dry sludge, and its fuel value $958 \times 6.2 = 5,900$ Btu. This is $100 \times 5,900/7,700 = 77\%$ of the fuel value of the dry solids.

26-8. Fertilizer Value. A large number of chemical elements are essential to the growth of the higher green plants. The most important ones are:

a. Carbon, oxygen, and hydrogen. They are secured freely from air and water.

b. Nitrogen, phosphorus, potassium, calcium, magnesium, sulfur, and iron. They are obtained in substantial quantities from the soil.

c. Boron, manganese, zinc, copper, and others. They are secured in minute quantities (trace-quantities) from the soil.

In addition, there are elements that, though not beneficial to plants, are valuable components of the food of man and animals: iodine, fluorine, chlorine, and sodium. The value of vitamins and hormones is not fully clarified as yet.

Sludges produced by waste waters contain many of these elements. In competition with commercial fertilizers, they are rated principally on their content of three fertilizing ingredients: nitrogen (N), phosphorus as phosphoric acid (P_2O_5), and potassium as potash (K_2O); but more particularly on the first two. Many sludges are also of value as soil builders or soil conditioners; i.e., as humus.

Nitrogen promotes the growth of leaf and stem. Phosphoric acid stimulates root growth, hastens ripening, and increases the resistance of plants to disease. Potash encourages vigorous growth, develops the woody parts of stems and the pulp of fruits, is needed for the formation of chlorophyll, and increases the resistance of plants to disease, but delays ripening. Humus improves the water-holding capacity and erosion resistance of soil, furnishes a useful substrate for soil bacteria that make nitrogen available as a plant food, and contributes in other ways to soil fertility.

The concentration of chemical fertilizer-ingredients is expressed as a percentage of the dry weight of the sludge. The nitrogen content of sludges produced by the treatment of domestic sewage varies in fresh sludges from 0.8 to 5% for plain-sedimentation solids (and proportionately less in sludges including chemical precipitating agents) to 3 to 10% for activated sludges. Trickling-filter humus contains 1.5 to 5% nitrogen, depending upon the length of storage of the sludge in the filter. Digestion reduces the nitrogen content of the sludge by 40 to 50%. The phosphoric acid content of most sewage sludges is small (1 to 3%), and that of potash even smaller (0.1 to 0.3%). For purposes of comparison, animal manures contain 1 to 4% of nitrogen and about the same percentage of phosphoric acid and potash. Animal tankage, blood, and fish scraps include 5 to 13% nitrogen and 0.5 to 14% phosphoric acid. Cottonseed meal and castor pomace are about as rich in nitrogen and phosphoric acid as animal tankage, blood, and fish scraps. In addition they contain 1 to 2% potash.

Nitrogen and humus content are ordinarily the determining factors in the utilization of sewage sludges. These sludges are applied directly, or they are used as a fertilizer base (other needed elements being added) or as commercial fertilizer fillers. Not all the nitrogen present in sewage sludges is in forms that are directly available to plants. Because of this, determinations normally include those for nitrate, ammonia, and organic nitrogen. Nitrate nitrogen is directly available, ammonia nitrogen after conversion in the soil to nitrate, and organic nitrogen after breakdown and oxidation in the soil (Section 19-4). Nitrate and ammonia nitrogen are water soluble. The availability of organic nitrogen is indicated by the yield in alkaline or neutral permanganate solutions of ammonia. However, true usefulness of fertilizers in meeting the needs of different crops can be fully determined only by field tests. The presence of grease in sludge is not agriculturally desirable.

The utilization of sewage sludges is circumscribed by the hygienic hazards involved. Pathogenic bacteria, viruses, protozoa (cysts), and worms (eggs) can survive sewage treatment and be included in the sludge. There, they will persist for long times and cannot be fully destroyed by digestion or air-drying. Although the numbers of surviving organisms decrease appreciably in the normal course of events, only heat-dried sludge can be considered fully safe.

26-9. Flow Characteristics. All sludges are but pseudohomogeneous materials. The greater the divergence in characteristics of the included solids (for example, fresh plain-sedimentation solids compared with digested solids or activated sludge or any of these solids compared with alum or iron flocs), the greater is their lack of homogeneity. The presence of solids imposes a self-cleaning requirement on the velocity of flow. The solids are of such a nature that plastic or pseudoplastic rather than viscous conditions of flow obtain so long as a significant amount of solid matter is present in the liquid. The hydraulics of sludge flow are complicated by the fact that most sludges are *thixotropic*, i.e., their plastic properties are changed by stirring and turbulence. There may also be a release of gases or air during flow. The friction losses engendered are controlled by the temperature of the sludge, its solids content, and the nature of the solid matter. As might be expected, friction increases with solids content and decreases with temperature. In general, laminar or transitional flow persists up to much higher velocities than for water. For thick sewage sludges, this type of flow has been observed to obtain up to 1.5 to 4.5 fps in pipes 5 to 12 in. in diameter. At turbulent velocities, all sludges behave more like water.

The following relationship[2] for laminar flow of plastic liquids in pipes is based on Poiseuille's equation for viscous liquids:

$$\frac{h}{l} = \frac{32}{g}\frac{v}{d^2}\left(\frac{\eta}{\rho} + \frac{1}{6}\frac{\tau_y d}{\rho}\frac{d}{v}\right) \qquad \text{26-10}$$

[2] For derivation of a similar equation, see: H. E. Babbitt and D. H. Caldwell, "Laminar Flow of Sludge in Pipes," *Univ. Illinois Bull.* 319 (1939).

Here h is the loss of head in terms of the sludge; l and d are respectively the length and diameter of the pipe; v is the velocity of the liquid; ρ is its density; and η and τ_y are respectively its coefficient of rigidity and shearing stress at the yield point. The terms enclosed in the parentheses are analogous to the kinematic viscosity of a Newtonian liquid and possess the same dimensions.[3] When the solids content becomes small, the shearing stress at the yield point becomes zero and the coefficient of rigidity merges into the dynamic viscosity of the liquid ν. If we call the plastic-flow factors evaluated in the parentheses the coefficient of kinematic rigidity ν_p, the Reynolds number becomes $\mathbf{R} = vd/\nu_p$, and laminar flow may be expected to occur below a value of $\mathbf{R}$ of about 2,000 as it does also in viscous flow.

Values of η/ρ and τ_y/ρ for a given sludge may be determined from the results of sludge-flow tests or by means of a Stormer viscometer. Reported magnitudes for thick (10% solids) digested sludges lie in the vicinity of $\eta/\rho = 5 \times 10^{-4}$ sq ft per sec and $\tau_y/\rho = 8 \times 10^{-3}$ (ft/sec)^2. Fresh activated sludge, being high in water content (98% or better), has no measurable shearing resistance, and its value of η/ρ is substantially equal to that of the kinematic viscosity of water.

Example 26-4. Estimate for a 10%-solids, digested, plain-sedimentation sludge and a velocity of 2 fps (1) the loss of head in 100 ft of 12-in. pipe and (2) the expected range of laminar flow.

1. Assuming that η/ρ is 5×10^{-4} sq ft per sec and τ_y/ρ is 8×10^{-3} (ft/sec)^2, the loss of head is given by Equation 26-10 as:

$$h = \frac{32}{32.2}\left(\frac{2}{1}\right)100\left[5 \times 10^{-4} + \frac{1}{6}(8 \times 10^{-3})\frac{1}{2}\right] = 0.23 \text{ ft}$$

2. At $\nu_p = 5 \times 10^{-4} + \frac{1}{6}(8 \times 10^{-3})/v$ and $\mathbf{R} = 2,000 = v \times 1/\nu_p$, $v = 2.2$ fps.

When the flow is turbulent, the loss of head of fairly homogeneous sludges (digested sludges and activated sludge) is increased by not more than 1% for each per cent of solids in the sludge. Fresh, plain-sedimentation sludge is transported at losses that are 1.5 to 4 times those of water. For the transportation of sand and gritty materials, see Section 24-12. Requisite self-cleaning velocities can be gaged from the formulations presented in Section 15-2. When the velocities of flow are too small, the heavier and larger solids may settle out and form obstructions to flow. This reduces the cross-sectional area of the conduit and increases the velocity until there is scour of the deposited material. Under extreme conditions, however, complete stoppage of pipes may be experienced. Rates of sludge withdrawal

[3] Cm^2/sec or stokes in the cgs system; sq ft/sec $= 1.075 \times 10^{-3}$ stoke.

from tanks must not be made so large that water will break through. Pipe sizes must be selected accordingly.

Sludge pumps, like sewage pumps, must contend with solids of all kinds. For small rates of discharge, plunger and diaphragm pumps and compressed-air ejectors are employed. For higher rates of flow, centrifugal pumps (generally more than 4 in. in size) provide sufficient clearance to prevent clogging. The use of air lifts is normally confined to activated sewage sludge. Then depth of submergence is generally held to twice the head.

26-10. Quantities of Sludge. Measurement of the quantities of sludge that are produced by different treatment processes is a routine undertaking of water-purification and waste-water treatment works. Estimates of expected quantities can be made also from analyses of the water or waste water and from a knowledge of the removals of solids effected by different treatment processes and the changes produced by different sludge-treatment processes. Coagulating and precipitating chemicals as well as added suspended substances (such as activated carbon) increase the amounts of sludge that must be disposed of. Striking a solids balance on a weight basis is straightforward. Estimates of the associated volumes must depend upon general information relating to the water or solids content of the sludge and to the proportions and specific gravities of the constituent volatile and fixed solids.

The nature and characteristics of the solids fractions in domestic sewage may be summarized briefly as follows:

1. *Plain sedimentation* (primary treatment). The fresh sludge is composed of substantially 100% of the "settleable solids" in the raw sewage. Digestion destroys about 67% of the volatile matter in the sludge, about 25% becoming fixed solids.

2. *Chemical coagulation* (primary treatment). The fresh sludge generally includes the precipitated chemicals and from 70 to 90% of the solids suspended in the raw sewage depending upon the quantity and effectiveness of chemical dosage. Ferric chloride of molecular weight 162.2, for example, is precipitated as ferric hydrate of molecular weight 106.9. Hence each mg/l $FeCl_3$ produces 0.66 mg/l $Fe(OH)_3$. Digestion of the resulting sludge produces changes in composition that are substantially like those for plain sedimentation, primary sludge.

3. *Trickling filtration* (secondary treatment). Fresh trickling-filter humus is composed of originally non-settleable fractions of solids in the applied sewage that have been rendered settleable by biological flocculation and precipitation and that have been modified subsequently by decomposition during storage in the filter. Fixed-solid residues of decomposing suspended and dissolved volatile matter are largely washed out into the effluent. The proportion of destruction and loss varies with the length of storage. Limits of 30% for low-rate operation and 10% for high-rate operation may be assumed. There results a recovery in the secondary sedimentation units of humus quantities equivalent to 50 to 60%

of the non-settleable suspended solids applied to low-rate filters, the range for high-rate filters being 80 to 90%. The humus is generally mixed with primary sludge for digestion, the proportionate changes in composition of the mixture being much the same as for plain sedimentation, primary solids.

4. *Activation* (secondary treatment). The controlling fraction of sewage solids in fresh, excess activated sludge is substantially the same as that in trickling filters. The subsequent destruction of transferred materials during formation and recirculation of the activated flocs is much like that observed in high-rate trickling filters. A value of 5 to 10% may be assigned to it, depending upon the proportion of sludge return. This proportion governs the length of time that the activated sludge remains in circulation. The recovery of excess sludge in secondary settling units may be estimated at 80 to 90% of the applied non-settleable suspended solids. The excess sludge is generally allowed to settle with the primary sludge, or the excess sludge is mixed with the primary sludge for treatment and disposal. Digestion brings about much the same proportionate changes in sludge composition as for plain sedimentation, primary solids.

Calculation of actual quantities of sludge rests fundamentally on the base values for the composition of domestic sewage given in Table 20-4 and the efficiencies of removal indicated in Table 21-11. Corresponding information must be obtained for other waste waters. The commonly observed solids content of domestic sewage sludges is shown in Table 26-2.

TABLE 26-2. Proportion of Solids in Domestic Sewage Sludges

Treatment process	*Condition of sludge*	*% Solids*
1. Plain sedimentation	a. Fresh—depending upon method of sludge removal	2.5–5
	b. Digested—wet	10–15
2. Chemical precipitation	a. Fresh—increasing in moisture with amount of chemical used	2–5
	b. Digested—wet	10
3. Trickling filtration	a. Fresh humus alone—depending upon length of storage in filter	5–10
	b. Fresh humus mixed with 1a	3–6
	c. Digested 3b—wet	10
4. Activation	a. Fresh *—as pumped	0.5–1
	b. Thickened *	1–2
	c. Digested *—alone (a or b)	2–3
	d. Fresh—settled with 1a	4–5
	e. Digested—with 1a	6–8

* If primary sedimentation is curtailed, suitable adjustments must be made.

Example 26-5. Estimate for an activated-sludge plant treating domestic sewage and including primary and secondary sedimentation: (*a*) the weight of dry sludge solids in lb per 1,000 persons per day and lb per mg of sewage; (*b*) the volume of wet sludge in cu ft per 1,000 persons per day and gal per mg of sewage. Find in each case the separate and combined amounts of fresh sludge and the amounts of digested sludge if the primary sludge is digested alone and in combination with the secondary sludge. Assume a sewage flow of 80 gpcd and specific gravities of 2.5 for fixed solids and 1.0 for volatile solids.

1. Primary sludge—fresh. From Table 20-4, the daily per capita production of fresh sludge is 54 grams, 39 grams (or 72.2%) being volatile and 15 grams (or 27.8%) fixed. Since 1 lb = 454 grams, the weight of dry solids is: $54 \times 10^3/454 = 119$ lb per 1,000 persons daily, or $119 \times 10^6/(80 \times 10^3) = 1,490$ lb per mg. By Equation 26-2, the specific gravity of the dry solids is: $s_s = \dfrac{250}{100 + 1.5 \times 72.2} = 1.20$. Assuming 5% solids in the wet sludge (Table 26-2), Equation 26-3 gives the specific gravity of the wet sludge as: $s = \dfrac{120}{95 \times 1.20 + 5} = 1.008$. The volume of the wet sludge is, therefore: $119 \times 10^2/(5.0 \times 62.4 \times 1.008) = 37.8$ cu ft per 1,000 persons daily, or $37.8 \times 10^6 \times 7.48/(80 \times 10^3) = 3,530$ gal per mg.

2. Excess activated sludge—fresh. From Table 20-4, the daily per capita production of non-settleable suspended solids is 36 grams, 26 grams being volatile and 10 grams fixed. Assuming that 7.5% of the weight of volatile solids is destroyed during activation and that 87.5% of the remaining weight of solids is captured in the excess sludge, the pertinent figures are: $0.875 \times 0.925 \times 26 = 21$ grams of volatile solids (70%), $0.875 \times 10 = 9$ grams (30%) of fixed solids, and $(21 + 9) = 30$ grams of total solids. Converting as in (1) the dry solids are: 66 lb per 1,000 persons daily, or 826 lb per mg.

Calculating the specific gravity of the solids, as in (1): the specific gravity of the dry solids is found to be $s_s = 1.219$. Assuming 1.5% solids in the wet sludge (Table 26-2), the specific gravity of the wet sludge then becomes $s = 1.002$ and the volume of the wet sludge, again as in (1), 70.4 cu ft per 1,000 persons daily, or 6,580 gal per mg.

3. Combined primary and excess activated sludge—fresh. By addition, the dry solids (grams per capita daily) are: $(54 + 30) = 84$ grams total, $(39 + 21) = 60$ grams (71.4%) volatile, and $(15 + 9) = 24$ grams (28.6%) fixed; and correspondingly $(119 + 66) = 185$ lb per 1,000 persons daily, or $(1,490 + 826) = 2,316$ lb per mg.

The specific gravity of the dry solids is: $s_s = 1.206$ and, assuming 4.5% solids in wet sludge (Table 26-2), that of the wet sludge is: $s = 1.007$. The resulting volume of wet sludge then becomes 65.4 cu ft per 1,000 persons daily, or 6,110 gal per mg.

4. Primary sludge—digested. Assuming that 67% of the volatile matter is destroyed, 25% being converted into fixed solids, the pertinent figures are: $(1 - 0.67)39 = 13$ grams of volatile solids (37%), $[15 + 0.25(39 - 13)] = 22$ grams of fixed solids (63%), and $(13 + 22) = 35$ grams of total solids, or 77 lb per 1,000 persons daily and 963 lb per mg.

The specific gravity of the dry solids is now: $s_s = 1.607$ and, assuming 13% solids in the wet sludge (Table 26-2), the specific gravity of the wet sludge is: $s = 1.052$. The resulting volume of wet sludge is then: 9.0 cu ft per 1,000 persons daily, or 840 cu ft per mg.

5. Combined primary and excess activated sludge—digested. Assuming that 67% of the volatile matter is destroyed, 25% being converted into fixed solids, the pertinent figures are: $(1 - 0.67)60 = 20$ grams of volatile solids (37.0%), $[24 + 0.25(60 - 20)] = 34$ grams of fixed solids (63.0%), and $(20 + 34) = 54$ grams of total solids, or 119 lb per 1,000 persons daily, and 1,490 lb per mg.

The specific gravity of the dry solids is now: $s_s = 1.607$ and, assuming 7.0% solids in the wet sludge (Table 26-2), the specific gravity of the wet sludge is: $s = 1.027$. The resulting volume of wet sludge is then: 26.5 cu ft per 1,000 persons daily, or 2,480 cu ft per mg.

26-11. Sludge-Digestion Units. As indicated in Section 26-2, the anaerobic decomposition, or digestion, of putrescible solids is either made a concurrent function of the settling tank or of a separate unit to which the settled solids are transferred for treatment. Septic tanks perform the first function, separate sludge digestion units, called sludge digesters, the second.

a. Septic Tanks. In their simplest form, septic tanks are single-storied, settling basins in which the sludge is held sufficiently long to undergo partial and possibly complete digestion. Single-storied septic tanks possess a number of faults both as sedimentation and as digestion units. Septic action cannot be confined to the sludge proper, and the overlying water is deprived of its freshness. Gas-lifted solids rise into the flowing water. If they reach the tank surface, they may accumulate as unsightly scum in which digestion is retarded. Otherwise they may escape into the effluent. For these reasons, the use of single-storied septic tanks is almost exclusively confined to small, generally residential, installations, where their bad features are counterbalanced by their simplicity (see Section 30-7).

b. Two-Storied Septic Tanks. The idea of separating the decomposing sludge from the flowing sewage in a two-storied structure was conceived by Travis and brought to perfection by Imhoff. In the Imhoff, or Emscher,[4] tank, the settling solids slide down the incline of a trough-shaped false bottom of the settling compartment and through slots at the apex of the trough into the underlying digestion compartment (see Figure 22-9). The slope of the false bottom is made as steep as possible ($\leqq 1.2$ vertical:1 horizontal) in order to keep it clean. The slots overlap (about 10 in.), or are otherwise trapped, to keep gases or solids that rise within the digestion compartment out of the settling compartment. However, a small interchange of liquid does occur. In the Travis tank, a larger interchange is encouraged by purposely conducting a portion of the flow through the digestion compartment supposedly to wash out substances that might retard digestion.

In order to distribute the sludge load as uniformly as possible within the sludge compartment of long tanks, arrangements are generally made to reverse the direction of flow from time to time. Companion

---

[4] Named after the Emscher District in which the Travis tank was modified.

flow of sewage through the sludge compartment is reduced by throwing walls across the digestion compartment. To promote longitudinal equalization of sludge accumulation by sludge movement, these walls are slotted at the bottom. Where two or more settling compartments are used in a wide tank (in order to keep the depth of these compartments reasonably small) lateral interchange of flow through the digestion compartment is prevented by the use of longitudinal, dividing walls that reach to the bottom of the tank. The resulting exterior and interior walls of the tank create a number of sludge compartments. For structural economy and ease of sludge withdrawal, these are given hopper bottoms (slope = 1 vertical to 1, or 2, horizontal). The sludge compartments may be dimensioned for temporary storage of the settling solids or for complete digestion of the solids before their removal. The compartments may indeed be made sufficiently large to store sludge for protracted periods of time during which digested sludge cannot be air-dried or otherwise disposed of. Because the winter periods are generally most unfavorable for sludge disposal, this type of storage is called winter storage. The term operational storage is perhaps preferable. Other forms of two-storied tanks that include the essential features of Imhoff tanks may also be elaborated.

The digested sludge can be withdrawn through pipes 8 in. or more in diameter reaching into the center of the sludge-compartment hoppers and discharging 4 to 5 ft below the water level of the tank. Sludge gases are allowed to escape to the atmosphere through vents at least 18 in. wide (for access) and of an area equal to about 20% of the total superficial area of the tank; or the gases are captured in gas collectors. The accumulation of scum and foam makes it necessary to provide a freeboard of at least 18 in. in open vents. Foaming is normally confined (1) to the initial breaking-in, or ripening, period of the digestion process and (2) to a few weeks of the spring following a long period of slow digestion associated with low temperatures. Otherwise foaming does not occur in the presence of an adequate amount of seeding (well-ripened) sludge, unless the waste water contains foaming substances such as some synthetic detergents used in household and industry.

The feature that detracts most from the economy of two-storied tanks, in which sludge is to be fully digested, is the relatively great depth of tank required. This is related to the impossibility of heating the digestion compartment effectively and the resulting large size of the lower story. Since two-storied septic tanks cannot compete economically with heated digesters, they are no longer employed in large installations. However, they are useful in plants of small size in which the even more undesirable features of single-storied septic tanks are to be avoided. Adequate operating supervision and attendance must then be provided. In such plants, digestion gases are very rarely collected or utilized.

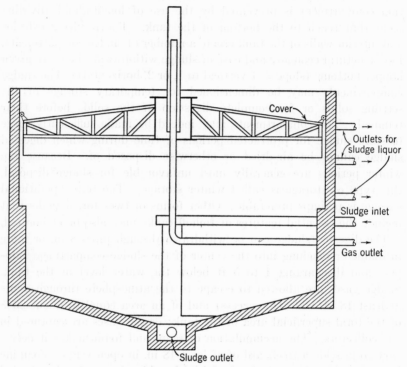

Figure 26-4. Sludge digester with floating cover.

c. Sludge Digesters. Almost any pattern of storage tank can serve as a sludge digester. Design is generally concerned with requisite digestion capacity and, in the most advanced designs, with gas collection and tank heating. Storage of gas and winter storage of digested sludge may be included in the tank itself, or they may be kept separate. A single tank or multiple tanks that operate in parallel or in series may be used. Unheated tanks from which gas is not to be collected and winter-storage tanks are generally left open. Otherwise digesters are covered (see Figure 26-4). Since sludge is admitted intermittently (one or more times a day) and withdrawn at less frequent intervals, the volume of sludge in the tank fluctuates. If gas is to be collected, the collection system must be protected against the entrance of air and the formation of explosive air-gas mixtures. Floating covers that rise and fall with the variations in gas and sludge volume will provide this protection. They may be elaborated into gas holders. Fixed covers should preferably be employed only if the gas-collection system includes a gas holder that acts as a balancing unit.

The incoming sludge generally enters sludge digesters at middepth, in order to mix it with the digesting sludge and secure the advantages of seeding and buffering. Digested sludge is withdrawn from the bottom under hydrostatic pressure. Excess water and sludge moisture released by digestion are called digester, sludge, or tank liquor. Outlets for this liquor are provided between the highest sludge-solids level and the lowest scum-solids level. Ordinarily this "neutral" zone begins 3 or 4 ft below the maximum flowline and can be tapped by 3 or 4 outlets placed about 2 ft apart vertically. Sampling pipes attached to these outlets identify the one that yields the clearest liquor at any particular time.

The accumulation of scum can be held in check in various ways: (1) by providing a large depth of tank relative to its surface area at flowline level, (2) by mechanical destruction of the scum with scum breakers, (3) by pumping tank liquor onto the scum or wetting it down with sprays of water, and (4) by recirculating gas into the digester bottom. A large depth-area ratio produces a high release of gas per unit area. This keeps the scum in motion and mixes the sludge in the tank. It also makes for good seeding and for rapid heat transfer in heated tanks. The proper dimensioning of digesters is, therefore, of importance.

Sludge liquor is the often troublesome by-product of sludge digestion. In single digesters, it occupies valuable space and is usually high in immediate BOD and suspended solids. To improve its quality, it must generally be subjected to treatment before disposal: either by itself (for example, by chemical coagulation, chlorination, and perhaps sand filtration) or in the general treatment works (by being returned to the plant influent, for example). The waste liquor from sludge filters and from sludge elutriators is much like sludge liquor and should be subjected to similar treatment before disposal.

A better grade of sludge liquor can be produced, and the design of high-temperature digestion units can be functionalized to a certain degree by placing two or more tanks in series (multistage digestion). The first or lead tank holds the sludge for a week or two during which the gas production of digesting solids is normally most active. This tank is equipped for heating and gas collection and sometimes also for stirring. No attempt is made to withdraw sludge liquor. The second tank then holds the sludge for the further length of time necessary to carry digestion to technical completion. The second tank may be left unheated but is generally equipped for gas collection. A floating roof, often elaborated into a gas holder that stores the gas from both tanks, is useful. In the second tank, the rate of digestion is relatively much slower than in the first. As a result, clear liquor separates from the sludge and can be withdrawn without much difficulty. The second tank may provide space for winter or operational storage, or this task may be assigned to a third tank which is then generally left uncovered.

26-12. Requisite Capacity of Digestion Tanks. The basic capacity of digestion tanks is a function of the sludge load, time required for digestion, and loss of sludge moisture (sludge liquor). Operational storage of gas and sludge (winter storage) is an added element. Capacities are expressed in a number of different ways, among them: cu ft of tank volume per capita; cu ft per lb of solids (on a dry basis) added daily; and cu ft per lb of volatile solids (on a dry basis) added daily. Operational or loading parameters are the reciprocals of these capacities. The basic per capita capacity is determined in accordance with the general rules laid down in Section 26-10. The assumption is generally made that the rate of loss of sludge moisture or reduction in sludge volume, like the rate of gasification (Figure 19-12) is substantially constant. It follows that progress of decomposition is parabolic and that the average difference in the volume of the fresh and digested solids is about $\frac{2}{3}$ the final difference. Formulated,

$$C = [V_f - \tfrac{2}{3}(V_f - V_d)]t \qquad\qquad 26\text{-}11$$

where C is the basic tank capacity in cubic feet per capita; V is the daily per capita volume of sludge in cubic feet (the subscripts f and d denoting the fresh and digested volumes respectively); and t is the time in days required for digestion. The latter is a function of tank temperature (Section 19-6) and can be estimated from Figure 19-12 for plain-sedimentation sludge. Characteristic values are summarized in Table 26-3. At a normal sewage temperature of 60 F, for example, the digestion period extends over 56 days.

TABLE 26-3.   Digestion Time of Plain-Sedimentation Sludge at Different Temperatures

Temperature, F	50	60	70	80	90	100	110	120	130	140
Digestion period, days	75	56	42	30	25	24	26	16	14	18
Type of digestion		——Mesophilic——					——Thermophilic——			

The design capacity includes, in addition to the basic space requirement, allowances for sludge liquor, scum, and gas. A factor of safety,
generally less than 2, is applied to the total.

Example 26-6. Find the basic capacity of (a) the sludge compartment of an
Imhoff tank in which plain-sedimentation primary sludge is to be digested at an
average temperature of 60 F and (b) a heated digestion tank in which (1) the
same sludge is to be digested at 90 F and (2) a mixture of primary and activated
sludge is to be digested also at 90 F. Assume the per capita volumes of sludge
calculated for domestic sewage in Example 26-5, namely, 37.8 cu ft of fresh and
9.0 cu ft of digested primary sludge and 65.4 cu ft of fresh and 26.5 cu ft of
digested combined sludge, all per 1,000 persons daily.

a. The digestion period at 60 F is about 56 days. Hence by Equation 26-11, the
required capacity of the Imhoff tank, is: $C = [37.8 - \frac{2}{3}(37.8 - 9.0)]56/1,000 = 1.04$
cu ft per capita.

b. The digestion period at 90 F is about 25 days.

1. Hence the required per capita digester capacity for primary sludge is: $C = 1.04$
$\times \frac{25}{56} = 0.46$ cu ft per capita.

2. For the combined primary and activated sludge, this must be raised to: $C' =$
$[65.4 - \frac{2}{3}(65.4 - 26.5)]25/1,000 = 0.99$ cu ft per capita. The assumption is made
in this connection that the mixed sludge digests as rapidly as the primary sludge.

Winter storage can be calculated from the volume occupied by the
fully digested sludge. The requisite capacity of small septic tanks
is discussed in Section 30-7.

26-13. Heat Requirements of Digestion Tanks. The heat supplied
to heated sludge-digestion tanks must be sufficient (1) to raise the
temperature of the incoming sludge to that of the tank; (2) to offset
the heat lost from the tank through its walls, bottom, and cover; and
(3) to compensate for heat lost in piping and other structures between
the source of heat and the tank. The amount of heat entering into
the digestion reactions and used up in the evaporation of water into
the sludge gases is so small that it need not be taken into consideration in engineering computations.

The specific heat of most sludges is substantially the same as that
of water. The heat loss Q through the walls, bottom, and cover of a
tank is a function of the temperature difference ΔT, the tank area A,
and the coefficient of heat flow C, or

$$Q = CA(\Delta T) \qquad\qquad 26\text{-}12$$

The value of C depends upon a number of things: motion of the fluids
(sludge inside and air or water outside of the tank), thickness of
specific portions of the tank and their relative conductance, and opportunities for radiation. For concrete tanks, rough over-all values
for C in Btu per sq ft per hr are 0.10, 0.15, and 0.30 for exposures to

dry earth, air, and wet earth respectively. For equal exposure of all parts of a digester, heat is conserved best if the tank geometry conforms as closely as possible to a sphere as structural economy will permit. The largest ratio of sludge volume to tank surface is thereby obtained. For unequal exposures, the portions through which the greatest losses per unit area occur should be kept at a minimum.

The heat requirements of digesters can be supplied in a number of different ways, among which the following are common: (1) the incoming sludge is heated outside of the tank in a countercurrent heat exchanger; (2) hot water is circulated through fixed or moving coils inside the tank; and (3) gas is burned under water or in a heater submerged in the sludge. Heat transfer is analogous to heat loss. For stationary heating surfaces, the coefficient of heat flow in British thermal units per square foot per hour has approximate values of 8 to 12 for sludge of ordinary thickness and 35 to 45 for thin sludge or water. Moving surfaces increase the heat flow to about 60 Btu per sq ft per hr. From submerged burners, there is direct absorption of the heat of combustion. Caking of sludge on the surface of heating units is controlled by keeping the temperature of the heating surface at less than 140 F and by moving the unit through the sludge or inducing motion of the sludge past it either mechanically or thermally.

Example 26-7. A cylindrical digester 20 ft in diameter is built of concrete and surrounded by dry earth or provided with equivalent insulation. The side walls are 16 ft high, and the roof rises 1 ft to a central, insulated gas dome and is exposed to the air. The bottom slopes 4 ft to a central sludge-withdrawal pipe. The daily weight of sludge added to the tank is 13,000 lb. Find: (a) the daily heat requirements of the tank when the temperatures of the incoming sludge, digesting sludge, earth, and air are 50, 90, 40, and 20 F respectively and the coefficient of heat flow is 0.20 Btu per sq ft per hr; (b) the required area of stationary heating coils through which water is circulated at an incoming temperature of 130 F and with a temperature drop of 10 F if the coefficient of heat flow is 10 Btu per sq ft per hr; and (c) the daily volume of heating water that must be circulated through the coils.

a. Heat requirements.

1. The area of the tank exposed to earth is: $\pi \times 20(16 + \frac{1}{2}\sqrt{10^2 + 4^2}) = 1,344$ sq ft. The area of roof exposed to air is: $\pi \times 10\sqrt{10^2 + 1^2} = 316$ sq ft.

2. Heat requirements of the incoming sludge: $Q = 13,000 \times (90 - 50) = 520,000$ Btu per day.

3. Exposure loss: $Q = 0.20 \times 24[1,344(90 - 40) + 316(90 - 20)] = 430,000$ Btu per day.

4. Total heat requirements: $Q = (520,000 + 430,000) = 950,000$ Btu per day.

b. Area of heating coils.

1. Average temperature of heating water: $(130 - 5) = 125$ F.

2. Area of coils: $A = 950,000/[24 \times 10(125 - 90)] = 113$ sq ft.

c. Recirculating water.
1. Temperature drop: 10 F = 10 Btu per lb.
2. Weight of water: 950,000/10 = 95,000 lb per day.
3. Volume of water: 95,000/8.34 = 11,400 gpd = 8 gpm.

The calculated heat requirements do not take into account possible losses between the heat source and the digester. The utilization of digester gas for heating purposes is considered in the next section of this chapter.

26-14. Utilization of Digester Gas. The normal composition, volume, and fuel value of sludge-digester gas have been discussed in Section 26-6. In addition to methane (combustible) and carbon dioxide (non-combustible), sludge gas always contains water vapor; occasionally hydrogen sulfide; and, more rarely, hydrogen (combustible) and nitrogen (inert). Hydrogen sulfide is an extremely toxic gas. Brief exposure (30 min or less) to concentrations as low as 0.1% by volume may terminate fatally. When hydrogen sulfide is burnt, sulfur dioxide, a very corrosive gas, may be formed. For use in gas engines with exhaust gas heaters, not more than 10 grains of hydrogen sulfide [5] should be present in 100 cu ft of gas (0.015% by volume).

The fuel value of sludge gas can be put to use in various ways both within treatment plants and for non-plant purposes. The following are common: (1) plant-heating purposes—digesters, incinerators, buildings, and hot-water supply; (2) plant-power production—pumping, air and gas compression, and operation of other mechanical equipment; (3) minor plant uses—gas supply to the plant laboratory for gas burners and refrigerators; and (4) motor fuel for municipal cars and trucks. The first two purposes are met by burning the gas (*a*) in a furnace or under a gas-fired hot-water or steam boiler or (*b*) in a gas engine equipped with water jacket and exhaust-gas heat exchanger. The third purpose may be accomplished by direct use of the gas under the available plant pressure or by the bottling of the gas. The fourth purpose involves the bottling of the gas under high pressure in steel containers.

Collection, storage, and utilization of sludge gas are economically justified only when the treatment works are of sufficient size to warrant skilled attendance. Gas storage is either included in the design of digesters, or separate holders are provided. The collection, storage, and distribution system must be kept under pressure at all times if the formation of explosive mixtures of gas and air is to be avoided.

---

[5] 1 lb = 7,000 grains, and 1 cu ft of H_2S weighs 0.095 lb.

Combustion of methane takes place as follows: $CH_4 + 2O_2 = CO_2 + 2H_2O$. Since air contains about 21% of oxygen by volume, at least $2/0.21 = 9.5$ cu ft of air are required to burn 1.0 cu ft of methane. If the gas contains 72% methane, therefore, at least $9.5 \times 0.72 = 6.8$ cu ft of air are required to burn the methane in 1.0 cu ft of digester gas. Explosive mixtures of methane and air are obtained over a range of 5.6 to 13.5% of methane by volume. Maximum flame speed occurs at 9.6%. Above 13.5% the mixture burns quietly after ignition. Violent explosions with loss of life have occurred in sewage works.

The operating, protecting, and regulating devices of gas collection and distribution systems include: (1) condensate traps and drains for water vapor; (2) flame traps that will prevent flash-backs from gas burners and engines; (3) pressure-regulating valves; and (4) waste-gas burners. Gas lines and their appurtenances must be protected against freezing, and all vents must terminate in the open. Gas storage may be effected without compressors under a head of 3 to 6 in. of water. The economical pressure for cylindrical and spherical pressure tanks is about 40 psig. Bottled gas is placed under a pressure of about 5,000 psig. Before being compressed, the gas may be passed through scrubbers to remove unwanted constituents: carbon dioxide, hydrogen sulfide, and water vapor.

Hot-water boilers are neither as efficient (about 60%) nor as trouble-free (sulfur dioxide corrosion) as steam boilers with heat exchangers for hot-water heating (about 80%). Gas engines that are equipped for hot-water utilization have a water-heating efficiency of about 50% and a direct power efficiency of 22 to 27% depending upon the engine load (half load to full load respectively). Conversion of gas-engine power into electrical power and use of electric motor-driven equipment entail a loss of about 25% of the engine power. For equal performance in automotive engines about 160 cu ft of sludge gas containing 72% of methane (110,000 Btu) may be substituted for a gallon of gasoline (122,000 Btu).

Example 26-8. If the 13,000 lb of sewage sludge added daily to the digester in Example 26-7 are assumed to contain 5% solids, 72.2% of which are volatile, and if 67% of the volatile matter is assumed to be destroyed in producing gas that is composed of 72% methane and 28% carbon dioxide by volume, estimate: (1) the volume of gas produced and its calorific power; (2) the power made available from a gas engine equipped with a waste-gas boiler for the purpose of heating the digester and from an electrical generator driven by the engine; and (3) the volume of gas that is available for plant purposes other than digester heating (950,000 Btu per day) or that must be burnt in a waste-gas burner.

1. Gas production. The volatile matter destroyed is: $13,000 \times 0.05 \times 0.722 \times 0.67 = 315$ lb. At 1.25 lb of gas per lb of volatile matter destroyed and the given

gas composition, the gas yield is: $1.25 \times 315/(0.72 \times 0.0446 + 0.28 \times 0.1225) =$ 5,930 cu ft daily, or $5,930 \times 958 \times 0.72 = 4.1 \times 10^6$ Btu daily.

2. Power of gas engine and generator. If the gas engine has a water-heating efficiency of 50%, the daily heat input of the engine must be $950,000/0.50 = 1.9 \times 10^6$ Btu. At 2,545 Btu per hp-hr and 0.7457 kw-hr per hp-hr, and at an engine efficiency of 25% and a generator and motor efficiency of 75%, the heat and gas consumed are: $2,545/0.25 = 10,000$ Btu per brake hp-hr, and $10^4/(958 \times 0.72) =$ 14.5 cu ft of gas per brake hp-hr. The engine power is then $(1.9 \times 10^6)/(24 \times 10^4)$ $= 8.0$ hp; and the electrical power $8.0 \times 0.75 \times 0.7457 = 4.4$ kw. [If all of the available gas were supplied to the engine, the engine and generator power would be raised $(4.1 \times 10^6)/(1.9 \times 10^6) = 2.2$ fold.]

3. Volume of excess gas. With $(4.1 \times 10^6 - 1.9 \times 10^6) = 2.2 \times 10^6$ Btu not used by the engine, the volume of excess gas is $(2.2 \times 10^6)/(0.72 \times 958) = 3,190$ cu ft daily.

As has been shown in Section 25-14, the energy requirements of diffused-air, activated-sludge units are about 550 hp-hr or 410 kw-hr per million cu ft of free air daily when the air pressure is 7 psig. It follows from the calculations given in Example 26-8, that 550×14.5 $= 8,000$ cu ft of gas are needed to deliver a million cu ft of air at a pressure of 7 psig by means of an engine-driven compressor or $8,100/0.75 = 10,700$ cu ft of gas when electric drive is employed. The flexibility of electrical operation, including the possibility of using purchased electricity when the gas supply fails, often justifies the installation of electrical equipment. Stand-by fuel must otherwise be provided in the form of municipal gas, gasoline, or oil. Stand-by equipment varies in accordance with the selected sources of energy.

Since 10^6 cu ft of air daily will treat about 1 mgd of sewage from 10^4 people in activated-sludge units, and since the gas production from primary solids and activated sludge is about 1.25 cu ft per capita, the available gas supply of 1.25×10^4 cu ft daily is normally sufficient to provide the necessary engine (and where wanted electrical) power and to keep the sludge digestion tanks at optimum mesophilic temperatures. Where primary treatment and sludge digestion are employed, the gas yield of about 1 cu ft per capita is normally more than adequate for the principal plant purposes.

Sludge Drying, Incineration, and Disposal

26-15. Chemical Conditioning and Elutriation. Coagulation of the solids dispersed in sludge (called chemical conditioning) increases the rate at which water can be removed from the sludge by filtration through cloth or by drying on sand beds.

a. Chemical Conditioning. Common conditioning chemicals for sewage sludge are listed in Table 26-4. In this table, all but lime

TABLE 26-4. Common Conditioning Chemicals for Sewage Sludge

Conditioning chemical	Chemical symbol	Molecular weight
Ferric chloride	$FeCl_3$	162.2
Chlorinated copperas	$FeSO_4Cl$	187.4
Ferric sulfate	$Fe_2(SO_4)_3$	399.9
Aluminum sulfate	$Al_2(SO_4)_3 \cdot 18H_2O$	666.4
Lime	CaO	56.1

are coagulating agents. Before these agents can combine with the solids fraction of the sludge, they must satisfy the coagulant demand of the liquid fraction of the sludge which is exerted by the alkalinity or bicarbonates (see Section 23-2). The alkalinities of digested sewage sludges are quite high; in some instances a hundredfold those of fresh sludges. As a precipitant of bicarbonates (see Section 23-3), lime may be substituted for the portion of the coagulant that combines with the liquid fraction. Lime does not form floc with this fraction; only a precipitate.

The coagulant or conditioner requirements of sludge are generally expressed as a percentage ratio of the pure chemical to the weight of the solids fraction on a dry basis. In accordance with what has been said, the requirements may be divided into two parts: (1) the liquid-fraction requirement and (2) the solids-fraction requirement. The liquid-fraction requirement is approximated closely by the stoichiometry of the idealized chemical reactions. The solids-fraction requirement is a matter of experience. For ferric chloride, Genter [6] has developed the relationship:

$$p_c = [1.08 \times 10^{-4} Ap/(1 - p)] + 1.6p_v/p_f \qquad 26\text{-}13$$

where A is the alkalinity of the sludge moisture in mg/l of $CaCO_3$, and p_c, p, p_v, and p_f are respectively the percentages of chemical ($FeCl_3$), moisture, volatile matter, and fixed solids in the sludge, all on a dry basis.[7] The term for the solids fraction ($1.6p_v/p_f$) is derived from

[6] A. L. Genter, "Computing Coagulant Requirements in Sludge Conditioning," *Trans. Am. Soc. Civil Engrs., 111,* 641 (1946).

[7] 1 mg/l $CaCO_3$ (100) combines with ($\frac{2}{3} \times 162.2/100$) = 1.08 mg/l of $FeCl_3$ (162.2) in accordance with the equation: $2FeCl_3 + 3Ca(HCO_3)_2 \rightleftarrows 2Fe(OH)_3 + 3CaCl_2 + 6CO_2$.

operating results for the vacuum filtration of ferric chloride treated sewage sludge. Since this term is a function of the volatile-matter content of the sludge, coagulant requirements can be reduced in magnitude by digestion of the sludge prior to coagulating it for dewatering. By contrast, the magnitude of the term for the liquid fraction $[1.08 \times 10^{-4} Ap/(1-p)]$ is greatly increased by digestion. It can be reduced either by the use of lime as a precipitant or by washing out a share of the alkalinity of the sludge with water of low alkalinity. This is called elutriation.

b. *Elutriation.* The elutriation of sludge can be carried out in single or multiple tanks by single or repeated washings, the wash water being used serially if desired. During washing, the sludge is kept in suspension by air or mechanical agitation. Serial use of wash water is called countercurrent elutriation.

If a total of R volumes of elutriating water with an alkalinity of W mg/l is added for each volume of moisture in the sludge, and the alkalinity of the sludge moisture before elutriation is A mg/l, the alkalinity of the elutriated sludge moisture E in mg/l can be found by striking a balance between the alkalinities entering and leaving the elutriating tank or tanks. The following examples in which the subscripts denote the sequence of operations will indicate the development of general formulations:

1. Multiple elutriation of sludge in a single tank. In this scheme, $1/n$th of the elutriating water is used in each washing operation. See (a) in Figure 26-5. Hence:

$$(1/n)RW + A = (1/n)RE_1 + E_1$$

$$(1/n)RW + E_1 = (1/n)RE_2 + E_2$$

$$\cdots \cdots \cdots \cdots \cdots \cdots \cdots \cdots$$

$$(1/n)RW + E_{n-2} = (1/n)RE_{n-1} + E_{n-1}$$

$$(1/n)RW + E_{n-1} = (1/n)RE_n + E_n$$

2. Countercurrent elutriation in multiple tanks. In this scheme, the clean wash water is introduced into the last tank which receives the partially elutriated sludge from the next to the last tank, the wash water from the last tank being used to wash the sludge coming into the next to the last tank. Proceeding serially in this manner (see Figure 26-5b), to the first tank:

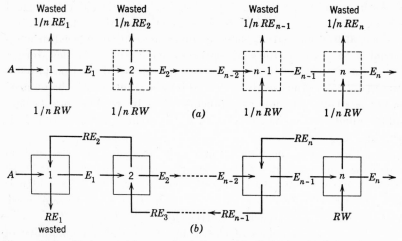

Figure 26-5. Sludge washing or elutriation. (a) Multiple elutriation in single tank. (b) Countercurrent elutriation in multiple tanks.

$$RW + E_{n-1} = RE_n + E_n$$
$$RE_n + E_{n-2} = RE_{n-1} + E_{n-1}$$
$$\cdot \cdot \cdot \cdot \cdot \cdot \cdot \cdot \cdot \cdot \cdot \cdot \cdot \cdot$$
$$RE_3 + E_1 = RE_2 + E_2$$
$$RE_2 + A = RE_1 + E_1$$

If we solve respectively for the alkalinity E_n of the final sludge and for the ratio of wash water to sludge R the following general equations are obtained:

1. Single tank, multiple elutriation (n stages):

$$E_n = \frac{A + W[(R/n + 1)^n - 1]}{(R/n + 1)^n} \qquad \text{26-14}$$

and

$$R = n\left[\left(\frac{A - W}{E - W}\right)^{1/n} - 1\right] \qquad \text{26-15}$$

2. Multiple tank, countercurrent elutriation (n tanks):

$$E_n = \frac{A + W(R^n + R^{n-1} \cdots + R)}{R^n + R^{n-1} \cdots + R + 1}$$

or

$$E_n = \frac{A(R - 1) + WR(R^n - 1)}{R^{n+1} - 1} \qquad \text{26 16}$$

and

$$(R^{n+1} - 1)/(R - 1) = (A - W)/(E - W) \qquad 26\text{-}17$$

The ratio of elutriating water to wet sludge commonly employed is about 2 to 1. Reduction in the necessary amounts of conditioning chemicals is reflected in increased heat values of the dried cake and reduced heat requirements for drying and incineration. The wash water is treated or disposed of along with digestion-tank and sludge-filter liquor.

Example 26-9. A digested sludge with 45% volatile solids on a dry basis and 90% moisture has an alkalinity of 3,000 mg/l. Find the percentage of ferric chloride that must be added to this sludge prior to vacuum filtration: (a) if the sludge is not elutriated, and (b) if the sludge is elutriated in two tanks by countercurrent operation in a ratio of 3 to 1 with water of 20 mg/l alkalinity. Find also (c) the elutriation ratio that will reduce the alkalinity of the sludge to 300 mg/l by countercurrent and two-stage elutriation.

a. Unelutriated sludge. By Equation 26-13: $p_c = (1.08 \times 10^{-4})\ 3{,}000(^{90}/_{10}) +$ $1.6(^{45}/_{55}) = 4.22\%$ of $FeCl_3$ on a dry-weight basis.

b. Elutriated sludge, countercurrent operation. By Equation 26-16: $E_2 = (3{,}000 \times$ $2 + 20 \times 3 \times 8)/26 = 250$ mg/l. By Equation 26-13: $p_c = (1.08 \times 10^{-4})$ $250(^{90}/_{10}) + 1.6(^{45}/_{55}) = 1.55\%$ of $FeCl_3$ on a dry-weight basis.

c. Elutriation ratio. By Equation 26-17: $(R^3 - 1)/(R - 1) = (3{,}000 - 20)/$ $(300 - 20) = 10.64$, or $(R^2 + R + 1) = 10.64$, whence $R = 2.64$ by countercurrent elutriation.

By Equation 26-15: $R = 2\left[\left(\dfrac{3{,}000 - 20}{300 - 20}\right)^{1/2} - 1\right]$, or $R = 4.54$ for two washings by multiple elutriation. This is 70% more wash water than is needed in the countercurrent operation.

26-16. Vacuum Filtration. The dewatering of sludge by filtration through cloth is an operation that has been taken over from the chemical industries. The art of dewatering solids has advanced from the

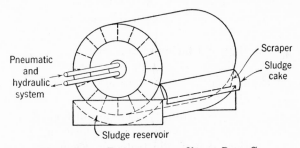

Figure 26-6. Drum vacuum filter. *Dorr Co.*

batch or discontinuous operation of chamber, or leaf, filter presses to the continuous, automatic operation of vacuum filters. Among these, the revolving-drum filter is most widely used (see Figure 26-6). The filtering medium is cotton or woolen cloth of suitable weight and weave. The cloth is stretched and wired over a supporting layer of copper mesh which covers the sides of the drum and overlies a series of cells running the length of the drum. These cells can be placed under vacuum or pressure. The drum revolves at a peripheral speed of 1 fpm or less. As it revolves, it passes through a reservoir of the sludge that is to be dewatered. A vacuum of sufficient magnitude (12 to 26 in. of mercury) is applied to the submerged cells (from 15 to 40% of the filter surface) to attach a mat of sludge of suitable thickness to the cloth. The emerging mat is placed under a drying vacuum of effective magnitude (20 to 26 in. of mercury), and the sludge liquor is drawn into the vacuum cells and drained from them for treatment and disposal with other sludge liquors. The dried cake is removed from the drum by a scraper and carried away for heat-drying, incineration, or disposal. If necessary, a slight pressure is applied to the cell of the drum which is just about to engage the scraper. This lifts the cake from the cloth and facilitates its removal.

The sludge cake is usually from $\frac{1}{16}$ in. to $\frac{1}{4}$ in. thick. Its solids content is as high as 32% for plain-sedimentation sludge (raw or digested) and as low as 20% for raw, activated sludge. Digested, activated sludge may be dewatered to about 25% solids content. Trickling-filter sludge and mixtures of different sludges span the gap. The solids content of dewatered, trickling-filter humus depends upon the length of storage of the sludge in the filter. The cake-producing capacity of vacuum filters varies ordinarily from 2 to 6 lb per sq ft per hr on a dry basis. Low yields are obtained with fresh, chemical sludge and activated sludge, high yields with digested, plain-sedimentation sludge. Filter speeds and vacuums are varied to suit operating conditions. Power requirements of drum filters and ancillary pneumatic and hydraulic equipment lie in the vicinity of $\frac{1}{8}$ hp per sq ft of filter area.

26-17. Heat Drying and Incineration. Sewage sludge is heat-dried to less than 10% moisture when it is to be sold as a commercial fertilizer. Heat-drying may also precede the use of sludge as a fuel for sludge-drying or other plant purposes. The dried sludge is then burnt in a furnace. Two types of rotary driers are in use: the kiln (direct-indirect) drier common to the lime and cement industry, and the cage-mill (flash-drier) system illustrated in Figure 26-7. Drying is promoted by adding a sufficient amount of previously dried sludge to the incoming cake to reduce the moisture of the mixture to about 50%. Drying gases are passed through the tumbling mixture in the cage mill and carry the dried dust to a cyclone in which it is separated from the transporting gases. The temperature of the drying gases is reduced from 1,000 F or higher to about 225 F. Volatilized-sludge odors are destroyed by incineration at about 1,250 F. The heat of the gases is conserved by countercurrent flow. In drying kilns, sludge movement is also countercurrent.

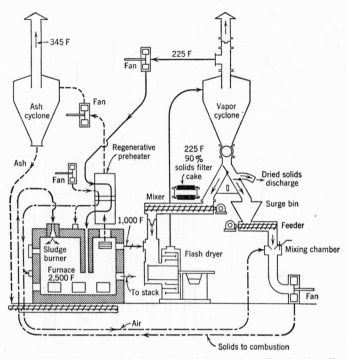

Figure 26-7. Heat-drying and incineration of filter cake. *Combustion Engineering Co.*

Spray-drying of sludge in a heated vacuum chamber has been tried with indifferent success.

Sludge-burning furnaces are operated at temperatures of about 2,500 F. The furnace gases are passed through a regenerative preheater in which air and the recirculated exhaust gases from the flash-drier are brought up to temperature before they are introduced respectively into the drying element and the furnace. Fly ash is removed from the furnace gases in a cyclone.

In the multiple-hearth incinerator shown in Figure 26-8, filter cake is fed onto the topmost hearth and moved (rabbled) from hearth to hearth by plows or teeth attached to horizontal, hollow (for air cooling) arms branching from a vertical, central, hollow shaft. The sludge cake loses moisture, ignites, burns, and cools. Hearth temperatures rise to a maximum in the center of the incinerator. The exhaust gases are passed through a preheater or recuperator for the purpose of heating the air blown into the furnace to support combustion. The cold-

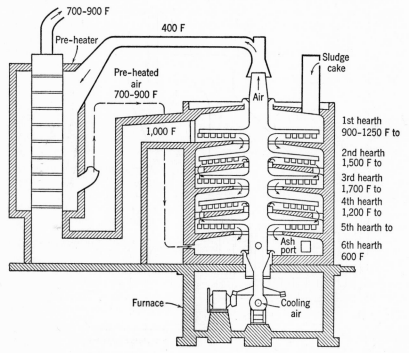

Figure 26-8. Multiple-hearth furnace for the incineration of filter cake. *Nichols Herreshoff Corp.*

air intake is through the hollow shaft to which the rabble arms are attached.

Heat requirements are determined by the temperature of the sludge and its moisture content and by the efficiency of the furnace. If the temperature of the sludge is 60 F, the heat requirements are 1,124 Btu per lb of moisture. Furnace efficiency usually varies between 45 and 70% in terms of total heat recovery (including credits on stack gas and latent heat of evaporation) and total heat input. Multiple-hearth furnaces have a combined efficiency of evaporation and incineration of about 55%. Sludge cake produced by the vacuum filtration of chemically conditioned, raw, plain-sedimentation sludge and of mixtures of it with fresh, trickling-filter or activated sludge will ordinarily supply sufficient heat for self-incineration. Digested sludge, on the other hand, is almost always inadequate in heat value to support its own destruction by burning. Auxiliary fuel must be used. Sludge-digester gas may serve this purpose.

Example 26-10. An activated-sludge plant produces 7,000 gpd of excess activated sludge from 1 mgd of sewage. The sludge contains 1.5% solids of which 70% are volatile on a dry basis. In conditioning the sludge for dewatering on a vacuum filter, 6% of $FeCl_3$ on a dry basis is added. Find (a) the required vacuum filter area and (b) the auxiliary heat required to incinerate the filter cake. The specific gravity of the wet sludge may be taken as 1.002.

a. Area of vacuum filter. The daily weight of dry solids is:

$$7,000 \times 8.34 \times 1.002 \times 1.5 \times 10^{-2} = 880 \text{ lb}$$

Assuming that each per cent of $FeCl_3$ increases the dry solids in the ratio of the molecular weight of $Fe(OH)_3$ to that of $FeCl_3$, or 106.8 to 162.2, the added chemical increases the weight of sludge by 0.66% for each per cent of ferric chloride. Hence the additional weight is $6 \times 0.66 \times 880/100 = 35$ lb. Assuming an allowable filter loading of 2.5 lb per sq ft per hr, the required filter area is then found to be $(880 + 35)/(24 \times 2.5) = 15.2$ sq ft.

b. Auxiliary heat for incineration. By Equation 26-9, the fuel value of the filter cake is:

$$Q = 107 \left(\frac{100 \times 70}{100 - 6 \times 0.66} - 5 \right) \left(\frac{100 - 6 \times 0.66}{100} \right) = 7,000 \text{ Btu per lb}$$

If the filter cake contains 20% solids and the efficiency of evaporation and incineration is 55%, the heat requirements are $1,124(100 - 20)/(20 \times 0.55) = 8,100$ Btu per lb. Auxiliary heat must, therefore, be provided in an amount of $(880 + 35)(8,100 - 7,000) = 1.0$ million Btu per day.

26-18. Air-Drying. Under favorable climatic conditions (dryness and warmth), well-digested sludge will dry in a week or two when it is run onto a porous bed to a depth of 8 to 12 in. No odor troubles are encountered. The drying of fresh sludge, on the other hand, gives rise to bad odors, and the sludge will not dry satisfactorily in layers of reasonable thickness. Therefore, air-drying is more or less confined to well-digested sludges.

Drying beds usually consist of graded layers of gravel or crushed stone beneath 4 to 6 in. of filter sand (see Figure 26-9). Agricultural tile pipes or sewer pipes laid with open joints serve as underdrains in much the same way as in intermittent sand filters (Section 25-2). The beds are subdivided to meet plant-operating conditions. Their width is so chosen that the vehicle used for removing the dried sludge can be loaded conveniently. Common values for small plants are 20 ft or less. The length is generally held below 100 ft. This is the distance sludge may be expected to flow from a single outlet when the surface slope of the bed is 0.5% or less. Concrete posts and reinforced-concrete slabs or cypress planks rising about 12 in. above bed level confine the sludge to the bed and its subdivisions.

Glass enclosures of the green-house variety or sheds similar to the platform sheds of railroad stations will protect the sludge against rain. If the enclosures are properly ventilated, the number of dryings per year can be increased by 33 to 100%. In the northern part of the United States, about 5 dryings of 8 in. of wet digested sludge are

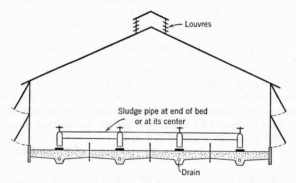

Figure 26-9. Glass-covered sludge-drying beds. *After Imhoff and Fair.*

feasible per year on open beds. Bed-dried, digested sludge contains about 40% solids. Its volume is about half that of the wet sludge. The sludge is removed by hand-forking or by mechanical, sludge loaders or strippers.

In air-drying, moisture is lost to the atmosphere by evaporation and to the bed by percolation. Both evaporation and percolation are important.

Example 26-11. If the production of digested plain-sedimentation solids is 9 cu ft per 1,000 persons daily (Example 26-5), find (*a*) the area of open sludge-drying bed, in sq ft per capita, that must be provided in the northern United States and (*b*) the volume of sludge cake, in cu yd per capita, that must be removed annually.

a. Area of bed. Assuming 5 dryings of sludge 8 in. in depth annually, the bed area is $(9 \times 365)/(5 \times 1,000 \times \frac{8}{12}) = 1.0$ sq ft per capita. This is a common figure for open beds in the northern United States.

b. Volume of sludge cake. Assuming 50% reduction in volume of sludge during drying, the volume of dried cake becomes $0.5 \times 9 \times 365/(27 \times 1,000) = 6 \times 10^{-2}$ cu yd per capita annually.

26-19. Sludge Handling and Disposal. The flow characteristics of wet sludge have been described in Section 9 of this chapter. Both free-flow and pressure conduits are employed. Partially dewatered sludge (sludge paste or filter cake) can be transported on belt conveyors. Granular (heat-dried) sludge can be moved pneumatically or by belt or screw conveyors. All types of sludge can be handled in industrial cars and suitably constructed automotive equipment.

Sludge may be disposed of in any one of the states in which it is produced, i.e., as wet sludge (both raw and digested), filter cake, sludge cake from air-drying beds, and heat-dried sludge. Alum and iron

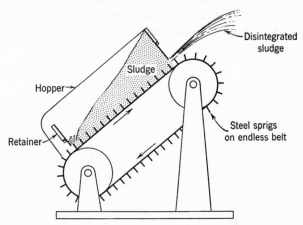

Figure 26-10. Sludge disintegrator. *Royer Co.*

precipitates from water-purification plants may be discharged into sewers. If they are to be disposed of in streams of small size, they should preferably be lagooned before discharge. Lagoons are natural depressions in the ground, or earth basins excavated for that purpose. They may or may not be provided with overflows and underdrains. Heavy precipitates of calcium and magnesium from water-softening plants may be partially dewatered and used as fill for low-lying lands. Their possible reclamation is discussed in Section 23-9. Wet, sewage sludge may be pumped onto land and plowed under. Digested sludge is more suitable for this purpose than raw sludge. In favorable circumstances, sewage sludges may be discharged into water. Seacoast communities may transport either wet or partially dewatered fresh or digested sludge to dumping grounds at sea. Specially designed sludge tankers and scows or barges are used for this purpose. Wet, digested sludge may be discharged into large streams (more particularly in times of flood runoff) without creating a nuisance, or it may be pumped to deep-lying and hydraulically active portions of tidal estuaries. Sludge lagoons may be used both for the digestion of raw sludge and for the storage and consolidation of digested sludge. The odors produced by raw sludge must be taken into cognizance in this connection. Low-lying land can be filled by lagooning or by the dumping of filter-cake or air-dried sludge. Inclusion of partially dewatered sludge or sludge cake in sanitary land fills is a possibility. Air-dried sludge as well as filter cake may be hauled away by farmers to serve as a soil builder. Disintegration of the sludge for this purpose is of some value (see Figure 26-10). As described in Section 26-8, dried sludge is commonly used as a fertilizer or fertilizer base, or it is incinerated. The ash from incinerators can be disposed of as fill, or it can be dumped at sea.

DISINFECTION, DESTRUCTION OF AQUATIC GROWTHS, AND REMOVAL OF ODORS AND TASTES

27-1. General Considerations. The safety and palatability of water often hinge upon the elimination or destruction of two groups of living organisms: (1) the pathogenic bacteria and other microorganisms that may infect man through his use of contaminated water and (2) the algae and related water blooms that may render water esthetically unfit for human consumption. The creation or intensification of odors and tastes is, at times, associated with the destruction of these organisms. A discussion of the removal of odors and tastes from water is, therefore, made a part of the present chapter. For convenience in presentation, attention is given, furthermore, to other matters that are allied to the methods of treatment employed, or to the objectives that are to be attained. Among these matters are: the destruction of water weeds in reservoirs, streams, and oxidation ponds; the destruction of undesirable growths in water conduits, water-purification plants, waste-water conduits, and waste-water-treatment works; the control of odors in sewers and sewage-treatment plants; the reduction in BOD that may result from disinfection; and the enhancement of treatment efficiency produced by agents such as chlorine.

Disinfection

27-2. Definitions and Requirements. Pathogenic bacteria and other potentially infective microorganisms are *removed* from water and waste waters in varying degree by most of the conventional treatment processes that have been discussed in the preceding chapters of this book. These organisms are also *destroyed* in significant numbers in the course of water treatment. A few examples of removal and destruction follow:

1. Physical removal: sedimentation; chemical coagulation; chemical precipitation; filtration; and biological flocculation and precipitation (Chapters 22 to 25).

793

2. Natural die-away: storage of water for a protracted period of time before, during, and following treatment; and storage of sludge, in which are concentrated the organisms that have been removed from suspension (Chapters 26 and 28).

3. Destruction by predators: [1] natural purification of polluted waters; filtration processes in which biological activity is significant (slow sand filtration, intermittent sand filtration, and irrigation); biological flocculation and precipitation; and anaerobic decomposition of sludge (Chapters 24 to 26 and 28).

4. Destruction by chemicals introduced for purposes other than disinfection: caustic alkalinity resulting from the lime softening of water (Chapter 23).

Although polluted waters are rendered less infective and possibly noninfective by such treatment methods, the term *disinfection* is used in practice in a more specific sense to describe the more unique treatment processes, such as the boiling of water, or the chlorination of water, that have as their sole objective the killing of infective organisms. The term *sterilization* is not synonymous but implies the total destruction of all living things in the medium treated. The preparation of sterile water is generally confined to medical practice.

To be of service, water disinfectants must meet the following general requirements: (1) they must be able to destroy the kinds and numbers of pathogenic organisms potentially present in the water or waste water that is to be disinfected; (2) they must be able to accomplish their task within the time available for disinfection, within the range of water temperatures encountered, and within the fluctuations in composition, concentration, and condition of the water or waste water experienced; (3) their use must not render the water toxic or unpalatable to the consumer or otherwise objectionable for the purposes that the water is to serve; and (4) they must be obtainable at reasonable cost, safe and easy to handle, and conveniently applicable to the water that is to be disinfected. It is desirable, furthermore, (1) that the disinfecting agent be of such a nature that its strength or concentration in the treated water can be quickly determined, and (2) that, where necessary, the agent will persist within the treated water in sufficient concentration to provide "residual" protection against recontamination.

Because of the limitations of available analytical techniques, determination of the efficiency of disinfection is measured, in all but experimental studies, by the reduction of indicator organisms (usually coliform organisms) to a concentration that, by inference, is acceptable for the water that is subjected to disinfection. In laboratory ex-

---

[1] Antibiotic substances produced by living organisms may also play a part. The presence of antibiotic factors in algal growths and in activated sludge has been reported.

periments, either pure cultures of pathogens or of organisms harvested from carriers or cases of the disease under study are employed. Use of the latter is to be preferred, unless comparative experiments show the cultured organisms to be equally resistant. A tie-in of results obtained by concurrent exposure of indicator organisms, such as *Esch. coli*, will furnish useful information on what may be expected in disinfection practice.

27-3. Means of Disinfection. The disinfection of water for general sanitary purposes can be accomplished by many different means. A classified list of the more common ones is given below:

1. HEAT. Raising water to its boiling point and holding it there for 15 to 20 min will disinfect it. Since no important water-borne diseases are caused by spore-forming bacteria, or other heat-resistant organisms, this is a safe practice which is often resorted to as an emergency measure. Maintenance of the time-temperature relationships that have been found to be satisfactory for the pasteurization of milk should be equally useful.

2. LIGHT. Exposure of water to sunlight for a protracted period of time is a natural means of disinfection. Irradiation of water by ultraviolet light of suitable wave length offers an intensified and controllable engineering means. Disinfection is then accomplished by exposure of water in thin films to the emanations from mercury-vapor lamps. These lamps must be encased in quartz or in special glass envelopes that are transparent to the intense and destructive, invisible light of 2,537 angstrom units (A) emitted by the mercury-vapor arc. To insure disinfection, the water must be sufficiently free from suspended matter and other substances that might shade the organisms against the light. Time and intensity of exposure must also be adequate.[2] Other forms of radiant energy, too, are destructive to living organisms, but they have not yet found engineering application.

3. CHEMICAL DISINFECTANTS. Exposure for an adequate length of time to chemicals of the following kinds in adequate concentration will disinfect water:

a. *Oxidizing chemicals.* For the disinfection of water the following are important: (1) The halogens—chlorine, bromine, and iodine—released in suitable form from suitable.sources; and (2) other oxidizing agents such as potassium per-

---

[2] Radiant energy occurs in discrete units or quanta $E = kc\lambda$, where E is the energy of a single quantum in ergs, k is Planck's constant (6.62×10^{-27} erg-sec), c is the velocity of light (3×10^{10} cm/sec), and λ is the wave length of radiation in cm. A germicidal unit is defined as 100 milliwatts per square centimeter for radiations of wave length 2,537 A. The relative effectiveness of other radiations may be identified accordingly.

The attenuation of radiant energy is given by Equation 17-14. The coefficient of attenuation of ultraviolet light of 2,537 A varies from 0.03 cm^{-1} for filtered waters to 0.2 cm^{-1} for unfiltered waters supplied to municipalities in North America. Exposures of *Esch. coli* to 3,000, 1,500, and 750 milliwatt-sec/cm² are reported to produce 99.99, 99, and 90% kills respectively.

About 2% of the incident radiation of 2,537 A from a source of ultraviolet light is reflected at the water surface. The reflectivity of aluminum is 90%. (Lewis R. Koller, *Ultraviolet Radiation,* John Wiley & Sons, New York, 1952.)

manganate and ozone. Of the halogens, liquid chlorine and a number of chlorine compounds have been found to be most generally and most economically useful. Bromine (Br_2) has been employed on a limited scale for the disinfection of swimming-pool water, and iodine has been used for the disinfection of small quantities of drinking water. Elemental iodine (I_2) may be released from tablets of tetraglycine hydroperiodide for such disinfection. Potassium permanganate and ozone have a more limited use because of cost, ozone, in addition, because of difficulty of production and application to water. Ozone is particularly effective in the destruction of odors. It also bleaches color. The oxidizing capacity (Table 18-6) of a compound is not necessarily a measure of its disinfecting efficiency. Hydrogen peroxide, for example, is a strong oxidant but a poor disinfectant.

b. Metal ions. The ions of silver are notably destructive in minute concentrations,[3] but long periods of exposure are required, and the use of silver is costly. Copper ions are strongly algicidal (Section 27-14) but only weakly bactericidal.

c. Alkalies and acids. Pathogens will not survive in water that is highly alkaline or highly acid, e.g., at very high or very low pH values. As previously mentioned, destruction of living organisms by caustic lime may be incidental to water softening by lime.

d. Surface-active chemicals. Of these, the cationic detergents are strongly destructive, the anionic detergents only weakly so. The neutral detergents occupy an intermediate position. The disinfecting powers of the detergents have been used only selectively in wash waters and rinse waters. Their toxicity is yet to be fully explored.

For general municipal and industrial water needs, but one of the means included in this list (chlorination) is both of proved efficiency and economy, and but one more (heat) can be resorted to with assurance of success through individual action in times of emergency (when "boil-water orders" are issued by public authorities). Because chlorine and some of its compounds meet the general requirements for disinfection so well, and because they are used almost to the exclusion of other disinfecting agents, the discussion of disinfection which is to follow will be concerned very largely with the principles and practice of chlorination.

27-4. Theory of Disinfection. The disinfection of water and waste waters is concerned almost wholly with the destruction of single-celled organisms: bacteria, protozoa, and viruses; more particularly bacteria. This explains, in part, the success that can be attained in chemical disinfection by the addition of disinfecting substances in relatively minute amounts (fractions of a milligram per liter of free chlorine, for example). The fact that the required concentration of disinfectant is small and that much of it is normally inactivated in the course of disinfection or prior to use of the disinfected water, explains,

[3] As low as 15 $\mu g/l$ (micrograms per liter, or closely parts per billion).

furthermore, why suitably disinfected water can be ingested with impunity by man and the higher animals and why less highly organized living things, such as fish in fishbowls supplied with chlorinated water, are also not harmed.

Green and Stumpf [4] have shown that disinfecting chlorine compounds react with certain of the enzymes that are essential to the metabolic processes of living cells and that death results from the inactivation of these key substances. There are reasons for assuming, therefore, that destruction of these essential links in the life requirements of living cells is the primary action of disinfectants, even when a radical process, such as heat, eventually coagulates the entire protoplasmic content of the cell. Since the enzymes involved are created within the cell plasm, disinfection proceeds theoretically in two steps: (1) penetration of the cell wall by the disinfectant and (2) reaction of the cell enzymes with the disinfectant.

In terms of the gross effects that generally govern engineering practices, the factors that establish the efficiency of disinfection are:

1. The nature of the organisms to be destroyed and their concentration and condition in the water to be disinfected. Non-spore-forming bacteria are less resistant to disinfection than are spore-forming bacteria. But spore formers, as previously stated, are, fortunately, of little sanitary significance. Among the bacteria of enteric origin *Esch. coli* appears to be somewhat more resistant than the pathogenic groups. As a result, it is a useful test organism. The cysts of the enteric pathogenic protozoön *E. histolytica* are known to be quite resistant, but little is known about the resistance of the viruses. Concentration of organisms enters into the problem of chemical disinfection only when the number of organisms present in a given volume of water is sufficiently high to compete for the disinfectant. Clumping of bacteria, such as the staphylococci, protects the cells inside the clump.

2. The nature and concentration of the disinfectant employed in terms of the products that it releases when it is placed in the water to be disinfected. As will be shown later, for example, chlorine and many of its compounds used in water disinfection may form in water one or more different substances of varying disinfecting efficiency.

3. The nature of the water to be disinfected. Suspended matter will shelter embedded organisms against chemical disinfection and destructive light rays. Organic matter will use up oxidizing chemicals. Other substances will react with chemical disinfectants and change their structure. The resulting compounds may be less efficient and even innocuous.

4. The temperature of the water to be disinfected. The higher the temperature, the more rapid is the kill.

5. The time of contact. The longer the time, the greater is the opportunity for destruction. In pure water of a given temperature, destruction of a given

[4] D. E. Green and P. K. Stumpf, "The Mode of Action of Chlorine," *J. Am. Water Works Assoc.*, *38*, 1301 (1946).

species of organisms by a given species of disinfectant is a time-concentration process. When light is the disinfectant, its intensity at the cell surface is the concentration factor. When heat is the disinfectant, the temperature of the water is itself a measure of the concentration of the disinfectant.

27-5. Kinetics of Disinfection. Under ideal conditions, all cells of a single species of organism will be equally susceptible to a single species of disinfectant; both cells and disinfectant will be uniformly dispersed in the water; the disinfectant will remain substantially constant in concentration throughout the period of contact; and the water will contain no interfering substances. The rate of disinfection, under ideal conditions, is then a function of the following variables: (a) the time of contact; (b) the concentration of the disinfectant; (c) the number of organisms; and (d) the temperature of the water.

 $a.$ *Time of Contact.* The effect of contact time on the killing of organisms by disinfectants is generally expressed in terms of Chick's Law.[5] This states that the number of organisms destroyed, y, per unit of time is proportional to the number of organisms remaining, N, the initial number being N_0. Hence

$$dy/dt = k(N_0 - y) \qquad 27\text{-}1$$

where k is the coefficient of proportionality or the rate constant with dimension $[t^{-1}]$. Integration between the limits $y = 0$ at $t = 0$ and $y = y$ at $t = t$ gives the equation

$$\log_e \frac{N_0 - y}{N_0} = \log_e \frac{N}{N_0} = -kt \qquad \text{or} \qquad \frac{N}{N_0} = e^{-kt} \qquad 27\text{-}2$$

A plot of $\log N/N_0$ against t, therefore, traces a straight line with slope $-k \log e = -k'$ and intercept 1 (or 100%) at $t = 0$. When $kt = 1$ or $k't = 0.4343$, the rate of survival, or mean lethal dose, is 0.368.

Departures from Chick's Law are not uncommon, even when the conditions of test are as nearly ideal as possible. The rate of kill, instead of being constant, may increase or decrease with time. An increase can be explained in at least two ways: (1) as a combination of slow diffusion of chemical disinfectants through the cell wall and a rate of killing dependent upon the rising concentration of disinfecting material inside the cell; and (2) on the assumption that a lethal number of centers in the organism must be reached by the disinfectant. A linear relation may then be created by plotting $\log N/N_0$ against t^m, or of $\log \log N/N_0$ against t. The exponent m will have a value

[5] Harriet Chick, "Investigation of the Laws of Disinfection," *J. Hygiene, 8*, 92 (1908).

greater than unity (see Figure 27-1). A decrease is generally explained as being due to variation in resistance of different cells within the same culture of organisms. However, a decline in the concentration of the disinfectant as well as other interfering factors may be responsible. Linear relations may result when, as before, N/N_0 is plotted functionally against t. However, other formulations are also possible (see Equation 28-1).

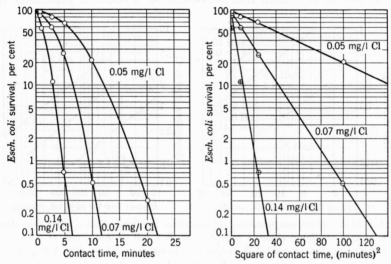

Figure 27-1. Length of survival of *Esch. coli* in pure water at pH 8.5 and a temperature of 2 to 5 C.

b. Concentration of Disinfectant. Commonly observed changes in disinfecting efficiency with concentration of the disinfectant can be expressed mathematically by the equation

$$c^n t_r = \text{Constant} \qquad\qquad 27\text{-}3$$

Here, c is the concentration of the disinfectant; t_r is the time required to effect a constant percentage kill of the organisms to be destroyed; and the exponent n is generally called the coefficient of dilution. Values of $n > 1$ indicate that the efficiency of the disinfectant decreases rapidly as it is diluted; values of $n < 1$ that the time of contact is more important than the dosage. When $n = 1$, concentration and time are of equal weight.

Equation 27-3 is purely empirical. It plots as a straight line on double logarithmic paper, the slope of the line being $-1/n$ (see Figure 27-2).

c. Concentration of Organisms. No significant difference is generally observed between the killing of high and low concentrations of organisms. Where a difference is observed, at very great differences in concentration of cell substance, for example, it can be formulated as

$$c^p/N_r = \text{Constant} \qquad\qquad 27\text{-}4$$

Here c is again the concentration of the disinfectant; N_r is the concentration of organisms that is reduced by a constant percentage in

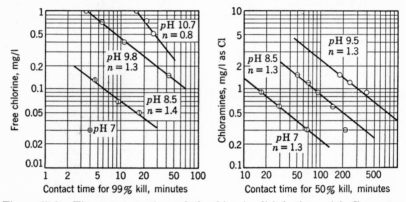

Figure 27-2. Time-concentration relationships in disinfection. (*a*) Concentration of free available chlorine required for 99% kill of *Esch. coli* at 2 to 5 C. (*b*) Concentration of combined available chlorine required for 50% kill of *Esch. coli* at 2 to 5 C.

a given time; and p is the concentration exponent of the disinfectant. Like Equation 27-3, this equation is merely an expression for the correlation of observations.

d. Temperature of Disinfection. If either the rate of diffusion through the cell wall or the rate of reaction with an enzyme determines the rate of disinfection, its variation with temperature is identified most conveniently by the van't Hoff-Arrhenius equation (Equation 18-73) written in the following form:

$$\log \frac{t_1}{t_2} = \frac{E(T_2 - T_1)}{2.303RT_1T_2} = \frac{E(T_2 - T_1)}{4.575T_1T_2} \qquad 27\text{-}5$$

The symbols T_2 and T_1 stand for two temperatures (normally in degrees Kelvin) between which the rates are to be compared; t_1 and t_2 are the times required for equal percentages of kill to be effected at these temperatures and at a fixed concentration of disinfectant; E is the activation energy (normally in calories) and a constant characteristic of the reaction; [6] and R is the gas constant (1.99 cal per deg C, for example). When $T_2 - T_1 = 10$, the ratio t_1/t_2, called Q_{10}, is approximately related to E, in the vicinity of 20 C, as follows (Equation 18-76):

$$\log Q_{10} = \log t_a/t_b = E/39,000 \qquad\qquad 27\text{-}6$$

Here t_a and t_b are the times required for equal percentages of kill at temperatures T_a and T_b that are 10 C apart.

The temperature dependence of the disinfecting action of aqueous chlorine and chloramines (Sections 27-6 and 27-7) in the destruction of *Esch. coli*, computed from the work of Butterfield et al.,[7] is shown in Table 27-1.

TABLE 27-1.   Temperature Dependence of the Disinfecting Action of Aqueous Chlorine and Chloramines in the Destruction of *Esch. coli* in Clean Water

Type of chlorine	pH	E, cal	Q_{10}
Aqueous chlorine	7.0	8,200	1.65
	8.5	6,400	1.42
	9.8	12,000	2.13
	10.7	15,000	2.50
Chloramines	7.0	12,000	2.08
	8.5	14,000	2.28
	9.5	20,000	3.35

The magnitudes of E throw some light on the nature of the disinfecting process (see Section 18-17).

27-6. Disinfection by Chlorine.   The first use of chlorine as a disinfectant for municipal water supplies in America was in 1908 when George A. Johnson and John L. Leal employed chloride of lime for the continuous disinfection of the water supply of Jersey City, N. J.[8]

The element chlorine is the second member of the seventh column of the periodic table.   Surrounding its nucleus is an outer shell of seven electrons.   Since this structure has great stability, atoms of chlorine show a strong tendency to acquire an extra electron to complete a shell of eight.   This tendency manifests itself as oxidizing activity.   Correspondingly, elemental chlorine is a powerful oxidizing agent and functions as an oxidizer in a great majority of its chemical reactions.

[6] The higher the value of E, the slower is the reaction.

[7] C. T. Butterfield et al., "Influence of pH and Temperature on the Survival of Coliforms and Enteric Pathogens when Exposed to Free Chlorine," *U. S. Public Health Rept. 58*, 1837 (1943).

[8] J. L. Leal, "The Sterilization Plant of the Jersey City Water Supply Company at Boonton, N. J.," *Proc. Am. Water Works Assoc.*, 100 (1909).

The addition to water of chlorine or its disinfecting compounds is observed to release the following groups of substances:

1. Hypochlorous acid (HOCl), hypochlorite ion (OCl^-), and elemental chlorine (Cl_2). The distribution of the three species in this group depends upon the pH of the water. Elemental chlorine, from chlorine gas, is present for but a fleeting moment in waters within the normal pH zone. The two prevailing species (HOCl and OCl^-) are referred to in practice as "free available chlorine."

2. Monochloramine (NH_2Cl), dichloramine ($NHCl_2$), and nitrogen trichloride (NCl_3). The presence of ammonia, or organic nitrogen, that will react to form the simple chloramines, is essential to the production of these compounds. The distribution of the three species in this group is again a function of the pH of the water. Nitrogen trichloride is not formed in significant amounts within the normal pH zone unless the "break point" (Section 27-9) is approached. The two prevailing species (NH_2Cl and $NHCl_2$) are referred to in practice as "combined available chlorine."

3. Complex organic chloramines, more especially in sewage.

The disinfecting power of the different species of chlorine compounds varies widely. Therefore, the chemistry of chlorination must be known if chlorine and its compounds are to be employed intelligently and efficiently in the disinfection of water and waste waters.

The concentration in water of free available chlorine and of combined available chlorine is generally determined colorimetrically by the *ortho*-tolidine-arsenite (OTA) test. This test depends upon the fact that free available chlorine reacts much faster with *ortho*-tolidine than does combined available chlorine. For the identification of free available chlorine, therefore, sodium arsenite (a reducing agent) is added to stop the reaction *after* the free available chlorine has reacted and, at least approximately, *before* the combined available chlorine has reacted.

As a strong oxidizing agent, chlorine reacts with reducing substances to produce the so-called "chlorine demand." In the reactions included under this heading, the chlorine atom manifests its great tendency to gain electrons. It is thereby changed into chloride ion or organic chloride, depending upon the nature of the substances present in water. These substances include inorganic Fe^{++}, Mn^{++}, NO_2^-, and H_2S, along with the greater part of the organic material (living and dead) in the water. The reaction of the inorganic reducing substances is generally rapid and stoichiometric; that of the organic material is generally slow, and its extent depends upon the excess of concentration of available chlorine present. Since the amount of organic material in natural waters that serve as drinking-water supplies is closely related to their natural color or stain, the organic chlorine demand of these waters can often be approximately estimated from the depth of color. Similarly, the organic chlorine demand of waste waters bears some relation to their BOD or, more closely, to the oxygen absorbed from permanganate or dichromate.

The occurrence of these reactions is a complicating factor in the use of chlorine as a disinfectant, for one must provide sufficient chlorine to take care of these side reactions along with the disinfecting reactions. It is for this reason that chlorine residuals after a specified time of contact, such as 10 min, are made the basis for standards of accomplishment or comparison. The demand is a function of temperature, concentration, and time. Determination of its magnitude must take all these factors into account. The chlorine used up in disinfection is part of the demand.

27-7. Free Available Chlorine. The solution of elemental chlorine in water is characterized by the following equilibrium equations:

 a. Hydrolysis:

$$Cl_2 + H_2O \rightleftarrows HOCl + H^+ + Cl^- \qquad\qquad 27\text{-}7$$

$$(HOCl)(H^+)(Cl^-)/(Cl_2) = K_h \qquad\qquad 27\text{-}8$$

 b. Ionization:

$$HOCl \rightleftarrows H^+ + OCl^- \qquad\qquad 27\text{-}9$$

$$(H^+)(OCl^-)/(HOCl) = K_i$$

or

$$(OCl^-)/(HOCl) = K_i/(H^+) \qquad\qquad 27\text{-}10$$

Solutions of hypochlorites, such as chloride of lime and calcium hypochlorite, establish the same ionization equilibrium in water. When calcium hypochlorite is used, for example, the reactions leading up to this equilibrium are

$$Ca(OCl)_2 \rightarrow Ca^{++} + 2OCl^- \qquad\qquad 27\text{-}11$$

and

$$H^+ + OCl^- \rightleftarrows HOCl \qquad\qquad 27\text{-}9$$

The value of the hydrolysis constant K_h, 4.5×10^{-4} $(mols/l)^2$ at 25 C, is of such magnitude that no measurable concentration of Cl_2 exists in solution when the pH value of the chlorinated water is more than about 3.0 and the total chlorine concentration is less than about 1,000 mg/l.

At ordinary water temperatures, the hydrolysis of chlorine is essentially complete within a very few seconds, and the ionization of hypochlorous acid produced is an essentially instantaneous, reversible

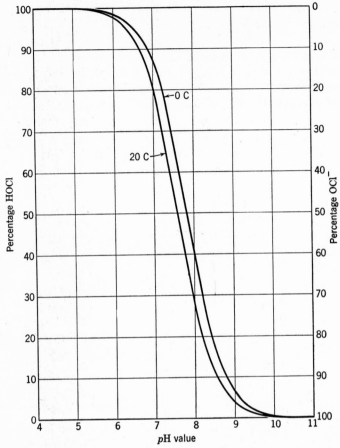

Figure 27-3. Distribution of hypochlorous acid and hypochlorite ion in water at different pH values and temperatures. *After Morris.*

reaction. The value of the ionization constant K_i varies in magnitude with temperature as shown in Table 27-2.

TABLE 27-2.   Values of the Ionization Constant of Hypochlorous Acid at Different Temperatures

Temperature, C	0	5	10	15	20	25
$K_i \times 10^8$, mols/l.	1.5	1.7	2.0	2.2	2.5	2.7

The relative distribution of HOCl and OCl$^-$ at various pH values is shown in Figure 27-3. It is calculated from Equation 27-10 and Table 27-2 as

$$\frac{(HOCl)}{(HOCl) + (OCl^-)} = \frac{1}{1 + (OCl^-)/(HOCl)} = \frac{1}{1 + K_i/(H^+)} \quad 27\text{-}12$$

At 20 C and pH 8, for example, the percentage distribution of HOCl is $100 \times [1 + 2.5 \times 10^{-8}/10^{-8}]^{-1} = 100/3.5 = 29\%$. This equilibrium relationship, therefore, permits the identification of the species of chlorine that constitute free available chlorine.

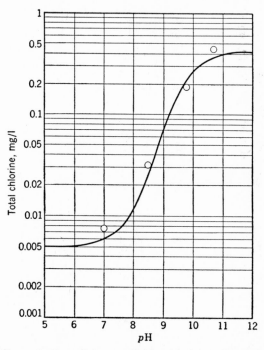

Figure 27-4.   Concentration of free available chlorine required for 99% kill of *Esch. coli* in 30 min. at 2 to 5 C.

The relative colicidal efficiency (concentration of aqueous, or free available, chlorine required to kill 99% of *Esch. coli* in 30 min at 2 to 5 C) is presented in Figure 27-4. The mirrored images exhibited between Figures 27-3 and 27-4 suggest a higher killing efficiency for HOCl than for OCl$^-$ (in the approximate ratio of 80:1 for the conditions of test). By assuming an additive efficiency for the two species, one can calculate a theoretical curve for the total amount of chlorine required to produce a given percentage of kill in a specified time at various pH values as follows:

If parentheses stand for the required concentration of the species of chlorine, C is the concentration of HOCl alone required to produce the desired kill, p equals the proportionate efficiency of OCl^- ion in relation to that of HOCl, and R is the required total chlorine, then

$$R = (HOCl) + (OCl^-) = (HOCl)\left[1 + \frac{(OCl^-)}{(HOCl)}\right]$$

By Equation 27-10, therefore,

$$R = HOCl\left[1 + \frac{K_i}{(H^+)}\right]$$

Since

$$C = (HOCl) + p(OCl^-) = \frac{R}{1 + K/(H^+)} + p\frac{K_i}{(H^+)}\left[\frac{R}{1 + K_i/(H^+)}\right]$$

it follows that

$$R = C\frac{1 + K_i/(H^+)}{1 + pK_i/(H^+)} \qquad\qquad 27\text{-}13$$

Example 27-1. From the data presented in Table 27-1 and Figures 27-2a and 27-3, draw a comparison between the disinfecting characteristics of HOCl and OCl^- ion based upon the results presented for pH values of 7.0 and 10.7.

1. At pH 7.0 about 80% of the disinfecting chlorine is present as HOCl; the coefficient of dilution n is 1.5, indicating that concentration of the disinfectant is more important than the time of contact; the energy of activation E is 8,200 cal and, hence, falls within the range of activation energies for diffusion processes; and the concentration of chlorine required for 99% kill of *Esch. coli* in 10 min at 2 to 5 C is 0.017 mg/l, or $C^n t = 0.017^{1.5} \times 10 = 2.2 \times 10^{-2}$.

2. At pH 10.7 almost 100% of the disinfecting chlorine is present as OCl^- ion; the coefficient of dilution n is 0.8, indicating that time of contact is more important than concentration of the disinfectant. The energy of activation E is 15,000 cal and hence falls within the range of activation energies for chemical reactions; and the concentration of chlorine residual for 99% kill of *Esch. coli* in 10 min at 2 to 5 C is 1.7 mg/l, or $C^n t = 1.7^{0.8} \times 10 = 15.3$.

It appears, therefore, that the rate-determining processes for HOCl are different from those for OCl^- ion. The proportionate disinfecting efficiency p of OCl^- ion, for 99% kill of *Esch. coli* in 30 min, is about $0.005/0.042 = 0.012$ or 1.2%. Substitution of $p = 0.012$, $C = 0.005$, and $K_i = 2.2 \times 10^{-8}$ in Equation 27-13 gives the following numerical expression for the total chlorine required for a 99% kill of *Esch. coli* in 30 min at 2 to 5 C:

$$R = 0.005\frac{1 + (1.6 \times 10^{-8})/(H^+)}{1 + (1.9 \times 10^{-10})/(H^+)}$$

This is the basis of the curve shown in Figure 27-4. At pH 8.0, for example,

$$R = 0.005\frac{1 + (1.6 \times 10^{-8})/10^{-8}}{1 + (1.9 \times 10^{-10})/10^{-8}} = 0.013 \text{ mg/l.}$$

27-8. Combined Available Chlorine. The most important reaction of chlorine with nitrogen compounds is that of hypochlorous acid with ammonia. This is a stepwise process for which the successive reactions are:

$$NH_3 + HOCl \rightarrow NH_2Cl + H_2O \qquad 27\text{-}14$$

$$NH_2Cl + HOCl \rightarrow NHCl_2 + H_2O \qquad 27\text{-}15$$

$$NHCl_2 + HOCl \rightarrow NCl_3 + H_2O \qquad 27\text{-}16$$

When the pH is greater than 6 and the molar ratio of chlorine (or hypochlorite) to ammonia (or ammonium ions) is not greater than one, the formation of monochloramine predominates. The rate of the first step is very much dependent upon the pH of the solution. It is described by Equation 18-59 as follows:

$$-dc/dt = Kc_{Cl}c_{NH_3} \qquad 18\text{-}59$$

where dc/dt is the instantaneous rate of reaction in mols of HOCl or NH_3, and c_{Cl} and c_{NH_3} are respectively the concentrations of chlorine and ammonia in mols per liter. The rate is maximal at a pH of 8.3 and decreases rapidly in both directions. Its measured magnitude per minute is 8.9×10^{-3} at pH 4.6, 5.8×10^{-1} at pH 6.5, and 7.4×10^{-3} at pH 12.1. At pH 8.3, 25 C, 0.8 mg/l of chlorine, and 0.32 mg/l of ammonia nitrogen, the reaction is 99% complete in about 1 min; at pH 5, the corresponding time is 210 min; at pH 11, it is 50 min. The rate of the reaction also varies greatly with temperature. The value of Q_{10} lies between 2.0 and 2.5, depending upon the pH.

In the past, the distribution of the chloramines has been assumed to be in accord with the following equilibrium equation:

$$2NH_2Cl + H^+ \rightleftarrows NH_4^+ + NHCl_2 \qquad 27\text{-}17$$

whence

$$\frac{(NH_4^+)(NHCl_2)}{(H^+)(NH_2Cl)^2} = K_e \qquad 27\text{-}18$$

The magnitude of the equilibrium constant is 6.7×10^5 at about 25 C, and the equations predict the formation of 84% dichloramine at pH 5 and 94% monochloramine at pH 9 when the chlorine ammonia ratio is equimolar or 5 to 1 on a weight basis. Morris[9] and Palin[10] have

[9] J. C. Morris, unpublished research, Harvard University, 1951.

[10] A. T. Palin, "The Estimation of Free Chlorine and Chloramine in Water," *J. Inst. Water Engrs.*, *3*, 100 (1949).

shown, however, that the distribution is actually governed by the relative rates of formation of monochloramine and dichloramine, which change with the relative concentrations of chlorine and ammonia as well as with pH and temperature. Figure 27-5 shows the distribution at equimolar concentrations of chlorine and ammonia or at a weight ratio of chlorine (Cl_2) to ammonia (N) of 5 to 1.

A comparison of diagrams (a) and (b) in Figure 27-2 shows that combined available chlorine is a much less efficient colicidal agent than

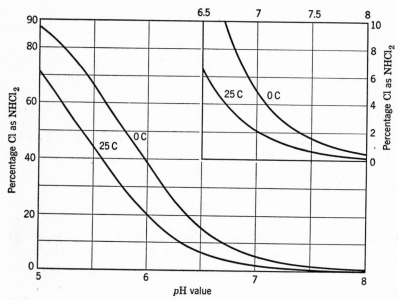

Figure 27-5. Distribution of chloramines at equimolar concentrations of chlorine and ammonia. [Cl_2:NH_3 (as N) = 5.] *After Morris.*

free available chlorine. The value of the dilution coefficient $n = 1.3$ suggests that concentration of the disinfectant is somewhat more important than time of contact, and the magnitudes of $E = 12,000$ to 20,000 recorded in Table 27-1 lie within the range of chemical reactions.

27-9. Break-Point Reactions of Ammonia. Oxidation of ammonia and reduction of chlorine are noted when the molar ratio of chlorine to ammonia is greater than one. A substantially complete oxidation-reduction process occurs in the neighborhood of a ratio of 2 to 1 and leads, in the course of time, to the disappearance of all the ammonia and oxidizing chlorine from the solution. This phenomenon is called the "break point." It is generally illustrated by a diagram such as that shown in Figure 27-6. Between A and B, molar ratios of chlorine to ammonia are less than one, and the residual oxidizing chlorine is essentially all monochloramine. Between B and C, oxidation of ammonia and reduction of chlorine increase, until complete oxidation-reduction occurs at C, the break point. In this region, again, the residual oxidizing chlorine is essentially all monochloramine. Beyond C, unreacted hypochlorite remains in solution, and the presence of some nitrogen trichloride is observed, depending upon the pH.

The rate of the break-point reaction is strongly dependent upon pH. A maximum rate occurs between pH 7 and 8. However, no clear-cut picture of the complex reactions involved can as yet be presented, and

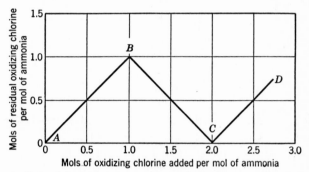

Figure 27-6. Schematic diagram of the break point. *After Morris.*

the student must be referred to current publication for up-to-date information. Time requirements are determined in practice by test.

Important advantages of chlorinating to and, if desired, beyond the break point to obtain free available chlorine residuals are: (1) that most odors and tastes normal to water are thereby destroyed and (2) that rigorous disinfection is insured. In the presence of undecomposed urea, nitrogen trichloride is very likely to be found. It gives rise to bad odors and tastes.

27-10. Dechlorination. When large amounts of chlorine have been added to water (for example, to insure disinfection in the time available before the water is to be used or to destroy odors and tastes), unwanted residuals can be removed by dechlorination. Intensive use of chlorine in this manner without the break-point reaction is called "superchlorination and dechlorination." There are a number of methods of dechlorination, among them: the addition of reducing chemicals; passage through beds of granular activated carbon; and aeration. The reducing agents include sulfur dioxide, SO_2; sodium bisulfite, $NaHSO_3$; and sodium sulfite, Na_2SO_3. The bisulfite is ordinarily used in practice, because it is cheaper and more stable than the sulfite.

Samples of water that are collected for bacteriological analysis are usually dechlorinated by including sodium thiosulfate ($Na_2S_2O_3$) in the sampling bottles either as a solution or in crystalline form. Granular activated carbon absorbs chlorine into its pores where the chlorine oxidizes the carbon to carbon dioxide. Contact with powdered activated carbon cannot generally be made long enough to produce this result. Chlorine, hypochlorous acid, dichloramine, and nitrogen trichloride are sufficiently volatile to be removed by aeration. Other species of chlorine are not.

The theoretical reactions of dechlorinating agents follow:

$$SO_2 + Cl_2 + 2H_2O \rightarrow H_2SO_4 + 2HCl \qquad 27\text{-}19$$

$$NaHSO_3 + Cl_2 + H_2O \rightarrow NaHSO_4 + 2HCl \qquad 27\text{-}20$$

$$2Na_2S_2O_3 + Cl_2 \rightarrow Na_2S_4O_6 + 2NaCl \qquad 27\text{-}21$$

$$C + 2Cl_2 + 2H_2O \rightarrow CO_2 + 4HCl \qquad 27\text{-}22$$

27-11. Technical Properties of Chlorine and Related Compounds. Chlorine gas (Cl_2) can be liquefied at room temperatures, at a pressure of 5 to 10 atm, for storage and shipment in steel cylinders or tanks. One pound of the liquid will produce 5 cu ft of gas. Under conditions of use, withdrawal of gas lowers the temperature of the stored fluid. If the rate of withdrawal is to remain constant, the heat loss must be supplied from without. But direct application of heat at temperatures in excess of 125 F is dangerous. Since reliquefaction of chlorine in measuring and dosing equipment produces erratic results, chlorine containers and gas lines must be kept cooler than the dispensing equipment.

The solubility of chlorine gas in water is about 7,300 mg/l at 68 F and 1 atm. Below 49.2 F, chlorine combines with water to form chlorine hydrate ($Cl_2 \cdot 8H_2O$ usually), called chlorine ice. The hydrate interferes with the proper operation of feeding equipment. Feed or sealing water that comes into contact with the gas should, therefore, be kept above 49.2 F.

Chlorine gas is highly toxic and must be handled with due care and adequate safeguards. Its odor threshold in air is about 3.5 ppm by volume. Coughing is induced when its concentration reaches 30 ppm, and exposures for 30 min to concentrations of 40–60 ppm are dangerous. At a concentration of 1,000 ppm, the gas is rapidly fatal.

Where the use of chlorine is large—in municipal water and sewage works, for example—liquid chlorine is the cheapest form of chlorine that can be employed. In small installations and for emergency, or other specialized uses, some of the compounds of chlorine are more satisfactory, among them: the hypochlorites of calcium, $Ca(OCl)_2$, and sodium, $(NaOCl)$; chlorinated lime, $CaClOCl$, and certain organic complexes such as Halazone, $HOOC-C_6H_4-SO_2NCl_2$. The purposeful combination of chlorine with ammonia and the release of chlorine dioxide, ClO_2, from sodium chlorite, $NaClO_2$, create other useful chlorine disinfectants. Chlorinated lime (a loose combination of chlorine with slaked lime), calcium hypochlorite, sodium chlorite, and the common organic chlorine compounds are solids. Sodium hypochlorite is produced as a liquid (see Table A-5).

Of the substances that may be used in combination with chlorine, or as antichlors (chlorine-reducing substances), ammonia and sulfur dioxide are gases that can be liquefied, stored, handled, and dispensed like chlorine. Ammonia is available also as ammonium hydroxide (aqua ammonia) and ammonium sulfate. Sodium bisulfite $(NaHSO_3)$, a solid, may take the place of SO_2.

The strength of chlorine compounds, i.e., their oxidizing power, is commonly expressed in terms of their "available chlorine." Use of this term is analogous to that of alkalinity as $CaCO_3$. "Chlorine equivalent" would be a more accurate designation. The oxidizing power of chlorine compounds is proportional to their amount of chlorine with a valence number greater than -1. Calculation of the percentage of "available chlorine" of a given compound is based on (1) the mols of equivalent chlorine, or number of mols of chlorine that would have an oxidizing capacity equivalent to one mol of the compound; (2) the actual percentage by weight of chlorine present in the compound; and (3) the proportion by weight of the pure compound present in the commercial product. Chlorinated lime, for example, contains as its essential constituent about 62.5% of calcium oxychloride, $CaClOCl$ (molecular weight 127), with Cl_2 mols (molecular weight 71) of equivalent chlorine. Therefore, the actual weight of chlorine present is $62.5 \times 71/127 = 35\%$ of the total, and the available chlorine is also 35%. The oxidizing ability of non-chlorinous compounds can also be expressed in terms of available chlorine.

27-12. Application of Chlorine and Related Compounds. Liquid chlorine, ammonia, and sulfur dioxide are generally added to water in controlled amounts through orifice flow meters called respectively chlorinators, ammoniators, and sulfonators. For a given dosage, the pressure drop across the orifice is kept constant. In devices that are operated under pressure, this is done by providing a pressure-reducing, pressure-compensating valve which keeps the influent pressure constant regardless of pressure changes in the container from which the gas is drawn. In devices that are operated under a vacuum, the drop in pressure across the orifice is regulated by controlling the vacuum on the outlet side of the orifice, the inlet side also being under partial vacuum. The advantages of vacuum-feed devices in lessening gas leakage are obvious. Some pressure devices are based on regulated volumetric displacement of the gas (bubblers).

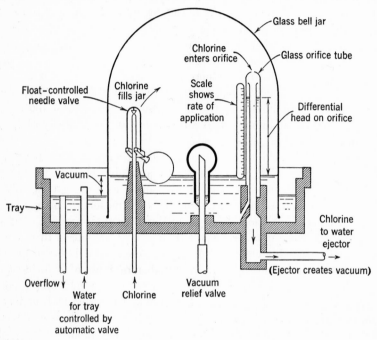

Figure 27-7. Control features of a vacuum-type chlorinator. *Wallace & Tiernan Co.*

The measured gas flow may be introduced directly into water through diffusers, or it may be dissolved in a small flow of water that passes through the gas-flow regulating device and carries a solution of the gas to the point of application. Escape of gas through water in direct feed is not uncommon. Solution feed is preferred for this reason. A flow diagram of a vacuum-type, solution-feed chlorinator is presented in Figure 27-7. Portable chlorinators are used to supply chlorine for the disinfection of water mains, wells, tanks, and masonry reservoirs that have been newly constructed or that have undergone repairs. The initial concentration of the chlorine applied for these purposes is about 50 mg/l. Dosage is repeated until a residual of about 1 mg/l is obtained. The structure is then flushed out thoroughly before being placed in service.

Solutions of chlorinating, ammoniating, and sulfonating compounds are commonly fed through chemical reagent feeders (Section 23-8). For the chlorination of new mains, suitable amounts of calcium hypochlorite are sometimes placed in the main during construction. Manufacture of chlorine at the treatment works by the electrolysis of brine in electrolytic cells is possible, but it has not found significant use.

The dosages of chlorine that are generally required in the marginal (minimal) treatment of water and sewage may be gaged from Tables 27-3 and 27-4. Suitable adjustments of the values given must be

TABLE 27-3.   Minimum Chlorine Residuals for Drinking Water at 20 C

After Butterfield

pH value	6 to 7	7 to 8	8 to 9	9 to 10	10 to 11
Free available chlorine, mg/l after 10 min	0.2	0.2	0.4	0.8	0.8
Combined available chlorine, mg/l after 60 min	1.0	1.5	1.8	1.8	...

TABLE 27-4.   Probable Amounts of Chlorine Required to Secure a Chlorine Residual of 0.5 mg/l after 15 min in Sewage and Sewage Effluents

Type of sewage or effluent	Probable amounts of chlorine, mg/l
Raw sewage, depending on strength and staleness	6 to 24
Settled sewage, depending on strength and staleness	3 to 18
Chemically precipitated sewage, depending on strength	3 to 12
Trickling-filter effluent, depending upon performance	3 to 9
Activated-sludge effluent, depending upon performance	3 to 9
Intermittent-sand-filter effluent, depending upon performance	1 to 6

made for temperature effects and for variations in the quality of different waters or the strength of different waste waters. The capacities of feeding equipment must cover a sufficiently wide span to insure adequate dosage under all the conditions that may be encountered. To the values in this table must be added the chlorine demand of the water. For the chlorine residuals commonly prescribed in swimming pools, see Section 21-4.

Satisfactory disinfection of secondary sewage effluents, represented by 99.9% destruction of *Esch. coli* and 37 C bacterial count, is generally obtained when the chlorine residuals after 15 to 30 min of contact lie between 0.2 and 1.0 mg/l. A residual of 0.5 mg/l after 15 min appears to be a safe average.

In municipal water supplies, chlorination is often the only treatment process. Where other treatment methods are included, disinfecting chlorine may be added to the raw water (prechlorination), the partially treated water, or the finished water (postchlorination). The water may be chlorinated more than once; also after it leaves the plant. Where the distribution system contains open reservoirs, for example, the water may be rechlorinated in the distribution system.

27-13. Other Uses of Chlorine. In the operation of water and waste-water works, chlorine has been found useful for a number of purposes other than disinfection. Some of these purposes are outlined below:

1. Destruction or control of undesirable growths of algae and related organisms in water and waste waters. See Section 27-14.

2. Destruction and prevention of growth of iron-fixing and slime-forming bacteria in pipelines and other water conduits and of slime-forming bacteria in sewers and sewage-treatment works.

3. Destruction of filter flies (*Psychoda*) and of ponding slime growths in trickling filters.

4. Improvement of the coagulation of water and waste waters and of the separation of grease from waste waters.

5. Control of odors in water and waste waters.

6. Stabilization of settling-tank sludges in water-purification works.

7. Prevention of anaerobic conditions in sewerage systems and sewage-treatment works, by delaying or reducing decomposition.

8. Control of odors associated with the treatment of sewage sludge, including its drying.

9. Destruction of hydrogen sulfide in water and waste waters, and the protection of concrete, mortar, and paint against the corrosive action of this gas.

10. Reduction of the immediate oxygen requirements of returned activated sludge and of digester liquor returned to the treatment plant.

11. Reduction or delay of the BOD of waste waters that are to be discharged into receiving waters.

12. Preparation at the plant of the coagulant chlorinated copperas.

Of these purposes, the reduction of BOD by chlorination deserves special mention. Four kinds of reactions are conceivably involved in BOD reduction by chlorination: (1) direct oxidation of BOD-exerting compounds; (2) formation with nitrogen compounds of bactericidal chloroamines by substitution of chlorine for hydrogen; (3) formation with carbon compounds of substances that are no longer decomposable, again by substitution of chlorine for hydrogen; and (4) addition of chlorine to unsaturated compounds to form non-decomposable substances. Often quoted is the observation that the application to sewage of enough chlorine to produce a measurable residue after 15 min will reduce the 5-day, 20-C BOD by 15 to 35%; or in the ratio of about 2 mg/l of BOD to 1 mg/l of chlorine. However, present knowledge is not sufficiently well founded to permit the use of these figures. Snow [11] has shown that the reduction in BOD depends not only upon the concentration of chlorine employed but also upon the condition of the sewage treated. In his studies, chlorination of fresh sewage to a trace of residual at 15 min gave a reduction of but 10%, whereas the value for stale sewage was 25 to 40%. Doses as high as 100 to 300 mg/l were required to secure a reduction of 35% in fresh sewage. Chlorination by very high doses to the break point eliminated 75% of the BOD. Aeration of sewage prior to chlorination enhanced the BOD reduction of fresh sewage. The reductions obtained for all aerobic samples were due both to a reduction of the first-stage demand and the rate of BOD exertion. In anaerobic, chlorinated sewage, the rate of BOD was stepped up.

The use of chlorine in taste and odor control is discussed in Section 27-20.

Destruction of Aquatic Growths

27-14. Control of Plankton. The control of the plankton of lakes, ponds, and reservoirs, and to a lesser extent of streams, is an important and often vexing problem in the management of surface waters that serve as water supplies or as receiving waters. Among the nuisances created by the, often sudden, "blooming" of a single genus or a few genera are: nauseous odors and tastes; killing of fish; interference with stock watering; poisoning of water fowl and cattle; poisoning of mussels; shortening of filter runs in water-purification plants; growths in pipes and other water conduits; and interference with industrial water uses. The characteristics of the odors and tastes associated with different organisms vary widely (see Table 27-5). Consumer complaints are ordinarily registered when the concentration of odor-producing organisms lies above 500 to 1,000 areal standard units of 400 square microns. The bitter taste imparted to water by the chlorophyllaceous flagellate *Synura* becomes objectionable, however, whenever the presence of the organism can be detected. Small amounts of chlorine, intended for disinfection, may intensify the odors and tastes of microorganisms in much the same way as they intensify the tastes due to phenols. On the other hand, high concentrations of

[11] W. B. Snow, "Biochemical Oxygen Demand of Chlorinated Sewage," *Sewage and Ind. Wastes*, *24*, 689 (1952).

chlorine will destroy both the organisms and their odor-producing oils or cell matter.

The nature of the plankton has been described in Section 19-2, and the control of catchment areas and reservoirs in the development of surface water supplies has been discussed in Chapter 10. Some attention is given, furthermore, to plankton growths in connection with the self-purification of water (Chapter 28). The present section is, therefore, confined to a consideration of the destruction of the plankton.

The use of copper sulfate for the eradication of algae and other microscopic organisms from reservoirs was suggested in 1904 by Moore and Kellerman.[12] Since then, this chemical has been applied more widely than any other as an algicide. The use of chlorine is supplemental rather than competitive. It destroys organisms that are more sensitive to it than to copper ions, oxidizes odors released when plankton growths are killed by copper and undergo decay, and delays decay and consequent depletion of oxygen. Activated carbon has been applied with some success in small reservoirs to shut out the sunlight essential to the growth of chlorophyllaceous organisms. It is useful also in removing odors and tastes due to algae. The addition of lime in amounts sufficient to produce caustic alkalinity deprives the plankton of needed carbon dioxide.

The mechanism and kinetics of destruction of plankton organisms by copper and chlorine are analogous to those of disinfection. However, the rate of kill at the concentrations normally employed is relatively slow. For copper sulfate it is days rather than minutes. Destruction of large growths by copper sulfate and by small concentrations of chlorine is accompanied (1) by an intensification of odors and (2) by a rise in number of the saprophytic bacteria which feed upon the cell substances released by the plankton carcasses. This may cause so serious a depletion of dissolved oxygen that fish are killed. Destruction of one plankton genus may be followed by the rapid rise of another. A treated body of water must, therefore, be watched carefully. Remedial, supplementary treatment of the water with chlorine or activated carbon may be indicated. The amounts of copper sulfate and of chlorine required to kill some of the most troublesome organisms are shown in Table 27-5. The values given in Table 27-5 apply to relatively soft, warm (15 C, or 60 F) waters. Each 10 mg/l of alkalinity may raise the required dosage of copper

[12] G. T. Moore and K. F. Kellerman, "A Method of Destroying or Preventing the Growth of Algae and Certain Pathogenic Bacteria in Water Supplies," *U. S. Bur. Plant Ind.*, Bull. 64 (1904).

TABLE 27-5.   Concentration of Copper and Chlorine Required to Kill
Troublesome Growths of Organisms

After Hale

	Organism	Trouble	Copper sulfate, mg/l	Chlorine, mg/l
Algae				
Diatoms	Asterionella, Synedra, Tabellaria	Odor: aromatic to fishy	0.1–0.5	0.5–1.0
	Fragilaria, Navicula	Turbidity	0.1–0.3	. . . . . .
	Melosira	Turbidity	0.2	2.0
Green	Eudorina,* Pandorina *	Odor: fishy	2–10	. . . . . .
	Volvox *	Odor: fishy	0.25	0.3–1.0
	Chara, Cladophora	Turbidity, scum	0.1–0.5	. . . . . .
	Coelastrum, Spirogyra	Turbidity, scum	0.1–0.3	1.0–1.5
Blue-green	Anabaena, Aphanizomenon	Odor: moldy, grassy, vile	0.1–0.5	0.5–1.0
	Clathrocystis, Coelosphaerium	Odor: grassy, vile	0.1–0.3	0.5–1.0
	Oscillatoria	Turbidity	0.2–0.5	1.1
Higher bacteria	Beggiatoa (sulfur)	Odor: decayed, pipe growths	5.0	. . . . . .
	Crenothrix (iron)	Odor: decayed, pipe growths	0.3–0.5	0.5
Protozoa (chlorophyllaceous flagellates)	Ceratium	Odor: fishy, vile	0.2–0.3	0.3–1.0
	Glenodinium	Odor: fishy	0.2–0.5	. . . . . .
	Peridinium	Odor: fishy	0.5–2.0	. . . . . .
	Cryptomonas, Mallomonas	Odor: aromatic	0.2–0.5	. . . . . .
	Dinobryon	Odor: aromatic to fishy	0.2	0.3–1.0
	Synura	Taste: cucumber	0.1–0.3	0.3–1.0
	Uroglenopsis	Odor: fishy. Taste: oily	0.1–0.2	0.3–1.0
Crustacea	Cyclops	†	. . . . . .	1.0–3.0
	Daphnia	†	2.0	1.0–3.0
Miscellaneous	Chironomus (bloodworm)	†	. . . . . .	15–50
	Craspedacusta (jellyfish)	†	0.3	. . . . . .

* These organisms are classified also as flagellate protozoa.
† These organisms are individually visible and cause consumer complaints.

sulfate by as much as 5% because it promotes the precipitation of the
copper as copper carbonate. Carbon dioxide reduces precipitation by
decreasing the pH and OH^-. If the CO_2 content of the water to be
treated is small, the dosage is, therefore, increased by about 5%. The
algicidal Q_{10} value of copper sulfate lies in the vicinity of 1.3. Stage
of growth of the organisms is also a determining factor. Organic
matter competes for copper as well as for chlorine, and dosage may
have to be increased by 2% for each 10 mg/l of organic matter present.

The tolerance of fish to copper sulfate lies between 0.14 mg/l (trout)
and 2.1 mg/l (black bass), i.e., within the range of concentrations
required to destroy plankton growths. However, the number killed
is generally small, because dosage is based, not upon the total volume
of water in the body to be treated, but only upon the volume contained
within the limited (usually uppermost) strata in which the plankton
occurs (Section 17-8). Therefore, fish can seek refuge in the untreated
waters. When a massive killing of fish follows the destruction, or
natural death, of intense algal blooms, the likely cause is not the copper

sulfate that may have been used, but the depletion of oxygen due to the decay of the algae and the adherence of dead algal cells to the gills of the fish.

The quantities of copper normally needed for plankton control fall well below the concentration of 3 mg/l allowed under the federal drinking-water standards.

27-15. Application of Algicides. Destruction of large pulses of plankton growths should not be necessary. Steps should be taken to prevent propagation leading to heavy infestations as soon as limnologic and microscopic evidences sound a warning. Prevention of such propagation requires adequate sampling and an understanding of the responses of different kinds of organisms to season (heat and light) and water movement. Except for *Synura*, which should be destroyed whenever its presence can be detected, bodies of water from which drinking-water supplies are taken should, as a rule, be treated whenever the concentration of microscopic organisms exceeds 500 to 1,000 areal standard units. The destruction of some of the flagellates such as *Synura* is sometimes complicated by their growth under the sheet of ice that covers bodies of water during the winter.

Small reservoirs, more particularly distribution reservoirs, and basins can be protected or treated by adding algicides to their influent waters. Dry-feed or solution-feed apparatus suited to the chemical to be applied are used for this purpose. Seeding of such reservoirs from upland storages can also be prevented by such means. Where large reservoirs, or portions of them, are to be treated, the algicide must be applied from a boat. A common method of applying copper sulfate is to place crystals of this chemical in burlap bags that are dragged through the water. To cover areas of moderate size, the boat may take a zigzag course across the surface, form a "reflected" zigzag pattern on the return run, and cover the shore waters more intensively by finally traversing a perimetral course within about 20 ft of the shore line. For large areas, a pattern of parallel paths 20 to 100 ft apart may be traced first in one direction and then at right angles to it.

The solubility of copper sulfate as $CuSO_4 \cdot 5H_2O$ is high. It varies from 19.5% by weight at 32 F (0 C) to 31.3% at 86 F (30 C). The rate of solution of crystals of copper sulfate (including 5 molecules of water) is sufficiently slow, however, to make the bag method effective.

Dry-feed or solution-feed machines may be used instead. Dusters of the orchard-spray variety and special broadcasting equipment have also been employed successfully. Chlorination apparatus of the type described in Section 27-12 is used for the application of liquid chlorine, hypochlorites, and chloramines. A combination of copper sulfate, chlorine, and ammonia will form cupric chloramine and tends to prevent precipitation of the copper. Powdered activated carbon for "blacking out" sunlight from small basins can be dispersed from bags, added to the influent, or ejected onto the surface as a slurry. Its use can be confined to sunny days.

27-16. Destruction of Water Weeds. Most of the higher aquatic plants are perennial and propagate by means of runners, tubers, buds, or stem fragments; few depend upon seed reproduction. Since vegetative propagation is relatively slow and seed reproduction is successful only when the seeds find suitable lodging, objectionable growths of water weeds are relatively rare. Under favorable conditions, however, weeds may propagate so rapidly that they create a serious nuisance, especially in shallow bodies of water. The limiting depth of prevalence of attached weeds is about 40 ft. The discharge of waste waters that are rich in fertilizing elements, such as nitrogen and phosphorus, will promote heavy weed infestation of receiving waters and of oxidation or fish ponds.

There are five ways of destroying these aquatic growths: draining, dredging, cutting, dragging, and poisoning. If the weeded area can be drained during hot weather, the exposed plants will die, and their roots will be destroyed. Dredging will remove the entire plant. Cutting and dragging offer but temporary relief. Flowering weeds should be cut before they have had a chance to go to seed. Since copper and chlorine in reasonable concentration are not effective against large aquatic plants, other chemical agents must be employed to poison them. Unfortunately, the compounds that are effective may also be toxic to man, or to fish, in the concentrations that must be used. Compounds of chlorinated benzene, such as *ortho*-dichlorobenzene, although toxic to fish, have been used successfully in bodies of water from which drinking water is drawn. These substances are sprayed upon the water and settle onto the weeds to destroy them. More than one dose must generally be applied to control growth. The killing of fish is kept down by proceeding from the shore outward and thereby causing the fish to migrate into deep water. The required dosage of commercial *ortho*-dichlorobenzene is 0.4 to 1.2 gal per 1,000 sq ft.

Arsenical compounds such as sodium arsenite will destroy a variety of water weeds. Their use is limited to waters that do not serve as sources of drinking water for man or cattle. The development of new herbicides gives promise of eventually providing effective non-toxic weed killers that can be used with safety. Mention should be made in this connection of the growth-regulating substances of the dichlorphenoxyacetic acid type, sodium chlorate and ammonium sulfamate. Some of these have been used successfully for the control of (1) marginal growths, such as willows, that encroach upon bodies of water and (2) emergent vegetation, such as the water hyacinth and water chestnut. The required dosage of sodium arsenite is about 20 lb per 1,000 sq ft, and kill is improved if the weeds are cut before applying the chemical.

Proper design of reservoirs will keep weeds from establishing themselves (Section 10-4); and control of pollution will minimize their prevalence.

27-17. Destruction of Other Organisms. A number of other problems in biological control occur in water supply and waste-water disposal. A few examples will illustrate their range. Copper sulfate has been used in concentrations of 0.5 to 2.0 mg/l to destroy the snail hosts of the flukes that cause swimmer's itch (Section 1-5). It has also been employed to control root growths in house sewers. Caustic alkalinity as well as chlorine have been found to kill *Cyclops*, the intermediate host of guinea worm (Section 1-5). Chlorine as well as storage of water for a day or two at temperatures prevailing in the tropics have destroyed the cercariae of the pathogenic schistosomes (blood flukes). Chironomid larvae (blood worms) have been screened from returned activated sludge which they were destroying. Insecticides, such as DDT, have found use in the control of adult filter flies (Section 25-4).

Removal of Odors and Tastes

27-18. Available Processes. The origin and nature of odors and tastes in drinking water have been discussed in Sections 1-6, 19-2, and 20-5. The most pronounced odors of sewage (Section 20-12) and other decomposable waste waters are produced when they, or the solids removed from them, become septic. Some industrial wastes, however, have characteristic odors of their own which are not changed by septicity. Odor and taste troubles can generally be avoided by proper planning and management of water supplies and waste-water works. Their correction is often a part of treatment processes that serve other primary purposes. Coagulation, sedimentation, filtration, and biological treatment (including sludge treatment) are examples. But there are certain processes in which odor and taste removal or control is the principal objective or the specific purpose. These include: (1) aeration; (2) oxidation by chemicals such as chlorine (including the hypochlorites and chlorinated lime), combinations of chlorine with ammonia, chlorine dioxide, and ozone, and (3) adsorption onto substances such as activated carbon.

Aeration will remove from water only odors and tastes that are dissolved in it as gases or that are otherwise sufficiently volatile (i.e., of low boiling point) to escape rapidly at an air-water interface. The concentration of gases, furthermore, must be such that the water is supersaturated with them in terms of their partial pressure in the air with which the water is brought into contact. Hydrogen sulfide (boiling point -62 C) is the principal odorous gas that can be removed from water to a substantial degree by aeration. The odors associated with algae and related organisms are examples of volatile substances that can often be reduced below their threshold values. But so-called phenolic substances and their chloro compounds, which are created by the marginal chlorination of water containing phenolic substances, are non-volatile and will not respond to aeration. The phenolic compounds involved are hydroxy derivatives of benzene and include phenol, cresol, and similar substances released by chemical industries, gas-manufacturing establishments, and coke plants. The boiling point of phenol (C_6H_5OH) is 182 C and that of *ortho*-chlorphenol $(Cl \cdot C_6H_4 \cdot OH)$ 176 C. As previously mentioned, chlorphenols may be objectionable in quantities as low as 1 $\mu g/l$.

Destruction of odors by oxidizing chemicals is successful when the chemical reaction involved is such as to produce non-odorous substances. The production of non-odorous substances is not uncommon. One of the simplest oxidizing reactions is that between chlorine and hydrogen sulfide to precipitate sulfur. The stronger the oxidizing agent, the more certain is the destruction of the offending substances. Hence the effectiveness of break-point chlorination. The production of chlorphenol by marginal chlorination and the intensification of tastes when water containing *Synura* or other microscopic organisms is chlorinated speak against halfway measures.

Adsorption of odor- and taste-producing substances is widely effective. Activated carbon possesses especially high adsorptive properties and is almost the only substance used for this purpose in water-works practice. The efficiency of adsorption of a substance from water is inversely proportional to its solubility in water. Since many of the odorous substances in water are organic compounds and but slightly soluble, they are generally adsorbed with ease.

27-19. Aeration. As shown in other chapters of this book, the aeration of water and sewage serves many purposes other than odor removal. The physics of gas exchange by aeration has, therefore, been presented in Section 17-5. The hydraulics and pneumatics of aeration have been discussed in Sections 25-12 and 25-14 in connection with trickling filters and activated-sludge units respectively. Natural aeration, so important to the self-purification of water, is treated in

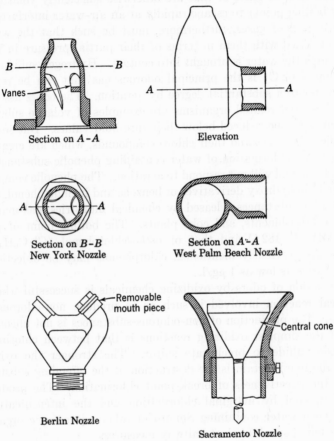

Figure 27-8. Aerator nozzles. The coefficients of discharge of these nozzles vary from 0.85 to 0.92.

Section 28-9. The reader is referred to these sections for a statement of the principles that also underlie the design and operation of aerators intended for the removal of odors and tastes from water.

Aerating devices used specifically for the removal of volatile substances from water commonly take one of the following three forms: (1) injection aerators in which air is blown into the water in substantially the same way as in activated-sludge aeration units; (2) gravity aerators in which the water cascades over a flight of steps or troughs, flows in a thin sheet over an inclined plane that may be studded with baffles to increase the turbulence of the water, drops through the air from perforated pans or perforated pipes, or percolates through porous materials similar to trickling filters; and (3) fountain aerators in which the water is sprayed upward into the air through perforated pipes or pipes equipped with nozzles. Combinations of fountain aerators and beds of contact material similar to trickling filters have also been employed. Injection aerators or air-diffusion

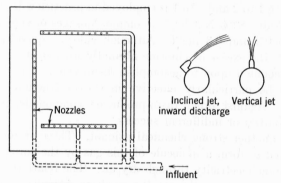

Figure 27-9. Plan of fountain aerator.

units for the removal of gases or volatile matter are designed in substantially the same way as activated-sludge units. The detention period is seldom less than 15 min or more than 45 min, and the amount of air may be as low as 0.005 and as high as 0.2 cu ft per gallon of water treated.

The most effective fountain aerators take the form of pipes equipped with nozzles that break up the spray into small droplets. Examples of nozzles are shown in Figure 27-8, and an arrangement of piping is sketched in Figure 27-9. Operating heads are seldom less than 4 ft or more than 30 ft. The floating-cone nozzle is particularly useful for variable heads.

The use of aerators for odor and taste removal has decreased markedly since the introduction of powdered activated carbon into water-works practice. Aerators may be expected to find continuing employment, however, for the removal of carbon dioxide and hydrogen sulfide and for the addition of oxygen.

27-20. Chemical Oxidation. Chlorine is used as a chemical oxidant as well as a disinfectant in break-point chlorination and superchlorination (Sections 27-9 and 27-10). It may be applied to water for the specific purpose of odor and taste reduction also as chlorine dioxide

($ClO_2 $), a strong oxidizing agent. Chlorine dioxide, a gas in pure form, is produced as needed from sodium chlorite ($NaClO_2$) by allowing a solution of this solid to react with a strong chlorine solution (7,500 mg/l of Cl_2 or a pH value of <3.5), or more rarely with an acidified solution of calcium or sodium hypochlorite.

$$2NaClO_2 + Cl_2 \rightarrow 2ClO_2 + 2NaCl \qquad 27\text{-}23$$

The theoretical ratio of chlorine to sodium chlorite is 1 to 2.6, but a ratio between 1 to 2 and 1 to 1 is employed in practice with commercial sodium chlorite (82% $NaClO_2$). Common dosages of chlorine dioxide lie between 0.2 and 0.3 mg/l. Although chlorine dioxide is itself a disinfectant, the excess of chlorine normally used in its generation is commonly counted upon to accomplish disinfection. Chlorine dioxide appears to be particularly effective in the destruction of phenolic substances. Against other taste-producing compounds, it has been used with partial or indifferent success.

Ozone is another strong chemical oxidant. Three atoms of oxygen are combined to form a molecule of this gas by the corona discharge of high-voltage electricity through dry air. The relatively small partial pressure of ozone in the air, the resulting difficulty of its solution in water, and the "fixing" of some residual odors in treated water have militated against the exploitation of this otherwise very promising substance. The energy use in producing ozone is 0.2 kw-hr per gram of ozone at 15,000 volts, and but 0.5 to 1% of the air's oxygen is converted into ozone. From 1 to 4 mg/l of ozone are required for deodorizing or for disinfection. Modern ozonizing plants include besides contact tanks the following equipment for the production of ozone: air cleaners, blowers, refrigerative driers, adsorptive driers, ozone generators, and cooling-water services. The power requirement for this ancillary equipment is from 25 to 35% of the power needed for the generation of the ozone. Contact tanks similar in construction to the air-diffusion units of activated-sludge tanks provide a detention of about 10 min for the absorption of the gas.

27-21. Adsorption. The principles of adsorption have been discussed in Section 18-19. Activated carbon is the chief means employed for the removal of odors and tastes from water by adsorption. Although a wide variety of other raw materials can also be employed, activated carbon is generally produced from wood. The raw material is charred at a temperature below 500 C and then activated by slow burning at temperatures above 800 C. The adsorptive capacity of different activated carbons for pure phenol, called their "phenol value," offers a basis for their general comparison. However, the phenol value does not necessarily reflect their relative efficiency in removing specific odors and tastes. The phenol value is defined as the mg/l of activated carbon required to reduce 100 μg/l of phenol by 90%. Most commercial carbons used in water treatment possess a phenol value between 15 and 30. Granular activated carbon is generally a millimeter or less in diameter; powdered activated carbon is normally ground to such size that 50% will pass a 300-mesh sieve and 95% a 200-mesh sieve. The adsorptive capacity of finely divided activated carbon can be understood when it is realized that 1 cu ft of this substance is estimated to present a surface of about 3,000,000 sq ft to the water in which it is suspended.

Determination of the phenol value and of the dosage of powdered activated carbon required to reduce odors and tastes to desired threshold values is based upon the relationships expressed by the Freundlich adsorption isotherm. If c_0 is the concentration of odor or phenol in the water to be treated and c is the residual concentration produced by the addition of m units of activated carbon, the equilibrium equation states that

$$\log \frac{c_0 - c}{m} = \log K + \frac{1}{n} \log c \qquad 27\text{-}24$$

Hence the values of K and $1/n$ can be read respectively as the intercept at $c = 1$ and as the slope of the straight line of best fit on double logarithmic paper. The coefficient K is a measure of the fundamental effectiveness of the adsorbent; the coefficient n is a measure of the change in rate of effectiveness with relative dosage. It follows from Equation 27-24 that the phenol value includes both the coefficient K and the coefficient n. Specifically, it is expressed as $\log m = 1.9542 - (\log K + 1/n)$ because $c_0 - c = 90$ and $c = 10$.

It is generally simpler and sufficiently precise to find the dosage required to reach a certain threshold odor or taste from a plot of experimental results. Either an arithmetic or a double logarithmic plot can be used. In an arithmetic plot, carbon dosage in mg/l is made the ordinate and threshold odor or taste values the abscissa (see Figure 27-10a). In such a plot, the experimental points should straddle the desired threshold value. Satisfactory extrapolation is possible by double logarithmic plotting of $(c_0 - c)/m$ against c (see Figure 27-10b). For the data plotted in Figure 27-10, the dosage of activated carbon required to reduce the threshold odor value from 20 to 4 is 7 mg/l.

Activated carbon may be applied to water to correct existing odors and tastes or to prevent their intensification by chlorine. The addition of carbon should be kept flexible. Introduction in advance of coagulation of the raw water allows substantial removal of the carbon particles prior to filtration, stabilization of the precipitated sludge,

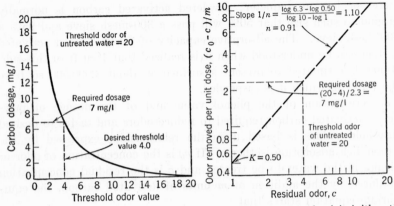

Figure 27-10. Determination of carbon dosage for taste control. (*a*) Arithmetic plotting of experimental results. (*b*) Double-logarithmic plotting of experimental results.

and buffering against rapidly changing water quality in terms of odors and tastes. Deposition of carbon on filter beds is more economical but contributes to more rapid loss of head. Addition of carbon to reservoirs has been mentioned in Section 27-15. Required dosages vary from a few milligrams per liter to over 10 mg/l.

Powdered activated carbon is generally shipped in paper bags (Table A-5). It should be isolated in storage to protect the plant against dust and carbon fires, and it should be kept dry to prevent caking. But it may be fed dry or suspended as a slurry in water.

THE NATURAL OR SELF-PURIFICATION OF WATER

28-1. General Considerations. To cure the ills of water to which it is subjected (1) during its natural passage over and through the ground from the clouds to the sea and (2) by the manifold uses to which it is put by man, the engineer—like the physician who gives aid to a sick patient—must often place reliance on the healing power of nature.[1] Given a chance to exert itself, this healing force will rid polluted water of corruption, even as the marshaling of the natural defenses of the body will cleanse a sick man of disease. It behooves the engineer, therefore, to become familiar not only with the syndrome of pollution and methods for its prevention or cure but also with the forces of natural or self-purification, which will of themselves cause a remission of the symptoms of pollution. He must be able (1) to identify the origins and intensities of pollution, (2) to measure and estimate the magnitudes of the forces of natural purification, (3) to recognize the limitations of these forces, and (4) to prescribe either a regimen that will bring about a spontaneous cure or one in which sufficient external remedial aid is given to insure recovery.

The natural forces of purification are many and varied: physical, chemical, and biological. They are closely interrelated and mutually dependent. Individually, most of them have already been described in the preceding chapters of this book. They enter in one way or another into the different treatment methods that have been devised for the purification of water and waste waters. There, they are purposely intensified in order to accomplish, in brief time and in small space, the changes that are normally brought about in nature only during a protracted period of time and over long distances or wide areas.

It is the purpose of the present chapter to evaluate the significant forces of self-purification and to demonstrate the application of existing

[1] The *vis medicatrix naturae* recognized by early medical philosophers.

knowledge to the solution of some of the engineering problems encountered in the sanitary management of natural waters. For reasons that will be suggested presently, the discussion of self-purification will hinge, in particular, on that of streams polluted by domestic sewage and similar waste waters.

28-2. Patterns of Pollution and Natural Purification. When domestic sewage or a similar polluting substance is discharged into water, a succession of changes in water quality takes place. If the sewage is emptied into a lake in which the currents about the outfall are sluggish and shift their direction with the wind, the changes occur in close proximity to each other, move their location sporadically, and cause much overlap. As a result, the pattern of change is not crisply distinguished. If, on the other hand, the water moves steadily away from the outfall, as in a stream, the successive changes occur in different river reaches and establish a profile of pollution and natural purification so well defined that it can be subjected to mathematical analysis and generalization. In most streams, this pattern is by no means static. It shifts longitudinally along the course of the stream and is modified in intensity with changes in season and hydrography. The intensity rises during the warmer months and at low river stages. It is suppressed in winter and when the stream is in flood. Ice cover imposes a pattern of its own. A decrease in the pollutional load is similar to an increase in stream runoff.

When a single, large charge of sewage or other putrescible matter is poured into a clean stream, the water becomes turbid, sunlight is shut out of the depths, and green plants, which by photosynthesis remove carbon dioxide from the water and release oxygen to it, die off. Scavenging organisms increase in number until they match the food supply. The intensity of their life activities is mirrored by the intensity of the biochemical oxygen demand. The oxygen resources of the water are drawn upon heavily. In an overloaded stream, the dissolved oxygen may become exhausted. Nitrogen, carbon, sulfur, and other important nutritional elements run through their natural cycles (Section 19-4), and sequences of microbic population groups manage to break down the sewage matters in accordance with the nutritional requirements and environmental adaptiveness of the constituent organisms.

Depending upon the hydrography of the stream, suspended matter is carried along with the water or removed to the bottom by sedimentation. The bottom (benthal) deposits may be laid down in thicknesses varying from a thin pollutional carpet to heavy sludge banks. Decomposition of these deposits differs appreciably from that in the flowing water. In the presence of oxygen dissolved in the supernatant water, benthal decomposition changes with depth of deposit from largely aerobic to largely anaerobic conditions. The influence of the benthal factor upon the stream varies accordingly.

The initial effect of pollution, on a stream, is to degrade the physical quality of the water. As decomposition becomes active, there is a shift to chemical degradation that is biologically induced. At the same time, there is a biological degradation in terms of the variety and organization of the living things that persist or make their appearance. In the course of time, or flow, the energy values of a single charge of polluting substances are used up. The biochemical oxygen demand is then decreased in intensity, and the rate of absorption of oxygen from the atmosphere, which at first has lagged behind the rate of oxygen utilization, falls into step with it and eventually overwhelms it. The water becomes clear. Green plants flourish once again and release oxygen to the water by photosynthesis. Other higher aquatic organisms, including game fish, which are notably intolerant to pollution, reappear and thrive as in a balanced aquarium. The stream waters are returned to normal purity. Self-purification has gradually been completed. Recovery has taken place.

The natural purification of polluted waters is never fast, and heavily polluted streams may traverse long distances during the time required to accomplish a significant degree of purification.

The self-purification of polluted ground waters departs significantly from that of surface waters. The variety of living organisms that seize upon the pollutional substances for food is greatly restricted in the confinement and darkness of the pore space of the soil. But this reduction in biological forces is more than counterbalanced by the introduction of the physical force of filtration. In general, the rate of purification is stepped up greatly, and time and distance of pollutional travel shrink to smaller values.

If pollution is kept within bounds, it will contribute to the fertility of the water. The growth of useful aquatic life may thereby be promoted. Then fish will browse in increased numbers in the aquatic meadows that derive the elements for their growth from the nitrogen and other fertilizing constituents of the waste matters. The use of settled sewage for the fertilizing of fish ponds is an example of controlled pollution; as is the possibility of harvesting proteinaceous plankton from oxidation ponds (Section 28-15). In the fertilization of water by domestic sewage, however, the danger of spreading disease through plant or animal foods must never be lost from sight.

28-3. Parameters of Pollution and Natural Purification.

Pollution and natural purification may be measured physically, chemically, and biologically. No single yardstick tells the full story. Depending upon the nature of the polluting substances and the uses that the receiving body of water (or water taken from it) is to serve, measurements may include determinations such as turbidity, color, odor, nitrogen in its various forms, BOD, dissolved oxygen and other gases, mineral substances of many kinds, bacteria, and larger aquatic organisms.

When waters that have been polluted are to be used for municipal purposes or as bathing waters, for example, the progress of bacterial self-purification as measured by the prevalence of the coliform group of organisms may be the principal determinant. The concentration of coliform organisms then reflects (1) the relative hazard of infection incurred by ingesting the water and (2) the degree of purification to which the water must be subjected before it can be used with safety. When pollutional nuisance of receiving waters is to be avoided, the DO and BOD, taken together, are generally relied upon to delineate the profile of pollution and natural purification on which engineering calculations of permissible pollutional loadings are based. The BOD, as shown in Section 19-5, records in a comprehensive manner the pollutional load placed on the receiving water or remaining in it at any time, while the DO identifies the capacity of the body of water to assimilate the imposed load with or without the aid of reaeration by oxygen absorbed from the atmosphere. The standards of water quality discussed in Chapter 21 will serve as a guide to the tests that are meaningful in given circumstances. The significance of biological indicators of contamination and pollution has been discussed in Section 19-3.

A single example [2] of observed changes in terms of some of the generally useful parameters of pollution and natural purification is illustrated in Figure 28-1. The samples on which all but the benthal results are based were collected during midsummer and represent the condition of the stream waters during warm weather when the greatest demands are normally made upon it by the pollutional load. Since bottom deposits are garnered over a long period of time, the bottom-dwelling organisms are characteristic of the average condition of the stream during the period of accumulation. That time of flow, rather than distance of flow, is the controlling factor is strikingly shown by the improvement in water quality effected by passage of the stream through the lake that occupies the lower reaches. The tributaries

[2] From a survey by the United States Public Health Service of the Mississippi River at Minneapolis and St. Paul before treatment of the metropolitan sewage.

entering from the left in Figure 28-1 were themselves heavily polluted. The waters of the other tributary were of significantly better quality than that of the main stream.

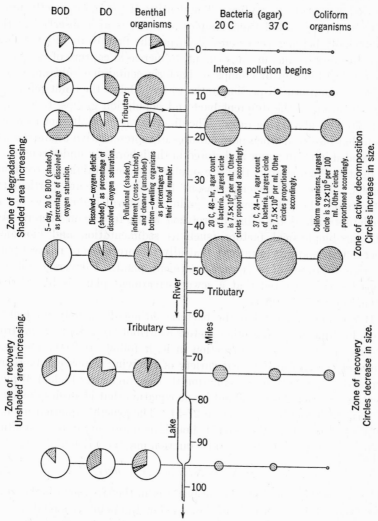

Figure 28-1. Pollution and self-purification of a large stream.

28-4. Rates of Bacterial Self-Purification.

The discharge into a receiving water of sewage and other waste waters that are rich in decomposable matter vastly increases the number and genera of saprophytic bacteria that are essential to self-purification. The multiplying organisms are derived in part from the waste water, in part from the receiving waters. Other saprophytes enter from other sources. Only after they have come into balance with the food supply under the prevailing environmental conditions does the number and variety of saprophytes begin to decline. The density of the more strictly intestinal bacteria isolated from samples of water is also observed to rise appreciably below a sewer outfall during the first 10 to 12 hr of flow. But this may be due, in some extent, to increased capture of organisms by the breaking-up of clumps of bacteria-containing substances and their more uniform dispersion in the water. Below the points of modal concentration of the different bacterial population groups, their numbers drop off at varying rates. The die-away is normally not identical with that observed when pure cultures of representative organisms are suspended in clean water and stored in the laboratory under conditions of light and temperature that are similar to those obtaining in receiving waters. There are several reasons for this. Two are particularly important: (1) the presence, in polluted, natural bodies of water, of predators such as the ciliated protozoa which feed upon bacteria and (2) the biophysical factors (such as sedimentation and biological flocculation and precipitation) that ally the processes of natural purification to those of a sewage-treatment plant. Conversely, it has indeed been suggested that a sewage-treatment plant is like a river wound up in small space.

If we acknowledge that the bacteria do not die merely for lack of food, but that numerous other factors contribute to their removal from the flowing water and destruction in it, it follows that the die-away curve of bacteria in the great variety of receiving waters can be represented broadly only by an equation that characterizes biological purification (Section 25-9) and not by an equation that identifies die-away in terms of Chick's law (Section 27-5). The general equation for rate of purification (Equation 25-15) should, therefore, apply to most situations. To suit our purposes, this equation may be written as follows: [3]

$$(N_0 - y)/N_0 = N/N_0 = (1 + nkt)^{-1/n} \qquad 28\text{-}1$$

Here, N_0 is the modal number of bacteria in the stream; y is the number removed during a time of flow t below the point of modal density to leave a number N; k (or $k' = k \log e$) is the initial die-away con-

---

[3] Phelps suggests using the equation $N/N_0 = pe^{-k_1 t} + (1 - p)e^{-k_2 t}$ on the assumption that a given population group is composed of two different fractions: a less resistant fraction $0 > p \gtrless 1$ with a die-away constant k_1 and a more resistant fraction $1 < (1 - p) \geqq 0$ with a die-away constant $k_2 < k_1$. (E. B. Phelps, *Stream Sanitation*, John Wiley & Sons, New York, p. 211, 1944.) Equation 28-2 is obtained when $p = 1$.

stant for a specific bacterial population group in the environments created within the receiving water; and n is its associated coefficient of non-uniformity. Equation 28-1 merges into the form known as Chicks law only when $n = 0$ (i.e. uniformity of removal). It then becomes: [3]

$$(N_0 - y)/N_0 = N/N_0 = e^{-kt} \qquad 28\text{-}2$$

The variation of N/N_0 with kt described by these equations is shown in Figure 25-11.

Both k and n vary in magnitude with the nature of the stream, the concentration of pollution, and the temperature of the water. Only in very clean and quiescent bodies of water can the value of k be expected to be as low as that observed in laboratory experiments on the die-away of pure cultures in pure water. Polluted, shallow, and turbulent streams offer (1) relatively extensive surfaces for contact between the flowing water and surface growths and (2) mixing of the waters or contact opportunity. If such streams are fairly heavily polluted, their initial rates of die-away (k values) are very high. The opposite is true of deep, sluggish streams with a high dilution factor. Rapid purification is accompanied by greater non-uniformity, or higher n values, because heavy pollution is quickly succeeded by a cleaner environment that possesses poorer purification powers. As a result, die-aways of the lower proportions (5% or less) of coliform organisms, for example, take substantially the same length of time in the two types of streams. A lowering of water temperature decreases the k values and increases the n values; i.e., the initial rate of die-away is decreased while the non-uniformity of purification is increased. Bacterial self-purification is thereby delayed.

We arrive at the apparently anomalous conclusion that the destruction of enteric bacteria is more rapid: (1) in heavily polluted streams than in clean streams; (2) in warm weather than in cold weather; and (3) in shallow turbulent streams than in deep sluggish bodies of water.

Example 28-1. The observed removal of coliform organisms in a small stream [4] (A) and a large stream [5] (B), during summer weather, are shown in Table 28-1. Estimate the values of k and n.

TABLE 28-1. Observed Removal of Coliform Organisms (Example 28-1)

Time of flow, hr	10	20	100
Removal: Stream A,[4] %	97.5	97.9	98.9
Stream B,[5] %	36	59	98.7

[4] After Kittrell and Kochtitzky, *Sewage Works J. 19,* 1044 (1947).

[5] After Frost and Streeter, Ohio River from Cincinnati to Louisville.

Plotting the data on semilogarithmic paper will show that the results recorded for Stream B are closely approximated by a straight line with a slope of 0.044 per hr, whereas no such simple fit is possible for Stream A.

For high values of k and n, Equation 28-1 can be transformed into the following approximate relationship for the determination of n:

$$n = (\log t_2/t_1)/(\log p_1/p_2) \quad \text{where } p = N/N_0 \qquad 28\text{-}3$$

Applying this approximation to the observed die-aways in Stream A, $n = 3.98$, 2.49, and 2.80, averaging 3.09. The corresponding values of k (Equation 28-1) are then: 2,880, 2,470, 3,650, and average 3,000. Using $k = 3,000$ and $n = 3.09$ for Stream A, and $k = 0.044$ and $n = 0$ for Stream B, the calculated removals of coliforms are shown in Table 28-2.

TABLE 28-2. Calculated Removal of Coliform Organisms (Example 28-2)

Time of flow, hr	10	20	100
Removal: Stream A, %	97.5	98.0	98.8
Stream B, %	36	59	98.8

It should be noted that after 100 hr of flow the percentage removals are essentially the same in both streams. At that time, the rate of die-away in Stream B is $kN = 0.044\ (100 - 98.7) = 5.7 \times 10^{-2}\%$ per hr instead of 4.4% per hr, whereas that in Stream A, as suggested by Equation 25-14, has been reduced from an initial value of $3 \times 10^5\%$ per hr to:

$$k \left(\frac{N}{N_0}\right)^n N = 3,000 \left(\frac{100 - 98.9}{100}\right)^{3.09} (100 - 98.9) = 2.93 \times 10^{-3}\ \% \text{ per hr}$$

The time required for bacterial self-purification is seen to be long. The associated distance of travel may be very great. Ordinarily, it is so great indeed that English bacteriologists concluded many years ago that the streams of their country were never long enough to insure the bacteriological safety of receiving waters, even when the initial pollution was not sufficiently intense to create a nuisance.

The die-away of coliforms inoculated into natural sea water under laboratory conditions is reported to be many times as rapid (about 25 times) as in sea water that has been autoclaved.[6] The lethal factors, or substances, involved are apparently organic in nature and heat labile. The elaboration of antibiotic substances by marine organisms may explain this observation. The rapid disappearance of coliform bacteria from sewage-polluted sea water accounts for the observation that a dilution factor of 200 to 250 will reduce the coliform organisms in sewage to 10 per ml or less, whereas dispersion unac-

[6] B. H. Ketchum, C. L. Carey, and Margaret Briggs, "Preliminary Studies on the Viability and Dispersal of Coliform Bacteria in the Sea," *Limnological Aspects of Water Supply and Waste Disposal*, Am. Assoc. Advance. Sci., Washington, D. C., p. 64, 1949.

companied by rapid die-away would call for a dilution factor more than 10^3 times as great.

28-5. The Oxygen Economy of Polluted Waters. In nature, clean waters are saturated with dissolved oxygen, or nearly so. Normally, therefore, waste matters discharged into natural waters undergo aerobic decomposition. Only when the supply of oxygen present in solution or taken into solution—principally from the atmosphere—cannot keep pace with the biochemical oxygen demand of the waste matters does the receiving water, and with it the type of decomposition, become anaerobic. Although the ultimate result of both types of decomposition is a purified water, the conditions associated with each are as different as those obtaining in an activated-sludge unit on the one hand and in a septic tank on the other. Under aerobic conditions, the receiving waters remain reasonably clean in appearance and free from odor. Within limits, such waters continue to support their normal animal and plant populations. Under anaerobic conditions, by contrast, the waters become black, unsightly, and malodorous, and their normal fauna and flora are destroyed. A septic receiving water usually creates a nuisance that makes itself felt over long reaches of the stream, because anaerobic decomposition is so much slower than aerobic decomposition.

For the maintenance of normally satisfactory conditions, therefore, the oxygen economy of the receiving water is of paramount consideration. In order to maintain a balanced ledger, biochemical oxygen demand on the debit side must not exceed available oxygen supply on the credit side. Exertion of the BOD results in *deoxygenation* of the receiving waters. Absorption of oxygen from the atmosphere and from oxygen released by green plants during photosynthesis results in *reoxygenation* or *reaeration* of the receiving waters. The interplay between deoxygenation and reaeration produces the dissolved-oxygen profile of a stream called the *oxygen sag* (Section 28-10).

28-6. Deoxygenation of Polluted Waters. It is generally assumed that the demands made upon the oxygen resources of polluted streams by the living organisms engaged in the utilization and the accompanying destruction or stabilization of decomposable substances are the same as those recorded in the laboratory when samples of waste water that have been mixed with convenient amounts of synthetic dilution water are subjected to BOD tests (Section 19-5). This assumption overlooks the fact that the biophysical as well as the biochemical environment of BOD bottles cannot possibly be like that of every kind of stream, even when the temperature of incubation of the bottles is that of the stream water. Fortunately, for engineering predictions of the deoxygenation of large and important streams, the correlation between (1) laboratory observations of the BOD of polluted waters and (2) field investigations of the reaction of such streams to pollution is usually high.

When, by contrast, streams are shallow and turbulent, the rate of deoxygenation is stepped up appreciably and for much the same reasons as bacterial self-purification. Deoxygenation may indeed approach that experienced in submerged biological treatment systems. At the same time, the rate of BOD drops off along the course of the stream below the point of maximum pollution, again in accordance with the experience with bacterial die-away in streams. In such situations, adjustments in estimates must be made and it is not possible to apply generalized laboratory results directly to the solution of deoxygenation problems. Adjustments must be made also: (1) when the decomposition of the waste matters in the stream progresses far enough to pass beyond the first-stage BOD into the nitrification stage; (2) when the BOD of the waste waters themselves lies within the nitrification stage (biologically treated sewage, for example) or is close to it; and (3) when part of the pollutional load is transferred to the stream bottom where it undergoes benthal decomposition.

The 5-day, 20 C BOD of domestic sewages upon which engineering calculations of deoxygenation are generally based has been shown in Table 20-4. If the waste waters are composed of combined sewage, or, if they contain industrial wastes, or other polluting (oxygen-demanding) substances, the pollutional load can be accounted for in terms of the equivalent domestic population. As stated in Section 20-17, the population equivalent of combined sewage is generally of the order of 1.4 times the tributary population. The population equivalents of industrial wastes are discussed in Chapter 29.

28-7. Rate of Deoxygenation by the Suspended and Dissolved Load.

If the decomposition of waste matters discharged into a stream falls within the first-stage BOD and the rate of BOD of these waste matters is constant and known for a given temperature, the oxygen demands made upon a large, relatively deep, and sluggish stream can be calculated from the formulations given in Section 19-5: $y = L(1 - e^{-kt})$, (Equation 19-2); $L = L_0 e^{C_L(T - T_0)}$, (Equation 19-9); and $k = k_0 e^{C_k(T - T_0)}$, (Equation 19-8). Here, y is the BOD exerted in time t; L is the first-stage BOD of the waste matter at the point of pollution; e is the Napierian base; k is the rate of BOD; C_L and C_k are the temperature characteristics; T is the temperature of the receiving water; and the subscripts zero denote the reference values of k, L, T, y, and t. In terms of these reference values (k_0, T_0, y_0, and t_0) and of C_L and C_k, the BOD y exerted in a given time t and at a given temperature T is:

$$y = y_0 e^{C_L(T-T_0)} \frac{1 - e^{-k_0 t e^{C_k(T-T_0)}}}{1 - e^{-k_0 t_0}} \qquad 28\text{-}4$$

Similarly, the ultimate first-stage BOD is:

$$L = y_0 e^{C_L(T-T_0)}/(1 - e^{-k_0 t_0}) \qquad 28\text{-}5$$

The rate of deoxygenation at the instant of time t is given by the first derivative of Equation 19-2, or

$$dy/dt = k(L - y) = kLe^{-kt} \qquad 28\text{-}6$$

For dy/dt in per cent of the first-stage demand per unit of time,

$$dy/dt = 100ke^{-kt} = 100k_0 e^{C_k(T-T_0)} e^{-k_0 t e^{C_k(T-T_0)}} \qquad 28\text{-}7$$

Example 28-2. A mixture of domestic sewage and river water has a 5-day, 20 C BOD of 18.0 mg/l, none of which settles out. Find (*a*) its 2-day, 30 C BOD, (*b*) its rate of BOD after 2 days, and (*c*) its ultimate first-stage BOD on the assumption that the BOD rate constant at 20 C is 0.23 per day and that the temperature characteristics of the first-stage demand and of the rate constant are respectively 0.020 and 0.046 per degree C. See Tables A-7 and A-8 for values of e^{-x}.

a. In accordance with Equation 28-4:

$$y = 18.0 e^{0.020 \times 10} \frac{1 - e^{-0.23 \times 2 e^{0.046 \times 10}}}{1 - e^{-0.23 \times 5}}$$

$$= 18.0 \times 1.22 \frac{1 - e^{-0.46 \times 1.58}}{1 - e^{-1.15}} = \frac{18.0 \times 1.22(1 - 0.483)}{1 - 0.317} = 16.6 \text{ mg/l}$$

b. By Equation 28-7:

$$dy/dt = 100 \times 0.23 \times e^{0.046 \times 10} \times e^{-0.23 \times 2 e^{0.046 \times 10}}$$

$$= 100 \times 0.23 \times 1.58 \times 0.483 = 17.5\%$$

per day of the first-stage demand after two days, compared with an initial rate:

$$dy/dt = 100 \times 0.23 \times e^{0.046 \times 10} = 100 \times 0.23 \times 1.58 = 36.4\%$$

of the first-stage demand per day at the outset.

c. By Equation 28-5:

$$L = 18.0 \frac{e^{0.020 \times 10}}{(1 - e^{-0.23 \times 5})} = \frac{18.0 \times 1.22}{0.683} = 32.2 \text{ mg/l (at 30 C)}$$

compared with $L_0 = 32.2/1.22 = 26.3$ mg/l (at 20 C).

The oxygen demand of waste matters that are emptied into a small, relatively shallow, and rapid stream can be calculated from the general formulation given in Section 25-9 or Section 28-4. For comparison with Equation 19-2, which is a special case of this formulation ($n = 0$), we may write: [7]

$$y = L[1 - (1 + nkt)^{-1/n}]$$ 28-8

Use of this formulation requires a knowledge of the coefficient of non-uniformity n which varies widely in streams of the kind under consideration.

The rate of deoxygenation of these streams is

$$\frac{dy}{dt} = k\left(\frac{L - y}{n}\right)^{n}(L - y) = kL[1 + nkt]^{-1/n}$$ 28-9

The rate of BOD of polluted sea water appears to vary with the concentration of the sea water. In low concentrations (up to about 25%), k is larger than in fresh water. In straight sea water it is less. No change appears to take place in the magnitude of the first-stage demand. A second stage is observed, but it is retarded.[8]

There is, as yet, no satisfactory formulation of the nitrification stage of the BOD curve. The relationship of nitrified sewage effluents to stream sanitation has been discussed in Section 25-10.

28-8. Rate of Deoxygenation by the Benthal Load. Mud and sludge deposits are composites of settleable solids that have been laid down and impounded, generally over long periods of time during which stream currents were too sluggish (1) to prevent the sedimentation of suspended matter or (2) to encourage bottom scour. If the overriding waters contain dissolved oxygen, aerobic conditions are maintained at the surface of the accumulating organic debris. Diffusion of oxygen into the deposits is normally too slow, however, to carry enough oxygen to the deeper strata to keep them from becoming anaerobic.

The sludge-water interface is by no means static. During periods of sedimentation, settling solids form new surface layers. During periods of scour, the deposits are churned up. The entire sludge load may indeed be resuspended and moved away. Some bottom-dwelling organisms, such as the sludge worms and insect larvae (Figure 19-6), ingest subsurface debris and cast their fecal pellets upon the mud surface; other organisms burrow into the deposits and expose the spoil to the flowing water. Gases of decomposition are produced within the sludge. If they are released in sufficient volume, they may

[7] This equation is identical with Equation 28-1.

[8] H. B. Gotaas, "The Effect of Sea Water on the Biochemical Oxidation of Sewage," *Sewage Works J. 21*, 818 (1949).

buoy some of the sludge into the supernatant water (and even to the water surface). Hydrography determines the degree of deposition as well as the rate of scour, whereas temperature establishes the intensity of decomposition or sludge activity. Because the processes of decomposition in deep deposits are largely anaerobic, their rate of stabilization is normally much slower than that of the suspended and dissolved pollutional load.

The deposition of bottom deposits is not necessarily detrimental to the sanitary economy of a stream. In fact, it may be of considerable help. Transfer of the settleable load to the stream bottom delays the demands made upon the supply of dissolved oxygen and reduces them in proportion to the degree of anaerobic stabilization of the sediments. The winter's accumulation may be washed away by spring freshets (the spring housecleaning of the stream) and give the waters a new start at the beginning of what is usually the most dangerous season: summer, when stream flows are low and rates of decomposition are high.

Although the rate of deoxygenation by the benthal load can be formulated by Equation 28-8, the magnitudes of the constants that should be applied in different circumstances are not sufficiently well known to make the formulation widely useful. Use of the following approximate relationship is, therefore, suggested for the determination of the maximum, daily, benthal oxygen demand of an accumulating sediment: [9]

$$y_m = 3.14 \times 10^{-2} y_0 C_T w \frac{5 + 160w}{1 + 160w} \sqrt{t_a}$$

$$= 3.14 \times 10^{-2} y_0 C_T w' \frac{5 + 0.02w'}{1 + 0.02w'} \sqrt{t_a} \qquad 28\text{-}10$$

Here y_m is the maximum daily benthal oxygen demand either in grams per square meter (for w) or in lb per acre (for w'); y_0 is the 5-day, 20-C BOD in grams per kilogram of volatile matter. $C_T = y/y_0$ is the temperature factor of Equation 28-4 for $t = t_0 = 5$ days and $T_0 = 20$ C; w and w' are respectively the daily rates of deposition of volatile solids in kilograms per square meter and pounds per acre; and t_a is the time in days up to 365 days during which accumulation takes place.

Example 28-3. On a daily per capita basis, the 5-day, 20-C BOD of 39 grams of volatile settleable solids of a domestic sewage is 19 grams (Table 20-4), 10

[9] G. M. Fair, E. W. Moore, and H. A. Thomas, Jr., "The Natural Purification of River Muds and Pollutional Sediments," *Sewage Works J. 13*, 270, 756 (1941).

grams of volatile solids being deposited daily per square meter of stream bottom during a period of 100 days. Find the maximum daily benthal oxygen demand of the accumulating sediment if the water temperature remains constant at 20 C.

Since a BOD of 19 grams produced by 39 grams of volatile solids equals $19 \times 1,000/39 = 500$ grams per kilogram of volatile matter, and since the temperature factor C_T is unity at 20 C, Equation 28-10 states that

$$y_m = 3.14 \times 10^{-2} \times 500 \times 1 \times 10 \times 10^{-3} \frac{5 + 160 \times 10 \times 10^{-3}}{1 + 160 \times 10 \times 10^{-3}} \sqrt{100}$$

$$= 4.0 \text{ grams per sq m daily}$$

If the deposits are laid down in equal increments and they remain sufficiently thin to be decomposed aerobically, their maximum daily rate of deoxygenation will equal the BOD exerted by a single day's accession of settleable solids during a period of time equal to the period of sludge accumulation. This follows from the fact that the deposit will include the following: (1) the first day's batch of solids which is exerting its first-day demand; (2) the preceding day's batch which is exerting its second-day demand; (3) the second preceding day's batch which is exerting its third-day demand, etc., back to the beginning of sludge accumulation. In these circumstances, for example, the solids accumulating in 5 days at a daily rate of 10 grams of volatile matter per square meter of stream bottom and possessing a 5-day, 20 C BOD of 500 grams per kilogram of volatile matter, may be estimated to reach a maximum rate of deoxygenation of $500 \times 10 \times 10^{-3} = 5$ grams per square meter daily if the temperature is 20 C.

Scour of sludge deposits or the lifting of sludge masses into the supernatant waters may exert sudden, sometimes overpowering, oxygen demands upon receiving waters. Such occurrences are similar to the degrading effects of rising sludge in septic tanks. In the normal course of events, some of the products of anaerobic decomposition (from the nitrogen-containing substances, for example) leach into the supernatant water where they are oxidized. This is a complicating factor in stream sanitation. The seasonal destruction of bottom-dwelling organisms, too, may create abnormal oxygen demands. If they are washed into ponds, lakes, reservoirs, and backwaters, they may form secondary sludge deposits with high BOD values.

28-9. Atmospheric Reoxygenation of Polluted Waters. Aside from the oxygen released by green plants during photosynthesis, the oxygen dissolved in streams and other bodies of water and needed for the maintenance of an aerobic biological environment is derived in nature from the atmosphere with which these waters are in contact. Although photosynthesis may make considerable amounts of oxygen available, oxygenation by green plants is confined: (a) to waters that are not

sufficiently degraded by pollution to destroy the green plants, which
are fairly intolerant of pollution; (b) to waters that have sufficiently
recovered from pollution to reestablish the presence of green plants;
(c) to the hours of daylight; and (d) to the warmer (growing) seasons
of the year. During the night, green aquatic plants abstract oxygen
from the water. There results a diurnal cycle of dissolved oxygen
within waters that are rich in vegetation, the amplitude of this cycle
varying with the intensity of sunlight and the density of the plant
population. For these reasons, then, this source of oxygen, important
as it may be in the total oxygen economy of natural waters, cannot
generally be included in engineering calculations of the oxygen balance
of polluted waters. Reliance can be placed only on the oxygen absorbed from the atmosphere at the air-water interface. Ice cover
shuts off the air contact, and winter conditions may, in certain circumstances, produce worse oxygen deficits than summer conditions,
in spite of lowered rates of deoxygenation and higher oxygen-satura-
tion values of cold waters.

The rate at which water that is not saturated with oxygen absorbs
this gas from the atmosphere has been discussed in Section 17-5. If,
in Equation 17-9, $(c_s - c_0) = D_a$, $(c_s - c_t) = D$, and $K_g = r$, where
D_a is the initial dissolved-oxygen deficit, D is the deficit after time
t, and r is the rate of reoxygenation of the body of water, we may write

$$D = D_a e^{-rt} \qquad \text{28-11}$$

and

$$dD/dt = -rD \qquad \text{28-12}$$

In accordance with Section 17-5, the magnitude of r is not only a function of water temperature but also of the area of the air-water interface in relation to the volume of water and the renewal of this interface by the film-reducing movements of the water and of the air above
it. The variation of r with temperature can be formulated in accordance with the van't Hoff-Arrhenius equation as

$$r = r_0 e^{C_r(T - T_0)} \qquad \text{28-13}$$

Here C_r is the temperature characteristic of the rate of reoxygenation
r, and T is the temperature of the water, the subscript zero designating
the reference values. Within the range of normal water temperatures,
the magnitude of C_r derived from Becker's observations (Section 17-5)
is about 0.018 when the water temperature is measured in degrees C.

The variation of r with surface exposure and depth and with the
rate at which the water is mixed by vertical and horizontal currents

that distribute the absorbed oxygen through the water and bring new volumes of undersaturated water into contact with the atmosphere is very great. For want of a satisfactory definition of mixing effects we must at present be satisfied with over-all values that have been observed in studies of standing and flowing waters. See Section 28-11.

Example 28-4. A large polluted stream flowing at low velocity contains 2.2 mg/l of dissolved oxygen at 15 C. Find: (a) the amount of oxygen added during 2 days of flow; (b) the maximum rate of reoxygenation if decomposition is sufficiently active to keep the dissolved-oxygen content of the stream at 2 mg/l. Assume a rate of reoxygenation of 0.40 per day at 20 C and a temperature characteristic of 0.018.

The DO saturation value of fresh water at 15 C is 10.2 mg/l (Table A-6). Hence the DO deficit of the stream is: $D_a = (10.2 - 2.2) = 8.0$ mg/l.

a. In accordance with Equation 28-13: $r = 0.40e^{0.018(15 - 20)} = 0.40 \times 0.91 = 0.36$.

By Equation 28-11, therefore: $D = 8.0e^{-0.37 \times 2} = 8.0 \times 0.47 = 3.8$ mg/l.

b. By Equation 28-12: $dD/dt = -0.37 \times 8 = -3.0$ mg/l per day. In accordance with the statement of the problem, this is also the rate of deoxygenation.

28-10. The Dissolved-Oxygen Sag. The interplay of the deoxygenation of polluted waters (BOD) and their reoxygenation, or reaeration, from the atmosphere creates a spoon-shaped profile of the dissolved-oxygen (DO) deficit along the path of water movement. This profile is called "the dissolved oxygen sag." Its genesis is portrayed in Figure 28-2. The general mathematical properties of the sag curve, which underlie engineering calculations of the permissible pollutional loading of receiving waters, have been formulated in the classical studies of Streeter and Phelps.[10]

The basic differential equation that identifies the combined action of deoxygenation and reaeration states that the net rate of change in the DO deficit (dD/dt) is equal to the sum of (1) the oxygen utilization by BOD in the absence of reaeration $[dD/dt = k(L_a - y)]$ and (2) the rate of oxygen absorption by reaeration in the absence of BOD $(dD/dt = -rD)$, or

$$dD/dt = k(L_a - y) - rD \qquad \text{28-14}$$

Integration between the limits D_a at the point of pollution, or reference point, $[t = 0, (L_a - y) = L_a]$ and D at any point distant a time of flow t from the reference point yields the equation

$$D = \frac{kL_a}{r - k} (e^{-kt} - e^{-rt}) + D_a e^{-rt} \qquad \text{28-15}$$

[10] H. W. Streeter and E. B. Phelps, *U. S. Pub. Health Bull.* 146 (1925).

This relationship may be used to find any point on the oxygen-sag curve. If, in Equation 28-15, the ratio of the rates of reaeration and

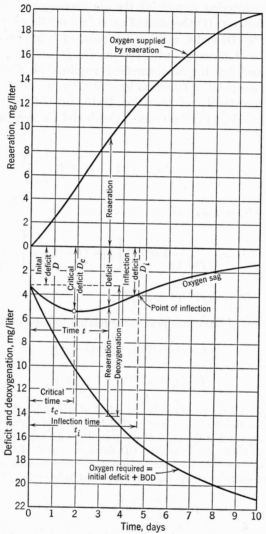

Figure 28-2. The dissolved-oxygen sag and its components: deoxygenation and reaeration.

deoxygenation r/k which may be termed the rate of self-purification f of the particular body of water is used insofar as possible, the expression becomes

$$D = \frac{L_a}{f-1} e^{-kt} \left\{ 1 - e^{-(f-1)kt} \left[1 - (f-1)\frac{D_a}{L_a} \right] \right\} \qquad 28\text{-}16$$

From an engineering standpoint the sag curve possesses two points of particular interest: (1) the point of maximum deficit, or critical point, with coordinates D_c and t_c and (2) the point of inflection, or point of maximum rate of recovery, with coordinates D_i and t_i. The critical point is defined by the mathematical requirement $dD/dt = 0$ and $d^2D/dt^2 < 0$; the point of inflection by $d^2D/dt^2 = 0$. If we perform the necessary differentiation of Equation 28-15, we obtain the following simplified expressions for the times t_c and t_i and the associated deficits D_c and D_i:[11, 12]

$$t_c = \frac{1}{k(f-1)} \log_e \left\{ f\left[1 - (f-1)\frac{D_a}{L_a} \right] \right\} \qquad 28\text{-}17$$

or

$$D_c = L_a e^{-kt_c}/f \qquad 28\text{-}18$$

and

$$t_i = \frac{1}{k(f-1)} \log_e \left\{ f^2 \left[1 - (f-1)\frac{D_a}{L_a} \right] \right\} \qquad 28\text{-}19$$

or

$$D_i = L_a e^{-kt_i}(f+1)/f^2 \qquad 28\text{-}20$$

The coordinates of these two points are related to each other as follows:

$$t_i - t_c = (\log_e f)/[k(f-1)] \qquad 28\text{-}21$$

and

$$D_i/D_c = e^{-k(t_i-t_c)}(f+1)/f \qquad 28\text{-}22$$

Example 28-5. A large stream possesses a rate of self-purification $f = 2.4$ and a rate of deoxygenation $k = 0.23$ per day. The DO deficit of the mixture of stream water and waste water at the point of reference D_a is 3.2 mg/l, and its first-stage BOD L_a is 20.0 mg/l. Find: (a) the DO deficit at a point 1 day distant from the point of reference; (b) the magnitudes of the critical time and critical deficit; and (c) the magnitudes of the inflection time and inflection deficit.

a. By Equation 28-16: $D = \dfrac{20.0}{1.4} e^{-0.23} \left[1 - e^{-1.4\times0.23}\left(1 - \dfrac{1.4\times3.2}{20.0}\right) \right] = 5.0$ mg/l.

b. By Equation 28-17: $t_c = \dfrac{1}{0.23\times1.4} \log_e \left[2.4\left(1 - \dfrac{1.4\times3.2}{20.0}\right) \right] = 1.93$ days, and by Equation 28-18: $D_c = 20.0e^{-0.23\times1.93}/2.4 = 5.3$ mg/l.

[11] G. M. Fair, "The Dissolved Oxygen Sag—an Analysis," *Sewage Works J.*, 11, 445 (1939).

[12] For the special case $f = 1$, $D = (ktL_a + D_a)e^{-kt}$; $t_c = (1 - D_a/L_a)/k$; $t_i = 2 - D_a/L_a)/k$; and $t_i - t_c = 1/k$.

c. By Equation 28-21: $t_i = 1.93 + (\log_e 2.4)/(0.23 \times 1.4) = 4.65$ days, and by Equation 28-22: $D_i = 5.3e^{-0.23 \times 2.72}/(3.4/2.4) = 4.0$ mg/l.

If part of the pollutional load settles in the immediate vicinity of the point of pollution, the benthal oxygen demand may be calculated in accordance with Equation 28-10 and assumed to be an added DO deficit at this point. If the deposited load is dispersed over a long river stretch, Equation 28-14 may be expanded to include the rate of removal of BOD due to benthal decomposition.[13] The resulting relationships are:

$$dD/dt = kL_a e^{-(k+d)t} - rD \qquad\qquad 28\text{-}23$$

and

$$D = \frac{kL_a}{r - (k+d)} [e^{-(k+d)t} - e^{-rt}] + D_a e^{-rt} \qquad 28\text{-}24$$

The coefficient of deposition d must reflect (1) the composition of the waste waters and the receiving water and (2) the relative quiescence of the receiving water. In times of considerable turbulence, scour of deposited sludge may render d negative. This then represents an added load.

28-11. Allowable BOD Loading of Receiving Waters. Inspection of Equations 28-16 to 28-18 shows that the pollutional load L_a that can be placed upon a particular receiving water is determined by the magnitudes of the following parameters: (1) its deoxygenation constant k; (2) its self-purification constant $f = r/k$; (3) its critical deficit D_c; and (4) its initial deficit D_a.

1. As pointed out in Section 28-7, the value of the deoxygenation constant k may be expected to vary widely in different receiving waters and along the course of these waters. Only the magnitude $k = 0.23$ per day for large streams of normal velocity appears to be well founded. Departure from this value is expected to be particularly great in shallow, swift streams filled with boulders and debris.

2. Present information on the self-purification constant $f = r/k$ supports the values at 20 C listed in Table 28-3.

This classification of different bodies of water is not sharply defined. Each class merges into its adjacent class, and there is appreciable variation within the types described, as well as within different reaches of the same body of water. In accordance with Equations 28-13 and 19-8, the variation of the self-purification constant $f = r/k$ with temperature is given by the relationship

$$f = f_0 e^{(C_r - C_k)(T - T_0)} = f_0 C_f^{(T - T_0)} \qquad\qquad 28\text{-}25$$

For values of $C_r = 0.018$ and $C_k = 0.046$ within the range of normal water temperatures, $C_f = -0.028$, i.e., the magnitude of f decreases with rising temperatures

---

[13] H. A. Thomas, Jr., "Pollution Load Capacity of Streams," *Water and Sewage Works,* *95,* 409 (1948).

TABLE 28-3. Values of the Self-Purification Constant f

Nature of receiving water	Magnitude of f at 20 C
Small ponds and backwaters	0.5–1.0
Sluggish streams and large lakes or impoundments	1.0–1.5
Large streams of low velocity	1.5–2.0
Large streams of moderate velocity	2.0–3.0
Swift streams	3.0–5.0
Rapids and waterfalls	Above 5.0

and increases with falling temperatures by about 3% compounded per degree C.

3. If septic conditions are to be avoided, the maximum magnitude of the critical deficit D_c is the DO saturation value S of the receiving water, e.g., 9.2 mg/l at 20 C in fresh water. For the support of game fish, such as trout, the DO content must not fall below about 5 mg/l, which gives an allowable critical deficit of but 4.2 mg/l at 20 C.

4. For given values of k, f, and D_c, the initial deficit D_a establishes two boundary values for the maximum loading that can be imposed on a receiving water: (a) an upper limit associated with zero initial deficit or full DO saturation $(D_a = 0)$ and (b) a lower limit associated with an initial deficit equal to the critical deficit $(D_a = D_c)$. These boundary restrictions result in the following boundary relationships for the maximum loading of receiving waters and for the coordinates of the characteristic points of the oxygen sag.

a. For $D_a = 0$ and $D_c \gtrless S$, Equations 28-17, -18, -19, and -22 take the following forms: [14]

$$t_c' = (\log_e f)/[k(f - 1)] \qquad\qquad 28\text{-}26$$

$$L_a'/D_c = f^{f/(f-1)} = f e^{kt_c'} \qquad\qquad 28\text{-}27$$

$$t_i' = 2t_c' \qquad\qquad 28\text{-}28$$

$$D_i'/D_c = (f + 1)D_c/L_a' \qquad\qquad 28\text{-}29$$

b. For $D_a = D_c \gtrless S$, the corresponding forms of Equations 28-17, -18, -19, and -22 are:

$$t_c'' = 0 \qquad\qquad 28\text{-}30$$

$$L_a''/D_c = f \qquad\qquad 28\text{-}31$$

$$t_i'' = (\log_e f)/[k(f - 1)] = t_c' \qquad\qquad 28\text{-}32$$

$$D_i'' = D_i' \qquad\qquad 28\text{-}33$$

The ratio of the upper to the lower limit of maximum loading, therefore, equals

$$L_a'/L_a'' = f^{1/(f-1)} = e^{kt_c'} \qquad\qquad 28\text{-}34$$

Inspection of these boundary equations shows that the allowable loading and the coordinates of the characteristic points of the oxygen sag become simple functions of the coefficient of self-purification when the loading is expressed in terms

---

[14] For the special case $f = 1$, $t_c' = 1/k$, and $L_a'/D_c = e = 2.718$.

of the critical deficit and the critical time is expressed in terms of the product kt_c. It follows that the important parameters of the sag curve can be generalized in such fashion that their values need to be computed but once. They can then be recorded in tabular form, or graphically as in Figure 28-3. Loading curves between the upper and lower boundary values are included in Figure 28-3 in order to make this diagram more widely useful.

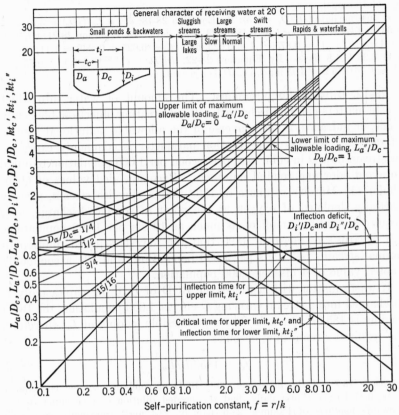

Figure 28-3. Allowable loading of receiving waters and associated coordinates of the critical point and the point of inflection of the dissolved-oxygen sag.

Example 28-6. Find from Figure 28-3 for a water temperature of 20 C and a minimum DO content of 4.0 mg/l (1) the allowable loading and (2) the co-ordinates of the characteristic points of the oxygen sag of a stream with a rate of self-purification $f = 2.4$ and a rate of deoxygenation $k = 0.23$ per day under the following conditions: (a) maximal, $D_a = 0$, (b) minimal, $D_a = D_c$, and (c) intermediate, $D_a = 0.50D_c$ (characteristic points by calculation).

Since the DO saturation value at 20 C is 9.2 mg/l, the critical deficit of the stream is: $D_c = (9.2 - 4.0) = 5.2$ mg/l.

1. Allowable loading.

   a. Maximal $(D_a/D_c = 0)$: $L_a'/D_c = 4.5$; or $L_a' = 4.5 \times 5.2 = 23.4$ mg/l.
   b. Minimal $(D_a/D_c = 1.0)$: $L_a''/D_c = 2.4$; or $L_a'' = 2.4 \times 5.2 = 12.5$ mg/l.
   c. Intermediate $(D_a/D_c = 0.5)$: $L_a/D_c = 3.9$; or $L_a = 3.9 \times 5.2 = 20.3$ mg/l.
   2. Coordinates of characteristic points.
   a. Maximal $(D_a/D_c = 0)$: $kt_c' = 0.62$; or $t_c' = 0.62/0.23 = 2.7$ days. $kt_i' = 1.24$; or $t_i' = 1.24/0.23 = 5.4$ days. $D_i/D_c = 0.76$; or $D_i = 0.76 \times 5.2 = 3.95$ mg/l.
   b. Minimal $(D_a/D_c = 1.0)$: $t_c'' = 0$ by definition. $t_i'' = t_c' = 2.7$ days. $D_i'' = D_i' = 3.95$ mg/l.
   c. Intermediate $(D_a/D_c = 0.5)$: By Equation 28-18: $e^{kt_c} = L_a/(fD_c) = 3.9/2.4 = 1.63$, and $kt_c = 0.489$; or $t_c = 0.489/0.23 = 2.1$ days. By Equation 28-21: $k(t_i - t_c) = (\log_e f)/(f - 1) = 0.8755/1.4 = 0.625$, and $kt_i = (0.625 + 0.489) = 1.11$; or $t_i = 1.11/0.23 = 4.8$ days. By Equation 28-22: $D_i/D_c = e^{-0.625}(3.4/2.4) = 0.758$; or $D_i = 0.76 \times 5.2 = 3.95$ mg/l, i.e., D_i is constant.

28-12. Dilution Requirements. The amount of water into which waste matters can be discharged without creating objectionable conditions, or nuisance, is the converse of the allowable pollutional loading of receiving waters. The dilution parameter is commonly expressed as stream flow Q in cubic feet per second per 1,000 population required to avoid odor and related nuisances. Recommended values of Q include: (1) Hazen's estimate of 1898 that a sluggish stream, already partially depleted of oxygen at the point of sewage discharge, may require a diluting runoff of as much as 10 cfs per 1,000 population; (2) Stearns's estimate of 1890 that the lowest required dilution of normal streams is 2.5 cfs per 1,000 population; and (3) a commonly quoted value of 4 cfs per 1,000 population.

   If waste matter with a first-stage BOD of L lb per capita daily is discharged into a stream carrying Q cfs per 1,000 population, the BOD loading is $185.5L/Q$ mg/l. For a permissible loading of L_a, therefore, the required stream flow becomes

$$Q = 185.5L/L_a \qquad\qquad 28\text{-}35$$

   Example 28-7. If the first-stage, 20-C BOD of combined sewage is assumed to be 0.25 lb per capita daily, find the needed dilution corresponding to the allowable loadings of Example 28-6, namely, 23.4 mg/l (maximal), 20.6 mg/l (intermediate), and 12.5 mg/l (minimal) for a DO residual of 4.0 mg/l.

   By Equation 28-35, $Q = 185.5 \times 0.25/L_a = 46.4/L_a$ cfs or, respectively, 2.0, 2.3, and 3.7 cfs per 1,000 persons daily depending upon the magnitude of the initial deficit $(D_a = 0, 2.6,$ and 5.2 mg/l respectively).

28-13. Sewage Fields in Lakes and Coastal Waters. The natural progress of dispersion of waste waters in lakes and coastal waters is slow. The turbulence common to streams and other flowing waters is absent. Also, the waste waters are generally lower in density than the receiving waters, because the waste waters are warmer than the receiving waters and the receiving waters possess an inherently greater density when they are salt or brackish. The rate of chemical diffusion being relatively insignificant, natural mixing of the unlike waters then becomes a function of wind, currents, and (in the sea) tide. The work to be done if mixing is to disperse the wastes uniformly in the receiving waters is great (see Section 17-7). As a result, the proper design of outfalls challenges the ingenuity of the engineer. Thorough hydrographic exploration of the receiving water is an important matter which usually requires much effort, if dilution is to be effective. Dispersion of pollutants and opportunity for natural purification become especially significant when water intakes, bathing beaches, shellfish layings, and shore properties are to be protected. In lakes and ponds, normal and wind-induced currents should be studied to find the most favorable location of outfalls. In tidal waters, tidal currents and the volume of the tidal prism must be known.

A number of different methods are used singly, or in combination, to prevent the formation of a sewage field of considerable thickness and area at the surface of the receiving water: (1) the waste water is discharged in small amounts at a number of different points; (2) the outfall is constructed with multiple outlets that are suitably spaced and designed to accomplish as much mixing as possible; and (3) the outfall is submerged in order to induce vertical as well as horizontal dispersion of the waste matters. Horizontal or inclined, submerged discharge is more effective than vertical discharge, because the longer path followed by the rising sewage or waste water offers better opportunity for mixing. The flow pattern traced by the waste water is much like that of a smoke plume from a chimney. When the rising column of waste water reaches the surface, it spreads out horizontally in the same manner as smoke under conditions of atmospheric inversion.

Observations by the California State Board of Health [15] show that the area of the "sleek" field that is created by the discharge of raw sewage through submerged outfalls into salt water is related to the tributary population roughly as follows:

$$A = P(11.5 - 3.5 \log P) \qquad\qquad 28\text{-}36$$

where A is the area in acres and $P (\lesseqgtr 1,000)$ is the population in thousands. This relationship is useful in making a first estimate of the length of outfall required to keep beach waters free from sleek and associated bacterial contamination. Looking at dilution as a treatment process, it is evident that the areal rate of treatment is relatively small.

15 *Eng. News-Rec.*, *123*, 690 (1939).

For a per capita discharge of Q gpd, the areal rate of treatment Q' in gallons per day per acre becomes roughly

$$Q' = 1{,}000Q/(11.5 - 3.5 \log P) \qquad 28\text{-}37$$

At best, this is an areal loading of the order of magnitude of intermittent sand filters.

More exactly, the area and configuration of sewage fields is a function of the following physical factors: rate of discharge; diameter, direction, and submergence of outlet nozzle; and speed of water currents. These control the thickness and horizontal spread of the field and the associated mixing or dilution. Use of multiple outlets will normally produce some overlap but will remain advantageous. Empirical formulations of the extent of sewage fields in sea water have been developed by Rawn and Palmer.[16]

28-14. Control Works. The volume of waste water that can safely be emptied into a natural, receiving body of water can be increased not only by the proper location and design of outfalls and by suitable treatment of the waste water before discharge but also by (a) regulation of waste discharge, (b) control of the flow of the receiving water (low-water regulation), (c) strengthening the power for self-purification of the receiving water, and (d) limitation of sludge deposition. The husbanding, by suitable control works, of the forces of self-purification that inhere in natural bodies of water is an important engineering responsibility.

a. *Regulation of Discharge.* Fluctuation in flow or volume of the receiving water, variations in other hydrographic conditions, and changes in season may justify the storage of waste waters in basins or lagoons (often for protracted periods of time) in order to adjust the release of waste matters to the load capacity of the receiving waters. Fluctuations in rate of flow and in strength of waste water can be ironed out at the same time or by similar means. The impounded wastes can then be released in quantities and concentrations that stand in optimal ratios to the flow, or volume, and to the self-purifying power of the receiving water. Water intakes may be safeguarded, in some situations, by confining the discharge of waste waters to certain periods of time and withdrawal of water to the remaining time. Tidal waters can be protected by release of waste waters during certain stages of the tide (normally the falling tide). Disposal into streams of particularly dangerous or obnoxious wastes, or wastes diffi-

---

[16] A. M. Rawn and H. K. Palmer, "Predetermining the Extent of a Sewage Field in Sea Water," *Trans., Am. Soc. Civil Engrs., 94,* 1036 (1929).

cult of treatment, and of sewage sludge can sometimes be confined to the high-water stages of the receiving water and to periods of cold weather. The impounding of wastes for selective discharge into inland waters at convenient times has been found to be particularly applicable to industrial wastes (especially when they are seasonally produced) and to sewage sludges. The impounding of municipal sewage is uncommon, except on the seacoast.

Treatment of waste waters before discharge may be adjusted also to the seasonally changing requirements of receiving waters. Chemical precipitation or biological treatment processes (provided as part of a treatment plant, for example) may be placed in operation only during the summer months, while the receiving water is at low stage and its oxygen demand is high. Complete treatment may be confined to the bathing season. Disinfection of treatment-plant effluents may also be confined to the bathing season or to the season for harvesting shellfish from the receiving waters. At other times, treatment may be carried no farther than plain sedimentation.

b. Low-Water Regulation. It is usually immaterial whether the pollutional load imposed on a unit volume of water is reduced by modifying the concentration or rate of discharge of the waste water or by regulating the flow of diluting water. In terms of the oxygen sag, maintenance of adequate clean-water flows does not only supply dissolved oxygen directly, it also increases the rate of reaeration of the polluted waters by greater turbulence or by enlarging the water surface, generally by both. The direct effect of dilution on the concentration of waste matters and living organisms is self-evident.

The diluting waters may be supplied (1) from upstream storage of flood waters in impounding reservoirs, (2) by diversion of waters from nearby catchment areas, or (3) by pumping water from lower reaches of a stream or from a lake or other body of water back into critical stretches. Low-water regulation should be part of the regional development of available water resources. Upstream reservoirs may then be designed to serve the multiple purposes dictated by the water economy of the area. These may include water supply, power development, flood control, navigation, irrigation, recreation, and the conservation of useful aquatic life.

c. Regulation of Natural Purification. The amount of self-purification that can be accomplished in a receiving water can be increased (1) if the time of passage through a given stretch of water is lengthened; (2) if the rate of reaeration is stepped up; and (3) if the accumulation of sludge deposits is controlled.

Impounding reservoirs that lie below the point of pollution lengthen the time of flow, expand the water surface, and cause the deposition of suspended solids. The combined effect is well illustrated in Figure 28-1. However, the sludge load that can be placed on such reservoirs is strictly limited. Sedimentation of waste waters that carry large amounts of suspended matter should generally precede their discharge into receiving waters that include impounding reservoirs or natural storage in ponds and lakes. Impounding reservoirs must be designed to maintain a favorable oxygen balance during self-purification. If the pollutional load becomes too heavy, relative to stream flow and reservoir surface, the purification processes that establish themselves in the reservoir will become offensive; more oxygen is then used up than can be supplied; the water becomes septic; all living things that depend upon free oxygen for respiration die off; and the reservoir does more harm than good. Oxidation ponds (see Section 28-15) are an interesting example of controlled self-purification by impoundage of undiluted waste waters.

The oxygen supply of a receiving water can be increased by the provision of aeration works. Air may be injected into a stream for this purpose, or the water may be aerated by passage over cascades or similar constructions that improve reoxygenation. As shown by Equation 28-27 and Equation 28-31, the permissible loading of a stream is increased by the factor $f^{1/(f-1)}$ when the receiving water is saturated with oxygen at the point of pollution.[17]

The addition to a receiving water of nitrates to supply needed oxygen is but an emergency measure. Chlorination and the addition of ferric chloride, likewise, are resorted to only in emergencies (see Section 27-13).

d. *Regulation of Sludge Deposition.* Streams that are not subjected to flood-scour are forced to digest benthally, in the course of a year, far greater quantities of sludge than are flood-scoured streams. Absence of scour may also reduce the permeability of river channels that furnish ground water to the valley by bottom and lateral seepage from the river bed. Scouring capacity may be lost when large storage works are constructed in river valleys or when flood waters are diverted into other water sheds.

Scour can be regulated by controlling the discharge from impounding reservoirs and by canalizing receiving streams. The mechanical re-

---

[17] This factor is largest when the coefficient of self-purification is smallest, e.g., it has magnitudes of 4.0, 2.7, 2.0, and 1.6 for values of $f = 0.5$, 1.0, 2.0, and 4.0 respectively.

moval of sludge deposits by dredging is seldom justified economically.

28-15. Oxidation Ponds. Oxidation ponds are shallow basins excavated in the ground for the purpose of purifying settled sewage or other waste water by storage under climatic conditions that favor the growth of algae: namely, warmth and sunshine. Bacterial decomposition of the waste matters releases carbon dioxide; heavy growths of algae develop; ammonia and other plant-growth substances are used up; and dissolved oxygen is kept at a high level. The driving force in this type of self-purification is photosynthesis supported by a symbiosis between saprophytic bacteria and algae.

If oxidation ponds are made 3 to 4 ft deep and hold the sewage for 3 to 4 weeks, a remarkable destruction of coliform organisms (possibly due in part to the production of antibiotic substances by the algae) and a satisfactory reduction in BOD are observed. The effluent is high in DO; often supersaturated during the daytime. The pond waters are so rich in algal cells that some thought has been given to harvesting these cells as a source of protein for animal feed. Allowable surface loadings approach those of intermittent sand filters, but removal efficiencies are somewhat poorer. BOD loadings in the vicinity of 45 lb of 5-day 20 C BOD per acre are generally employed. Oxidation ponds must be cleaned after an interval of several years, and weeds must be kept under control (see Section 27-16).

Where oxidation ponds have been used for fish culture, settled municipal sewage has been diluted with clean water, and their surface loading has been decreased. Weed growths have then been controlled by raising ducks on the ponds.[18]

[18] In North America, oxidation ponds have found good use in the Southwest. Fish ponds have been managed successfully in Western Europe.

29-1. Water and Waste-Water Problems of Industry. Industries require large volumes of water for cooling purposes, steam generation, manufacturing processes, and sanitation. In the production of basic commodities like metals, chemicals, foods, and textiles, the tonnage of water may well exceed that of other raw materials. Finishing and fabrication processes generally need smaller, but nevertheless appreciable, amounts of water. Most of the water used becomes waste water and may carry a heavy burden of polluting substances. For economy of water supply and waste-water disposal, plants that need large amounts of water are commonly located on sizable rivers, lakes, or tidal estuaries. Upon these they impress their presence in numerous ways that are of concern to the water engineer. The supply of water to a given industry and the removal of its waste-waters must be based upon an understanding of the manufacturing processes that require water and produce waste water. A discussion of even the most common industrial processes, however, falls beyond the scope of this book. Standard treatises on industrial chemistry are heavy tomes.

The industrial revolution created industry and concentrated it in areas served by power, transportation, skilled labor, and markets. The march of industrialization and urbanization has continued ever since and, with it, the competition for water. Demands for, and on, water have become more and more pressing, until in some regions of the world industries can no longer, with ease, find sites where good water is abundant and the discharge of waste water is not a matter of serious import. As a result, surveys of available water resources have become a heavy responsibility in the location of new plants. In the interest of the public as well as industry, quantity and quality requirements of needed waters must be projected well into the future and placed in balance with the total water economy. Necessary considerations include the amount of water available, the variability of its quality, the cost of water purification, the hazards of drought and flood, the danger of upstream pollution, the downstream effects of waste discharge, and the cost of waste-water treatment. The regional economy is best served by long-range integrated plans for both urban and industrial development.

Water Supply for Industries

29-2. Quantity and Quality Requirements. The amounts of water used by industry vary widely not only with the type of industrial operation but also with the following: (1) the availability and cost of water; (2) the difficulty of waste-water disposal; (3) the nature of the processes and equipment employed; and (4) the attention given by management and public authorities to water conservation. Among possible measures of conservation by management are: (1) the recirculation of cooling water through ponds or towers; (2) the use of countercurrent washing equipment; (3) the reuse of slightly soiled water (either in the same process after repurification, or in other processes that do not require water of high quality); and (4) the prevention of waste, such as letting flushing lines run continuously. Ranges in amounts of process waters for different industries are given in Table 29-3. To them must be added the water evaporated in the generation of steam for power or other purposes. If the quantities consumed are broken down according to their quality requirements, it may be found that a large percentage of the water, such as cooling water, need not be of high sanitary or chemical quality, although the remaining water, such as high-pressure boiler feed-water and water used in food processing, may have to comply with very strict quality specifications.

The quality tolerances for process waters vary with the manufacturing process and with the quality of the goods to be produced. The point at which it becomes economical to improve the available supply is found through comparisons between (1) the cost of treatment and (2) the increase in value of the product together with the decrease in costs of operation, maintenance, and replacement of equipment. Rising costs, higher standards of production, closer quality control of manufactured articles, and deterioration of water sources have made for a growing awareness of the importance of water quality in industry. When the available water is treated, therefore, the maximum economical improvement in its quality is commonly sought. Tolerances of impurities in the treated water are generally stricter than those for untreated waters that would be used if they were available.

Many industrial products or operations call for water that is clear, colorless, tasteless, relatively soft, free from iron, manganese, hydrogen sulfide, and organic matter, and of approved bacteriological quality. Examples are: bottled beverages, fine chemicals, canned goods, processed milk, ice, packed meat, edible oils, laundering operations, and the printing and dyeing of textiles. Most soft municipal waters are of this nature. Process waters drawn from a private source, however, may have to be purified. The principles of treatment discussed for municipal water supplies apply equally well to the large body of process waters.

Wash waters should be soft when soap is the detergent and when deposition of residues by evaporating rinse water is to be avoided. Among industries that are sensitive to hardness are laundries, electroplating plants, milk plants, ice plants, and textile mills. They generally soften or demineralize the available water. Breweries, distilleries, and bakeries, on the other hand, require relatively hard water for some manufacturing operations and may have to add hardness. Pulp and paper mills, tanneries, oil refineries, and steel mills do not commonly need water of municipal quality. But they may have other requirements. Paper pulp and low-quality paper can be made with colored water that contains as much as 50 mg/l of turbidity, but it should be low in iron and manganese, hardness, and carbon dioxide. Formation of organic slimes and mineral scales must also be kept under control. By contrast, high-quality paper can be manufactured only with high-quality water. The situation is much the same in tanning. In oil refineries and steel mills, water is used primarily for steam production and cooling. Quality requirements for the cooling water of these industries are much the same as those for cooling waters in general (Section 29-6). In the rolling of steel, however, a chloride content above 150 mg/l in cooling water causes rapid deterioration of rolls. Quality tolerances for a variety of process waters are summarized in Table 29-1.

Quality requirements for boiler feed-water are discussed in Section 29-5.

29-3. Selection of Source. Industrial water supplies are either purchased from a municipality or developed privately. Multiple sources of supply are common. Examples are cooling water drawn from a stream, lake, or estuary; process water or water used for special cooling purposes drawn from the ground; and drinking water and, possibly, boiler feed-water purchased from a municipality. Use of multiple sources by large industries may render the planning, design, and management of their supplies quite complex. The cost and safety

TABLE 29-1. Quality Tolerances for Industrial Process Waters *

All values are expressed in parts per million.

Industry or use	Turbidity	Color	Hardness as CaCO₃	Iron as Fe	Manganese as Mn	Total solids	Alkalinity as CaCO₃	Odor taste	Hydrogen sulfide	Other requirements
Air conditioning				0.5 †	0.5			Low	1	No corrosiveness or slime formation
Baking	10	10		0.2 †	0.2			Low	0.2	Potable water
Brewing, light beer	10			0.1 †	0.1	500	75	Low	0.2	Potable, NaCl less than 275 ppm, pH 6.5–7.0
dark beer	10			0.1 †	0.1	1,000	150	Low	0.2	Potable, NaCl less than 275 ppm, pH 7.0 or more
Canning, legumes general	10		25–75	0.2 †	0.2			Low	1	Potable
Carbonated beverages	2	10	250	0.2(0.3) †	0.2	850	50–100	Low	1	Potable, organic color plus oxygen consumed less than 10 ppm
Confectionery				0.2 †	0.2	100		Low	0.2	Potable
Food, general	10			0.2 †	0.2			Low		Potable
Ice	5	5		0.2 †	0.2			Low	0.2	Potable, SiO₂ less than 10 ppm
Laundering			50	0.2 †	0.2					
Plastics, clear, uncolored	2	2		0.02 †	0.02	200				
Paper and pulp, ground wood	50	20	180	1.0 †	0.5					No grit or corrosiveness
Kraft pulp	25	15	100	0.2 †	0.1	300				
soda and sulfite	15	10	100	0.1 †	0.05	200				
high-grade light papers	5	5	50	0.1 †	0.05	200				
Rayon (Viscose), pulp production	5	5	8	0.05 †	0.03	100				No slime formation Al₂O₃ less than 8 ppm. SiO₂ less than 25 ppm. Cu less than 5 ppm, pH 7.8 to 8.3
manufacture	0.3		55	0.0	0.0		Total 50, hydroxide 8			
Tanning	20	10–100	50–135	0.2 †	0.2					
Textiles, general	5	20		0.25 †	0.25		Total 135, hydroxide 8			
dyeing	5	5–20		0.25 †	0.25	200				
Wool scouring		70		1.0 †	1.0			Low		Constant composition, residual alumina less than 0.5 ppm
Cotton bandage	5	5		0.2 †	0.2			Low		

* Progress Report, Committee on Quality Tolerances of Water for Industrial Uses. *J. New Eng. Water Works Assoc.*, *54*, 271 (1940).
† Limit given applies to both iron alone and the sum of iron and manganese.

of an industrial water supply must be weighed against all other factors that govern production costs.

Many of the difficulties encountered in industrial water supply stem from the concentration of too many industries in too small an area. Resulting heavy overdrafts on ground-water sources then point to the eventual impairment of water quality and to the possible depletion of the supply. Manufacturers should, therefore, be encouraged to scatter their plants and to anticipate the effects of future expansion of their own and other industries upon the abundance and quality of available water resources.

29-4. Selection of Treatment Processes. The cost of water treatment and the associated economic gain are important elements in comparisons of alternate sources of supply. Necessary studies may be stimulated also by the deterioration of existing supplies or by demands for better quality or quality control of manufactured products. The situation is again more complex than for municipal supplies. Not only may the water have to be "tailored" to fit specific uses, but the number of treatment processes from which a selection can be made is generally larger than for public supplies. By way of illustration, hardness is removed from industrial water supplies, in practice, by at least ten different processes: (1) cold lime, (2) cold lime-soda, (3) cold lime-barium, (4) hot lime-soda, (5) hot phosphate, (6) sodium-cation exchange, (7) lime followed by sodium-cation exchange, (8) hydrogen-cation exchange, (9) hydrogen-cation exchange followed by anion exchange, and (10) distillation. Actually, the selection of suitable processes is not as difficult as the number of choices might lead one to suspect. When the desired characteristics of the raw and finished waters have been defined, along with other factors such as the quantity to be treated, the space available, and the ease of operation, many of the possible treatment processes are automatically eliminated.

The ways of purifying water discussed in Chapters 22, 23, 24, and 27 are applicable also to industrial supplies. But there are some treatment processes that are peculiarly suited to specific industrial needs. The preparation of boiler feed-water and of cooling water are examples. These are discussed in the two succeeding sections of this chapter.

29-5. Feed Water for Boilers. In the operation of boilers, foaming, priming, scale formation, caustic embrittlement, and corrosion mount with operating pressures. Foaming and priming entrain moisture and solids in steam. The solids carried over may then be deposited in steam lines and in turbines and other equipment. The intercrystalline cracking of boiler metal, called "caustic embrittlement," is associated (1) with localized stresses that have strained the metal beyond its elastic limit and (2) with a high concentration of caustic soda in the absence of an adequate concentration of sulfate in the feed water. Failure generally occurs at riveted seams and similar places of confined extent that have been subjected to stresses of high intensity. Table 29-2 suggests feed-water tolerances for

TABLE 29-2. Feed-Water Quality Tolerances for Boilers Operated at Different Pressures *

All values but the pH value are expressed in parts per million.

Measure of quality	Pressure, psig			
	0 to 150	150 to 250	250 to 400	Over 400
Turbidity	20	10	5	1
Color	80	40	5	2
Oxygen consumed	15	10	4	3
Dissolved oxygen (O_2) †	1.5	0.1	0	0
Hydrogen sulfide (H_2S) ‡	5	3	0	0
Total hardness ($CaCO_3$)	80	40	10	2
Sulfate carbonate ratio ($Na_2SO_4 : Na_2CO_3$)	1:1	2:1	3:1	..
Aluminum oxide (Al_2O_3)	5	0.5	0.05	0.01
Silica (SiO_2)	40	20	5	0
Bicarbonate ($HCO_3{}^-$)	50	30	5	0
Carbonate ($CO_3{}^=$)	200	100	40	20
Hydroxide (OH^-)	50	40	30	15
Total solids §	3,000 to 500	2,500 to 500	1,500 to 100	50
Minimum pH value	8.0	8.4	9.0	9.6

* Progress Report, Committee on Quality Tolerances of Water for Industrial Uses. *J. New Eng. Water Works Assoc.*, *54*, 261 (1940).
† Feed-water entering boiler.
‡ Except when odor in live steam is objectionable.
§ Depends on design of boiler.

different pressures. The values listed take into account (1) that reductions in turbidity, color, organic matter (as measured by oxygen consumed), and total solids decrease foaming and priming; (2) that reductions in hardness, silica, and alumina alleviate scale formation; (3) that maintenance of a high ratio of sulfate to carbonates controls caustic embrittlement; and (4) that elimination of oxygen, reduction of bicarbonate ions, and increase in pH suppress corrosion. Municipal water supplies, as well as private water supplies, must generally be suitably prepared for use in high-pressure boilers.

Water suited to the boiler pressure can be, and often is, softened and demineralized by the procedures described in Sections 23-3 and 23-5. Since boiler feed-water must be heated in any event and treatment becomes more efficient at elevated temperatures, hot processes are often substituted for cold processes: chemical reactions are quicker; the solubility of important precipitates is lower; the agglomeration of

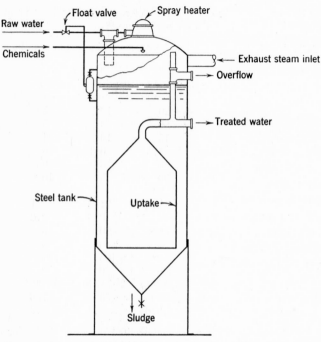

Figure 29-1.   Enclosed, heated water softener.   *Permutit Co.*

flocs is prompter; and the rate of settling of precipitates is faster. Whereas a settling period of 8 to 10 hours is required in cold, lime-soda softening, for example, only 2 to 3 hours are needed at 100 F and but one hour at 212 F.

Hot softeners are generally operated at temperatures of 212 F or more.   For this reason, reaction tanks are made of steel and covered. As shown in Figure 29-1, the cold water enters the tank through a float-controlled valve that holds the water surface at the desired level. Solutions of chemicals are automatically proportioned to the inflow which is heated by steam as it enters the tank.   Tanks are generally elaborated to include a mixing and flocculating chamber, a settling compartment, and a conical sludge hopper.   The softened water is drawn from the settling compartment and passed through a pressure filter to remove colloidal precipitates before it is fed to the boiler. Crushed, anthracite-coal or other non-siliceous grains are used as the filtering medium, in order to avoid silica pick-up. The filter is backwashed with hot softened water, and the wash water is returned to the softener. Sludge and boiler blowdown, too, are sometimes recirculated through the softener in order to economize on chemicals.

High boiler pressures, as indicated in Table 29-2, call for more effective silica removal, for deactivation, and for acid treatment to prevent scaling, corrosion, and caustic embrittlement.

a. Softening. The principal methods of softening are hot lime-soda softening and hot phosphate softening. The hot lime-soda process does not differ in its elements from the cold process (Section 23-3a), but it is more economical of space and chemicals and produces a softer water. An excess of 20 to 25 mg/l of sodium carbonate will reduce the hardness to about 20 to 25 mg/l and will prevent scale formation in boilers operated at pressures less than 250 psig. At higher pressures, calcium tends to combine with silica to form silicate as well as carbonate scales.

Phosphates and caustic soda will precipitate calcium as tricalcium phosphate and magnesium as magnesium hydroxide. Magnesium may also be precipitated in the absence of caustic soda; probably by the hydrolysis of magnesium phosphate. The addition of caustic soda has the advantage of removing silicates. Both the calcium and magnesium precipitates are substantially insoluble at elevated temperatures. Water of very low hardness can, therefore, be produced. The process is generally employed to soften water of low hardness (60 mg/l or less), and for the secondary treatment of water following softening with lime or lime and soda, which remove the bulk of the hardness at low cost. Numerous phosphates, ranging from monosodium phosphate to phosphoric acid, find use. Acid phosphates are often chosen to soften water of high carbonate alkalinity. Caustic soda must be added when the phosphate is to be converted to the trisodium form. Anhydrous disodium phosphate (Na_2HPO_4, mol. wt. 142), for example, is converted to trisodium phosphate in accordance with the following reaction:

$$Na_2HPO_4 + NaOH \rightleftarrows Na_3PO_4 + H_2O \qquad 29\text{-}1$$

It is seen that 28 lb of NaOH (mol. wt. 40) are required to convert 100 lb of disodium phosphate to trisodium phosphate.

The reactions which result in precipitation of hardness (Tables 18-1 and 18-2) are:

$$Na_3PO_4 \rightleftarrows 3Na^+ + PO_4^{\equiv} \qquad 29\text{-}2$$

$$3Ca^{++} + 2PO_4^{\equiv} \rightleftarrows Ca_3(PO_4)_2 \downarrow \qquad 29\text{-}3$$

$$NaOH \rightleftarrows Na^+ + OH^- \qquad 29\text{-}4$$

$$Mg^{++} + 2OH^- \rightleftarrows Mg(OH)_2 \downarrow \qquad 23\text{-}10$$

To assure complete precipitation, an excess of 5 to 10 mg/l of phosphate is added, and the pH is maintained at approximately 9.7. Phosphates may be fed to lime-soda softened water either in the boiler (internal treatment) or before the water enters the boiler (external treatment). Internal treatment to maintain an excess of 40 to 60 mg/l of phosphate in boiler "saline" minimizes scale formation and renders the precipitates sufficiently fluid to be removed with the blowdown. In external treatment, anthracite-coal pressure filters will clear the water of colloids and of floc not removed by sedimentation.

When hot, phosphate-softened water is passed through equipment such as economizers and closed heaters, in which there is a marked rise in temperature, after-precipitation may occur unless the water has been stabilized by lowering its pH value, or the formation of scales is prevented by adding organic inhibitors. Required dosages and resultant water quality are determined in accordance with the principles laid down in Sections 23-3 and 23-6.

b. *Removal of Silica.* Natural waters may contain more than 100 mg/l of silica in solution. This silica forms troublesome scales of calcium and magnesium silicates and analcite ($Na_2O_3 \cdot Al_2O_3 \cdot 4SiO_2 \cdot 2H_2O$) in high-pressure boilers and deposits hard, glassy scales on turbine blades when it is carried over in steam. Silica can be removed by highly basic anion exchangers after the decarbonation step of the common, ion-exchange, demineralizing process. Fluosilicates are also removed. Distillation frees water from silica along with all other minerals. The principles of ion exchange and distillation have been discussed in Section 23-5. Quite different in action is the adsorption of silica on hydrous precipitates of magnesium and iron oxides.

Hot-process removal of silica by magnesium is ordinarily ancillary to hot lime-soda or hot phosphate softening. Separate treatment of cold as well as hot water is also effective. The compounds employed include magnesium sulfate, dolomitic lime, calcium magnesite, magnesium carbonate, and magnesium oxide. Magnesium oxide is preferred for the hot removal of silica because of its high effectiveness, and because its use does not increase the dissolved-solids content of the water or call for an increase in lime and soda when the water is to be softened. The natural magnesium hardness of the water which is precipitated in softening assists in the removal of silica.

As an adsorption reaction, the removal of silica by magnesium hydroxide is described by the Freundlich adsorption isotherm (Equation 18-80). Accordingly, the removal per unit weight of hydrous oxide declines with increasing amounts of silica to be removed. The dosage of magnesium oxide required must be determined by trial, in much the same way as the removal of odors and tastes by activated carbon (Section 27-21). Sludge recirculation for fuller utilization of the adsorptive powers of the hydrate is more or less standard.

The reactions in cold water are qualitatively the same as in hot water, but their efficiencies are lower. Treatment is most effective when magnesium hydroxide is precipitated in place, preferably from carbonates or bicarbonates. The bicarbonate and free carbon dioxide content of raw water may be put to use for the recovery of magnesium by passing the raw water through a dissolver to which the sludge is recirculated. If insufficient magnesium is taken up, carbon dioxide may be blown in to promote solution.

Because their solubility increases with temperature, hydrous ferric oxides are normally added only to cold water. From 10 to 20 mg/l of ferric sulfate are required for each mg/l of silica to be removed. Considerable quantities of anions are released. This, together with the expense, limits the application of ferric hydroxide to feed waters that are turbid and must be coagulated in any case.

c. Deactivation. In order to control corrosion, oxygen is removed from boiler feed-water by deaeration, external chemical treatment, or internal chemical treatment. Polyphosphates are widely used for internal treatment because of their corrosion-inhibiting properties. As sequestering agents, they reduce scaling by causing boiler salines to precipitate as soft sludges that can be removed by blowdown.

Deaeration of boiler water to remove oxygen and carbon dioxide, and incidentally nitrogen, is accomplished by boiling or atomizing the water at elevated temperatures. Deaerating heaters (Figure 29-2) may be operated above, at, or below atmospheric pressure. For hot-process softening, a deaeration unit is ordinarily built into the feed-water heater. As shown in Figure 29-2, feed water, which has been warmed in a vent condenser that recovers most of the steam used for heating and deaeration, is sprayed into the steam chamber at the top of the heater along with trap returns. The water is heated by the steam and loses all but about 0.4 mg/l of its dissolved oxygen. The hot water then passes in countercurrent flow against the incoming steam through a scrubber. More heat is added, and the dissolved oxygen is further reduced. The now slightly superheated water falls into the deaerated water-storage compartment, where flashing completes the removal of oxygen usually to less than 0.007 mg/l. Gases escape from the system through the vent condenser, along with a small amount of steam.

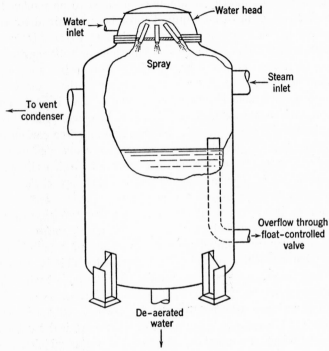

Figure 29-2. De-aerating heater. *Permutit Co.*

Residual dissolved oxygen may be removed by maintaining in the boiler water an excess of up to 30 mg/l of sodium sulfite (Na_2SO_3, mol. wt. 126.1). The oxidation-reduction reaction is:

$$2Na_2SO_3 + O_2 \rightleftarrows 2Na_2SO_4 \qquad\qquad 29-5$$

and it proceeds quite rapidly in hot water, especially in the presence of an excess of sodium sulfite.

d. Reduction of Alkalinity and pH. Boiler feed-waters (in particular sodium-cation-exchange, softened waters) are treated with acid to reduce their alkalinity and to increase their sulfate-to-carbonate ratio. Acid is added either before or after softening. The acid can also be introduced by passing a portion of the water through a cation exchanger operated on the hydrogen cycle (split treatment). Sulfuric acid will not only acidify the water but will also increase the sulfate to carbonate ratio. The acid reacts with alkaline constituents of the water to form carbon dioxide. This is removed in the deaerating heater. The total dissolved-solids content of the water is little affected.

When part of the water is softened in a sodium-cation exchanger and the balance is passed through a hydrogen-cation exchanger, the sulfuric and hydrochloric acid produced will destroy the alkalinity of the mixed water. The quality of the mixture can be controlled by varying the proportions of water treated in each kind of exchanger. If the sulfate content of the raw water is quite low, sodium sulfate may have to be added to the softened water in order to reach the desired sulfate-carbonate ratio.

29-6. Cooling Water. Cooling water should not form scales, deposit sediment, promote the growth of slimes, or cause corrosion. However, the most troublesome "contaminant" of cooling water is often the heat which raises the temperature of natural waters that must serve one industry after another along a water course. Downstream industries have, indeed, been put out of operation during droughts because the temperature of needed cooling water was too high. In the processing of food and beverages, cooling water should be as good as drinking water in bacterial purity and freedom from toxic metals. Otherwise, almost any source of water, including sea water, treated sewage, and polluted river water can be used for cooling purposes. Cross-connections with water supplies of higher quality must then be scrupulously avoided. Because of their seasonally uniform and low temperature, ground waters are drawn upon heavily as cooling waters. During the winter, a shift is sometimes made to surface waters.

Cooling waters may have to be treated before use in order to reduce or prevent scaling, corrosion, and the formation of slimes in heat exchangers, condensers, and engine jackets, as well as on other cooling surfaces. Cooling-water systems are of three types: (1) once-through systems, (2) open recirculating systems, and (3) closed recirculating systems. Means for the control of scale formation and corrosion vary accordingly.

In once-through systems, the water can be stabilized (Section 23-6) at a point at which protective layers of calcium carbonate are maintained on cooling surfaces, and a sequestering or surface-active agent can be added to prevent excessive deposition at points of high temperature. Included in the surface active agents are polyphosphates (Section 23-7), tannins, starches, and lignins. These can be used singly or in different combinations. They broaden the solubility range of scale-forming substances and counterbalance the oversaturation of scale-forming minerals.

In open recirculating systems, the evaporation of water in cooling ponds or towers increases its dissolved-solids concentration, while windage loss removes dissolved solids from the system.[1] The cycles of concentration through which the water passes equal the sum of the evaporation and windage losses divided by the windage loss, all expressed as proportions or percentages of the total water use. If the windage loss is not high enough, the mineral concentration can be held within desired limits (1) by bleeding recirculating water from the system, (2) by softening or demineralizing the make-up water, or (3) by lowering the alkalinity of the recirculating water with acid. In other respects, scaling and corrosion can be reduced as in once-through systems. However, larger concentrations of surface-active agents (30 to 100 mg/l) are usually needed to offset the increased dissolved-solids concentration of the recirculating water.

In closed cooling systems, there is but little make-up water, and scaling is reduced. Corrosion is decreased for the same reason and because the water is not aerated. Corrosion may be further reduced by stabilization, deactivation, vacuum deaeration, or the addition of inhibitors.

Slime and algal growths in condensers and other heat exchangers may seriously impair their operation. Where such growths are allowed to develop, they must be cleaned out periodically. This is a costly operation when it requires dismantling of the equipment. It is generally cheaper to add to the cooling water chemicals, such as copper sulfate, chlorine, and chloramine, that will either prevent the formation of growths or destroy existing growths (Chapter 27). Ordinarily, the chemicals are added intermittently in heavy doses. An example is the application of chlorine in amounts that will produce an excess of several milligrams per liter of free available chlorine for 30 min a day to prevent slime growths in the main condensers of a power plant. Sodium pentachlorphenate is another useful agent. From 20 to 40 mg/l will generally control sliming in recirculated cooling water. Since pentachlorphenate is an irritant and toxic to man, it must be handled and applied with caution. Poisonous chemicals such as this should not be added to cooling-water systems, unless there is certainty that

---

[1] Evaporation loss is about 1% for each drop in temperature of 10 F through the pond or tower. Windage losses are 1.0 to 5.0% for spray ponds, 0.3 to 1.0% for atmospheric towers, and 0.1 to 0.3% for mechanical-draft towers.

no cross-connection can or will be established with drinking-water supplies or with supplies of process water that enters into manufactured products.

Disposal of Industrial Waste-Waters

29-7. Nature of Industrial Waste-Waters. Most industrial waste-waters are derived from cooling, washing, flushing, extracting, impregnating, chemical treatment, and similar operations. They are as varied in quantity and nature as the products and processes of the mills from which they drain. Their spectrum ranges from the discharge of great volumes of cooling water that is "contaminated" only with heat to the emptying of relatively small but concentrated baths that are so loaded with inorganic and organic substances as to be on the verge of jelling. Quite different in origin are the drainage waters from coal mines and the brines from oil fields. Coal-mine drainage may continue to give trouble long after the working of the mines has been stopped.

The discharge or treatment of the waste-waters of certain industries has been known to cause far worse difficulties than the discharge or treatment of the domestic sewage of the community in which the industries are situated. Toxic metals and chemicals may destroy the biological activity of streams and municipal sewage-treatment works and render receiving waters unfit for further use. In the manufacture of organic chemicals, the wastes may impart to receiving waters tastes and odors that are almost impossible of removal in water-purification plants. Strong acids and alkalies may render receiving waters corrosive and expensive to purify. Suspended solids may settle in receiving waters and smother aquatic life. Excessive concentrations of organic matter may overtax municipal sewage-treatment works and rapidly exhaust the natural purifying capacity of receiving waters. Oils, dyes, and floating solids may render receiving waters and their banks unsightly and interfere with the rights of riparian owners.

The tests that identify the strength and characteristics of domestic sewage cannot be applied to the analysis of industrial waste-waters, unless this is done with an understanding of their limitations and unless they are supplemented by tests that evaluate more specific properties of the waste-waters. Toxic wastes, for example, may have a high chemical demand for oxygen but exert a biochemical oxygen demand that is quite low, although much organic matter is present. Reduction of toxic constituents below threshold limits (by dilution in the laboratory or in receiving waters) will permit biological activity to establish itself. The total oxygen demand may then increase with increasing dilution of the waste, although the chemical oxygen demand is decreased. To cite another example, the chemical tests commonly included in a sanitary water analysis will not record the presence or danger of toxic metals or of toxic organic and inorganic complexes. Higher organisms, such as fingerlings or minnows, may have to be placed in graded dilutions of the waste-water with receiving water in order to measure the nature and intensity of poisoning effects. Since toxic chemicals are often specific in their physiological action, even such tests may be of but limited value. The ecology of a receiving water is affected by the destruction of any one group of the many living organisms through which the food chain of self-purification is maintained. The synergistic, or combined, effect of different toxic chemicals may be more marked than their isolated actions.

The quantity and strength of waste waters from a given industry vary within wide limits depending on the manufacturing processes employed and the methods of their control in different plants. The approximate composition of waste-waters that possess high BOD values is listed in Table 29-3. The total weight of BOD discharged from a plant employing relatively few people may equal that of the domestic sewage from a city of fair size.

As stated in Section 20-17, the population equivalent of the BOD of industrial waste waters is the ratio of their BOD to the per capita BOD normally exerted by domestic or combined sewage. Average figures are 0.119 lb per capital daily for domestic sewage and 0.165 lb per capita daily for combined sewage, in 5 days at 20 C. The population equivalent of 0.5 mgd of waste water from a vegetable canning plant containing 2,500 mg/l of 5-day 20 C BOD, for example, is $2,500 \times 8.32 \times 0.5/0.119 = 87,400$ people in terms of domestic sewage and $87,400 \times 0.119/0.165 = 63,000$ people in terms of combined sewage. If a plant like this is situated in a community of but 10,000 people, the BOD load contributed by the cannery during the canning season overshadows that of the domestic or combined sewage load. Similar comparative calculations can be made for suspended solids and other characteristic pollutants.

Because of the variety and complexity of industrial operations and requirements and because of the wide differences in local sanitary needs, the equitable and economical solution of industrial waste-water disposal problems calls for cooperative studies (1) by men who are experienced in manufacturing processes and (2) by sanitary engineers who are expert in the treatment and disposal of industrial waste waters.

29-8. Reduction, Recovery, and Re-Use of Water and Waste Matters. In critical situations, or in the interest of preserving water assets and reducing the cost of sewage treatment, the pollution of receiving waters

TABLE 29-3.   Approximate Quantities and Concentration of Industrial Waste-Waters

After E. W. Moore

Waste water	Production unit	Gallons per unit	Suspended solids, mg/l	5-day BOD, mg/l	Special characteristics
Beet sugar *	1 ton beets	3,000–4,000	800	450	Without Steffens' waste †
		...		700–2,000	With Steffens' waste
Brewery	1 barrel beer	300–1,000	250–650	500–1,200	...
Cannery	1 ton stock	2,500–8,000	200–3,000	300–4,000	...
Coal washing	1 ton coal	600–2,400	3,000–150,000	...	Fine coal
Distillery	1 bushel grain	45–55	20,000–40,000	15,000–20,000	Starchy
	100 gal molasses	200–300	...	20,000–30,000	High in potash
Gas and coke	1 ton coal	200–400	200–3,000	1,000–6,000	Phenols 1,000–5,000 mg/l in untreated liquor
Laundry	100 lb clothes	1,500	400–1,000	300–1,000	Alkaline
Malthouse *	100 bushel barley	800	...	400	...
Milk plant	1,000 lb milk	100–225	...	300–2,000	Lactose, sours readily
Oil-well brine	1 gal oil	4–2,800	...	...	Total solids 11,000 to 325,000 mg/l
Packing house, small	1 hog ‡	1,000–1,500	500–1,500	600–2,000	High in fats, proteins
large	1 hog ‡	500–800	400–1,000	350–1,000	...
Paper-making	1 ton paper	5,000–100,000	500	20–100	Fiber, clay
Paper pulp, ground-wood	1 ton pulp	0–12,000	100–150	20	...
sulfite	1 ton pulp	30,000–100,000	...	400	Lignin, sulfites
sulfite cooker-liquor	1 ton pulp	2,000–3,600	...	16,000–25,000	...
Tannery	100 lb hides	600–700	1,000–5,000	500–5,000	High in lime
Textile, cotton kier §	100 lb goods	120–250	...	1,000–1,600	High in caustic alkali
kier-liquor only	100 lb goods	30	...	4,000–8,000	...
cotton kier and bleach	100 lb goods	1,000–1,600	...	100–200	High in oxidizing agents
Flax retting *	1 ton straw	5,300	...	1,800–2,800	...
Fulling *			4,000	520	...
Silk boiling *	100 lb silk	850	100–500	700–1,000	...
Sulfur dye (dye-bath only)	100 lb goods	500–1,800	...	1,000–2,000	Sulfides
Wool-scouring, batch	100 lb wool	160–500	1,000–170,000	200–10,000	Wool grease
countercurrent	100 lb wool	40–100	1,000–170,000	200–10,000	Wool grease

* Data from one source only.

† The Steffens process precipitates tricalcium sucrate from beet juices that have yielded their crystallizable sugar. Steffens' waste is the liquor filtered from the sucrate.

‡ 1 steer = 2.5 hogs; 1 sheep or calf = 1 hog.

§ A kier is a tub.

or the loading of sewage-treatment works by industrial waste waters can be reduced in a variety of ways: (1) by altering manufacturing processes to decrease the volume and concentration of waste waters, (2) by developing means for the recovery of useful and marketable by-products from the waste waters or industrial processes, and (3) by treatment and re-use of process waters within the plant. Only when these possibilities have been exhausted should the waste waters be allowed to be (1) discharged into municipal sewers (either in their raw state or after treatment) or (2) treated by themselves preparatory to direct disposal into available receiving waters or onto land.

A significant reduction in the volume and concentration of waste waters can be effected in almost all industries in which draining, rinsing, and spillage are important sources of waste matters. The following are illustrative examples: (1) reduction of the loss of milk, whey, and buttermilk in the manufacture of milk products (a) by fuller drainage of cans, churns, and other vessels prior to washing, and (b) by introduction of a preliminary, low-volume, cold-water rinse from which food products can be recovered by evaporation; (2) adequate drainage (assisted by shaking) of plated pieces upon their removal from electroplating baths and use of preliminary, low-volume, rinse waters to make up or replenish the baths; (3) reduction of spillage in dyeing, printing, chemical treating, food processing, as well as other operations, in which floor washings become water-carried wastes; and (4) use of countercurrent washing and rinsing of wool which reduces the amount of water by 80%.

Examples of the recovery of salable or usable industrial wastes are the recovery of (1) copper and sulfuric acid from spent copper-pickling liquor, (2) copperas from spent steel-pickling liquor, (3) alkalies from mercerizing processes, (4) feed from distillery slop, (5) fiber from paper-mill wastes, and (6) palm oil from cold-rolling-mill wastes. Economic factors that may militate against recovery of waste materials are: (1) fluctuating or glutted markets and (2) the necessity for establishing separate marketing organizations for by-products because they are so unlike the articles of manufacture themselves.

Examples of process waters that can be re-used are: (1) the "white waters" of paper mills,[2] the development of objectionable slime growths being controlled by chlorination; (2) the flume and wash waters of the beet-sugar industry after sedimentation or lagooning, and (3) the

---

[2] White water contains fiber, size, dye, and loading materials that have passed through the wires, showers, and felts of paper-making machines. They will support heavy growths of slime-forming organisms, both lower and higher bacteria.

spent dye baths or rinse waters of textile mills. The last-named waters can be used for the preparation of dye solutions.

29-9. Disposal with Domestic Sewage. The discharge of industrial waste-waters into municipal sewerage systems may be advantageous (1) when the waste waters become more amenable to treatment after they have been mixed with domestic sewage; (2) when treatment of combined wastes is more economical because of the increased size of the operation, and (3) when treatment of the combined wastes is more effective and economical because of the technical and sanitary supervision available in the municipal works. Waste waters should not be emptied into public sewers when there is evidence that their admission would result in (1) nuisances or hazards, (2) clogging or damage to the sewers, or (3) interference with existing treatment processes. Greases and oils, inflammable solvents, hot liquids, concentrated acids and alkalies, poisonous substances, putrescent materials, and large and heavy solids are examples of objectionable waste matters. They may have to be removed from waste waters or modified by preliminary treatment at the industrial plant before discharge into the public sewerage system. Sometimes the blending of different wastes or the regulated release of waste waters (either uniformly or in proportion to the flow of domestic sewage) is all that is needed.

Biological treatment processes have a marked ability to adapt themselves to toxic wastes, especially when the concentration of toxic substances is raised gradually and a sufficiently long breaking-in period is allowed. Shock loads, however, may be fatal. Of the biological growths, trickling-filter slimes are quite resistant to variable loadings; activated sludges are not. High BOD, suspended-matter content, or volume of industrial waste waters may demand additional plant capacity to handle the industrial load.

In the public interest, operating authorities should be empowered: (1) to exclude objectionable or dangerous wastes from sewerage systems; (2) to specify the manner of waste-water discharge into such systems; (3) to require pretreatment of industrial waste waters; and (4) to determine, negotiate, and levy appropriate charges upon industry for acceptance and disposal of water-carried industrial wastes.

29-10. Methods of Separate Treatment and Disposal. Available methods for treating and disposing of industrial waste-waters by themselves are generally quite like those for domestic sewage. They include: screening; lagooning; sedimentation with or without neutralization, coagulation, or precipitation; biological treatment; and ultimate disposal of the treated liquids into receiving waters or onto land.

Racks find some use. More often, however, fine screens take their place in order to recover fibers or stock and to remove gross suspended matters. In paper mills and in food-processing plants, for example, screens with 20 to 60 meshes to the inch or more and of the self-cleaning, shaker or drum type, are widely employed (Figure 29-3). Useful screenings are recovered; waste screenings are buried, burned, or spread on land.

Plain sedimentation and storage in lagoons is common in the canning, mining, and chemical industries. If the waste solids are predominantly organic, their decomposition may exhaust the dissolved oxygen of the

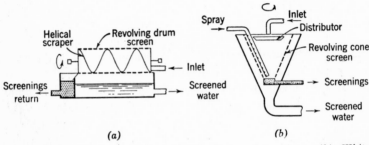

Figure 29-3.   Screens or save-alls: (a) *Shevlin* revolving drug; (b) *Whitman* revolving cone.

lagooned waters and give rise to foul gases including hydrogen sulfide. Nitrates may then have to be added. The oxygen in nitrates is more readily available to living organisms than that in sulfates.

For treatment beyond screening and plain sedimentation, most industries resort to chemical precipitation because of its flexibility and because of the expense of constructing and maintaining biological treatment units. The common water coagulants (alum, ferrous sulfate and lime, ferric sulfate and ferric chloride) are generally employed. But some wastes respond better to other chemical precipitants. Examples are: calcium chloride for laundry wastes, and alkalized starches for coal-washing wastes. The types and dosages of effective coagulants cannot be predicted. Experimentation in the laboratory and in pilot plants is, generally, necessary. Neutralization or adjustment of pH is accomplished with chemicals such as lime, soda ash, sulfuric acid, and carbon dioxide.

Both fill-and-draw and continuous-flow settling tanks find use. The former are often best suited to small plants or works in which the characteristics of the waste water fluctuate rapidly; the latter where flows are large and wastes are quite uniform in amount and character.

Fill-and-draw plants usually consist of two or more tanks equipped with mixers and with liquid and sludge draw-off pipes (see Figure 29-4). When a tank unit has been filled, the waste water is mixed to uniform consistency. The quantities of chemical required for the

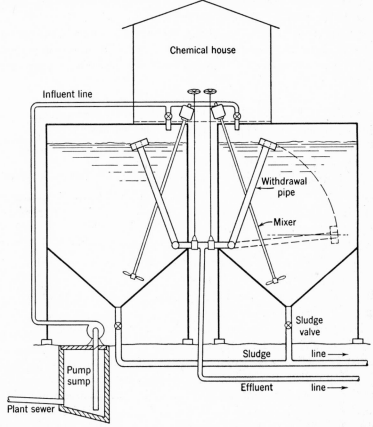

Figure 29-4. Fill-and-draw plant for the clarification of industrial waste waters by chemicals.

batch are determined by jar tests and added to the tank. Mixing is continued until a good floc has formed. The tank contents are then allowed to come to rest, and the solids are permitted to settle. After that, the supernatant liquid is siphoned off through a draw-off pipe that sinks automatically with the liquid surface. The sludge is discharged to a drying bed, to a sludge lagoon, or, if it is putrescible, to a digestion tank. Retention in the settling tank of some sludge may reduce coagulant requirements for the next batch. The liquid draw-off pipe may be operated by floats, or it may be lowered on a chain that is released by a timer or by a constant-speed motor. A propeller in the side of the tank, paddles on vertical or horizontal shafts, or turbines may serve as mixers. The sludge may be removed hydrostatically, by scrapers, or by pumps.

Chemical treatment in continuous-flow tanks is similar to that in sewage-treatment works and in water-purification plants.

The loading and operation of biological treatment units are functions of the strength of the wastes and the nature of their constituents. As is true with sewage, the weight of BOD removed by a unit area or volume of filter ordinarily increases with the loading, whereas the percentage removal declines. Commonly, there are advantages in recirculating effluent when the BOD of the waste waters approaches 1,000 mg/l. Trickling filters can handle a number of toxic wastes quite satisfactorily. Among them are phenol, formaldehyde, cyanide, and sulfide wastes. In order to distribute the loading and acclimate the filter to the permissible load, the waste may have to be diluted for some time with sewage or with waste water that is free from toxic materials. Pilot tests will identify permissible loadings and the effects of substances that may produce slime growths or precipitates that clog the filter. Activated-sludge treatment should rarely be tried without pilot tests, even when it has been applied successfully to similar waste waters. Foaming and bulking may be too severe in the presence of strong or toxic industrial wastes.

Suitably screened or settled effluents may be sprayed onto land when industries are situated far from satisfactory receiving waters. Spray disposal is particularly useful when manufacturing operations reach their peak during the summer and fall or at a time when evapotranspiration is high and the water table is low. Waste waters from vegetable and fruit canneries are examples. Portable irrigation pipes equipped with rotating nozzles are often used. Rates of application and frequency of change of area are determined by irrigation experience and from field tests. Industrial waste waters may also be carried onto land in the ways commonly employed for the disposal of sewage.

Sludge disposal is generally in accordance with sewage-plant practice. The sludge removed from many industrial waste-waters is relatively stable and can be disposed of without digestion. Where space is available, the lagooning of sludge is generally favored.

29-11. Wastes Containing Mineral Impurities. Examples of waste waters that contain large or detrimental amounts of mineral impurities are steel-pickling liquors, copper-bearing wastes, electroplating wastes, gas- and coke-plant wastes, oil-field brines and petroleum-refinery wastes, and mining wastes.

a. Steel Pickling Liquors. Steel and iron are pickled in acid (normally sulfuric acid) prior to cold working, galvanizing, plating, or similar operations. The acid concentration of the pickling bath declines from an initial value of 5 to 15% to one of 1.5 to 5% while its concentration of ferrous iron rises as high as 4 to 30%. Neutralization of the spent pickling liquor, which contains other impurities as well, is costly and leaves large volumes of sludge. Processes for the recovery of ferrous sulfate or acid include: (1) evaporation of water to crystallize impurities; (2) crystallization of ferrous sulfate by cooling or by the addition of organic solvents; (3) use of scrap iron to neutralize residual acidity followed by evaporation to recover copperas; (4) recovery of sulfur and iron oxides by roasting recovered copperas; (5) electrolytic recovery of iron; and (6) dewatering and processing of the sludge after neutralization with lime to produce building and insulating materials. Diluteness of the waste, presence of extraneous impurities, and a limited market for ferrous sulfate impose formidable barriers to profitable recoveries.

b. Copper-Bearing Wastes. Pickling and washing of copper and its alloys after hot working and annealing leaves copper in the waste liquors. Very small amounts of copper (less than 1 mg/l) will interfere with the life of streams and biological sewage-treatment works. The relatively high cost of copper makes its recovery more profitable than that of ferrous sulfate or iron. Available methods are: (1) electrolytic treatment of the pickling liquor to recover copper and regenerate the acid; (2) crystallization of copper sulfate, which may require neutralization of spent acid with copper oxide scale; (3) lime neutralization followed by sedimentation; and (4) passage through iron turnings or other scrap iron or steel, iron being dissolved and an equivalent amount of copper being precipitated as recoverable metal.

c. Wastes Containing Chromates and Cyanides. Chromates, or hexavalent chromium ($CrO_4^=$ and $Cr_2O_7^=$) and sodium cyanide (NaCN) are widely used in electroplating and other electrolytic operations. The concentration and composition of the toxic waste waters varies widely. About 1 mg/l of chromate (as Cr) or cyanide (as CN) appears to be the permissible limit of these substances in sewage that is to be treated biologically. Reduction of spillage, draining of processed pieces, prewashing, use of wash waters to make up new solutions, and recovery of spent baths are measures of control. Chromates may be removed by precipitation with a barium salt and an alkali or with ferrous sulfate. They may be reduced to the relatively non-toxic trivalent chromic or chromite forms (Cr^{+++} or CrO_2^-) by passage over scrap iron. Cyanides can be removed by acidification and aeration, or by precipitation with ferrous sulfate and lime. Chlorination in alkaline solution will convert them to less toxic cyanates such as NaOCN. The addition of acids to cyanide wastes releases highly toxic hydrogen cyanide (HCN). This must be guarded against.

d. Gas and Coke Plant Wastes. Vapor condensates from manufactured gas and from the quenching of coke throw considerable quantities of ammonia, phenols, cresols, sulfides, cyanides, and thiocyanates into the waste waters. They have a high oxygen demand, are toxic, and impart to receiving waters tastes and odors that are difficult to remove. Phenol appears to be the principal offender (Section 27-21). Acclimated trickling filters can oxidize phenolic waters that contain several hundred milligrams per liter of phenol. Activated sludge is less tolerant, but 50 mg/l will not cause injury in favorable circumstances.

Recovery of ammonia from gas- and coke-plant wastes is common. The spent liquors, which contain lime used to free the ammonia as well as most of the remaining contaminants, may then be evaporated or subjected to phenol recovery: (1) by solvents, such as benzol, benzene, pyridine, and tricresyl phosphate; (2) by adsorption on activated carbon; or (3) by distillation. Otherwise the wastes may be treated on trickling filters, either with domestic sewage or after dilution with treated sewage effluents or other waters.

e. Oil-Field Brines and Petroleum-Refinery Wastes. Oil-field brines, which average about 3.3 times the amount of oil pumped, contain as much as 32.5% total solids and 20% chlorides. Their solids load may indeed be ten times that of normal sea water. Although they are usually less heavily mineralized than this, most oil-field brines are sufficiently saline to destroy fresh-water life unless they are highly diluted. Since heavy concentrations of dissolved solids can be removed satisfactorily only by distillation at great expense, the economical disposal of brines remains a challenge. Methods of disposal include: (1) storage in ponds for evaporation and seepage and (2) recharge of deep saline strata by pumping, often as a means of increasing the yield of oil. Seepage from lagoons may render ground-waters salty and clog water-bearing formations. The oil in brines and refinery wastes may be removed by flotation and skimming. Gas flotation increases the yield. Hydrogen sulfide, mercaptans, phenols, and similar substances may have to be removed when receiving waters serve as sources of water supply.

f. Mining Wastes. Mining wastes include (1) the mineralized and acid water pumped or drained from mines and (2) the waste waters from the washing and processing of coal or ore. Acid coal-mine drainage and coal-washing wastes are a widespread source of trouble. The acidity and iron content of coal-mine drainage is due to the oxidation of iron pyrites (FeS) to ferrous sulfate and sulfuric acid. Estimates of the amount of sulfuric acid reaching streams in the United States run into several million tons per annum. No satisfactory method for reducing this acid load has as yet been found. Included in methods tried are: (1) the flooding of abandoned mines; (2) the sealing of mine entrances with water traps to exclude the oxygen needed to form acids; (3) the reduction of seepage into mines by diversion of surface streams or by other drainage works; and (4) the neutralization of the drainage waters by the addition of lime or by their passage through beds of limestone. Local geology, topography, and hydrology will identify the most effective method and its probable degree of success. Attainable results are often disappointing. The application of inactivating coatings to exposed surfaces is in the experimental stage.

The suspended matter in coal-washing wastes can be removed by sedimentation with or without coagulation. An alkalized solution of potato starch is a good coagulant.

29-12. Wastes Containing Organic Impurities. The most important organic wastes are produced by milk-processing plants, meat-packing establishments, breweries and distilleries, and canneries.

a. Milk-Processing Wastes. Milk-plant wastes contain washings (1) from cans, pasteurizers, coolers, churns, and other equipment, and (2) from the plant floor. Their BOD is high (up to several thousand milligrams per liter), and their decomposition is rapid. Reduction of spillage, fuller drainage of cans and equipment, and recovery of solids from first rinsings will reduce losses. Treatment methods include: (1) chemical precipitation with lime and iron in dosages up to 500 mg/l; (2) activated-sludge treatment possibly aided by small amounts of iron coagulant; and (3) trickling filtration. Treatment on trickling filters is common. Dosing rates range from 0.5 to 1.5 mgad without recirculation of effluent and from 2 to 6 mgad (net) with recirculation. The liquid going to the filter should have a BOD of less than 400 mg/l. If the effluent BOD must be low, the BOD of the applied waters must be reduced. Double filtration with alternation of the leading filter has been quite successful. It provides relief for the leading filter after it has been dosed for a time with concentrated wastes.

b. *Meat-Packing Wastes.* Packing-plant and abattoir wastes contain blood, grease, excreta, paunch contents, liquors from rendering and other processing operations, and floor washings. The larger the plant, the more economical does recovery become, and the smaller is the resulting weight of solids lost per animal slaughtered. Meat-packing wastes are treated in ways common to the treatment of domestic sewage. Consideration must be given to the strength of the applied wastes. This may be high.

c. *Brewery and Distillery Wastes.* The principal waste material of breweries and distilleries is spent grain. The food values of this residue are high and can be recovered profitably as a feed for hogs and cattle either as liquid slop or as dry feed. Alternate methods of disposal are: (1) use as fertilizer; (2) re-use of part of the distillery slop to make up new mash; and (3) anaerobic fermentation. Wastes that contain less suspended but more dissolved organic matter (for example, steepings and washings) may possess such high BOD values that they must be evaporated or treated biologically. Suspended solids are generally removed by sedimentation prior to biological treatment.

d. *Vegetable- and Fruit-Processing Wastes.* The characteristics of vegetable- and fruit-processing wastes vary within wide limits with the raw materials and the process. BOD values range up to 60,000 mg/l, and the wastes may be strongly acid or alkaline. Treatment and disposal is peculiarly difficult because of the seasonal nature of the industry and because of the shifting from one vegetable or fruit to another as the season advances. Screening and lagooning or irrigation are used most often. Screenings are buried, burned, spread on land, or used for feed. Lagoons, less than 5 ft deep, should hold 125% of the seasonal volume of waste waters. About 25% of these waters is stored over the winter in order to dilute and seed the next year's batch. Water is discharged from the lagoons by evaporation and seepage and by withdrawal into receiving waters during spring freshets. Nuisances due to the depletion of oxygen can be combated by the addition, to waste waters of average strength, of sodium nitrate at a rate of 200 lb or less for each pack of 1,000 No. 2 cases. Disposal by irrigation requires suitable land areas. Waste water to depths as high as 600 in. per year has been sprayed onto sandy areas covered with underbrush and forest litter.

29-13. Wastes Containing Both Organic and Mineral Impurities. Examples of such wastes are those of the textile industry, laundries, tanneries, and paper mills.

a. Textile Wastes. These wastes are derived from deterging and fiber preparation, and from dyeing, printing, and finishing processes. The variety of fibers (wool, cotton, silk, linen, synthetics, etc.) is great, and the kinds and colors or goods produced are numerous. As a result, textile waste waters vary in composition and strength more than other industrial waste waters. Only a few examples of their disposal are given below.

The scouring of wool produces a water-carried waste that contains dirt, manure, burrs, spent soap, and large amounts of wool grease. Grease can be recovered by lowering the pH of the settled waste with sulfuric acid to a value of 3 or 4 (acid cracking) to break the soap emulsion. In the acid tanks, most of the fat settles as a sludge, the remainder rises to the surface. Chlorination, aeration, coagulation, pressing, and centrifuging also find use in the recovery process. Extraction by solvents prior to scouring yields wool grease of high quality (lanolin).

Cotton kiering is the boiling of woven goods in water containing 0.5 to 3.0% of caustic and soda. Gums, pectins, vegetable impurities, and sizing are separated from the fiber. The resulting waste water is highly alkaline and has a BOD of thousands of milligrams per liter. Neutralization with sulfuric acid or carbon dioxide must precede biological treatment on filters. Alkaline bleaching wastes will neutralize or decolorize acid or colored wastes. Bleaching wastes may also be combined with kier liquors for disposal. Mercerizing wastes are sufficiently concentrated to justify recovery of the caustic by dialysis or evaporation.

Dye wastes are deeply colored. High acidity or alkalinity, or the dye itself, may render them destructive to aquatic life. They can be treated chemically (by coagulation, bleaching, or absorption) or biologically (on trickling filters or in activated-sludge units). Decolorization is rarely complete. Waste waters from dyeing, printing, and finishing operations are so variable in volume and composition that experimentation should precede the selection of a plan of treatment. Table 29-4 illustrates the variety of treatment methods that may be employed.

b. Laundry Wastes. Laundry wastes contain (1) spent soaps, synthetic detergents, bleaches, and (2) dirt and grease. They respond to coagulation with alum or ferric coagulants in combination with calcium chloride or sulfuric acid. Dosages range from 1 to 5 lb per 1,000 gal.

c. Tannery Wastes. Roughly half of the BOD (several thousand mg/l) of tannery wastes is concentrated in liquors from the preliminary processes of soaking, liming, dehairing, and fleshing the hides ("beam-

TABLE 29-4. Examples of Processes Recommended for the Treatment of Textile Wastes *

Type of manufacture	Process of manufacture	Water consumption, gpd	Average BOD, mg/l	Recommended treatment	Anticipated reduction of BOD, %
Cotton thread	Lime-sour, bleaching, kier boiling, machine-vat dyeing	40,000	550	Precipitation with copperas and lime	60
Finishing cotton piece	Bleaching-kier boil; dyeing and printing	274,000	605	Segregation of print waste; coagulation by copperas and lime; aeration of effluent	65
Elastic webbing and brake linings	Kier boiling; dyeing, impregnating of linings	80,000	422	Screening; coagulation with copperas and lime; aeration	60
Silk manufacture	Degumming, bleaching, dyeing, printing	1,200,000	460	Cracking of gum suds; incineration of print wastes; coagulation with ferric sulfate	65
Cotton finishing	Bleaching; kier boil, printing, dyeing	80,000	540	Coagulation of wastes by copperas and lime; aeration	65
Cotton and rayon finishing	Bleaching, soap boiling, sizing, dyeing	100,000	390	Collection of concentrated wastes; coagulation by copperas and lime; aeration	50
Fish lines	Spinning, dyeing, impregnating, finishing silk and cotton lines	500	180	Discharge of wastes into lagoon and filtration	100
Finishing cotton cloth	Alkali and peroxide kier boil; mercerizing, printing, dyeing, finishing	438,000	478	Storage in open-air lagoon for a week; coagulation with ferric sulfate and lime; incineration of print wastes	65
Rayon goods	Bleaching, dyeing, sizing, and finishing	125,000	1,920	Storage in tanks; coagulation with ferric sulfate and lime	68
Woolen cloths	Wool scouring, weaving, dyeing, finishing cloth	120,000	936	Cracking with acid; coagulation with ferric sulfate and lime	75
Felt	Washing, carding, felting, dyeing of wool	109,000	156	Screening; filtration through limestone	45
Laundry	Washing clothes	300,000	920	Storage in tanks; coagulation with alum and calcium chloride	84

* Fourth Biennial Report of the State Water Commission of Connecticut (1931 to 1933).

house wastes"[3]), and the other half from the tanning and finishing processes. Preliminary processing removes highly putrescible materials; final processing introduces toxic chemicals, such as sulfides and chromates, as well. Variations in the characteristics of the wastes within a given tannery and between tanneries are high. Treatment methods include screening, flocculation, sedimentation, and biological filtration. Success of treatment depends on adequate blending and neutralization of the various waste waters.

d. *Paper-Mill Wastes.* Production of wood pulp by the sulfite, soda, or sulfate processes is common. Wastes from sulfite mills do the most damage to receiving waters and are the most difficult to treat. Ponding, digestion, and evaporation have been tried in addition to patented processes that recover sulfur dioxide or sulfites. Caustic soda is usually recovered from soda- and sulfate-pulping liquors. "Black liquor" containing wastes cooked from the wood fibers is evaporated, and the solids are burned to produce "black ash." This material is added to fresh soda ash to make up "green liquor" which, in turn, is causticized with quicklime, settled, and filtered to produce "white liquor," which is used in the pulping process. Activated carbon is a salable by-product. It is prepared from residues of soda recovery.

Waste waters from the reclamation of old paper carry ink and clay filler removed from the paper, as well as spent caustic and soda ash from the processing baths. Recovery of chemicals from these waste waters has not been found profitable.

The wastes from beaters, refiners, and paper-making machines ("white waters") contain about 5% fiber and 45% clay. These are recovered by screening and sedimentation, or the water is recirculated after it has been chlorinated to prevent the development of slime growths.

29-14. Radioactive Wastes. Radioactive materials comprise all isotopes,[4] the nuclei of which undergo spontaneous disintegration. The quantity of radioactivity is measured by the number of disintegrations that take place in a unit of time. The standard unit, called a curie,[5] is 3.7×10^{10} disintegrations per second. This is the rate of nuclear transformation of 1 gram of radium. Each radioisotope decays at a characteristic rate that is unaffected by heat or pressure. The transformation is described by Equation 28-2 when N is the quantity of the

---

[3] From the process of working or dressing hides over a beam or in a beaming machine.

[4] Isotopes are chemical elements that differ slightly in atomic weight but occupy the same place in the periodic system and possess the same nuclear charge.

[5] Named after Pierre and Marie Curie who discovered radium.

isotope remaining at time t measured from the instant when N_0 was present. Rates are conventionally expressed in terms of the "half-life" rather than the rate constant k of the element. The half-life of a radioisotope is the time required for half of it to decay. Solution of Equation 28-2 for $N/N_0 = 0.5$ gives $k = 0.69/$half-life. The half-lives of radioisotopes range from 10^{-11} sec to more than 10^{10} years.

Radioactive waste waters originate primarily (1) in hospitals and research laboratories and in the laundries serving them and (2) in water-cooled nuclear reactors and in chemical plants that process reactor fuels. The radioactivity of fuel-processing wastes is of a much higher order of magnitude than that of radioactive waste waters from hospitals, laboratories, and laundries. Curies [6] must be dealt with rather than microcuries, μc.

Fuel-processing wastes are now stored in tanks, usually after concentration by evaporation. How these wastes will be contained ultimately and whether they can be safely and economically discharged into the atmosphere or disposed of in the ocean are matters that are yet to be determined.

Radioactive phosphorus (P^{32}) and iodine (I^{131}) are frequently used as tracers in research work. Their half-lives are 14.3 and 8 days respectively. P^{32} and I^{131} can be disposed of into sewers if transient concentrations in excess of 100 $\mu c/l$ are avoided by regulated release, dilution, or storage prior to disposal. Storage for 10 half-lives reduces the concentration of isotopes with short half-lives to about 0.1% of their original amount.

The permissible increase in radioactivity of public waters is currently set at 10^{-7} $\mu c/ml$ for unknown mixtures of isotopes. For specific isotopes, the permissible limit is much higher: 2×10^{-4} $\mu c/ml$ for P^{32} and 3×10^{-5} $\mu c/ml$ for I^{131}. These figures are useful [7] guides in judging the amounts of radioactivity that can safely be discharged into natural waters.

Other limitations on the disposal of radioisotopes in sewage are: (1) the contamination of plumbing systems; (2) hazards to personnel at treatment plants; and (3) the use of sludge and effluent in the cultivation of crops. Algae and higher plants will concentrate in their cells numerous chemical elements from both water and fertilizers. Radioactive elements, such as P^{32}, may be included. However, if the half-life of the radioisotope is short, radioactive decay will greatly reduce

[6] One curie = 10^6 microcuries.

[7] National Bureau of Standards, "Maximum Permissible Amounts of Radioisotopes in the Human Body and Maximum Permissible Concentrations in Air and Water," *Handbook* 52 (1953).

the activity of the element before it can find its way back into the food supply of man.

Radioactive substances can be removed from water and waste water in a number of different ways, the selection of which must depend on the nature of the substances involved and their physical condition in the water or waste water. Straub [8] lists the following methods: evaporation, carrier precipitation (coagulation), sand filtration, ion exchange (including natural clays), electrodialysis, metallic displacement or scrubbing, differential volatility, electrolytic separation, solvent extraction, biological processes, and crystallization.

The maximum removal of radioactivity in biological sewage-treatment systems is about 95%. A much lower removal is experienced for radioisotopes that are not utilized by, or readily adsorbed on, biological slimes, or that occur in company with an abundance of nonradioactive atoms of the same element.[9]

[8] Conrad P. Straub, "Observations on the Removal of Radioactive Materials from Waste Solutions," *Sewage and Ind. Wastes, 23,* 188 (1951).

[9] C. C. Ruchhoft and L. R. Setter, "Application of Biological Methods in the Treatment of Radioactive Wastes," *Sewage and Ind. Wastes, 25,* 48 (1953).

30

RURAL WATER SUPPLY AND WASTE-WATER DISPOSAL —SWIMMING POOLS

30-1. General Considerations. The term *rural* is used in this chapter to describe those situations in which the needs and amenities of water supply and waste-water disposal are normally satisfied by the development of relatively small and compact systems that are individually owned, developed, and managed and kept within the property lines of the owner. Normally, this implies the construction of wanted or required systems through individual rather than community effort. But there have been developments in villages and communities with scattered dwellings and other buildings in which the local government has taken the initiative and responsibility for the construction and care of the individualized systems. The property owner, as well as the community, then enjoys the benefits of adequate planning, design, construction, management, and supervision. In the absence of such community undertakings, unfortunately, the necessary works are all too seldom designed by qualified engineers. In consequence, they may satisfy their purpose but poorly, both in a sanitary and economic sense. Reasonably good results can be secured, however, (1) if the engineering departments of central health authorities prepare and make available to the public manuals of design, construction, and operation that fit the conditions encountered in the area governed by them, and (2) if these authorities are ready to provide needed advice and supervision as well as regulation and take an active interest in determining and safeguarding the quality of rural water supplies and in eliminating sanitary hazards due to improper disposal of human excreta and other waste matters.

In the long run, peri-urban or "fringe" areas are best served by the extension of central water lines and sewers. Where these areas lie outside of the political boundaries of the central community, this may be done through the incorporation of "water and sewer districts" that comprise more than a single unit of local government.

Although the individual systems are small and often primitive, the over-all problem of rural water supply and waste disposal is a large and challenging one. Its sanitary and economic implications must be gaged not only by the size of the population that lives under rural conditions, but also by the numbers of people that visit rural areas, vacation in them, and purchase food, drink, and other commodities from roadside eating places, food stands, filling stations, and other commercial undertakings. Recreational areas, summer camps for children and adults, logging camps, construction camps, and military camps are part of the complex as well. The design and operation of swimming pools, too, present individualized problems of water management. Hence these pools are also discussed in this chapter.

30-2. Amounts of Water and Waste Water. The quantities of water used under rural conditions and the resulting amounts of waste water vary in magnitude from the values common to urban areas described in Chapter 5 to much smaller amounts. The minimum use of piped water in dwellings is about 20 gpcd, the average about 50 gpcd. The water requirements of rural schools, overnight camps, and rural factories (excluding manufacturing uses) are about 25 gpcd, of restaurants about 10 gpcd on a patronage basis, and of work or construction camps about 45 gpcd. By contrast, resort hotels need about 100 gpcd and rural sanatoria or hospitals about twice this amount.

On farms, live-stock and irrigation needs are additional. The drinking-water requirements of farm animals vary from 15 gpcd for dairy cows and 12 gpcd for horses, mules, and steers, to 4 gpcd for hogs and 2 gpcd for sheep. Chickens consume but 0.04 gpcd and turkeys but 0.07 gpcd. The over-all water requirements for dairy cows, including water for cleansing and cooling, are about 35 gpcd. Green-houses may need as much as 70 gpcd per 1,000 sq ft, and garden crops about half this amount.

Military water requirements vary from an absolute minimum of 0.5 gpcd for troops in combat through 2 to 5 gpcd for troops on the march or in bivouac and 15 gpcd for troops in temporary camps up to 50 or more gpcd for permanent military installations.

The quantities of waste water are of the same order of magnitude, but due allowance must be made for waters that do not reach the waste-disposal system.

As discussed in Chapter 14, the rates of water use and waste-water production are given by the water requirements and discharge capacities of the different fixtures. In comparison with municipal sewage, the water-carried wastes of rural habitations and similar buildings are likely to be smaller and more fluctuating in volume; fresher and more concentrated; and quite warm, greasy, and soapy as flushes of wash water are released. Discharge is largely confined to 16 hr of the day, with substantially no flow at night.

30-3. Sanitary Safeguards. Rural water supply and waste-water disposal must rely, to a considerably greater degree than their municipal counterparts, on safeguards that are inherent in their construction and that do not receive the benefit of supervisory control or operation. To this purpose, rural water supplies should be collected, wherever possible, from sources that are certain to deliver, at all times, water that is safe and of satisfactory quality. Furthermore, the collecting system itself should be such that the water cannot be impaired in quality. Purification should be resorted to only when safe and satisfactory sources are non-existent. It should then be as simple and foolproof as possible in conception and execution. Like municipal supplies, the collected water should be conducted to the points of use without danger of its contamination. The necessity of disposing of the spent water supply in a safe manner must be kept in mind, and the method of waste-water disposal must be chosen to prevent danger both to the system from which it draws its water and to that of a neighboring user. The interrelationship between waste disposal and water supply is very intimate indeed.

Because of the natural purifying capacity of the ground, rural water supplies are generally drawn from the ground through springs, infiltration galleries, and wells. Where ground water is highly mineralized or unavailable, rain water is next best in general safety and quality. Only in uninhabited upland areas do ponds and streams lend themselves to exploitation without the necessity of purifying the waters taken from them.

Because of the natural purifying capacity of the ground, waste waters from dwellings as well as non-water-carried human excreta are most safely and esthetically disposed of by being discharged into the ground. Contamination of the surface soil and of surface water is thereby avoided. In addition, potentially dangerous wastes are rendered inaccessible to flies, rodents, and domestic animals, and the mechanical transfer of infection to man is prevented. The fact that ground water is thereby endangered requires that the disposal systems be located and constructed with a full understanding of the hazards involved.

Factors to be considered in this dual use of the ground are: (1) the nature of the geological formations from which the water is drawn; (2) the nature of the soil into which the excreta or waste waters are discharged; (3) the direction of flow of the ground water and its hydraulic gradient under draft (including the cone of depression induced by pumpage of water); (4) the quantities of water and waste water involved; and (5) the distance of travel, both horizontal and vertical, from the place of excreta or sewage disposal to the ground-water intake. No generally applicable values can be assigned to the distance that pollution may be expected to travel through the ground. As a matter of safety, it is assumed that these distances are never less than 10 ft even under the most favorable conditions: when the soil is constituted of fine-grained sand, for example, and has a high filtering effect. A minimum cover of 10 ft of fine-grained, homogeneous soil is required for the protection of ground waters against pollution by surface wash. When privies and sewage-disposal works are present, they are placed on the downward slope of the ground, the distance from the water intake being made as great as possible (see Figure 30-1). Under favorable geological conditions, distances are chosen to exceed about 50 ft when pit-privies are employed, 100 ft when sewage is settled in tight septic tanks before discharge into subsurface irrigation systems, and 150 ft when bored-hole latrines or cesspools are used. In addition, all sewers and supposedly tight treatment tanks are kept at least 50 ft from the ground-water intake. Within this distance, sewers should be constructed of cast-iron pipe with lead-calked joints. Fractured ground or rock can never be considered safe.

The immediate vicinity of the ground-water intake presents the gravest dangers. For this reason, surface runoff is led away from the intake structure and the structure itself, whether it be a spring, gallery, or well, is made watertight until it has penetrated into the ground-water-bearing stratum.

All parts of the water-supply system should be thoroughly flushed and disinfected before being placed in use. Calcium hypochlorite is most conveniently employed as the disinfectant. A concentration of active chlorine between 50 and 100 mg/l should be reached. The chlorinated water should be held in the system or circulated through it for 12 hours. After that the system should be flushed until all noticeable traces of chlorine have disappeared.

Water Supply

30-4. Collection and Pumping. Some of the details of construction that must be incorporated in collection works for ground water in order to prevent contamination of the water at the source are illustrated in Figures 30-2 to 30-4. They have the following features in common: (1) diversion of surface water from the intake structure; (2) drainage

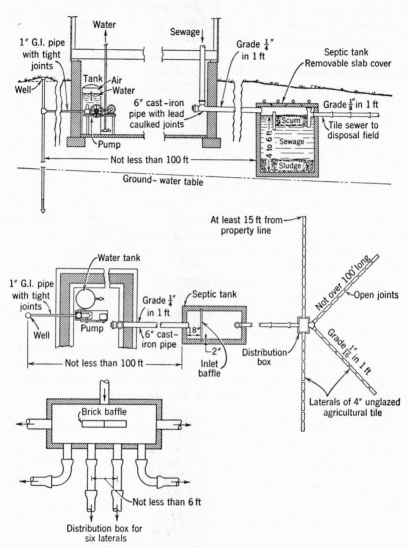

Figure 30-1. Typical rural water-supply and waste-water-disposal system. Water is obtained from a driven well and distributed by pneumatic pressure. Waste water is treated in a septic tank and discharged through a subsurface irrigation system.

of overflow or spillage waters from the intake structure; (3) water-tightness of the intake works for at least 10 ft below the ground surface and, if necessary, until the aquifer is reached; and (4) prevention of back-flow into the intake.

The development of rain-water supplies has been discussed in Section 2-4. Waste of the first flush of water by diversion from the cistern or of water diverted when the "switch-to-waste" is not changed

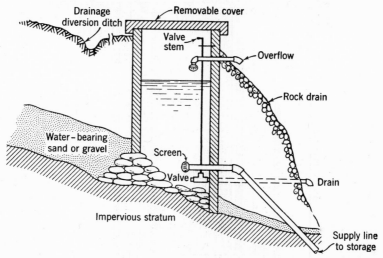

Figure 30-2. Water supply from spring. *After U. S. Public Health Service.*

into the storage position is avoided by introduction of a "flush-water tank" such as that shown in Figure 30-5.

Other considerations that enter into the development of rural water supplies are: (1) minimum yield of source, (2) maximum demand of user, (3) available or needed storage, (4) pressure conditions or requirements, and (5) needed purification. The minimum yield of the source is determined at the end of the dry season (August or September in the northern United States). Timing the recovery after draft or the filling of a vessel of known capacity establishes the rate of flow. Peak demand rates are found in accordance with the fixture loadings discussed in Section 14-3. Storage in cisterns or pneumatic tanks, or in spring cribs or large-diameter wells, dampens direct demands on the source. Pressure requirements are met either by gravity flow (when the source is situated sufficiently high above the service outlets) or by pumping. The latter may be direct or through a pneumatic tank.

Where electric power is not available, the pumps used in rural water supplies are operated by hand, wind, water, or gasoline engines. Windmills are generally loaded to operate in a 10- or 15-mph wind. They

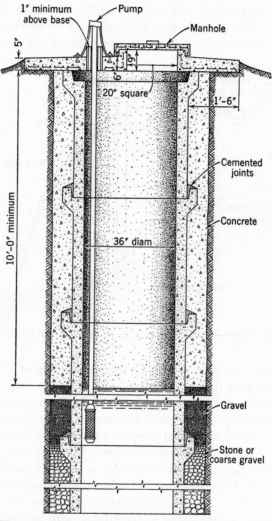

Figure 30-3. Water supply from dug well. *After U. S. Department of Agriculture.*

start to pump in winds of about half these velocities and reach their maximum output in winds of about twice these speeds. In large areas of North America, needed wind velocities do not occur during as much as two-thirds the time, and storage of water must be planned accord-

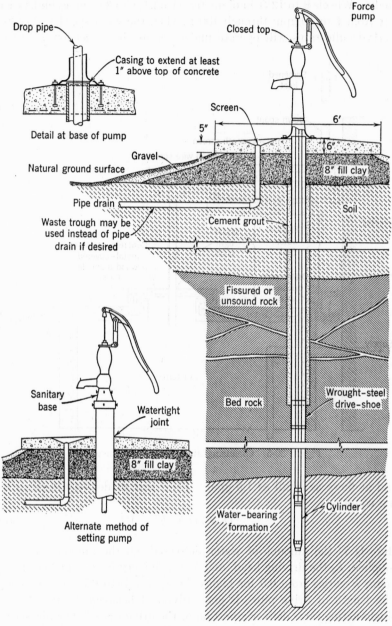

Figure 30-4.   Water supply from driven well. *After Virginia State Department of Health.*

ingly. Wheels 6 to 12 ft in diameter with 2½- to 4½-in. cylinders will lift from 1 to 10 gpm through 100 ft when the wind speed is 15 mph. Hydraulic rams will operate under driving heads as low as 20 in.

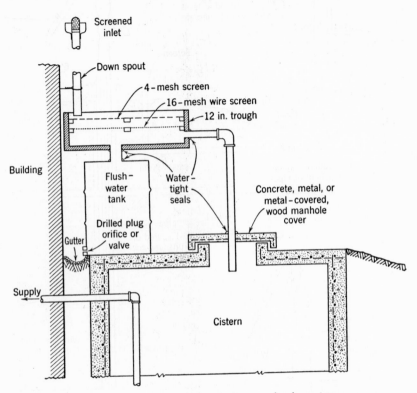

Figure 30-5. Cleansing and storage of rain water.

and at flows as small as 1.5 gpm. Their rate of delivery is given by the equation

$$Q = kQ_sh_d/h \qquad 30\text{-}1$$

Here Q is the amount of water delivered, Q_s the amount of water supplied, h_d the driving head, and h the delivery head. The efficiency factor k varies from 0.5 for high delivery heads to 0.75 for low ones. The length of drive pipes is generally held between 25 and 250 ft. Single-acting rams deliver a portion of the drive water. Double-acting rams use water from one source to pump water from another. When the two sources are thereby interconnected, the drive source must be of satisfactory quality if pollution of the supply is to be avoided.

Electrically driven pumps are of numerous designs. Reciprocating pumps mounted on or beside pneumatic tanks are often used for shallow wells. To lift water more than 25 ft, including dynamic friction, rod-operated cylinder pumps are driven through pump jacks at the well head. Ejectors or jets combined with centrifugal pumps, installed at the ground surface, will permit a 100-ft suction lift. In these combination units, water is lifted to the centrifugal pump through the

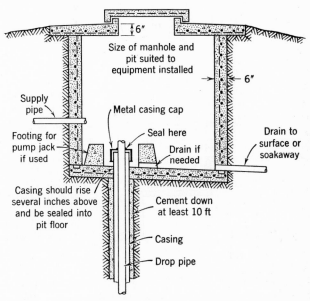

Figure 30-6. Pit for an electric pump.

suction pipe by forcing part of the discharge of the centrifugal pump through a pressure pipe and through a jet in the suction lift. The jet is similar in construction to a boiler-water injector. It attaches to the suction lift below the water surface of the well but above the foot-valve and strainer.

When electric pumps at the well head must be placed below ground level to prevent freezing, the pit must be watertight and properly drained. As shown in Figure 30-6, the drain is installed in such fashion that there is no opportunity for surface or other water to back into the pit and flow back into the well column.

30-5. Storage and Purification. The masonry reservoirs of rural water supplies are called cisterns. Elevated storage is secured by placing cisterns on elevated ground, by the construction of tanks in the attic of the building to be served, or by the use of elevated tanks.

Pressure can also be provided by the employment of hydropneumatic tanks. These are placed either at the intake or in the cellar of the building served. The tight tank, usually constructed of steel and often galvanized, holds both air and water. The air, instead of being displaced, is compressed by the water. If the pressure in a tank of volume V is p when the tank holds its maximum volume of water V_w, the pressure p_0 when the tank is just empty is given by the isothermal relationship

$$p_0 V = p(V - V_w) \quad \text{or} \quad p_0 = p(1 - V_w/V) \qquad 30\text{-}2$$

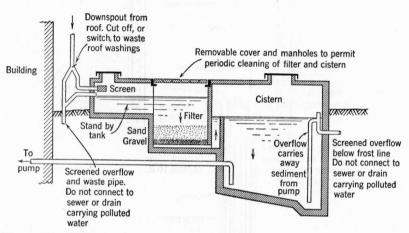

Figure 30-7. Filtration and storage of rain water. Capacities of the component structures are determined by the intensity and distribution of rainfall.

The air pressure may be kept between these limits, or it may be increased for certain purposes, such as fire fighting, by adding an air compressor and air-storage tank to the system.

All types of water-purification problems are encountered in rural water supplies. The filtration of roof water before cistern storage is illustrated in Figure 30-7. The stand-by tank and filter must be large enough to hold and filter the maximum rainfall expected in a given period, such as a day. Similar arrangements can be employed to improve the sanitary quality of other waters of doubtful purity. Pressure filters (see Figure 30-13) are more elaborate and expensive. Also they require regular and careful supervision. Zeolite softeners and other ion-exchange units look much like pressure filters and are operated in much the same manner. Iron-bearing ground waters that issue from their source sparklingly clear but become rust-colored on exposure to air (by oxidation and precipitation of the iron) are best treated in manganese-cation exchange units (Section 23-5). Addition of hexametaphosphates to otherwise untreated iron-bearing water may keep the iron from precipitating. But this requires skillful management. It is more often advisable to seek an iron-free source instead.

Some soft, ground waters contain much carbon dioxide and are extremely corrosive. If such waters are passed through marble or limestone chips, calcium is taken into solution and the carbon dioxide is reduced proportionately. The hardness of the water is increased, but its corrosiveness is decreased. A period of contact of about two hours with chips an inch or less in diameter ordinarily suffices. If the water is drawn from a dug well or spring, a layer of chips placed in the well or spring crib may be of some benefit. Where cisterns or gravity tanks are employed, they may incorporate a contact compartment filled with chips through which the water must pass on its way to storage. In pressure systems, the chips are conveniently placed in a tank similar in construction to a pressure filter or hot-water boiler. The period of contact is then more irregular, however.

The chlorination of polluted rural supplies is made possible of accomplishment by the use of dosing devices that proportion the addition of a chlorine solution to the flow of water. To avoid the continual maintenance problem involved, the householder may prefer to insure the safety of the water that is to be used for drinking and culinary purposes by boiling it. As previously stated, it is best to seek an inherently safe and satisfactory supply.

Excreta and Waste-Water Disposal

30-6. Disposal of Excreta and Waste Waters without Water Carriage. In the absence of plumbing systems, soapy and greasy waters from the kitchen and from hand basins and wash tubs are emptied onto the ground or into soakage pits and human excreta are deposited in privies. Apart from their general significance in the protection of the health of rural areas, privies are of concern to sanitary engineers (1) in evaluating the need for and economy of private and public sewerage and sewage disposal and (2) in making privy construction an integral part of the general plan for the collection and disposal of sanitary wastes.

Privies are so-called because they provide privacy during defecation. Their name does not indicate their more important purpose of disposing of human excreta in a safe and clean fashion. Privacy and protection against the elements are insured by the superstructure of privies; sanitary requirements principally by their substructure. Both components are held as simple as possible to meet the economic needs of the population that they must serve. The superstructure must either be tight with a self-closing door and openings for light and ventilation screened against flies and other insects, or the seat lid must be self-closing. However, a self-closing lid is uncomfortable and may soil clothing. The substructure provides for the safe storage of the excreta. To this purpose, it must be sealed against entrance by flies and other vermin as well as surface runoff. The fecal solids accumulate, but they are reduced in volume by compaction and decomposition. The annual per capita production of fecal solids is about 1.5 cu ft for adults and about half this amount for children. The annual production of urine is about twelve times as great. But the urine leaches into the soil in some constructions and evaporates to a considerable extent in others. Not all of the urine, furthermore, is excreted in privies. Provision of screened ventilators for the substructure brings air to the underside of the privy seat and prevents condensation of moisture on it. It also helps to carry away odors.

The features of construction of a number of privies are illustrated in Figure 30-8. In North America, the *pit privy* (see Figure 30-8a) is most widely used because of its economy and sanitary safety. Feces are stored in the pit; urine seeps into the soil. A pit capacity of 50 cu ft will serve a family of average size for several years. After that a new pit is dug and cribbed, and the privy structure is moved over it, the remaining volume of the old pit (desirably about 18 in. in depth) being filled with earth. Pits will not contaminate ground water provided that (1) they are dug into ordinary ground, not shale, limestone, or fissured rock; (2) they lie several feet above the ground-water table; and (3) surface drainage and other waste waters are kept out of the pit. Pit privies are about 5 ft deep. In the *bored-hole latrine*, a hole, usually less than 18 in. in diameter but more than 12 ft deep, is substituted for the pit. The hole generally penetrates into the ground-water stream. This endangers nearby ground water, but it promotes anaerobic digestion of fecal solids and longer use of the hole. Depth, furthermore, keeps flies, which naturally shun darkness, from the excreta. The bored-hole latrine has been used with success among people that prefer to defecate while squatting rather than sitting. The top of the hole is then protected by a slab with slanting foot rests adjacent to a slot through which the excreta fall into the hole.

The *concrete-vault privy* (see Figure 30-8c) is intended for use in areas where the ground-water table is high or space is small. To prevent pollution of the ground water, the vault must be constructed

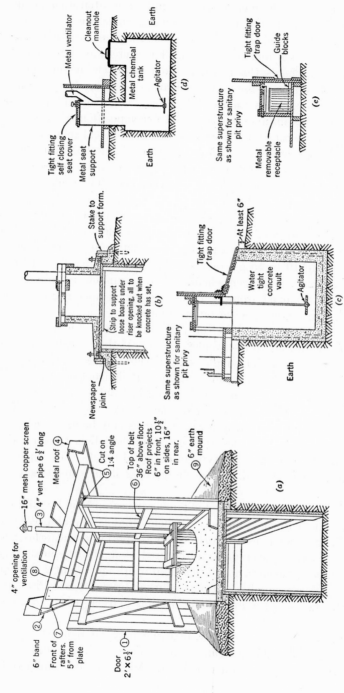

Figure 30-8. Disposal of excreta without water carriage. (a) Pit privy. (b) Detail of slab and riser
for pit privy. (c) Concrete-vault privy. (d) Chemical toilet. (e) Removable receptacle privy. After U. S. Public Health Service and New York State Department of Health.

of reinforced, dense concrete. Concrete vaults are often used in rural schools and similar institutions. Depending upon the size of the population to be served, they are built as single or multiple units. When the vault fills, it must be cleaned. The excreta are removed and buried. In rural schools, this is usually done at the end of the summer recess, in order to permit the excreta to rot and become less unsightly and malodorous before they must be handled. High concentrations of urine are generally unfavorable to rapid decomposition of the feces. In order to promote anaerobic decomposition of the fecal solids in more dilute solution, concrete-vault privies may be elaborated into *septic-tank privies*. Water is added to the tank as needed. An overflow commonly leads to a subsurface drain or cesspool. The tank must be pumped out from time to time.

In *chemical toilets* (see Figure 30-8d), a metal tank takes the place of the concrete vault, and stabilization of putrescible matter is effected by caustic added to the water in the tank. A charge of 25 lb of caustic soda dissolved in 10 to 15 gal of water is generally placed in a tank of 125-gal capacity. The spent chemical and accumulating liquids and solids must be removed from time to time. The tank contents are either drained into a cesspool or pumped out.

Removable receptacle privies, or pail privies (see Figure 30-8e), require regular and careful scavenger service, if they are to serve as sanitary conveniences. The night soil collected in the receptacle is disposed of safely by burial or incineration. Pails from privies on the fringe of a sewered community may be flushed out with water in a station connected to a main drain of the sewerage system. In the absence of sewerage, disposal into water courses may be dangerous. A caustic solution may be added to the receptacle. This converts the pail privy into the "commode" type of chemical toilet. The capacity of the pail is about 10 gal, and a charge of 2 lb of caustic soda is generally used.

The sanitary facilities employed in temporary camps and by military forces in the field range from the "cat hole" that is dry and filled in by the individual after use to fairly elaborate portable platforms and seats that are placed over pits and covered by tents or shielded by canvas. Straddle trenches, a foot or less in width and about 2 ft deep, will care for large numbers of men during brief stops. Pits and trenches should be filled and their location marked when camp is broken.

When pits are not fly-tight, fly breeding may be reduced by the judicious use of insecticides. Odors can be decreased by adding lime to the pit or spraying it with a deodorant. Adding easily combustible fuels such as hay and fuel oil and burning out the pit is principally of psychological value. Shallow burial of privy contents with a cover of about 18 in. leads to their rapid destruction. Composting of night soil with garbage and other organic waste materials is satisfactory only under proper supervision and with the control of fly breeding. Incineration is expensive and difficult of operation and maintenance. Use of night soil as a fertilizer presents numerous sanitary hazards.

30-7. Disposal of Water-Carried Wastes. In the presence of plumbing systems, the waste waters from rural dwellings and similar buildings are normally disposed of in the ground. The capacity of the soil to receive these wastes is then of controlling importance. The absorptive capacity of the soil is greatly increased if the settleable portion of the solid fraction of the waste waters is removed before the soil is called upon to receive the residual, largely liquid, fraction. This separation is accomplished in devices that incorporate, by as simple means as possible, removal of suspended matter by sedimentation and, since the devices can be cleaned with convenience only after long intervals of time (1 to 3 years), also digestion and consolidation of the deposited sludge and scum. Attached to these primary treatment facilities, and included in them when the amount of waste water is relatively small and the absorptive capacity of the soil is relatively large, are leaching or irrigation facilities that carry the liquid fraction into the soil. The combination of sedimentation and digestion is accomplished more often than not in (1) leaching cesspools or (2) septic tanks (or tight cesspools) with attached subsurface absorption fields or seepage pits. The absorption fields are referred to also as subsurface disposal or purification fields, and as subsurface irrigation or seepage areas. Underdrainage of the disposal areas is not common. Leaching cesspools are called seepage pits when they receive the effluent of septic tanks.

When the volumes of waste water are large, the use of Imhoff tanks and sand beds, or trickling filters, may become more economical. Their design and operation is like that of municipal installations. However, they are generally covered or placed below the surface of the ground.

When the absorptive capacity of the soil is poor, subsurface sand beds or sand-filter trenches may have to be employed in small installations, too. Insofar as volume of flow is concerned, the line of separation between small and large facilities is generally drawn at about 10,000 gpd.

A leaching-cesspool and seepage-pit installation is shown in Figure 30-9 and a septic-tank and absorption field in Figure 30-1. Details of a large septic tank with dosing siphon are given in Figure 30-10.

A sand-filter trench and a subsurface sand filter are illustrated in Figure 30-11.

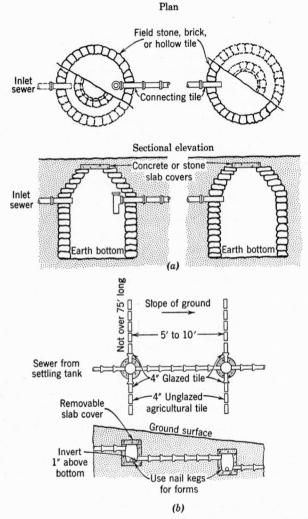

Figure 30-9. Cesspools: (a) Leaching cesspool and seepage pit; (b) Tight cesspool and seepage trenches on steep slope. *After New York State Department of Health.*

a. Sedimentation and Storage. The required volume V of cesspools and septic tanks is a function of the contributory population P, the rate of sewage discharge Q, the nominal detention period t, and the volume of sludge to be stored S, or

$$V = PQt + SP \qquad\qquad 30\text{-}3$$

Because the wide fluctuations in flow that occur in small systems interfere with sedimentation, the minimum nominal detention period must be set at about 4 hr for the largest tanks, in which the smallest disturbance is experienced. For the smallest units, in which disturbance is a maximum and settling efficiency a minimum, a much longer nominal period, such as 12 or 13 hr, must be provided. The nominal detention period is thereby made a function of PQ, such as $t = (1.3 - 0.3 \log PQ)$ for t in days and Q in gpd. The volume of sludge that must be stored can be calculated in accordance with the principles laid down in Chapter 26. For domestic wastes, the per capita volume is found to be about 30 gal if the tank is cleaned once a year or if there is a 50% loss of sludge during 2 years of storage. In the terms given, the required tank volume in gallons becomes

$$V = (1.3 - 0.3 \log PQ)PQ + 30P \qquad\qquad 30\text{-}4$$

For flows of 50 gpcd, this equation is closely approximated by the relation

$$V = 2.8(PQ)^{0.86} \qquad\qquad 30\text{-}5$$

Because of the uncertainties involved in water use and in the construction and operation of small units, a total tank capacity equal to 1.5 times the daily flow (i.e., $V = 1.5PQ$) for flows up to 1,000 gpd and equal to the daily flow (i.e., $V = PQ$) for flows between 1,000 and 10,000 gpcd will generally make for reasonably effective installations. For satisfactory operation, the settling and digestion units should possess a total useful volume of not less than 500 gal and a depth below the water line of at least 4 ft with a minimum freeboard of 1 ft.

Cesspools and seepage pits are masonry-lined pits 6 to 10 ft deep and not less than 3 ft in diameter. The bottom of these devices is left unlined, and the masonry walls of leaching cesspools and seepage pits below the influent sewer are laid dry. To increase pit capacity without making it too deep, pairs of pits may be placed in series. Both pits may be lined or unlined, or the first pit may serve as a septic tank and the second as a leaching device (see Figure 30-9). Leaching cesspools may be used for the combined wastes of a building or for all but the toilet wastes. If the latter, they may be classed as seepage pits.

Septic tanks are generally constructed of reinforced concrete. They possess a single compartment or are divided into two compartments by an overflow wall or a concrete baffle pierced by 4-in. holes 12 in. on centers and 12 to 18 in. below the water line. Subdivision increases the efficiency of sedimentation. The first compartment is generally made twice as large as the second, because it receives both the shock of fluctuating flows and the largest amount of solids. A dosing chamber may be added to control the flows into the disposal field (see Figures 30-1 and 30-10).

Rural kitchen sinks are often equipped with *grease traps*. In large institutions, separate traps of substantial capacity are sometimes inserted in the kitchen line close to the kitchen and ahead of the septic

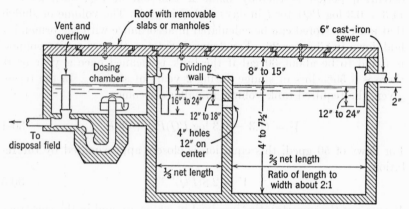

Figure 30-10. Two-compartment septic tank with dosing chamber.

tank. Traps holding about 2½ gal per capita and not less than 30 gal will generally cool the incoming wastes sufficiently quickly to permit separation of the grease. In construction, grease traps are not unlike small septic tanks. For satisfactory operation, the influent pipe should terminate at least 6 in. below the water line, while the effluent pipe should take off about 6 in. from the bottom. Grease traps must be cleaned regularly. See Figure 14-10.

b. Leaching or Absorption. The absorptive capacity of soils for sewage is not only a function of their hydraulic permeability but also of their capacity to cleanse pore space of the solids that escape from settling devices or that are built up by the life activities of zoogleal organisms. These develop on soil grains in the same manner as in intermittent sand filters and trickling filters. Biological activity is most rapid under the aerobic conditions that can be maintained near the surface of the soil. In the light of experience with existing systems, the New York State Department of Health [1] has correlated the allowable loading of leaching devices with the results of standardized seepage

[1] *Bull.* 1 (1938); but see also "Studies on Household Sewage Disposal Systems," *U. S. Pub. Health Service,* 1949 and 1950.

tests. Test holes 1 ft square are filled with water to a depth of 6 in. The time for the water surface to drop 1 in. is then noted. The bottom of the test hole must be placed at the operating level of the leaching device: at the depth of seepage trenches (generally 18 in.) and below the bottom of a test pit dug to half the proposed depth of a leaching cesspool or seepage pit. The correlation noted by the New York State Department of Health is expressed closely by the following equations: [2]

For seepage trenches,

$$Q = 30/(t + 7.5) \hspace{3cm} 30\text{-}6$$

For seepage pits,

$$Q = 40/(t + 7.5) \hspace{3cm} 30\text{-}7$$

Here Q is the permissible loading or rate of discharge in gpd per sq ft and t is the time in minutes during which the seepage water is lowered 1 in. in the test pits. For very short and very long seepage times (such as 1 min or less and above 30 min) the equations give more conservative values than actual observations. Cesspools and seepage pits or trenches should not be employed when the seepage time exceeds an hour. Very dry soil must be wetted before the test is conducted. The useful seepage area equals the bottom area of seepage trenches and the area of the bottom and the outside area of the permeable side walls of seepage pits. The permissible loading of seepage pits is a third greater than that of seepage trenches, because of the greater head of water in pits. Seepage pits are used in small installations and when the lower layers of soil are hydraulically more suitable than the upper ones. The bottom of cesspools should not be included as seepage area.

Significant details of *subsurface irrigation systems* are shown in Figures 30-1 and 30-9. To promote biological action in the soil, the depth of seepage trenches should be kept shallow (18 to 36 in.). In small systems a single line of open-jointed, agricultural, tile pipe 4 in. in diameter may suffice to distribute the sewage in the seepage trench. Where more than one lateral and trench must be used, a distribution box should be employed. When the total length of seepage trenches exceeds 1,000 ft, a dosing chamber should be added to the septic tank in order to distribute the load as uniformly as possible over all parts of the system. To do this, the chamber is given a capacity equal to the total internal volume of the irrigation pipes. In small systems, the discharge of plumbing fixtures is normally sufficiently great in rate and volume to act as a dosing mechanism. Uniform loading is aided by laying irrigation pipes on uniform slopes of about 0.5% in the

[2] By contrast, the experimental rate of seepage is $Q = 900/t$.

absence of dosing tanks and about 0.3% in their presence. The pattern of the irrigation pipes is dictated by the topography of the disposal area. During the growing season and in warm weather, evaporation from the soil and transpiration by plants reduce the downward percolation in the disposal area considerably.

In tight soils, seepage trenches may be elaborated into *sand-filter trenches*. As shown in Figure 30-11, these trenches are wider (up to

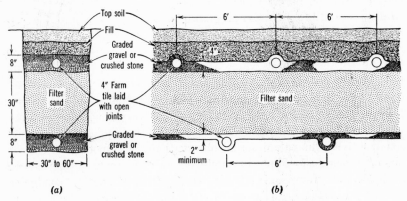

Figure 30-11. Subsurface filters: (*a*) sand-filter trench; (*b*) sand filter.

5 ft) and include, below the irrigation pipe, (1) a bed of filter sand 30 in. deep and (2) a collecting pipe 4 in. in diameter laid in gravel and crushed stone in much the same fashion as the irrigation pipe. The underdrain must terminate in a ditch leading to a water course or empty directly into a natural body of water. As shown in Figure 30-11, too, *subsurface sand beds* constitute a maximal artificial development of the filtering capacity of the subsurface. The allowable loading of the filter trenches or beds is about 1 gpd per sq ft. This corresponds to a seepage test time of about 23 min. Alternating dosing siphons that throw the tank effluent into half the area at a time may be required in large installations, in order to effect adequate dosage and provide a longer resting period for the filter sand.

Example 30-1. A septic tank and subsurface irrigation system are to serve a rural school with a population of 100 pupils and teachers. Tests at trench depth record a seepage time of 10 minutes. Determine the requisite volume of a septic tank, the requisite storage capacity of its dosing chamber, and the requisite length of subsurface irrigation tiles.

From Section 30-2, the expected daily flow of sewage is: $Q = 25 \times 100 = 2,500$ gpd. However, since the school is in use for half a day only, the rate of sewage flow must be expected to be at about double the daily rate of flow, or 5,000 gpd. By Equation 30-4, the volume of the septic tank is: $V = (1.3 - 0.3 \log 5,000)5,000$

+ 30 × 100 = 3,950 gal, or 530 cu ft. By Equation 30-6, the permissible loading of the seepage trenches is $Q = 30/(10 + 7.5) = 1.71$ gpd per sq ft, and the required length of tile drains is: 5,000/1.71 = 2,920 ft, or about 30 ft per capita.

The volume of sewage to be stored in the dosing chamber, therefore, is: 2,920 × π × 9/(4 × 144) = 140 cu ft for 3-in. tile or 140 × 16/9 = 250 cu ft for 4-in. tile.

Swimming Pools

30-8. Sanitary Requirements for Swimming Pools. Standards of quality for bathing waters have been discussed in Section 21-4. In developing standards of design for swimming pools, the engineer must have in mind: (1) the protection of the bather (*a*) against infection transmitted through pool water, (*b*) against infection transmitted outside of the pool, and (*c*) against physical injury within and outside of the pool; (2) the maintenance of the pool and its waters and of the pool surroundings in a clean, comfortable, and attractive condition; (3) the protection of the pool water itself as well as the supply from which it is drawn against back-flow from the drainage system of the pool and that into which it empties; and (4) the provision of auxiliary facilities that will insure the comfort and cleanliness of the bather before he enters the pool or re-enters it after using the toilet.

Modern swimming pools are designed for the recirculation of pool water and its continuous repurification, reheating, and redisinfection, including the maintenance of desirable concentrations of active disinfectant (usually chlorine or chloramine) in the pool water at all times. Recirculation introduces some interesting problems, both hydraulic and sanitary, in water-supply and waste-water piping, and in water purification and conditioning. A recirculated pool and its appurtenances are outlined in Figures 30-12 and 30-13.

Pool sanitation is promoted by the proper design and operation of auxiliary facilities (dressing rooms, toilets, showers, drinking fountains, heating, lighting, and ventilation) and by the sanitary supervision of the bather both before and after he is permitted to enter the pool. The taking of a cleansing shower before the bather enters the pool and after he has visited the toilet should be enforced. Footbaths containing 0.3 to 0.6% active chlorine do not afford adequate protection against the spread of athlete's foot (epidermophytosis), but thorough cleaning and disinfection of all walkways is helpful. Persons ill with respiratory diseases, infections of the mucous surfaces, and skin lesions should, insofar as practicable, be excluded from the pool and its environs. Bathing-suits (if used) and towels should be owned and washed by the bathing establishment. There should be no common

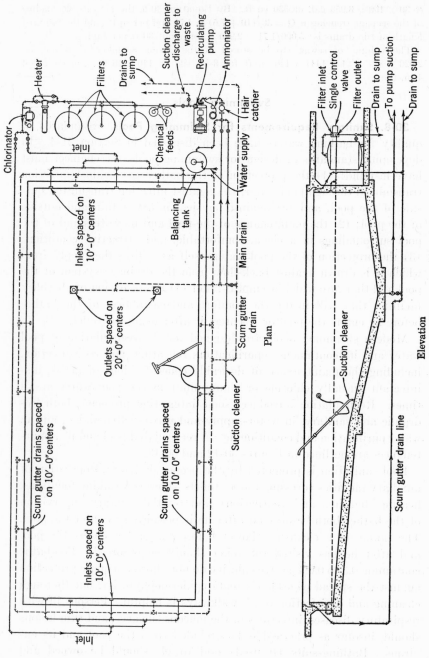

Figure 30-12. Recirculated swimming pool. After Figure 8.2, *Water Conditioning Handbook*, Permutit Co., New York, 1943.

toilet articles. Lifeguards should be present whenever the pool is in use and should maintain good order in the interest of safety. When pools are empty or in the process of being filled, entrances to them should be locked.

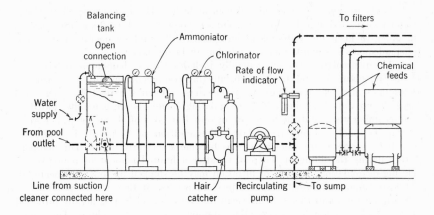

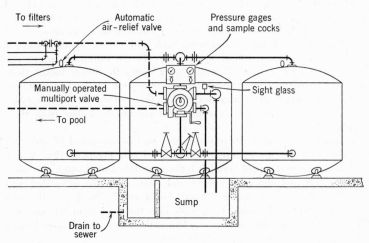

Figure 30-13. Purification of recirculated swimming-pool water. After Figure 8.2, *Water Conditioning Handbook,* Permutit Co., New York, 1943.

The design and operation of outdoor pools should approximate as closely as possible that of indoor pools with due allowances for the special situations that are created at them.

30-9. Design, Equipment, and Operation of Swimming Pools. Recommended practice for the design, equipment, and operation of swimming pools is summarized from time to time by the American Public Health Association,[3] similar organizations, and public health authorities. Some of the matters covered that are of interest to sanitary engineers are outlined below.

1. Pools are normally recirculated continuously. The turnover ratio (ratio of water recirculated in a day to pool volume) should be at least 2 and preferably 3 in order to keep the water clean and safe. Fill-and-draw operation does not offer adequate safeguards under conditions of heavy use.

2. The recirculating system generally includes pumps, hair-catchers, chemical feeds (for alum and soda), filters, disinfecting equipment (usually a chlorinator, sometimes also an ammoniator), and heaters. When the pool is being filled or make-up water is being added, coagulating chemicals are generally added to the incoming water and the filters are operated at rates of about 2 gpm per sq ft. When the pool is being recirculated, the addition of chemicals is ordinarily omitted as soon as the pool water has become sufficiently clear. This happens either during the filling of the pool or after a limited amount of recirculation. During recirculation, the rate of filtration may be stepped up to 3 gpm per sq ft. At least three and probably four filters are needed, if they are to provide the wash water for a unit that is being cleaned. Alum coagulant is generally provided as filter alum, sometimes as crystalline ammonia or potassium alum. The reduction in alkalinity and pH value associated with alum coagulation is normally made up by the use of soda ash, sometimes in the form of washing soda. Ammonia from ammonia alum coagulation as well as ammonia contributed by bathers converts added chlorine to chloramine in proportionate amounts.

3. Use of a make-up or balancing tank will permit drawing water from the municipal or primary supply system for (1) the initial charge of pool water, (2) make-up water, and (3) water for washing the filters (other than filtered, pool water) without objectionable cross-connection of the two supplies. Use of a sump, into which all drainage water from the pool system empties with adequate air gaps for discharge into a sewer, will prevent back-flow from the sewerage system.

4. Displacement of water through the pool is controlled by inlet and outlet arrangements that are hydraulically balanced (see Figure 30-12). Water may be withdrawn from the pool through bottom outlets and through the scum gutters. Scum gutters act also as overflows and carry away the scum that accumulates on the surface of the water. They should not be used as spit troughs since there is bound to be some back-wash into the pool from the gutter. The lip of the gutter generally serves as a handrail. Floor drains should intercept the drainage from walkways around the pool.

5. Bather safety is affected by areal crowding and pool depth. The minimum area of a pool is a function of the number of persons using it at one time (the bathing load). Common minimum requirements are 10 sq ft per person for areas shallower than 5 ft and 27 sq ft for areas deeper than this. In arriving at these figures, it is assumed that at any one time only half the *non-swimmers* and two-thirds the *swimmers* are in the pool. The area within 10 ft of the end

---

[3] "Recommended Practice for Design, Equipment, and Operation of Swimming Pools and Other Public Bathing Places," 1949.

of a diving board is generally permitted to contain but three bathers, with three times that number waiting their turn to use the board. Controlling depths are those for non-swimmers (3 to 5 ft with floor slopes of not more than 1 in 15) and for divers (from 6 to 12 ft depending on the height of the diving board above the water surface). Pool dimensions are otherwise set by the requirements for athletic competitions; multiples of 5 yd for length (not less than 20 yd) and multiples of 5, 6, or 7 ft for the subdivision of the pool width into convenient swimming lanes.

6. In spite of a high degree of water cleanness and bather cleanliness, slime growths (often teaming with saprophytes) will develop on the walls and bottom of swimming pools, mucous and oily substances will rise to the surface, and hair, lint, and epithelial cells will sink to the bottom. Floating substances are best skimmed off or flushed off into the scum gutters. Slime growths and bottom accumulations are removed by brushes that operate as suction cleaners. They are called pool-cleaning tools (see Figure 30-12).

7. Water quality is a function of the number of bathers, the capacity of the pool, and the amount of clean water introduced into it. Based on observations by public health authorities, these factors may be related empirically and in part rationally in terms that are shown below.

a. Recirculated Pools. Aside from cleansing of the pool itself, recirculated pools depend for their sanitary safety (1) on purification and disinfection of the pool water and (2) on the carrying of an active disinfectant (such as chlorine) into the pool in such concentration that disinfection of the pool water will be a nearly immediate and continuous process. Useful bathing load relations are:

$$p_r = \frac{Q}{G}\frac{R}{B} = 0.02\,\frac{C}{T}\frac{R}{B} \qquad\qquad 30\text{-}8$$

$$P_r = \frac{kQ}{T^2} = 3.84\,\frac{C}{T^3} \qquad\qquad 30\text{-}9$$

Here p_r is the maximum number of bathers per hour; P_r the maximum number of bathers that may be admitted to the pool during the hours that it is in use; Q the gallons per hour of purified and disinfected water entering the pool from the recirculation system; C the capacity of the pool in gallons; T the turnover or replacement period of the pool in hours, $T = C/Q$; R the number of hours in a day during which the pool water is recirculated; B the number of hours in a day during which the pool is in use; G a coefficient with dimensions of gallons of recirculated water added to the pool per bather; and k a coefficient reflecting the conditions under which the pool is used. The New York State Department of Health, as indicated in Equations 30-8 and 30-9, has suggested a value of $G = 50$ gal per bather, $1/G = 0.02$, and $k = 3.84$.   C. A. Hyatt [4] allows Wayne Becker's value of $k = 3.84$ in Equation 30-9 to vary over a wide range according to (1) conditions of pool use and (2) cap, suit, and bather control.

b. *Flowing-Through Pools.*   Flowing-through pools are natural ponds, impounded pools, and completely artificial pools that are supplied with water of good sanitary quality.   They depend for their sanitary safety on relatively rapid replacement of the pool water. When G is less than 500 gal per bather, it is generally agreed that the influent should be chlorinated in much the same way as for recirculated pools.   The pool itself should preferably be chlorinated daily.   Bathing loads are formulated as follows:

$$p_f = \frac{Q}{G}\frac{R}{B} = \frac{0.16C}{T^3}\frac{R}{B} \qquad\qquad 30\text{-}10$$

$$P_f = 0.16\frac{C}{T^3}B \qquad\qquad 30\text{-}11$$

Here the subscript f denotes a flowing-through pool, Q is the gallons per hour of clean water entering the pool, and R is the number of hours in a day during which clean water is added to the pool.   The New York State Department of Health, as indicated in Equations 30-10 and 30-11, has suggested a value of $G = 6.25T^2$, or $(1/G = 0.16/T^2)$.

Example 30-2.   The capacity of two pools, (a) a recirculated pool, and (b) a flowing-through pool, is 80,000 gal for each.   Recirculation and inflow are continuous at a rate of 10,000 gph, and the pools are open for use during 12 hr. Find the maximum allowable hourly and daily bathing loads.

The turnover or replenishment period is: $T = 80,000/10,000 = 8$ hr.

a. By Equation 30-8: $p_r = 0.02(80,000/8)(^{24}\!/_{12}) = 400$ bathers per hour.
    By Equation 30-9: $P_r = 3.84 \times 80,000/(8)^3 = 600$ bathers per day.
b. By Equation 30-10: $p_f = 0.16[80,000/(8)^3](^{24}\!/_{12}) = 50$ bathers per hour.
    By Equation 30-11: $P_r = 0.16[80,000/(8)^3]12 = 300$ bathers per day.

Since the amounts of water added per bather in the flowing-through pool is but 400 gal, namely, 6.25×64, the water added to the flowing-through pool should preferably be chlorinated.   The allowable loads can then be increased.

From what has been said in items 5 and 7 of this section, two permissible loadings of swimming pools may be found: a permissible areal loading to provide for the physical safety of the bather and a permissible water-supply loading to insure the sanitary safety of the

[4] "Minimum Sanitary Requirements for Swimming Pools and Bathing Places," *Illinois Dept. Pub. Health*, 1938.

pool water. In the operation of a given pool, the maximum areal loading can be reached by bringing the turnover or replacement period and the hours of recirculation or inflow and hours of use of the pool into balance with the permissible areal loading.

The disinfection of large bodies of natural water of doubtful quality is difficult and uncertain of results. It has been tried with varying success (1) by pumping, chlorinating, and dispersing off-shore water into the bathing area, and (2) by feeding chlorine into the water from boats moving along the shore.

TABLE A-1. Abbreviations

The abbreviations used in this book are shown in the following schedule. There is no differentiation between the singular and the plural unless it is noted. Chemical symbols are listed in Table A-4.

A	angstrom units	kw	kilowatt
atm	atmosphere	l	liter
AM	before noon	lb	pound
ave	average	MAF	mean annual flow
bbl	barrel	m	meter
Bé	Baumé degrees	me	milliequivalent
BOD	biochemical oxygen demand (in 5 days at 20 C, unless otherwise stated)	mg	million gallons, also milligram
		mgad	million gallons per acre per day
Btu	British thermal unit		
C	Centigrade degrees	mgd	million gallons per day
cal	calorie	min	minute
cc	cubic centimeter	ml	milliliter
cfm	cubic foot per minute	mm	millimeter
cfs	cubic foot per second	mol	gram molecular weight
cgs	centimeter-gram-second system	mols	gram molecular weights
		mph	mile per hour
cm	centimeter	MPN	Most Probable Number
csm	cubic foot per second per square mile	$m\mu$	millimicron
		μ	micron
cu	cubic	μc	microcurie
deg	degree	μg	microgram
DC	direct current	N	normal
DO	dissolved oxygen	No.	number
emf	electromotive force	PM	after noon
F	Fahrenheit degree	ppb	part per billion
fpm	foot per minute	ppm	part per million
fps	foot per second	psi	pound per square inch
ft	foot	psia	pound per square inch, absolute
gal	gallon		
gpad	gallon per acre per day	psig	pound per square inch, gage
gpcd	gallon per capita per day	R	Reynolds number
gpd	gallon per day	rpm	revolution per minute
gph	gallon per hour	sec	second
gpm	gallon per minute	sq	square
hp	horsepower	U. S.	United States
hr	hour	wt	weight
in.	inch	yd	yard

TABLE A-2.   Weights and Measures

The American and English weights and measures referred to in this book are alike except for the gallon.   The U. S. gallon is employed.   The U. S. billion, which equals 1,000 million, is also employed.

Length

Miles	Yards	Feet	Inches	Centimeters
1	1,760	5,280	..	.....
..	1	3	36	91.4
..	.....	1	12	30.5
..	.....	.....	1	2.54

1 m = 100 cm = 3.28 ft

Area

Square miles	Acres	Square feet	Square inches	Square centimeters
1	640	......	..	......
..	1	43,560	...	......
..	...	1	144	929
..	...	......	1	6.45

1 sq m = 10.8 sq ft

Volume

Cubic feet	Imperial gallons	U. S. gallons	U. S. quarts	Liters	Cubic inches
1	6.23	7.48	29.92	28.32	1,728
..	1	1.2	4.8	4.536	277.4
..	....	1	4	3.785	231
..	....	....	1	0.946	57.75
..	....	....	1.057	1	61.02

1 Imperial gal weighs 10 lb   1 U. S. gal weighs 8.34 lb
1 cu ft of water weighs 62.4 lb

Velocity

Miles per day	Feet per second	Inches per minute	Centimeters per second
1	0.0611	44	......
..	1	720	30.5
..	......	1	0.043

Time

Days	Hours	Minutes	Seconds
1	24	1,440	86,400
..	1	60	3,600
..	..	1	60

TABLE A-2. Weights and Measures (*Continued*)

Weight

Tons	Pounds	Grams	Grains
1	2,000	...	....
..	1	454	7,000
..	.....	1	15.43

1 grain per gal = 17.1 mg/l = 142.9 lb per mg
1 ppm = 1 mg/l = 8.34 lb per mg

Discharge

Cubic feet per second	Million gallons daily	Gallons per minute
1	0.646	449
1.547	1	694

1 mgd per acre ft = 0.430 gpm per cu yd

Pressure

Pounds per square inch	Feet of water	Inches of mercury
1	2.31	2.04
0.433	1	0.883
0.491	1.133	1

1 atm = 14.7 psi = 29.9 in. Hg

Power

Kilowatts	Horsepower	Foot-pounds per second
1	1.341	738
0.746	1	550

Work and energy

Kilowatt-hours	Horsepower-hours	British thermal units
1	1.341	3,410
0.746	1	2,540

Temperature

Degree Fahrenheit = $32 + \frac{9}{5} \times$ degrees Centigrade

0	5	10	15	20	25	30	35	40	45	50	55	60	C
32	41	50	59	68	77	86	95	104	113	122	131	140	F

TABLE A-3.   Viscosity and Density of Water

Calculated from International Critical Tables, 1928 and 1929.

Tempera- ture, C	Density ρ, γ (grams/cm^3), also s	Absolute viscosity μ, centipoises *	Kinematic viscosity ν, centistokes †
0	0.99987	1.7921	1.7923
1	0.99993	1.7320	1.7321
2	0.99997	1.6740	1.6741
3	0.99999	1.6193	1.6193
4	1.00000	1.5676	1.5676
5	0.99999	1.5188	1.5188
6	0.99997	1.4726	1.4726
7	0.99993	1.4288	1.4288
8	0.99988	1.3872	1.3874
9	0.99981	1.3476	1.3479
10	0.99973	1.3097	1.3101
11	0.99963	1.2735	1.2740
12	0.99952	1.2390	1.2396
13	0.99940	1.2061	1.2068
14	0.99927	1.1748	1.1756
15	0.99913	1.1447	1.1457
16	0.99897	1.1156	1.1168
17	0.99880	1.0876	1.0888
18	0.99862	1.0603	1.0618
19	0.99843	1.0340	1.0356
20	0.99823	1.0087	1.0105
21	0.99802	0.9843	0.9863
22	0.99780	0.9608	0.9629
23	0.99757	0.9380	0.9403
24	0.99733	0.9161	0.9186
25	0.99707	0.8949	0.8975
26	0.99681	0.8746	0.8774
27	0.99654	0.8551	0.8581
28	0.99626	0.8363	0.8394
29	0.99597	0.8181	0.8214
30	0.99568	0.8004	0.8039
31	0.99537	0.7834	0.7870
32	0.99505	0.7670	0.7708
33	0.99473	0.7511	0.7551
34	0.99440	0.7357	0.7398
35	0.99406	0.7208	0.7251
36	0.99371	0.7064	0.7109
37	0.99336	0.6925	0.6971
38	0.99299	0.6791	0.6839
39	0.99262	0.6661	0.6711

* 1 centipoise $= 10^{-2}$ (gram mass)/(cm)(sec).

† 1 centistoke $= 10^{-2}$ cm^2/sec.

TABLE A-4.   Atomic Numbers, Weights, and Valences of Some Chemical
Elements *

Element	Symbol	Atomic number	International atomic weight (1952)	Valence
Aluminum	Al	13	26.98	3
Arsenic	As	33	74.91	3, 5
Barium	Ba	56	137.36	2
Boron	B	5	10.82	3
Bromine	Br	35	79.92	1, 3, 5, 7
Cadmium	Cd	48	112.41	2
Calcium	Ca	20	40.08	2
Carbon	C	6	12.01	2, 4
Chlorine	Cl	17	35.46	1, 3, 5, 7
Chromium	Cr	24	52.01	2, 3, 6
Cobalt	Co	27	58.94	2, 3
Copper	Cu	29	63.54	1, 2
Fluorine	F	9	19.00	1
Gold (aurum)	Au	79	197.2	1, 3
Hydrogen	H	1	1.008	1
Iodine	I	53	126.92	1, 3, 5, 7
Iron (ferrum)	Fe	26	55.85	2, 3
Lead (plumbum)	Pb	82	207.21	2, 4
Magnesium	Mg	12	24.32	2
Manganese	Mn	25	54.93	2, 3, 4, 6, 7
Mercury (hydrargyrum)	Hg	80	200.61	1, 2
Nickel	Ni	28	58.69	2, 3
Nitrogen	N	7	14.01	3, 5
Oxygen	O	8	16.00	2
Phosphorus	P	15	30.98	3, 5
Platinum	Pt	78	195.23	2, 4
Potassium (kalium)	K	19	39.10	1
Selenium	Se	34	78.96	2, 4, 6
Silicon	Si	14	28.09	4
Silver (argentum)	Ag	47	107.88	1
Sodium (natrium)	Na	11	23.00	1
Strontium	Sr	38	87.63	2
Sulfur	S	16	32.07	2, 4, 6
Tin (stannum)	Sn	50	118.70	2, 4
Zinc	Zn	30	65.38	2

* Elements encountered in radioactive wastes are not included.   For a complete list, see *Handbook of Chemistry and Physics*, Chemical Rubber Publishing Company, Cleveland, Ohio.

TABLE A-5.   Chemicals Used in

No.	Chemical name and formula (1)	Molecular weight (2)	Common or trade name (3)	Available forms (4)	Weight, lb/cu ft (5)	Solubility, lb/gal (6)
1	Activated carbon C	12.0	Aqua Nuchar, Hydrodarco, Norite	Black granular powder	15	Insoluble (suspension used)
2	Aluminum sulfate $Al_2(SO_4)_3 \cdot 14H_2O$	594.4	Alum, filter alum, sulfate of alumina	Ivory white: Powder Granule Lump	35–45 60–63 62–67	4.2 (60 F)
3	Ammonium aluminum sulfate $Al_2(SO_4)_3(NH_4)_2SO_4 \cdot 24H_2O$	906.6	Ammonium alum, crystal alum	Lump Nut, pea Powdered	64–68 62–65 60	0.3 (32 F) 8.3 (212 F)
4	Ammonium chloride NH_4Cl	53.5	Sal ammoniac	White, lump, crystal		
5	Ammonium sulfate $(NH_4)_2SO_4$	132.1	Sulfate of ammonia	White to brown crystals	42.5	6.3 (68 F)
6	Anhydrous ammonia NH_3	17.0	Ammonia	Colorless gas		3.9 (32 F) 3.1 (60 F) 1.8 (125 F)
7	Aqua ammonia NH_4OH	35.1	Ammonia water, ammonium hydroxide, ammonium hydrate	Water-white liquid		Complete
8	Bentonite $H_2O(Al_2O_3 \cdot Fe_2O_3 \cdot 3MgO) \cdot 4SiO_2 \cdot nH_2O$		Colloidal clay, Wilkinite, Volclay	Powder, pellet, mixed sizes	60	Insoluble (suspension used)
9	Calcium hydroxide $Ca(OH)_2$	74.1	Hydrated lime, slaked lime	White powder: Light Dense	26–48 40–70	0.014 (68 F) 0.012 (90 F)
10	Calcium oxide CaO	56.1	Quicklime, burnt lime, unslaked lime	Lump Pebble Granule	56–65 60–65 50–70	Slakes
11	Calcium hypochlorite $Ca(OCl)_2 \cdot 4H_2O$	215.1	HTH, Perchloron, Pittchlor	White, granule, powder	52.5	
12	Chlorinated lime $CaO \cdot 2CaOCl_2 \cdot 3H_2O$	346.3	Chloride of lime, bleaching powder	White powder	48	
13	Chlorine Cl_2	71.0	Chlorine gas, liquid chlorine	Green-yellow gas, light-orange liquid		0.07 (60 F) 0.04 (100 F)
14	Chlorine dioxide ClO_2	67.5	Chlorine dioxide	Yellow-red gas		0.02 (30 mm)
15	Copper sulfate $CuSO_4 \cdot 5H_2O$	249.7	Blue vitriol, blue stone	Crystal Lump Powder	75–90 73–80 60–64	1.6 (32 F) 2.2 (68 F) 2.6 (86 F)
16	Di-sodium phosphate $Na_2HPO_4 \cdot 12H_2O$	358.2	DSP, basic sodium phosphate, secondary sodium phosphate	Crystal	60–64	0.4 (32 F) 0.4 (86 F)
17	Ferric chloride $FeCl_3$ (35–45% solution)		Ferrichlor, chloride of iron	Dark-brown syrupy liquid		Complete
	$FeCl_3 \cdot 6H_2O$	270.3	Crystal ferric chloride	Yellow-brown lump		4.0 (86 F) 5.0 (98 F)
	$FeCl_3$	162.2	Anhydrous ferric chloride	Green-black powder		

Water and Waste-Water Treatment *

No.	Commercial strength (7)	Shipping containers (8)	Suitable handling materials (9)	Feeding characteristics (10)	Uses (11)
1		Bags, bulk	Dry: iron, steel; wet: rubber, silicon iron, stainless steel	Hopper agitation required for dry feed	Taste and odor control, dechlorination, sludge stabilization
2	15–22% Al$_2$O$_3$	100–200-lb bags, 300–400-lb bbls, bulk (carloads)	Dry: iron, steel; solution: lead, rubber silicon iron, stoneware, asphaltum	5-min agitation to dissolve; 1% solution has pH 3.4	Coagulation
3	11% Al$_2$O$_3$	Bags, bbls, bulk	Duriron, lead, rubber, silicon iron, stoneware	1% solution has pH 3.5, even solubility	For feed in solution pots; coagulant and source of ammonia
4		100-lb kegs, 200–550-lb bbls, 800–1,200-lb hogsheads	Iron, rubber	Hygroscopic; volatilizes	Source of ammonia
5		100-lb bags	Rubber, plastics, ceramics	Cakes in dry feed, add CaSO$_4$ for free flow	Source of ammonia
6	99–100% NH$_3$	50-lb, 100-lb, 150-lb cylinders	Iron, steel, glass, nickel, Monel		To form combined residual chlorine for disinfection
7	26 Bé†; 29.4% NH$_3$	Carboys, 750-lb drums, 8,000-gal tank cars	Iron, steel, glass, nickel, Monel		To form combined residual chlorine for disinfection
8		100-lb bags	Iron, steel		Coagulant aid and floc-weighting agent
9	85–99% Ca(OH)$_2$ 63–73% CaO	50-lb bags, 100-lb bbls, bulk (carload)	Asphalt, cement, iron, rubber, steel	Hopper agitation required for dry feed	Softening, coagulation, water stabilization, and as caustic agent
10	75–99% CaO	50-lb bags, 100-lb bbls, bulk (carload)	Asphalt, cement, iron, rubber, steel	Sat sol pH 12.4; time, temp, amt water critical for slaking	Softening, coagulation, water stabilization, source of Ca(OH)$_2$
11	70% available Cl$_2$	5-lb cans, 100-, 300-, 800-lb drums	Glass, rubber, stoneware, wood	1–3% available Cl$_2$ solution used	Disinfection, source of Cl$_2$
12	25–37% available Cl$_2$	100-, 300-, 800-lb drums	Glass, rubber, stoneware, wood	Deteriorates	Disinfection, source of Cl$_2$
13	99.8 Cl$_2$	100-, 150-, 200-, 2,000-lb cylinders, 16-, 30-ton tank cars	Gas: copper, iron, steel; liquid: glass, hard rubber, lead, silver		Disinfection, control of odors, H$_2$S, and as general oxidant
14	26.3% available Cl$_2$	Generated as used	Plastics, soft rubber (avoid hard rubber)		Taste and odor control, disinfection
15	99% CuSO$_4$	100-lb bags, 450-lb bbls, drums	Asphalt, silicon iron, stainless steel		Algae control
16	19–19.5% P$_2$O$_5$	125-lb kegs, 200-lb bags, 325-lb bbls	Cast iron, steel	1% solution pH 9.1	Softening
17	37–48% FeCl$_3$, 12–17% Fe	5-, 13-gal carboys, trucks, tank cars	Glass, rubber, stoneware, synthetic resins		Coagulation, sludge conditioning
	59–61% FeCl$_3$, 20–21% Fe	300-lb bbls		Hygroscopic, store in tight containers, no dry feed	
	98% FeCl$_3$, 34% Fe	500-lb casks, 100-, 300-, 400-lb kegs			

TABLE A-5. Chemicals Used in Water

No.	Chemical name and formula (1)	Molecular weight (2)	Common or trade name (3)	Available forms (4)	Weight, lb/cu ft (5)	Solubility, lb/gal (6)
18	Ferric sulfate $Fe_2(SO_4)_3 \cdot 9H_2O$	562.0	Ferrifloc, Ferrisul	Red-brown powder, granule	70–72	Soluble in 2–4 parts cold water
19	Ferrous sulfate $FeSO_4 \cdot 7H_2O$	277.9	Green vitriol, copperas	Green crystal, granule, lump	63–66	
20	Fluosilicic acid H_2SiF_6	144.1	Fluosilicic acid	Liquid		1.2 (68 F)
21	Hydrogen fluoride HF	20.0	Hydrofluoric acid	Liquid		
22	Ozone O_3	48.0	Ozone	Colorless gas		
23	Potassium aluminum sulfate $K_2SO_4 \cdot Al_2(SO_4)_3 \cdot 24H_2O$	948.8	Potash alum	Lump Granule Powder	62–67 60–65 60	0.5 (32 F) 1.0 (68 F) 1.4 (86 F)
24	Sodium aluminate $Na_2O \cdot Al_2O_3$	163.9	Soda alum	White or greenish-yellow crystal, liquid 27 Bé	50–60	3.0 (68 F) 3.3 (86 F)
25	Sodium bisulfite $Na_2S_2O_5$	190.1	Sodium metabisulfite	Powder	74–85	4.5 (68 F) 6.8 (212 F)
26	Sodium carbonate Na_2CO_3	106.0	Soda ash 58%	White powder: Extra light Light Dense	 23 35 65	1.5 (68 F) 2.3 (86 F)
27	Sodium chloride NaCl	58.5	Common salt, salt	Rock Fine	50–60 58–70	2.9 (32 F) 3.0 (68 F)
28	Sodium chlorite $NaClO_2$	90.5	Technical sodium chlorite	Light-orange powder, flake		
29	Sodium fluoride NaF	42.0	Fluoride	Blue or white powder: Light Dense	 50 75	0.35 (most temperatures)
30	Sodium hexa-metaphosphate $(NaPO_3)_6$	612.0	Calgon, glassy phosphate, vitreous phosphate	Crystal flake, powder	47	1–4.2
31	Sodium hydroxide NaOH	40.0	Caustic soda, soda lye	Flake, lump, liquid		2.4 (32 F) 4.4 (68 F) 4.8 (104 F)
32	Sodium hypochlorite NaOCl	74.5	Sodium hypochlorite	Light-yellow liquid		
33	Sodium silicofluoride Na_2SiF_6	188.1	Sodium silicofluoride	Nile blue or yellowish-white powder	72	0.03 (32 F) 0.06 (72 F) 0.12 (140 F)
34	Sodium silicate $Na_2O \cdot SiO_2$	122.1	Water glass	Opaque viscous liquid		Complete
35	Sodium sulfite Na_2SO_3	126.1	Sulfite	Powder	80–91	1.2 (32 F) 2.3 (132 F)
36	Sodium thiosulfate $Na_2S_2O_3 \cdot 5H_2O$	248.2	Hypo, sodium hyposulfite	Standard: Crystal Rice Fine Granules	 64–65 65 70 61	6.2 (32 F)
37	Sulfur dioxide SO_2	64.1	Sulfur dioxide	Colorless gas		

and Waste-Water Treatment (*Continued*) *

No.	Commercial strength (7)	Shipping containers (8)	Suitable handling materials (9)	Feeding characteristics (10)	Uses (11)
18	90–94% $Fe_2(SO_4)_3$ 25–26% Fe	100-, 175-lb bags, 400-, 425-lb drums	Ceramics, lead, plastics, rubber, 18-8 stainless steel	Mildly hygroscopic	Coagulation
19	55% $FeSO_4$, 20% Fe	Bags, bbls, bulk	Asphalt, concrete, lead, tin, wood	Hygroscopic, cakes in storage	Coagulation
20	35% approx	Rubber-lined drums	Rubber-lined steel		Fluoridation
21	70%	Steel drums, tank cars	Steel	Below 60% steel cannot be used	Fluoridation
22		Generated at site of use	Aluminum, ceramics, glass		Taste and odor control, disinfection
23	10–11% Al_2O_3	Bags, bbls, bulk (carloads)	Lead, leadlined rubber, stoneware	1% solution pH 3.5, even solubility	For feed in solution pots, coagulation
24	55% Al_2O_3, 35% Na_2O, 5% excess NaOH	100-, 150-lb bags, 250-, 440-lb drums	Iron, plastics, rubber, steel	Hopper agitation required for dry feed	Coagulation
	32% $Al_2O_3 \cdot Na_2O$, 10% NaOH	Solution			
25	93% $Na_2S_2O_5$, 62% SO_2	Drums	Ceramics, chrome, glass, lead, nickel, rubber	1% solution pH 4.6	Dechlorination
26	99.4% Na_2CO_3, 58% Na_2O	Bags, bbls, bulk (carloads)	Iron, rubber, steel	Hopper agitation for dry feed for light and extra light, 1% solution pH 11.2	Softening, pH contro
27	98% NaCl	Bags, bbls, bulk (carloads)	Bronze, cement, rubber		Regeneration of zeolites
28	82% $NaClO_2$, 30% available Cl_2	100-lb drums	Metals (avoid cellulose materials)	Generates ClO_2 at pH 3.0	To produce ClO_2
29	90–95% NaF	Bags, bbls, fiber drums, kegs	Iron, lead, steel	4% solution pH 6.6	Fluoridation
30	66% P_2O_5 (unadjusted)	100-lb bags	Hard rubber, plastics, stainless steel	0.25% solution has pH 6.0–8.3	Corrosion control, to prevent precipitation
31	98.9% NaOH, 74–76% Na_2O	100-, 700-lb drums, bulk (trucks, tank cars)	Cast iron, rubber, steel	Solid hygroscopic, 1% solution has pH 12.9	Softening, pH control, filter cleaning
32	12–15% available Cl_2	5-, 13-gal carboys, 1,300-, 2,000-gal tank trucks	Ceramics, glass, plastics, rubber		Disinfection, source of Cl_2
33	99% Na_2SiF_6	Bags, bbls, fiber drums	Iron, lead, steel	1% solution has pH 3.5	Fluoridation
34	38–42 Bé	Drums, bulk (tank trucks, tank cars)	Cast iron, rubber, steel	1% solution has pH 12.3	Corrosion control, coagulant aid
35	93–99% Na_2SO_3	Bags, bbls	Cast iron, steel	1% solution has pH 9.8	Oxygen removal in boilers
36	98–99% $Na_2S_2O_3$	Bags, bbls, drums, kegs	Cast iron, low-carbon steel, stoneware		Dechlorination of biological samples
37	100% SO_2	100-, 150-, 200-lb cylinders	Dry-steel		Dechlorination and to clean filters

TABLE A-5.   Chemicals Used in Water

No.	Chemical name and formula (1)	Molecular weight (2)	Common or trade name (3)	Available forms (4)	Weight, lb/cu ft (5)	Solubility, lb/gal (6)
38	Sulfuric acid H_2SO_4	98.1	Vitriol, oil of vitriol	Solution 60, 66 Bé		Complete
39	Tetrasodium pyrophosphate $Na_4P_2O_7 \cdot 10H_2O$	446.2	TSPP, alkaline sodium pyrophosphate	White powder	68	0.6 (80 F) 3.3 (212 F)
40	Trisodium phosphate $Na_3PO_4 \cdot 12H_2O$	380.2	TSP, tertiary sodium phosphate, normal sodium phosphate	Crystal: Coarse Medium Standard	56 58 61	0.1 (32 F) 13.0 (158 F)

* This table has been compiled from information contained in Appendix 3, *Water Quality and Treatment*, American Water Works Association, New York, 2nd Ed., 1950.

and Waste-Water Treatment (*Continued*) *

No.	Commercial strength (7)	Shipping containers (8)	Suitable handling materials (9)	Feeding characteristics (10)	Uses (11)
38	60 Bé, 77.7% H_2SO_4, 66 Bé, 93.2% H_2SO_4	Bottles, carboys, drums, trucks, tankcars	Concentrated-iron, steel; dilute-glass, lead, porcelain, rubber	0.5% solution has pH 1.2	pH control
39	53% P_2O_5	125-lb kegs, 200-lb bags, 325-lb bbls	Cast iron, steel	1% solution has pH 10.8	Corrosion control, water stabilization
40	19% P_2O_5	125-lb kegs, 200-lb bags, 325-lb bbls	Cast iron, steel	1% solution has pH 11.9	Hot-process softening, cleaning compound

† Bé = degrees on a Beaumé hydrometer. For liquids heavier than water Bé = $145(1 - 1/s)$, where s is the specific gravity of the liquid. For liquids lighter than water, 0 Bé equals the specific gravity of a 10% solution of NaCl and 60 Bé equals a specific gravity of 0.745.

TABLE A-6.   Saturation Values of Dissolved Oxygen in Fresh and Sea Water Exposed to an Atmosphere Containing 20.9% Oxygen under a Pressure of 760 mm of Mercury *

Calculated by G. C. Whipple and M. C. Whipple from measurements of C. J. J. Fox.

Tempera-ture, C	Dissolved oxygen (mg/l) for stated concentrations of chloride, mg/l					Difference per 100 mg/l chloride
	0	5,000	10,000	15,000	20,000	
0	14.62	13.79	12.97	12.14	11.32	0.0165
1	14.23	13.41	12.61	11.82	11.03	.0160
2	13.84	13.05	12.28	11.52	10.76	.0154
3	13.48	12.72	11.98	11.24	10.50	.0149
4	13.13	12.41	11.69	10.97	10.25	.0144
5	12.80	12.09	11.39	10.70	10.01	.0140
6	12.48	11.79	11.12	10.45	9.78	.0135
7	12.17	11.51	10.85	10.21	9.57	.0130
8	11.87	11.24	10.61	9.98	9.36	.0125
9	11.59	10.97	10.36	9.76	9.17	.0121
10	11.33	10.73	10.13	9.55	8.98	.0118
11	11.08	10.49	9.92	9.35	8.80	.0114
12	10.83	10.28	9.72	9.17	8.62	.0110
13	10.60	10.05	9.52	8.98	8.46	.0107
14	10.37	9.85	9.32	8.80	8.30	.0104
15	10.15	9.65	9.14	8.63	8.14	.0100
16	9.95	9.46	8.96	8.47	7.99	.0098
17	9.74	9.26	8.78	8.30	7.84	.0095
18	9.54	9.07	8.62	8.15	7.70	.0092
19	9.35	8.89	8.45	8.00	7.56	.0089
20	9.17	8.73	8.30	7.86	7.42	.0088
21	8.99	8.57	8.14	7.71	7.28	.0086
22	8.83	8.42	7.99	7.57	7.14	.0084
23	8.68	8.27	7.85	7.43	7.00	.0083
24	8.53	8.12	7.71	7.30	6.87	.0083
25	8.38	7.96	7.56	7.15	6.74	.0082
26	8.22	7.81	7.42	7.02	6.61	.0080
27	8.07	7.67	7.28	6.88	6.49	.0079
28	7.92	7.53	7.14	6.75	6.37	.0078
29	7.77	7.39	7.00	6.62	6.25	.0076
30	7.63	7.25	6.86	6.49	6.13	.0075

* For other barometric pressures the solubilities vary approximately in proportion to the ratios of these pressures to the standard pressures.

TABLE A-7. Values of the Exponential e^{-x} for x Ranging from 0.0 to 3.09

x	0	1	2	3	4	5	6	7	8	9
0.0	1.000	0.990	0.980	0.970	0.961	0.951	0.942	0.932	0.923	0.914
0.1	0.905	.896	.887	.878	.869	.861	.852	.844	.835	.827
0.2	.819	.811	.803	.794	.787	.779	.771	.763	.756	.748
0.3	.741	.733	.726	.719	.712	.705	.698	.691	.684	.677
0.4	.670	.664	.657	.651	.644	.638	.631	.625	.619	.613
0.5	.607	.600	.595	.589	.583	.577	.571	.566	.560	.554
0.6	.549	.543	.538	.533	.527	.522	.517	.512	.507	.502
0.7	.497	.492	.487	.482	.477	.472	.468	.463	.458	.454
0.8	.449	.445	.440	.436	.432	.427	.423	.419	.415	.411
0.9	.407	.403	.399	.395	.391	.387	.383	.379	.375	.372
1.0	.368	.364	.361	.357	.353	.350	.347	.343	.340	.336
1.1	.333	.330	.326	.323	.320	.317	.313	.310	.307	.304
1.2	.301	.298	.295	.292	.289	.287	.284	.281	.278	.275
1.3	.273	.270	.267	.264	.262	.259	.257	.254	.252	.249
1.4	.247	.244	.242	.239	.237	.235	.232	.230	.228	.225
1.5	.223	.221	.219	.217	.214	.212	.210	.208	.206	.204
1.6	.202	.200	.198	.196	.194	.192	.190	.188	.186	.185
1.7	.183	.181	.179	.177	.176	.173	.172	.170	.169	.167
1.8	.165	.164	.162	.160	.159	.157	.156	.154	.153	.151
1.9	.150	.148	.147	.145	.144	.142	.141	.139	.138	.137
2.0	.135	.134	.133	.131	.130	.129	.127	.126	.125	.124
2.1	.122	.121	.120	.119	.118	.116	.115	.114	.113	.112
2.2	.111	.110	.109	.108	.106	.105	.104	.103	.102	.101
2.3	.100	.0993	.0983	.0973	.0963	.0954	.0944	.0935	.0926	.0916
2.4	.0907	.0898	.0889	.0880	.0872	.0863	.0854	.0846	.0837	.0829
2.5	.0821	.0813	.0805	.0797	.0789	.0781	.0773	.0765	.0758	.0750
2.6	.0743	.0735	.0728	.0721	.0714	.0707	.0700	.0693	.0686	.0679
2.7	.0672	.0665	.0659	.0652	.0646	.0639	.0633	.0627	.0602	.0614
2.8	.0608	.0602	.0596	.0590	.0584	.0578	.0573	.0567	.0561	.0556
2.9	.0550	.0545	.0539	.0534	.0529	.0523	.0518	.0513	.0508	.0503
3.0	.0498	.0493	.0488	.0483	.0478	.0474	.0469	.0464	.0460	.0455

TABLE A-8. Values of the Exponential e^{-x} for x Ranging from 3.00 to 10.00

x	e^{-x}	x	e^{-x}	x	e^{-x}	x	e^{-x}	x	e^{-x}
3.00	0.0498	4.00	0.0183	5.00	0.00674	6.0	0.00248	8.0	0.000335
3.05	.0474	4.05	.0174	5.05	.00641	6.1	.00224	8.1	.000304
3.10	.0450	4.10	.0166	5.10	.00610	6.2	.00203	8.2	.000275
3.15	.0429	4.15	.0158	5.15	.00580	6.3	.00184	8.3	.000249
3.20	.0408	4.20	.0150	5.20	.00552	6.4	.00166	8.4	.000225
3.25	.0388	4.25	.0143	5.25	.00525	6.5	.00150	8.5	.000203
3.30	.0369	4.30	.0136	5.30	.00499	6.6	.00136	8.6	.000184
3.35	.0351	4.35	.0129	5.35	.00475	6.7	.00123	8.7	.000167
3.40	.0334	4.40	.0123	5.40	.00452	6.8	.00111	8.8	.000151
3.45	.0317	4.45	.0117	5.45	.00430	6.9	.00101	8.9	.000136
3.50	.0302	4.50	.0111	5.50	.00409	7.0	.000912	9.0	.000123
3.55	.0287	4.55	.0106	5.55	.00389	7.1	.000825	9.1	.000112
3.60	.0273	4.60	.0101	5.60	.00370	7.2	.000747	9.2	.000101
3.65	.0260	4.65	.00956	5.65	.00352	7.3	.000676	9.3	.000091
3.70	.0247	4.70	.00910	5.70	.00335	7.4	.000611	9.4	.000083
3.75	.0235	4.75	.00865	5.75	.00319	7.5	.000553	9.5	.000075
3.80	.0224	4.80	.00823	5.80	.00303	7.6	.000500	9.6	.000068
3.85	.0213	4.85	.00783	5.85	.00288	7.7	.000453	9.7	.000061
3.90	.0202	4.90	.00745	5.90	.00274	7.8	.000410	9.8	.000055
3.95	.0193	4.95	.00708	5.95	.00261	7.9	.000371	9.9	.000050
4.00	.0183	5.00	.00674	6.00	.00248	8.0	.000335	10.0	.000045

REFERENCE WORKS

Municipal Water Supply

American Water Works Association, *Water Quality and Treatment,* Published by the Association, New York, 2nd Ed., 1950.

Babbitt, H. E., and J. J. Doland, *Water Supply Engineering,* McGraw-Hill Book Co., New York, 4th Ed., 1949.

Baker, M. N., *The Quest for Pure Water,* American Water Works Association, New York, 1948.

Hardenbergh, W. A., *Water Supply and Purification,* International Textbook Co., Scranton, Pa., 3rd Ed., 1952.

Hoover, C. P., *Water Supply and Treatment,* National Lime Association, Washington, D. C., 1943.

Institution of Water Engineers, *Manual of British Water Supply Practice,* W. Heffer & Sons, Cambridge, England (American Water Works Association, New York), 1950.

Ryan, W. J., *Water Treatment and Purification,* McGraw-Hill Book Co., New York, 2nd Ed., 1946.

Turneaure, F. E., and H. L. Russell, *Public Water Supplies,* John Wiley & Sons, New York, 4th Ed., 1940.

Municipal Sewerage

Babbitt, H. E., *Sewerage and Sewage Treatment,* John Wiley & Sons, New York, 7th Ed., 1953.

Hardenbergh, W. A., *Sewerage and Sewage Treatment,* International Textbook Co., Scranton, Pa., 3rd Ed., 1950.

Imhoff, Karl, and G. M. Fair, *Sewage Treatment,* John Wiley & Sons, New York, 1940.

Keefer, C. E., *Sewage Treatment Works,* McGraw-Hill Book Co., New York, 1940.

Metcalf, Leonard, and H. P. Eddy, *American Sewerage Practice,* McGraw-Hill Book Co., New York, 3 Vol., 1915 to 1935.

Rudolfs, Willem, *Principles of Sewage Treatment,* National Lime Association, Washington, D. C., 1941.

Municipal Water Supply and Sewerage

Escritt, L. B., and Sidney F. Rich, *The Work of the Sanitary Engineer,* Macdonald & Evans, London, 1949.

Isaac, P. C. G., *Public Health Engineering,* E. & F. N. Spon, London, 1953.

Maxcy, K. F., *Rosenau, Preventive Medicine and Hygiene,* Appleton-Century-Crofts, New York, 7th Ed., 1951. Sections on water by E. W. Moore; section on sewage by G. M. Fair.

Phelps, E. B., *Public Health Engineering* (Vol. 1, Part 2, in collaboration with C. J. Velz), John Wiley & Sons, New York, 1948.

Steel, E. W., *Water Supply and Sewerage*, McGraw-Hill Book Co., New York, 3rd Ed., 1953.

Water Supply and Drainage of Buildings

Babbitt, H. E., *Plumbing*, McGraw-Hill Book Co., New York, 2nd Ed., 1950.

Day, L. J., *Standard Plumbing Details*, John Wiley & Sons, New York, 1938.

Plum, Svend, *Plumbing Practice and Design*, John Wiley & Sons, New York, 1943.

Industrial Water Supply and Waste-Water Disposal

Besselievre, E. B., *Industrial Waste Treatment*, McGraw-Hill Book Co., New York, 1952.

Betz, W. H. and L. D., *Handbook of Industrial Water Conditioning*, Published by the authors, Philadelphia, 1950.

Eldridge, E. F., *Industrial Waste Treatment Practice*, McGraw-Hill Book Co., New York, 1942.

Nordell, Eskell, *Water Treatment for Industrial and Other Uses*, Reinhold Publishing Corp., New York, 1951.

Rudolfs, Willem, Editor, *Industrial Wastes*, Reinhold Publishing Corp., New York, 1953.

Southgate, B. A., *Treatment and Disposal of Industrial Waste Waters*, H. M. Stationery Office, London, 1948.

Rural Water Supply and Waste-Water Disposal

Ehlers, V. M., and E. W. Steel, *Municipal and Rural Sanitation*, McGraw-Hill Book Co., New York, 4th Ed., 1950.

Wright, F. B., *Rural Water Supply and Sanitation*, John Wiley & Sons, New York, 1939.

Statistical Methods

Croxton, F. E., *Elementary Statistics*, Prentice-Hall, New York, 1953.

Hoel, P. G., *Introduction to Mathematical Statistics*, John Wiley & Sons, New York, 1947.

Yule, G. U., and M. G. Kendall, *Theory of Statistics*, J. B. Lippincott Co., London, 1940.

Hydrology

Blair, T. A., *Weather Elements*, Prentice-Hall, New York, 1946.

Foster, E. E., *Rainfall and Runoff*, The Macmillan Co., New York, 1948.

Grover, N. C., and A. W. Harrington, *Stream Flow*, John Wiley & Sons, New York, 1943.

Johnstone, Don, and W. P. Cross, *Elements of Applied Hydrology*, Ronald Press Co., New York, 1949.

Linsley, R. K., M. A. Kohler, and J. L. H. Paulhus, *Applied Hydrology*, McGraw-Hill Book Co., New York, 1949.

Mead, D. W., *Hydrology*, McGraw-Hill Book Co., New York, 2nd Ed., 1950.

Meinzer, O. E., *Hydrology*, McGraw-Hill Book Co., New York, 1942.

Muskat, Morris, *Flow of Homogeneous Fluids through Porous Media*, McGraw-Hill Book Co., New York, 1937.

Thomas, H. E., *The Conservation of Ground Water*, McGraw-Hill Book Co., New York, 1951.

BIBLIOGRAPHY

Tolman, C. F., *Ground Water,* McGraw-Hill Book Co., New York, 1937.

Wisler, C. O., and E. F. Brater, *Hydrology,* John Wiley & Sons, New York, 1949.

Hydraulics and Structures

Creager, W. P., J. D. Justin, and Julian Hinds, *Engineering for Dams,* John Wiley & Sons, New York, 1945.

Davis, C. V., Editor, *Handbook of Applied Hydraulics,* McGraw-Hill Book Co., New York, 2nd Ed., 1952. Sections on water by T. R. Camp; sections on sewage by S. A. Greeley and W. E. Stanley.

Kristal, F. A., and F. A. Annett, *Pumps,* McGraw-Hill Book Co., New York, 2nd Ed., 1953.

National Resources Committee, *Low Dams,* U. S. Government Printing Office, Washington, D. C., 1939.

Rouse, Hunter, Editor, *Engineering Hydraulics,* John Wiley & Sons, New York, 1950.

Chemistry

American Society for Testing Materials, *Manual on Industrial Water,* Published by the Society, Philadelphia, 1953.

American Public Health Association and American Water Works Association, *Standard Methods for the Examination of Water and Sewage,* American Public Health Association, New York, 9th Ed., 1949, 10th Ed., 1954.

Bull, H. B., *Physical Biochemistry,* John Wiley & Sons, New York, 2nd Ed., 1951.

Hodgman, C. D., Editor, *Handbook of Chemistry and Physics,* Chemical Rubber Publishing Co., Cleveland, 34th Ed., 1952.

Clark, W. M., *Topics in Physical Chemistry,* Williams & Wilkins, Baltimore, 1952.

Daniels, Farrington, *Outlines of Physical Chemistry,* John Wiley & Sons, New York, 1950.

Frost, A. A., and R. G. Pearson, *Kinetics and Mechanism,* John Wiley & Sons, New York, 1953.

Glasstone, Samuel, *Textbook of Physical Chemistry,* D. Van Nostrand & Co., New York, 2nd Ed., 1946.

Gurney, R. W., *Ionic Processes in Solution,* McGraw-Hill Book Co., New York, 1953.

Taylor, E. W., *The Examination of Waters and Water Supplies,* Blakiston Co., Philadelphia, 6th Ed., 1949.

Weiser, H. B., *Colloid Chemistry,* John Wiley & Sons, New York, 2nd Ed., 1949.

Biology

Frobisher, Martin, Jr., *Fundamentals of Bacteriology,* W. B. Saunders Co., Philadelphia, 4th Ed., 1950.

Maxcy, K. F., *Rosenau, Preventive Medicine and Hygiene,* Appleton-Century-Crofts, New York, 7th Ed., 1951.

Muenscher, W. C., *Aquatic Plants of the United States,* Comstock Publishing Co., Ithaca, N. Y., 1944.

Needham, J. G. and P. R., *A Guide to the Study of Fresh-Water Biology,* Comstock Publishing Co., Ithaca, N. Y., 1938.

Pratt, H. S., *A Manual of the Common Invertebrate Animals,* Blakiston Co., Philadelphia, 1935.

Prescott, S. C., C-E. A. Winslow, and Mac Harvey McCrady, *Water Bacteriology. With Special Reference to Sanitary Water Analysis*, John Wiley & Sons, New York, 6th Ed., 1946.

Robbins, W. W., A. S. Crafts, and R. N. Raynor, *Weed Control*, McGraw-Hill Book Co., New York, 1942.

Smith, G. M., *The Fresh-Water Algae of the United States*, McGraw-Hill Book Co., New York, 1933.

Stephenson, Marjory, *Bacterial Metabolism*, Longmans, Green & Co., London, 2nd Ed., 1939.

West, T. F., J. E. Hardy, and J. H. Ford, *Chemical Control of Insects*, John Wiley & Sons, New York, 1952.

ZoBell, C. E., *Marine Microbiology*, Chronica Botanica Co., Waltham, Mass., 1946.

Limnology and Stream Sanitation

Phelps, E. B., *Stream Sanitation*, John Wiley & Sons, New York, 1944.

Welch, P. S., *Limnology*, McGraw-Hill Book Co., New York, 1935.

Welch, P. S., *Limnological Methods*, Blakiston Co., Philadelphia, 1948.

Whipple, G. C., G. M. Fair, and M. C. Whipple, *The Microscopy of Drinking Water*, John Wiley & Sons, New York, 4th Ed., 1927.

SERIAL PUBLICATIONS

Professional Societies

American Chemical Society: *Industrial and Engineering Chemistry*, monthly.

American Geophysical Union: *Transactions*, bimonthly.

American Public Health Association: *American Journal of Public Health*, monthly; *Yearbook*.

American Society of Civil Engineers: *Transactions*, annual; *Proceedings*, printed as separates, formerly monthly; *Civil Engineering*, monthly; *Manuals of Engineering Practice*.

American Water Works Association: *Journal*, monthly.

British Waterworks Association, London: *Journal*, several times a year.

Federation of Sewage and Industrial Wastes Associations: *Sewage and Industrial Wastes* (formerly Sewage Works Journal), monthly; *Manuals of Practice*.

Institute of Sewage Purification, London: *Journal and Proceedings*, annual.

Institution of Civil Engineers, London: *Journal*, monthly.

Institution of Sanitary Engineers, London: *Journal*, several times a year.

Institution of Water Engineers, London: *Journal*, 6 to 8 times a year.

New England Water Works Association: *Journal*, quarterly.

Governmental Agencies

U. S. Geological Survey: *Water Supply Papers*.

U. S. Public Health Service: *Public Health Reports*, monthly; *Public Health Engineering Abstracts*, monthly; *Public Health Bulletins*.

U. S. Weather Bureau: *Climatological Data*, monthly; *Monthly Weather Review*.

Water Pollution Research Laboratory, Department of Scientific and Industrial Research, Britain: *Water Pollution Research, Summary of Current Literature*, monthly.

Magazines

Case-Sheppard-Mann Publishing Co., New York: *Wastes Engineering*, monthly; *Water Works Engineering*, monthly.

Gillette Publishing Co., Chicago: *Water and Sewage Works*, monthly.

McGraw-Hill Publishing Co., New York: *Engineering News-Record*, weekly.

Public Works Journal Corp., New York: *Public Works*, monthly.

MONOGRAPHS AND PAPERS

Supplementing References Noted in Text

Chapter 1. Elements of Water Sanitation

American Association for the Advancement of Science, *Dental Caries and Fluorine*, Published by the Association, Washington, D. C., 1946.

American Public Health Association, "Century of Progress through Sanitation," *Am. J. Public Health, 43*, Supplement (1953).

Arnold, F. A., H. T. Dean, and J. W. Knutson, "Effect of Fluoridated Water Supplies on Dental Caries Prevalence," *Pub. Health Rept. 69*, 141 (1953).

Baker, M. N., *The Quest for Pure Water*, American Water Works Association, New York, 1948.

Comly, H. H., "Cyanosis in Infants Caused by Nitrates in Well Water," *J. Am. Med. Assoc., 129*, 1112 (1945).

Cort, W. W., "Studies on Schistosome Dermatitis, XI. Status of Knowledge after More than 20 Years," *Am. J. Hyg., 52*, 251 (1950).

Cox, C. R., "Gastroenteritis and Public Water Supplies," *A Symposium on Hydrobiology*, Wisconsin University Press, Madison, Wis., 1941.

Draffin, J. O., *The Story of Man's Quest for Water*, Garrard Press, Champaign, Ill., 1939.

Faber, H. A., "Fundamentals of Water Fluoridation," *J. New Eng. Water Works Assoc., 66*, 66 (1952).

Jellison, W. L., D. C. Epler, E. Kuhns, and G. M. Kohl, "Tularemia in Man from a Domestic Rural Water Supply," *Pub. Health Rept., 65*, 1219 (1950).

Kehoe, R. A., Jacob Cholak, and E. J. Largent, "The Hygienic Significance of the Contamination of Water with Certain Mineral Constituents," *J. Am. Water Works Assoc., 36*, 645 (1944).

Maxcy, K. F., "Supposed Involvement of Water Supplies in Poliomyelitis Transmission," *J. Am. Water Works Assoc., 41*, 696 (1949).

Maxcy, K. F., and H. A. Howe, "The Significance of the Finding of the Virus of Infantile Paralysis in Sewage. A Review," *Sewage Works J., 15*, 1101 (1943).

McClendon, J. F., and J. C. Hathaway, "Inverse Relation between Iodine in Food and Water and Goiter, Simple and Exophthalmic," *J. Am. Med. Assoc., 82*, 1668 (1924).

Neefe, J. R., and Joseph Stokes, Jr., "An Epidemic of Infectious Hepatitis Apparently Due to a Water-Borne Agent," *J. Am. Med. Assoc., 128*, 1063 (1945).

Newitt, A. W., T. M. Koppa, and D. W Gudekunst, "Water-Borne Outbreak of *Brucella melitensis* infection," *Am. J. Public Health, 29*, 738 (1939).

Okun, D. A., "Public Health Importance of Water-Supply and Waste-Disposal Works," *Proc. Am. Soc. Civil Engrs., 79*, 252 (1953).

Parker, R. R., E. A. Steinhaus, G. M. Kohls, and W. L. Jellison, "Contamination of Natural Waters and Mud with *Pasteurella tularensis,*" *Nat. Inst. Health Bull.* 193 (1951).

Rawn, A. M., and Committee, "Salvage of Sewage," *Trans. Am. Soc. Civil Engrs., 107,* 1652 (1942).

Rudolfs, Willem, L. L. Falk, and R. A. Ragotzkie, "Literature Review of the Occurrence and Survival of Enteric Pathogenic and Related Organisms in Soil, Water, Sewage, and Sludges, and on Vegetation," *Sewage and Ind. Wastes, 22,* 1261, 1417 (1950); also see *23,* 253, 656, 739, 853 (1951).

Sears, W. H., "Pumping Water. An Historical Review," *J. New Eng. Water Works Assoc., 49,* 119 (1935).

Smith, Geddes, *Plague on Us,* Commonwealth Fund, New York, 1948.

Symposium, "Historic Review of the Development of Sanitary Engineering in the United States during the Past One Hundred and Fifty Years," *Trans. Am. Soc. Civil Engrs., 92,* 1207 (1928).

Symposium on the History of Civil Engineering, "Sanitary Engineering," Part VII, *Trans. Am. Soc. Civil Engrs., CT* 556 (1952).

U. S. Public Health Service, "Epidemic Amebic Dysentery," *Nat. Inst. Health Bull.* 166 (1936).

U. S. Public Health Service, "Manual of Recommended Water-Sanitation Practice," *Pub. Health Bull.* 296 (1946).

U. S. Public Health Service, "Studies on Schistosomiasis," *Nat. Inst. Health Bull.* 189 (1947).

Walton, Graham, "Survey of Literature Relating to Infant Methemoglobinemia Due to Nitrate-Contaminated Water," *Am. J. Public Health, 41,* 986 (1951).

Wheeler, R. E., J. B. Lackey, and S. Schott, "A Contribution to the Toxicity of Algae," *Pub. Health Rept. 57,* 1695 (1942).

Chapter 2. Water Supply Systems

Bogert, C. L., Editor, *Glossary, Water and Sewage Control Engineering,* American Public Health Association, New York, 1950.

Greeley, S. A., and Committee, "Fundamental Considerations in Rates and Rate Structures for Water and Sewage Works," *Ohio State Law J., 12,* 151 (1951).

Howson, L. R., "Future Costs and Their Effects on Engineering Budgets," *Trans. Am. Soc. Civil Engrs., 112,* 701 (1947).

National Board of Fire Underwriters, *Standard Schedule for Grading Cities and Towns of the United States with Reference to Their Fire Defenses and Physical Conditions,* Published by the Board, New York, 1942.

Sampson, G. A., "The Cost of Small Surface-Water Supplies in New England," *J. New Eng. Water Works Assoc., 53,* 121 (1939).

Shaw, A. L., and E. S. Chase, "Economics of Water Purification," *J. New Eng. Water Works Assoc., 52,* 131 (1938).

U. S. Public Health Service, *Inventory of Water and Sewage Facilities in the United States, 1945,* Government Printing Office, Washington, D. C., 1948.

Chapter 3. Waste-Water Disposal Systems

Bogert, C. L., Editor, *Glossary, Water and Sewage Control Engineering,* American Public Health Association, New York, 1950.

Camp, T. R., "Pollution Abatement Policy," *Trans. Am. Soc. Civil Engrs., 116,* 252 (1951).

Federation of Sewage Works Associations, "Municipal Sewer Ordinances," *Manual of Practice* 3 (1949).

Federation of Sewage Works Associations, "Occupational Hazards in the Operation of Sewage Works," *Manual of Practice* 1 (1944).

Friel, F. S., "Financing Sewage Works," *Sewage Works J.*, *19*, 379 (1947).

Greeley, S. A., "Organizing and Financing Sewage Treatment Projects," *Trans. Am. Soc. Civil Engrs.*, *109*, 248 (1944).

Klassen, C. W., "Integrating a State Water-Pollution-Control Program with a Regional Water-Resources Plan," *Am. J. Public Health*, *43*, 438 (1953).

Rousculp, J. A., "Relation of Rainfall and Runoff to Cost of Sewers," *Trans. Am. Soc. Civil Engrs.*, *104*, 1473 (1939).

Schroepfer, George J., "Economics of Sewage Treatment," *Trans. Am. Soc. Civil Engrs.*, *104*, 210 (1939).

Stone, R. V., Jr., H. B. Gotaas, and V. W. Bacon, "Economic and Technical Status of Water Reclamation from Sewage and Industrial Wastes," *J. Am. Water Works Assoc.*, *44*, 503 (1952).

Tolman, S. L., "Ground Garbage. Its Effect upon the Sewer System and Sewage-Treatment Plant," *Sewage Works J.*, *19*, 441 (1947).

U. S. Public Health Service, *Inventory of Water and Sewage Facilities in the United States, 1945*, Government Printing Office, Washington, D. C., 1948.

Velz, C. J., "How Much Should Sewage Treatment Cost?", *Eng. News-Rec.*, *141*, No. 16, 84 (1948).

Chapter 4. Statistical Analysis of Quantitative Information

Beard, L. R., "Statistical Analysis in Hydrology," *Trans. Am. Soc. Civil Engrs.*, *108*, 1110 (1943).

Herdan, G., and M. L. Smith, *Small Particle Statistics*, Elsevier Publishing Co., Houston, Tex., 1953.

Chapter 5. Quantities of Water and Waste Water

Population

Bureau of the Census, *17th Decennial Census of the United States*, Government Printing Office, Washington, D. C., 1952.

McLean, J. E., "More Accurate Population Estimates by Means of Logistic Curves," *Civil Eng.*, *22*, 133, 886 (1952).

Pearl, Raymond, *The Natural History of Population*, Oxford University Press, New York, 1939.

Smith, T. L., *Population Analysis*, Prentice-Hall, New York, 1948.

Thompson, W. S., *Plenty of People*, Ronald Press, New York, Rev. ed., 1948.

Water Consumption and Waste-Water Flow

Folwell, A. P., "Maximum Daily and Hourly Water Consumption in American Cities," *J. New Eng. Water Works Assoc.*, *46*, 389 (1932).

Horne, R. W., "Control of Infiltration and Storm Flow in the Operation of Sewerage Systems," *Sewage Works J.*, *17*, 209 (1945).

Langbein, W. B., "Municipal Water Use in the United States," *J. Am. Water Works Assoc.*, *41*, 997 (1949).

Larson, B. O., and H. E. Hudson, Jr., "Residential Water Use and Family Income," *J. Am. Water Works Assoc., 43,* 603 (1951).

Lewis, L. L., and L. H. Polderman, "Modern Air Conditioning. What It Means to the Water Utility," *J. Am. Water Works Assoc., 28,* 1181 (1936).

Metcalf, Leonard, "Effect of Water Rates and Growth of Population upon Per Capita Consumption," *J. Am. Water Works Assoc., 15,* 1 (1926).

Mowry, C. W., "Water Consumption during Fires," *J. New Eng. Water Works Assoc., 46,* 93 (1932).

Stanley, W. R., "Peak-Demand Loads in Water-Supply Systems," *J. New Eng. Water Works Assoc., 65,* 217 (1951).

Chapter 6. Elements of Hydrology

American Society of Civil Engineers, "Hydrology Handbook," *Manuals of Engineering Practice* 28 (1949).

Bernard, Merrill, "Hydrometeorology. A Coordination of Meteorology and Hydrology," *Trans. Am. Geophys. Union, 19,* Part II, 598 (1938).

Hoover, M. D., "Effect of Removal of Forest Vegetation upon Water Yields," *Trans. Am. Geophys. Union, 25,* 973 (1944).

Horton, R. E., "The Field, Scope, and Status of the Science of Hydrology," *Trans. Am. Geophys. Union, 12,* 189 (1931).

Meinzer, O. E., "Outline of Ground-Water Hydrology," *U. S. Geol. Survey Water Supply Paper* 494 (1923).

Symposium, "Consumptive Use of Water," *Trans. Am. Soc. Civil Engrs., 117,* 948 (1952).

Thornthwaite, C. W., and Benjamin Holzman, "Measurement of Evaporation from Land and Water Surfaces," *U. S. Dept. Agr. Tech. Bull.* 817 (1942).

Veihmeyer, F. J., "Evaporation from Soils and Transpiration," *Trans. Am. Geophys. Union, 19,* 612 (1938).

Wilm, H. G., "Methods for the Measurement of Infiltration," *Trans. Am. Geophys. Union, 22,* 678 (1941).

Chapter 7. Rainfall and Runoff

Bernard, Merrill, "An Approach to Determine Stream Flow," *Trans. Am. Soc. Civil Engrs., 100,* 347 (1935).

Cook, H. L., "The Infiltration Approach to the Calculation of Surface Runoff," *Trans. Am. Geophys. Union, 27,* 726 (1946).

Gumbel, E. J., "Floods Estimated by the Probability Method," *Eng. News-Rec., 134,* 833 (1945).

Gumbel, E. J., and H. von Schelling, "The Distribution of the Number of Exceedances," *Ann. Math. Statistics, 21,* 247 (1950).

Horton, R. E., "Determining the Mean Precipitation on a Drainage Basin," *J. New Eng. Water Works Assoc., 38,* 1 (1924).

Hoyt, J. C., "Droughts of 1930–1934 and 1936," *U. S. Geol. Survey Water Supply Papers, 680, 820* (1936, 1938).

Hoyt, W. G., and others, "Studies of Relations of Rainfall and Runoff in the United States," *U. S. Geol. Survey Water Supply Papers* 772 (1936).

Jarvis, C. S., "Flood Flow Characteristics," *Trans. Am. Soc. Civil Engrs., 89,* 985 (1926).

Jarvis, C. S., "Floods in the United States," *U. S. Geol. Survey Water Supply Papers* 771 (1936).

Kinnison, H. B., and B. R. Colby, "Flood Formulas Based on Drainage-Basin Characteristics," *Trans. Am. Soc. Civil Engrs., 110,* 849 (1945).

Lane, E. W., and Kai Lei, "Stream-Flow Variability," *Trans. Am. Soc. Civil Engrs., 115,* 1084 (1950).

Linsley, R. K., Jr., "Simple Procedure for the Day to Day Forecasting of Runoff from Snow Melt," *Trans. Am. Geophys. Union, 24,* Part III, 62 (1943).

Paulsen, C. G., "The Measurement and Computation of Flood Discharge," *Trans. Am. Geophys. Union, 20,* 177 (1939).

Sherman, L. K., "Stream Flow from Rainfall by the Unit-Graph Method," *Eng. News-Rec., 108,* 501 (1932).

U. S. Department of Agriculture, *Snow Surveying,* Miscellaneous Publications, 1940.

Yarnell, D. L., "Rainfall Intensity-Frequency Data," *U. S. Dept. Agr. Misc. Publ.* 204 (1935).

Chapter 8. Storage and Regulation of Runoff

Bell, H. S., "Stratified Flow in Reservoirs and Its Use in Prevention of Silting," *U. S. Dept. Agr. Misc. Publ.* 491 (1942).

Clark, C. O., "Storage and the Unit Hydrograph," *Trans. Am. Soc. Civil Engrs., 110,* 1419 (1945).

Cummings, N. W., "The Reliability and Usefulness of the Energy Equations for Evaporation," *Trans. Am. Geophys. Union, 27,* 81 (1946).

Grover, N. C., and C. S. Howard, "The Passage of Turbid Water through Lake Mead," *Trans. Am. Soc. Civil Engrs., 103,* 720 (1938).

Hickox, G. H., "Evaporation from a Free Water Surface," *Trans. Am. Soc. Civil Engrs., 111,* 1 (1946).

Mitchell, P. B., "Reservoir-Site Investigation and Economics," *J. Inst. Water Engrs., 5,* 445 (1951).

Riesbol, H. W., "Snow Hydrology for Multiple-Purpose Reservoirs," *Proc. Am. Soc. Civil Engrs., 79,* 189 (1953).

Rutter, E. J., Q. B. Graves, and F. F. Snyder, "Flood Routing," *Trans. Am. Soc. Civil Engrs., 104,* 275 (1939).

Wisler, C. O., and E. F. Brater, "A Direct Method of Flood Routing," *Trans. Am. Soc. Civil Engrs., 107,* 1519 (1942).

Witzig, B. J., "Sedimentation in Reservoirs," *Trans. Am. Soc. Civil Engrs., 109,* 1047 (1944).

Chapter 9. Ground Water

Casagrande, Arthur, "Classification and Identification of Soils," *Trans. Am. Soc. Civil Engrs., 113,* 901 (1948).

Geyer, R. L., "Depth Determinations from Seismic Data," *J. New Eng. Water Works Assoc., 65,* 185 (1951).

Horton, R. E., "Determination of Infiltration Capacity for Large Drainage Basins," *Trans. Am. Geophys. Union, 18,* Part II, 371 (1937).

Lewis, M. R., "Rate of Flow of Capillary Moisture," *U. S. Dept. Agr. Tech. Bull.* 579 (1937).

McGuinness, C. L., "Recharge and Depletion of Ground-Water Supplies," *Trans. Am. Soc. Civil Engrs., 112,* 972 (1947).

Meinzer, O. E., "The Occurrence of Ground Water in the United States, with a Discussion of Principles," *U. S. Geol. Survey Water Supply Paper* 489 (1923, reprinted 1950).

Rose, H. E., "On the Permeability of Cemented Beds and Sandstones," *J. Inst. Water Engrs.*, *4*, 535 (1950).

Sherman, L. K., "Determination of Infiltration Rates from Surface Runoff," *Trans. Am. Geophys. Union*, *19*, Part II, 430 (1938).

Slichter, C. S., "Theoretical Investigation of the Motion of Ground Waters," *U. S. Geol. Survey, 19th Annual Report*, Part II, 1899.

Stickel, J. F., L. E. Blakeley, and B. B. Gordon, "Geophysics of Water," *J. Am. Water Works Assoc.*, *44*, 23 (1952).

Waring, G. A., and O. E. Meinzer, "Bibliography and Index of Publications Relating to Ground Water Prepared by the Geological Survey and Cooperating Agencies," *U. S. Geol. Survey Water Supply Paper* 992 (1947).

Chapter 10. Collection of Surface Water

Houser, G. C., "Pollution of Reservoirs by Gulls and Other Birds," *J. New Eng. Water Works Assoc.*, *45*, 15 (1931).

Lischer, V. C., and H. O. Hartung, "Intakes on Variable Streams," *J. Am. Water Works Assoc.*, *44*, 873 (1952).

Merriman, Thaddeus, "The Law of Interstate Waters and Its Application to the Case of the Delaware River," *J. New Eng. Water Works Assoc.*, *45*, 199 (1931).

Purcell, L. T., "The Aging of Reservoir Waters," *J. Am. Water Works Assoc.*, *31*, 1775 (1939).

Saville, C. M., "Compensating Reservoirs and Diversion of Water," *J. New Eng. Water Works Assoc.*, *40*, 249 (1926).

Symposium, "Multipurpose Reservoirs," *Trans. Am. Soc. Civil Engrs.*, *115*, 790 (1950).

Task Group Report, "Erosion Control in Reservoir Areas," *J. Am. Water Works Assoc.*, *45*, 790 (1953).

Thomas, H. A., Jr., R. S. Kleinschmidt, F. L. Parker, and C. G. Bell, Jr., "Radioactive Fallout in Massachusetts Surface Waters," *J. Am. Water Works Assoc.*, *45*, 562 (1953).

Weston, A. D., "Sanitary Protection of Water Sheds. Are We Overdoing or Underdoing It?", *J. New Eng. Water Works Assoc.*, *65*, 256 (1951).

Chapter 11. Collection of Ground Water

Anderson, Keith, *Water Well Handbook*, Missouri Well Drillers Association, Rolla, Mo., 2nd Ed., 1948.

Balch, L. R., "Hydraulics of Deep Wells," *J. Am. Water Works Assoc.*, *22*, 727 (1930).

Baumann, Paul, "Experiments with Fresh-Water Barrier to Prevent Sea-Water Intrusion," *J. Am. Water Works Assoc.*, *45*, 521 (1953).

Baumann, Paul, "Ground-Water Movement Controlled through Spreading," *Trans. Am. Soc. Civil Engrs.*, *117*, 1024 (1952).

Bennison, E. W., *Ground Water: Its Development, Uses, and Conservation.* Edward E. Johnson, St. Paul, Minn., 1947.

Brown, R. H., "Selected Procedure for Analyzing Aquifer Test Data," *J. Am. Water Works Assoc.*, *45*, 844 (1953).

Conkling, Harold, "Administrative Control of Underground Water: Physical and Legal Aspects," *Trans. Am. Soc. Civil Engrs.*, *102*, 753 (1937).

Jacob, C. E., "Drawdown Test to Determine Effective Radius of Artesian Well," *Trans. Am. Soc. Civil Engrs.*, *112*, 1047 (1947).

Kazman, R. G., "River Infiltration as a Source of Ground-Water Supply," *Trans. Am. Soc. Civil Engrs., 113,* 404 (1948).

Lee, C. H., "The Interpretation of Water Level in Wells and Test Holes," *Trans. Am. Geophys. Union, 15,* 540 (1934).

Chapter 12.   Transmission of Water

Aldrich, E. H., "Solution of Transmission Problems of a Water System," *Trans. Am. Soc. Civil Engrs., 103,* 1579 (1938).

Killam, E. T., and Committee, "Pipeline Friction Coefficients," *J. New Eng. Water Works Assoc., 49,* 235 (1935).

Eames, D. D., "Economics of Pumping Equipment," *J. New Eng. Water Works Assoc., 52,* 214 (1938).

Harris, C. W., "An Engineering Concept of Flow in Pipes," *Trans. Am. Soc. Civil Engrs., 115,* 909 (1950).

Hazen, Richard, "Pumps and Pumping Stations," *J. New Eng. Water Works Assoc., 67,* 114 (1953).

Kennison, K. R., "The Design of Pipelines," *J. New Eng. Water Works Assoc., 47,* 27 (1933).

Leggett, R. F., and C. B. Crawford, "Soil Temperatures and Water Works Practice," *J. Am. Water Works Assoc., 44,* 923 (1952).

Niles, T. M., "Selection of Pumping Equipment," *J. Am. Water Works Assoc., 45,* 170 (1953).

Panel Discussion, "Standard Allowances for Water Hammer," *J. Am. Water Works Assoc., 44,* 977 (1952).

Parmakian, John, "Air-Inlet Valves for Steel Pipe Lines," *Trans. Am. Soc. Civil Engrs., 115,* 438 (1950).

Symposium, "Entrainment of Air in Flowing Water," *Trans. Am. Soc. Civil Engrs., 108,* 1393 (1943).

Chapter 13.   Distribution of Water

American Society of Civil Engineers, "Location of Underground Utilities," *Manuals of Engineering Practice* 14 (1937).

Atkinson, Alan, "The Relining of Water Mains *in situ*," *J. Inst. Water Engrs., 4,* 293 (1950).

Black, C. A., and W. T. Calaway, "A Study of Jute and Other Yarning Materials," *J. Am. Water Works Assoc., 44,* 707 (1952).

Camp, T. R., "Economic Pipe Sizes for Water-Distribution Systems," *Trans. Am. Soc. Civil Engrs., 104,* 190 (1939).

Camp, T. R., "Hydraulics of Distribution Systems.   Some Recent Developments in Methods of Analysis," *J. New Eng. Water Works Assoc., 57,* 334 (1943).

Gavett, Weston, "Computation of Flows in Distribution Systems," *J. Am. Water Works Assoc., 35,* 267 (1943).

McIlroy, M. S., "Water Distribution Systems Studied by a Complete Electrical Analogy," *J. New Eng. Water Works Assoc., 65,* 299 (1951).

National Board of Fire Underwriters, *Fire-Engine Tests and Fire-Stream Tables,* Published by the Board, New York, 4th Ed., 1931.

Chapter 14.   Water Supply and Drainage of Buildings

Cronkright, A. B., and A. P. Miller, "Plumbing and Public Health," *Pub. Health Bull.* 256 (1940).

Dawson, F. M., and A. A. Kalinske, "Design and Operation of Grease Interceptors," *Sewage Works J.,* *16,* 482 (1944).

Eaton, H. N., and J. L. French, "Fixture-Unit Ratings as Used in Plumbing-System Design," Housing and Home Finance Agency, *Housing Research Paper* 15 (1951).

Halpin, H. E., "Automatic Sprinkler-Systems and Their Water Supplies," *J. New Eng. Water Works Assoc., 50,* 255 (1936).

Taylor, S. H., "Water Department Regulation of Pipes within Buildings," *J. New Eng. Water Works Assoc., 50,* 129 (1936).

Chapter 15. Flow in Sewers and Their Appurtenances

Allen, K., "The Clarification of Sewage by Fine Screens," *Trans. Am. Soc. Civil Engrs., 78,* 880 (1915).

Einstein, H. A., "Formulas for the Transportation of Bed Load," *Trans. Am. Soc. Civil Engrs., 107,* 561 (1942).

Hands, G. E., "Fundamentals of Sewage Pumping," *Sewage and Ind. Wastes, 23,* 959 (1951).

Johnson, C. F., "Determination of Kutter's *n* for Sewers Partly Filled," *Trans. Am. Soc. Civil Engrs., 109,* 223 (1944).

Kennedy, R. R., "Design of Sewage Pumping Stations," *Sewage and Ind. Wastes, 23,* 451 (1951).

Larson, C. L., and L. G. Straub, "Grate Inlets for Surface Drainage of Streets and Highways," *St. Anthony Falls Hydraulic Laboratory Bull.* 2, Univ. Minnesota, Minneapolis, 1949.

Stegmaier, R. B., Jr., "Storm Water Overflows," *Sewage Works J., 14,* 1264 (1942).

Vanoni, V. A., "Transportation of Suspended Sediment by Water," *Trans. Am. Soc. Civil Engrs., 111,* 67 (1946).

Chapter 16. Collection of Sewage and Storm Drainage

Greely, S. A., "Sewage Disposal Project of Buffalo, New York," *Trans. Am. Soc. Civil Engrs., 105,* 1604 (1940).

Gregory, J. H., R. H. Simpson, Orris Bonney, and R. A. Allton, "Intercepting Sewers and Storm Stand-by Tanks at Columbus, Ohio," *Trans. Am. Soc. Civil Engrs., 99,* 1295 (1934).

Hicks, W. I., "A Method of Computing Urban Runoff," *Trans. Am. Soc. Civil Engrs., 109,* 1217 (1944).

Izzard, C. F., "Hydraulics of Runoff from Developed Areas," *Proc. Highway Research Board* (1946).

Izzard, C. F., and others, "Surface Drainage," *Highway Research Board Research Report* 11-B (1950).

McKee, J. E., "Loss of Sanitary Sewage through Storm-Water Overflows," *J. Boston Soc. Civil Engrs., 34,* 55 (1947).

Pomeroy, Richard, and F. D. Bowlus, "Progress Report on Sulfide Control Research," *Sewage Works J., 18,* 597 (1946).

Seaver, C., and D. T. Sampson, "Principles of Storm-Water Runoff Derived from a Study of Sewer Gagings," *Municipal Engrs. J., 35,* 69 (1949).

Chapter 17. Physical Properties of Water

Adeney, W. E., and H. G. Becker, "The Determination of the Rate of Solution of Atmospheric Nitrogen and Oxygen by Water," *Phil. Mag., 38*, 317 (1919); *39*, 385 (1920).

Arnold, J. M., "A Kinetic Theory of Diffusion in Liquid Systems," *J. Am. Chem. Soc., 52*, 3937 (1930).

Scouller, W. D., and W. Watson, "The Solution of Oxygen from Air Bubbles," *Surveyor, 86*, 15 (1934).

Chapter 18. Elements of Water Chemistry

Babor, J. A., and G. W. Thiessen, *How to Solve Problems in Physical Chemistry*, Thomas Y. Crowell, New York, 1944.

Camp, T. R., "Corrosiveness of Water to Metals," *J. New Eng. Water Works Assoc., 60*, 189, 282 (1946).

Langelier, W. F., "Chemical Equilibria in Water Treatment," *J. Am. Water Works Assoc., 38*, 169 (1946).

Speller, F. N., *Corrosion*, McGraw-Hill Book Co., New York, 3rd Ed., 1951.

Uhlig, H. H., Editor-in-Chief, *The Corrosion Handbook*, John Wiley & Sons, New York, 1948.

Chapter 19. Biology of Water and Waste Water

Baines, S., H. A. Hawkes, C. H. Hewitt, and S. H. Jenkins, "Protozoa as Indicators in Activated Sludge Treatment," *Sewage and Ind. Wastes, 25*, 1023 (1953).

Buswell, A. M., Irene Van Meter, and J. R. Gerke, "Study of the Nitrification Phase of the BOD Test," *Sewage and Ind. Wastes, 22*, 508, 1297 (1950).

Clark, H. F., E. E. Geldreich, H. J. Jeter, and P. W. Kabler, "The Membrane Filter in Sanitary Bacteriology," *Public Health Rept. 66*, 951 (1951).

Cram, E. B., "The Effect of Various Treatment Processes on the Survival of Helminth Ova and Protozoan Cysts in Sewage," *Sewage Works J., 15*, 1119 (1943).

Gotaas, H. B., "The Effect of Sea Water on the Biochemical Oxidation of Sewage," *Sewage Works J., 21*, 818 (1949).

Holtje, R. H., "The Biology of Sewage Sprinkling Filters," *Sewage Works J., 15*, 14 (1943).

Thomas, H. A., Jr., "Slope Method of Evaluating the Constants of the First-Stage BOD Curve," *Sewage Works J., 9*, 425 (1937).

Woodward, R. L., "Deoxygenation of Sewage. A Discussion," *Sewage and Ind. Wastes, 25*, 918 (1953).

Chapter 20. Examination of Water and Waste Water

Cox, C. R., *Laboratory Control of Water Purification*, Case-Sheppard-Mann Publishing Corp., New York, 1946.

Dye, J. F., "Calculation of Effect of Temperature on pH, Free Carbon Dioxide, and the Three Forms of Alkalinity," *J. Am. Water Works Assoc., 44*, 356 (1952).

Flett, Lawrence, and L. F. Hoyt, "Detergent Compounds. Their Composition and Behavior," *Sewage and Ind. Wastes, 25*, 245 (1953). (See also pp. 255, 262, and 277.)

Hopkins, E. S., *Water Purification Control*, Williams & Wilkins, Baltimore, 3rd Ed., 1948.

Larson, T. E., and A. M. Buswell, "Calcium Carbonate Saturation Index and Alkalinity Interpretations," *J. Am. Water Works Assoc., 34,* 1667 (1942).

Moore, E. W., "The Precision of Microscopic Counts of Plankton in Water," *J. Am. Water Works Assoc., 44,* 208 (1952).

Ruchhoft, C. C., and W. A. Moore, "Chemical Oxygen Consumed and Its Relationship to B.O.D.," *Sewage and Ind. Wastes, 23,* 705 (1951).

Spaulding, C. H., "Quantitative Determination of Odor in Water," *Am. J. Public Health, 21,* 1038 (1931).

Theroux, F. R., E. F. Eldridge, and W. LeR. Mallmann, *Laboratory Manual for Chemical and Bacterial Analysis of Water and Sewage,* McGraw-Hill Book Co., New York, 3rd Ed., 1943.

Chapter 21.   Standards of Water Quality and Unit Operations of Water and Waste-Water Treatment

California State Water Pollution Control Board, *Water Quality Criteria,* Published by the Board, Sacramento, 1952.

Chase, E. S., and Committee, "A System of Sanitary Scoring of Water Supplies," *J. New Eng. Water Works Assoc., 40,* 416 (1926); *41,* 316 (1927).

Cox, C. R., "Acceptable Standards for Natural Waters Used for Bathing," *Trans. Am. Soc. Civil Engrs., 117,* 223 (1952).

McKee, J. E., and V. W. Bacon, "An Analysis of Water Quality Criteria," *Proc. Am. Soc. Civil Engrs., 79,* 231 (1953).

Schroepfer, G. J., "An Analysis of Stream Pollution and Stream Standards," *Sewage Works J., 14,* 1130 (1942).

U. S. Public Health Service, "Public Health Service Drinking-Water Standards," *Pub. Health Rept., 61,* 371 (1946).

Waring, F. H., "Significance of Nitrates in Water Supplies," *J. Am. Water Works Assoc., 41,* 147 (1949).

Chapter 22.   Sedimentation and Flotation

American Society of Civil Engineers, "Hydraulic Models," *Manuals of Engineering Practice* 25 (1942).

American Society of Civil Engineers, "Water Treatment Plant Design," *Manuals of Engineering Practice* 19 (1940).

Anderson, N. E., "Design of Final Settling Tanks for Activated Sludge," *Sewage Works J., 17,* 50 (1945).

Camp, T. R., "Studies of Sedimentation-Basin Design," *Sewage and Ind. Wastes, 25,* 1 (1953).

Dobbins, W. E., "Effect of Turbulence on Sedimentation," *Trans. Am. Soc. Civil Engrs., 109,* 629 (1944).

Fischer, A. J., and A. Hillman, "Improved Sewage Clarification by Preflocculation without Chemicals," *Sewage Works J., 12,* 280 (1940).

Gascoigne, G. B., "Grit Chambers for Sewage-Treatment Works," *Trans. Am. Soc. Civil Engrs., 91,* 496 (1927).

Hartung, H. O., and Committee, "Capacity and Loadings of Suspended-Solids Contact-Units," *J. Am. Water Works Assoc., 43,* 263 (1951).

Hawkesley, P. G. W., "The Effect of Concentration on the Settling of Suspensions and Flow Through Porous Media," *Some Aspects of Fluid Flow,* Edward Arnold & Co., London, 1951.

Herdan, G., and M. L. Smith, *Small Particle Statistics*, Elsevier Publishing Co., Houston, Tex., 1953.

Hopper, S. H., and M. C. McCowen, "A Flotation Process for Water Purification," *J. Am. Water Works Assoc., 44,* 719 (1952).

Hubbell, G. E., "Experiments with Inlet Devices for Sedimentation Tanks," *Sewage Works J., 6,* 774 (1934).

Kalinske, A. A., "Settling Rate of Suspensions in Solids Contact-Units," *Proc. Am. Soc. Civil Engrs., 79,* 186 (1953).

Lee, Ming, and H. E. Babbitt, "Constant-Velocity Grit-Chamber with Parshall-Flume Control," *Sewage Works J., 18,* 646 (1946).

McNown, J. S., and Jamil Malaika, "Effects of Particle Shape on Settling Velocity at Low Reynolds Numbers," *Trans. Am. Geophys. Union, 31,* 74 (1950).

Schroepfer, G. J., "Factors Affecting the Efficiency of Sewage Sedimentation," *Sewage Works J., 5,* 203 (1933).

Slade, J. J., "Sedimentation in Quiescent and Turbulent Basins," *Trans. Am. Soc. Civil Engrs., 102,* 289 (1937).

Thomas, H. A., Jr., and J. L. Dallas, "An Improved Settling-Tank Design," *J. Boston Soc. Civil Engrs., 39,* 354 (1952).

Wittwer, N. C., "Some Observations on Sewage Sedimentation," *Sewage Works J., 12,* 513 (1940).

Chapter 23. Chemical Coagulation, Precipitation, Ion Exchange, and Stabilization

Chemical Coagulation

Baylis, J. R., "Silicates as Aids to Coagulation," *J. Am. Water Works Assoc., 29,* 1355 (1937).

Bartow, Edward, A. P. Black, and W. E. Sansbury, "Formation of Floc by Ferric Coagulants," *Ind. Eng. Chem., 25,* 898 (1933).

Black, A. P., Owen Rice, and Edward Bartow, "Formation of Floc by Aluminum Sulfate," *Ind. Eng. Chem., 25,* 811 (1933).

Camp, T. R., "Flocculation and Flocculation Basins," *Proc. Am. Soc. Civil Engrs., 79,* 283 (1953).

Pearse, L., and Committee, "Chemical Treatment of Sewage," *Sewage Works J., 7,* 997 (1935).

Chemical Precipitation

Caldwell, D. H., and W. B. Lawrence, "Water Softening and Conditioning Problems," *Ind. Eng. Chem., 45,* 535 (1953).

Coffman, P. A., "Guides for Selection of Chemical Feeders," *J. New Eng. Water Works Assoc., 67,* 192 (1953).

Gedge, F. G., "Use of Commercial Carbon Dioxide in Lime Softening," *J. Am. Water Works Assoc., 41,* 159 (1949).

Graf, A. V., "Carbon Dioxide Treatment at St. Louis Water Works," *Eng. News-Rec., 99,* 643 (1927).

Hudson, H. W., and A. M. Buswell, "Soap Consumption and Water Quality," *J. Am. Water Works Assoc., 24,* 859 (1932).

Knox, W. H., "Water-Softening Plant Design," *Trans. Am. Soc. Civil Engrs., 104,* 1425 (1939).

Larson, T. E., "The Ideal Lime-Softened Water," *J. Am. Water Works Assoc., 43,* 649 (1951).

Larson, T. E., "Interpretation of Soap-Savings Data," *J. Am. Water Works Assoc.*, *40*, 296 (1948).

Mellen, A. F., "Recarbonation with Liquid Carbon Dioxide," *J. Am. Water Works Assoc.*, *42*, 204 (1950).

Ion Exchange and Other Desalting Processes

Aultman, W. W., "Resinous Ion Exchangers in Water Treatment," *Trans. Am. Soc. Civil Engrs.*, *117*, 361 (1952).

Howe, E. D., "Sea Water as a Source of Fresh Water," *J. Am. Water Works, Assoc.*, *44*, 690 (1952).

Langelier, W. F., "The Electrochemical Desalting of Sea Water with Perm-selective Membranes. A Hypothetical Process," *J. Am. Water Works Assoc.*, *44*, 845 (1952).

Lindsay, F. K., "High-Capacity Cation Exchangers," *J. Am. Water Works Assoc.*, *42*, 75 (1950).

Maier, F. J., "Defluoridation of Municipal Water Supplies," *J. Am. Water Works Assoc.*, *45*, 879 (1953).

Moore, E. W., "The Desalting of Saline Waters: A Review of the Present Status," *J. New Eng. Water Works Assoc.*, *65*, 319 (1951).

Showell, E. B., "Ion Exchange for Water Treatment," *J. Am. Water Works Assoc.*, *43*, 522 (1951).

Streicher, Lee, and A. E. Bowers, "Cation Exchangers for Municipal Water Softening," *J. Am. Water Works Assoc.*, *42*, 81 (1950).

Chemical Stabilization

Baylis, J. R., "Cast-Iron Pipe Coatings and Corrosion," *J. Am. Water Works Assoc.*, *45*, 807 (1953).

Hoover, C. P., "Stabilization of Lime-Softened Water," *J. Am. Water Works Assoc.*, *34*, 1425 (1942).

Powell, S. T., H. E. Bacon, and J. R. Lill, "Corrosion Prevention by Controlled Calcium Carbonate Scale," *Ind. Eng. Chem.*, *37*, 842 (1945).

Ryznar, J. S., "A New Index for Determining Amount of Calcium Carbonate Scale Formed by a Water," *J. Am. Water Works Assoc.*, *36*, 472 (1944).

Corrosion Control

Anderson, H. H., and Committee, "Technical Practices in Cathodic Protection," *J. Am. Water Works Assoc.*, *43*, 883 (1951).

Hay, H. R., "Water-Purification Methods Involving Sodium Silicates," *J. Am. Water Works Assoc.*, *36*, 626 (1944).

Lehrman, Leo, and H. L. Shuldener, "The Role of Sodium Silicate in Inhibiting Corrosion by Film Formation on Water Piping," *J. Am. Water Works Assoc.*, *43*, 175 (1951).

Logan, K. H., "Underground Corrosion," *Nat. Bur. Standards Catalog* C 13.4:450 (1945).

McKay, R. J., and Robert Worthington, *Corrosion Resistance of Metals and Alloys*, Reinhold Publishing Corp., New York, 1936.

Magoffin, L. E., "Use of Magnesium Anodes in Cathodic Protection of Tanks and Pipelines," *J. Am. Water Works Assoc.*, *44*, 407 (1952).

Powell, S. T., H. E. Bacon, and J. R. Lill, "Recent Developments in Corrosion Control," *J. Am. Water Works Assoc.*, *38*, 808 (1946).

Powell, S. T., and H. S. Burns, "Vacuum Deaeration," *Chem. & Met. Eng., 43,* 180 (1936).

Rice, Owen, "Sodium Hexametaphosphate as an Aid in the Control of Corrosion," *J. New Eng. Water Works Assoc., 54,* 25 (1940).

Schneider, W. R., "Corrosion and Cathodic Protection of Pipelines," *J. Am. Water Works Assoc., 44,* 413 (1952).

Wells, C. K., "Cathodic Protection of Steel Water Tanks," *J. Am. Water Works Assoc., 44,* 428 (1952).

Chemicals and Waste Chemicals

Coffman, P. A., "Guides for Selection of Chemical Feeders," *J. New Eng. Water Works Assoc., 67,* 192 (1953).

Harper, L. E., "Fluoride Chemical Feeding," *J. Am. Water Works Assoc., 43,* 744 (1951).

Sheen, R. T., and H. B. Lammers, "Recovery of Calcium Carbonate or Lime from Water-Softening Sludges," *J. Am. Water Works Assoc., 36,* 1145 (1944).

Chapter 24. Filtration

Baylis, J. R., "Experiences in Filtration," *J. Am. Water Works Assoc., 29,* 1010 (1937).

Baylis, J. R., "Experience with High-Rate Filtration," *J. Am. Water Works Assoc., 42,* 687 (1950).

Black, H. H., and C. H. Spaulding, "Diatomite Water Filtration Developed for Field Troops," *J. Am. Water Works Assoc., 36,* 1208 (1944).

Camp, T. R., "Experimental Study of Porous Plates for Use in Filter Bottoms for Rapid Filters," *J. New Eng. Water Works Assoc., 49,* 1 (1935).

Fair, G. M., "The Hydraulics of Rapid Sand Filters," *J. Inst. Water Engrs., 5,* 171 (1951).

Fair, G. M., and L. P. Hatch, "Fundamental Factors Governing the Streamline Flow of Water through Sand," *J. Am. Water Works Assoc., 25,* 1551 (1933).

Hatch, L. P., "Flow of Fluids through Granular Materials: Filtration, Expansion, Hindered Settling," *Trans. Am. Geophys. Union, 24,* 536 (1943).

Hazen, Allen, and E. D. Hardy, "Works for the Purification of the Water Supply of Washington, D. C.," *Trans. Am. Soc. Civil Engrs., 57,* 307 (1906).

Hazen, Richard, "Application of the Microstrainer to Water Treatment in Great Britain," *J. Am. Water Works Assoc., 45,* 723 (1953).

Hazen, Richard, "Elements of Filter Design," *J. Am. Water Works Assoc., 43,* 208 (1951).

Howard, G. W., "Transportation of Sand and Gravel in a Four-Inch Pipe," *Trans. Am. Soc. Civil Engrs., 104,* 1334 (1939).

Hulbert, Roberts, and F. W. Herring, "Studies on the Washing of Rapid Filters," *J. Am. Water Works Assoc., 21,* 1445 (1935).

Pettet, A. E. J., W. F. Collett, and J. I. Waddington, "Rapid Filtration of Sewage Effluents through Sand and Anthracite," *Sewage and Ind. Wastes, 24,* 835 (1952).

Rose, H. E., "Fluid Flow Through Beds of Granular Material," *Some Aspects of Fluid Flow,* Edward Arnold & Co., London, 1951.

Sanchis, J. M., and J. C. Merrell, Jr., "Studies on Diatomaceous Earth Filtration," *J. Am. Water Works Assoc., 43,* 475 (1951).

Streeter, H. W., "Experimental Studies of Water Purification. VI. General Summary and Conclusions," *Pub. Health Rept. 48*, 377 (1933).

Zack, S. I., "Mechanical Filtration of Effluents," *Sewage Works J., 9*, 466 (1937).

Chapter 25. Biological Flocculation and Precipitation

General

Bushee, R. J., "Mathematical Relationships in Sewage Treatment," *Sewage and Ind. Wastes, 22*, 166 (1951).

Fair, G. M., and H. A. Thomas, Jr., "The Concept of Interface and Loading in Submerged, Aerobic, Biological Sewage-Treatment Systems," *J. and Proc., Inst. Sewage Purif.*, Part 3, 235 (1950).

Howland, W. E., "Effect of Temperature on Sewage Treatment Processes," *Sewage and Ind. Wastes, 25*, 161 (1953).

Hutchins, W. A., "Sewage Treatment as Practiced in the Western States," *U. S. Dept. Agr. Tech. Bull. 675* (1939).

Smith, D. B., "Aerobic Biological Stabilization of Organic Substrates," *Sewage and Ind. Wastes, 24*, 1077 (1952).

Stone, Ralph, "Land Disposal of Sewage and Industrial Wastes," *Sewage and Ind. Wastes, 25*, 406 (1953).

Stone, Ralph, and W. F. Garber, "Sewage Reclamation by Spreading-Basin Infiltration," *Trans. Am. Soc. Civil Engrs., 117*, 1189 (1952).

Theriault, E. J., "The Clarification of Sewage," *Sewage Works J., 7*, 377 (1935).

Activated-Sludge Treatment

Ardern, Edward, and W. T. Lockett, "Experiments on the Oxidation of Sewage without the Aid of Filters," *J. Soc. Chem. Ind., 33*, 523, 1122 (1914).

Bloodgood, D. E., "Studies of Activated-Sludge Oxidation at Indianapolis," *Sewage Works J., 10*, 26 (1938).

Compressed Air and Gas Institute, *Compressed-Air Handbook*, Published by the Institute, New York, 1947.

Eckenfelder, W. W., Jr., "Aeration Efficiency and Design," *Sewage and Ind. Wastes, 24*, 1221, 1361 (1952).

Federation of Sewage Works Associations, "Air Diffusion in Sewage Works," *Manual of Practice* 5 (1952).

Harris, F. W., T. Cockburn, and T. Anderson, "Observations on the Biological and Physical Properties of Activated Sludge and the Principles of Its Application," *Surveyor, 70*, 30 (1926).

Ippen, A. T., L. G. Campbell, and C. E. Carver, Jr., "The Determination of Oxygen Absorption in Aeration Processes," *Mass. Inst. Tech., Hydrodynamics Lab., Technical Report* 7 (1952).

Keefer, C. E., and J. Meisel, "Activated-Sludge Studies," *Sewage Works J., 22*, 1117, 1518 (1950); *23*, 982 (1951).

Kraus, L. S., "Quantitative Relationships in the Activated-Sludge Process," *Sewage Works J., 21*, 613 (1949).

Lemke, A. A., "Flow of Air in Pipes," *Sewage and Ind. Wastes, 24*, 24 (1952).

McKee, J. E., and G. M. Fair, "Load Distribution in the Activated-Sludge Process," *Sewage Works J., 14*, 121 (1942).

Okun, D. A., "A System of Bio-Precipitation of Organic Matter from Sewage," *Sewage Works J., 21,* 763 (1949).

Parsons, A. S., and H. Wilson, "Notes on the Clarification Stage of the Activated-Sludge Process," *J. Roy. Sani. Inst., 48,* 506 (1928); also *Surveyor, 72,* 221 (1927).

Pearse, Langdon, and Committee, "Bulking of Sludge in the Activated-Sludge Process of Sewage Treatment," *Year Book,* American Public Health Association, *7,* 164 (1936–1937).

Pearse, Langdon, and Committee, "The Operation and Control of Activated-Sludge Sewage-Treatment Works," *Sewage Works J., 14,* 3 (1942).

Rohlich, G. A., "Oxidation-Reduction Potential Measurements in Activated Sludge and Activated-Sludge Sewage Mixtures," *Sewage Works J., 16,* 540 (1944).

Sawyer, C. N., and Leland Bradney, "Rising of Activated Sludge in Final Settling Tanks," *Sewage Works J., 17,* 1191 (1945).

Setter, L. R., and G. P. Edwards, "Modified Sewage Aeration," *Sewage Works J., 16,* 278 (1944).

Setter, L. R., W. T. Carpenter, and G. C. Winslow, "Practical Applications of Principles of Modified Sewage Aeration," *Sewage Works J., 17,* 669 (1945).

Thomas, H. A., Jr., and J. E. McKee, "Longitudinal Mixing in Aeration Tanks," *Sewage Works J., 16,* 42 (1944).

Townsend, D. W., "Loss of Head in Activated-Sludge Aeration-Channels," *Trans. Am. Soc. Civil Engrs., 100,* 558 (1935).

Whitehead, H. C., "Partial Purification of Sewage by Activated Sludge," *Surveyor, 68,* 449 (1925).

Trickling Filtration

Fair, G. M., "The Trickling-Filter Fly," *Sewage Works J., 6,* 966 (1934).

Greeley, S. A., "Considerations and Procedures in the Design of High-Rate Trickling-Filters," *Sewage Works J., 20,* 789 (1948).

Halvorson, H. O., G. M. Savage, and E. L. Piret, "Fundamental Factors Concerned in the Operation of Trickling Filters," *Sewage Works J., 8,* 888 (1936).

Jenks, H. N., "Experimental Study of Biofiltration," *Sewage Works J., 8,* 701 (1936).

Schaetzle, T. C., "Control of Psychoda Flies at Akron," *Sewage and Ind. Wastes, 24,* 124 (1952).

Velz, C. J., "A Basic Law for the Performance of Biological Beds," *Sewage Works J., 20,* 607 (1948).

Chapter 26. Sludge Treatment and Disposal

Sludge Digestion

Buswell, A. M., "Microbiology and Theory of Anaerobic Digestion," *Sewage Works J., 19,* 28 (1947).

Buswell, A. M., and W. D. Hatfield, "Anaerobic Fermentations," *Ill. Water Survey Bull.* 32 (1939).

Fair, G. M., and E. W. Moore, "Heat and Energy Relations in the Digestion of Sewage Solids," *Sewage Works J., 4,* 242, 428, 589, 728 (1932).

Fischer, A. J., and R. A. Greene, "Plant-Scale Tests on Thermophilic Digestion," *Sewage Works J., 17,* 718 (1945).

Langford, L. L., "Safety Considerations in the Design of Gas-Utilization Facilities," *Sewage Works J., 17,* 66 (1945).

Rankin, R. S., "Digester-Capacity Requirements," *Sewage Works J.*, *20*, 478 (1948).

Rawn, A. M., and E. J. Candell, "Some Effects of Anaerobic Digestion on Sewage Sludge," *Trans. Am. Soc. Civil Engrs.*, *115*, 181 (1950).

Rawn, A. M., A. P. Banta, and Richard Pomeroy, "Multiple-Stage Sewage-Sludge Digestion," *Trans. Am. Soc. Civil Engrs.*, *104*, 93 (1939).

Rudolfs, Willem, and Associates, "High and Low Temperature Digestion-Experiments," *Sewage Works J.*, *7*, 422, 781 (1935); *9*, 459, 728 (1937).

Schlenz, H. E., "Controlled Digestion," *Sewage Works J.*, *16*, 504 (1944).

Snell, J. R., "Anaerobic Digestion," *Sewage Works J.*, *14*, 1304 (1942); *15*, 56, 679 (1943).

Walraven, W. B., "Development of Power from Sewage-Sludge Gas," *Sewage Works J.*, *4*, 614 (1932).

Sludge Drying and Disposal

Federation of Sewage Works Associations, "Utilization of Sewage Sludge as Fertilizer," *Manual of Practice* 2 (1946).

Fischer, A. J., "The Economics of Various Methods of Sludge Disposal," *Sewage Works J.*, *9*, 248 (1936).

Flood, Frank, "Handling and Disposal of Screenings," *Sewage Works J.*, *3*, 223 (1931).

Genter, A. L., "Principles and Factors Influencing Vacuum Filtration of Sludge," *Sewage Works J.*, *13*, 1164 (1941).

Genter, A. L., "Small Sludge-Elutriation Plants," *Sewage Works J.*, *18*, 17 (1946).

Greeley, S. A., and Committee, "Standard Practice in Separate Sludge Digestion," *Trans. Am. Soc. Civil Engrs.*, *103*, 1662 (1938).

Halff, A. H., "An Investigation of the Rotary Vacuum-Filter Cycle," *Sewage and Ind. Wastes, 24*, 962 (1952).

Haseltine, T. R., "Measurement of Sludge-Drying-Bed Performance," *Sewage and Ind. Wastes, 23*, 1065 (1951).

Laboon, J. F., "Experimental Studies on the Concentration of Raw Sludge," *Sewage and Ind. Wastes, 24*, 423 (1952).

Pearse, Langdon, and Committee, "Friction of Sewage Sludge in Pipes," *Proc. Am. Soc. Civil Engrs.*, *55*, 1773 (1929).

Pearse, Langdon, and Committee, "Sludge Lagoons," *Sewage Works J.*, *20*, 817 (1948).

Schroepfer, G. J., "Incineration Problems," *Sewage Works J.*, *19*, 559 (1947).

Smith, F. E., "A Study of Sludge Disposal at Water-Purification Plants in New England," *J. New Eng. Water Works Assoc.*, *62*, 265 (1948).

Symposium, "Concentration of Sewage Sludge," *Trans. Am. Soc. Civil Engrs.*, *110*, 1557 (1945).

Symposium, "Dewatering, Incineration, and Use of Sewage Sludge," *Trans. Am. Soc. Civil Engrs.*, *110*, 179 (1945).

Symposium, "Pipeline Flow of Solids in Suspension," *Trans. Am. Soc. Civil Engrs.*, *107*, 1563 (1942).

Chapter 27. Disinfection, Destruction of Aquatic Growths, and Removal of Odors and Tastes

Disinfection

Butterfield, C. T., "Bactericidal Properties of Free and Combined Available Chlorine," *J. Am. Water Works Assoc., 40,* 1305 (1948); *Pub. Health Rept. 63,* 934 (1948).

Calvert, C. K., "Disinfection of New Mains," *J. Am. Water Works Assoc., 37,* 46 (1945).

Calvert, C. K., and Committee, "Control of Chlorination," *J. Am. Water Works Assoc., 35,* 1315 (1943).

Carlson, H. J., G. M. Ridenour, and C. F. McKhann, "Efficiency of Standard Purification Methods in Removing Poliomyelitis Virus from Water," *Am. J. Public Health, 32,* 1256 (1942); (see also p. 1366).

Chang, S. L., "Applicability of Oxidation-Potential Measurements in Determining the Concentration of Germicidally Active Chlorine in Water," *J. New Eng. Water Works Assoc., 59,* 79 (1945).

Chang, S. L., "Destruction of Microorganisms," *J. Am. Water Works Assoc., 36,* 1192 (1944).

Chang, S. L., and G. M. Fair, "Viability and Destruction of the Cysts of *Endameba histolytica*," *J. Am. Water Works Assoc., 33,* 1705 (1941).

Chang, S. L., and J. C. Morris, "Elemental Iodine as a Disinfectant for Drinking Water," *Ind. Eng. Chem., 45,* 1009 (1953).

Chang, S. L., P. C. G. Isaac, and Neva Baine, "Dynamics of the Removal of Bacterial Virus in Water by Flocculation with Aluminum Sulfate," *Am. J. Hyg., 57,* 253 (1953).

Eliassen, Rolf, and H. L. Krieger, "Control of Bacterial Numbers in Chlorinated Sewage Effluents," *Sewage and Ind. Wastes, 22,* 47 (1951).

Fair, G. M., J. C. Morris, S. L. Chang, Ira Weil, and R. P. Burden, "Behavior of Chlorine as a Water Disinfectant," *J. Am. Water Works Assoc., 40,* 1051 (1948).

Fair, G. M., S. L. Chang, and J. C. Morris, "The Dynamics of Water Chlorination," *J. New Eng. Water Works Assoc., 61,* 285 (1947).

Federation of Sewage and Industrial Wastes Associations, "Chlorination of Sewage and Industrial Wastes," *Manual of Practice* 4 (1951).

Griffin, A. E., "Review of the Progress in Break-Point Chlorination," *J. New Eng. Water Works Assoc., 61,* 145 (1947).

Hess, S. G., A. N. Diachishin, and Paul de Falco, Jr., "Bactericidal Effects of Sewage Chlorination," *Sewage and Ind. Wastes, 25,* 751, 907 (1953).

Horwood, M. P., J. P. Horton, and V. A. Minch, "Factors Influencing Bactericidal Action of Ultrasonic Waves," *J. Am. Water Works Assoc., 43,* 153 (1951).

Kabler, P. W., "Relative Resistance of Coliform Organisms and Enteric Pathogens in the Disinfection of Water with Chlorine," *J. Am. Water Works Assoc., 43,* 553 (1951).

Laux, P. C., "Break-Point Chlorination at Anderson," *J. Am. Water Works Assoc., 32,* 1027 (1940).

McCarthy, J. A., "Bromine and Chlorine Dioxide as Water Disinfectants," *J. New Eng. Water Works Assoc., 58,* 55 (1944).

Morris, J. C., S. L. Chang, G. M. Fair, and G. H. Conant, Jr., "Disinfection of Drinking Water under Field Conditions," *Ind. Eng. Chem., 45,* 1013 (1953).

Neefe, J. R., J. B. Baty, J. G. Reinhold, and Joseph Stokes, Jr., "Inactivation of the Virus of Infectious Hepatitis in Drinking Water," *Am. J. Public Health, 37,* 365 (1947).

Neefe, J. R., Joseph Stokes, J. B. Baty, and J. G. Reinhold, "Disinfection of Water Containing Causative Agent of Infectious (Epidemic) Hepatitis," *J. Am. Med. Assoc., 128,* 1076 (1945).

Palin, A. T., "Chemical Aspects of Chlorination," *J. Inst. Water Engrs., 4,* 565 (1950).

Riehl, M. L., H. H. Weiser, and B. T. Rheins, "Effect of Lime-Treated Water upon Survival of Bacteria," *J. Am. Water Works Assoc., 44,* 466 (1952).

Shapiro, Robert, and F. E. Hale, "An Investigation of the Katadyn Treatment of Water, with Particular Reference to Swimming Pools," *J. New Eng. Water Works Assoc., 51,* 113 (1937).

Smith, M. C., and Committee, "Chemical Hazards in Water-Works Plants," *J. Am. Water Works Assoc., 27,* 1225 (1935); *28,* 1772 (1936); *31,* 489 (1939).

Wattie, Elsie, and C. T. Butterfield, "Relative Resistance of *Escherichia coli* and *Eberthella typhosa* to Chlorine and Chloramines," *Pub. Health Rept. 59,* 1661 (1944).

Wolman, Abel, and L. H. Enslow, "Chlorine Absorption and the Chlorination of Water," *Ind. Eng. Chem., 11,* 209 (1919).

Destruction of Aquatic Growths

Goudey, R. F., "Chemical Weed Control," *J. Am. Water Works Assoc., 38,* 186 (1946).

Hale, F. E., *The Use of Copper Sulphate in the Control of Microscopic Organisms,* Phelps Dodge Refining Corp., New York, 1948.

Owen, Richard, "Removal of Phosphorus from Sewage-Plant Effluent with Lime," *Sewage and Ind. Wastes, 25,* 548 (1953).

Sawyer, C. N., "Fertilization of Lakes by Agricultural and Urban Drainage," *J. New Eng. Water Works Assoc., 61,* 109 (1947).

Sawyer, C. N., "Some New Aspects of Phosphates in Relation to Lake Fertilization," *Sewage and Ind. Wastes, 24,* 768 (1952).

Removal of Odors and Tastes

Aston, R. N., "Recent Developments in the Chlorine Dioxide Process," *J. Am. Water Works Assoc., 42,* 151 (1950).

Baylis, J. R., *Elimination of Taste and Odor in Water,* McGraw-Hill Book Co., New York, 1935.

Braidech, M. M., "Mechanics of Adsorption by Means of Activated Carbons," *J. Am. Water Works Assoc., 30,* 1299 (1938).

Braidech, M. M., and Committee, "Specifications and Tests for Powdered Activated Carbon," *J. Am. Water Works Assoc., 30,* 1133 (1938).

Helbig, W. A., "Taking Guesswork out of Activated-Carbon Dosage," *J. Am. Water Works Assoc., 30,* 1320 (1938).

Howard, N. J., "Progress in Superchlorination Treatment for Taste Prevention at Toronto, Ontario," *J. Am. Water Works Assoc., 23,* 373 (1931).

Taylor, E. J., "Philadelphia Ozonation Plant," *J. Am. Water Works Assoc., 41,* 322 (1949).

Chapter 28. The Natural or Self-Purification of Water

American Association for the Advancement of Science, *Limnological Aspects of Water Supply and Waste Disposal*, Published by the Association, Washington, D. C., 1948.

Caldwell, D. H., "Sewage Oxidation Ponds—Performance, Operation, and Design," *Sewage Works J., 18*, 433 (1946).

Crohurst, H. R., "A Study of the Pollution and Natural Purification of the Ohio River. IV," *Pub. Health Bull.* 204 (1933).

Crohurst, H. R., "A Study of the Pollution and Natural Purification of the Upper Mississippi River," *Pub. Health Bull.* 203 (1932).

Crohurst, H. R., and M. V. Veldee, "Report of an Investigation of the Pollution of Lake Michigan in the Vicinity of South Chicago and the Calumet and Indiana Harbors," *Pub. Health Bull.* 170 (1927).

Diachishin, J. M., S. G. Hess, and W. T. Ingraham, "Sewage Disposal in Tidal Estuaries," *Proc. Am. Soc. Civil Engrs., 79*, 167 (1953).

Hoskins, J. K., C. C. Ruchhoft, and L. G. Williams, "A Study of the Pollution and Natural Purification of the Illinois River. I. Surveys and Laboratory Studies," *Pub. Health Bull.* 171 (1927).

Kehr, R. W., and Others, "A Study of the Pollution and Natural Purification of the Scioto River," *Pub. Health Bull.* 276 (1941).

Ketchum, B. H., "The Flushing of Tidal Estuaries," *Sewage and Ind. Wastes, 23*, 198 (1951).

National Resources Committee, *Water Pollution in the United States*, Government Printing Office, Washington, D. C., 1939.

Oswald, W. J., H. B. Gotaas, H. F. Ludwig, and Victoria Lynch, "Algae Symbiosis in Oxidation Ponds," *Sewage and Ind. Wastes, 23*, 1337 (1951); *25*, 26, 692 (1953).

Parker, C. D., H. L. Jones, and W. S. Taylor, "Purification of Sewage in Lagoons," *Sewage and Ind. Wastes, 22*, 760 (1950).

Pearse, Langdon, and Committee, "Oxidation Ponds," *Sewage Works J., 20*, 1025 (1948).

Purdy, W. C., "A Study of the Pollution and Natural Purification of the Illinois River. II. The Plankton and Related Organisms," *Pub. Health Bull.* 198 (1930).

Purdy, W. C., and C. T. Butterfield, "Effect of Plankton Animals on Bacterial Death Rates," *Am. J. Pub. Health, 8*, 499 (1918).

Stommel, Henry, "Computation of Pollution in a Vertically Mixed Estuary," *Sewage and Ind. Wastes, 25*, 1065 (1953).

Stone, Ralph, and W. F. Garber, "Sewage Reclamation by Spreading-Basin Infiltration," *Proc. Am. Soc. Civil Engrs., 77*, 87 (1951).

Streeter, H. W., "A Formulation of Bacterial Changes Occurring in Polluted Waters," *Sewage Works J., 6*, 211 (1934).

Thomas, H. A., Jr., "Pollution-Load Capacity of Streams," *Water and Sewage Works, 95*, 409 (1948).

U. S. Public Health Service, "Water Pollution in the United States," *Pub. Health Service Publication* 64 (1951).

Velz, C. J., "Factors Influencing Self-Purification and Their Relation to Pollution Abatement," *Sewage Works J., 19*, 629 (1947); *21*, 309 (1949).

Chapter 29. Industrial Water Supply and Waste-Water Disposal

American Society for Testing Materials, *Manual on Industrial Water*, Published by the Society, Philadelphia, 1953.

Collins, W. D., W. L. Lamar, and E. W. Lohr, "The Industrial Utility of Public Water Supplies in the United States," *U. S. Geol. Survey Water Supply Paper* 658 (1934).

Doudoroff, Peter, and Max Katz, "Critical Review of Literature on the Toxicity of Industrial Wastes and Their Components to Fish," *Sewage and Ind. Wastes, 22,* 1432 (1950) ; *25,* 802 (1953).

Eliassen, Rolf, W. J. Kaufman, J. B. Nesbitt, and M. I. Goldman, "Studies on Radioisotope Removal by Water-Treatment Processes," *J. Am. Water Works Assoc., 43,* 615 (1951).

Geyer, J. C., and W. A. Perry, *Textile-Waste Treatment and Recovery*, Textile Foundation, Washington, D. C., 1937.

Mohlman, F. W., "Industrial Wastes: Possibilities of Recovery and Utilization," *Trans. Am. Soc. Civil Engrs., 114,* 338 (1949).

Moore, E. W., and Committee, "Quality Tolerances of Water for Industrial Uses," *J. New Eng. Water Works Assoc., 54,* 261 (1940) ; *64,* 412 (1950).

Powell, S. T., and H. E. Bacon, "Magnitude of Industrial Demand for Process Water," *J. Am. Water Works Assoc., 42,* 777 (1950).

Pye, D. J., "Chemical Fixation of Oxygen," *J. Am. Water Works Assoc., 39,* 1121 (1947).

Redfield, A. C., and L. A. Walford, "A Study of the Disposal of Chemical Waste at Sea," *Nat. Research Council Pub.* 201 (1951).

Ruchhoft, C. C., "The Possibilities of Disposal of Radioactive Wastes by Biological Treatment Methods," *Sewage Works J., 21,* 877 (1949).

Straub, C. P., R. J. Morton, and O. R. Placak, "Studies on the Removal of Radioactive Contaminants from Water," *J. Am. Water Works Assoc., 43,* 773 (1951).

Veatch, N. T., "Industrial Uses of Reclaimed Sewage Effluents," *Sewage Works J., 20,* 3 (1948) ; (see also pp. 15, 24, 36).

Wood, C. P., "Factors Controlling the Location of Various Types of Industry," *Trans. Am. Soc. Civil Engrs., 112,* 577 (1947).

Chapter 30. Rural Water Supply and Waste-Water Disposal. Swimming Pools

Rural Water Supply and Waste-Water Disposal

Bendixen, T. W., M. Berk, J. P. Sheehy, and S. R. Weibel, *Studies on Household-Sewage Disposal Systems, Part II*, Pub. Health Service, Environmental Health Center, Cincinnati, 1950.

New York State Department of Health, *Rural Water-Supply and Sewage Systems*, Published by the Department as *Bull.* 26 (1940) ; (similar bulletins are published by the health agencies of other states).

Ridenour, G. M., and I. O. Lacey, "Institutional Sewage and Sewage-Flow Characteristics," *Sewage Works J., 4,* 1046 (1932).

Weibel, S. R., C. P. Straub, and J. R. Thoman, *Studies on Household-Sewage Disposal Systems, Part I*, Public Health Service, Environmental Health Center, Cincinnati, 1949.

Swimming Pools

American Public Health Association, *Swimming Pools and Other Public Bathing Places*, Published by the Association, New York, 1949 [see also *Yearbook, American Public Health Association*, 99 (1951–1952)].

Kiker, J. E., Jr., "Diatomite Filters for Swimming Pools," *J. Am. Water Works Assoc., 41,* 801 (1949).

Stevenson, A. H., "Studies of Bathing-Water-Quality and Health," *Am. J. Public Health, 43,* 529 (1953).